AQUATIC SCIENCES AND FISHERIES INFORMATION SYSTEM

Aquatic Sciences and Fisheries Thesaurus

Descriptors Used in the Aquatic Sciences and Fisheries Information System

Compiled by

E. Fagetti
Food and Agriculture Organization of the United Nations Fisheries Department, Rome, Italy

D.W. Privett
Institute of Oceanographic Sciences, Wormley, Godalming, Surrey, U.K.

J.R.L. Sears
Cambridge Scientific Abstracts, Bethesda, MD, U.S.A.

D1304820

Published by
Cambridge Scientific Abstracts
for
Food and Agriculture Organization of the United Nations
Rome 1986

ISBN 0-88387-103-3

Preface

The Aquatic Sciences and Fisheries Information System (ASFIS) is an international information system for the science, technology and management of marine and freshwater environments, including their socio-economic and legal aspects. The system is maintained jointly by the Food and Agriculture Organization of the United Nations (FAO), the Intergovernmental Oceanographic Commission of Unesco (IOC), and the United Nations Ocean Economics and Technology Branch (OETB) with collaboration of the national ASFIS partners. The system's information outputs currently include: 1) the computer searchable ASFA database and its print product derivatives, *Aquatic Sciences and Fisheries Abstracts (ASFA)* and *ASFA Aquaculture Abstracts;* 2) *Marine Science Contents Tables (MSCT);* 3) *Freshwater and Aquaculture Contents Tables (FACT);* 4) the *ASFIS Meetings Register;* and 5) the *World List of Serial Titles in Aquatic Sciences and Fisheries.*

The *ASFIS Reference Series* comprises the rules, authority lists, formats, codes, etc. on which the system is based.

Cambridge Scientific Abstracts (CSA) of Bethesda, Maryland, USA has published this thesaurus for FAO. CSA also prepares the ASFA database and publishes *ASFA* and *ASFA Aquaculture Abstracts* under contract to FAO.

ACKNOWLEDGEMENTS

Compilation of this extensive terminology would not have been possible without the willing support of all personnel involved over many years in the development and production of Aquatic Sciences and Fisheries Abstracts. This support by past and present members of the ASFA Advisory Board and indexing staff whose names are listed on the editorial pages of ASFA is gratefully acknowledged. Thanks are also due to many specialists in the FAO Fisheries Department, in the Institute of Oceanographic Sciences at Wormley, UK and in the Institute of Offshore Engineering, UK, who have suggested descriptors and defined concepts relevant to their fields of speciality.

To the compilers of this edition of the Thesaurus goes the credit for their unique and valuable achievement. The enormous task of structuring the terminology for the aquatic biology, biological oceanography, and living resource aspects was undertaken by Dr. Elda Fagetti of the FAO Fisheries Department; her dedicated efforts launched the development of this Thesaurus on a sound foundation. The entries relevant to the expanded scope of ASFA into physical oceanography, ocean technology and non-living resource aspects were added by Dr. D.W. Privett of the UK Institute of Oceanographic Sciences, Wormley, working under contract to FAO. To Mr. J.R.L. Sears of Cambridge Scientific Abstracts, Bethesda, MD., USA, goes the credit for suggesting a large number of descriptors and editing online the final print version of this Thesaurus. In addition to the compilers, acknowledgement goes to Arnold Myers (Institute of Offshore Engineering, IOE) who contributed to the vocabulary in marine technology; to Cinda Yates Gainch (Division of the Unesco Libraries, Archives and Documentation Services), who adapted the SPINES software to the ASFIS Thesaurus requirements and carried out the initial computerisation process.

Last but not least in this list of names go acknowledgements to Mr. E.F. Akyüz, my predecessor as Chief, Fishery Information, Data and Statistics Service, FAO, who made possible the realisation of this Thesaurus, to Mr. R. Needham, head of the Research Information Unit which is responsible for development of all of the ASFIS Reference Series, and to the ASFA staff of the same unit who in one way or another were involved in this lengthy task, particularly Mrs. Giovanna Sebastiani-Corbellini and Mrs. Luciana Lombardi-Gianandrea, for their invaluable and patient help at the keyboarding and proofreading stages of the Thesaurus.

Robert R. Freeman
Chief, Fishery Information
Data and Statistics Service,
FAO, Rome, October 1986

Contents

Introduction

by

Elda Fagetti
FAO

1. PURPOSE AND COVERAGE OF THE ASFIS THESAURUS

1.1 Purpose

The ASFIS Thesaurus has been conceived so as to correspond to the objectives of the ASFIS system. It permits the subject indexing and retrieval of information on all aspects of aquatic sciences and technology, exploitation of living and non-living resources, related policy, social and economic aspects, processing and marketing of aquatic products, as recorded and stored in the Aquatic Sciences and Fisheries Information System's ASFA database. So far as can be ascertained, this is the only Thesaurus devoted to this broad field of knowledge. It supersedes the "Thesaurus of Terms for Aquatic Sciences and Fisheries" published in 1976 as FAO Fisheries Circular number 344.

1.2 Status of Thesaurus Development

It is perhaps worthwhile to emphasize that a technical thesaurus is not concerned with "semantic perfection" or exact hierarchy of scientific disciplines. Its structure is developed in accordance with the pragmatic requirements of information retrieval. The terminology presented in this publication has resulted from the experience gained in indexing over 300,000 records for Aquatic Sciences and Fisheries Abstracts during 1971-85. Extensive reference has been made to other related authority lists, thesauri, term glossaries and dictionaries. A list of these can be found in the bibliography. Nevertheless, terminology relevant to any area of scientific/technological development grows hand-in-hand with that development, and no thesaurus can ever be regarded as final.

The effort of compiling a more comprehensive Thesaurus for ASFIS and its ASFA database will take several more years. Rather than tolerate further delay in revising the now outdated 1976 edition, the ASFA Advisory Board has chosen to publish this Thesaurus now. Users may find some topics within the scope of ASFIS still not satisfactorily covered. To facilitate revision and up-dating, comments on and/or criticisms of the Thesaurus are welcome. Such comments/criticisms as well as suggestions for new terms to be added to the Thesaurus should be submitted on the forms found in this Thesaurus to:

> Fishery Information, Data and Statistics Service
> Attention: ASFA
> Fisheries Department
> Food and Agriculture Organization
>   of the United Nations
> 00100 Rome, Italy.

The Thesaurus covers only subject index terms and should be used in conjunction with the ASFIS Guidelines for Subject Categorisation and Indexing - (ASFIS-5) - and the other ASFIS indexing tools, namely ASFIS Geographic Authority List - (ASFIS-7) - for geographic indexing and the NODC Taxonomic Code, for taxonomic indexing.

1.3   Background

This thesaurus has evolved hand-in-hand with the rapid growth of interest in aquatic ecosystems (both marine and freshwater) during the last 20 years, and the accompanying problems in handling the rapidly increasing volume of relevant scientific and technical literature.

In 1964, as a result of a collaborative programme with the University of Rhode Island, FAO published a *List of classification terms and subject descriptors.* In 1970, when arrangements were being made for the cooperative publication of the *Aquatic Sciences and Fisheries Abstracts (ASFA)* journal, the Informations und Dokumentationsstelle of the Bundesforschungsanstalt für Fischerei (Hamburg, Germany FR), undertook to further develop and classify this list. This work resulted in a considerably enhanced terminology (1971, revised 1974) which was used to index citations appearing in ASFA during this period.

In this next phase, FAO structured this terminological authority to produce a draft structured thesaurus (1974) which was evaluated in the production of a new experimental index for the 1975 volume of ASFA and used to index ASFA documents until the revised and enlarged version was published by FAO (FAO, 1976). This was widely distributed among ASFA indexers and users, specialised libraries and information systems over the world. It has been translated into Spanish (Mileo, A.T., 1981 and 1985) and is being translated into French, following the IOC Executive Council recommendation of May 1979 (IOC/EC - X1.13) that "the Secretary of IOC makes arrangements when required for the translation of the terms in the enlarged ASFIS Thesaurus (ASFIS-6) through interested international institutions and member states, in particular in conjunction with ASFIS centres and other centres of excellence, having the necessary linguistic competence."

The widening of the ASFA scope in 1978 to cover also non-living resources and their exploitation called for additional appropriate terminology which has been developed hand-in-hand with the development of ASFA-2 during the past 8 years. The present ASFIS Thesaurus version includes therefore the original ASFA terminology in use since its origin plus additional terms relevant to the enlarged scope of ASFA or to the overall scope, in accordance with the development of the system.

As for the previous editions, additions to the terminology have been based mainly on suggestions received from the international network of ASFIS input centres as well as from other information systems which have used the ASFIS Thesaurus as controlled vocabulary. The development of terminology relevant to the enlarged scope of ASFA has made it necessary to introduce changes in some of the 1976 biological descriptors, mainly to avoid possible confusion between similar terms which have different meanings in relation to either biological or geological aspects. Other changes have been introduced to avoid compound descriptors with parentheses.

Changes have been kept to the strictly necessary in order to keep consistency in the ASFA indexing vocabulary already well established over several years. For additional descriptors or changed descriptors, information is included in their SN giving the year in which their use was initiated as far as possible. Changed descriptors are also cross-referred to corresponding descriptors used in previous years.

As demonstrated by the previous edition, the Thesaurus will continue to exercise its influence over the standardisation of the English terminology relevant to the science and technology of the aquatic environment. It has already been adopted in a variety of emerging national information systems. As an example, the Thesaurus is used to index Canada's annual bibliography of fisheries publications and it has provided the basis for a more specialised thesaurus for an information system on the Great Barrier Reef.

1.4   Field coverage of the ASFIS Thesaurus

The specialised field coverage of the ASFA Thesaurus can be divided into a core area which is treated in depth at very specific levels and peripheral areas requiring less refined treatment and treated only when relevant to the ASFA scope.

Strictly Core Areas

Aquatic natural and applied sciences such as:

Biology
Ecology
Environmental sciences
Oceanography
Limnology

Aquaculture
Geology
Geophysics
Meteorology and climatology
Fisheries sciences

Technology and Engineering such as:

Marine technology
Ship technology

Fishing technology
Fish food technology

Living and non-living resources exploitation and processing, such as:

Fishable stocks
Fishery products
Energy from the sea
Minerals from the sea

Cultured stocks
Freshwater from the sea
Chemicals from the sea
Oil and gas

Aquatic pollution and its effects in organisms

Aquatic environmental changes, conservation, public health

Social, economic and policy relevant aspects

Marginal or peripheral areas

Exact and natural sciences, such as:

Biology
Mathematics
Space sciences

Chemistry
Physics
Statistical sciences

Human and social sciences:

Development sciences
History
Pedagogy

Economics
International relations
Management

Applied sciences and technologies

Engineering relevant sciences
Medical sciences
Power technology

Information sciences
Transport technology
Potable and waste water treatment technology

2. RULES AND CONVENTIONS

2.1 Standardisation and control of terms

In order to allow for coincidence between the indexing language and the searching language the ASFIS Thesaurus includes two types of terms, descriptors and non-descriptors.

Descriptors or allowable (permitted) terms are those which have been accepted by the systems for describing a concept and which are therefore used in indexing and consequently also for retrieval. The present version of the ASFIS Thesaurus includes over 6,500 descriptors.

Non-descriptors or forbidden (or unauthorised) terms include true synonyms, quasi-synonyms, word forms, different (American) spelling or very specific terms which are grouped for indexing (or retrieval) purposes into a conceptually broader term. They are followed by a USE reference which leads to the relevant descriptor. Therefore they are also known in controlled language systems as "lead-in terms." The present version includes 3,400 non-descriptors.

2.1.1 Spelling rules

The following rules have been followed:

British English rather than American English has been adopted for the descriptors. Where American spelling is used, or where alternative English spellings are available, they have been cross-referred to the preferred descriptors.

2.1.2 Noun and adjective forms

All descriptors have a "substantive" (or "noun") form.

Usually "common" adjectives are pre-coordinated with nouns and entered as compound descriptors to avoid (i) inconsistency in indexing and (ii) false combinations during retrieval, for example: "marine" pre-coordinated in:

MARINE ORGANISMS
MARINE PARKS
MARINE POLLUTION
MARINE TECHNOLOGY, etc.

and "international" pre-coordinated in:

INTERNATIONAL AGREEMENTS
INTERNATIONAL LAW
INTERNATIONAL POLICY, etc.

Only a very small proportion of single word terms in adjectival or adverbial form are entered, with the instruction in SN "To be used only as a qualifier." This is for the benefit of practicality and flexibility, for adjectives in recurrent or common use, for example:

ANNUAL, MONTHLY, etc.

Prepositions are avoided in noun phrases (pluriterms), for example: "Technology transfer" instead of "Transfer of technology." The following exceptions were made because the form with the preposition is the most familiar:

LAW OF THE SEA, OIL AND GAS and its compound descriptors, EQUATIONS OF STATE

2.1.3 Singular and plural forms

The general rule adopted is that *plural form* be given preference, whenever possible. It was always adopted for generic processes, phenomena, operations, properties, materials, instruments, entities, for example:

FISHERIES
BIOLOGICAL PHENOMENA
CHEMICAL PROPERTIES
FISH DISEASES
MEASURING DEVICES

Singular form is used for specific processes, properties and phenomena, specific materials, proper chemical names and disciplinary areas, which are acceptable only in the singular:

DECANTATION
DENSITY
GUANO
GROWTH
IRIDIUM
CHEMISTRY

When singular or plural forms of a term imply two different concepts, compound descriptors are used to avoid ambiguities, for example:

"coating" as a process is entered as COATING PROCESSES
"coatings" as an entity is entered as a synonym of COATING MATERIALS.

2.1.4 Abbreviations, initials and acronyms

As a general rule, abbreviations for descriptors have been avoided. Exceptions are:

- abbreviations which are universally accepted and do not give rise to misinterpretations, especially when appearing in their clustered structure e.g. DDT, RNA
- if the expanded form of the term is excessively long.

However, the expanded form of the term appears always as a synonym with a cross-reference, or in the scope notes.

2.1.5 Alphabetisation

Alphabetisation is based on word-by-word arrangement, according to the following sequences: spaces, special characters (full stop, hyphen, parenthesis) and letter in usual order.

2.2 Multiple-word entries

Both single-word descriptors and multiple-word descriptors have been used. Multiple-word entries (consisting of two or more words) are necessary to modify, define or specify scientific and technical concepts. In the field of aquatic sciences, this is particularly needed because the distinct environments (marine, fresh and brackish water) frequently imply particular research disciplines (e.g. MARINE GEOLOGY), different flora and fauna (e.g. FRESHWATER MOLLUSCS), or specialised techniques (ESTUARINE FISHERIES). Other compound descriptors have been used to express concepts that should not be separated, for example BIOLOGICAL DEVELOPMENT; this helps to overcome retrieval problems associated with high-frequency usage of terms such as BIOLOGY and DEVELOPMENT.

Multiple-word descriptors are mainly entered with the words in their natural order, for example, MARINE POLLUTION and cross-referred to the hidden-words in the descriptors "pollution (marine)" as lead-in-terms. The first word in a multiple-word entry is always used in the singular form and the entry is cross-referred to the non-descriptor (and vice versa) when the plural is also in common use, for example FISHERY MANAGEMENT UF "fisheries management."

2.3 Use of characters

2.3.1 Character sets

The general rules adopted for the alphabetical structured list follows the SPINES printing format in which:

- all descriptors are printed in upper case, including those in scope notes
- all non-descriptors (UF references) and scope notes are printed in lower case. This rule is applied also to abbreviations in non-descriptors (e.g. the abbreviation of "biochemical oxygen demand" is "bod" not BOD).

2.3.2 Punctuation

Punctuation marks have been kept to a minimum

- Diacritical marks are avoided
- Prefixes are usually connected to the stem, for example
  MICROFORMS
  MICROHABITATS
- Hyphens have been retained only when this is common practice or when omission may alter the meaning of the term, for example:
  RHODAMINE B-DYE
  SHORT-CRESTED WAVES
  POLE-LINE FISHING
  AIR-ICE INTERFACE, etc.

  and for letter-word combinations, for example:

  X-RAY ANALYSIS
  S-WAVES

  The space occupied by the hyphen is:

  (i) Left blank for some compound adjectives, noun-noun combinations, where this is common practice, for example:
      IN SITU DENSITY

  (ii) dropped in attaching prefixes (adverbs) to the base word (stem), where this is common practice, for example:
      NONDESTRUCTIVE TESTING
      MULTISPECIES FISHERIES
      MONOSEX CULTURE

- Slash is used only for the following compound descriptors, because of their common use in the specialised languages:
  T/S DIAGRAMS and CATCH/EFFORT
- Periods and commas are used only in scope notes.
- Parentheses are used only for very few descriptors, as specified below, which need parenthetical definition and in non-desciptors resolved by inversion i.e. "reaction (chemical)" use CHEMICAL REACTIONS. Inversion was adopted, in general, with some exceptions, e.g.:

  RESERVOIRS (WATER)
  HABITAT IMPROVEMENT (CHEMICAL)
  HABITAT IMPROVEMENT (PHYSICAL)
  HABITAT IMPROVEMENT (FERTILIZATION)
  LOCATIONS (WORKING)

3. SELECTION AND DEFINITION OF TERMS

As already mentioned in the introduction the ASFIS controlled vocabulary has developed hand-in-hand with the development of the *Aquatic Sciences and Fisheries Abstracts* journal. The ASFA indexers suggested terms in accordance with their experience in indexing documents for ASFA entries. The compilers selected among the suggested terms those more frequently requested or those that were considered necessary for indexing at more specific levels. Specialised relevant nomenclature bulletins, dictionaries and thesauri, as listed in the bibliography, were consulted for term selection and definition.

3.1 Term Selection

The main sources of term selection were:

(1) *Thesaurus of Terms for Aquatic Sciences and Fisheries* (FAO, 1976)
(2) the indexing of ASFA-2 documents from 1978 to 1985 (a total of about 74,000)
(3) the suggestions of ASFA indexers, users and subject specialists
(4) the relevant FAO and other UN specialised agencies Terminology Bulletins
(5) Thesauri, Dictionaries and Glossaries as listed in the selected bibliography

3.2 Term definition

The inter-relationships given in the Thesaurus supply a kind of definition by grouping terms in their semantic relations. A rough definition of the terms, when this is needed, is given in the scope notes. Usually to:

- restrict the usage of a broad descriptor within the context of the of the ASFIS system's scope.
- clarify the exact meaning of key specialised terms
- to give the corresponding descriptors used in previous years
- to explain the meaning of certain non-English terms
- to indicate that the descriptor is to be used only as a qualifier
- to recommend, in the case of a few "umbrella terms," i.e. terms with a very broad meaning, to select and use a more specific, or alternative, descriptor, among those listed below as NTs or RTs.

4. SPECIFICITY AND PRE-COORDINATION LEVEL

Due to the wide scope of ASFIS which covers three well-defined aquatic environments and bio-ecological as well as physico-chemical oceanographic sciences and technologies, a high level of specificity is necessary to ensure precision performance both at the input and the retrieval stages. To avoid confusion of descriptors which have a different meaning if applied to bio-ecological aspects or to physico-chemical aspects, the pre-coordination of terms by multiword descriptors has been very frequently adopted e.g.

> BIOTESTING UF BIOLOGICAL TESTING, to distinguish from more general TESTING procedure etc.
> BIOLOGICAL DAMAGE to distinguish from DAMAGE as resulting from accident or fire.

The same pre-coordination level was adopted for the terminology which refers to a specific aquatic environment in order to give to the relevant descriptors more specificity as requested by the specialised technology in use, or by the organisms involved e.g.

> AQUACULTURE as broader term, but also MARINE AQUACULTURE, FRESHWATER AQUACULTURE and BRACKISHWATER AQUACULTURE.

Very general descriptors which are too generic or too conceptually broad for precise indexing and retrieval purposes have been included only with the function of recalling under a single generic "umbrella" term, the pre-coordinated specific descriptors among which to select the most relevant one e.g.

> CONTROL and EQUIPMENT followed by the hierarchical display of narrower pre-coordinated descriptors or PROPERTIES followed by a non-hierarchical list of pre-coordinated descriptors as related terms.

5. COMPUTER LOADING, CHECKING AND DEVELOPMENT

Following initial automation via SPINES, the Thesaurus was converted and edited at Cambridge Scientific Abstracts, leading to this print and online version of the ASFIS Thesaurus.

6. THESAURUS CLASSIFICATION, STRUCTURE AND NOTATION

6.1 Facet classification

The development of the ASFA 1976 Thesaurus version has followed the facet grouping of notions according to their nature. The ten facets of the 1976 version, namely *Operations; Properties and Characteristics; Natural phenomena; Materials and intellectual tools; Equipment; Science and technology; Organisms; Earth, space and time concepts; Economic, social and legal aspects; Residual concepts* have been increased by a new facet, *Constants,* in which to group relevant descriptors. The previous facet *Materials and intellectual tools* has been divided into two separate facets.

6.1.1 Classification of descriptors by facet

Because of the problems associated with the subject categorization of descriptors in a broad interdisciplinary field, the descriptors have been classified by facet. Complete facet listings are given as an appendix to the thesaurus.

The following facets have been used:

Operations

Descriptors which define operations carried out deliberately by man, which can be broadly grouped into:
- physical operations (e.g., PHOTOGRAPHY, FISH CULTURE, CHARTING)
- analytical operations (e.g., CHEMICAL ANALYSIS, WATER ANALYSIS)
- mathematical operations (e.g., STATISTICAL ANALYSIS, TIME SERIES ANALYSIS)

Properties and Characteristics

Descriptors which define properties of substances and characteristics of organisms, ecological communities, environment and phenomena, such as:
- physical properties (e.g., TRANSPARENCY, POROSITY, etc.)
- chemical properties, (e.g., ACIDITY, SOLUBILITY, pH, etc.)
- biological characteristics of organisms (e.g., TOXICITY, VULNERABILITY)
- characteristics of populations and communities by composition (e.g., POPULATION STRUCTURE, AGE COMPOSITION) and by quantity (BIOMASS, POPULATION DENSITY)
- characteristics of phenomena (e.g., WAVE PERIOD, WAVE VELOCITY)
- characteristics of environment (e.g., SEA LEVEL, ENVIRONMENTAL CONDITIONS)
- characteristics of materials and organisms by composition (e.g., FOOD COMPOSITION, CHEMICAL COMPOSITION)

Phenomena

Descriptors related with phenomena occurring in nature such as:
- physical phenomena (e.g., RADIOACTIVITY, REFRACTION)
- chemical phenomena (e.g., CORROSION, OXIDATION)
- biological phenomena (e.g., GROWTH, DISEASES)
- environmental phenomena (e.g., CURRENTS, STORMS, WIND EROSION)
- phenomena observed in nature and arising from human activities (e.g., MARINE POLLUTION, ENTRAINMENT)

Materials

Generic or specific names given to substances, objects of any sort, such as:
- chemical elements and compounds (e.g., OXYGEN, NITRATES)
- chemical products (e.g.. FERTILIZERS, DETERGENTS)
- organic substances (e.g., ENZYMES, VITAMINS, HORMONES, etc.)
- major components of natural environment (e.g., AIR, ROCKS, FRESH WATER)
- manufactured material (e.g., NETTING MATERIALS)
- industrial products (e.g., STICKWATER, FISH OILS)

Intellectual tools

- documentation material (e.g., CHARTS, PROFILES, ABSTRACTS, PHOTOGRAPHS, SECTIONS)
- data, including raw data (e.g., OCEANOGRAPHIC DATA, CATCH/EFFORT) and elaborated data (e.g., FISHERY STATISTICS, T/S DIAGRAMS)
- intellectual aids (e.g., MATHEMATICAL MODELS, COMPUTER PROGRAMMES, IDENTIFICATION KEYS)

Equipment and structures

Descriptors used for man-made equipment, devices, structures, etc.

- laboratory equipment (e.g., MICROSCOPES, CENTRIFUGES)
- field equipment (e.g., COLLECTING DEVICES, SAMPLERS)
- measuring devices (e.g., THERMOMETERS, FLOWMETERS)
- gear and equipment for exploitation of resources (e.g., FISHING NETS, OFFSHORE PLAT-FORMS) and navigation (e.g., NAVIGATIONAL BUOYS, RADIO AIDS)
- vehicles (e.g., FACTORY SHIPS, RESEARCH VESSELS, SATELLITES)
- industry plants (e.g., DESALINATION PLANTS, POWER PLANTS)

Sciences and Technology

This facet includes the descriptors for research disciplines (e.g., BOTANY, CHEMISTRY) and for applied sciences and technology (e.g., SANITARY ENGINEERING, OFFSHORE ENGINEERING)

Organisms

This facet brings together descriptors used for fossil organisms, (e.g., FOSSIL DIATOMS, FOSSIL SPORES) and living organisms (from subcellular through community level) usually defined according to:

- feeding habits (e.g., CARNIVORES, DETRITUS FEEDERS)
- taxonomic terminology (e.g., NEW SPECIES, TAXA)
- ecological terminology (e.g., DOMINANT SPECIES, INDICATOR SPECIES)
- anatomy (e.g., GLANDS, RESPIRATORY ORGANS, FINS)
- histology and cytology (e.g., TISSUES, CELLS)
- physiological systems (e.g., NERVOUS SYSTEM, MUSCULOSKELETAL SYSTEM)
- developmental stages (e.g., LARVAE, FINGERLINGS)
- community and associations (e.g., PLEUSTON, NEKTON)
- utilization by man (e.g., ORNAMENTAL FISH, COMMERCIAL SPECIES, etc.)

Earth, space and time concepts

Terms used for:

- landforms (e.g., LAKES, RIVERS)
- underwater features (e.g., SUBMARINE RIDGES, SUBMARINE VALLEYS)
- ecological divisions of aquatic environment (e.g., BENTHIC ENVIRONMENT, EPILIMNION, EUPHOTIC ZONE, NURSERY GROUNDS)
- space (e.g., EARTH ATMOSPHERE, TROPOSPHERE)
- geological time (e.g., QUATERNARY) and actual time (e.g., SPAWNING SEASONS)

Organizational aspects, socioeconomic, legal and personnel aspects

Terms which describe, for example:

- organizational aspects, (e.g., INTERNATIONAL ORGANIZATIONS, RESEARCH INSTITU-TIONS)
- sociological aspects (e.g., LABOUR, PUBLIC HEALTH, EDUCATION)
- economic aspects (e.g., NATURAL RESOURCES, TRADE)
- legal aspects (e.g., TERRITORIAL WATERS, OCEAN SPACE, LAW OF THE SEA)

Constants

Residual concepts

This facet includes miscellaneous terms which do not fall into the above categories, because they are very general, such as, TERMINOLOGY, CAPTIVITY, or because they represent rational concepts (e.g., NEW RECORDS, TROPHIC LEVELS, LIMITING FACTORS)

6.2   Thesaurus structural relations

As in the first edition, this Thesaurus is structured to display commonly accepted relationships – preferential, hierarchical and affinitive. A further development is represented by the full hierarchical display at an entry point plus complete hierarchical levels of broader and narrower terms.

6.3   Notation

6.3.1   Scope notes

SN (scope note), a rough definition of the scope of the term where this is needed (usually for limitation). Scope notes also indicate the date, year in which additional descriptors to the 1976 version entered into use ("Added in...") and the dates when previous descriptors were changed, in which case indication is also given of descriptors previously used ("Before...search...").

The scope notes of a few "umbrella" terms included in the thesaurus recommend the use of alternative or more specific descriptors as listed below, at hierarchical or related levels.

6.3.2   Alternative relations and synonymy

USE directs the user from a non-descriptor to the relevant descriptor; UF (used for) is the reciprocal relationship to USE.

The USE-UF cross-relationship is used in a variety of situations:

- for synonyms or near synonyms
  man-made lakes   USE   ARTIFICIAL LAKES
  chorology   USE   BIOGEOGRAPHY
- to indicate preference in spelling
  hematology   USE   HAEMATOLOGY
- to designate a mandatory generically broader descriptor
  coastal aquaculture   USE   MARINE AQUACULTURE
- to designate a preferred, closely related, descriptor
  commercialization   USE   MARKETING
- to indicate preferred (natural) word order
  reactions (chemical)   USE   CHEMICAL REACTIONS
  pollution (marine)   USE   MARINE POLLUTION
- to refer from specific commonly-used parameters to the phenomena or properties which they quantify, for example:
  metabolic rate   USE   METABOLISM
  respiratory quotients   USE   RESPIRATION
  fishing mortality coefficients   USE   FISHING MORTALITY

6.3.3   Hierarchical relations

ASFIS Thesaurus includes mainly generic hierarchical relations, in which the generic descriptor (broad term) represents a class of concepts expressed by its specific descriptors (narrower terms).

BT (broader term):   DISEASES (generic)
NT (narrower term):   FISH DISEASES
                         PLANT DISEASES

6.3.3.1   Level of hierarchies

A hierarchical class of concepts may have several levels of hierarchies, at the head of which is the broadest concept, known as the "top descriptor." The ASFIS Thesaurus displays all broader and narrower levels after the main entry, for which notation is as follows:

BT 1 = broader term at level 1
BT 2 = broader term at level 2
BT 3 = broader term at level 3
BT 4 = broader term at level 4

and the reciprocal cross-references of BT 4:

NT1, NT2, NT3, NT4 = narrower terms at the 4 levels.

6.3.4 Associative or affinitive relations

The non-hierarchical relations, direct the users to alternative descriptors in the event that the lead descriptor is conceptually inappropriate. They are known as related terms and entered as RT. Related terms in the ASFIS Thesaurus are displayed also:

- to indicate antinomy
  AESTIVATION   RT   HIBERNATION
- to suggest possible concurrent use of two concepts
  ESCAPEMENT   RT   MESH SELECTIVITY
- to indicate an affinitive relationship other than hierarchic
  AQUACULTURE   RT   AQUACULTURE TECHNIQUES (i.e. instrumental relationship)
  WATER POLLUTION   RT   POLLUTION EFFECTS (i.e. cause/effect relationship)

7.   GUIDELINES FOR TERM SELECTION BY USER

It is difficult to lay down a coherent set of rules for subject indexing where different research disciplines and technologies are involved, but users of this Thesaurus should be aware of certain general considerations:

Only the essential scientific technical concepts, which are necessary for retrieval of the document abstracted, should be indexed;

Be specific by using the available keyword at the nearest level of specificity.

Example: if a paper deals with migration of juvenile tuna to feeding grounds, do not use MIGRATIONS as descriptor but the more specific keyword FEEDING MIGRATIONS;

Use a combination of descriptors where needed, even if this involves the redundancy of using "stem-synonyms."

Example: if a paper deals with mesh selectivity of a certain type of fishing net for fishery regulation purposes, use both relevant descriptors MESH SELECTIVITY and MESH REGULATIONS plus other related descriptors, e.g., TRAWLS;

Use complimentary descriptors where needed for a particular aquatic environment (marine, freshwater and brackishwater environment) and its organisms.

Example: (a) if a paper deals with oyster culture in the Ribadeo estuary, use both descriptors OYSTER CULTURE and BRACKISHWATER AQUACULTURE;
(b) if a paper deals with the effects of pollution on an oceanic species, use both descriptors MARINE POLLUTION and POLLUTION EFFECTS plus the relevant taxonomic entry;

Descriptors referring to very broad concepts – "umbrella" terms – which have been included to facilitate retrieval of the related specific descriptors *should not* be used as main lead in index entries. They may serve as qualifiers of the main entry, for example

METHODOLOGY may serve as qualifier for a lead-in entry such as SHRIMP CULTURE when the paper dealt with describes methods in use;

Index always with subject descriptors plus the taxonomic entry (in the appropriate tag of the Indexing Form) those papers that deal with aquatic animals and plants, for which only vernacular names are given.

Example: (a) a paper dealing with tuna fishery in the World Ocean should be indexed by by the relevant subject descriptors TUNA FISHERIES and PELAGIC FISHERIES plus the taxonomic entry SCOMBRIDAE;
(b) a paper dealing with carp culture should be indexed by both relevant subject descriptors FRESHWATER AQUACULTURE and FISH CULTURE plus the taxonomic entry CYPRINIDAE;

Facets are important when selecting descriptors.

Example: a paper describing a new type of flowmeter should be indexed with a descriptor chosen from the facet "Equipment" - FLOWMETERS; however, if the paper deals also with methods for the measurement of current, the appropriate descriptor should be chose from those descriptors grouped in the the facet "Operation" - CURRENT MEASUREMENT.

BIBLIOGRAPHY

Aitchison, J. and A. Gilchrist. Thesaurus construction: a practical manual. London, Aslib, 95 p.
1972

American Geological Institute, Glossary Review Committee, Glossary of geology and related sciences, with
1966   supplement. Washington, American Geological Institute, 397 p.

Armstrong, T., B. Roberts and C. Swithinbank. Illustrated glossary of snow and ice. Spec. Publ. Scott Polar Res. Inst.,
1966   (4): 60 p.

Baker, B. B. Jr., W. R. Deebel and R. D. Geisenderfer (eds.). Glossary of oceanographic terms. Spec. Publ. U.S. Naval
1966   Oceanogr. Off., (SP.35): 204 p.

Bates, R. L. and Jackson, J. A. (eds.). Glossary of geology. Falls Church, VA., American Geological Institute, 749 p.
1980   2nd ed.

Bender, A. E. Dictionary of nutrition and food technology. London, Butterworths Scientific Publications, 1943 p.
1960

Breitling, W. Inventory, maintenance and development of FAO index terms. Rome, FAO, Documentation Centre,
1975   (DC/TH/O):pag. var.

Bundesforschungsanstalt für Fischerei. Aquatic sciences and fisheries thesaurus (ASFA documentation system).
1971   Hamburg, Bundesforschungsanstalt für Fischerei, Unpag. (mimeo).

_____. Informations und Dokumentationstelle. Aquatic sciences and fisheries thesaurus. Hamburg,
1974   Bundesforschungsanstalt für Fischerei, 388 p. (mimeo).

Bureau National des Données Oceaniques, Centre Oceanologique de Bretagne. Thesaurus oceanologie (Provisional
1976   edition). Paris, Bureau National de l'Information Scientifique et Technique, 256 p.

CNEXO, Thesaurus océanologie. Liste alphabetique et list alphabetique par facette. Brest, CNEXO, 2 vols: pag. var.
n.d.   (mimeo)

Collocott, T. C. (ed.). Chambers' dictionary of science and technology. London, W. & R. Chambers, Ltd., 1328 p.
1971

Cooper, D. G. The periodic table. London, Butterworths. 93 p. 2nd ed.
1960

Dennis, J. G. et al. (eds.). International tectonic lexicon: a prodrome. Stuttgart, Schweizerbart'sche VB for International
1979   Union of Geological Sciences, 153 p.

Duffy, D. E. Offshore glossary: an explanation of terms used in the offshore oil and gas industries. Southampton,
1980   Solent Exhibitions (~il) Ltd. for Channel Offshore '80, 20 p.

Engineers Joint Council. Thesaurus of engineering and scientific terms: a list of engineering and related scientific terms
1967   and their relationships for use as a vocabulary reference in indexing and retrieving technical information.
        New York, N.Y., Engineers Joint Council, 690 p.

Fairbridge, R. W. (ed.). The encyclopedia of oceanography. New York., Reinhold Publ. Corp., 1021 p.
1966

Fairbridge, R. W. and Bourgeois, J. (eds.), Encyclopedia of sedimentology. Stroudsburg, VA. Dowden, Hutchinson and
1978   Ross, Inc., 901 p.

FAO, Research Information Unit. Structured thesaurus of descriptors for the aquatic sciences and fisheries.
1974   Working document prepared for the ASFA Editorial Advisory Board Meeting, Moscow, October 1974.
        Rome, FAO, 186 p.

FAO. Trilingual dictionary of fisheries technological terms - curing. Rome, FAO, 85 p.
1960

—————— List of classification terms and subject descriptors. <u>FAO Fish. Tech. Pap.</u>, (48):57 p.
1964

—————— Environment. <u>FAO Terminol Bull</u>., (22):106 p.
1972

—————— Thesaurus of terms for aquatic sciences and fisheries. <u>FAO Fish. Circ.</u>, (344):242 p.
1976

—————— Fish culture. <u>FAO Terminol. Bull.</u>, (19):106 p.
1981

Firth, F. E. (ed.). The encyclopedia of marine resources. New York, N.Y., Van Nostrand Reinhold Co., 740 p.
1969

GEBCO Committee. Standardization of undersea feature names: guidelines proposal form, terminology. Monaco,
1981   International Hydrographic Bureau, 27 p.

Gilchrist, A. The thesaurus in retrieval. London, Aslib, 184 p.
1971

Godman, A. and E. M. F. Payne (eds.). Longman dictionary of scientific useage. London, Longman Group Ltd., 684 p.
1979

Hanson, H. Dictionary of ecology. London, P. Owen, 382 p.
1972

Hayakawa, S. I. (ed). Cassell's modern guide to synonyms and related words. Revised by P. J. Fletcher, London,
1971   Cassell, 707 p.

Heckman, G. <u>et al.</u>, (eds.). GEOREF: thesaurus and guide to indexing. Falls Church, VA., American Geological
1978   Institute, 456 p. 2nd ed.

Henderson, I. F. and W. D. Henderson. A dictionary of scientific terms. Edinburgh, Oliver and Boyd, 595 p.
1960

Holt, S. J. Multilingual vocabulary and notation for fishery dynamics. Rome, FAO, 42 p.
1960

Hunt, I. M. and D.G. Groves (eds.). A glossary of ocean sciences and undersea technology terms. Arlington, VA.,
1965   Compass Publications Inc., 1972 p.

Huschke, R. E. (ed). Glossary of meteorology. Boston, Mass., American Meteorological Society, 638 p.
1959

Hydrographer of the Navy. The mariner's handbook. London, Ministry of Defence, Hydrographic Department, 139 p.
1973

IAPSO Working Group on Symbols, Units and Nomenclature in Physical Oceanography. SUN report on the use in
1979   physical sciences of the ocean of the Systeme International d'Unites (SI) and related standards for
          symbols and terminology. <u>IAPSO Publ. Sci.</u>, (31):56 p.

Institution of Electrical Engineers. INSPEC thesaurus. London, Institution of Electrical Engineers, 395 p.
1979

International Atomic Energy Agency. INIS thesaurus. Vienna, IAEA, 702 p.
1977

International Hydrographic Organization. Hydrographic dictionary, Pt. 1. <u>Spec. Publ. Int. Hydrogr. Organ.</u>, (32):387 p.
1977

Landi, G. Initials and acronyms of bodies, activities and projects concerned with fisheries and aquatic sciences.
1975   FAO Fish. Circ., (110) Rev.2:91 p. (tri-lingual).

Leatherdale, D. Canadian agricultural thesaurus. Section 1: General-first approximation. Ottawa, Canada, Department
1971   of Agriculture, Scientific Information Section, Research Branch, unpag.

McIntosh, D. H. (comp.), Meterological glossary. London, HMSO, (Met.0.342). 319 p.
1972

Mileo, A.T. Descriptores alfabeticos espanol-ingles + facetas: traducción parcial correspondiente los
1981   descriptores del "Thesaurus of terms for Aquatic Sciences and Fisheries," FAO. Contrib. Tec. CIBIMA
(37):147 p.

Mileo, A.T., Tesauro de terminos para ciencias acuáticas y pesqueras (Traducción del "Thesaurus of terms for aquatic
1985   sciences and fisheries"). COPESCAL Doc.Tec., (3):202 p.

Moureau, M. and J. Delawnay. Principe et développement d'un thesaurus d'application: le thesaurus. Rev. Inst. Fr.
1971   Petrole, 26(10):962-80.

Moureau, M. and A. Girard. Étude comparée de la stratégie d'interrogation dans un systeme en langage organisé et
1971   dans un systeme en langage naturel. (Project No. DO2/01350). Rapp. Inst. Fr. Petrole Cent. Doc.,
(20185):16 p.

Myers, A. Marine technology micro-thesaurus. Edinburgh, Heriot-Watt University, Institute of Offshore Engineering, 74 p.
1978   (mimeo).

National Aeronautics and Space Administration. NASA Thesaurus, Vol 1. Alphabetical listing. Washington, D.C., U.S.
1976   Government Printing Office, 809 p.

National Computing Centre. NCC Thesaurus of computing terms. Manchester, NCC Publications, 147 p.
1976

Nédélec, C. (ed.). Catalogue of small-scale fishing gear. West Byfleet, Surrey, Fishing News (Books) Ltd., for FAO,
1975   191 p. (tri-lingual).

Parker, S. P. (ed.). McGraw-Hill encyclopedia of ocean and atmospheric sciences. New York, McGraw-Hill, Inc. 580 p.
1980

Pennak, R. W. Collegiate dictionary of zoology. New York, N.Y., Ronald Press Co., 566 p.
1964

Riley, G. P. and Skirrow, G. (eds.). Chemical oceanography. Vols. 1-7. London: Academic Press. 2nd ed.
1975-78

Schriner, C. R. et al., Environmental/chemical thesaurus. Oak Ridge, TN., Oak Ridge National Laboratory, 305 p.
1978   (ORNL/EIS-132):305 p.

Schureman, P. Tide and current glossary. Spec. Publ. U.S. Coast Geodetic Surv., 228:25 p.
1949

U.N. Secretariat. Law of the sea terminology. UN Terminol. Bull., (297)Rev.1:276 p.
1971

UNISIST. Guidelines for the establishment and development of monolingual thesauri. Paris, Unesco, SC/WS/555:37 p.
1973

U.S. Army Coastal Engineering Research Center. Shore protection manual. Vol. 3. Appendix A. Glossary of terms.
1977   Washington, D.C., Superintendent of Documents, 54 p. 3rd ed.

U.S. Department of the Interior, Bureau of Reclamation. Thesaurus of water resources terms: a collection of water
1971   resources and related terms for use in indexing technical information. Washington, D.C., Government
Printing Office, 339 p.

Visser, W. A. (ed.). Geological nomenclature. Utrecht, Scheltema and Holkema BV for Royal Geological and Mining
1980   Society of the Netherlands, 540 p.

Water Research Centre. AQUAline thesaurus. Chichester, Ellis Horwood Ltd., 684 p.
1980

Whitehead, H. An A-Z of offshore oil and gas. London, Kogan Page Ltd., 337 p.
1976

ASFIS Thesaurus

AAS
USE **ABSORPTION SPECTROSCOPY**

ABALONE FISHERIES
USE **GASTROPOD FISHERIES**

ABDOMEN
SN Added in 1980
UF peritoneum
BT1 BODY REGIONS
BT2 ANATOMICAL STRUCTURES
RT ANIMAL APPENDAGES
RT DIGESTIVE SYSTEM
RT TELSON

ABIOTIC DISEASES
USE **ENVIRONMENTAL DISEASES**

ABIOTIC FACTORS
SN Before 1982 search ENVIRONMENTAL FACTORS
UF density-independent factors
BT1 ENVIRONMENTAL FACTORS
RT DISSOLVED OXYGEN
RT ENVIRONMENTAL EFFECTS
RT LIGHT
RT SALINITY
RT WATER TEMPERATURE

ABLATION
SN Use only for processes resulting in removal and loss of ice from glaciers, floating ice, etc. For organ ablation use ORGAN REMOVAL
RT AIR-ICE INTERFACE
RT CALVING
RT EVAPORATION
RT GLACIERS
RT ICE
RT ICE ACCRETION
RT ICE CAPS
RT ICE ISLANDS
RT ICE MELTING
RT ICE SHELVES
RT ICE VOLUME
RT ICEBERGS
RT MELTING
RT SUBLIMATION
RT SUBLIMATION HEAT

ABNORMAL ORGANISMS
USE **ABNORMALITIES**

ABNORMALITIES
SN Restricted to living organisms
UF abnormal organisms
UF body deformations
UF malformations
NT1 GENETIC ABNORMALITIES
RT TERATOLOGY

ABSOLUTE AGE
UF actual age
BT1 AGE
RT CARBON 13
RT CARBON 14
RT EARTH AGE
RT GEOCHRONOMETRY
RT ISOCHRONES
RT LEAD 210
RT RADIOMETRIC DATING

ABSOLUTE FOOD DEFICIENCY
USE **STARVATION**

ABSOLUTE HUMIDITY
BT1 HUMIDITY

ABSOLUTE VELOCITY
USE **VELOCITY**

ABSOLUTE VORTICITY
BT1 VORTICITY
RT CONSERVATION OF VORTICITY
RT CORIOLIS PARAMETERS
RT RELATIVE VORTICITY

ABSORPTANCE
BT1 OPTICAL PROPERTIES
BT2 PHYSICAL PROPERTIES
BT3 PROPERTIES
RT ABSORPTION COEFFICIENT
RT ABSORPTION SPECTRA
RT LIGHT ABSORPTION
RT WAVE MOTION

ABSORPTION (CHEMISTRY)
USE **SORPTION**

ABSORPTION (FOOD)
USE **FOOD ABSORPTION**

ABSORPTION (LIGHT)
USE **LIGHT ABSORPTION**

ABSORPTION (PHYSICS)
NT1 LIGHT ABSORPTION
NT1 SOUND ABSORPTION
RT AMPLITUDE
RT ATTENUATION
RT REFLECTION
RT TRANSMISSION
RT WAVE MOTION

ABSORPTION (SOUND)
USE **SOUND ABSORPTION**

ABSORPTION COEFFICIENT
SN Before 1982 search also ABSORPTIVITY
UF absorptivity
RT ABSORPTANCE
RT EMISSIVITY
RT EXTINCTION COEFFICIENT
RT LIGHT ABSORPTION
RT LIGHT PENETRATION
RT OPTICAL PROPERTIES

ABSORPTION LOSS
USE **TRANSMISSION LOSS**

ABSORPTION SPECTRA
BT1 SPECTRA
RT ABSORPTANCE
RT ABSORPTION SPECTROSCOPY
RT LIGHT ABSORPTION
RT LIGHT PENETRATION
RT TURBIDITY

ABSORPTION SPECTROMETRY
USE **ABSORPTION SPECTROSCOPY**

ABSORPTION SPECTROSCOPY
UF aas
UF absorption spectrometry
UF atomic absorption spectroscopy
BT1 SPECTROSCOPIC TECHNIQUES
BT2 ANALYTICAL TECHNIQUES
RT ABSORPTION SPECTRA

ABSORPTIVITY
USE **ABSORPTION COEFFICIENT**

ABSTRACTS
UF summaries
BT1 DOCUMENTS
RT CONFERENCES

ABUNDANCE
SN For population studies use POPULATION NUMBER if given in number, or BIOMASS if given in weight
UF relative abundance
RT AVAILABILITY
RT BIOMASS
RT COMMERCIAL AVAILABILITY
RT FOOD AVAILABILITY
RT NATURAL RESOURCES
RT POPULATION NUMBER
RT QUANTITATIVE DISTRIBUTION
RT RESOURCE AVAILABILITY

ABUNDANCE (CHEMICAL)
USE **CHEMICAL COMPOSITION**

ABYSSAL CIRCULATION
SN World-wide deep circulation of ocean basins
BT1 OCEAN CIRCULATION
BT2 WATER CIRCULATION
BT3 WATER MOTION
RT ABYSSAL CURRENTS
RT BOTTOM TOPOGRAPHY EFFECTS

ABYSSAL CONES
USE **DEEP-SEA FANS**

ABYSSAL CURRENTS
BT1 BOTTOM CURRENTS
BT2 WATER CURRENTS
BT3 WATER MOTION
RT ABYSSAL CIRCULATION
RT BENTHIC CURRENTS
RT OCEAN CURRENTS

ABYSSAL ENVIRONMENT
USE **ABYSSAL ZONE**

ABYSSAL HILLS
BT1 SUBMARINE FEATURES
BT2 TOPOGRAPHIC FEATURES
RT RELIEF FORMS

ABYSSAL PLAINS
BT1 SUBMARINE FEATURES
BT2 TOPOGRAPHIC FEATURES
RT CONTINENTAL RISE
RT OCEAN BASINS
RT OCEAN FLOOR
RT PLAINS
RT SEACHANNELS

ABYSSAL ZONE
SN Zone below 1000 m depth
UF abyssal environment
RT ABYSSOBENTHIC ZONE
RT ABYSSOPELAGIC ZONE
RT BATHYSPHERES
RT BENTHIC ENVIRONMENT
RT PELAGIC ENVIRONMENT
RT TURBIDITY CURRENTS

ABYSSOBENTHIC ZONE
SN Benthic regions below 1000 m depth
BT1 BENTHIC ENVIRONMENT
BT2 AQUATIC ENVIRONMENT
BT3 ENVIRONMENTS
RT ABYSSAL ZONE
RT ABYSSOPELAGIC ZONE

ABYSSOPELAGIC ZONE
SN Pelagic regions below 1000 m depth
BT1 OCEANIC PROVINCE
BT2 PELAGIC ENVIRONMENT
BT3 AQUATIC ENVIRONMENT
BT4 ENVIRONMENTS
RT ABYSSAL ZONE
RT ABYSSOBENTHIC ZONE

ABYSSOPELAGIC ZONE (cont'd)
RT APHOTIC ZONE

ACANSTEROL
BT1 STEROLS
BT2 STEROIDS
BT3 LIPIDS
BT4 ORGANIC COMPOUNDS

ACCELERATION
NT1 CORIOLIS ACCELERATION
RT ACCELEROMETERS
RT CENTRIFUGAL FORCE
RT CENTRIPETAL FORCE
RT CORIOLIS FORCE
RT KINEMATICS
RT VELOCITY

ACCELEROMETERS
BT1 INSTRUMENTS
RT ACCELERATION
RT GRAVITY METERS
RT MEASURING DEVICES
RT SEISMOMETERS
RT TRANSDUCERS
RT WAVE BUOYS
RT WAVE RECORDERS

ACCEPTABILITY
SN Added in 1980
RT ACCEPTANCE TESTS
RT CODEX STANDARDS
RT EVALUATION
RT INSPECTION
RT PERFORMANCE ASSESSMENT
RT QUALITY CONTROL
RT RELIABILITY
RT STANDARDS
RT TESTING
RT TESTS

ACCEPTABILITY TESTS
USE **ACCEPTANCE TESTS**

ACCEPTANCE TESTS
SN Added in 1980
UF acceptability tests
BT1 TESTS
RT ACCEPTABILITY
RT FISH INSPECTION
RT FOOD TECHNOLOGY
RT INSPECTION
RT ORGANOLEPTIC PROPERTIES
RT PROCESSED FISHERY PRODUCTS
RT QUALITY CONTROL

ACCESS
SN Descriptor to be used only as a qualifier
NT1 PUBLIC ACCESS
NT1 UNDERWATER ACCESS
RT INSPECTION
RT MANAGEMENT

ACCESSORY RESPIRATORY ORGANS
USE **RESPIRATORY ORGANS**

ACCIDENT PREVENTION
BT1 HEALTH AND SAFETY
RT ACCIDENTS
RT DECK EQUIPMENT
RT DIVING REGULATIONS
RT GEAR HANDLING
RT HAZARDS
RT PROTECTION
RT SAFETY DEVICES
RT SAFETY REGULATIONS

ACCIDENTS
UF disasters (man-made)
UF man-made disasters
NT1 CHEMICAL SPILLS
NT1 COLLISIONS
NT1 DIVING ACCIDENTS
NT1 OIL SPILLS
NT1 RADIATION LEAKS
RT ACCIDENT PREVENTION
RT ALARM SYSTEMS
RT BLOWOUTS
RT CAPSIZING
RT DAMAGE
RT DISASTERS
RT DROWNING
RT EMERGENCIES
RT EMERGENCY VESSELS
RT FIRE
RT FIRE FIGHTING
RT FISSION PRODUCTS
RT GROUNDINGS
RT HAZARDS
RT INJURIES
RT LIABILITY
RT LIFEBOATS
RT MEDICINE
RT SAFETY DEVICES
RT SEARCH AND RESCUE
RT SURVIVAL AT SEA

ACCLIMATION
SN Adjustment of aquatic organisms to conditions in the laboratory
RT ACCLIMATIZATION
RT ADAPTATIONS
RT BAIT CULTURE
RT CAPTIVITY
RT TOLERANCE

ACCLIMATIZATION
SN Adjustment of organisms to conditions in the aquatic environment
UF adaptations (physiological)
UF physiological adaptations
RT ACCLIMATION
RT ADAPTATIONS
RT AQUACULTURE
RT AQUACULTURE TECHNIQUES
RT CAPTIVITY
RT TOLERANCE

ACCOMMODATION
UF living quarters
RT EVACUATION
RT FISHING VESSELS
RT OFFSHORE STRUCTURES
RT RESEARCH VESSELS
RT UNDERWATER HABITATS

ACCRETING PLATE BOUNDARIES
USE **DIVERGING PLATE BOUNDARIES**

ACCRETION
UF aggradation
NT1 BEACH ACCRETION
NT2 BEACH NOURISHMENT
NT1 CRUSTAL ACCRETION
NT1 ICE ACCRETION
NT2 ICING
RT SEDIMENTATION

ACCUMULATION
SN Descriptor to be used only as a qualifier
RT BIOACCUMULATION
RT FATE

ACCUMULATION OF IONS
USE **ION ACCUMULATION**

ACCUMULATION OF SEDIMENTS
USE **SEDIMENTATION**

ACCURACY
SN Use only as a qualifier
RT CALIBRATION
RT EQUIPMENT
RT INSTRUMENTS
RT MEASUREMENT
RT RELIABILITY
RT RESOLUTION
RT TESTS

ACETATE
BT1 CARBOXYLIC ACID SALTS

ACETONE
BT1 KETONES
BT2 ORGANIC COMPOUNDS

ACETYLCHOLINE
USE **NEUROTRANSMITTERS**

ACETYLENE
USE **ETHYNE**

ACID PRECIPITATION
USE **ACID RAIN**

ACID RAIN
SN Precipitation having a pH below 5.6 due to high concentrations of sulphate, nitrate, ammonium or other anions
UF acid precipitation
BT1 ATMOSPHERIC PRECIPITATIONS
BT2 HYDROMETEORS
RT FRESHWATER POLLUTION
RT INLAND WATER ENVIRONMENT
RT RAIN
RT RAINFALL

ACIDIFICATION
SN Added in 1980
RT ACIDITY
RT FISH SILAGE
RT PH

ACIDITY
BT1 CHEMICAL PROPERTIES
BT2 PROPERTIES
RT ACIDIFICATION
RT ALKALINITY
RT BUFFERS
RT INORGANIC ACIDS
RT PH
RT PH EFFECTS
RT WATER PROPERTIES

ACIDS (INORGANIC)
USE **INORGANIC ACIDS**

ACIDS (ORGANIC)
USE **ORGANIC ACIDS**

ACOUSTIC ANALOGS
USE **ACOUSTIC MODELS**

ACOUSTIC ARRAYS
BT1 ARRAYS
NT1 SONAR ARRAYS
NT1 TRANSDUCER ARRAYS
NT1 TRANSPONDER ARRAYS
RT ACOUSTIC EQUIPMENT
RT HYDROPHONES
RT SEISMIC ARRAYS
RT SONAR

ASFIS Thesaurus

ACOUSTIC ARRAYS (cont'd)
RT   TRANSDUCERS
RT   TRANSPONDERS

ACOUSTIC BAFFLES
USE   **ACOUSTIC INSULATION**

ACOUSTIC BEACONS
RT   ACOUSTIC EQUIPMENT
RT   ACOUSTIC NAVIGATION
RT   ACOUSTIC PINGERS
RT   ACOUSTIC TRANSPONDERS
RT   DYNAMIC POSITIONING
RT   LOCATING
RT   NAVIGATIONAL AIDS
RT   POSITIONING SYSTEMS
RT   TRACKING

ACOUSTIC CAVITATION
USE   **CAVITATION**

ACOUSTIC CHANNELS
USE   **SOUND CHANNELS**

ACOUSTIC COMMAND SYSTEMS
RT   ACOUSTIC EQUIPMENT
RT   ACOUSTIC TELEMETRY
RT   ACOUSTIC TRANSPONDERS
RT   REMOTE CONTROL

ACOUSTIC CURRENT METERS
BT1   CURRENT METERS
BT2   MEASURING DEVICES
RT   CURRENT SENSORS
RT   EULERIAN CURRENT MEASUREMENT

ACOUSTIC DATA
RT   ACOUSTIC PROPERTIES
RT   DATA
RT   LIMNOLOGICAL DATA
RT   OCEANOGRAPHIC DATA
RT   SEDIMENT PROPERTIES
RT   SOUND VELOCITY
RT   WATER PROPERTIES

ACOUSTIC DETECTION
USE   **SONAR DETECTION**

ACOUSTIC DEVICES
USE   **ACOUSTIC EQUIPMENT**

ACOUSTIC DIRECTION FINDING
USE   **ECHO RANGING**

ACOUSTIC DISTANCE MEASUREMENT
USE   **ECHO RANGING**

ACOUSTIC DOPPLER SONAR
USE   **DOPPLER SONAR**

ACOUSTIC EMISSION
RT   NONDESTRUCTIVE TESTING

ACOUSTIC EMISSION TESTING
USE   **NONDESTRUCTIVE TESTING**

ACOUSTIC EQUIPMENT
UF   acoustic devices
UF   acoustic systems
UF   instruments (acoustic)
BT1   EQUIPMENT
NT1   SOUND GENERATORS
NT2   PINGERS
RT   ACOUSTIC ARRAYS
RT   ACOUSTIC BEACONS
RT   ACOUSTIC COMMAND SYSTEMS
RT   ACOUSTIC TELEMETRY
RT   ACOUSTIC TRACKING SYSTEMS
RT   ACOUSTIC TRANSDUCERS
RT   ACOUSTIC TRANSPONDERS

ACOUSTIC EQUIPMENT (cont'd)
RT   ACOUSTICS
RT   DOPPLER SONAR
RT   ECHO INTEGRATORS
RT   ECHO SURVEYS
RT   ECHOSOUNDING
RT   ELECTROACOUSTIC DEVICES
RT   ELECTRONIC EQUIPMENT
RT   FISH COUNTERS
RT   FISHING OPERATIONS
RT   MICROPHONES
RT   NET SOUNDERS
RT   SONAR
RT   SONAR ARRAYS
RT   SONAR RECEIVERS
RT   SONAR TARGETS
RT   SONIC TAGS
RT   SOUND RECORDERS
RT   SOUND WAVES
RT   SUB-BOTTOM PROFILING
RT   SURVEYING EQUIPMENT
RT   TRANSPONDER ARRAYS

ACOUSTIC GENERATORS
USE   **SOUND GENERATORS**

ACOUSTIC HOLOGRAPHY
BT1   HOLOGRAPHY
RT   ACOUSTIC TOMOGRAPHY
RT   IMAGING TECHNIQUES
RT   SEISMIC DATA PROCESSING

ACOUSTIC IMAGERY
UF   acoustic sensing
BT1   IMAGERY
BT2   REMOTE SENSING
NT1   ACOUSTIC TOMOGRAPHY
NT1   SONAR IMAGERY
RT   ACOUSTIC IMAGES
RT   SODAR
RT   SONAR

ACOUSTIC IMAGES
RT   ACOUSTIC IMAGERY

ACOUSTIC IMPEDANCE
BT1   IMPEDANCE
RT   ACOUSTIC PROPERTIES
RT   SEDIMENT PROPERTIES
RT   SOUND VELOCITY

ACOUSTIC INSULATION
UF   acoustic baffles
UF   baffles (sound)
UF   sound insulation
BT1   INSULATING MATERIALS
BT2   MATERIALS
RT   ACOUSTIC PROPERTIES
RT   NOISE REDUCTION
RT   SOUND ABSORPTION
RT   SUPPRESSORS

ACOUSTIC INTENSITY
USE   **SOUND INTENSITY**

ACOUSTIC MEASUREMENT
USE   **SOUND MEASUREMENT**

ACOUSTIC MODELS
UF   acoustic analogs
BT1   ANALOG MODELS
BT2   MODELS
RT   ACOUSTICS

ACOUSTIC NAVIGATION
UF   doppler sonar navigation
UF   sonar navigation
UF   transponder navigation
BT1   NAVIGATION
RT   ACOUSTIC BEACONS

ACOUSTIC NAVIGATION (cont'd)
RT   DOPPLER SONAR
RT   DYNAMIC POSITIONING
RT   NAVIGATION UNDERWATER
RT   SONAR

ACOUSTIC PINGERS
RT   ACOUSTIC BEACONS

ACOUSTIC PROPERTIES
UF   sound properties
BT1   PHYSICAL PROPERTIES
BT2   PROPERTIES
RT   ACOUSTIC DATA
RT   ACOUSTIC IMPEDANCE
RT   ACOUSTIC INSULATION
RT   ACOUSTICS
RT   CAVITATION
RT   SEDIMENTS
RT   SEISMIC WAVES
RT   SOUND ATTENUATION
RT   SOUND INTENSITY
RT   SOUND VELOCITY
RT   TARGET STRENGTH

ACOUSTIC RADIATORS
USE   **SOUND GENERATORS**

ACOUSTIC RELEASE MECHANISMS
USE   **RELEASE MECHANISMS**

ACOUSTIC SENSING
USE   **ACOUSTIC IMAGERY**

ACOUSTIC SIZING TECHNIQUES
USE   **FISH SIZING**

ACOUSTIC SPECTRA
USE   **SOUND SPECTRA**

ACOUSTIC STRATIGRAPHY
USE   **SEISMIC STRATIGRAPHY**

ACOUSTIC SURVEYS
USE   **ECHO SURVEYS**

ACOUSTIC SURVEYS (ATMOSPHERE)
USE   **SODAR**

ACOUSTIC SYSTEMS
USE   **ACOUSTIC EQUIPMENT**

ACOUSTIC TAGS
USE   **SONIC TAGS**

ACOUSTIC TELEMETRY
BT1   TELEMETRY
BT2   COMMUNICATION SYSTEMS
RT   ACOUSTIC COMMAND SYSTEMS
RT   ACOUSTIC EQUIPMENT
RT   ACOUSTIC TRACKING SYSTEMS

ACOUSTIC TOMOGRAPHY
UF   tomography (acoustic)
BT1   ACOUSTIC IMAGERY
BT2   IMAGERY
BT3   REMOTE SENSING
RT   ACOUSTIC HOLOGRAPHY

ACOUSTIC TRACKING
USE   **TRACKING**

ACOUSTIC TRACKING SYSTEMS
UF   underwater tracking systems
RT   ACOUSTIC EQUIPMENT
RT   ACOUSTIC TELEMETRY
RT   ACTIVE SONAR
RT   DETECTION
RT   ECHO RANGING
RT   NAVIGATION UNDERWATER

ACOUSTIC TRACKING SYSTEMS (cont'd)
RT	PINGERS
RT	SURVEILLANCE AND ENFORCEMENT
RT	UNDERSEA WARFARE

ACOUSTIC TRANSDUCERS
BT1	TRANSDUCERS
NT1	HYDROPHONES
NT1	MICROPHONES
NT1	SONAR TRANSDUCERS
RT	ACOUSTIC EQUIPMENT
RT	ELECTROACOUSTIC DEVICES
RT	PIEZOELECTRIC TRANSDUCERS

ACOUSTIC TRANSPONDERS
UF	beacons (transponders)
BT1	TRANSPONDERS
NT1	SONAR TRANSPONDERS
RT	ACOUSTIC BEACONS
RT	ACOUSTIC COMMAND SYSTEMS
RT	ACOUSTIC EQUIPMENT
RT	ELECTRONIC EQUIPMENT
RT	NAVIGATIONAL AIDS
RT	SWALLOW FLOATS

ACOUSTIC WAVE ABSORPTION
USE	**SOUND ABSORPTION**

ACOUSTIC WAVE ATTENUATION
USE	**SOUND ATTENUATION**

ACOUSTIC WAVE DIFFRACTION
USE	**SOUND DIFFRACTION**

ACOUSTIC WAVE DISPERSION
USE	**SOUND DISPERSION**

ACOUSTIC WAVE PROPAGATION
USE	**SOUND PROPAGATION**

ACOUSTIC WAVE REFLECTION
USE	**SOUND REFLECTION**

ACOUSTIC WAVE REFRACTION
USE	**SOUND REFRACTION**

ACOUSTIC WAVE SCATTERING
USE	**SOUND SCATTERING**

ACOUSTIC WAVE TRANSMISSION
USE	**SOUND TRANSMISSION**

ACOUSTIC WAVES
USE	**SOUND WAVES**

ACOUSTICS
UF	underwater acoustics
BT1	PHYSICS
NT1	BIOACOUSTICS
NT1	ULTRASONICS
RT	ACOUSTIC EQUIPMENT
RT	ACOUSTIC MODELS
RT	ACOUSTIC PROPERTIES
RT	ECHO SURVEYS
RT	ECHOES
RT	ELECTROACOUSTIC DEVICES
RT	SONIC TAGS
RT	SOUND
RT	SOUND CHANNELS
RT	SOUND RECORDERS
RT	SOUND WAVES
RT	UNDERWATER NOISE

ACQUISITION
NT1	DATA ACQUISITION
RT	COSTS
RT	PURCHASING

ACRONYMS
SN	Added in 1980
RT	EQUIPMENT
RT	EXPEDITIONS
RT	INTERNATIONAL ORGANIZATIONS
RT	ORGANIZATIONS
RT	TERMINOLOGY

ACRYLIC ACID
BT1	ORGANIC ACIDS
BT2	ORGANIC COMPOUNDS

ACRYLICS
BT1	PLASTICS
BT2	MATERIALS

ACTIN
SN	Before 1982 search PROTEINS
BT1	PROTEINS
BT2	ORGANIC COMPOUNDS
RT	ANIMAL PHYSIOLOGY
RT	MUSCLES

ACTINIDE COMPOUNDS
NT1	ACTINIUM COMPOUNDS
NT1	AMERICIUM COMPOUNDS
NT1	BERKELIUM COMPOUNDS
NT1	CALIFORNIUM COMPOUNDS
NT1	CURIUM COMPOUNDS
NT1	NEPTUNIUM COMPOUNDS
NT1	PLUTONIUM COMPOUNDS
NT1	THORIUM COMPOUNDS
NT1	URANIUM COMPOUNDS
RT	ACTINIDES

ACTINIDES
BT1	METALS
RT	ACTINIDE COMPOUNDS
RT	ACTINIUM
RT	AMERICIUM
RT	BERKELIUM
RT	CALIFORNIUM
RT	CURIUM
RT	FERMIUM
RT	NEPTUNIUM
RT	NOBELIUM
RT	PLUTONIUM
RT	PROTACTINIUM
RT	THORIUM
RT	TRANSITION ELEMENTS
RT	URANIUM

ACTINIUM
BT1	CHEMICAL ELEMENTS
RT	ACTINIDES
RT	ACTINIUM COMPOUNDS
RT	ACTINIUM ISOTOPES
RT	RADIOACTIVITY
RT	TRANSITION ELEMENTS

ACTINIUM COMPOUNDS
BT1	ACTINIDE COMPOUNDS
RT	ACTINIUM
RT	CHEMICAL COMPOUNDS

ACTINIUM ISOTOPES
BT1	ISOTOPES
RT	ACTINIUM

ACTINOMETERS
BT1	RADIOMETERS
BT2	REMOTE SENSING EQUIPMENT
BT3	EQUIPMENT
NT1	PYRANOMETERS
NT1	PYRGEOMETERS
NT1	PYRHELIOMETERS
RT	MEASURING DEVICES
RT	METEOROLOGICAL INSTRUMENTS
RT	SOLAR RADIATION
RT	TERRESTRIAL RADIATION

ACTIVATED SLUDGE
USE	**SLUDGE**

ACTIVATION ANALYSIS
BT1	ANALYTICAL TECHNIQUES
NT1	NEUTRON ACTIVATION ANALYSIS

ACTIVE MARGINS
UF	convergent margins
UF	seismic margins
BT1	CONTINENTAL MARGINS
BT2	SUBMARINE FEATURES
BT3	TOPOGRAPHIC FEATURES
RT	EARTHQUAKES
RT	FOREARC BASINS
RT	ISLAND ARCS
RT	MARGINAL BASINS
RT	OROGENY
RT	PLATE BOUNDARIES
RT	PLATE CONVERGENCE
RT	PLATE MARGINS
RT	SUBDUCTION
RT	VOLCANISM

ACTIVE SONAR
BT1	SONAR
BT2	REMOTE SENSING EQUIPMENT
BT3	EQUIPMENT
NT1	DOPPLER SONAR
NT1	ECHOSOUNDERS
NT1	MULTIBEAM SONAR
NT1	SIDE SCAN SONAR
RT	ACOUSTIC TRACKING SYSTEMS
RT	ECHO RANGING
RT	ECHO SURVEYS
RT	FISH DETECTION
RT	INSONIFICATION
RT	SONAR DETECTION
RT	SONAR IMAGERY
RT	SONOGRAPHS

ACTIVITY COEFFICIENT
USE	**THERMODYNAMIC ACTIVITY**

ACTIVITY PATTERNS
UF	activity rhythms
RT	BEHAVIOUR
RT	BIOLOGICAL RHYTHMS
RT	FEEDING
RT	LOCAL MOVEMENTS
RT	LOCOMOTION
RT	MIGRATIONS

ACTIVITY RHYTHMS
USE	**ACTIVITY PATTERNS**

ACTUAL AGE
USE	**ABSOLUTE AGE**

ACYCLIC HYDROCARBONS
UF	branched chain saturated hydrocarbons
UF	straight chain saturated hydrocarbons
BT1	SATURATED HYDROCARBONS
BT2	HYDROCARBONS
BT3	ORGANIC COMPOUNDS
NT1	BUTANE
NT1	DODECANE
NT1	ETHANE
NT1	METHANE
NT1	PROPANE

ADAPTATIONS
SN	Used only as a qualifier. Use of a more specific term is recommended
BT1	BIOLOGICAL PHENOMENA
NT1	CAMOUFLAGE
NT1	CHROMATIC ADAPTATIONS
NT1	MIMICRY
NT1	OSMOTIC ADAPTATIONS

ASFIS Thesaurus

ADAPTATIONS (cont'd)
RT	ACCLIMATION
RT	ACCLIMATIZATION
RT	BEHAVIOUR
RT	ECOTYPES
RT	STIMULI
RT	SYNECOLOGY
RT	TOLERANCE

ADAPTATIONS (PHYSIOLOGICAL)
USE	**ACCLIMATIZATION**

ADAPTIVE COLOURATION
USE	**MIMICRY**

ADDITIONAL CATCH
USE	**BY CATCH**

ADDITIVES
UF	modifiers
NT1	FOOD ADDITIVES
RT	AGENTS
RT	ANTIFREEZES
RT	COAGULANTS
RT	ENZYME INHIBITORS
RT	FUELS
RT	PRESERVATIVES
RT	SOLVENTS

ADENOSINE DIPHOSPHATE
USE	**ADP**

ADENOSINE MONOPHOSPHATE
USE	**AMP**

ADENOSINE TRIPHOSPHATE
USE	**ATP**

ADHESION
UF	bonding
RT	ADHESIVES
RT	SEDIMENT STRUCTURE
RT	SURFACE PROPERTIES

ADHESIVES
SN	Added in 1980
UF	binders (adhesives)
UF	cements (adhesives)
UF	rubber (adhesives)
RT	ADHESION
RT	EPOXY RESINS
RT	FISH GLUE

ADIABATIC COOLING
USE	**ADIABATIC PROCESSES**

ADIABATIC HEATING
USE	**ADIABATIC PROCESSES**

ADIABATIC LAPSE RATES
SN	Use for adiabatic gradients in atmosphere
BT1	TEMPERATURE GRADIENTS
RT	ADIABATIC PROCESSES
RT	ADIABATIC TEMPERATURE GRADIENT
RT	AIR TEMPERATURE
RT	POTENTIAL TEMPERATURE

ADIABATIC PROCESSES
UF	adiabatic cooling
UF	adiabatic heating
BT1	ISOTHERMAL PROCESSES
RT	ADIABATIC LAPSE RATES
RT	ADIABATIC TEMPERATURE GRADIENT
RT	POTENTIAL DENSITY
RT	POTENTIAL TEMPERATURE
RT	THERMODYNAMICS

ADIABATIC TEMPERATURE GRADIENT
SN	Use for adiabatic gradient in water
BT1	TEMPERATURE GRADIENTS
RT	ADIABATIC LAPSE RATES
RT	ADIABATIC PROCESSES
RT	POTENTIAL TEMPERATURE
RT	WATER

ADJACENT SEAS
USE	**MARGINAL SEAS**

ADMINISTRATION
USE	**MANAGEMENT**

ADP
UF	adenosine diphosphate
BT1	NUCLEOTIDES
BT2	ORGANIC COMPOUNDS
RT	CHEMICAL COMPOUNDS
RT	PHOSPHATES

ADRENAL GLANDS
SN	Before 1982 search ENDOCRINE GLANDS
UF	suprarenal glands
BT1	ENDOCRINE GLANDS
BT2	GLANDS
BT3	SECRETORY ORGANS
RT	HORMONES
RT	KIDNEYS
RT	METABOLISM

ADSORBENTS
USE	**ADSORPTION**

ADSORPTION
SN	The taking up of one substance at the surface of another
UF	adsorbents
BT1	SORPTION
RT	CHROMATOGRAPHIC TECHNIQUES
RT	DIFFUSION
RT	DRYING
RT	EXCHANGE CAPACITY
RT	OIL REMOVAL
RT	OIL WATER SEPARATION
RT	OSMOSIS
RT	SEPARATION
RT	SURFACE PROPERTIES
RT	WATER POLLUTION TREATMENT

ADULTS
RT	DEVELOPMENTAL STAGES
RT	LIFE CYCLE
RT	SEXUAL MATURITY

ADVECTION
SN	Process of transport of property by mass motion
UF	marine advection
BT1	TRANSPORT PROCESSES
NT1	CONVECTION
NT2	ATMOSPHERIC CONVECTION
NT2	CELLULAR CONVECTION
NT2	FORCED CONVECTION
NT2	MANTLE CONVECTION
NT2	OCEANIC CONVECTION
NT1	HORIZONTAL ADVECTION
NT1	SALT ADVECTION
NT1	VERTICAL ADVECTION
RT	AIR
RT	ATMOSPHERIC CIRCULATION
RT	CIRCULATION
RT	CONVERGENCE ZONES
RT	HEAT TRANSPORT
RT	OCEANIC CONVERGENCES

ADVECTION FOG
USE	**FOG**

ADVERTISEMENTS
USE	**PUBLICITY MATERIAL**

AEOLIAN DEPOSITS
USE	**EOLIAN DEPOSITS**

AEOLIAN DUST
USE	**EOLIAN DUST**

AEOLIAN PROCESSES
USE	**EOLIAN PROCESSES**

AEOLIAN TRANSPORT
USE	**EOLIAN TRANSPORT**

AERATION
NT1	ARTIFICIAL AERATION
NT1	BIOAERATION
RT	AIR
RT	AIR BUBBLES
RT	BREAKING WAVES
RT	BUBBLES
RT	BUBBLING
RT	DISSOLVED OXYGEN
RT	MIXING PROCESSES
RT	OXYGEN
RT	OXYGENATION
RT	SELF PURIFICATION
RT	SEPARATION
RT	SEWAGE TREATMENT
RT	SLUDGE TREATMENT
RT	WATER CIRCULATION
RT	WATER FILTRATION
RT	WATER MIXING
RT	WATER POLLUTION TREATMENT
RT	WATER PURIFICATION
RT	WATER QUALITY CONTROL
RT	WATER TREATMENT

AERIAL EXPOSURE
USE	**AIR EXPOSURE**

AERIAL PHOTOGRAPHS
SN	Before 1982 search AERIAL PHOTOGRAPHY
BT1	PHOTOGRAPHS
BT2	AUDIOVISUAL MATERIAL
BT3	DOCUMENTS
RT	AERIAL PHOTOGRAPHY
RT	MAPPING
RT	SATELLITE MOSAICS

AERIAL PHOTOGRAPHY
BT1	PHOTOGRAPHY
BT2	IMAGERY
BT3	REMOTE SENSING
NT1	SATELLITE PHOTOGRAPHY
RT	AERIAL PHOTOGRAPHS
RT	AERIAL SURVEYS
RT	AIRBORNE SENSING
RT	AIRCRAFT
RT	GEOSENSING
RT	HELICOPTERS
RT	MAPPING
RT	PHOTOGRAMMETRY
RT	PHOTOGRAPHIC EQUIPMENT
RT	STEREOPHOTOGRAPHY

AERIAL SURVEYS
BT1	SURVEYS
RT	AERIAL PHOTOGRAPHY
RT	AIRBORNE EQUIPMENT
RT	AIRBORNE SENSING
RT	AIRCRAFT
RT	BALLOONS
RT	ELECTRONIC EQUIPMENT
RT	FISHERY SURVEYS
RT	HELICOPTERS

ASFIS Thesaurus

AERIAL SURVEYS (cont'd)
RT	ICE COVER
RT	ICE ROUTEING
RT	INFRARED DETECTORS
RT	REMOTE SENSING
RT	SATELLITES
RT	STOCK ASSESSMENT

AEROBIC BACTERIA
SN	See also the taxonomic index
BT1	BACTERIA
BT2	MICROORGANISMS
RT	SELF PURIFICATION

AEROBIC CONDITIONS
USE	**OXIC CONDITIONS**

AEROBIC RESPIRATION
BT1	RESPIRATION
RT	ANOXIA
RT	BIOCHEMICAL OXYGEN DEMAND
RT	CARBONATE COMPENSATION DEPTH
RT	COMPENSATION DEPTH
RT	DISSOLVED OXYGEN
RT	GILLS
RT	LUNGS
RT	OXYGEN CONSUMPTION
RT	RESPIRATORY ORGANS
RT	RESPIROMETERS

AEROBIC SEDIMENTS
USE	**OXIC SEDIMENTS**

AERODYNAMICS
BT1	FLUID DYNAMICS
BT2	FLUID MECHANICS
BT3	MECHANICS
BT4	PHYSICS

AEROMAGNETIC SURVEYS
BT1	SURVEYS
RT	AIRBORNE SENSING
RT	GEOMAGNETIC FIELD
RT	MAGNETIC EXPLORATION

AERONOMY
USE	**ATMOSPHERIC PHYSICS**

AEROSOLS
UF	atmospheric aerosols
UF	continental aerosols
UF	marine aerosols
BT1	COLLOIDS
NT1	RADIOACTIVE AEROSOLS
RT	AIR POLLUTION
RT	AIR SAMPLING
RT	AIR-WATER INTERFACE
RT	ATMOSPHERIC CHEMISTRY
RT	ATMOSPHERIC PARTICULATES
RT	BUBBLE BURSTING
RT	DUST
RT	FALLOUT
RT	SALT PARTICLES
RT	SPRAY
RT	SURFACE MICROLAYER
RT	TURBIDITY

AESTIVATION
RT	ANIMAL PHYSIOLOGY
RT	BODY TEMPERATURE
RT	DORMANCY
RT	ECOPHYSIOLOGY
RT	ENVIRONMENTAL EFFECTS
RT	HEAT BALANCE
RT	HIBERNATION
RT	METABOLISM
RT	PLANT PHYSIOLOGY
RT	TEMPERATURE TOLERANCE
RT	THERMOREGULATION

AETIOLOGY
SN	The medical study of the causation of diseases. Added in 1982
UF	etiology
BT1	MEDICINE
BT2	HEALTH AND SAFETY
RT	DISEASE CONTROL
RT	DISEASE DETECTION
RT	DISEASES

AFFERENT NERVES
USE	**NERVES**

AGAR
BT1	SEAWEED PRODUCTS
BT2	PROCESSED FISHERY PRODUCTS
BT3	FISHERY PRODUCTS
BT4	PRODUCTS
RT	ALGINATES
RT	CARBOHYDRATES
RT	CARRAGEENINS
RT	CHEMICAL EXTRACTION
RT	COLLOIDS
RT	CULTURE MEDIA
RT	POLYSACCHARIDES

AGAROSE
BT1	POLYSACCHARIDES
BT2	SACCHARIDES
BT3	CARBOHYDRATES
BT4	ORGANIC COMPOUNDS

AGE
SN	Use of a more specific term is recommended. Added in 1982
NT1	ABSOLUTE AGE
NT1	AGE OF SEAWATER
NT1	AGE OF TIDE
NT1	BIOLOGICAL AGE
NT2	AGE AT RECRUITMENT
NT1	EARTH AGE
NT1	WAVE AGE
RT	AGE DETERMINATION
RT	AGING
RT	GEOCHRONOMETRY
RT	RESIDENCE TIME

AGE (BIOLOGICAL)
USE	**BIOLOGICAL AGE**

AGE (ORGANISMS)
USE	**BIOLOGICAL AGE**

AGE AT FIRST MATURITY
USE	**AGE AT RECRUITMENT**

AGE AT RECRUITMENT
SN	Age at which fish are recruited as fishable stock. Added in 1982
UF	age at first maturity
BT1	BIOLOGICAL AGE
BT2	AGE
RT	AGE COMPOSITION
RT	RECRUITMENT

AGE COMPOSITION
SN	Year-class frequencies
BT1	POPULATION STRUCTURE
BT2	POPULATION CHARACTERISTICS
RT	AGE AT RECRUITMENT
RT	AGE DETERMINATION
RT	AGE GROUPS
RT	BIOLOGICAL AGING
RT	GROWTH
RT	RECRUITMENT
RT	SIZE DISTRIBUTION

AGE DETERMINATION
SN	Before 1982 search also AGEING METHODS. Restricted to age determination in aquatic organisms. For physical purposes use GEOCHRONOMETRY
UF	biological dating
UF	dating (biological)
UF	organism dating
NT1	OTOLITH READING
NT1	SCALE READING
RT	AGE
RT	AGE COMPOSITION
RT	AGE GROUPS
RT	BIOLOGICAL AGE
RT	BIOLOGICAL AGING
RT	FOSSILS
RT	GROWTH

AGE DETERMINATION (EARTH SCIENCES)
USE	**GEOCHRONOMETRY**

AGE GROUPS
SN	Before 1982 search AGE COMPOSITION. A group of fish at a given age
UF	0 group
RT	AGE COMPOSITION
RT	AGE DETERMINATION
RT	FISHERY SURVEYS

AGE-LENGTH RELATIONSHIPS
USE	**GROWTH CURVES**

AGE OF EARTH
USE	**EARTH AGE**

AGE OF SEAWATER
BT1	AGE
RT	RESIDENCE TIME
RT	SEA WATER
RT	SUBSURFACE WATER
RT	WATER MASSES

AGE OF TIDE
UF	tide (age)
BT1	AGE
RT	SPRING TIDES
RT	TIDAL RANGE
RT	TIDAL RESONANCE

AGEING
USE	**AGING**

AGEING (BIOLOGICAL)
USE	**BIOLOGICAL AGING**

AGENTS
SN	Use of a more specific term is recommended; consult terms listed below. Added in 1980
RT	ADDITIVES
RT	ANTICOAGULANTS
RT	ANTIFOULING SUBSTANCES
RT	ANTIFREEZES
RT	ANTIOXIDANTS
RT	ANTIPARASITIC AGENTS
RT	COAGULANTS
RT	DISPERSANTS
RT	DRUGS
RT	INHIBITORS
RT	MUTAGENS
RT	PRESERVATIVES
RT	SOLVENTS
RT	SURFACTANTS

AGENTS (ANTIPARASITIC)
USE	**ANTIPARASITIC AGENTS**

ASFIS Thesaurus

AGEOSTROPHIC FLOW
BT1	FLUID FLOW
BT2	FLUID MOTION
RT	GEOSTROPHIC FLOW
RT	GEOSTROPHY

AGGLUTININS
UF	haemagglutinins
BT1	ANTIBODIES
BT2	SERUM
BT3	BODY FLUIDS
RT	BACTERIA
RT	BLOOD CELLS

AGGRADATION
USE	**ACCRETION**

AGGREGATES
SN	Sand and gravel dredged and used as construction material
BT1	SEABED DEPOSITS
BT2	MINERAL DEPOSITS
BT3	MINERAL RESOURCES
BT4	NATURAL RESOURCES
RT	AGGREGATION
RT	DREDGING
RT	GRAVEL
RT	SAND
RT	SEDIMENTS

AGGREGATION
SN	Descriptor to be used only as a qualifier
RT	AGGREGATES

AGGREGATIONS (ECOLOGICAL)
USE	**ECOLOGICAL AGGREGATIONS**

AGGREGATIONS (ORGANISMS)
USE	**ORGANISM AGGREGATIONS**

AGGRESSION
USE	**AGGRESSIVE BEHAVIOUR**

AGGRESSIVE BEHAVIOUR
SN	Before 1982 search AGONISTIC BEHAVIOUR
UF	aggression
UF	aggressive mimicry
BT1	BEHAVIOUR
RT	AGONISTIC BEHAVIOUR
RT	PECKING ORDER
RT	TERRITORIALITY

AGGRESSIVE MIMICRY
USE	**AGGRESSIVE BEHAVIOUR**

AGING
SN	Before 1982 search also AGEING. Use of a more specific term is recommended. Added in 1980
UF	ageing
NT1	BIOLOGICAL AGING
RT	AGE

AGING (BIOLOGICAL)
USE	**BIOLOGICAL AGING**

AGONISTIC BEHAVIOUR
SN	Animal behaviour including threatening behaviour, posturing, and fleeing
BT1	BEHAVIOUR
RT	AGGRESSIVE BEHAVIOUR
RT	DISPLAY BEHAVIOUR

AGREEMENTS
USE	**INTERNATIONAL AGREEMENTS**

AGRICULTURAL POLLUTION
UF	pollution (agriculture)
BT1	POLLUTION
RT	AGRICULTURAL RUNOFF
RT	AGRICULTURE
RT	CHEMICAL POLLUTANTS
RT	CHEMICAL POLLUTION
RT	DDT
RT	EUTROPHICATION
RT	FERTILIZERS
RT	IRRIGATION
RT	PESTICIDES
RT	POLLUTION CONTROL
RT	WASTE WATER

AGRICULTURAL RUNOFF
UF	runoff from agricultural land
BT1	RUNOFF
BT2	DRAINAGE WATER
BT3	WATER
RT	AGRICULTURAL POLLUTION
RT	AGRICULTURE
RT	CHEMICAL POLLUTANTS
RT	CHEMICAL POLLUTION
RT	DDT
RT	FERTILIZERS
RT	IRRIGATION
RT	PESTICIDES
RT	WASTE WATER

AGRICULTURE
UF	life sciences (agriculture)
RT	AGRICULTURAL POLLUTION
RT	AGRICULTURAL RUNOFF
RT	AGROPISCICULTURE
RT	IRRIGATION
RT	RICE FIELD AQUACULTURE
RT	SOILS

AGROPISCICULTURE
SN	Combination or alternation of agriculture and freshwater aquaculture
UF	fish-cum-chicken culture
UF	fish-cum-duck culture
UF	fish-cum-pig culture
UF	integrated agriculture
NT1	RICE FIELD AQUACULTURE
RT	AGRICULTURE
RT	AQUACULTURE
RT	AQUACULTURE TECHNIQUES
RT	FISH CULTURE
RT	FISH PONDS
RT	FRESHWATER AQUACULTURE
RT	FRESHWATER FISH
RT	FROG CULTURE
RT	HERBIVOROUS FISH
RT	PLANT CULTURE
RT	POND CULTURE
RT	WASTEWATER AQUACULTURE
RT	WATER LEVELS

AIR
BT1	GASES
BT2	FLUIDS
RT	ADVECTION
RT	AERATION
RT	AIR BUBBLES
RT	AIR CONDITIONING
RT	AIR POLLUTION
RT	AIR TEMPERATURE
RT	EARTH ATMOSPHERE
RT	LIFE SUPPORT SYSTEMS
RT	OXYGEN
RT	OXYGEN DEMAND
RT	RESPIRATION

AIR BLADDER
USE	**SWIM BLADDER**

AIR-BREATHING FISH
SN	Added in 1982
BT1	FISH
BT2	AQUATIC ANIMALS
RT	FISH CULTURE
RT	FRESHWATER AQUACULTURE
RT	INTENSIVE CULTURE
RT	POND CULTURE

AIR BUBBLES
BT1	BUBBLES
RT	AERATION
RT	AIR
RT	AIR-WATER INTERFACE
RT	ARTIFICIAL AERATION
RT	BUBBLE BURSTING
RT	CAPILLARITY
RT	CAVITATION
RT	FOAMS
RT	GASES
RT	ICE PREVENTION
RT	SALT NUCLEI
RT	SURFACE MICROLAYER

AIR COMPRESSORS
USE	**COMPRESSORS**

AIR CONDITIONING
RT	AIR
RT	LIFE SUPPORT SYSTEMS
RT	UNDERWATER HABITATS
RT	VENTILATION

AIR CONTAMINATION
USE	**AIR POLLUTION**

AIR CUSHION VEHICLES
USE	**HOVERCRAFT**

AIR EXPOSURE
SN	Added in 1980
UF	aerial exposure
UF	exposure (to air)
RT	EXPOSURE TOLERANCE
RT	INTERTIDAL ENVIRONMENT

AIR FLOW OVER LAND
BT1	FLOW OVER SURFACES
BT2	FLUID FLOW
BT3	FLUID MOTION
RT	ATMOSPHERIC MOTION
RT	TOPOGRAPHIC EFFECTS

AIR FLOW OVER WATER
UF	flow over water surface
BT1	FLOW OVER SURFACES
BT2	FLUID FLOW
BT3	FLUID MOTION
RT	ATMOSPHERIC MOTION
RT	WAVE INTERACTIONS
RT	WAVE-AIR INTERACTION
RT	WIND WAVE GENERATION
RT	WIND-WAVE INTERACTION

AIR GUNS
BT1	SEISMIC ENERGY SOURCES

AIR-ICE INTERFACE
UF	ice-air interface
BT1	INTERFACES
RT	ABLATION
RT	EVAPORATION
RT	HEAT EXCHANGE
RT	ICE
RT	ICE CAPS
RT	SENSIBLE HEAT TRANSFER

AIR MASSES
NT1	POLAR AIR MASSES
RT	ATMOSPHERIC DISTURBANCES
RT	ATMOSPHERIC FRONTS
RT	FRONTOGENESIS

AIR MOTION
USE	**ATMOSPHERIC MOTION**

AIR POISONING
USE	**AIR POLLUTION**

AIR POLLUTION
SN	Including its effects on aquatic environment
UF	air contamination
UF	air poisoning
UF	atmospheric pollution
UF	pollution (air)
BT1	POLLUTION
RT	AEROSOLS
RT	AIR
RT	AIR SAMPLING
RT	ANTHROPOGENIC FACTORS
RT	ASHES
RT	ATMOSPHERIC CHEMISTRY
RT	ATMOSPHERIC PARTICULATES
RT	CLIMATIC CHANGES
RT	DUST
RT	FALLOUT
RT	FLY ASH
RT	FOSSIL FUELS
RT	HAZE
RT	ODOUR
RT	POLLUTANTS
RT	POLLUTION CONTROL
RT	PUBLIC HEALTH
RT	SMOKE
RT	SURFACE MICROLAYER
RT	TEMPERATURE INVERSIONS
RT	WASTES
RT	WATER POLLUTION

AIR PUMPS
USE	**PUMPS**

AIR SAMPLING
BT1	SAMPLING
RT	AEROSOLS
RT	AIR POLLUTION
RT	ATMOSPHERIC CHEMISTRY
RT	ATMOSPHERIC PARTICULATES

AIR-SEA COUPLING
RT	AIR-SEA INTERACTION
RT	METEOROLOGY
RT	OCEAN-ATMOSPHERE SYSTEM
RT	OCEAN-ICE-ATMOSPHERE SYSTEM

AIR-SEA EXCHANGES
USE	**AIR-WATER EXCHANGES**

AIR-SEA INTERACTION
RT	AIR-SEA COUPLING
RT	AIR-WATER EXCHANGES
RT	AIR-WATER INTERFACE
RT	INTERACTIONS
RT	METEOROLOGY
RT	OCEAN-ATMOSPHERE SYSTEM
RT	SEA SURFACE
RT	TELECONNECTIONS

AIR-SEA TRANSFER
USE	**AIR-WATER EXCHANGES**

AIR TEMPERATURE
UF	dry bulb temperature
BT1	TEMPERATURE
BT2	THERMODYNAMIC PROPERTIES
BT3	PHYSICAL PROPERTIES

AIR TEMPERATURE (cont'd)
BT4	PROPERTIES
RT	ADIABATIC LAPSE RATES
RT	AIR
RT	CARGOES
RT	CLIMATE
RT	CLIMATOLOGY
RT	COLD SEASON
RT	ENVIRONMENTAL CONDITIONS
RT	EVAPORATION
RT	HEAT
RT	ISOTHERMS
RT	METEOROLOGY
RT	POTENTIAL TEMPERATURE
RT	RADIOSONDES
RT	SOUTHERN OSCILLATION
RT	STORAGE CONDITIONS
RT	THERMOMETERS
RT	TROPOSPHERE
RT	WATER TEMPERATURE
RT	WEATHER
RT	WEATHER MAPS

AIR TRANSPORTATION
SN	Carriage of passengers and goods by air
BT1	TRANSPORTATION
RT	AIRCRAFT
RT	HELICOPTERS
RT	HELIDECKS
RT	HOVERCRAFT

AIR-WATER BOUNDARY LAYER
USE	**ATMOSPHERIC BOUNDARY LAYER**

AIR-WATER EXCHANGES
UF	air-sea exchanges
UF	air-sea transfer
UF	sea-air exchanges
UF	water-air exchanges
RT	AIR-SEA INTERACTION
RT	AIR-WATER INTERFACE
RT	AIR-WATER TEMPERATURE DIFFERENCE
RT	BOWEN RATIO
RT	BUBBLE BURSTING
RT	DRAG
RT	ELECTRIC CURRENTS
RT	ENERGY
RT	ENERGY TRANSFER
RT	EVAPORATION
RT	GAS EXCHANGE
RT	GASES
RT	HEAT EXCHANGE
RT	MOISTURE
RT	MOISTURE TRANSFER
RT	MOMENTUM
RT	MOMENTUM TRANSFER
RT	OCEAN-ATMOSPHERE SYSTEM
RT	PLANKTON
RT	SALT PARTICLES
RT	SEA SURFACE
RT	SENSIBLE HEAT
RT	SURFACE CHEMISTRY
RT	SUSPENDED PARTICULATE MATTER
RT	TEMPERATURE DIFFERENCES
RT	WAVE FOLLOWERS

AIR-WATER INTERFACE
UF	naviface
BT1	INTERFACES
RT	AEROSOLS
RT	AIR BUBBLES
RT	AIR-SEA INTERACTION
RT	AIR-WATER EXCHANGES
RT	AIR-WATER TEMPERATURE DIFFERENCE
RT	ATMOSPHERIC BOUNDARY LAYER
RT	ENERGY TRANSFER
RT	EOLIAN DUST
RT	EVAPORATION
RT	GAS EXCHANGE

AIR-WATER INTERFACE (cont'd)
RT	HEAT EXCHANGE
RT	LIGHT REFLECTION
RT	LIGHT REFRACTION
RT	MOISTURE TRANSFER
RT	MOMENTUM TRANSFER
RT	NEUSTON
RT	OCEANIC BOUNDARY LAYER
RT	PLEUSTON
RT	REFLECTANCE
RT	REFLECTED GLOBAL RADIATION
RT	SEA SURFACE
RT	SENSIBLE HEAT TRANSFER
RT	SOLAR RADIATION
RT	SURFACE MICROLAYER
RT	SURFACE PROPERTIES
RT	SURFACE RADIATION TEMPERATURE

AIR-WATER TEMPERATURE DIFFERENCE
BT1	TEMPERATURE DIFFERENCES
RT	AIR-WATER EXCHANGES
RT	AIR-WATER INTERFACE

AIRBORNE EQUIPMENT
UF	aircraft equipment
BT1	EQUIPMENT
RT	AERIAL SURVEYS
RT	AIRBORNE SENSING
RT	AIRCRAFT
RT	AXBTs
RT	ELECTRONIC EQUIPMENT
RT	INFRARED DETECTORS
RT	LASER BATHYMETERS
RT	SURVEYING EQUIPMENT

AIRBORNE LASER BATHYMETERS
USE	**LASER BATHYMETERS**

AIRBORNE REMOTE SENSING
USE	**AIRBORNE SENSING**

AIRBORNE SENSING
SN	Employing equipment carried by low flying aircraft and helicopters
UF	airborne remote sensing
BT1	GEOSENSING
RT	AERIAL PHOTOGRAPHY
RT	AERIAL SURVEYS
RT	AEROMAGNETIC SURVEYS
RT	AIRBORNE EQUIPMENT
RT	AIRCRAFT
RT	DEPTH MEASUREMENT
RT	HELICOPTERS
RT	ICE OBSERVATIONS
RT	INFRARED IMAGERY
RT	LASER BATHYMETERS
RT	REMOTE SENSING

AIRCRAFT
BT1	VEHICLES
NT1	HELICOPTERS
RT	AERIAL PHOTOGRAPHY
RT	AERIAL SURVEYS
RT	AIR TRANSPORTATION
RT	AIRBORNE EQUIPMENT
RT	AIRBORNE SENSING
RT	AIRPORTS
RT	ALTIMETRY
RT	AXBTs
RT	ELECTRONIC EQUIPMENT
RT	INSTRUMENT PLATFORMS
RT	METEOROLOGICAL OBSERVATIONS
RT	RADAR ALTIMETRY
RT	REMOTE SENSING
RT	SURVEYS
RT	TRANSPORTATION

ASFIS Thesaurus

AIRCRAFT EQUIPMENT
USE **AIRBORNE EQUIPMENT**

AIRGLOW
RT ATMOSPHERIC OPTICAL PHENOMENA
RT AURORA
RT CHEMILUMINESCENCE
RT LUMINESCENCE

AIRPORTS
RT AIRCRAFT
RT COASTAL STRUCTURES

AIRY WAVES
USE **LINEAR WAVES**

ALANINE
BT1 AMINO ACIDS
BT2 ORGANIC ACIDS
BT3 ORGANIC COMPOUNDS

ALARM SUBSTANCES
RT BEHAVIOUR
RT CHEMORECEPTION
RT OLFACTION

ALARM SYSTEMS
UF warning devices
NT1 DISTRESS SIGNALS
RT ACCIDENTS
RT DETECTION
RT DETECTORS
RT PROTECTION
RT SAFETY DEVICES
RT WARNING SERVICES
RT WARNING SYSTEMS

ALBACORE FISHERIES
USE **TUNA FISHERIES**

ALBEDO
RT OPTICAL PROPERTIES
RT RATIOS
RT REFLECTANCE
RT REFLECTION
RT SOLAR RADIATION
RT SURFACE PROPERTIES

ALBINISM
SN Complete or almost complete absence
   of pigment in aquatic organisms
RT CHROMATIC PIGMENTS
RT GENETIC ABNORMALITIES

ALBUMINS
SN Before 1980 search PROTEINS
UF ovalbumin
UF serum albumins
BT1 PROTEINS
BT2 ORGANIC COMPOUNDS
RT BIRD EGGS
RT BLOOD

ALCOHOLS
BT1 ORGANIC COMPOUNDS
NT1 CHOLINE
NT1 GLYCEROL
RT CARBOHYDRATES
RT CHEMICAL COMPOUNDS
RT STEROLS

ALDEHYDES
BT1 ORGANIC COMPOUNDS
RT ARABINOSE
RT GLUCOSE
RT MANNOSE
RT RIBOSE
RT XYLOSE

ALDRIN
BT1 CHLORINATED HYDROCARBONS
BT2 HALOGENATED HYDROCARBONS
BT3 HYDROCARBONS
BT4 ORGANIC COMPOUNDS
RT INSECTICIDES

ALGAE
SN In ASFA-1, use as taxonomic
   descriptor; in ASFA-2, use as
   subject descriptor
NT1 DIATOMS
NT1 ZOOXANTHELLAE
RT ALGAL BLOOMS
RT ALGAL CULTURE
RT ALGAL MATS
RT ALGAL SETTLEMENTS
RT STROMATOLITES

ALGAE CULTURE
USE **ALGAL CULTURE**

ALGAE RESOURCES
USE **BOTANICAL RESOURCES**

ALGAL BLOOMS
UF blooms
UF plankton blooms
UF sea blooms
UF water blooms
RT ALGAE
RT BIOLOGICAL POISONS
RT EUTROPHICATION
RT MORTALITY CAUSES
RT OXYGEN DEPLETION
RT PHYTOPLANKTON
RT PRIMARY PRODUCTION
RT RED TIDES

ALGAL CULTURE
SN Added in 1980
UF algae culture
UF algiculture
BT1 AQUACULTURE
NT1 PHYTOPLANKTON CULTURE
RT ALGAE
RT BRACKISHWATER AQUACULTURE
RT CULTURE TANKS
RT ENERGY RESOURCES
RT FERTILIZERS
RT FRESHWATER AQUACULTURE
RT LABORATORY CULTURE
RT MARINE AQUACULTURE
RT MASS CULTURE
RT SPORES

ALGAL MATS
BT1 BIOGENIC SEDIMENTARY STRUCTURES
BT2 SEDIMENTARY STRUCTURES
RT ALGAE
RT STROMATOLITES

ALGAL SETTLEMENTS
BT1 BIOLOGICAL SETTLEMENT
RT ALGAE
RT ARTIFICIAL SUBSTRATA
RT COLONIZATION
RT SETTLING BEHAVIOUR
RT SUBSTRATE PREFERENCES

ALGICIDES
BT1 PESTICIDES
RT CHEMICAL POLLUTANTS
RT CHEMICAL POLLUTION
RT HERBICIDES
RT PLANT CONTROL
RT TOXICANTS

ALGICULTURE
USE **ALGAL CULTURE**

ALGINATES
SN Industrial product derived from
   brown algae
UF seaweed meal
BT1 SEAWEED PRODUCTS
BT2 PROCESSED FISHERY PRODUCTS
BT3 FISHERY PRODUCTS
BT4 PRODUCTS
RT AGAR
RT CARRAGEENINS
RT CHEMICAL EXTRACTION
RT KELPS
RT ORGANIC ACIDS

ALGINIC ACID
BT1 POLYSACCHARIDES
BT2 SACCHARIDES
BT3 CARBOHYDRATES
BT4 ORGANIC COMPOUNDS
RT AMINO ACIDS

ALGOLOGISTS
SN Added in 1980
UF phycologists
BT1 BIOLOGISTS
BT2 SCIENTIFIC PERSONNEL
BT3 PERSONNEL
RT ALGOLOGY
RT DIRECTORIES
RT FISHERY BIOLOGISTS
RT PHYTOPLANKTON
RT PLANT PHYSIOLOGISTS
RT SEAWEEDS
RT TAXONOMISTS

ALGOLOGY
UF phycology
BT1 BOTANY
BT2 BIOLOGY
RT ALGOLOGISTS
RT AQUATIC PLANTS
RT HYDROBIOLOGY
RT MARINE SCIENCES
RT PHYTOBENTHOS
RT PHYTOPLANKTON
RT PLANT PHYSIOLOGY
RT SEAWEEDS

ALGORITHMS
SN Used only as a qualifier
RT COMPUTER PROGRAMS
RT MATHEMATICAL MODELS
RT NUMERICAL ANALYSIS

ALICYCLIC HYDROCARBONS
BT1 SATURATED HYDROCARBONS
BT2 HYDROCARBONS
BT3 ORGANIC COMPOUNDS

ALIEN SPECIES
USE **INTRODUCED SPECIES**

ALIMENTARY ORGANS
BT1 ANIMAL ORGANS
BT2 BODY ORGANS
NT1 DIGESTIVE TRACT
NT1 INTESTINES
NT1 LOPHOPHORES
NT1 PYLORIC CAECA
NT1 STOMACH
NT2 MASTICATORY STOMACH
RT ANATOMY
RT DIGESTIVE GLANDS
RT DIGESTIVE SYSTEM
RT MOUTH PARTS
RT RADULAE

ASFIS Thesaurus

ALIPHATIC HYDROCARBONS
USE   **SATURATED HYDROCARBONS**

ALKALI BASALTS
BT1	BASALTS
BT2	VOLCANIC ROCKS
BT3	IGNEOUS ROCKS
BT4	ROCKS
RT	PYROXENES
RT	VOLCANIC ISLANDS

ALKALI METAL COMPOUNDS
RT	CADMIUM COMPOUNDS
RT	CAESIUM COMPOUNDS
RT	POTASSIUM COMPOUNDS
RT	SODIUM COMPOUNDS

ALKALI METALS
BT1	METALS
RT	CAESIUM
RT	CHEMICAL ELEMENTS
RT	FRANCIUM
RT	LITHIUM
RT	POTASSIUM
RT	RUBIDIUM
RT	SODIUM

ALKALINE EARTH METAL COMPOUNDS
NT1	BARIUM COMPOUNDS
NT1	BERYLLIUM COMPOUNDS
NT1	CALCIUM COMPOUNDS
NT2	CALCIUM CARBONATES
NT2	CALCIUM PHOSPHATES
NT2	CALCIUM SULPHATES
NT1	MAGNESIUM COMPOUNDS
NT2	MAGNESIUM FLUORIDES
NT2	MAGNESIUM PHOSPHATES
NT2	MAGNESIUM SILICATES
NT2	MAGNESIUM SULPHATES
NT1	SODIUM COMPOUNDS
NT2	SODIUM CHLORIDE

ALKALINE EARTH METALS
BT1	METALS
RT	BARIUM
RT	BERYLLIUM
RT	CALCIUM
RT	CHEMICAL ELEMENTS
RT	MAGNESIUM
RT	RADIUM
RT	STRONTIUM
RT	YTTRIUM

ALKALINITY
SN	For a pH above 7
UF	causticity
BT1	CHEMICAL PROPERTIES
BT2	PROPERTIES
RT	ACIDITY
RT	BUFFERS
RT	PH
RT	WATER HARDNESS
RT	WATER PROPERTIES

ALKALOIDS
BT1	ORGANIC COMPOUNDS
RT	AQUATIC PLANTS
RT	CHEMICAL COMPOUNDS
RT	DRUGS

ALKANES
USE   **SATURATED HYDROCARBONS**

ALKENES
BT1	UNSATURATED HYDROCARBONS
BT2	HYDROCARBONS
BT3	ORGANIC COMPOUNDS
NT1	ETHENE

ALKYNES
BT1	UNSATURATED HYDROCARBONS
BT2	HYDROCARBONS
BT3	ORGANIC COMPOUNDS
NT1	ETHYNE

ALLERGIC REACTIONS
UF	allergies
BT1	BIOLOGICAL PHENOMENA
RT	FOOD POISONING
RT	HISTAMINES
RT	IMMUNOLOGY
RT	POISONOUS ORGANISMS
RT	TOXICITY

ALLERGIES
USE   **ALLERGIC REACTIONS**

ALLIGATOR CULTURE
USE   **REPTILE CULTURE**

ALLOCATION SYSTEMS
SN	Restricted to fisheries for division of a total catch between participants in the fishery. Added in 1982
UF	international allocation
UF	national allocation
RT	EXCLUSIVE ECONOMIC ZONE
RT	FISHERY POLICY
RT	SHARED STOCKS

ALLOCHTHONOUS DEPOSITS
RT	AUTOCHTHONOUS DEPOSITS
RT	EOLIAN DEPOSITS
RT	EXTRATERRESTRIAL MATERIAL
RT	GLACIAL DEPOSITS
RT	OLISTOLITHS
RT	SEDIMENTS
RT	VOLCANIC ROCKS

ALLOPATRIC POPULATIONS
SN	Populations of a same species living in different geographic areas
RT	GEOGRAPHICAL DISTRIBUTION
RT	SYMPATRIC POPULATIONS

ALLOYS
UF	metals (materials)
BT1	MATERIALS
NT1	FERROUS ALLOYS
NT2	STEEL
NT3	STAINLESS STEEL
NT1	NONFERROUS ALLOYS
RT	CHEMICAL ELEMENTS
RT	METALLURGY
RT	METALS

ALLUVIAL DEPOSITS
UF	alluvium
RT	ALLUVIAL FANS
RT	ALLUVIAL TERRACES
RT	CLASTICS
RT	COASTAL EROSION
RT	DELTAS
RT	EROSION
RT	FLOOD PLAINS
RT	FLUVIAL MORPHOLOGY
RT	FLUVIAL SEDIMENTATION
RT	FLUVIAL TRANSPORT
RT	GRAVEL
RT	LANDFORMS
RT	LEVEES
RT	RIVERS
RT	SAND
RT	SEDIMENT TRANSPORT
RT	SEDIMENTATION
RT	SEDIMENTS

ALLUVIAL FANS
BT1	LANDFORMS
BT2	TOPOGRAPHIC FEATURES
RT	ALLUVIAL DEPOSITS
RT	DEEP-SEA FANS
RT	DEPOSITION FEATURES
RT	FANS
RT	FLUVIAL FEATURES
RT	RIVER VALLEYS
RT	TERRACES

ALLUVIAL TERRACES
BT1	LANDFORMS
BT2	TOPOGRAPHIC FEATURES
RT	ALLUVIAL DEPOSITS
RT	RIVER VALLEYS
RT	TERRACES

ALLUVIUM
USE   **ALLUVIAL DEPOSITS**

ALMANACS
BT1	TABLES
BT2	DOCUMENTS
NT1	NAUTICAL ALMANACS
NT1	TIDE TABLES
RT	PREDICTION

ALPHA SPECTROSCOPY
BT1	SPECTROSCOPIC TECHNIQUES
BT2	ANALYTICAL TECHNIQUES

ALTERNATE REPRODUCTION
SN	Alternation of generations
BT1	REPRODUCTION

ALTERNATIVE NAME
USE   **SYNONYMY**

ALTIMETERS
RT	ALTIMETRY
RT	HEIGHT
RT	LASER ALTIMETERS
RT	MEASURING DEVICES
RT	RADAR ALTIMETERS

ALTIMETRY
NT1	LASER ALTIMETRY
NT1	RADAR ALTIMETRY
NT1	SATELLITE ALTIMETRY
RT	AIRCRAFT
RT	ALTIMETERS
RT	HEIGHT

ALTITUDE
USE   **HEIGHT**

ALUMINIUM
UF	aluminum
BT1	CHEMICAL ELEMENTS
RT	ALUMINIUM COMPOUNDS
RT	ALUMINIUM ISOTOPES
RT	BAUXITE
RT	FERROMANGANESE NODULES
RT	METALS
RT	TRACE METALS

ALUMINIUM COMPOUNDS
RT	ALUMINIUM
RT	CHEMICAL COMPOUNDS
RT	SILICON COMPOUNDS

ALUMINIUM ISOTOPES
BT1	ISOTOPES
RT	ALUMINIUM

ALUMINUM
USE · **ALUMINIUM**

AMBERGRIS
BT1 · ANIMAL PRODUCTS
RT · CETOLOGY
RT · INTESTINES

AMBIENT NOISE
UF · background noise (sound)
UF · noise (ambient)
UF · underwater ambient noise
BT1 · NOISE (SOUND)
NT1 · BIOLOGICAL NOISE
NT1 · SEDIMENT NOISE
NT1 · SHIPPING NOISE
NT1 · SURFACE NOISE
RT · PASSIVE SONAR
RT · UNDERWATER NOISE

AMERICIUM
BT1 · CHEMICAL ELEMENTS
RT · ACTINIDES
RT · AMERICIUM COMPOUNDS
RT · AMERICIUM ISOTOPES
RT · TRANSITION ELEMENTS
RT · TRANSURANIC ELEMENTS

AMERICIUM COMPOUNDS
BT1 · ACTINIDE COMPOUNDS
RT · AMERICIUM
RT · CHEMICAL COMPOUNDS

AMERICIUM ISOTOPES
BT1 · ISOTOPES
RT · AMERICIUM

AMINATION
BT1 · CHEMICAL REACTIONS
RT · DEAMINATION

AMINES
SN · Added in 1980
BT1 · ORGANIC COMPOUNDS
NT1 · HEXOSAMINES
NT2 · GLUCOSAMINE
NT1 · HYDROXYLAMINES
NT1 · NITROSAMINES
NT1 · PYRROLIDINE
RT · AMINO ACIDS

AMINO ACIDS
BT1 · ORGANIC ACIDS
BT2 · ORGANIC COMPOUNDS
NT1 · ALANINE
NT1 · ARGININE
NT1 · ASPARTIC ACID
NT1 · CYSTEINE
NT1 · CYSTINE
NT1 · GLUTAMIC ACID
NT1 · GLYCINE
NT1 · LEUCINE
NT1 · LYSINE
NT1 · METHIONINE
NT1 · ORNITHINE
NT1 · PHENYLALANINE
NT1 · PROLINE
NT1 · SERINE
NT1 · THREONINE
NT1 · TYROSINE
NT1 · VALINE
RT · ALGINIC ACID
RT · AMINES
RT · CHEMICAL COMPOUNDS
RT · NITROGEN COMPOUNDS
RT · ORGANIC CONSTITUENTS
RT · PEPTIDES
RT · PROTEIN SYNTHESIS
RT · PROTEINS

AMMOCETES
USE · **FISH LARVAE**

AMMONIA
UF · ammonium salts
BT1 · NITROGEN COMPOUNDS
RT · AMMONIUM COMPOUNDS
RT · BIODEGRADATION
RT · CHEMICAL COMPOUNDS
RT · GASES
RT · NITROGEN CYCLE
RT · NITROGEN FIXATION
RT · UREA
RT · VOLATILE COMPOUNDS

AMMONIUM
USE · **AMMONIUM COMPOUNDS**

AMMONIUM CHLORIDE
BT1 · AMMONIUM COMPOUNDS

AMMONIUM COMPOUNDS
SN · Before 1986 search also AMMONIUM
UF · ammonium
NT1 · AMMONIUM CHLORIDE
RT · AMMONIA

AMMONIUM SALTS
USE · **AMMONIA**

AMOEBOCYTES
SN · Before 1982 search CELLS
BT1 · CELLS
RT · BODY FLUIDS
RT · COELOM
RT · DIGESTION
RT · EXCRETION
RT · PHAGOCYTOSIS

AMP
UF · adenosine monophosphate
BT1 · NUCLEOTIDES
BT2 · ORGANIC COMPOUNDS
RT · CHEMICAL COMPOUNDS
RT · PHOSPHATES

AMPEROMETRIC TITRATION
USE · **TITRATION**

AMPHIBIAN CULTURE
USE · **FROG CULTURE**

AMPHIBIOTIC SPECIES
SN · Aquatic species during one part of the life cycle and terrestrial during therest of the life cycle. Added in 1980
BT1 · SPECIES
BT2 · TAXA
RT · AQUATIC ORGANISMS

AMPHIBIOUS VEHICLES
RT · HOVERCRAFT
RT · VEHICLES
RT · WETLANDS

AMPHIBOLES
BT1 · SILICATE MINERALS
BT2 · MINERALS

AMPHIBOLITE FACIES
BT1 · METAMORPHIC FACIES
BT2 · FACIES
RT · AMPHIBOLITES

AMPHIBOLITES
BT1 · METAMORPHIC ROCKS
BT2 · ROCKS
NT1 · HORNBLENDE
RT · AMPHIBOLITE FACIES

AMPHIDROMES
USE · **AMPHIDROMIC SYSTEMS**

AMPHIDROMIC POINT
USE · **AMPHIDROMIC SYSTEMS**

AMPHIDROMIC SYSTEMS
UF · amphidromes
UF · amphidromic point
RT · COTIDAL LINES

AMPHIHALINE FISH
USE · **AMPHIHALINE SPECIES**

AMPHIHALINE POTAMOTOCOUS SPECIES
USE · **ANADROMOUS SPECIES**

AMPHIHALINE SPECIES
SN · Aquatic species which pass periodically at well defined stages of their life cycle, from salt to fresh water and vice versa. Added in 1980
UF · amphihaline fish
BT1 · SPECIES
BT2 · TAXA
NT1 · ANADROMOUS SPECIES
NT1 · CATADROMOUS SPECIES
RT · ANADROMOUS MIGRATIONS
RT · CATADROMOUS MIGRATIONS
RT · OSMOREGULATION
RT · OSMOTIC ADAPTATIONS
RT · SALINITY TOLERANCE
RT · SPAWNING MIGRATIONS

AMPHIHALINE THALASSOTOCOUS SPECIES
USE · **CATADROMOUS SPECIES**

AMPLITUDE
SN · Use only as a qualifier
BT1 · DIMENSIONS
NT1 · WAVE AMPLITUDE
NT2 · TIDAL AMPLITUDE
RT · ABSORPTION (PHYSICS)
RT · ATTENUATION

ANABOLISM
BT1 · METABOLISM
RT · CATABOLISM

ANADROMOUS FISH
USE · **ANADROMOUS SPECIES**

ANADROMOUS MIGRATIONS
UF · upstream migrations
BT1 · SPAWNING MIGRATIONS
BT2 · MIGRATIONS
RT · AMPHIHALINE SPECIES
RT · ANADROMOUS SPECIES
RT · BRACKISHWATER FISH
RT · CATADROMOUS MIGRATIONS
RT · FISHWAYS
RT · HOMING BEHAVIOUR
RT · POTADROMOUS MIGRATIONS
RT · RANCHING
RT · SCREENS

ANADROMOUS SPECIES
SN · Having the habit to migrate from oceanic to coastal water or from salt water to freshwater to breed
UF · amphihaline potamotocous species
UF · anadromous fish
BT1 · AMPHIHALINE SPECIES
BT2 · SPECIES
BT3 · TAXA
RT · ANADROMOUS MIGRATIONS
RT · SPAWNING GROUNDS
RT · SPAWNING MIGRATIONS

ANADROMOUS SPECIES (cont'd)
RT   SPAWNING SEASONS

ANAEMIA
SN   Deficiency in red blood cells, haemoglobin or both. Added in 1980
UF   anemia
BT1   HAEMATOLOGICAL DISEASES
BT2   DISEASES
RT   ERYTHROCYTES
RT   HAEMOCYANINS
RT   HAEMOGLOBINS
RT   NUTRITION DISORDERS

ANAEROBIC BACTERIA
SN   See also the taxonomic index
BT1   BACTERIA
BT2   MICROORGANISMS
RT   ANAEROBIC DIGESTION
RT   ANAEROBIC RESPIRATION
RT   ANAEROBIOSIS
RT   BIODEGRADATION
RT   FERMENTATION

ANAEROBIC CONDITIONS
USE   **ANOXIC CONDITIONS**

ANAEROBIC DIGESTION
BT1   BIODEGRADATION
BT2   DEGRADATION
BT3   CHEMICAL REACTIONS
RT   ANAEROBIC BACTERIA
RT   ANAEROBIOSIS
RT   BIODEGRADABLE SUBSTANCES
RT   WASTE TREATMENT

ANAEROBIC RESPIRATION
BT1   RESPIRATION
RT   ANAEROBIC BACTERIA
RT   ANAEROBIOSIS
RT   FERMENTATION

ANAEROBIC SEDIMENTS
USE   **ANOXIC SEDIMENTS**

ANAEROBIONTS
USE   **ANAEROBIOSIS**

ANAEROBIOSIS
SN   Added in 1980
UF   anaerobionts
RT   ANAEROBIC BACTERIA
RT   ANAEROBIC DIGESTION
RT   ANAEROBIC RESPIRATION

ANAESTHESIA
SN   Apparatus and methods for anaesthesia of aquatic organisms
UF   anesthesia
UF   electroanaesthesia
RT   ANAESTHETICS
RT   DRUGS

ANAESTHETICS
UF   anesthetics
BT1   DRUGS
RT   ANAESTHESIA
RT   FIXATION
RT   INHIBITORS
RT   NARCOTICS

ANALCIME
USE   **ANALCITE**

ANALCITE
UF   analcime
BT1   ZEOLITES
BT2   SILICATE MINERALS
BT3   MINERALS

ANALOG DATA RECORDS
USE   **ANALOG RECORDS**

ANALOG MODELS
SN   Used only as a qualifier
UF   electronic models
BT1   MODELS
NT1   ACOUSTIC MODELS

ANALOG RECORDS
SN   Used only as a qualifier
UF   analog data records
BT1   GRAPHICS
BT2   AUDIOVISUAL MATERIAL
BT3   DOCUMENTS
NT1   BATHYTHERMOGRAMS
NT1   ECHOSOUNDER PROFILES
NT1   SEISMIC PROFILES
NT2   SEISMIC REFLECTION PROFILES
NT2   SEISMIC REFRACTION PROFILES
NT1   SEISMOGRAMS
NT1   TIDAL CURVES
NT1   TIDAL RECORDS
RT   DATA CONVERTERS
RT   DIGITAL RECORDS
RT   RECORDS

ANALOGS
SN   Used only as a qualifier
RT   MATHEMATICAL MODELS

ANALYSIS
SN   Used only as a qualifier. Use of a more specific term is recommended
RT   BIOCHEMICAL ANALYSIS
RT   CHEMICAL ANALYSIS
RT   CORE ANALYSIS
RT   CORE LAYER METHOD
RT   COST ANALYSIS
RT   DATA PROCESSING
RT   DYNAMIC ANALYSIS
RT   ECONOMIC ANALYSIS
RT   ELECTROANALYSIS
RT   ELECTROLYSIS
RT   HARMONIC ANALYSIS
RT   ISENTROPIC ANALYSIS
RT   MICROBIOLOGICAL ANALYSIS
RT   NUMERICAL ANALYSIS
RT   SEDIMENT ANALYSIS
RT   SHIPBOARD ANALYSIS
RT   STATISTICAL ANALYSIS
RT   TIDAL ANALYSIS
RT   TIME SERIES ANALYSIS
RT   VOLUMETRIC ANALYSIS
RT   WATER ANALYSIS
RT   WAVE ANALYSIS
RT   X-RAY SPECTROSCOPY

ANALYTICAL ERRORS
SN   Used only as a qualifier
BT1   ERRORS
RT   ANALYTICAL TECHNIQUES

ANALYTICAL TECHNIQUES
NT1   ACTIVATION ANALYSIS
NT2   NEUTRON ACTIVATION ANALYSIS
NT1   CHROMATOGRAPHIC TECHNIQUES
NT2   GAS CHROMATOGRAPHY
NT1   COLORIMETRIC TECHNIQUES
NT1   ELECTROPHORESIS
NT1   GRAVIMETRIC TECHNIQUES
NT1   INTERFEROMETRY
NT1   ION SELECTIVE ELECTRODE ANALYSIS
NT1   ISENTROPIC ANALYSIS
NT1   MICROSCOPY
NT2   ELECTRON MICROSCOPY
NT2   FLUORESCENCE MICROSCOPY
NT2   LIGHT MICROSCOPY
NT1   POLAROGRAPHY
NT1   SPECTROSCOPIC TECHNIQUES

ANALYTICAL TECHNIQUES (cont'd)
NT2   ABSORPTION SPECTROSCOPY
NT2   ALPHA SPECTROSCOPY
NT2   EMISSION SPECTROSCOPY
NT2   FLUORESCENCE SPECTROSCOPY
NT2   GAMMA SPECTROSCOPY
NT2   INFRARED SPECTROSCOPY
NT2   MASS SPECTROSCOPY
NT2   X-RAY SPECTROSCOPY
NT3   X-RAY DIFFRACTION ANALYSIS
NT3   X-RAY EMISSION ANALYSIS
NT3   X-RAY FLUORESCENCE ANALYSIS
NT1   STRIPPING ANALYSIS
NT1   TITRATION
NT1   WINKLER METHOD
RT   ANALYTICAL ERRORS
RT   AUTOMATED RECORDING
RT   BIOCHEMICAL ANALYSIS
RT   CENTRIFUGATION
RT   CHEMICAL ANALYSIS
RT   CHEMISTRY
RT   COMPOSITION
RT   FLUORESCENCE
RT   HYDROCARBON ANALYSIS
RT   LABORATORY EQUIPMENT
RT   METHODOLOGY
RT   SEDIMENT ANALYSIS
RT   SHIPBOARD ANALYSIS
RT   TECHNOLOGY
RT   TESTS
RT   WATER ANALYSIS

ANATASE
BT1   OXIDE MINERALS
BT2   MINERALS

ANATOMICAL STRUCTURES
SN   Added in 1980
NT1   BODY REGIONS
NT2   ABDOMEN
NT2   CEPHALOTHORAX
NT2   HEAD
NT2   THORAX
NT1   INTEGUMENTARY SYSTEM
NT2   FEATHERS
NT1   LYMPHATIC SYSTEM
NT1   NEUROSECRETORY SYSTEM
NT1   URINARY SYSTEM
RT   ANATOMY
RT   ANIMAL ORGANS
RT   ANIMAL PHYSIOLOGY
RT   BODY FLUIDS
RT   CELLS
RT   TISSUES

ANATOMY
BT1   BIOLOGY
RT   ALIMENTARY ORGANS
RT   ANATOMICAL STRUCTURES
RT   ANIMAL ORGANS
RT   ANIMAL REPRODUCTIVE ORGANS
RT   AUDITORY ORGANS
RT   BODY ORGANS
RT   BONES
RT   CIRCULATORY SYSTEM
RT   COMPARATIVE STUDIES
RT   ENDOSKELETON
RT   EXCRETORY ORGANS
RT   HISTOLOGY
RT   NERVOUS SYSTEM
RT   ORGANISM MORPHOLOGY
RT   OSTEOLOGY
RT   PHYSIOLOGY
RT   RESPIRATORY ORGANS
RT   SECRETORY ORGANS
RT   SENSE ORGANS
RT   SKELETON
RT   TEETH

ASFIS Thesaurus

ANCHOR STATIONS
USE **CRUISE STATIONS**

ANCHORAGES
UF roadsteads
NT1 HARBOURS
NT2 FERRY TERMINALS
NT2 FISHING HARBOURS
NT2 NAVAL BASES
NT2 TANKER TERMINALS
NT3 DEEP-WATER TERMINALS
NT3 OFFSHORE TERMINALS
RT ANCHORING
RT ANCHORS
RT TERRITORIAL WATERS

ANCHORING
RT ANCHORAGES
RT ANCHORS
RT BERTHING
RT BUOYS
RT BURYING
RT CHAIN
RT DRIFT
RT GEOTECHNOLOGY
RT MOORING SYSTEMS
RT OFFSHORE STRUCTURES
RT PIPELINE CONSTRUCTION
RT SEMISUBMERSIBLE PLATFORMS
RT SHIP MOORING SYSTEMS

ANCHORS
UF ship anchors
RT ANCHORAGES
RT ANCHORING
RT BERTHING
RT DROGUES

ANCHOVY FISHERIES
USE **CLUPEOID FISHERIES**

ANCIENT SHORELINES
USE **STRANDLINES**

ANDALUSITE
BT1 SILICATE MINERALS
BT2 MINERALS

ANDESITE
BT1 VOLCANIC ROCKS
BT2 IGNEOUS ROCKS
BT3 ROCKS

ANDROGENESIS
SN Added in 1980
BT1 REPRODUCTION

ANDROGENS
USE **SEX HORMONES**

ANELASTICITY
BT1 MECHANICAL PROPERTIES
BT2 PHYSICAL PROPERTIES
BT3 PROPERTIES
RT DEFORMATION
RT ELASTICITY

ANEMIA
USE **ANAEMIA**

ANEMOMETERS
SN Use only for mechanically operated
anemometers (cups, propellers,
vanes, etc.).
UF cup anemometers
BT1 MEASURING DEVICES
RT FLOWMETERS
RT TURBULENCE MEASUREMENT
RT WIND DIRECTION
RT WIND MEASURING EQUIPMENT

ANEMOMETERS (cont'd)
RT WIND SPEED
RT WINDS

ANESTHESIA
USE **ANAESTHESIA**

ANESTHETICS
USE **ANAESTHETICS**

ANGLING
SN Restricted to sport fishing only
BT1 CATCHING METHODS
NT1 BAIT FISHING
RT BAIT
RT FISHING
RT HOOKS
RT POLE-LINE FISHING
RT REEF FISHERIES
RT SALMON FISHERIES
RT SPORT FISHING
RT WORM FISHING

ANGULAR DISTRIBUTION
BT1 OPTICAL PROPERTIES
BT2 PHYSICAL PROPERTIES
BT3 PROPERTIES

ANGULAR MOMENTUM
BT1 MOMENTUM
RT CONSERVATION OF ANGULAR MOMENTUM

ANHYDRITE
BT1 SULPHATE MINERALS
BT2 MINERALS
RT AUTHIGENIC MINERALS
RT CHEMICAL SEDIMENTS
RT EVAPORITES

ANIMAL APPENDAGES
SN Projections of the body
UF appendages
UF appendages (animal)
NT1 ANTENNAE
NT1 BARBELS
NT1 BYSSUS
NT1 CILIA
NT1 LOCOMOTORY APPENDAGES
NT2 FINS
NT3 BONY FINS
NT2 WINGS
NT1 TELSON
NT1 TENTACLES
NT2 SENSE TENTACLES
RT ABDOMEN
RT CEPHALOTHORAX
RT FLAGELLA
RT LOCOMOTION
RT SENSE FUNCTIONS
RT THORAX

ANIMAL ASSOCIATIONS
USE **ECOLOGICAL ASSOCIATIONS**

ANIMAL BEHAVIOUR
USE **BEHAVIOUR**

ANIMAL BODY REGIONS
USE **BODY REGIONS**

ANIMAL COMMUNICATION
SN Added in 1980
UF biocommunication
UF communication (behaviour)
UF zoosemiotics
RT BEHAVIOUR
RT SOUND PRODUCTION
RT VOCALIZATION BEHAVIOUR

ANIMAL DISEASES
SN Before 1982 search DISEASES
UF aquatic animal diseases
BT1 DISEASES
NT1 FISH DISEASES
NT2 BOIL DISEASE
NT2 BUBBLE DISEASE
NT2 GILL DISEASE
NT2 PEDUNCLE DISEASE
NT2 REDMOUTH DISEASE
NT2 SUNBURN
NT2 ULCERATIVE DERMAL NECROSIS
NT2 WHIRLING DISEASE
RT AQUATIC ANIMALS
RT DISEASE CONTROL
RT ENVIRONMENTAL DISEASES
RT INFECTIOUS DISEASES
RT NUTRITION DISORDERS
RT THERAPY

ANIMAL FEED
USE **FEED**

ANIMAL FOSSILS
BT1 FOSSILS
NT1 FOSSIL FORAMINIFERA
NT1 FOSSIL PTEROPODS
NT1 FOSSIL RADIOLARIA
RT AQUATIC ANIMALS

ANIMAL GROWTH
USE **GROWTH**

ANIMAL HEAD
USE **HEAD**

ANIMAL MANURE
USE **MANURE**

ANIMAL METABOLISM
SN Before 1982 search METABOLISM
BT1 METABOLISM
RT ANIMAL PHYSIOLOGY
RT CONVERSION FACTORS
RT DIGESTION
RT ENDOCRINOLOGY

ANIMAL MIGRATIONS
USE **MIGRATIONS**

ANIMAL MORPHOLOGY
SN Before 1982 search MORPHOLOGY
(ORGANISMS)
UF morphology (animal)
BT1 ORGANISM MORPHOLOGY
BT2 BIOLOGY
RT ANIMAL PHYSIOLOGY
RT AQUATIC ANIMALS
RT BODY REGIONS
RT BODY SIZE
RT INTEGUMENTARY SYSTEM

ANIMAL NAVIGATION
SN Added in 1980
UF bird navigation
UF navigation (animal)
RT HOMING BEHAVIOUR
RT LOCOMOTION
RT LOCOMOTORY APPENDAGES
RT MIGRATIONS
RT ORIENTATION
RT WINGS

ANIMAL NUTRITION
UF finfish nutrition
UF fish nutrition
UF nutrition (animal)
BT1 NUTRITION
NT1 DEFAECATION
NT1 DIGESTION

ANIMAL NUTRITION (cont'd)
NT1	FOOD ABSORPTION
NT1	FOOD CONSUMPTION
NT1	FOOD CONVERSION
NT1	INGESTION
RT	ANIMAL PHYSIOLOGY
RT	DIETS
RT	FEEDING BEHAVIOUR
RT	HETEROTROPHY
RT	NUTRITIONAL REQUIREMENTS
RT	POWDERED PRODUCTS

ANIMAL OIL EXTRACTION
UF	extraction (animal oil)
UF	oil extraction (animal)
BT1	PROCESSING FISHERY PRODUCTS
BT2	FISHERY INDUSTRY
BT3	INDUSTRIES
NT1	FISH OIL EXTRACTION
RT	AQUATIC MAMMALS
RT	CHEMICAL EXTRACTION
RT	SEPARATION
RT	SOLVENTS
RT	WHALING

ANIMAL ORGANS
SN	Added in 1980
UF	organs (animal)
BT1	BODY ORGANS
NT1	ALIMENTARY ORGANS
NT2	DIGESTIVE TRACT
NT2	INTESTINES
NT2	LOPHOPHORES
NT2	PYLORIC CAECA
NT2	STOMACH
NT3	MASTICATORY STOMACH
NT1	BLADDERS
NT2	GALL BLADDER
NT2	SWIM BLADDER
NT1	EXCRETORY ORGANS
NT2	KIDNEYS
NT2	SPLEEN
NT1	PHOTOPHORES
NT1	RESPIRATORY ORGANS
NT2	GILLS
NT2	LARYNX
NT2	LUNGS
NT2	TRACHEA
NT1	SENSE ORGANS
NT2	AUDITORY ORGANS
NT2	BALANCE ORGANS
NT3	STATOCYSTS
NT2	CHEMORECEPTORS
NT2	LATERAL LINE
NT2	MECHANORECEPTORS
NT2	OLFACTORY ORGANS
NT2	PHOTORECEPTORS
NT3	EYES
NT4	COMPOUND EYES
NT4	EYESTALKS
NT4	RETINAS
NT2	TACTILE ORGANS
NT2	TASTE ORGANS
NT1	VOCAL ORGANS
RT	ANATOMICAL STRUCTURES
RT	ANATOMY
RT	ANIMAL PHYSIOLOGY
RT	BODY REGIONS
RT	TISSUES

ANIMAL ORIENTATION
USE	**ORIENTATION BEHAVIOUR**

ANIMAL PATHOLOGY
USE	**PATHOLOGY**

ANIMAL PHYSIOLOGISTS
SN	Added in 1980
BT1	PHYSIOLOGISTS
BT2	BIOLOGISTS
BT3	SCIENTIFIC PERSONNEL
BT4	PERSONNEL
RT	ANIMAL PHYSIOLOGY
RT	DIRECTORIES
RT	ZOOLOGISTS

ANIMAL PHYSIOLOGY
SN	Before 1982 search PHYSIOLOGY
UF	physiology (animal)
BT1	PHYSIOLOGY
BT2	BIOLOGY
NT1	AVIAN PHYSIOLOGY
NT1	FISH PHYSIOLOGY
NT1	MAMMALIAN PHYSIOLOGY
RT	ACTIN
RT	AESTIVATION
RT	ANATOMICAL STRUCTURES
RT	ANIMAL METABOLISM
RT	ANIMAL MORPHOLOGY
RT	ANIMAL NUTRITION
RT	ANIMAL ORGANS
RT	ANIMAL PHYSIOLOGISTS
RT	AQUATIC ANIMALS
RT	BIOLUMINESCENCE
RT	DIAPAUSE
RT	DIVING PHYSIOLOGY
RT	ENDOCRINOLOGY
RT	ENZYME INHIBITORS
RT	MYOSIN
RT	ORGAN REMOVAL
RT	REPRODUCTION
RT	RESPIRATION
RT	ZOOLOGY

ANIMAL PLANKTON
USE	**ZOOPLANKTON**

ANIMAL POPULATIONS
SN	Added in 1982
UF	populations (animal)
BT1	NATURAL POPULATIONS
NT1	SPAWNING POPULATIONS
RT	AQUATIC ANIMALS
RT	POPULATION CHARACTERISTICS
RT	STOCKS
RT	ZOOLOGY

ANIMAL PRODUCTS
UF	aquatic animal products
NT1	AMBERGRIS
NT1	CORAL
NT1	GUANO
NT1	PEARLS
NT1	SHELLS
NT1	SPONGES
RT	AQUATIC ANIMALS
RT	AQUATIC BIRDS
RT	FISHERY RESOURCES
RT	LIVING RESOURCES
RT	WAXES

ANIMAL REPRODUCTIVE ORGANS
SN	Before 1982 search REPRODUCTIVE ORGANS (ANIMAL). For sexual reproduction only
UF	gonads
UF	reproductive organs (animal)
UF	reproductive system
UF	sexual glands
NT1	OVARIES
NT1	TESTES
RT	ANATOMY
RT	HERMAPHRODITISM
RT	REPRODUCTION
RT	SELF FERTILIZATION
RT	SEX CHARACTERS

ANIMAL REPRODUCTIVE ORGANS (cont'd)
RT	SEX HORMONES
RT	SEX REVERSAL
RT	SEXUAL CELLS
RT	SEXUAL REPRODUCTION
RT	STERILITY

ANIMAL WASTES
USE	**ORGANIC WASTES**

ANIMALS (AQUATIC)
USE	**AQUATIC ANIMALS**

ANION EXCHANGE
USE	**ION EXCHANGE**

ANIONS
UF	negative ions
BT1	IONS
RT	ELECTROLYSIS
RT	ION EXCHANGE

ANISOTROPIC ROCKS
RT	ANISOTROPY
RT	SEISMOLOGY

ANISOTROPY
BT1	PHYSICAL PROPERTIES
BT2	PROPERTIES
RT	ANISOTROPIC ROCKS
RT	ISOTROPIC MATERIALS
RT	ISOTROPY
RT	MAGNETIC SUSCEPTIBILITY
RT	MECHANICAL PROPERTIES
RT	OPTICAL PROPERTIES
RT	ORIENTATION

ANNOTATION
USE	**BIBLIOGRAPHIC INFORMATION**

ANNUAL
SN	Descriptor to be used only as a qualifier
BT1	PERIODICITY
RT	ANNUAL RANGE
RT	ANNUAL REPORTS
RT	ANNUAL VARIATIONS
RT	BIENNIAL
RT	SEASONAL VARIATIONS

ANNUAL RANGE
SN	Descriptor to be used only as a qualifier
BT1	EXTREME VALUES
RT	ANNUAL
RT	ANNUAL VARIATIONS

ANNUAL REPORTS
BT1	REPORT LITERATURE
BT2	DOCUMENTS
RT	ANNUAL
RT	INTERNATIONAL ORGANIZATIONS
RT	MUSEUMS
RT	ORGANIZATIONS
RT	PROGRESS REPORTS
RT	RESEARCH INSTITUTIONS
RT	RESEARCH PROGRAMMES

ANNUAL VARIATIONS
SN	Used only as a qualifier
UF	year to year variations
UF	yearly changes
BT1	PERIODIC VARIATIONS
BT2	TEMPORAL VARIATIONS
RT	ANNUAL
RT	ANNUAL RANGE
RT	HORIZONTAL DISTRIBUTION
RT	REGIONAL VARIATIONS
RT	SEASONAL VARIATIONS
RT	TEMPORAL DISTRIBUTION

ANODES
BT1	ELECTRODES
BT2	ELECTRICAL EQUIPMENT
BT3	EQUIPMENT
NT1	SACRIFICIAL ANODES

ANODIC STRIPPING VOLTAMMETRY
USE	**STRIPPING ANALYSIS**

ANOMALIES
NT1	DYNAMIC HEIGHT ANOMALY
NT1	GEOID ANOMALIES
NT1	GRAVITY ANOMALIES
NT2	BOUGUER ANOMALIES
NT2	FREE AIR ANOMALIES
NT1	MAGNETIC ANOMALIES
NT1	SPECIFIC VOLUME ANOMALIES
NT2	THERMOSTERIC ANOMALIES
NT1	TEMPERATURE ANOMALIES

ANORTHITE
BT1	FELDSPARS
BT2	SILICATE MINERALS
BT3	MINERALS

ANORTHOCLASE
BT1	FELDSPARS
BT2	SILICATE MINERALS
BT3	MINERALS

ANORTHOSITE
RT	GABBROS

ANOXIA
SN	Deficiency or absence of oxygen in the blood and tissues
BT1	OXYGEN DEPLETION
RT	AEROBIC RESPIRATION
RT	ASPHYXIA
RT	BIOLOGICAL STRESS
RT	BLOOD
RT	HYPOXIA
RT	MORTALITY CAUSES
RT	NECROSES
RT	OXYGEN

ANOXIC BASINS
SN	Water basins, without vertical circulation, characterized by a total absence of dissolved oxygen and a higher sulphides production
UF	anoxic waters
RT	ANOXIC CONDITIONS
RT	ANOXIC SEDIMENTS
RT	BASINS
RT	DEGRADATION
RT	HYDROGEN SULPHIDE
RT	MARGINAL SEAS
RT	OXYGEN
RT	OXYGEN DEPLETION
RT	SULPHUR COMPOUNDS
RT	SUSPENDED ORGANIC MATTER

ANOXIC CONDITIONS
SN	Depletion of dissolved oxygen in any specific aquatic environment
UF	anaerobic conditions
RT	ANOXIC BASINS
RT	DEGRADATION
RT	DISSOLVED OXYGEN
RT	FISH KILL
RT	FJORDS
RT	OXIC CONDITIONS
RT	OXYGEN
RT	OXYGEN CONSUMPTION
RT	OXYGEN DEPLETION
RT	POLLUTION EFFECTS
RT	SAPROPELS
RT	STAGNANT WATER
RT	WINTERKILL

ANOXIC SEDIMENTS
UF	anaerobic sediments
BT1	SEDIMENTS
RT	ANOXIC BASINS
RT	FJORDS
RT	HYDROGEN SULPHIDE
RT	LACUSTRINE SEDIMENTATION
RT	LAKE DEPOSITS
RT	ORGANIC MATTER
RT	OXIC SEDIMENTS
RT	OXYGEN
RT	OXYGEN DEPLETION
RT	SAPROPELS

ANOXIC WATERS
USE	**ANOXIC BASINS**

ANS
USE	**AUTONOMIC NERVOUS SYSTEM**

ANTARCTIC CONVERGENCE
UF	antarctic polar front (ocean)
BT1	POLAR CONVERGENCES
BT2	OCEANIC CONVERGENCES
BT3	CONVERGENCE ZONES
RT	FRONTS

ANTARCTIC FRONT
SN	Use only for the semi-permanent front separating continental and maritime air masses over the Southern Ocean
UF	antarctic polar front (atmospheric)
BT1	ATMOSPHERIC CONVERGENCES
BT2	CONVERGENCE ZONES
RT	FRONTS
RT	POLAR AIR MASSES
RT	POLAR METEOROLOGY

ANTARCTIC POLAR FRONT (ATMOSPHERIC)
USE	**ANTARCTIC FRONT**

ANTARCTIC POLAR FRONT (OCEAN)
USE	**ANTARCTIC CONVERGENCE**

ANTARCTIC WATERS
USE	**POLAR WATERS**

ANTARCTIC ZONE
BT1	POLAR ZONES
BT2	CLIMATIC ZONES

ANTENNAE
SN	A pair of anterior appendages, normally of sensory function
UF	antennulae
BT1	ANIMAL APPENDAGES
RT	ORIENTATION BEHAVIOUR
RT	SENSE FUNCTIONS

ANTENNULAE
USE	**ANTENNAE**

ANTHROPOGENIC EFFECTS
USE	**MAN-INDUCED EFFECTS**

ANTHROPOGENIC FACTORS
SN	Influences exercised by man and his activities on an organism or biotic community. Added in 1980
BT1	ENVIRONMENTAL FACTORS
RT	AIR POLLUTION
RT	ENVIRONMENTAL CONDITIONS
RT	LIMITING FACTORS
RT	POLLUTION EFFECTS

ANTI-SUBMARINE WARFARE
USE	**UNDERSEA WARFARE**

ANTIBACTERIALS
USE	**ANTIBIOTICS**

ANTIBIOTIC RESISTANCE
USE	**CONTROL RESISTANCE**

ANTIBIOTICS
UF	antibacterials
BT1	DRUGS
RT	ANTIHELMINTHIC AGENTS
RT	ANTIPROTOZOAL AGENTS
RT	BACTERIAL DISEASES
RT	BACTERIOCIDES
RT	CONTROL RESISTANCE
RT	DISEASES
RT	FUNGAL DISEASES
RT	FUNGICIDES
RT	PATHOGENIC BACTERIA
RT	PROTOZOAN DISEASES
RT	TERPENES
RT	THERAPY
RT	TUBERCULOSIS
RT	VIRAL DISEASES

ANTIBODIES
UF	antitoxins
BT1	SERUM
BT2	BODY FLUIDS
NT1	AGGLUTININS
RT	ANTIGENS
RT	BIOLOGICAL POISONS
RT	DEFENCE MECHANISMS
RT	IMMUNITY
RT	IMMUNOLOGY
RT	IMMUNOPRECIPITATION
RT	SEROLOGICAL STUDIES
RT	SEROLOGICAL TAXONOMY
RT	TARGET CELLS
RT	TOXICITY
RT	VACCINES

ANTICHOLINESTERASES
USE	**CHOLINESTERASE INHIBITORS**

ANTICLINES
BT1	FOLDS
BT2	GEOLOGICAL STRUCTURES
NT1	DOMES
RT	ANTICLINORIA
RT	SALT DOMES
RT	SYNCLINES

ANTICLINORIA
BT1	FOLDS
BT2	GEOLOGICAL STRUCTURES
RT	ANTICLINES
RT	GEOSYNCLINES
RT	SYNCLINORIA

ANTICOAGULANTS
RT	AGENTS
RT	COAGULANTS
RT	DISPERSANTS
RT	PRESERVATIVES

ANTICORROSION MATERIAL
USE	**CORROSION CONTROL**

ANTICYCLONES
UF	midlatitude anticyclones
RT	ANTICYCLONIC MOTION
RT	ATMOSPHERIC PRESSURE
RT	CLIMATOLOGY
RT	CYCLONES
RT	ISOBARS
RT	SEA LEVEL PRESSURE
RT	WEATHER

ANTICYCLONES (cont'd)
RT	WINDS

ANTICYCLONIC EDDIES
USE	**CURRENT RINGS**

ANTICYCLONIC GYRES
USE	**GYRES**

ANTICYCLONIC MOTION
RT	ANTICYCLONES
RT	CYCLONIC MOTION
RT	FLUID MOTION
RT	MOTION
RT	ROTATION

ANTICYCLONIC RINGS
USE	**CURRENT RINGS**

ANTIDUNES
BT1	BED FORMS
BT2	SEDIMENTARY STRUCTURES
RT	TRANSVERSE BED FORMS

ANTIFOULING COATINGS
USE	**ANTIFOULING SUBSTANCES**

ANTIFOULING SUBSTANCES
UF	antifouling coatings
RT	AGENTS
RT	ARSENIC COMPOUNDS
RT	BIODEGRADATION
RT	BIOLOGICAL DAMAGE
RT	CHEMICAL CONTROL
RT	COATING MATERIALS
RT	FOULING
RT	FOULING CONTROL
RT	FOULING ORGANISMS

ANTIFREEZES
UF	freezing point depressants
RT	ADDITIVES
RT	AGENTS
RT	DE-ICING
RT	FREEZING
RT	REFRIGERATION

ANTIFUNGALS
USE	**FUNGICIDES**

ANTIGENS
RT	ANTIBODIES
RT	BACTERIA
RT	BLOOD CELLS
RT	BLOOD GROUPS
RT	GLYCOPROTEINS
RT	IMMUNOPRECIPITATION
RT	SEROLOGICAL STUDIES
RT	VACCINES

ANTIHELMINTHES PESTICIDES
USE	**ANTIHELMINTHIC AGENTS**

ANTIHELMINTHIC AGENTS
SN	Before 1982 search PESTICIDES
UF	antihelminthes pesticides
BT1	PESTICIDES
RT	ANTIBIOTICS
RT	DISEASE CONTROL
RT	PARASITIC DISEASES

ANTIMONY
BT1	CHEMICAL ELEMENTS
RT	ANTIMONY COMPOUNDS
RT	ANTIMONY ISOTOPES

ANTIMONY COMPOUNDS
RT	ANTIMONY
RT	CHEMICAL COMPOUNDS

ANTIMONY ISOTOPES
BT1	ISOTOPES
RT	ANTIMONY

ANTIOXIDANTS
SN	Added in 1980
RT	AGENTS
RT	CHEMICAL COMPOUNDS
RT	CORROSION
RT	CORROSION CONTROL
RT	FOOD ADDITIVES
RT	OXIDATION
RT	PAINTS

ANTIPARASITIC AGENTS
SN	Before 1982 search PESTICIDES
UF	agents (antiparasitic)
BT1	PESTICIDES
NT1	ANTIPROTOZOAL AGENTS
RT	AGENTS
RT	DISEASE CONTROL
RT	PARASITIC DISEASES

ANTIPROTOZOAL AGENTS
SN	Before 1982 search PESTICIDES
UF	antiprotozoals
UF	protozoal pesticides
BT1	ANTIPARASITIC AGENTS
BT2	PESTICIDES
RT	ANTIBIOTICS
RT	DISEASE CONTROL
RT	PARASITIC DISEASES
RT	PROTOZOAN DISEASES

ANTIPROTOZOALS
USE	**ANTIPROTOZOAL AGENTS**

ANTISEPTIC AGENTS
USE	**DISINFECTANTS**

ANTISEPTIC CHEMICALS
USE	**DISINFECTANTS**

ANTISEPTICS
USE	**DISINFECTANTS**

ANTITOXINS
USE	**ANTIBODIES**

APATITE
BT1	PHOSPHATE MINERALS
BT2	MINERALS

APHOTIC ZONE
RT	ABYSSOPELAGIC ZONE
RT	BATHYPELAGIC ZONE
RT	DEEP WATER
RT	DISPHOTIC ZONE
RT	EUPHOTIC ZONE
RT	INLAND WATER ENVIRONMENT
RT	LENITIC ENVIRONMENT
RT	LIGHT PENETRATION
RT	MARINE ENVIRONMENT

APLANOSPORES
USE	**SPORES**

APPENDAGES
USE	**ANIMAL APPENDAGES**

APPENDAGES (ANIMAL)
USE	**ANIMAL APPENDAGES**

APPLICATION
USE	**UTILIZATION**

APPRAISAL
USE	**EVALUATION**

APPROXIMATION
SN	Used only as a qualifier
UF	estimation
BT1	NUMERICAL ANALYSIS
BT2	MATHEMATICAL ANALYSIS
NT1	BOUSSINESQ APPROXIMATION
NT1	CLOSURE APPROXIMATION
NT1	LEAST SQUARES METHOD
RT	ERRORS
RT	FINITE DIFFERENCE METHOD
RT	PREDICTION
RT	STATISTICAL ANALYSIS

AQUACULTURE
UF	aquaculture industry
UF	aquatic agriculture
UF	aquiculture
NT1	ALGAL CULTURE
NT2	PHYTOPLANKTON CULTURE
NT1	BRACKISHWATER AQUACULTURE
NT1	CORAL FARMING
NT1	FISH CULTURE
NT2	BAIT CULTURE
NT1	FRESHWATER AQUACULTURE
NT1	FROG CULTURE
NT1	MARINE AQUACULTURE
NT1	PEARL CULTURE
NT1	PLANT CULTURE
NT1	REPTILE CULTURE
NT1	SEAWEED CULTURE
NT1	SHELLFISH CULTURE
NT2	CRUSTACEAN CULTURE
NT3	BRINE SHRIMP CULTURE
NT3	CRAB CULTURE
NT3	CRAYFISH CULTURE
NT3	LOBSTER CULTURE
NT3	PRAWN CULTURE
NT3	SHRIMP CULTURE
NT2	MOLLUSC CULTURE
NT3	CLAM CULTURE
NT3	MUSSEL CULTURE
NT3	OYSTER CULTURE
NT3	SCALLOP CULTURE
NT3	SQUID CULTURE
NT1	SPONGE CULTURE
NT1	TURTLE CULTURE
NT1	WORM CULTURE
NT1	ZOOPLANKTON CULTURE
RT	ACCLIMATIZATION
RT	AGROPISCICULTURE
RT	AQUACULTURE DEVELOPMENT
RT	AQUACULTURE ECONOMICS
RT	AQUACULTURE PRODUCTS
RT	AQUACULTURE REGULATIONS
RT	AQUACULTURE STATISTICS
RT	AQUACULTURE TECHNIQUES
RT	AQUACULTURISTS
RT	AQUATIC SCIENCES
RT	ARTIFICIAL AERATION
RT	ARTIFICIAL FEEDING
RT	ARTIFICIAL SPAWNING GROUNDS
RT	ARTIFICIAL UPWELLING
RT	BALANCED DIETS
RT	BASIC DIETS
RT	BREEDING
RT	BROOD STOCKS
RT	COASTAL LAGOONS
RT	COST ANALYSIS
RT	CULTURE TANKS
RT	CULTURED ORGANISMS
RT	DIETARY DEFICIENCIES
RT	EXPERIMENTAL CULTURE

ASFIS Thesaurus

AQUACULTURE (cont'd)
RT	FEEDING EXPERIMENTS
RT	FISH PONDS
RT	FOOD ORGANISMS
RT	FORAGE FISH
RT	HABITAT IMPROVEMENT
RT	HATCHERIES
RT	INBREEDING
RT	INDUSTRIAL PRODUCTION
RT	INLAND LAGOONS
RT	LABORATORY CULTURE
RT	LAGOONS
RT	MANURE
RT	OXBOW LAKES
RT	PELLET FEEDS
RT	PREDATOR CONTROL
RT	PROPERTY RIGHTS
RT	REARING
RT	SEED COLLECTION
RT	SEEDING (AQUACULTURE)
RT	SHELTERS
RT	STOCKING (ORGANISMS)
RT	TEMPERATURE PREFERENCES
RT	WATER RIGHTS
RT	WATER USE

AQUACULTURE DEVELOPMENT
BT1	RESOURCE DEVELOPMENT
RT	AQUACULTURE
RT	AQUACULTURE ECONOMICS
RT	AQUACULTURE ENTERPRISES
RT	AQUACULTURE PRODUCTS
RT	AQUACULTURE REGULATIONS
RT	AQUACULTURE SYSTEMS
RT	DEVELOPMENT PROJECTS
RT	EXPERIMENTAL CULTURE
RT	FISHERY ORGANIZATIONS
RT	INTERNATIONAL COOPERATION
RT	SCALLOP CULTURE
RT	SMALL SCALE AQUACULTURE
RT	SQUID CULTURE
RT	TRANSPLANTATION
RT	WATER LEVELS

AQUACULTURE ECONOMICS
SN	Before 1982 search FISHERY ECONOMICS
UF	farmed fish economics
UF	fish culture economics
BT1	FISHERY ECONOMICS
BT2	ECONOMICS
RT	AQUACULTURE
RT	AQUACULTURE DEVELOPMENT
RT	AQUACULTURE ENTERPRISES
RT	AQUACULTURE PRODUCTS
RT	AQUACULTURE STATISTICS
RT	COST ANALYSIS
RT	ECONOMIC FEASIBILITY
RT	ECONOMIC MODELS
RT	FINANCING
RT	MARKETING
RT	PRICING
RT	TRADE

AQUACULTURE EFFLUENTS
SN	Added in 1982
UF	effluents (aquaculture)
BT1	WASTES
RT	ENVIRONMENTAL LEGISLATION
RT	EUTROPHICATION
RT	FRESHWATER AQUACULTURE
RT	INTENSIVE CULTURE
RT	POLLUTION CONTROL
RT	POND CULTURE
RT	WASTE WATER
RT	WASTEWATER TREATMENT
RT	WATER QUALITY

AQUACULTURE ENTERPRISES
SN	Added in 1980
UF	aquaculture industries
UF	commercial aquaculture
BT1	INDUSTRIES
RT	AQUACULTURE DEVELOPMENT
RT	AQUACULTURE ECONOMICS
RT	AQUACULTURE PRODUCTS
RT	AQUACULTURE SYSTEMS
RT	CULTURE EFFECTS
RT	FINANCING

AQUACULTURE EQUIPMENT
SN	Added in 1980
BT1	EQUIPMENT
NT1	CAGES
NT2	FLOATING CAGES
NT2	SUBMERGED CAGES
NT1	FEEDING EQUIPMENT
RT	AQUACULTURE FACILITIES
RT	AQUACULTURISTS
RT	AQUARIA
RT	ARTIFICIAL AERATION
RT	CULTURE TANKS
RT	DESIGN
RT	FLOOD CONTROL
RT	GEAR MATERIALS
RT	GRADING
RT	HARVESTING MACHINES
RT	HATCHERIES
RT	MECHANIZATION
RT	RAFT CULTURE
RT	RECIRCULATING SYSTEMS
RT	SCREENS
RT	WATER FILTRATION
RT	WATER PUMPS
RT	WATER TREATMENT

AQUACULTURE FACILITIES
SN	Added in 1980
NT1	HATCHERIES
RT	AQUACULTURE EQUIPMENT
RT	AQUACULTURE TECHNIQUES
RT	AQUACULTURISTS
RT	ARTIFICIAL LAKES
RT	BREEDING PONDS
RT	DESALINATION PLANTS
RT	FISH PONDS
RT	FLOOD CONTROL
RT	NURSERY PONDS
RT	PITS
RT	RESERVOIRS (WATER)
RT	SITE SELECTION
RT	STOCKING PONDS

AQUACULTURE INDUSTRIES
USE	**AQUACULTURE ENTERPRISES**

AQUACULTURE INDUSTRY
USE	**AQUACULTURE**

AQUACULTURE LAW
USE	**AQUACULTURE REGULATIONS**

AQUACULTURE LICENSING
USE	**AQUACULTURE REGULATIONS**

AQUACULTURE PRODUCTS
SN	Organisms or products derived from aquaculture practices. Added in 1980
BT1	PRODUCTS
RT	AQUACULTURE
RT	AQUACULTURE DEVELOPMENT
RT	AQUACULTURE ECONOMICS
RT	AQUACULTURE ENTERPRISES
RT	AQUACULTURE REGULATIONS
RT	AQUACULTURE STATISTICS
RT	CULTURED ORGANISMS
RT	FISHERY PRODUCTS
RT	LIVING RESOURCES

AQUACULTURE PRODUCTS (cont'd)
RT	PROCESSED FISHERY PRODUCTS
RT	SEED (AQUACULTURE)

AQUACULTURE REGULATIONS
UF	aquaculture law
UF	aquaculture licensing
BT1	LEGISLATION
RT	AQUACULTURE
RT	AQUACULTURE DEVELOPMENT
RT	AQUACULTURE PRODUCTS
RT	RENTAL
RT	WASTE WATER
RT	WATER QUALITY

AQUACULTURE SITES
USE	**SITE SELECTION**

AQUACULTURE STATISTICS
SN	Referring to statistical data on cultivated aquatic organisms and harvested products
BT1	FISHERY STATISTICS
RT	AQUACULTURE
RT	AQUACULTURE ECONOMICS
RT	AQUACULTURE PRODUCTS
RT	SEAWEED STATISTICS
RT	TRADE

AQUACULTURE SYSTEMS
SN	Added in 1980
NT1	AQUARIUM CULTURE
NT1	BATCH CULTURE
NT1	CONTINUOUS CULTURE
NT1	EXPERIMENTAL CULTURE
NT1	EXTENSIVE CULTURE
NT1	INTENSIVE CULTURE
NT1	MASS CULTURE
NT1	OPEN SYSTEMS
NT1	RECIRCULATING SYSTEMS
NT1	SMALL SCALE AQUACULTURE
NT1	VALLICULTURE
RT	AQUACULTURE DEVELOPMENT
RT	AQUACULTURE ENTERPRISES
RT	AQUACULTURE TECHNIQUES
RT	AQUACULTURISTS
RT	LABORATORY CULTURE
RT	OZONATION
RT	ULTRAVIOLET STERILIZATION

AQUACULTURE TECHNIQUES
NT1	BOTTOM CULTURE
NT1	CAGE CULTURE
NT1	HYBRID CULTURE
NT1	MONOCULTURE
NT1	MONOSEX CULTURE
NT1	OFF-BOTTOM CULTURE
NT1	OVERWINTERING TECHNIQUES
NT1	POLYCULTURE
NT1	POND CULTURE
NT1	RACEWAY CULTURE
NT1	RAFT CULTURE
NT1	SILO CULTURE
NT1	THERMAL AQUACULTURE
NT1	TRAY CULTURE
NT1	WARM-WATER AQUACULTURE
NT1	WASTEWATER AQUACULTURE
RT	ACCLIMATIZATION
RT	AGROPISCICULTURE
RT	AQUACULTURE
RT	AQUACULTURE FACILITIES
RT	AQUACULTURE SYSTEMS
RT	AQUACULTURISTS
RT	ARTIFICIAL AERATION
RT	ARTIFICIAL FEEDING
RT	BRACKISHWATER AQUACULTURE
RT	CULTURE TANKS
RT	EXPERIMENTAL CULTURE
RT	FRESHWATER AQUACULTURE
RT	HABITAT IMPROVEMENT

ASFIS Thesaurus

AQUACULTURE TECHNIQUES (cont'd)

RT	HATCHERIES
RT	INDUCED BREEDING
RT	LABORATORY CULTURE
RT	MARINE AQUACULTURE
RT	PLANT CULTURE
RT	REARING
RT	RICE FIELD AQUACULTURE
RT	SEED (AQUACULTURE)
RT	SEED COLLECTION
RT	SELECTIVE BREEDING
RT	SITE SELECTION
RT	STOCKING (ORGANISMS)
RT	WATER PURIFICATION

AQUACULTURISTS

SN	Added in 1980
BT1	TECHNICIANS
BT2	EXPERTS
BT3	PERSONNEL
RT	AQUACULTURE
RT	AQUACULTURE EQUIPMENT
RT	AQUACULTURE FACILITIES
RT	AQUACULTURE SYSTEMS
RT	AQUACULTURE TECHNIQUES
RT	DIRECTORIES
RT	HATCHERIES

AQUARIA

UF	aquarium systems
UF	oceanaria
RT	AQUACULTURE EQUIPMENT
RT	AQUARIOLOGY
RT	ARTIFICIAL AERATION
RT	ARTIFICIAL FEEDING
RT	BATCH CULTURE
RT	CAPTIVITY
RT	CONTINUOUS CULTURE
RT	MUSEUMS
RT	ORNAMENTAL FISH
RT	REARING
RT	WATER FILTRATION
RT	WATER PUMPS

AQUARIOLOGY

RT	AQUARIA
RT	ARTIFICIAL AERATION
RT	ARTIFICIAL FEEDING
RT	BACTERIOCIDES
RT	CAPTIVITY
RT	CLEANING BEHAVIOUR
RT	LABORATORY EQUIPMENT
RT	ORNAMENTAL FISH
RT	REARING
RT	WATER FILTERS
RT	WATER FILTRATION

AQUARIUM CULTURE

SN	Added in 1982
BT1	AQUACULTURE SYSTEMS
RT	FISH CULTURE
RT	ORNAMENTAL FISH
RT	WATER PUMPS

AQUARIUM FISH

USE	**ORNAMENTAL FISH**

AQUARIUM SYSTEMS

USE	**AQUARIA**

AQUATIC AGRICULTURE

USE	**AQUACULTURE**

AQUATIC ANIMAL DISEASES

USE	**ANIMAL DISEASES**

AQUATIC ANIMAL PRODUCTS

USE	**ANIMAL PRODUCTS**

AQUATIC ANIMALS

SN	Any microscopic or macroscopic animal organisms living permanently or developing a part of their life cycle in an aquatic environment
UF	animals (aquatic)
UF	aquatic fauna
NT1	AQUATIC BIRDS
NT2	MARINE BIRDS
NT3	GUANO BIRDS
NT1	AQUATIC INSECTS
NT1	AQUATIC MAMMALS
NT2	MARINE MAMMALS
NT1	AQUATIC REPTILES
NT1	BRACKISHWATER MOLLUSCS
NT1	FISH
NT2	AIR-BREATHING FISH
NT2	BAIT FISH
NT2	BRACKISHWATER FISH
NT2	FOOD FISH
NT2	FORAGE FISH
NT2	FRESHWATER FISH
NT3	COARSE FISH
NT2	GAME FISH
NT2	HERBIVOROUS FISH
NT2	MARINE FISH
NT3	REEF FISH
NT2	ORNAMENTAL FISH
NT2	POISONOUS FISH
NT2	TRASH FISH
NT2	TROPICAL FISH
NT1	FRESHWATER CRUSTACEANS
NT1	FRESHWATER MOLLUSCS
NT1	MARINE CRUSTACEANS
NT1	MARINE INVERTEBRATES
NT1	MARINE MOLLUSCS
RT	ANIMAL DISEASES
RT	ANIMAL FOSSILS
RT	ANIMAL MORPHOLOGY
RT	ANIMAL PHYSIOLOGY
RT	ANIMAL POPULATIONS
RT	ANIMAL PRODUCTS
RT	AQUATIC ORGANISMS
RT	BIOGEOGRAPHY
RT	COMMERCIAL SPECIES
RT	FRESHWATER ECOLOGY
RT	GILLS
RT	HYDROBIOLOGY
RT	MARINE ECOLOGY
RT	RARE SPECIES
RT	VERNACULAR NAMES
RT	ZOOBENTHOS
RT	ZOOLOGY
RT	ZOOPLANKTON

AQUATIC BIOLOGISTS

USE	**BIOLOGISTS**

AQUATIC BIOLOGY

USE	**HYDROBIOLOGY**

AQUATIC BIRDS

UF	birds (aquatic)
BT1	AQUATIC ANIMALS
NT1	MARINE BIRDS
NT2	GUANO BIRDS
RT	ANIMAL PRODUCTS
RT	AVIAN PHYSIOLOGY
RT	FEATHERS
RT	FLIGHT BEHAVIOUR
RT	FLYING
RT	IMPRINTING
RT	MIGRATIONS
RT	MIGRATORY SPECIES
RT	NESTING
RT	NESTS
RT	ORNITHOLOGISTS

AQUATIC BIRDS (cont'd)

RT	ORNITHOLOGY
RT	PECKING ORDER
RT	WINGS

AQUATIC BOTANICAL RESOURCES

USE	**BOTANICAL RESOURCES**

AQUATIC COMMUNITIES

UF	communities (ecological)
NT1	BENTHOS
NT2	MEIOBENTHOS
NT2	PHYTOBENTHOS
NT2	ZOOBENTHOS
NT1	EPIPSAMMON
NT1	NEKTON
NT1	NEUSTON
NT1	PERIPHYTON
NT1	PLANKTON
NT2	CRYOPLANKTON
NT2	NANNOPLANKTON
NT2	PHYTOPLANKTON
NT2	ZOOPLANKTON
NT3	HOLOPLANKTON
NT3	ICHTHYOPLANKTON
NT3	MEROPLANKTON
NT3	SAPROPLANKTON
NT1	PLEUSTON
NT1	PSAMMON
NT1	SESTON
RT	AQUATIC ENVIRONMENT
RT	AQUATIC ORGANISMS
RT	BIOCOENOSIS
RT	BIOLOGICAL CHARTS
RT	BIOTA
RT	BRACKISHWATER ECOLOGY
RT	CLIMAX COMMUNITY
RT	COMMUNITY COMPOSITION
RT	ECOLOGICAL ASSOCIATIONS
RT	ECOLOGICAL SUCCESSION
RT	ECOSYSTEM DISTURBANCE
RT	ECOSYSTEM MANAGEMENT
RT	ECOSYSTEM RESILIENCE
RT	ECOSYSTEMS
RT	FRESHWATER ECOLOGY
RT	HABITAT
RT	MARINE ECOLOGY
RT	NICHES
RT	ORGANISM AGGREGATIONS
RT	SYNECOLOGY

AQUATIC DRUGS

SN	Drugs of aquatic origin and their medical uses
BT1	DRUGS
RT	BOTANICAL RESOURCES
RT	MEDICINE
RT	NATURAL RESOURCES
RT	PLANT UTILIZATION

AQUATIC ECOLOGY

USE	**ECOLOGY**

AQUATIC ENVIRONMENT

SN	Environment of all types of hydrosphere
UF	environment (aquatic)
BT1	ENVIRONMENTS
NT1	BENTHIC ENVIRONMENT
NT2	ABYSSOBENTHIC ZONE
NT2	BATHYAL-BENTHIC ZONE
NT2	LITTORAL ZONE
NT3	EULITTORAL ZONE
NT3	SUBLITTORAL ZONE
NT3	SUPRALITTORAL ZONE
NT1	BRACKISHWATER ENVIRONMENT
NT1	INLAND WATER ENVIRONMENT
NT2	LENITIC ENVIRONMENT
NT2	LOTIC ENVIRONMENT
NT1	INTERSTITIAL ENVIRONMENT

AQUATIC ENVIRONMENT (cont'd)
- NT1   MARINE ENVIRONMENT
- NT2   INTERTIDAL ENVIRONMENT
- NT1   PELAGIC ENVIRONMENT
- NT2   NERITIC PROVINCE
- NT2   OCEANIC PROVINCE
- NT3   ABYSSOPELAGIC ZONE
- NT3   BATHYPELAGIC ZONE
- NT3   EPIPELAGIC ZONE
- NT3   MESOPELAGIC ZONE
- RT   AQUATIC COMMUNITIES
- RT   AQUATIC SCIENCES
- RT   BIOTOPES
- RT   ECOSYSTEMS
- RT   ENVIRONMENT MANAGEMENT
- RT   ENVIRONMENTAL CONDITIONS
- RT   ENVIRONMENTAL EFFECTS
- RT   ENVIRONMENTAL FACTORS
- RT   ENVIRONMENTAL IMPACT
- RT   ENVIRONMENTAL SURVEYS
- RT   EXPLORATORY BEHAVIOUR
- RT   HABITAT
- RT   LIGHT PENETRATION
- RT   SWAMPS
- RT   WATER
- RT   WATER DEPTH
- RT   WETLANDS

AQUATIC FAUNA
- USE   **AQUATIC ANIMALS**

AQUATIC HABITAT
- USE   **HABITAT**

AQUATIC INSECTS
- SN   Restricted to aquatic insects and their larvae
- UF   insects (aquatic)
- BT1   AQUATIC ANIMALS
- RT   BIOLOGICAL CONTROL
- RT   BIOLOGICAL VECTORS
- RT   BORING ORGANISMS
- RT   COMPOUND EYES
- RT   DIAPAUSE
- RT   ECDYSONS
- RT   EMERGENCE
- RT   ENTOMOLOGISTS
- RT   ENTOMOLOGY
- RT   FOOD ORGANISMS
- RT   INFESTATION
- RT   INSECT EGGS
- RT   INSECT LARVAE
- RT   MALARIA
- RT   MOULTING
- RT   NYMPHS
- RT   TRACHEA
- RT   WINGS

AQUATIC LIVING RESOURCES
- USE   **LIVING RESOURCES**

AQUATIC MAMMALS
- UF   mammals (aquatic)
- BT1   AQUATIC ANIMALS
- NT1   MARINE MAMMALS
- RT   ANIMAL OIL EXTRACTION
- RT   CARCASSES
- RT   CETOLOGY
- RT   COMMERCIAL SPECIES
- RT   CULLING
- RT   DIVING
- RT   DIVING PHYSIOLOGY
- RT   ECHOLOCATION
- RT   FISHERY RESOURCES
- RT   FOETUS
- RT   HUNTING
- RT   LACTATION
- RT   MAMMALIAN PHYSIOLOGY
- RT   MAMMALOGISTS
- RT   MAMMALOGY

AQUATIC MAMMALS (cont'd)
- RT   OCEANODROMOUS MIGRATIONS
- RT   PARTURITION
- RT   PREGNANCY
- RT   STRANDING
- RT   VERNACULAR NAMES
- RT   VOCALIZATION BEHAVIOUR
- RT   WHALING

AQUATIC NATURAL RESOURCES
- USE   **NATURAL RESOURCES**

AQUATIC ORGANISMS
- SN   Use of a more specific term is recommended
- UF   organisms (aquatic)
- NT1   BORING ORGANISMS
- NT1   BURROWING ORGANISMS
- NT1   CULTURED ORGANISMS
- NT1   DANGEROUS ORGANISMS
- NT1   ESTUARINE ORGANISMS
- NT1   FOOD ORGANISMS
- NT1   FOULING ORGANISMS
- NT1   FRESHWATER ORGANISMS
- NT1   HETEROTROPHIC ORGANISMS
- NT2   CARNIVORES
- NT2   DECOMPOSERS
- NT2   DETRITUS FEEDERS
- NT2   FILTER FEEDERS
- NT2   HERBIVORES
- NT2   OMNIVORES
- NT2   PLANKTON FEEDERS
- NT2   PREDATORS
- NT2   SCAVENGERS
- NT1   LUMINOUS ORGANISMS
- NT1   MARINE ORGANISMS
- NT1   NOXIOUS ORGANISMS
- NT1   POISONOUS ORGANISMS
- NT1   TEST ORGANISMS
- NT1   TUBE DWELLERS
- RT   AMPHIBIOTIC SPECIES
- RT   AQUATIC ANIMALS
- RT   AQUATIC COMMUNITIES
- RT   AQUATIC PLANTS
- RT   BIOLOGICAL CHARTS
- RT   CLONES
- RT   HYDROBIOLOGY
- RT   LIVING RESOURCES
- RT   MICROORGANISMS
- RT   NICHES
- RT   ORGANISM AGGREGATIONS
- RT   SPECIES

AQUATIC PLANT CULTURE
- USE   **PLANT CULTURE**

AQUATIC PLANT RESOURCES
- USE   **BOTANICAL RESOURCES**

AQUATIC PLANT UTILIZATION
- USE   **PLANT UTILIZATION**

AQUATIC PLANTS
- SN   Any microscopic or macroscopic vegetal organism living in aquatic environment, excluding bacteria and viruses
- UF   hydrophytes
- UF   plants (aquatic)
- RT   ALGOLOGY
- RT   ALKALOIDS
- RT   AQUATIC ORGANISMS
- RT   BIOGEOGRAPHY
- RT   BOTANICAL RESOURCES
- RT   BOTANY
- RT   COMMERCIAL SPECIES
- RT   FISHERY RESOURCES
- RT   FOULING
- RT   FRESHWATER ECOLOGY
- RT   FUNGI

AQUATIC PLANTS (cont'd)
- RT   GERMINATION
- RT   HYDROBIOLOGY
- RT   LIVESTOCK FOOD
- RT   MARINE ECOLOGY
- RT   PHYTOBENTHOS
- RT   PHYTOHORMONES
- RT   PHYTOPLANKTON
- RT   PHYTOSOCIOLOGY
- RT   PLANT DISEASES
- RT   PLANT MORPHOLOGY
- RT   PLANT PHYSIOLOGY
- RT   PLANT POPULATIONS
- RT   PLANT UTILIZATION
- RT   PLEUSTON
- RT   POLLEN
- RT   POLLINATION
- RT   RARE SPECIES
- RT   STARCH
- RT   STOMATA
- RT   TURIONS
- RT   VERNACULAR NAMES
- RT   WEEDS

AQUATIC POLLUTION
- USE   **WATER POLLUTION**

AQUATIC REPTILES
- SN   Added in 1982
- UF   reptiles (aquatic)
- BT1   AQUATIC ANIMALS
- RT   COMMERCIAL SPECIES
- RT   FISHERY RESOURCES
- RT   HERPETOLOGY
- RT   REPTILE CULTURE
- RT   TURTLE CULTURE
- RT   VERNACULAR NAMES

AQUATIC SCIENCES
- NT1   FRESHWATER SCIENCES
- NT1   MARINE SCIENCES
- RT   AQUACULTURE
- RT   AQUATIC ENVIRONMENT
- RT   EARTH SCIENCES
- RT   EXPLOITATION
- RT   FISHERIES
- RT   HYDROSPHERE
- RT   LIMNOLOGY
- RT   OCEANOGRAPHY
- RT   RESOURCES

AQUATIC WEED CONTROL
- USE   **PLANT CONTROL**

AQUATIC WEED UTILIZATION
- USE   **PLANT UTILIZATION**

AQUICULTURE
- USE   **AQUACULTURE**

ARABINOSE
- BT1   MONOSACCHARIDES
- BT2   SACCHARIDES
- BT3   CARBOHYDRATES
- BT4   ORGANIC COMPOUNDS
- RT   ALDEHYDES

ARACHIDONIC ACID
- BT1   ORGANIC ACIDS
- BT2   ORGANIC COMPOUNDS

ARAGONITE
- BT1   CARBONATE MINERALS
- BT2   MINERALS
- RT   CALCIUM CARBONATES
- RT   PTEROPOD OOZE

ARCHAEOLOGY
UF	archeology
UF	excavation (archaeology)
UF	marine archaeology
UF	nautical archaeology
RT	FOSSILS
RT	HYDROGRAPHIC SURVEYS
RT	PALAEONTOLOGY
RT	SURVEYING UNDERWATER
RT	UNDERWATER EQUIPMENT
RT	UNDERWATER EXPLORATION

ARCHEAN
USE	**PRECAMBRIAN**

ARCHEOLOGY
USE	**ARCHAEOLOGY**

ARCHIPELAGIC APRONS
BT1	SUBMARINE FEATURES
BT2	TOPOGRAPHIC FEATURES
RT	DEEP-SEA FANS
RT	ISLAND SLOPE
RT	OCEANIC ISLANDS
RT	SEAMOUNTS

ARCHIPELAGIC WATERS
USE	**ARCHIPELAGOES**

ARCHIPELAGOES
UF	archipelagic waters
RT	ISLANDS
RT	OCEAN SPACE

ARCHIVES
SN	Added in 1982
UF	correspondence (letters)
UF	manuscripts (historical)
BT1	DOCUMENTS
RT	HISTORICAL ACCOUNT
RT	LOGBOOKS
RT	RECORDS
RT	STORAGE CONDITIONS

ARCHIVISTS
USE	**LIBRARIANS**

ARCS (ISLAND)
USE	**ISLAND ARCS**

ARCTIC ENVIRONMENT
USE	**ARCTIC ZONE**

ARCTIC SEA SMOKE
USE	**FOG**

ARCTIC WATERS
USE	**POLAR WATERS**

ARCTIC ZONE
UF	arctic environment
BT1	POLAR ZONES
BT2	CLIMATIC ZONES
RT	PERMAFROST
RT	POLAR METEOROLOGY
RT	POLAR OCEANOGRAPHY

AREA
SN	Used only as a qualifier
UF	surface area
BT1	DIMENSIONS
RT	HYPSOMETRIC CURVES
RT	SIZE
RT	SURFACES

ARENACEOUS DEPOSITS
RT	ARENITES
RT	SAND
RT	SEDIMENTS

ARENITES
BT1	CLASTICS
BT2	SEDIMENTS
RT	ARENACEOUS DEPOSITS
RT	GRAYWACKE
RT	PLACERS
RT	SAND
RT	SANDSTONE

ARGILLACEOUS DEPOSITS
RT	CLAY MINERALS
RT	CLAYS
RT	LUTITES
RT	MARL
RT	MARLSTONE
RT	SEDIMENTS
RT	SLATES

ARGININE
BT1	AMINO ACIDS
BT2	ORGANIC ACIDS
BT3	ORGANIC COMPOUNDS

ARGON
BT1	CHEMICAL ELEMENTS
RT	RARE GASES

ARGON ISOTOPES
BT1	ISOTOPES
RT	POTASSIUM-ARGON DATING

ARID ENVIRONMENTS
RT	CLIMATIC ZONES
RT	COASTAL UPWELLING
RT	DESERTS
RT	DROUGHTS
RT	PLAYAS
RT	SABKHAS

ARKSHELL FISHERIES
USE	**CLAM FISHERIES**

AROMA
USE	**ODOUR**

AROMATIC COMPOUNDS
USE	**AROMATICS**

AROMATIC HYDROCARBONS
SN	Before 1982 search also AROMATICS
UF	monocyclic hydrocarbons
UF	polycyclic hydrocarbons
BT1	UNSATURATED HYDROCARBONS
BT2	HYDROCARBONS
BT3	ORGANIC COMPOUNDS
NT1	BENZENE
NT1	NAPHTHALENE
NT1	PCB
NT1	XYLENE
RT	CHEMICAL COMPOUNDS
RT	CHEMICAL POLLUTANTS
RT	CHEMICAL POLLUTION

AROMATICS
UF	aromatic compounds
NT1	PHENOLS
RT	CHEMICAL COMPOUNDS
RT	ORGANIC COMPOUNDS

ARRAYS
NT1	ACOUSTIC ARRAYS
NT2	SONAR ARRAYS
NT2	TRANSDUCER ARRAYS
NT2	TRANSPONDER ARRAYS
NT1	CURRENT METER ARRAYS
NT1	SEISMIC ARRAYS
NT1	THERMISTOR CHAINS
NT1	THERMOCOUPLE ARRAYS
RT	BUOY SYSTEMS
RT	EQUIPMENT

ARSENATES
BT1	ARSENIC COMPOUNDS

ARSENIC
BT1	CHEMICAL ELEMENTS
RT	ARSENIC COMPOUNDS

ARSENIC COMPOUNDS
NT1	ARSENATES
RT	ANTIFOULING SUBSTANCES
RT	ARSENIC
RT	CHEMICAL COMPOUNDS

ARSENIC ISOTOPES
BT1	ISOTOPES

ARTEMIA CULTURE
USE	**BRINE SHRIMP CULTURE**

ARTERIES
USE	**BLOOD VESSELS**

ARTICULATED COLUMNS
UF	articulated structures
BT1	OFFSHORE STRUCTURES
BT2	HYDRAULIC STRUCTURES
RT	GAS FLARING
RT	LOADING BUOYS
RT	SINGLE POINT MOORINGS

ARTICULATED STRUCTURES
USE	**ARTICULATED COLUMNS**

ARTIFICIAL AERATION
SN	Aeration systems used in aquaria, aquaculture, diving and lakes
BT1	AERATION
RT	AIR BUBBLES
RT	AQUACULTURE
RT	AQUACULTURE EQUIPMENT
RT	AQUACULTURE TECHNIQUES
RT	AQUARIA
RT	AQUARIOLOGY
RT	BUBBLE DISEASE
RT	DIVING
RT	GASES
RT	HABITAT IMPROVEMENT (CHEMICAL)
RT	LABORATORY CULTURE
RT	ZOOPLANKTON CULTURE

ARTIFICIAL FECUNDATION
USE	**INDUCED BREEDING**

ARTIFICIAL FEED
USE	**FEED**

ARTIFICIAL FEEDING
BT1	FEEDING
NT1	SELECTIVE FEEDING
RT	AQUACULTURE
RT	AQUACULTURE TECHNIQUES
RT	AQUARIA
RT	AQUARIOLOGY
RT	BALANCED DIETS
RT	BALANCED RATIONS
RT	BASIC DIETS
RT	BODY CONDITIONS
RT	BRINE SHRIMP CULTURE
RT	BRINE SHRIMP EGGS
RT	CONTROLLED CONDITIONS
RT	DEFICIENCY DISEASES
RT	DIETARY DEFICIENCIES
RT	DIETS
RT	DIGESTIBILITY
RT	FEED
RT	FEED COMPOSITION
RT	FEED EFFICIENCY
RT	FEED PREPARATION
RT	FEEDING EQUIPMENT

ASFIS Thesaurus

ARTIFICIAL FEEDING (cont'd)		**ARTIFICIAL REEFS** (cont'd)		**ARTISANAL FISHING** (cont'd)	
RT	FEEDING EXPERIMENTS	RT	REEFS	RT	PROCESSED FISHERY PRODUCTS
RT	FOOD ORGANISMS	RT	SHELTERS	RT	RIVER FISHERIES
RT	FOOD PREFERENCES	RT	SPORT FISHING	RT	ROW BOATS
RT	IMPRINTING			RT	WOMEN
RT	INTENSIVE CULTURE	**ARTIFICIAL SATELLITES**			
RT	LABORATORY CULTURE	USE	**SATELLITES**	**ARTISANAL WHALING**	
RT	NUTRITION DISORDERS			SN	Added in 1982
RT	NUTRITIONAL REQUIREMENTS	**ARTIFICIAL SEAWATER**		UF	shore whaling
RT	PALATABILITY	UF	synthetic sea water	BT1	WHALING
RT	PELLET FEEDS	BT1	SEA WATER	RT	ARTISANAL FISHING
RT	REARING	BT2	WATER		
RT	SINGLE CELL PROTEINS	RT	STANDARD SEA WATER	**ASBESTOS**	
RT	WORM CULTURE			RT	FIRE FIGHTING
RT	ZOOPLANKTON CULTURE	**ARTIFICIAL SEAWEED**		RT	FIRE PREVENTION
		UF	seaweed (artificial)	RT	THERMAL INSULATION
ARTIFICIAL HABITATS		RT	CURRENT SCOURING		
USE	**UNDERWATER HABITATS**	RT	PIPELINE PROTECTION	**ASCORBIC ACID**	
		RT	SCOUR PROTECTION	USE	**VITAMIN C**
ARTIFICIAL HARBOURS		RT	SCOURING		
SN	Purpose-built anchorages	RT	SEABED PROTECTION	**ASCOSPORES**	
	constructed on an open coast. Use	RT	SEAWEEDS	USE	**SPORES**
	of a more specific term is	RT	SHORE PROTECTION		
	recommended			**ASCP**	
BT1	COASTAL STRUCTURES	**ARTIFICIAL SHELTERS**		USE	**SINGLE CELL PROTEINS**
BT2	HYDRAULIC STRUCTURES	USE	**SHELTERS**		
NT1	MARINAS			**ASDIC**	
NT1	MILITARY PORTS	**ARTIFICIAL SPAWNING**		USE	**SONAR**
RT	BREAKWATERS	USE	**INDUCED BREEDING**		
RT	DEFENCE CRAFT			**ASEISMIC MARGINS**	
RT	HARBOURS	**ARTIFICIAL SPAWNING GROUNDS**		USE	**PASSIVE MARGINS**
RT	OFFSHORE DOCKING	SN	Any man-made arrangement put into		
RT	PORT INSTALLATIONS		water bodies for fish to spawn.	**ASEISMIC RIDGES**	
RT	SECURITY		Added in 1980	BT1	SUBMARINE RIDGES
RT	SHIP TECHNOLOGY	BT1	SPAWNING GROUNDS	BT2	SUBMARINE FEATURES
RT	SITE SELECTION	RT	AQUACULTURE	BT3	TOPOGRAPHIC FEATURES
		RT	ARTIFICIAL REEFS	RT	MICROCONTINENTS
ARTIFICIAL INTELLIGENCE		RT	FISH CULTURE	RT	SEISMIC RIDGES
UF	expert systems	RT	SHELTERS		
RT	COMPUTER PROGRAMS			**ASEISMIC ZONES**	
		ARTIFICIAL SUBSTRATA		BT1	EARTH STRUCTURE
ARTIFICIAL ISLANDS		NT1	CULTCH	RT	SEISMIC ZONES
BT1	OFFSHORE STRUCTURES	RT	ALGAL SETTLEMENTS		
BT2	HYDRAULIC STRUCTURES	RT	COLONIZATION	**ASEXUAL REPRODUCTION**	
NT1	ICE RAFTS	RT	LARVAL SETTLEMENT	BT1	REPRODUCTION
NT1	SAND STRUCTURES	RT	SETTLING BEHAVIOUR	NT1	BUDDING
RT	ICE ISLANDS	RT	SUBSTRATA	RT	CLONES
RT	ISLANDS	RT	SUBSTRATE PREFERENCES	RT	CONIDIA
				RT	GEMMULES
ARTIFICIAL LAKES		**ARTIFICIAL UPWELLING**		RT	PLANT REPRODUCTIVE STRUCTURES
UF	man-made lakes	SN	Added in 1980	RT	RESTING SPORES
BT1	LAKES	RT	AQUACULTURE	RT	SPORANGIA
BT2	INLAND WATERS	RT	NUTRIENTS (MINERAL)	RT	SPORES
RT	AQUACULTURE FACILITIES	RT	OTEC	RT	VEGETATIVE REPRODUCTION
RT	COLONIZATION	RT	TEMPERATURE DIFFERENCES		
RT	DAMS	RT	THERMAL POWER	**ASH (VOLCANIC)**	
RT	INTRODUCED SPECIES	RT	UPWELLING	USE	**VOLCANIC ASH**
RT	RESERVOIRS (WATER)	RT	WATER SUPPLY		
RT	TRANSPLANTATION			**ASH CONTENT**	
		ARTISANAL AQUACULTURE		RT	ASHES
ARTIFICIAL MANURE		USE	**SMALL SCALE AQUACULTURE**	RT	CHEMICAL ANALYSIS
USE	**MANURE**			RT	CHEMICAL PROPERTIES
		ARTISANAL FISHING			
ARTIFICIAL REARING		SN	Mainly for local human food	**ASH LAYERS**	
USE	**REARING**		subsistence using primitive gears	RT	TEPHRA
			and vessels	RT	VOLCANIC ASH
ARTIFICIAL REEFS		UF	small scale fishing		
SN	Artificial structures introduced or	BT1	FISHING OPERATIONS	**ASHES**	
	built in marine or brackish coastal	RT	ARTISANAL WHALING	NT1	FLY ASH
	waters creating a sheltered space	RT	BOATS	RT	AIR POLLUTION
	for fishing or aquaculture	RT	CANOE FISHERIES	RT	ASH CONTENT
UF	reefs (artificial)	RT	CANOES	RT	FERTILIZERS
BT1	OFFSHORE STRUCTURES	RT	COASTAL FISHERIES	RT	VOLCANIC ASH
BT2	HYDRAULIC STRUCTURES	RT	ESTUARINE FISHERIES		
RT	ARTIFICIAL SPAWNING GROUNDS	RT	FISHERIES	**ASPARTIC ACID**	
RT	ATTRACTING TECHNIQUES	RT	FISHING	BT1	AMINO ACIDS
RT	HABITAT IMPROVEMENT (PHYSICAL)	RT	HANDLINING	BT2	ORGANIC ACIDS
RT	MARINE AQUACULTURE	RT	LABOUR	BT3	ORGANIC COMPOUNDS
RT	REEF FISH	RT	LAGOON FISHERIES		
RT	REEF FISHERIES	RT	LAKE FISHERIES		

ASPHALT
BT1	PETROLEUM HYDROCARBONS
BT2	HYDROCARBONS
BT3	ORGANIC COMPOUNDS
RT	OIL SANDS
RT	PETROLEUM RESIDUES

ASPHYXIA
SN	State of suspended animation as a result of deficiency of oxygen in the blood
UF	suffocation
RT	ANOXIA
RT	HYPERCAPNIA
RT	MORTALITY CAUSES

ASSEMBLING
USE	**CONSTRUCTION**

ASSIMILATION (FOOD)
USE	**FOOD CONVERSION**

ASSOCIATED SPECIES
SN	Species which have a predator/prey or competitive relationship with the exploited species. Added in 1982
UF	dependent species
UF	interdependent species
BT2	TAXA
BT1	SPECIES
RT	COMMERCIAL SPECIES
RT	COMPETITION
RT	PREDATION

ASSOCIATION CONSTANTS
RT	CONSTANTS

ASSOCIATIONS
USE	**ORGANIZATIONS**

ASSOCIATIONS (ANIMAL)
USE	**ECOLOGICAL ASSOCIATIONS**

ASSOCIATIONS (ECOLOGICAL)
USE	**ECOLOGICAL ASSOCIATIONS**

ASTACICULTURE
USE	**CRAYFISH CULTURE**

ASTATINE
BT1	CHEMICAL ELEMENTS
RT	ASTATINE COMPOUNDS
RT	ASTATINE ISOTOPES
RT	HALOGENS

ASTATINE COMPOUNDS
BT1	HALOGEN COMPOUNDS
RT	ASTATINE
RT	CHEMICAL COMPOUNDS

ASTATINE ISOTOPES
BT1	ISOTOPES
RT	ASTATINE

ASTHENOSPHERE
BT1	EARTH STRUCTURE
RT	ISOSTASY
RT	LITHOSPHERE
RT	LOW-VELOCITY LAYER
RT	MAGMA
RT	MESOSPHERE (EARTH)
RT	MOHO
RT	PLATE TECTONICS
RT	UPPER MANTLE

ASTRONOMICAL TIDES
BT1	TIDES
BT2	TIDAL MOTION
NT1	HIGHEST ASTRONOMICAL TIDES
NT1	LOWEST ASTRONOMICAL TIDES

ASTRONOMICAL TIDES (cont'd)
RT	EXTREME VALUES
RT	TIDAL AMPLITUDE

ASTRONOMY
RT	CELESTIAL NAVIGATION
RT	EARTH ORBIT
RT	EXTRATERRESTRIAL MATERIAL
RT	MOON
RT	MOON PHASES
RT	NAUTICAL ALMANACS
RT	SATELLITES
RT	SOLAR ACTIVITY
RT	SOLAR ECLIPSE
RT	SOLAR RADIATION
RT	SUN

ATLASES
BT1	DOCUMENTS
NT1	OCEANOGRAPHIC ATLASES
RT	BOTTOM TOPOGRAPHY
RT	CARTOGRAPHY
RT	CLIMATOLOGICAL CHARTS
RT	EXPEDITION REPORTS
RT	GAZETEERS
RT	GEOGRAPHY
RT	GEOLOGICAL MAPS
RT	GRAPHIC METHODS
RT	HYDROGRAPHIC CHARTS
RT	MAPS

ATMOSPHERE (EARTH)
USE	**EARTH ATMOSPHERE**

ATMOSPHERE (LIFE SUPPORT)
USE	**LIFE SUPPORT SYSTEMS**

ATMOSPHERE (PLANETARY)
USE	**PLANETARY ATMOSPHERES**

ATMOSPHERE EVOLUTION
SN	Evolution of planetary atmospheres
UF	evolution (atmosphere)
RT	ATMOSPHERIC CHEMISTRY
RT	EARTH
RT	EARTH ATMOSPHERE
RT	EARTH HISTORY
RT	GEOCHEMISTRY
RT	SEAWATER EVOLUTION
RT	SEDIMENT CHEMISTRY

ATMOSPHERE-OCEAN SYSTEM
USE	**OCEAN-ATMOSPHERE SYSTEM**

ATMOSPHERIC AEROSOLS
USE	**AEROSOLS**

ATMOSPHERIC BOUNDARY LAYER
UF	air-water boundary layer
UF	planetary boundary layer
UF	surface boundary layer
BT1	BOUNDARY LAYERS
BT2	LAYERS
RT	AIR-WATER INTERFACE
RT	ATMOSPHERIC FRONTS
RT	ATMOSPHERIC TURBULENCE
RT	CELLULAR CONVECTION
RT	HEAT TRANSFER
RT	MOISTURE TRANSFER
RT	MOMENTUM TRANSFER
RT	TROPOSPHERE
RT	WAVE INTERACTIONS
RT	WAVE-AIR INTERACTION
RT	WIND PROFILES
RT	WIND STRESS

ATMOSPHERIC CHEMISTRY
UF	atmospheric composition
BT1	CHEMISTRY
RT	AEROSOLS
RT	AIR POLLUTION
RT	AIR SAMPLING
RT	ATMOSPHERE EVOLUTION
RT	ATMOSPHERIC GASES
RT	ATMOSPHERIC PARTICULATES
RT	ATMOSPHERIC SCIENCES
RT	CARBON DIOXIDE
RT	CLIMATIC CHANGES
RT	DUST
RT	DUST CLOUDS
RT	EARTH ATMOSPHERE
RT	FALLOUT
RT	HYDROMETEORS
RT	OZONE
RT	RADIOACTIVE AEROSOLS

ATMOSPHERIC CIRCULATION
UF	circulation (atmosphere)
UF	general circulation (atmospheric)
BT1	ATMOSPHERIC MOTION
NT1	MERIDIONAL ATMOSPHERIC CIRCULATION
RT	ADVECTION
RT	CIRCULATION
RT	CORIOLIS FORCE
RT	HEAT TRANSPORT
RT	OCEAN CIRCULATION
RT	PLANETARY WINDS
RT	SOUTHERN OSCILLATION
RT	WINDS

ATMOSPHERIC COMPOSITION
USE	**ATMOSPHERIC CHEMISTRY**

ATMOSPHERIC CONDITIONS
USE	**WEATHER**

ATMOSPHERIC CONVECTION
BT1	CONVECTION
BT2	ADVECTION
BT3	TRANSPORT PROCESSES
RT	ATMOSPHERIC MOTION

ATMOSPHERIC CONVERGENCES
BT1	CONVERGENCE ZONES
NT1	ANTARCTIC FRONT
NT1	INTERTROPICAL CONVERGENCE ZONE
NT1	POLAR FRONTS
RT	ATMOSPHERIC FRONTS
RT	CONVERGENCE
RT	FRONTS

ATMOSPHERIC DEPRESSIONS
NT1	TROPICAL DEPRESSIONS
NT2	HURRICANES
RT	WEATHER

ATMOSPHERIC DIFFUSION
BT1	DIFFUSION
BT2	TRANSPORT PROCESSES
RT	TURBULENT DIFFUSION

ATMOSPHERIC DISTURBANCES
SN	Use of a more specific term is recommended
RT	AIR MASSES
RT	ATMOSPHERIC FRONTS
RT	ATMOSPHERIC MOTION
RT	BAROMETRIC WAVES
RT	HIGH PRESSURE RIDGES
RT	HIGH PRESSURE SYSTEMS
RT	LOW PRESSURE SYSTEMS
RT	LOW PRESSURE TROUGHS
RT	METEOROLOGY
RT	TORNADOES
RT	TROPICAL DEPRESSIONS

ASFIS Thesaurus

ATMOSPHERIC ELECTRICAL PHENOMENA
USE **ATMOSPHERIC ELECTRICITY**

ATMOSPHERIC ELECTRICITY
UF   atmospheric electrical phenomena
UF   st elmo's fire
BT1   ELECTRICITY
NT1   AURORA
NT1   LIGHTNING
RT   ATMOSPHERIC PHYSICS
RT   IONOSPHERE

ATMOSPHERIC FALLOUT
USE   **FALLOUT**

ATMOSPHERIC FORCING
UF   meteorological forcing
RT   ATMOSPHERIC PRESSURE
RT   HURRICANES
RT   MIXED LAYER DEPTH
RT   OCEANIC RESPONSE
RT   RESPONSE TIME
RT   SURFACE MIXED LAYER
RT   THERMAL STRUCTURE
RT   WIND STRESS

ATMOSPHERIC FRONTS
UF   cold fronts
UF   fronts (meteorology)
UF   meteorological fronts
UF   occluded fronts
UF   warm fronts
BT1   FRONTS
RT   AIR MASSES
RT   ATMOSPHERIC BOUNDARY LAYER
RT   ATMOSPHERIC CONVERGENCES
RT   ATMOSPHERIC DISTURBANCES
RT   FRONTAL FEATURES
RT   FRONTOGENESIS
RT   METEOROLOGY
RT   TROPOSPHERE
RT   WEATHER FORECASTING

ATMOSPHERIC GASES
BT1   GASES
BT2   FLUIDS
RT   ATMOSPHERIC CHEMISTRY

ATMOSPHERIC MOTION
UF   air motion
NT1   ATMOSPHERIC CIRCULATION
NT2   MERIDIONAL ATMOSPHERIC CIRCULATION
NT1   WINDS
NT2   GALE FORCE WINDS
NT2   GEOSTROPHIC WINDS
NT2   GRADIENT WINDS
NT2   LOCAL WINDS
NT3   BREEZES
NT4   LAND AND SEA BREEZES
NT4   LAND BREEZES
NT4   SEA BREEZES
NT3   MISTRAL
NT2   PLANETARY WINDS
NT3   MONSOONS
NT3   TRADE WINDS
NT4   EQUATORIAL EASTERLIES
NT3   WESTERLIES
NT4   EQUATORIAL WESTERLIES
RT   AIR FLOW OVER LAND
RT   AIR FLOW OVER WATER
RT   ATMOSPHERIC CONVECTION
RT   ATMOSPHERIC DISTURBANCES
RT   ATMOSPHERIC TURBULENCE
RT   EARTH ATMOSPHERE
RT   FLUID DYNAMICS
RT   HEAT TRANSPORT
RT   HORIZONTAL MOTION
RT   LEE WAVES
RT   METEOROLOGY
RT   MOTION

ATMOSPHERIC MOTION (cont'd)
RT   PLANETARY WAVES
RT   VERTICAL MOTION
RT   VORTICITY
RT   WATERSPOUTS

ATMOSPHERIC OPTICAL PHENOMENA
RT   AIRGLOW
RT   ATMOSPHERIC PHYSICS
RT   AURORA
RT   GREENFLASH
RT   HAZE
RT   LIGHT
RT   MIRAGES
RT   OPTICS
RT   VISIBILITY

ATMOSPHERIC PARTICULATES
UF   dust (atmospheric)
UF   particulate matter (air)
UF   particulates (atmospheric)
BT1   PARTICULATES
NT1   SALT PARTICLES
RT   AEROSOLS
RT   AIR POLLUTION
RT   AIR SAMPLING
RT   ATMOSPHERIC CHEMISTRY
RT   DUST
RT   FALLOUT
RT   FLY ASH
RT   POLLEN
RT   SMOKE
RT   SPORES

ATMOSPHERIC PHYSICS
UF   aeronomy
BT1   PHYSICS
NT1   CLOUD PHYSICS
RT   ATMOSPHERIC ELECTRICITY
RT   ATMOSPHERIC OPTICAL PHENOMENA
RT   ATMOSPHERIC SCIENCES
RT   EARTH ATMOSPHERE
RT   METEOROLOGY

ATMOSPHERIC POLAR FRONTS
USE   **POLAR FRONTS**

ATMOSPHERIC POLLUTION
USE   **AIR POLLUTION**

ATMOSPHERIC PRECIPITATIONS
SN   Before 1982 use PRECIPITATIONS (ATMOSPHERIC)
UF   precipitation (atmospheric)
UF   precipitation (meteorology)
BT1   HYDROMETEORS
NT1   ACID RAIN
NT1   HAIL
NT1   SNOW
RT   CLOUDS
RT   GLACIERS
RT   ISOHYETS
RT   METEOROLOGY
RT   RAIN
RT   RAINFALL
RT   RIVER DISCHARGE
RT   SALINITY
RT   WATER RESOURCES
RT   WATERSHEDS
RT   WEATHER
RT   WEATHERING

ATMOSPHERIC PRESSURE
UF   barometric pressure
UF   pressure (atmospheric)
BT1   PRESSURE
BT2   PHYSICAL PROPERTIES
BT3   PROPERTIES
NT1   SEA LEVEL PRESSURE
RT   ANTICYCLONES

ATMOSPHERIC PRESSURE (cont'd)
RT   ATMOSPHERIC FORCING
RT   BAROMETERS
RT   BAROMETRIC WAVES
RT   CLIMATE
RT   CLIMATOLOGY
RT   EARTH ATMOSPHERE
RT   HYPSOMETRY
RT   ISOBARS
RT   LOW PRESSURE SYSTEMS
RT   METEOROLOGICAL CHARTS
RT   METEOROLOGY
RT   PRESSURE FIELD
RT   RADIOSONDES
RT   SIGMA-T
RT   STORM SURGES
RT   WEATHER
RT   WEATHER FORECASTING
RT   WINDS

ATMOSPHERIC RADIATION
USE   **DOWNWARD LONG WAVE RADIATION**

ATMOSPHERIC SCIENCES
RT   ATMOSPHERIC CHEMISTRY
RT   ATMOSPHERIC PHYSICS
RT   CLIMATOLOGY
RT   EARTH ATMOSPHERE
RT   EARTH SCIENCES
RT   METEOROLOGY

ATMOSPHERIC TIDES
SN   Tidal motion in the atmosphere
UF   tides (atmospheric)
BT1   TIDAL MOTION
RT   EARTH TIDES
RT   EQUILIBRIUM TIDES
RT   METEOROLOGICAL TIDES
RT   TIDES

ATMOSPHERIC TURBIDITY
USE   **HAZE**

ATMOSPHERIC TURBULENCE
BT1   TURBULENCE
BT2   FLUID MOTION
NT1   CLEAR AIR TURBULENCE
NT1   GUSTS
RT   ATMOSPHERIC BOUNDARY LAYER
RT   ATMOSPHERIC MOTION
RT   LAMINAR FLOW
RT   METEOROLOGY
RT   TURBULENCE MEASUREMENT
RT   TURBULENT DIFFUSION
RT   TURBULENT FLOW
RT   WINDS

ATOLL LAGOONS
BT1   LAGOONS
RT   ATOLLS

ATOLLS
UF   coral islands
BT1   ISLANDS
BT2   LANDFORMS
BT3   TOPOGRAPHIC FEATURES
RT   ATOLL LAGOONS
RT   BIOGENIC DEPOSITS
RT   CORAL
RT   CORAL REEFS
RT   LAGOONS
RT   REEFS
RT   SEA LEVEL CHANGES
RT   TROPICAL ENVIRONMENT

ATOMIC ABSORPTION SPECTROSCOPY
USE   **ABSORPTION SPECTROSCOPY**

ATOMIC ENERGY	
USE	**NUCLEAR ENERGY**

ATOMIC FLUORESCENCE SPECTROSCOPY	
USE	**FLUORESCENCE SPECTROSCOPY**

ATOMIC PHYSICS	
USE	**NUCLEAR PHYSICS**

ATOMIC POWER PLANTS	
USE	**NUCLEAR POWER PLANTS**

ATP
UF	adenosine triphosphate
BT1	NUCLEOTIDES
BT2	ORGANIC COMPOUNDS
RT	CHEMICAL COMPOUNDS
RT	LIGASES

ATTACHMENT (BIOLOGICAL)	
USE	**BIOLOGICAL ATTACHMENT**

ATTACHMENT (LAMPREYS)	
USE	**LAMPREY ATTACHMENT**

ATTACHMENT (PARASITES)	
USE	**PARASITE ATTACHMENT**

ATTACHMENT ORGANS
SN	Added in 1982
BT1	BODY ORGANS
RT	BIOLOGICAL ATTACHMENT
RT	PARASITE ATTACHMENT

ATTENUANCE
BT1	OPTICAL PROPERTIES
BT2	PHYSICAL PROPERTIES
BT3	PROPERTIES
RT	BEAM TRANSMITTANCE
RT	EXTINCTION COEFFICIENT
RT	LIGHT ATTENUATION
RT	TRANSMITTANCE

ATTENUATION
SN	Use of a more specific term is recommended
NT1	LIGHT ATTENUATION
NT1	SEISMIC ATTENUATION
RT	ABSORPTION (PHYSICS)
RT	AMPLITUDE
RT	DAMPING
RT	SIGNAL-TO-NOISE RATIO
RT	TRANSMISSION
RT	WAVE ATTENUATION
RT	WAVE DISPERSION
RT	WAVE MOTION

ATTENUATION (LIGHT)	
USE	**LIGHT ATTENUATION**

ATTENUATION (WATER WAVES)	
USE	**WAVE ATTENUATION**

ATTENUATION COEFFICIENT	
USE	**EXTINCTION COEFFICIENT**

ATTRACTING TECHNIQUES
SN	Use of artificial or natural objects or artificial stimuli (light, electricity, etc.) to attract and concentrate fish and other aquatic animals for fishing purposes
UF	fish attracting
UF	luring
RT	ARTIFICIAL REEFS
RT	AUTOMATED FISHING PLATFORMS
RT	BAIT
RT	CATCHING METHODS
RT	ELECTRIC FISHING

ATTRACTING TECHNIQUES (cont'd)
RT	ELECTRIC STIMULI
RT	FISHING GEAR
RT	LIGHT FISHING
RT	PUMP FISHING
RT	SHELTERS

AUDIO RECORDINGS
UF	gramophone records
UF	sound recordings
UF	tape recordings (sound)
BT1	AUDIOVISUAL MATERIAL
BT2	DOCUMENTS
RT	BIOACOUSTICS
RT	MAGNETIC TAPE RECORDINGS
RT	MAGNETIC TAPES
RT	RECORDS
RT	SOUND PRODUCTION
RT	SOUND RECORDERS

AUDIOVISUAL MATERIAL
UF	visual aids
BT1	DOCUMENTS
NT1	AUDIO RECORDINGS
NT1	FILMS
NT1	FILMSTRIPS
NT1	GRAPHICS
NT2	ANALOG RECORDS
NT3	BATHYTHERMOGRAMS
NT3	ECHOSOUNDER PROFILES
NT3	SEISMIC PROFILES
NT4	SEISMIC REFLECTION PROFILES
NT4	SEISMIC REFRACTION PROFILES
NT3	SEISMOGRAMS
NT3	TIDAL CURVES
NT3	TIDAL RECORDS
NT2	ENGINEERING DRAWINGS
NT2	GRAPHS
NT3	GROWTH CURVES
NT3	HODOGRAPHS
NT4	CURRENT ELLIPSES
NT4	EKMAN SPIRAL
NT3	HYPSOMETRIC CURVES
NT3	T/S DIAGRAMS
NT3	WAVE REFRACTION DIAGRAMS
NT2	MAP GRAPHICS
NT3	CURRENT ROSES
NT3	ISOPLETHS
NT4	CONTOURS
NT4	CORANGE LINES
NT4	COTIDAL LINES
NT4	ISOBARS
NT4	ISOCHRONES
NT4	ISOHALINES
NT4	ISOHYETS
NT4	ISOMAGNETIC LINES
NT4	ISOPACHS
NT4	ISOPYCNICS
NT4	ISOSTERES
NT4	ISOTHERMS
NT3	STREAMLINES
NT3	VERTICAL SECTIONS
NT4	GEOLOGICAL SECTIONS
NT4	HYDROGRAPHIC SECTIONS
NT3	WIND ROSES
NT3	WIND VECTORS
NT2	MAPS
NT3	BIOLOGICAL CHARTS
NT3	CLIMATOLOGICAL CHARTS
NT3	CONTROL CHARTS
NT3	ENVIRONMENTAL CHARTS
NT3	FISHERY CHARTS
NT3	GEOLOGICAL MAPS
NT4	GRAVITY CHARTS
NT4	ISOPACH MAPS
NT4	MAGNETIC CHARTS
NT3	HYDROGRAPHIC CHARTS
NT4	BATHYMETRIC CHARTS
NT4	CURRENT CHARTS
NT4	DENSITY CHARTS

AUDIOVISUAL MATERIAL (cont'd)
NT4	ICE CHARTS
NT4	SALINITY CHARTS
NT4	TEMPERATURE CHARTS
NT4	TIDAL CHARTS
NT3	METEOROLOGICAL CHARTS
NT4	WEATHER MAPS
NT3	NAVIGATIONAL CHARTS
NT4	LATTICE CHARTS
NT4	PILOT CHARTS
NT3	POLLUTION MAPS
NT3	TOPOGRAPHIC MAPS
NT3	TRACK CHARTS
NT1	MICROFORMS
NT1	PHOTOGRAPHS
NT2	AERIAL PHOTOGRAPHS
NT2	UNDERWATER PHOTOGRAPHS
NT3	BOTTOM PHOTOGRAPHS
NT1	SATELLITE MOSAICS
NT1	SLIDES (PHOTOGRAPHIC)
NT1	VIDEOTAPE RECORDINGS
RT	EDUCATION
RT	MAGNETIC TAPES
RT	SCALE MODELS
RT	TRAINING AIDS

AUDITION
BT1	SENSE FUNCTIONS
RT	AUDITORY ORGANS
RT	AUDITORY STIMULI
RT	SOUND PRODUCTION

AUDITORY ORGANS
UF	ears
UF	phonoreceptors
BT1	SENSE ORGANS
BT2	ANIMAL ORGANS
BT3	BODY ORGANS
RT	ANATOMY
RT	AUDITION
RT	AUDITORY STIMULI
RT	ECHOLOCATION
RT	HEAD
RT	MECHANICAL STIMULI
RT	SOUND PRODUCTION
RT	VOCALIZATION BEHAVIOUR

AUDITORY STIMULI
BT1	STIMULI
RT	AUDITION
RT	AUDITORY ORGANS
RT	SOUND PRODUCTION
RT	VOCALIZATION BEHAVIOUR

AUGITE
BT1	PYROXENES
BT2	SILICATE MINERALS
BT3	MINERALS

AURORA
UF	auroral activity
BT1	ATMOSPHERIC ELECTRICITY
BT2	ELECTRICITY
RT	AIRGLOW
RT	ATMOSPHERIC OPTICAL PHENOMENA
RT	IONOSPHERE

AURORAL ACTIVITY	
USE	**AURORA**

AUSTAUSCH COEFFICIENTS	
USE	**EXCHANGE COEFFICIENTS**

AUTECOLOGY
SN	Ecological study of a single individual or many individuals of a given species
BT1	ECOLOGY
RT	BEHAVIOUR
RT	BIOLOGICAL RHYTHMS

AUTECOLOGY (cont'd)
RT	ENVIRONMENTAL CONDITIONS
RT	ENVIRONMENTAL EFFECTS
RT	LIFE HISTORY
RT	MIGRATIONS
RT	PARASITOLOGY

AUTHIGENES
USE	**AUTHIGENIC MINERALS**

AUTHIGENESIS
BT1	DIAGENESIS
BT2	SEDIMENTATION
RT	AUTHIGENIC MINERALS
RT	CHEMICAL SEDIMENTS

AUTHIGENIC MINERALS
UF	authigenes
UF	authigenic sediments
BT1	SEDIMENTS
NT1	EVAPORITES
NT1	IRONSTONE
NT1	JASPILITE
RT	ANHYDRITE
RT	AUTHIGENESIS
RT	CHEMICAL SEDIMENTS
RT	GYPSUM
RT	HALITE
RT	PHOSPHATE DEPOSITS
RT	PHOSPHORITE
RT	SUBMARINE CEMENTS

AUTHIGENIC SEDIMENTS
USE	**AUTHIGENIC MINERALS**

AUTOBIOGRAPHIES
USE	**BIOGRAPHIES**

AUTOCHTHONOUS DEPOSITS
RT	ALLOCHTHONOUS DEPOSITS
RT	BIOGENIC DEPOSITS
RT	CHEMICAL SEDIMENTS
RT	SEDIMENTS

AUTOCORRELATION
SN	Used only as a qualifier
UF	autocorrelation functions
BT1	CORRELATION ANALYSIS
BT2	STATISTICAL ANALYSIS
BT3	MATHEMATICAL ANALYSIS
RT	CROSS CORRELATION

AUTOCORRELATION FUNCTIONS
USE	**AUTOCORRELATION**

AUTOLYSIS
SN	Self digestion by the action of enzymes
BT1	CHEMICAL REACTIONS
RT	DEGRADATION
RT	ENZYMES

AUTOMATED CARTOGRAPHY
UF	computer-aided cartography
BT1	MAPPING
BT2	GRAPHIC METHODS
RT	AUTOMATED RECORDING
RT	AUTOMATION
RT	BATHYMETRIC DATA
RT	CARTOGRAPHY

AUTOMATED DATA PROCESSING
USE	**DATA PROCESSING**

AUTOMATED FISHING PLATFORMS
SN	Floating platforms provided with different means to attract and catch fish and other aquatic animals
BT1	CATCHING METHODS
RT	ATTRACTING TECHNIQUES

AUTOMATED FISHING PLATFORMS (cont'd)
RT	AUTOMATION
RT	ELECTRIC FISHING
RT	HARVESTING MACHINES
RT	LIGHT FISHING
RT	PUMP FISHING

AUTOMATED RECORDING
SN	Automated techniques for determination of physico-chemical properties of water
UF	automated techniques
RT	ANALYTICAL TECHNIQUES
RT	AUTOMATED CARTOGRAPHY
RT	AUTOMATION
RT	DATA BUOYS
RT	WATER ANALYSIS
RT	WATER PROPERTIES

AUTOMATED TECHNIQUES
USE	**AUTOMATED RECORDING**

AUTOMATION
SN	Added in 1982
RT	AUTOMATED CARTOGRAPHY
RT	AUTOMATED FISHING PLATFORMS
RT	AUTOMATED RECORDING
RT	COMPUTERS
RT	CONTROL
RT	DATA PROCESSING
RT	REMOTE CONTROL
RT	ROBOTS

AUTONOMIC NERVOUS SYSTEM
SN	Before 1982 search NERVOUS SYSTEM
UF	ans
UF	parasympathetic nervous system
UF	sympathetic nervous system
BT1	NERVOUS SYSTEM

AUTOPILOTS
RT	NAVIGATION SYSTEMS
RT	NAVIGATIONAL AIDS

AUTORADIOGRAPHIC TECHNIQUES
USE	**AUTORADIOGRAPHY**

AUTORADIOGRAPHY
UF	autoradiographic techniques
BT1	RADIOGRAPHY
RT	RADIOACTIVE TRACERS

AUTOTOMY
SN	Voluntary separation of a part of the body
RT	LESIONS
RT	PROTECTIVE BEHAVIOUR
RT	REGENERATION

AUTOTROPHY
BT1	NUTRITIONAL TYPES
RT	PLANT NUTRITION

AUTUMN
SN	Added in 1980
UF	fall
UF	fall season
BT1	SEASONS

AUXINS
SN	Added in 1980
BT1	GROWTH REGULATORS
RT	PHYTOHORMONES
RT	PLANT PHYSIOLOGY

AVAILABILITY
SN	Used only as a qualifier. Use of a more specific term is recommended
NT1	COMMERCIAL AVAILABILITY
NT1	FOOD AVAILABILITY

AVAILABILITY (cont'd)
NT1	RESOURCE AVAILABILITY
RT	ABUNDANCE

AVAILABLE POTENTIAL ENERGY
USE	**POTENTIAL ENERGY**

AVIAN PHYSIOLOGY
SN	Before 1982 search PHYSIOLOGY
UF	bird physiology
BT1	ANIMAL PHYSIOLOGY
BT2	PHYSIOLOGY
BT3	BIOLOGY
RT	AQUATIC BIRDS
RT	FLIGHT BEHAVIOUR

AVITAMINOSIS
USE	**VITAMIN DEFICIENCIES**

AVOIDANCE
USE	**AVOIDANCE REACTIONS**

AVOIDANCE REACTIONS
SN	Before 1982 search AVOIDANCE
UF	avoidance
UF	net avoidance
BT1	BEHAVIOUR
RT	BIOLOGICAL SAMPLING
RT	CATCHABILITY
RT	ESCAPEMENT
RT	FISHING GEAR
RT	FISHING NETS
RT	GEAR SELECTIVITY
RT	MIGRATIONS
RT	NEKTON COLLECTING DEVICES
RT	PLANKTON COLLECTING DEVICES
RT	WATER POLLUTION
BT1	BATHYTHERMOGRAPHS
BT2	PROFILERS

AXBTs
SN	Air-deployed expendable bathythermographs
BT1	BATHYTHERMOGRAPHS
BT2	PROFILERS
RT	AIRBORNE EQUIPMENT
RT	AIRCRAFT
RT	MEASURING DEVICES
RT	WATER TEMPERATURE
RT	XBTs

AXONS
USE	**NEURONES**

AZIMUTH
RT	DIRECTION

AZINES
BT1	ORGANIC COMPOUNDS
NT1	PYRIDINES
NT1	PYRIMIDINES
NT1	QUINOLINES

BACK-ARC BASINS
USE	**MARGINAL BASINS**

BACKGROUND NOISE (SOUND)
USE	**AMBIENT NOISE**

BACKRUSH
USE	**BACKWASH**

BACKSCATTER
UF	sound backscatter
BT1	SOUND SCATTERING
RT	FORWARD SCATTERING
RT	REVERBERATION
RT	SCATTEROMETERS

BACKSHORE
BT1 BEACH FEATURES
RT BERMS
RT FORESHORE

BACKWASH
UF backrush
RT BEACH MORPHOLOGY
RT WAVE EFFECTS
RT WAVE RUNUP
RT WAVES ON BEACHES

BACKWATERS
SN Water held back from the main flow
of a river
RT DAMS
RT FLOODS
RT LAGOONS
RT RESERVOIRS (WATER)
RT STREAM FLOW

BACTERIA
SN Use of a more specific term is
recommended. In ASFA-1, use as
taxonomic descriptor; in ASFA-2,
use as subject descriptor
BT1 MICROORGANISMS
NT1 AEROBIC BACTERIA
NT1 ANAEROBIC BACTERIA
NT1 PATHOGENIC BACTERIA
RT AGGLUTININS
RT ANTIGENS
RT BACTERIA COLLECTING DEVICES
RT BACTERIAL COUNTERS
RT BACTERIAL DISEASES
RT BACTERINS
RT BACTERIOLOGY
RT BACTERIOPHAGES
RT BIOEROSION
RT BIOLUMINESCENCE
RT CHEMOSYNTHESIS
RT CHEMOTAXONOMY
RT CULTURE MEDIA
RT DECOMPOSERS
RT ENDOTOXINS
RT FILTER FEEDERS
RT FOOD POISONING
RT MICROBIAL CONTAMINATION
RT MICROBIOLOGICAL ANALYSIS
RT MICROBIOLOGICAL CULTURE
RT NANNOPLANKTON
RT NITRIFICATION
RT NITROGEN CYCLE
RT OXIDATION
RT PHOSPHORUS CYCLE
RT SAPROPHYTES
RT SINGLE CELL PROTEINS
RT SPORES
RT STERILIZATION

BACTERIA COLLECTING DEVICES
BT1 COLLECTING DEVICES
RT BACTERIA
RT MICROBIOLOGICAL CULTURE

BACTERIAL COUNTERS
BT1 COUNTERS
RT BACTERIA
RT BACTERIOLOGY

BACTERIAL DISEASES
UF bacterioses
BT1 INFECTIOUS DISEASES
BT2 DISEASES
NT1 TUBERCULOSIS
NT1 VIBRIOSIS
RT ANTIBIOTICS
RT BACTERIA
RT BACTERINS
RT BACTERIOLOGY

BACTERIAL DISEASES (cont'd)
RT BOIL DISEASE
RT BOTULISM
RT DISINFECTION
RT DRUGS
RT ENDOTOXINS
RT IMMUNIZATION
RT PATHOGENIC BACTERIA
RT PEDUNCLE DISEASE
RT REDMOUTH DISEASE

BACTERIAL GILL DISEASE
USE **GILL DISEASE**

BACTERIAL HAEMORRHAGIC SEPTICAEMIA
USE **SEPTICAEMIA**

BACTERIAL VACCINES
USE **VACCINES**

BACTERICIDES
USE **BACTERIOCIDES**

BACTERINS
SN Added in 1980
BT1 VACCINES
BT2 DRUGS
RT BACTERIA
RT BACTERIAL DISEASES
RT PATHOGENS

BACTERIOCIDES
UF bactericides
BT1 PESTICIDES
RT ANTIBIOTICS
RT AQUARIOLOGY
RT BACTERIOLOGY
RT CHEMICAL CONTROL

BACTERIOLOGISTS
SN Added in 1980
BT1 MICROBIOLOGISTS
BT2 BIOLOGISTS
BT3 SCIENTIFIC PERSONNEL
BT4 PERSONNEL
RT BACTERIOLOGY
RT DIRECTORIES
RT MICROBIOLOGY

BACTERIOLOGY
BT1 MICROBIOLOGY
BT2 BIOLOGY
RT BACTERIA
RT BACTERIAL COUNTERS
RT BACTERIAL DISEASES
RT BACTERIOCIDES
RT BACTERIOLOGISTS
RT BACTERIOPHAGES
RT BIOASSAYS
RT ENDOTOXINS
RT EPIDEMIOLOGY
RT MICROBIOLOGICAL CULTURE
RT PARASITOLOGY

BACTERIOPHAGES
RT BACTERIA
RT BACTERIOLOGY
RT BIOLOGICAL CONTROL
RT VIRUSES

BACTERIOPLANKTON
USE **NANNOPLANKTON**

BACTERIOSES
USE **BACTERIAL DISEASES**

BAFFLES (SOUND)
USE **ACOUSTIC INSULATION**

BAIT
SN Including natural (dead or living)
and artificial baits (lures,
chemical baits, etc.)
UF fishing bait
UF lures
RT ANGLING
RT ATTRACTING TECHNIQUES
RT BAIT FISH
RT BAIT FISHING
RT COMMERCIAL FISHING
RT HOOKS
RT LINE FISHING
RT SPORT FISHING
RT TRAP FISHING
RT WORM CULTURE

BAIT CULTURE
SN Before 1982 search FISH CULTURE
UF bait farming
UF bait fish culture
BT1 FISH CULTURE
BT2 AQUACULTURE
RT ACCLIMATION
RT BAIT FISH
RT BRACKISHWATER AQUACULTURE
RT COMMERCIAL FISHING
RT CULTURES
RT FRESHWATER AQUACULTURE
RT HATCHERIES
RT SPORT FISHING
RT TUNA FISHERIES

BAIT FARMING
USE **BAIT CULTURE**

BAIT FISH
BT1 FISH
BT2 AQUATIC ANIMALS
RT BAIT
RT BAIT CULTURE
RT BAIT FISHING
RT CLUPEOID FISHERIES
RT LINE FISHING
RT LONGLINING
RT PURSE SEINING
RT SPORT FISHING
RT TRAP FISHING

BAIT FISH CULTURE
USE **BAIT CULTURE**

BAIT FISHING
SN Added in 1980
BT1 ANGLING
BT2 CATCHING METHODS
RT BAIT
RT BAIT FISH
RT FISHING
RT FISHING GEAR
RT FRESHWATER FISH
RT ICE FISHING
RT RECREATION
RT RESERVOIR FISHERIES
RT SPORT FISHING
RT TUNA FISHERIES
RT WORM FISHING

BALANCE (ECOLOGICAL)
USE **ECOLOGICAL BALANCE**

BALANCE OF NATURE
USE **ECOLOGICAL BALANCE**

ASFIS Thesaurus

BALANCE ORGANS
BT1	SENSE ORGANS
BT2	ANIMAL ORGANS
BT3	BODY ORGANS
NT1	STATOCYSTS

BALANCED DIETS
SN	Added in 1980
BT1	DIETS
RT	AQUACULTURE
RT	ARTIFICIAL FEEDING
RT	CULTURED ORGANISMS

BALANCED POLYMORPHISM
USE	**BIOPOLYMORPHISM**

BALANCED RATIONS
RT	ARTIFICIAL FEEDING
RT	NUTRITIONAL REQUIREMENTS
RT	NUTRITIVE VALUE

BALEENS
SN	Added in 1980
UF	whalebones
BT1	MOUTH PARTS
RT	FEEDING

BALLAST
RT	BALLAST TANKS
RT	BUOYANCY
RT	BUOYANCY FLOATS
RT	FLOATING
RT	LOADS (FORCES)
RT	STABILITY

BALLAST TANKS
RT	BALLAST
RT	UNDERWATER VEHICLES

BALLOONS
UF	meteorological balloons
RT	AERIAL SURVEYS
RT	INSTRUMENT PLATFORMS
RT	METEOROLOGICAL INSTRUMENTS
RT	RADIOSONDES
RT	WIND MEASURING EQUIPMENT

BANKS
USE	**FINANCIAL INSTITUTIONS**

BANKS (TOPOGRAPHY)
RT	EMBANKMENTS
RT	LEVEES
RT	MUD BANKS
RT	RELIEF FORMS
RT	RIVER BANKS
RT	SAND BANKS
RT	SHOALS
RT	SUBMARINE BANKS
RT	TOPOGRAPHIC FEATURES

BARBELS
SN	Added in 1980
BT1	ANIMAL APPENDAGES
RT	FISH
RT	TACTILE ORGANS

BARGES
SN	Do not use for drilling structures
BT1	SURFACE CRAFT
BT2	VEHICLES
NT1	CRANE BARGES
NT1	PIPELAYING BARGES
RT	FLOATING STRUCTURES
RT	MARINE TRANSPORTATION
RT	PONTOONS
RT	TOWING
RT	WORK PLATFORMS
RT	WORKOVER BARGES

BARITE
BT1	SULPHATE MINERALS
BT2	MINERALS
RT	BARIUM
RT	PLACERS

BARIUM
BT1	CHEMICAL ELEMENTS
RT	ALKALINE EARTH METALS
RT	BARITE
RT	BARIUM COMPOUNDS
RT	BARIUM ISOTOPES
RT	MAGNESIUM

BARIUM COMPOUNDS
BT1	ALKALINE EARTH METAL COMPOUNDS
RT	BARIUM
RT	CHEMICAL COMPOUNDS

BARIUM ISOTOPES
BT1	ISOTOPES
RT	BARIUM

BAROCLINIC FIELD
RT	BAROCLINIC MODE
RT	BAROCLINIC MOTION
RT	FIELDS

BAROCLINIC FLOW
USE	**BAROCLINIC MOTION**

BAROCLINIC INSTABILITY
BT1	INSTABILITY
RT	BAROCLINIC MODE
RT	BAROCLINIC MOTION
RT	BAROTROPIC INSTABILITY
RT	ENERGY TRANSFER
RT	MESOSCALE EDDIES
RT	POTENTIAL VORTICITY
RT	ROSSBY PARAMETER

BAROCLINIC MODE
UF	baroclinicity
UF	baroclinity
RT	BAROCLINIC FIELD
RT	BAROCLINIC INSTABILITY
RT	BAROCLINIC MOTION
RT	BAROTROPIC MODE
RT	FLUID MOTION
RT	INTERNAL TIDES
RT	ISOBARIC SURFACES
RT	ISOPYCNIC SURFACES
RT	ISOSTERIC SURFACES
RT	MODES
RT	STRATIFICATION
RT	STRATIFIED FLOW

BAROCLINIC MOTION
UF	baroclinic flow
UF	baroclinic waves
BT1	FLUID MOTION
RT	BAROCLINIC FIELD
RT	BAROCLINIC INSTABILITY
RT	BAROCLINIC MODE
RT	BAROTROPIC MOTION
RT	INTERNAL TIDES
RT	STRATIFIED FLOW

BAROCLINIC TIDES
USE	**INTERNAL TIDES**

BAROCLINIC WAVES
USE	**BAROCLINIC MOTION**

BAROCLINICITY
USE	**BAROCLINIC MODE**

BAROCLINITY
USE	**BAROCLINIC MODE**

BAROGRAPHS
USE	**BAROMETERS**

BAROMETERS
UF	barographs
BT1	MEASURING DEVICES
RT	ATMOSPHERIC PRESSURE
RT	MANOMETERS
RT	PRESSURE
RT	SEA LEVEL PRESSURE

BAROMETRIC CURRENTS
USE	**WIND-DRIVEN CURRENTS**

BAROMETRIC PRESSURE
USE	**ATMOSPHERIC PRESSURE**

BAROMETRIC WAVES
RT	ATMOSPHERIC DISTURBANCES
RT	ATMOSPHERIC PRESSURE

BAROTROPIC FIELD
RT	BAROTROPIC MODE
RT	BAROTROPIC MOTION
RT	FIELDS

BAROTROPIC FLOW
USE	**BAROTROPIC MOTION**

BAROTROPIC INSTABILITY
BT1	INSTABILITY
RT	BAROCLINIC INSTABILITY
RT	BAROTROPIC MODE
RT	ENERGY TRANSFER
RT	POTENTIAL VORTICITY
RT	UNSTEADY FLOW

BAROTROPIC MODE
UF	barotropy
RT	BAROCLINIC MODE
RT	BAROTROPIC FIELD
RT	BAROTROPIC INSTABILITY
RT	BAROTROPIC MOTION
RT	CONSERVATION OF VORTICITY
RT	FLUID MOTION
RT	ISOBARIC SURFACES
RT	ISOPYCNIC SURFACES
RT	ISOSTERIC SURFACES
RT	MODES
RT	STRATIFICATION

BAROTROPIC MOTION
UF	barotropic flow
UF	barotropic waves
BT1	FLUID MOTION
RT	BAROCLINIC MOTION
RT	BAROTROPIC FIELD
RT	BAROTROPIC MODE
RT	TIDES

BAROTROPIC TIDES
BT1	TIDES
BT2	TIDAL MOTION

BAROTROPIC WAVES
USE	**BAROTROPIC MOTION**

BAROTROPY
USE	**BAROTROPIC MODE**

BARRAGES
SN	Fixed structures built for the purpose of containing water for irrigation, power generation, recreation, flood control, etc.
BT1	HYDRAULIC STRUCTURES
NT1	DAMS

BARRAGES (cont'd)
NT1	ENCLOSURES
NT1	TIDAL BARRAGES
NT1	WEIRS
RT	BARRIERS
RT	COASTAL ENGINEERING
RT	COASTAL STRUCTURES
RT	COASTAL ZONE
RT	COASTAL ZONE MANAGEMENT
RT	CONTAINMENT
RT	RECREATIONAL WATERS
RT	STORM SURGE BARRIERS
RT	STRUCTURAL ENGINEERING

BARRIER BEACHES
BT1	BEACHES
BT2	COASTAL LANDFORMS
BT3	LANDFORMS
BT4	TOPOGRAPHIC FEATURES
RT	BARRIER ISLANDS

BARRIER ISLANDS
BT1	COASTAL LANDFORMS
BT2	LANDFORMS
BT3	TOPOGRAPHIC FEATURES
RT	BARRIER BEACHES
RT	BARRIER REEFS
RT	BARRIER SPITS
RT	BEACH ACCRETION
RT	COASTAL LAGOONS
RT	DEPOSITION FEATURES
RT	ISLANDS
RT	TIDAL INLETS

BARRIER REEFS
BT1	CORAL REEFS
BT2	BIOGENIC DEPOSITS
RT	BARRIER ISLANDS
RT	FRINGING REEFS
RT	LAGOONS

BARRIER SPITS
UF	bay barriers
UF	nehrung
BT1	SPITS
BT2	BEACH FEATURES
RT	BARRIER ISLANDS
RT	BAYS
RT	COASTAL LAGOONS
RT	LONGSHORE SEDIMENT TRANSPORT

BARRIERS
SN	Use of a more specific term is recommended
NT1	BUBBLE BARRIERS
NT1	FISHING BARRIERS
NT1	FLOATING BARRIERS
NT1	ICE BARRIERS
RT	BARRAGES
RT	BIOTIC BARRIERS
RT	BREAKWATERS
RT	COASTAL FISHERIES
RT	CONTAINMENT
RT	DAMS
RT	INLAND FISHERIES
RT	LAGOON FISHERIES
RT	POTS
RT	STORM SURGE BARRIERS

BARRIERS (BIOLOGICAL)
USE	**BIOTIC BARRIERS**

BARRIERS (FISHING)
USE	**FISHING BARRIERS**

BARS
USE	**NEARSHORE BARS**

BASALT-SEAWATER INTERACTION
BT1	HYDROTHERMAL ACTIVITY
RT	HALMYROLYSIS
RT	HYDROTHERMAL ALTERATION
RT	PALAGONITE

BASALTIC GLASS
USE	**VOLCANIC GLASS**

BASALTIC LAVA
USE	**BASALTS**

BASALTIC LAYER
USE	**SIMA**

BASALTS
UF	basaltic lava
BT1	VOLCANIC ROCKS
BT2	IGNEOUS ROCKS
BT3	ROCKS
NT1	ALKALI BASALTS
NT1	OCEANITE
NT1	THOLEIITE
NT1	THOLEIITIC BASALT
RT	LAVA

BASELINE STUDIES
SN	Studies conducted in advance of an anticipated environmental change or for long-term comparison of environmental or ecological conditions. Added in 1980
UF	baseline surveys
UF	ecological baseline studies
RT	ECOLOGY
RT	LONG-TERM CHANGES
RT	MONITORING
RT	POLLUTION
RT	POLLUTION EFFECTS
RT	RECLAMATION
RT	RESOURCE AVAILABILITY
RT	SURVEYS

BASELINE SURVEYS
USE	**BASELINE STUDIES**

BASEMENT (GEOLOGY)
USE	**BASEMENT ROCK**

BASEMENT ROCK
UF	basement (geology)
BT1	EARTH STRUCTURE
RT	EARTH CRUST
RT	IGNEOUS ROCKS
RT	METAMORPHIC ROCKS
RT	MOHO
RT	ROCKS

BASIC DIETS
SN	Added in 1980
BT1	DIETS
RT	AQUACULTURE
RT	ARTIFICIAL FEEDING
RT	CULTURED ORGANISMS

BASIDIOSPORES
USE	**SPORES**

BASINS
RT	ANOXIC BASINS
RT	FOREARC BASINS
RT	LAKE BASINS
RT	MARGINAL BASINS
RT	OCEAN BASINS
RT	RIVER BASINS
RT	SEDIMENTARY BASINS
RT	STRUCTURAL BASINS
RT	TOPOGRAPHIC FEATURES

BASKET CULTURE
USE	**CAGE CULTURE**

BATCH CULTURE
SN	Culture of organisms in homogeneous developmental stages. Added in 1980
BT1	AQUACULTURE SYSTEMS
RT	AQUARIA
RT	CONTINUOUS CULTURE
RT	CRUSTACEAN CULTURE
RT	CULTURE TANKS
RT	CULTURES
RT	HATCHERIES
RT	LABORATORY CULTURE
RT	SEED (AQUACULTURE)
RT	SEED PRODUCTION

BATCH PROCESSING
SN	Added in 1982
UF	batch processing data
BT1	DATA PROCESSING
RT	COMPUTER PROGRAMS
RT	COMPUTERS

BATCH PROCESSING DATA
USE	**BATCH PROCESSING**

BATFISH
USE	**UNDULATORS**

BATHING
SN	Before 1982 search RECREATIONAL SWIMMING
UF	recreation (swimming)
UF	recreational swimming
BT1	RECREATION
RT	DANGEROUS ORGANISMS
RT	DROWNING
RT	SHARK ATTACKS
RT	SURFING
RT	WATER QUALITY

BATHOLITHS
BT1	IGNEOUS INTRUSIONS
RT	IGNEOUS DIKES
RT	IGNEOUS ROCKS
RT	LACCOLITHS
RT	PLUTONS

BATHYAL-BENTHIC ZONE
SN	Benthic regions between 500 and 1000 m depth
BT1	BENTHIC ENVIRONMENT
BT2	AQUATIC ENVIRONMENT
BT3	ENVIRONMENTS
RT	BATHYAL ZONE
RT	BATHYPELAGIC ZONE
RT	MESOPELAGIC ZONE

BATHYAL ZONE
SN	Zone between 500 and 1000 m depth
RT	BATHYAL-BENTHIC ZONE
RT	BATHYPELAGIC ZONE
RT	BENTHIC ENVIRONMENT
RT	PELAGIC ENVIRONMENT

BATHYGENESIS
USE	**EPEIROGENY**

BATHYMETERS
BT1	MEASURING DEVICES
NT1	LASER BATHYMETERS
RT	BATHYMETRIC CHARTS
RT	BATHYMETRY
RT	BATHYTHERMOGRAPHS
RT	LIMNOLOGICAL EQUIPMENT
RT	OCEANOGRAPHIC EQUIPMENT
RT	WATER DEPTH

ASFIS Thesaurus

BATHYMETRIC CHARTS
BT1	HYDROGRAPHIC CHARTS
BT2	MAPS
BT3	GRAPHICS
BT4	AUDIOVISUAL MATERIAL
RT	BATHYMETERS
RT	BATHYMETRIC DATA
RT	BATHYMETRIC PROFILES
RT	BATHYMETRIC SURVEYS
RT	BATHYMETRY
RT	BOTTOM TOPOGRAPHY
RT	DEPTH MEASUREMENT
RT	ECHOSOUNDING
RT	GEOLOGICAL MAPS
RT	HYDROGRAPHIC SURVEYING
RT	HYDROGRAPHIC SURVEYS
RT	HYDROGRAPHY
RT	ISOBATHS
RT	SEAFLOOR MAPPING
RT	SOUNDINGS
RT	SUBMARINE FEATURES
RT	TOPOGRAPHIC MAPS
RT	VERTICAL DISTRIBUTION
RT	WATER DEPTH

BATHYMETRIC DATA
BT1	OCEANOGRAPHIC DATA
BT2	DATA
NT1	SOUNDINGS
RT	AUTOMATED CARTOGRAPHY
RT	BATHYMETRIC CHARTS
RT	BATHYMETRIC PROFILES
RT	BATHYMETRY
RT	GEOLOGICAL DATA
RT	LIMNOLOGICAL DATA
RT	PLOTTING
RT	WATER DEPTH

BATHYMETRIC DISTRIBUTION
USE	**VERTICAL DISTRIBUTION**

BATHYMETRIC OBSERVATIONS
USE	**SOUNDINGS**

BATHYMETRIC PROFILES
BT1	HYDROGRAPHIC SECTIONS
BT2	VERTICAL SECTIONS
BT3	MAP GRAPHICS
BT4	GRAPHICS
RT	BATHYMETRIC CHARTS
RT	BATHYMETRIC DATA
RT	BATHYMETRY
RT	BEACH PROFILES
RT	ECHOSOUNDER PROFILES
RT	HORIZONTAL PROFILES
RT	THALWEG
RT	WATER DEPTH

BATHYMETRIC SURVEYS
BT1	HYDROGRAPHIC SURVEYS
BT2	SURVEYS
RT	BATHYMETRIC CHARTS
RT	BATHYMETRY
RT	CARTOGRAPHY
RT	WATER DEPTH

BATHYMETRY
SN	To be used only for the operation of measuring water depth, i.e. surface to seabed
UF	depth sounding (water)
UF	sounding (water depth)
UF	water depth measurement
BT1	DEPTH MEASUREMENT
BT2	MEASUREMENT
NT1	LASER BATHYMETRY
RT	BATHYMETERS
RT	BATHYMETRIC CHARTS
RT	BATHYMETRIC DATA
RT	BATHYMETRIC PROFILES

BATHYMETRY (cont'd)
RT	BATHYMETRIC SURVEYS
RT	BOTTOM TOPOGRAPHY
RT	DEEP WATER
RT	ECHOSOUNDING
RT	HYDROGRAPHIC SURVEYING
RT	HYDROGRAPHIC SURVEYS
RT	HYDROGRAPHY
RT	ISOBATHS
RT	LASER BATHYMETERS
RT	MORPHOMETRY
RT	NAVIGATION
RT	SEAFLOOR MAPPING
RT	SOUNDING LINES
RT	SOUNDINGS
RT	SUBMARINE FEATURES
RT	WATER DEPTH

BATHYPELAGIC ZONE
SN	Waters between about 500 and 4000 m depth
BT1	OCEANIC PROVINCE
BT2	PELAGIC ENVIRONMENT
BT3	AQUATIC ENVIRONMENT
BT4	ENVIRONMENTS
RT	APHOTIC ZONE
RT	BATHYAL ZONE
RT	BATHYAL-BENTHIC ZONE

BATHYSPHERES
BT1	OBSERVATION CHAMBERS
BT2	MANNED VEHICLES
BT3	UNDERWATER VEHICLES
BT4	VEHICLES
RT	ABYSSAL ZONE
RT	UNDERWATER EXPLORATION

BATHYTHERMOGRAMS
BT1	ANALOG RECORDS
BT2	GRAPHICS
BT3	AUDIOVISUAL MATERIAL
BT4	DOCUMENTS
RT	BATHYTHERMOGRAPHIC DATA
RT	BATHYTHERMOGRAPHS

BATHYTHERMOGRAPHIC DATA
UF	data (bathythermographic)
BT1	OCEANOGRAPHIC DATA
BT2	DATA
RT	BATHYTHERMOGRAMS
RT	BATHYTHERMOGRAPHS
RT	TEMPERATURE SECTIONS
RT	WATER DEPTH
RT	WATER TEMPERATURE

BATHYTHERMOGRAPHS
UF	mechanical bathythermographs
BT1	PROFILERS
NT1	AXBTs
NT1	XBTs
RT	BATHYMETERS
RT	BATHYTHERMOGRAMS
RT	BATHYTHERMOGRAPHIC DATA
RT	DEPTH RECORDERS
RT	LIMNOLOGICAL EQUIPMENT
RT	MEASURING DEVICES
RT	OCEANOGRAPHIC EQUIPMENT
RT	THERMOMETERS
RT	WATER DEPTH
RT	WATER TEMPERATURE

BATTERIES
UF	electric batteries
BT1	ELECTRIC POWER SOURCES
RT	ELECTRICAL EQUIPMENT
RT	ELECTROMAGNETIC POWER
RT	UNDERWATER PROPULSION

BAUXITE
BT1	OXIDE MINERALS
BT2	MINERALS
RT	ALUMINIUM
RT	CLAY MINERALS

BAY BARRIERS
USE	**BARRIER SPITS**

BAY DYNAMICS
BT1	SHELF DYNAMICS
BT2	WATER CIRCULATION
BT3	WATER MOTION
RT	BAYS
RT	ESTUARINE DYNAMICS
RT	NEARSHORE DYNAMICS
RT	WAVE DYNAMICS

BAYS
BT1	COASTAL INLETS
BT2	COASTAL WATERS
RT	BARRIER SPITS
RT	BAY DYNAMICS
RT	COASTAL ZONE
RT	ESTUARIES
RT	HEADLANDS
RT	INLETS (WATERWAYS)
RT	WATER BODIES

BEACH ACCRETION
BT1	ACCRETION
NT1	BEACH NOURISHMENT
RT	BARRIER ISLANDS
RT	BEACH EROSION
RT	BEACH FEATURES
RT	BEACH MORPHOLOGY
RT	BEACH RIDGES
RT	BEACHES
RT	BERMS
RT	DEPOSITION FEATURES
RT	PROGRADATION
RT	SAND
RT	SHINGLE

BEACH BERMS
USE	**BERMS**

BEACH CUSPS
BT1	BEACH FEATURES
RT	BED FORMS
RT	EDGE WAVES
RT	LONGSHORE CURRENTS
RT	NEARSHORE DYNAMICS
RT	RIP CURRENTS
RT	SHOALING
RT	SHOALING WAVES
RT	SWELL
RT	WAVE EFFECTS
RT	WAVE REFRACTION
RT	WAVE SETUP

BEACH EROSION
BT1	COASTAL EROSION
BT2	EROSION
RT	BEACH ACCRETION
RT	BEACH FEATURES
RT	BEACH MORPHOLOGY
RT	BEACHES
RT	COAST DEFENCES
RT	DUNE STABILIZATION
RT	EROSION FEATURES
RT	GROYNES
RT	SHORE PROTECTION
RT	TIDAL EFFECTS
RT	WAVE EFFECTS

BEACH FACE
USE **FORESHORE**

BEACH FEATURES
NT1	BACKSHORE
NT1	BEACH CUSPS
NT1	BEACH RIDGES
NT2	CHENIERS
NT1	BERMS
NT1	DUNES
NT1	FORESHORE
NT1	NEARSHORE BARS
NT2	BREAK-POINT BARS
NT2	LONGSHORE BARS
NT2	TRANSVERSE BARS
NT1	RIP CHANNELS
NT1	RUNNELS
NT1	SPITS
NT2	BARRIER SPITS
NT1	SURF ZONE
NT1	TOMBOLOS
NT1	WAVE-CUT PLATFORMS
RT	BEACH ACCRETION
RT	BEACH EROSION
RT	BEACH MORPHOLOGY
RT	BEACH SURVEYS
RT	BEACHES
RT	BED FORMS
RT	HEADLANDS
RT	MICROTOPOGRAPHY
RT	NEARSHORE DYNAMICS
RT	SAND RIPPLES
RT	TOPOGRAPHIC FEATURES

BEACH GRADIENT
USE **BEACH SLOPE**

BEACH MORPHOLOGY
UF	beach processes
BT1	COASTAL MORPHOLOGY
BT2	GEOMORPHOLOGY
BT3	GEOLOGY
BT4	EARTH SCIENCES
RT	BACKWASH
RT	BEACH ACCRETION
RT	BEACH EROSION
RT	BEACH FEATURES
RT	BEACH NOURISHMENT
RT	BEACH PROFILES
RT	BEACHES
RT	NEARSHORE DYNAMICS
RT	SEA LEVEL VARIATIONS
RT	STORM SURGES
RT	TERRACES
RT	TIDAL CYCLES
RT	WAVE EFFECTS

BEACH NOURISHMENT
BT1	BEACH ACCRETION
BT2	ACCRETION
RT	BEACH MORPHOLOGY
RT	LONGSHORE SEDIMENT TRANSPORT

BEACH PLATFORMS
USE **WAVE-CUT PLATFORMS**

BEACH PROCESSES
USE **BEACH MORPHOLOGY**

BEACH PROFILES
BT1	HORIZONTAL PROFILES
BT2	PROFILES
RT	BATHYMETRIC PROFILES
RT	BEACH MORPHOLOGY
RT	BEACH SLOPE
RT	BEACHES
RT	BREAK-POINT BARS
RT	TOPOGRAPHIC SURVEYING
RT	WAVE EFFECTS

BEACH RIDGES
BT1	BEACH FEATURES
NT1	CHENIERS
RT	BEACH ACCRETION
RT	CUSPATE FORELANDS
RT	DEPOSITION FEATURES
RT	SHINGLE

BEACH ROCK
USE **BEACHROCK**

BEACH SEINES
BT1	SEINE NETS
BT2	FISHING NETS
BT3	FISHING GEAR
RT	BOAT SEINES
RT	COASTAL FISHERIES
RT	INLAND FISHERIES

BEACH SLOPE
UF	beach gradient
RT	BEACH PROFILES
RT	BEACHES
RT	GRADIENTS
RT	BEACH FEATURES

BEACH TEMPERATURE
USE **SEDIMENT TEMPERATURE**

BEACHES
UF	ocean beaches
UF	sandy beaches
UF	shingle beaches
BT1	COASTAL LANDFORMS
BT2	LANDFORMS
BT3	TOPOGRAPHIC FEATURES
NT1	BARRIER BEACHES
NT1	RAISED BEACHES
RT	BEACH ACCRETION
RT	BEACH EROSION
RT	BEACH FEATURES
RT	BEACH MORPHOLOGY
RT	BEACH PROFILES
RT	BEACH SLOPE
RT	COASTAL EROSION
RT	COASTAL ZONE
RT	COASTS
RT	DUNES
RT	GEOMORPHOLOGY
RT	INTERTIDAL ENVIRONMENT
RT	ISLANDS
RT	LAKE MORPHOLOGY
RT	LITTORAL ZONE
RT	NEARSHORE DYNAMICS
RT	RECREATIONAL WATERS
RT	RUNNELS
RT	SAND
RT	SURF
RT	WAVE PROCESSES ON BEACHES

BEACHROCK
UF	beach rock
BT1	CARBONATE ROCKS
RT	SEDIMENTARY ROCKS

BEACONS (DISTRESS)
USE **DISTRESS SIGNALS**

BEACONS (TRANSPONDERS)
USE **ACOUSTIC TRANSPONDERS**

BEAM TRANSMITTANCE
BT1	TRANSMITTANCE
BT2	OPTICAL PROPERTIES
BT3	PHYSICAL PROPERTIES
BT4	PROPERTIES
RT	ATTENUANCE
RT	BEAM TRANSMITTANCE METERS
RT	LIGHT ATTENUATION

BEAM TRANSMITTANCE METERS
UF	transparency meters
BT1	LIGHT MEASURING INSTRUMENTS
BT2	MEASURING DEVICES
RT	BEAM TRANSMITTANCE
RT	WATER TRANSPARENCY

BEAM TRAWLERS
USE **TRAWLERS**

BEAM TRAWLS (BOTTOM)
USE **BOTTOM TRAWLS**

BEAM TRAWLS (MIDWATER)
USE **MIDWATER TRAWLS**

BEARING CAPACITY
BT1	STRENGTH
BT2	MECHANICAL PROPERTIES
BT3	PHYSICAL PROPERTIES
BT4	PROPERTIES
RT	COMPACTION
RT	GEOTECHNICAL DATA
RT	LOADS (FORCES)
RT	PENETROMETERS
RT	PILE DRIVING
RT	SEDIMENT PROPERTIES
RT	SHEAR STRENGTH

BEAUFORT SCALE
UF	beaufort wind scale
RT	BREEZES
RT	GALE FORCE WINDS
RT	SEA STATE SCALES

BEAUFORT WIND SCALE
USE **BEAUFORT SCALE**

BED FORMS
SN	Before 1986 search also BEDFORMS
UF	bedforms
BT1	SEDIMENTARY STRUCTURES
NT1	ANTIDUNES
NT1	GRAVEL WAVES
NT1	MUD BANKS
NT1	OBSTACLE MARKS
NT1	PLOUGHMARKS
NT1	POCK MARKS
NT1	SAND BANKS
NT1	SAND BARS
NT1	SAND PATCHES
NT1	SAND RIBBONS
NT1	SAND RIPPLES
NT1	SAND WAVES
NT1	SCOUR HOLLOWS
NT1	SEACHANNELS
NT1	SEAMOATS
NT1	SEDIMENT DRIFTS
NT1	TRANSVERSE BED FORMS
RT	BEACH CUSPS
RT	BEACH FEATURES
RT	CONTOUR CURRENTS
RT	CURRENT SCOURING
RT	DUNES
RT	EROSION FEATURES
RT	FLUVIAL FEATURES
RT	HYDROLOGY
RT	ICEBERG SCOURING
RT	NEARSHORE BARS
RT	NEARSHORE DYNAMICS
RT	OSCILLATORY FLOW
RT	SEDIMENT-WATER INTERFACE
RT	TIDAL CURRENTS
RT	TOPOGRAPHIC FEATURES
RT	WAVE SCOURING
RT	WAVE-SEABED INTERACTION

ASFIS Thesaurus

BED FRICTION
USE **BOTTOM FRICTION**

BED LOAD
UF	bedload
UF	bottom load
UF	traction load
BT1	SEDIMENT LOAD
RT	RIVER BEDS
RT	SALTATION
RT	SEDIMENT TRANSPORT
RT	SHELF GEOLOGY
RT	SHELF SEDIMENTATION
RT	SUSPENDED LOAD
RT	TRACTION

BED ROUGHNESS
UF	bottom roughness
BT1	ROUGHNESS
BT2	SURFACE PROPERTIES
BT3	PROPERTIES
RT	BENTHIC BOUNDARY LAYER
RT	BOTTOM FRICTION
RT	CHANNEL FLOW
RT	DRAG COEFFICIENT
RT	FORM DRAG
RT	RIVER BEDS

BED SHEAR STRESS
USE **BOTTOM STRESS**

BED STRESS
USE **BOTTOM STRESS**

BEDDING STRUCTURES
SN	Use of a more specific term is recommended
BT1	SEDIMENTARY STRUCTURES
NT1	CURRENT MARKS
NT2	FLUTE CASTS
NT2	SCOUR MARKS
NT2	SOLE MARKS
NT1	RIPPLE MARKS
NT1	VARVES

BEDFORMS
USE **BED FORMS**

BEDLOAD
USE **BED LOAD**

BEHAVIOR
USE **BEHAVIOUR**

BEHAVIOUR
SN	Use of a more specific term is recommended
UF	animal behaviour
UF	behavior
NT1	AGGRESSIVE BEHAVIOUR
NT1	AGONISTIC BEHAVIOUR
NT1	AVOIDANCE REACTIONS
NT1	CHROMATIC BEHAVIOUR
NT1	CLEANING BEHAVIOUR
NT1	COMPETITIVE BEHAVIOUR
NT1	DISPLAY BEHAVIOUR
NT1	EXPLORATORY BEHAVIOUR
NT1	FEEDING BEHAVIOUR
NT2	CANNIBALISM
NT1	FLIGHT BEHAVIOUR
NT1	HOMING BEHAVIOUR
NT1	HYDROSTATIC BEHAVIOUR
NT1	LEARNING BEHAVIOUR
NT2	IMPRINTING
NT1	ORIENTATION BEHAVIOUR
NT2	KINESIS
NT2	TAXIS
NT3	CHEMOTAXIS
NT3	PHOTOTAXIS
NT3	RHEOTAXIS

BEHAVIOUR (cont'd)
NT1	PARENTAL BEHAVIOUR
NT1	PROTECTIVE BEHAVIOUR
NT1	REPRODUCTIVE BEHAVIOUR
NT2	COURTSHIP
NT1	SETTLING BEHAVIOUR
NT1	SEXUAL BEHAVIOUR
NT1	SOCIAL BEHAVIOUR
NT2	DOMINANCE HIERARCHIES
NT3	PECKING ORDER
NT2	SCHOOLING BEHAVIOUR
NT1	TERRITORIALITY
NT1	VOCALIZATION BEHAVIOUR
RT	ACTIVITY PATTERNS
RT	ADAPTATIONS
RT	ALARM SUBSTANCES
RT	ANIMAL COMMUNICATION
RT	AUTECOLOGY
RT	BEHAVIOURAL RESPONSES
RT	BIOLOGICAL RHYTHMS
RT	BIOTELEMETRY
RT	ECHOLOCATION
RT	ECOLOGY
RT	ECTOCRINES
RT	ENVIRONMENTAL EFFECTS
RT	ETHOLOGY
RT	GRAVITY EFFECTS
RT	INSTINCT
RT	INTERSPECIFIC RELATIONSHIPS
RT	INTRASPECIFIC RELATIONSHIPS
RT	MIGRATIONS
RT	NICHES
RT	PHENOLOGY
RT	PHEROMONES
RT	PRESSURE EFFECTS
RT	SPECIES
RT	STIMULI
RT	SYNECOLOGY
RT	SYNERGISM
RT	TRACKING
RT	TROPISM
RT	VERTEBRATE ZOOLOGY
RT	ZOOLOGY

BEHAVIOURAL RESPONSES
SN	As observed in experimental conditions. Added in 1980
RT	BEHAVIOUR
RT	CONTROLLED CONDITIONS
RT	STIMULI

BENCH MARKS
RT	DATUM LEVELS
RT	LEVELLING
RT	SEA LEVEL MEASUREMENT
RT	SURVEYING

BENDING
USE **DEFORMATION**

BENDS
USE **DECOMPRESSION SICKNESS**

BENIOFF SEISMIC ZONE
USE **BENIOFF ZONE**

BENIOFF ZONE
UF	benioff seismic zone
BT1	EARTH STRUCTURE
RT	LITHOSPHERE
RT	PLATE TECTONICS
RT	SEISMIC ZONES
RT	SUBDUCTION ZONES
RT	TRENCHES (OCEANIC)

BENJAMIN FEIR INSTABILITY
BT1	INSTABILITY
RT	WAVE TRAINS

BENTHIC ALGAE
USE **PHYTOBENTHOS**

BENTHIC BOUNDARY LAYER
UF	benthic layer
UF	bottom boundary layer
BT1	BOUNDARY LAYERS
BT2	LAYERS
RT	BED ROUGHNESS
RT	BENTHIC CURRENTS
RT	BOTTOM EKMAN LAYER
RT	BOTTOM MIXED LAYER
RT	DEEP LAYER
RT	WATER COLUMN
RT	WAVE-SEABED INTERACTION

BENTHIC COMMUNITIES
USE **BENTHOS**

BENTHIC CURRENTS
SN	Water currents at +4000 m depth
BT1	BOTTOM CURRENTS
BT2	WATER CURRENTS
BT3	WATER MOTION
RT	ABYSSAL CURRENTS
RT	BENTHIC BOUNDARY LAYER
RT	BOTTOM EKMAN LAYER
RT	OCEAN CURRENTS

BENTHIC ENVIRONMENT
UF	benthic regions
BT1	AQUATIC ENVIRONMENT
BT2	ENVIRONMENTS
NT1	ABYSSOBENTHIC ZONE
NT1	BATHYAL-BENTHIC ZONE
NT1	LITTORAL ZONE
NT2	EULITTORAL ZONE
NT2	SUBLITTORAL ZONE
NT2	SUPRALITTORAL ZONE
RT	ABYSSAL ZONE
RT	BATHYAL ZONE
RT	BENTHOS
RT	INTERSTITIAL ENVIRONMENT
RT	INTERTIDAL ENVIRONMENT
RT	LENITIC ENVIRONMENT
RT	LOTIC ENVIRONMENT
RT	MARINE ENVIRONMENT
RT	SEDIMENT-WATER INTERFACE
RT	SUBSTRATA

BENTHIC FAUNA
USE **ZOOBENTHOS**

BENTHIC FLORA
USE **PHYTOBENTHOS**

BENTHIC FRONTS
BT1	OCEANIC FRONTS
BT2	FRONTS

BENTHIC INFAUNA
USE **BURROWING ORGANISMS**

BENTHIC LAYER
USE **BENTHIC BOUNDARY LAYER**

BENTHIC REGIONS
USE **BENTHIC ENVIRONMENT**

BENTHON
USE **BENTHOS**

BENTHOS
UF	benthic communities
UF	benthon
UF	epibenthos
UF	macrobenthos
UF	microbenthos
BT1	AQUATIC COMMUNITIES
NT1	MEIOBENTHOS

BENTHOS (cont'd)
NT1	PHYTOBENTHOS
NT1	ZOOBENTHOS
RT	BENTHIC ENVIRONMENT
RT	BENTHOS COLLECTING DEVICES
RT	BURROWING ORGANISMS
RT	ECOLOGICAL ZONATION
RT	INTERSTITIAL ENVIRONMENT
RT	SEAFLOOR SAMPLING
RT	SESSILE SPECIES
RT	SUBSTRATA
RT	TUBE DWELLERS

BENTHOS COLLECTING DEVICES
BT1	COLLECTING DEVICES
RT	BENTHOS
RT	SEAFLOOR SAMPLING
RT	ZOOBENTHOS

BENTONITE
BT1	CLASTICS
BT2	SEDIMENTS
RT	LUTITES
RT	MONTMORILLONITE
RT	SEDIMENTARY ROCKS
RT	VOLCANIC ASH

BENZENE
BT1	AROMATIC HYDROCARBONS
BT2	UNSATURATED HYDROCARBONS
BT3	HYDROCARBONS
BT4	ORGANIC COMPOUNDS

BERKELIUM
BT1	CHEMICAL ELEMENTS
RT	ACTINIDES
RT	BERKELIUM COMPOUNDS
RT	BERKELIUM ISOTOPES
RT	TRANSITION ELEMENTS
RT	TRANSURANIC ELEMENTS

BERKELIUM COMPOUNDS
BT1	ACTINIDE COMPOUNDS
RT	BERKELIUM
RT	CHEMICAL COMPOUNDS

BERKELIUM ISOTOPES
BT1	ISOTOPES
RT	BERKELIUM

BERMS
UF	beach berms
BT1	BEACH FEATURES
RT	BACKSHORE
RT	BEACH ACCRETION
RT	DEPOSITION FEATURES
RT	OVERWASH
RT	SAND

BERTHING
SN	Use for both docking vessel and action of securing vessel to mooring buoy
UF	docking
UF	mooring ships
NT1	OFFSHORE DOCKING
RT	ANCHORING
RT	ANCHORS
RT	MOORING BUOYS
RT	OFFSHORE TERMINALS
RT	POSITIONING SYSTEMS
RT	SHIP MOORING SYSTEMS

BERYLLIUM
BT1	CHEMICAL ELEMENTS
RT	ALKALINE EARTH METALS
RT	BERYLLIUM COMPOUNDS
RT	BERYLLIUM ISOTOPES

BERYLLIUM COMPOUNDS
BT1	ALKALINE EARTH METAL COMPOUNDS
RT	BERYLLIUM
RT	CHEMICAL COMPOUNDS

BERYLLIUM ISOTOPES
BT1	ISOTOPES
RT	BERYLLIUM

BETA-PLANE
RT	CORIOLIS PARAMETERS
RT	EQUATORIAL DYNAMICS
RT	ROSSBY PARAMETER
RT	VORTICITY

BETA SPIRALS
RT	CORIOLIS PARAMETERS

BIBLIOGRAPHIC INFORMATION
UF	annotation
UF	bibliographic studies
RT	BIBLIOGRAPHIES
RT	DOCUMENTATION
RT	DOCUMENTS
RT	INFORMATION HANDLING
RT	INFORMATION RETRIEVAL

BIBLIOGRAPHIC STUDIES
USE	**BIBLIOGRAPHIC INFORMATION**

BIBLIOGRAPHIES
UF	reading lists
BT1	DOCUMENTS
NT1	PERSONAL BIBLIOGRAPHIES
RT	BIBLIOGRAPHIC INFORMATION
RT	DOCUMENTATION
RT	INFORMATION RETRIEVAL
RT	LITERATURE REVIEWS

BICARBONATES
BT1	CARBON COMPOUNDS

BIENNIAL
SN	Descriptor to be used only as a qualifier
BT1	PERIODICITY
RT	ANNUAL

BILATERAL AGREEMENTS
SN	Added in 1980
UF	bilateral aid
BT1	LEGISLATION
RT	ECONOMICS
RT	FOREIGN FISHING
RT	INTERNATIONAL AGREEMENTS
RT	JOINT VENTURES
RT	TERRITORIAL WATERS

BILATERAL AID
USE	**BILATERAL AGREEMENTS**

BILE
SN	Before 1982 search BODY FLUIDS
UF	bile pigments
UF	bile salts
BT1	BODY FLUIDS
RT	FATS
RT	GALL BLADDER
RT	LIVER
RT	METABOLISM

BILE PIGMENTS
USE	**BILE**

BILE SALTS
USE	**BILE**

BILLFISHERIES
USE	**TUNA FISHERIES**

BILLOWS
UF	kelvin-helmholtz billows
BT1	FLUID MOTION
RT	INTERNAL WAVES
RT	KELVIN-HELMHOLTZ INSTABILITY

BINDERS (ADHESIVES)
USE	**ADHESIVES**

BIOACCUMULATION
SN	biological uptake and accumulation or concentration in the tissues
BT1	BIOLOGICAL PHENOMENA
RT	ACCUMULATION
RT	CHEMICAL POLLUTANTS
RT	CHEMICAL POLLUTION
RT	EXCRETION
RT	FATE
RT	FOOD CHAINS
RT	HEAVY METALS
RT	LETHAL EFFECTS
RT	PESTICIDES
RT	POLLUTANT IDENTIFICATION
RT	POLLUTION EFFECTS
RT	POLLUTION TOLERANCE
RT	RADIOACTIVE WASTES
RT	RADIOISOTOPES
RT	SUBLETHAL EFFECTS
RT	TOXICITY TOLERANCE

BIOACOUSTICS
BT1	ACOUSTICS
BT2	PHYSICS
RT	AUDIO RECORDINGS
RT	BIOLOGICAL NOISE
RT	BIOLOGY
RT	BIOPHYSICS
RT	BIOTELEMETRY
RT	SOUND PRODUCTION
RT	VOCALIZATION BEHAVIOUR

BIOAERATION
SN	Sewage purification by oxidation. Added in 1982
BT1	AERATION
RT	SEWAGE
RT	SLUDGE

BIOASSAYS
UF	biological assays
UF	biological testing
UF	testing (biological)
NT1	BIOTESTING
RT	BACTERIOLOGY
RT	DRUGS
RT	LETHAL LIMITS
RT	POLLUTANT IDENTIFICATION
RT	SURVIVAL
RT	TEST ORGANISMS
RT	TESTS
RT	TOXICANTS
RT	TOXICITY
RT	TOXICITY TESTS

BIOCALCARENITE
BT1	CARBONATE ROCKS
RT	CALCARENITE

BIOCENOSIS
USE	**BIOCOENOSIS**

BIOCHEMICAL ANALYSIS
RT	ANALYSIS
RT	ANALYTICAL TECHNIQUES
RT	BIOCHEMICAL COMPOSITION
RT	BIOCHEMISTRY
RT	COMPOSITION

BIOCHEMICAL ANALYSIS (cont'd)
RT	ELECTROPHORESIS
RT	NUTRITIVE VALUE
RT	ORGANIC CONSTITUENTS

BIOCHEMICAL COMPOSITION
BT1	COMPOSITION
RT	BIOCHEMICAL ANALYSIS
RT	BIOCHEMISTRY
RT	ORGANIC CONSTITUENTS
RT	PLANKTON EQUIVALENTS
RT	WATER CONTENT

BIOCHEMICAL CYCLES
BT1	CYCLES
RT	BIOGEOCHEMICAL CYCLE
RT	CHEMICAL CYCLES
RT	CHEMICAL DEGRADATION
RT	NUTRIENT CYCLES

BIOCHEMICAL OXYGEN DEMAND
SN	Before 1982 search also BIOLOGICAL OXYGEN DEMAND
UF	biological oxygen demand
UF	bod
BT1	OXYGEN DEMAND
RT	AEROBIC RESPIRATION
RT	BIOCHEMICAL PHENOMENA
RT	CHEMICAL OXYGEN DEMAND
RT	COAGULATION
RT	DISSOLVED OXYGEN
RT	INDICATOR SPECIES
RT	METABOLISM
RT	OXYGEN
RT	OXYGENATION
RT	RESPIRATION
RT	SELF PURIFICATION
RT	WATER QUALITY

BIOCHEMICAL PHENOMENA
SN	Added in 1980
NT1	CALCIFICATION
NT1	DECALCIFICATION
NT1	PROTEIN DENATURATION
NT1	PROTEIN SYNTHESIS
RT	BIOCHEMICAL OXYGEN DEMAND
RT	BIOCHEMISTRY
RT	BIODEGRADATION
RT	BIOLOGICAL PHENOMENA
RT	CHEMICAL REACTIONS
RT	FERMENTATION
RT	METABOLISM
RT	NITROGEN FIXATION

BIOCHEMISTRY
UF	physiochemistry
BT1	CHEMISTRY
NT1	CYTOCHEMISTRY
NT1	HISTOCHEMISTRY
RT	BIOCHEMICAL ANALYSIS
RT	BIOCHEMICAL COMPOSITION
RT	BIOCHEMICAL PHENOMENA
RT	BIOGEOCHEMICAL CYCLE
RT	BIOGEOCHEMISTRY
RT	CARBOHYDRATES
RT	CARBON CYCLE
RT	ENZYME INHIBITORS
RT	ENZYMES
RT	METABOLISM
RT	PHARMACOLOGY
RT	PHYSIOLOGY
RT	PROTEINS
RT	SPECIFICITY
RT	VITAMINS

BIOCIDES
USE	**PESTICIDES**

BIOCLIMATOLOGY
SN	The study of the effects of climate on living organisms. Added in 1982
UF	biological climatology
UF	biometeorology
BT1	CLIMATOLOGY
RT	CLIMATE
RT	HYDROCLIMATE
RT	PHENOLOGY
RT	TEMPERATURE EFFECTS

BIOCOENOSIS
SN	A group of plants and animals forming a natural community
UF	biocenosis
RT	AQUATIC COMMUNITIES
RT	BIOTA
RT	BIOTOPES
RT	COMMUNITY COMPOSITION
RT	ECOLOGICAL ASSOCIATIONS
RT	HABITAT
RT	OVERCROWDING

BIOCOMMUNICATION
USE	**ANIMAL COMMUNICATION**

BIOCONTROL
USE	**BIOLOGICAL CONTROL**

BIODEGRADABLE SUBSTANCES
SN	Substances able to be broken down by microorganisms. Added in 1980
RT	ANAEROBIC DIGESTION
RT	BIODEGRADATION
RT	HAZARD ASSESSMENT

BIODEGRADATION
UF	microbial degradation
BT1	DEGRADATION
BT2	CHEMICAL REACTIONS
NT1	ANAEROBIC DIGESTION
RT	AMMONIA
RT	ANAEROBIC BACTERIA
RT	ANTIFOULING SUBSTANCES
RT	BIOCHEMICAL PHENOMENA
RT	BIODEGRADABLE SUBSTANCES
RT	BIOGEOCHEMICAL CYCLE
RT	DECOMPOSERS
RT	DEGENERATION
RT	FOULING ORGANISMS
RT	NITROGEN CYCLE
RT	NUTRIENT CYCLES
RT	OIL WASTES
RT	OXIDATION
RT	SEWAGE PONDS
RT	SEWAGE TREATMENT
RT	SLUDGE TREATMENT
RT	WASTEWATER TREATMENT
RT	WATER POLLUTION TREATMENT

BIODEPOSITION
USE	**DETRITUS**

BIODETERIORATION
USE	**BIOLOGICAL DAMAGE**

BIOELECTRICITY
SN	The production of electricity by living animals. Added in 1982
BT1	BIOLOGICAL PROPERTIES
BT2	PROPERTIES
RT	BIOPHYSICS
RT	DEFENCE MECHANISMS
RT	ELECTRIC ORGANS

BIOENERGETIC STUDIES
USE	**BIOENERGETICS**

BIOENERGETICS
SN	Energy transformation in living organisms and aquatic ecosystems. Before 1982 search ENERGY BUDGET
UF	bioenergetic studies
RT	CONVERSION FACTORS
RT	ECOSYSTEMS
RT	ENERGY BUDGET
RT	FOOD CHAINS
RT	FOOD CONSUMPTION
RT	METABOLISM

BIOENGINEERING
USE	**BIOTECHNOLOGY**

BIOEROSION
SN	Added in 1980
UF	erosion (biological)
RT	BACTERIA
RT	BIOLOGICAL DAMAGE
RT	BORING ORGANISMS
RT	EROSION
RT	FUNGI

BIOEVOLUTION
USE	**EVOLUTION**

BIOFACIES
BT1	FACIES
RT	BIOSTRATIGRAPHY
RT	ECOLOGY
RT	FOSSILS
RT	PALAEONTOLOGY
RT	SEDIMENTATION

BIOFILTERS
SN	Added in 1980
UF	biological filters
UF	filters (biological)
UF	subgravel filters
RT	RECIRCULATING SYSTEMS
RT	WATER TREATMENT

BIOGENESIS
SN	Before 1982 search EVOLUTION
BT1	BIOLOGICAL PHENOMENA
RT	BIOGENY
RT	EVOLUTION
RT	REPRODUCTION

BIOGENIC DEPOSITS
UF	biogenic sediments
NT1	CORAL REEFS
NT2	BARRIER REEFS
NT2	FRINGING REEFS
NT1	ORGANIC SEDIMENTS
NT2	PEAT
NT2	SAPROPELS
NT1	SILICEOUS SEDIMENTS
RT	ATOLLS
RT	AUTOCHTHONOUS DEPOSITS
RT	OOZES

BIOGENIC MATERIAL
SN	Material of biological origin. Added in 1980
UF	biogenous material
BT1	MATERIALS
RT	DETRITUS
RT	SUSPENDED ORGANIC MATTER
RT	TROPHODYNAMIC CYCLE

BIOGENIC SEDIMENTARY STRUCTURES
BT1	SEDIMENTARY STRUCTURES
NT1	ALGAL MATS
NT1	STROMATOLITES
NT1	TRACE FOSSILS
NT2	FOSSILIZED TRACKS
RT	BIOTURBATION
RT	CORAL REEFS

BIOGENIC SEDIMENTS
USE **BIOGENIC DEPOSITS**

BIOGENOUS MATERIAL
USE **BIOGENIC MATERIAL**

BIOGENY
SN The science of the evolution of
    organisms, comprising ontogeny and
    phylogeny. Before 1982 search
    EVOLUTION
RT BIOGENESIS
RT EVOLUTION

BIOGEOCHEMICAL CYCLE
SN Complete cycle between organic
    matter in aquatic ecosystems.
    Before 1982 search BIOCHEMICAL CYCLE
BT1 CYCLES
NT1 NUTRIENT CYCLES
NT2 CARBON CYCLE
NT2 NITROGEN CYCLE
NT2 PHOSPHORUS CYCLE
NT2 SILICON CYCLE
RT BIOCHEMICAL CYCLES
RT BIOCHEMISTRY
RT BIODEGRADATION
RT BIOGEOCHEMISTRY
RT BIOLOGICAL CLOCKS
RT CHEMICAL DEGRADATION
RT DETRITUS
RT GEOCHEMICAL CYCLE
RT NUTRIENTS (MINERAL)
RT OXIDATION
RT PHOTOSYNTHESIS
RT PRIMARY PRODUCTION
RT SUSPENDED PARTICULATE MATTER

BIOGEOCHEMISTRY
BT1 GEOCHEMISTRY
BT2 CHEMISTRY
RT BIOCHEMISTRY
RT BIOGEOCHEMICAL CYCLE
RT BIOLOGY
RT NUTRIENT CYCLES
RT PYROLYSIS
RT SEDIMENT CHEMISTRY
RT SULPHATE REDUCTION

BIOGEOGRAPHY
UF chorology
UF phytogeography
UF zoogeography
BT1 GEOGRAPHY
RT AQUATIC ANIMALS
RT AQUATIC PLANTS
RT BIOLOGICAL CHARTS
RT BIOLOGY
RT BOTANY
RT CLIMATOLOGY
RT CONTINENTAL DRIFT
RT COSMOPOLITE SPECIES
RT DISTRIBUTION RECORDS
RT ECOLOGICAL DISTRIBUTION
RT ECOLOGY
RT ENDEMIC SPECIES
RT ENDEMISM
RT FAUNAL PROVINCES
RT GEOGRAPHICAL DISTRIBUTION
RT HYDROCLIMATE
RT ICHTHYOLOGY
RT INVERTEBRATE ZOOLOGY
RT MAPPING
RT MAPS
RT PHYTOSOCIOLOGY
RT SPECIES
RT VERTEBRATE ZOOLOGY
RT ZOOLOGY

BIOGRAPHIES
UF autobiographies
BT1 DOCUMENTS
RT DOCUMENTATION
RT SCIENTIFIC PERSONNEL

BIOHERMS
BT1 REEFS
RT CORAL REEFS
RT LIMESTONE

BIOINDICATOR ORGANISMS
USE **INDICATOR SPECIES**

BIOINDICATORS
USE **INDICATOR SPECIES**

BIOLOGICAL AGE
SN Added in 1980
UF age (biological)
UF age (organisms)
BT1 AGE
NT1 AGE AT RECRUITMENT
RT AGE DETERMINATION
RT BIOLOGICAL AGING
RT GROWTH
RT LIFE CYCLE
RT LONGEVITY

BIOLOGICAL AGING
SN Added in 1980
UF ageing (biological)
UF aging (biological)
UF senescence
BT1 AGING
RT AGE COMPOSITION
RT AGE DETERMINATION
RT BIOLOGICAL AGE
RT GROWTH
RT LIFE CYCLE
RT LONGEVITY

BIOLOGICAL ASSAYS
USE **BIOASSAYS**

BIOLOGICAL ATTACHMENT
SN Added in 1982
UF attachment (biological)
NT1 PARASITE ATTACHMENT
RT ATTACHMENT ORGANS

BIOLOGICAL BALANCE
USE **ECOLOGICAL BALANCE**

BIOLOGICAL CHARTS
SN Distributional charts of aquatic
    organisms, aquatic communities,
    living resources and their migrations
BT1 MAPS
BT2 GRAPHICS
BT3 AUDIOVISUAL MATERIAL
BT4 DOCUMENTS
RT AQUATIC COMMUNITIES
RT AQUATIC ORGANISMS
RT BIOGEOGRAPHY
RT DISTRIBUTION RECORDS
RT FISHERY RESOURCES
RT GEOGRAPHICAL DISTRIBUTION
RT QUANTITATIVE DISTRIBUTION

BIOLOGICAL CLASSIFICATION
USE **TAXONOMY**

BIOLOGICAL CLIMATOLOGY
USE **BIOCLIMATOLOGY**

BIOLOGICAL CLOCKS
RT BIOGEOCHEMICAL CYCLE
RT BIOLOGICAL RHYTHMS
RT CIRCADIAN RHYTHMS
RT NYCTIMERAL RHYTHMS

BIOLOGICAL COLLECTIONS
SN Museum collections and comparative
    collections of aquatic organisms
BT1 COLLECTIONS
RT SORTING CENTRES

BIOLOGICAL COMPETITION
USE **COMPETITION**

BIOLOGICAL CONTROL
SN Use of organisms or viruses to
    control parasites, aquatic weeds or
    other pests
UF biocontrol
BT1 CONTROL
RT AQUATIC INSECTS
RT BACTERIOPHAGES
RT BIOLOGICAL VECTORS
RT FOULING CONTROL
RT HERBIVOROUS FISH
RT MORTALITY CAUSES
RT PEST CONTROL
RT PLANT CONTROL
RT PREDATOR CONTROL
RT PROTOZOAN DISEASES
RT VIRAL DISEASES
RT VIRUSES

BIOLOGICAL CORROSION
USE **BIOLOGICAL DAMAGE**

BIOLOGICAL CULTURE
USE **LABORATORY CULTURE**

BIOLOGICAL DAMAGE
SN Damages caused by aquatic
    organisms. Added in 1980
UF biodeterioration
UF biological corrosion
UF biological deterioration
UF damage (biological)
RT ANTIFOULING SUBSTANCES
RT BIOEROSION
RT BORING ORGANISMS
RT CHEMICAL CONTROL
RT DANGEROUS ORGANISMS
RT FOULING ORGANISMS

BIOLOGICAL DATA
UF data (biological)
BT1 DATA
RT BIOLOGICAL SAMPLING
RT BIOLOGICAL SURVEYS
RT CENSUS

BIOLOGICAL DATING
USE **AGE DETERMINATION**

BIOLOGICAL DETERIORATION
USE **BIOLOGICAL DAMAGE**

BIOLOGICAL DEVELOPMENT
SN Before 1982 search DEVELOPMENT
    (BIOLOGICAL). Restricted to
    development processes of organisms
UF development (biological)
NT1 EMBRYONIC DEVELOPMENT
NT1 LARVAL DEVELOPMENT
RT DEVELOPMENTAL STAGES
RT EMBRYOLOGY
RT GROWTH
RT LIFE CYCLE
RT ONTOGENY
RT RESOURCE DEVELOPMENT

ASFIS Thesaurus

BIOLOGICAL DRIFT
UF	drift (biological)
BT1	DISPERSION
RT	BIOTIC BARRIERS
RT	FISH LARVAE
RT	INVERTEBRATE LARVAE
RT	WIND-DRIVEN CURRENTS

BIOLOGICAL ENGINEERING
USE	**BIOTECHNOLOGY**

BIOLOGICAL EQUILIBRIUM
USE	**ECOLOGICAL BALANCE**

BIOLOGICAL FERTILIZATION
SN	Added in 1980
UF	external fertilization
UF	fertilization (biological)
UF	internal fertilization
UF	reproductive fertilization
UF	syngamy
BT1	SEXUAL REPRODUCTION
BT2	REPRODUCTION
RT	POLYSPERMY
RT	SEXUAL CELLS
RT	SPERMATOPHORES

BIOLOGICAL FILTERS
USE	**BIOFILTERS**

BIOLOGICAL HALF LIFE
SN	Time required by the body to eliminate one-half of the administered dose of any substance by regular process of elimination. Added in 1980
UF	biological half time
UF	half life (biological)
UF	half-life (effective)
RT	BODY BURDEN
RT	RADIOISOTOPES
RT	RADIONUCLIDE KINETICS

BIOLOGICAL HALF TIME
USE	**BIOLOGICAL HALF LIFE**

BIOLOGICAL INSTITUTIONS
BT1	RESEARCH INSTITUTIONS
BT2	ORGANIZATIONS
RT	LIMNOLOGICAL INSTITUTIONS
RT	OCEANOGRAPHIC INSTITUTIONS

BIOLOGICAL LIMNOLOGY
USE	**FRESHWATER ECOLOGY**

BIOLOGICAL MEMBRANES
SN	Added in 1980
UF	membranes (biological)
RT	CELL MEMBRANES
RT	ION EXCHANGE
RT	ION TRANSPORT

BIOLOGICAL NOISE
SN	Sound emitted by marine animals present on echo trace. Added in 1982
UF	fish sounds
UF	marine biological noise
BT1	AMBIENT NOISE
BT2	NOISE (SOUND)
RT	BIOACOUSTICS
RT	SOUND PRODUCTION
RT	SOUND WAVES

BIOLOGICAL OCEANOGRAPHY
USE	**MARINE ECOLOGY**

BIOLOGICAL OXYGEN DEMAND
USE	**BIOCHEMICAL OXYGEN DEMAND**

BIOLOGICAL PHENOMENA
SN	Added in 1980
UF	phenomena (biological)
NT1	ADAPTATIONS
NT2	CAMOUFLAGE
NT2	CHROMATIC ADAPTATIONS
NT2	MIMICRY
NT2	OSMOTIC ADAPTATIONS
NT1	ALLERGIC REACTIONS
NT1	BIOACCUMULATION
NT1	BIOGENESIS
NT1	BIOLOGICAL RHYTHMS
NT2	CIRCADIAN RHYTHMS
NT2	NYCTIMERAL RHYTHMS
NT1	BIOSYNTHESIS
NT1	DEGENERATION
NT1	EVOLUTION
NT1	METAMORPHOSIS
NT2	MOULTING
NT1	MUTATIONS
NT1	REGENERATION
RT	BIOCHEMICAL PHENOMENA
RT	BIOLUMINESCENCE
RT	ENCYSTMENT
RT	INTERSPECIFIC RELATIONSHIPS
RT	INTRASPECIFIC RELATIONSHIPS

BIOLOGICAL POISONS
SN	Before 1982 search POISONS (BIOLOGICAL)
UF	biotoxins
UF	poisons (biological)
UF	toxins
UF	venoms
NT1	CIGUATOXIN
NT1	ENDOTOXINS
NT1	NEUROTOXINS
NT1	TETRODOTOXIN
RT	ALGAL BLOOMS
RT	ANTIBODIES
RT	DETOXIFICATION
RT	HAZARDOUS MATERIALS
RT	LETHAL EFFECTS
RT	LETHAL LIMITS
RT	METABOLITES
RT	POISONOUS ORGANISMS
RT	RED TIDES
RT	SUBLETHAL EFFECTS
RT	TOXICITY
RT	TOXICOLOGY
RT	VENOM APPARATUS

BIOLOGICAL POLLUTANTS
SN	Pollutants having a biological origin
BT1	POLLUTANTS
RT	BIOLOGICAL PRODUCTION
RT	CULTURE EFFECTS
RT	MICROBIAL CONTAMINATION
RT	MICROBIOLOGICAL ANALYSIS

BIOLOGICAL POLYMORPHISM
USE	**BIOPOLYMORPHISM**

BIOLOGICAL PRODUCTION
SN	Organic production in aquatic environment, including dynamic parameters. Before 1982 search PRODUCTION (BIOLOGICAL)
UF	natural increase
UF	natural production
UF	organic production
UF	production (biological)
UF	production rate
UF	productivity
NT1	PRIMARY PRODUCTION
NT1	SECONDARY PRODUCTION
RT	BIOLOGICAL POLLUTANTS

BIOLOGICAL PRODUCTION (cont'd)
RT	BIOMASS
RT	DENSITY DEPENDENCE
RT	ECOSYSTEMS
RT	ENVIRONMENTAL EFFECTS
RT	FERTILITY
RT	FOOD CHAINS
RT	FOOD WEBS
RT	GRAZING
RT	NUTRIENT CYCLES
RT	NUTRIENTS (MINERAL)
RT	OXYGEN DEMAND
RT	PLANKTON
RT	PLANKTON EQUIVALENTS
RT	TROPHIC LEVELS
RT	TROPHODYNAMIC CYCLE
RT	UPWELLING
RT	YIELD

BIOLOGICAL PROPERTIES
BT1	PROPERTIES
NT1	BIOELECTRICITY
NT1	BIOLOGICAL RESISTANCE
NT2	COLD RESISTANCE
NT2	CONTROL RESISTANCE
NT2	DISEASE RESISTANCE
NT2	DROUGHT RESISTANCE
NT2	DRUG RESISTANCE
NT2	PARASITE RESISTANCE
NT1	EURYHALINITY
NT1	EURYTHERMY
NT1	FECUNDITY
NT1	HETEROSIS
NT1	HOMOIOTHERMY
NT1	IMMUNITY
NT1	LONGEVITY
NT1	NEOTENY
NT1	POIKILOTHERMY
NT1	SEXUAL MATURITY
NT1	STENOHALINITY
NT1	STENOTHERMY
NT1	TOLERANCE
NT2	EXPOSURE TOLERANCE
NT2	POLLUTION TOLERANCE
NT2	SALINITY TOLERANCE
NT2	TEMPERATURE TOLERANCE
NT2	TOXICITY TOLERANCE
NT1	TOXICITY
NT1	VULNERABILITY
RT	BIOLUMINESCENCE
RT	COLOUR
RT	FLUORESCENCE
RT	INSTINCT
RT	ODOUR
RT	ORGANOLEPTIC PROPERTIES
RT	PHOSPHORESCENCE
RT	PHYSICOCHEMICAL PROPERTIES
RT	TASTE

BIOLOGICAL RAFTING
SN	Transport of sediment by aquatic organisms
BT1	RAFTING
BT2	SEDIMENT TRANSPORT
RT	BIOTURBATION
RT	SEDIMENTS

BIOLOGICAL RESISTANCE
SN	Use of a more specific term is recommended. Added in 1980
UF	resistance (biological)
BT1	BIOLOGICAL PROPERTIES
BT2	PROPERTIES
NT1	COLD RESISTANCE
NT1	CONTROL RESISTANCE
NT1	DISEASE RESISTANCE
NT1	DROUGHT RESISTANCE
NT1	DRUG RESISTANCE
NT1	PARASITE RESISTANCE
RT	ECOPHYSIOLOGY

BIOLOGICAL RESISTANCE (cont'd)
RT	ENVIRONMENTAL EFFECTS
RT	RESISTANCE MECHANISMS
RT	TOLERANCE

BIOLOGICAL RESOURCES
USE	**LIVING RESOURCES**

BIOLOGICAL RHYTHMS
SN	A repeated cyclic change in the behaviour of organisms
UF	biorhythms
UF	endogenous rhythms
UF	rhythms (biological)
BT1	BIOLOGICAL PHENOMENA
NT1	CIRCADIAN RHYTHMS
NT1	NYCTIMERAL RHYTHMS
RT	ACTIVITY PATTERNS
RT	AUTECOLOGY
RT	BEHAVIOUR
RT	BIOLOGICAL CLOCKS
RT	ECOLOGICAL DISTRIBUTION
RT	PHENOLOGY
RT	PHOTOPERIODICITY
RT	VERTICAL DISTRIBUTION
RT	VERTICAL MIGRATIONS

BIOLOGICAL SAMPLING
SN	Before 1982 search SAMPLING (BIOLOGICAL). Sampling methods and techniques for aquatic animals & plants
UF	sampling (biological)
BT1	SAMPLING
RT	AVOIDANCE REACTIONS
RT	BIOLOGICAL DATA
RT	BIOLOGICAL SURVEYS
RT	BIOMETRICS
RT	CENSUS
RT	COLLECTING DEVICES
RT	ESCAPEMENT
RT	STATISTICAL SAMPLING

BIOLOGICAL SCIENCES
USE	**BIOLOGY**

BIOLOGICAL SELECTION
USE	**BIOSELECTION**

BIOLOGICAL SETTLEMENT
SN	Before 1982 search SETTLEMENT (BIOLOGICAL)
UF	settlement (biological)
NT1	ALGAL SETTLEMENTS
NT1	LARVAL SETTLEMENT
RT	COLONIZATION
RT	SETTLING BEHAVIOUR
RT	SUBSTRATE PREFERENCES

BIOLOGICAL SPECIATION
SN	Before 1982 search SPECIATION (BIOLOGICAL)
UF	speciation (biological)
RT	BIOSELECTION
RT	BREEDING
RT	ECOTYPES
RT	EVOLUTION
RT	GENETICS
RT	ISOLATING MECHANISMS
RT	MUTATIONS
RT	NEW SPECIES
RT	PHYLOGENETICS
RT	PHYLOGENY
RT	POPULATION GENETICS
RT	SPECIES
RT	TAXONOMY

BIOLOGICAL STRESS
SN	Before 1982 search FATIGUE (BIOLOGICAL). Physiological condition of a tissue, organ or organism which is unable to respond normally to a stimulus without rest
UF	fatigue (biological)
UF	stress (biological)
UF	stress (physiological)
RT	ANOXIA
RT	MORTALITY CAUSES
RT	MUSCLES
RT	MUSCULOSKELETAL SYSTEM
RT	STIMULI
RT	STRESS

BIOLOGICAL SURVEYS
BT1	SURVEYS
NT1	PLANKTON SURVEYS
NT2	ICHTHYOPLANKTON SURVEYS
RT	BIOLOGICAL DATA
RT	BIOLOGICAL SAMPLING
RT	COMMUNITY COMPOSITION

BIOLOGICAL TESTING
USE	**BIOASSAYS**

BIOLOGICAL TISSUES
USE	**TISSUES**

BIOLOGICAL TRANSPLANTATION
USE	**TRANSPLANTS**

BIOLOGICAL VECTORS
SN	Organisms serving as passive carrier of a disease agent. Before 1982 search VECTORS (BIOLOGICAL)
BT1	VECTORS
RT	AQUATIC INSECTS
RT	BIOLOGICAL CONTROL
RT	HOSTS
RT	HYGIENE
RT	PARASITES
RT	PARASITIC DISEASES
RT	PARASITOLOGY
RT	PATHOLOGY
RT	PROTOZOAN DISEASES

BIOLOGISTS
SN	Added in 1980
UF	aquatic biologists
UF	hydrobiologists
BT1	SCIENTIFIC PERSONNEL
BT2	PERSONNEL
NT1	ALGOLOGISTS
NT1	BOTANISTS
NT1	FISHERY BIOLOGISTS
NT1	GENETICISTS
NT1	MICROBIOLOGISTS
NT2	BACTERIOLOGISTS
NT2	MYCOLOGISTS
NT2	VIROLOGISTS
NT1	PHYSIOLOGISTS
NT2	ANIMAL PHYSIOLOGISTS
NT2	PLANT PHYSIOLOGISTS
NT1	TAXONOMISTS
NT1	ZOOLOGISTS
NT2	CARCINOLOGISTS
NT2	ENTOMOLOGISTS
NT2	ICHTHYOLOGISTS
NT2	MALACOLOGISTS
NT2	MAMMALOGISTS
NT3	CETOLOGISTS
NT2	ORNITHOLOGISTS
RT	DIRECTORIES

BIOLOGY
SN	Before 1982 search BIOLOGICAL SCIENCES. Use of a more specific term is recommended
UF	biological sciences
UF	life sciences (biology)
NT1	ANATOMY
NT1	BOTANY
NT2	ALGOLOGY
NT1	CRYOBIOLOGY
NT1	CYTOLOGY
NT2	KARYOLOGY
NT1	EMBRYOLOGY
NT1	FISHERY BIOLOGY
NT1	FUNCTIONAL MORPHOLOGY
NT1	GENETICS
NT2	POPULATION GENETICS
NT1	HAEMATOLOGY
NT1	HISTOLOGY
NT1	HYDROBIOLOGY
NT1	MICROBIOLOGY
NT2	BACTERIOLOGY
NT2	MYCOLOGY
NT2	VIROLOGY
NT1	ORGANISM MORPHOLOGY
NT2	ANIMAL MORPHOLOGY
NT2	CELL MORPHOLOGY
NT2	PLANT MORPHOLOGY
NT1	PHYSIOLOGY
NT2	ANIMAL PHYSIOLOGY
NT3	AVIAN PHYSIOLOGY
NT3	FISH PHYSIOLOGY
NT3	MAMMALIAN PHYSIOLOGY
NT2	DIVING PHYSIOLOGY
NT2	ECOPHYSIOLOGY
NT2	ELECTROPHYSIOLOGY
NT2	ENDOCRINOLOGY
NT2	HUMAN PHYSIOLOGY
NT2	NEUROPHYSIOLOGY
NT2	PLANT PHYSIOLOGY
NT1	ZOOLOGY
NT2	CONCHOLOGY
NT2	INVERTEBRATE ZOOLOGY
NT3	CARCINOLOGY
NT3	ENTOMOLOGY
NT3	MALACOLOGY
NT2	VERTEBRATE ZOOLOGY
NT3	HERPETOLOGY
NT3	ICHTHYOLOGY
NT3	MAMMALOGY
NT4	CETOLOGY
NT3	ORNITHOLOGY
NT3	OSTEOLOGY
RT	BIOACOUSTICS
RT	BIOGEOCHEMISTRY
RT	BIOGEOGRAPHY
RT	BIOPHYSICS
RT	BIOTECHNOLOGY
RT	ECOLOGY
RT	LIFE HISTORY
RT	PARASITOLOGY

BIOLUMINESCENCE
SN	Biological fluorescence and phosphorescence produced by photogenic or luminous organs or organisms
BT1	LUMINESCENCE
RT	ANIMAL PHYSIOLOGY
RT	BACTERIA
RT	BIOLOGICAL PHENOMENA
RT	BIOLOGICAL PROPERTIES
RT	CHEMILUMINESCENCE
RT	FLUORESCENCE
RT	LIGHT
RT	PHOSPHORESCENCE
RT	PHOTOPHORES
RT	SPECTRAL COMPOSITION

ASFIS Thesaurus

BIOMASS
UF	live weight
UF	population abundance (weight)
UF	population size (in weight)
UF	standing crop (in weight)
UF	standing stock (in weight)
BT1	POPULATION CHARACTERISTICS
RT	ABUNDANCE
RT	BIOLOGICAL PRODUCTION
RT	PLANKTON EQUIVALENTS
RT	POPULATION DENSITY
RT	POPULATION NUMBER
RT	QUANTITATIVE DISTRIBUTION
RT	STOCK ASSESSMENT
RT	YIELD

BIOMATHEMATICS
USE	**BIOMETRICS**

BIOMETEOROLOGY
USE	**BIOCLIMATOLOGY**

BIOMETRICS
UF	biomathematics
UF	biometry
UF	biostatistics
RT	BIOLOGICAL SAMPLING
RT	BODY REGIONS
RT	FISHERY BIOLOGY
RT	MATHEMATICS
RT	NUMERICAL TAXONOMY
RT	STATISTICAL ANALYSIS
RT	STATISTICS
RT	TAXONOMY

BIOMETRY
USE	**BIOMETRICS**

BIONOMICS
USE	**ECOLOGY**

BIOPHYSICS
BT1	PHYSICS
RT	BIOACOUSTICS
RT	BIOELECTRICITY
RT	BIOLOGY
RT	PHYSIOLOGY

BIOPLASM
USE	**CYTOPLASM**

BIOPOLYMORPHISM
SN	Before 1982 search POLYMORPHISM (BIOLOGICAL)
UF	balanced polymorphism
UF	biological polymorphism
UF	genetic polymorphism
UF	polymorphism (biological)
UF	transient polymorphism
NT1	CYCLOMORPHOSIS
RT	ORGANISM MORPHOLOGY
RT	POPULATION GENETICS
RT	SEROLOGICAL STUDIES
RT	SEXUAL DIMORPHISM

BIORHYTHMS
USE	**BIOLOGICAL RHYTHMS**

BIOSELECTION
SN	Added in 1980
UF	biological selection
UF	selection (biological)
NT1	GENETIC DRIFT
NT1	NATURAL SELECTION
NT1	SEXUAL SELECTION
RT	BIOLOGICAL SPECIATION
RT	EVOLUTION
RT	MUTATIONS
RT	PHYLOGENY

BIOSOCIOLOGY
USE	**SYNECOLOGY**

BIOSTATISTICS
USE	**BIOMETRICS**

BIOSTRATIGRAPHY
BT1	STRATIGRAPHY
BT2	GEOLOGY
BT3	EARTH SCIENCES
RT	BIOFACIES
RT	FOSSIL ASSEMBLAGES
RT	FOSSILS
RT	PALAEONTOLOGY
RT	STRATIGRAPHIC CORRELATION

BIOSYNTHESIS
BT1	BIOLOGICAL PHENOMENA
RT	BIOTECHNOLOGY
RT	CHEMOSYNTHESIS
RT	ENZYMATIC ACTIVITY
RT	PEARLS
RT	PHOTOSYNTHESIS

BIOTA
SN	Collective flora and fauna of a given region, a specific habitat or a biotope
RT	AQUATIC COMMUNITIES
RT	BIOCOENOSIS
RT	COMMUNITY COMPOSITION
RT	HABITAT

BIOTECHNOLOGY
SN	Engineering methods of achieving biosynthesis of animal and plant products, including genetic engineering. Before 1986 search also BIOENGINEERING
UF	bioengineering
UF	biological engineering
BT1	ENGINEERING
RT	BIOLOGY
RT	BIOSYNTHESIS
RT	BIOTELEMETRY
RT	FERMENTATION
RT	MEDICINE
RT	ULTRASTRUCTURE

BIOTELEMETRY
SN	Instrumentation and application of the technique of remote signaling by means of ultrasonic or radio signals from a transmitter on or in an animal. Before 1982 search TELEMETRY
UF	marine biotelemetry
UF	underwater biotelemetry
BT1	TELEMETRY
BT2	COMMUNICATION SYSTEMS
RT	BEHAVIOUR
RT	BIOACOUSTICS
RT	BIOTECHNOLOGY
RT	ECOLOGY
RT	MIGRATIONS
RT	ORIENTATION
RT	SONIC TAGS
RT	TAGGING
RT	TRACKING

BIOTESTING
SN	Bioassays for testing degree of toxicity. Added in 1982
BT1	BIOASSAYS
RT	CHEMICAL POLLUTANTS
RT	CHEMICAL POLLUTION
RT	LETHAL EFFECTS
RT	SUBLETHAL EFFECTS
RT	TOXICITY
RT	TOXICITY TESTS

BIOTIC BARRIERS
SN	Biotic limitations affecting the dispersal and/or survival of organisms. Added in 1980
UF	barriers (biological)
RT	BARRIERS
RT	BIOLOGICAL DRIFT
RT	BIOTIC FACTORS

BIOTIC DISEASES
USE	**INFECTIOUS DISEASES**

BIOTIC ENVIRONMENT
USE	**BIOTIC FACTORS**

BIOTIC FACTORS
SN	Before 1982 search ENVIRONMENTAL FACTORS
UF	biotic environment
UF	density-dependent factors
BT1	ENVIRONMENTAL FACTORS
RT	BIOTIC BARRIERS
RT	DENSITY DEPENDENCE
RT	FOOD AVAILABILITY
RT	GROUP EFFECTS
RT	INTERSPECIFIC RELATIONSHIPS
RT	STOCKING DENSITY

BIOTIC NATURAL RESOURCES
USE	**LIVING RESOURCES**

BIOTIC PRESSURE
SN	Activities of an enlarging population to maintain itself and spread
UF	population pressure
UF	pressure (populations)
RT	COMPETITION
RT	FOOD AVAILABILITY
RT	NATURAL MORTALITY
RT	POPULATION CONTROL
RT	POPULATION DENSITY
RT	PRESSURE

BIOTIN
USE	**VITAMIN B**

BIOTITE
BT1	MICAS
BT2	SILICATE MINERALS
BT3	MINERALS
RT	KIMBERLITES

BIOTOPES
BT1	HABITAT
RT	AQUATIC ENVIRONMENT
RT	BIOCOENOSIS
RT	ECOLOGICAL ASSOCIATIONS
RT	MICROHABITATS
RT	NICHES

BIOTOXINS
USE	**BIOLOGICAL POISONS**

BIOTURBATION
SN	Sediments disturbance by organisms
BT1	SEDIMENT MIXING
RT	BIOGENIC SEDIMENTARY STRUCTURES
RT	BIOLOGICAL RAFTING
RT	BURROWING ORGANISMS
RT	BURROWS
RT	DIAGENESIS
RT	MIXING PROCESSES
RT	SEDIMENTS
RT	TRACE FOSSILS

BIPOLAR DISTRIBUTION
SN	Used only as a qualifier
UF	bipolarity
BT1	HORIZONTAL DISTRIBUTION
BT2	GEOGRAPHICAL DISTRIBUTION
BT3	DISTRIBUTION
RT	CETOLOGY
RT	COSMOPOLITE SPECIES

BIPOLARITY
USE	**BIPOLAR DISTRIBUTION**

BIRD EGGS
SN	Added in 1980
BT1	EGGS
BT2	SEXUAL CELLS
BT3	CELLS
RT	ALBUMINS
RT	CLUTCH
RT	HATCHING
RT	NESTING
RT	NESTS

BIRD FLIGHT BEHAVIOUR
USE	**FLIGHT BEHAVIOUR**

BIRD FLYING
USE	**FLYING**

BIRD NAVIGATION
USE	**ANIMAL NAVIGATION**

BIRD PHYSIOLOGY
USE	**AVIAN PHYSIOLOGY**

BIRDS (AQUATIC)
USE	**AQUATIC BIRDS**

BIRDS (MARINE)
USE	**MARINE BIRDS**

BIRNESSITE
BT1	OXIDE MINERALS
BT2	MINERALS

BIRTH
USE	**PARTURITION**

BISEXUALITY
USE	**HERMAPHRODITISM**

BISMUTH
BT1	CHEMICAL ELEMENTS
RT	BISMUTH COMPOUNDS
RT	BISMUTH ISOTOPES
RT	HEAVY METALS
RT	METALS

BISMUTH COMPOUNDS
RT	BISMUTH
RT	CHEMICAL COMPOUNDS

BISMUTH ISOTOPES
BT1	ISOTOPES
RT	BISMUTH

BITUMENS
UF	pitch (mineral)
BT1	PETROLEUM HYDROCARBONS
BT2	HYDROCARBONS
BT3	ORGANIC COMPOUNDS
RT	OIL SANDS
RT	PETROLEUM RESIDUES

BLADDERS
SN	Any membrane sac containing gas or fluid
BT1	ANIMAL ORGANS
BT2	BODY ORGANS
NT1	GALL BLADDER

BLADDERS (cont'd)
NT1	SWIM BLADDER
RT	EXCRETORY ORGANS

BLASTING
SN	Controlled use of explosives
RT	DETONATORS
RT	EXPLOSIONS
RT	EXPLOSIVES

BLASTOSPORES
USE	**SPORES**

BLIND SPOT
USE	**RETINAS**

BLOCK FILLETS
USE	**FISH FILLETS**

BLOOD
UF	blood liquids
UF	plasma (blood)
BT1	BODY FLUIDS
RT	ALBUMINS
RT	ANOXIA
RT	BLOOD CELLS
RT	BLOOD GROUPS
RT	CIRCULATORY SYSTEM
RT	COAGULATION
RT	CONNECTIVE TISSUES
RT	ELECTROPHORESIS
RT	HAEMATOLOGY
RT	HAEMOCYANINS
RT	HYPERCAPNIA
RT	LIPOPROTEINS
RT	MYOGLOBINS
RT	SEROLOGICAL STUDIES

BLOOD CELLS
UF	haematoblasts
BT1	CELLS
NT1	ERYTHROCYTES
NT1	LEUKOCYTES
NT1	LYMPHOCYTES
NT1	MACROPHAGES
RT	AGGLUTININS
RT	ANTIGENS
RT	BLOOD
RT	BLOOD VESSELS
RT	CHOLESTEROL
RT	CIRCULATORY SYSTEM
RT	ELECTROPHORESIS
RT	HAEMOGLOBINS
RT	HAEMOPOIESIS

BLOOD CHEMISTRY
USE	**HAEMATOLOGY**

BLOOD CIRCULATION
UF	blood flow
UF	circulation (blood)
RT	BLOOD PRESSURE
RT	BLOOD VESSELS
RT	CIRCULATION
RT	CIRCULATORY SYSTEM
RT	HEART

BLOOD DISEASES
USE	**HAEMATOLOGICAL DISEASES**

BLOOD FLOW
USE	**BLOOD CIRCULATION**

BLOOD GROUPS
SN	Types of blood classified on the basis of the different antigens present. Added in 1980
UF	blood types
RT	ANTIGENS
RT	BLOOD

BLOOD GROUPS (cont'd)
RT	HAEMATOLOGY

BLOOD LIQUIDS
USE	**BLOOD**

BLOOD PRESSURE
BT1	PRESSURE
BT2	PHYSICAL PROPERTIES
BT3	PROPERTIES
RT	BLOOD CIRCULATION
RT	CIRCULATORY SYSTEM

BLOOD TYPES
USE	**BLOOD GROUPS**

BLOOD VESSELS
UF	arteries
UF	veins
UF	venules
BT1	CIRCULATORY SYSTEM
RT	BLOOD CELLS
RT	BLOOD CIRCULATION
RT	CONNECTIVE TISSUES
RT	HAEMORRHAGE
RT	HEART

BLOOMS
USE	**ALGAL BLOOMS**

BLOWOUT CONTROL
BT1	CONTROL
RT	BLOWOUTS

BLOWOUT PREVENTERS
RT	BLOWOUTS
RT	WELLHEADS

BLOWOUTS
SN	Pertains to oil and gas well blowouts
RT	ACCIDENTS
RT	BLOWOUT CONTROL
RT	BLOWOUT PREVENTERS
RT	FIRE
RT	FIRE HAZARDS

BLUE WHALE UNIT
UF	bwu
RT	QUOTA REGULATIONS
RT	WHALING
RT	WHALING REGULATIONS
RT	WHALING STATISTICS

BLUEPRINTS
USE	**ENGINEERING DRAWINGS**

BOAT DREDGES
USE	**DREDGES**

BOAT SEINES
UF	danish seines
UF	pair seines
UF	scottish seines
BT1	SEINE NETS
BT2	FISHING NETS
BT3	FISHING GEAR
RT	BEACH SEINES
RT	SEINERS
RT	SEINING

BOATING
SN	Added in 1980
UF	canoeing
UF	sailing
RT	RECREATION

BOATS
UF	rafts
BT1	SURFACE CRAFT
BT2	VEHICLES
RT	ARTISANAL FISHING
RT	CANOES
RT	CATAMARANS
RT	COASTAL FISHERIES
RT	DREDGES
RT	FISHING VESSELS
RT	INLAND FISHERIES
RT	LIFT-NETS
RT	PROPULSION SYSTEMS
RT	RESEARCH VESSELS
RT	SPEEDOMETERS
RT	TRANSPORTATION

BOD
USE	**BIOCHEMICAL OXYGEN DEMAND**

BODY BURDEN
SN	Added in 1980
RT	BIOLOGICAL HALF LIFE
RT	POLLUTANTS
RT	RADIOACTIVE CONTAMINATION
RT	RADIOACTIVITY
RT	RADIONUCLIDE KINETICS

BODY CAVITIES
SN	Before 1982 search BODY CAVITY
NT1	COELOM
NT1	MANTLE CAVITY
RT	BODY WALLS
RT	HAEMOLYMPH

BODY CONDITIONS
SN	Added in 1980
UF	fat content
RT	ARTIFICIAL FEEDING
RT	BODY WEIGHT
RT	CONDITION FACTOR
RT	FEED COMPOSITION
RT	NUTRITION
RT	NUTRITIONAL REQUIREMENTS

BODY DEFORMATIONS
USE	**ABNORMALITIES**

BODY FLUIDS
UF	body liquids
NT1	BILE
NT1	BLOOD
NT1	COELOMIC FLUIDS
NT1	HAEMOLYMPH
NT1	LYMPH
NT1	SERUM
NT2	ANTIBODIES
NT3	AGGLUTININS
RT	AMOEBOCYTES
RT	ANATOMICAL STRUCTURES
RT	CIRCULATORY SYSTEM
RT	COLLOIDS
RT	ELECTROPHORESIS
RT	FLUIDS
RT	HAEMATOLOGY
RT	MUCUS
RT	SEROLOGICAL STUDIES
RT	URINE

BODY LIQUIDS
USE	**BODY FLUIDS**

BODY ORGANS
SN	A part of an organism that forms a structural and functional unit. Added in 1980
UF	organs (body)
NT1	ANIMAL ORGANS
NT2	ALIMENTARY ORGANS
NT3	DIGESTIVE TRACT

BODY ORGANS (cont'd)
NT3	INTESTINES
NT3	LOPHOPHORES
NT3	PYLORIC CAECA
NT3	STOMACH
NT4	MASTICATORY STOMACH
NT2	BLADDERS
NT3	GALL BLADDER
NT3	SWIM BLADDER
NT2	EXCRETORY ORGANS
NT3	KIDNEYS
NT3	SPLEEN
NT2	PHOTOPHORES
NT2	RESPIRATORY ORGANS
NT3	GILLS
NT3	LARYNX
NT3	LUNGS
NT3	TRACHEA
NT2	SENSE ORGANS
NT3	AUDITORY ORGANS
NT3	BALANCE ORGANS
NT4	STATOCYSTS
NT3	CHEMORECEPTORS
NT3	LATERAL LINE
NT3	MECHANORECEPTORS
NT3	OLFACTORY ORGANS
NT3	PHOTORECEPTORS
NT4	EYES
NT3	TACTILE ORGANS
NT3	TASTE ORGANS
NT2	VOCAL ORGANS
NT1	ATTACHMENT ORGANS
NT1	PLANT ORGANS
NT2	HOLDFASTS
NT2	LEAVES
NT2	PLANT REPRODUCTIVE STRUCTURES
NT3	TURIONS
NT2	RHIZOMES
NT2	ROOTS
NT2	STEMS
NT2	THALLUS
RT	ANATOMY
RT	ORGAN REMOVAL
RT	ORGANOGENESIS
RT	PHYSIOLOGY
RT	REGENERATION
RT	TRANSPLANTS

BODY REGIONS
SN	Added in 1980
UF	animal body regions
BT1	ANATOMICAL STRUCTURES
NT1	ABDOMEN
NT1	CEPHALOTHORAX
NT1	HEAD
NT1	THORAX
RT	ANIMAL MORPHOLOGY
RT	ANIMAL ORGANS
RT	BIOMETRICS
RT	BODY SHAPE
RT	BODY SIZE
RT	BODY TEMPERATURE

BODY SHAPE
SN	Added in 1980
RT	BODY REGIONS
RT	BODY SIZE
RT	LENGTH-WEIGHT RELATIONSHIPS

BODY SIZE
RT	ANIMAL MORPHOLOGY
RT	BODY REGIONS
RT	BODY SHAPE
RT	BODY WEIGHT
RT	LENGTH-WEIGHT RELATIONSHIPS

BODY TEMPERATURE
BT1	TEMPERATURE
BT2	THERMODYNAMIC PROPERTIES
BT3	PHYSICAL PROPERTIES
BT4	PROPERTIES
RT	AESTIVATION
RT	BODY REGIONS
RT	HEAT BALANCE
RT	HIBERNATION
RT	HOMOIOTHERMY
RT	HYPERTHERMIA
RT	HYPOTHERMIA
RT	METABOLISM
RT	POIKILOTHERMY
RT	THERMAL STIMULI
RT	THERMOREGULATION

BODY WALLS
NT1	MANTLE
RT	BODY CAVITIES
RT	SKIN

BODY WAVES
SN	Use of a more specific term is recommended
BT1	SEISMIC WAVES
BT2	ELASTIC WAVES
NT1	P-WAVES
NT1	S-WAVES

BODY WEIGHT
RT	BODY CONDITIONS
RT	BODY SIZE
RT	LENGTH-WEIGHT RELATIONSHIPS

BOEHMITE
BT1	OXIDE MINERALS
BT2	MINERALS

BOGS
USE	**MARSHES**

BOIL DISEASE
SN	Before 1982 search PARASITIC DISEASES
UF	bubonic disease
UF	fish furuncolosis
UF	furuncolosis
UF	red boil disease
BT1	FISH DISEASES
BT2	ANIMAL DISEASES
BT3	DISEASES
RT	BACTERIAL DISEASES
RT	MUSCLES
RT	PARASITIC DISEASES

BOILING POINT
BT1	TRANSITION TEMPERATURES
BT2	TEMPERATURE
BT3	THERMODYNAMIC PROPERTIES
BT4	PHYSICAL PROPERTIES
RT	COLLIGATIVE PROPERTIES
RT	PHASE CHANGES

BOLUSES
BT1	WATER MASS INTRUSIONS
RT	CASCADING
RT	OVERFLOW

BONDING
USE	**ADHESION**

BONE NECROSIS
UF	osteonecrosis
RT	DIVING PHYSIOLOGY
RT	UNDERWATER MEDICINE

BONES
BT1	ENDOSKELETON
BT2	SKELETON
BT3	MUSCULOSKELETAL SYSTEM
NT1	SKULL
NT1	VERTEBRAE
RT	ANATOMY
RT	CALCIFICATION
RT	CARTILAGE
RT	CONNECTIVE TISSUES
RT	DECALCIFICATION
RT	OSTEOLOGY
RT	OTOLITHS

BONITO FISHERIES
USE	**TUNA FISHERIES**

BONY FINS
UF	bony rays
BT1	FINS
BT2	LOCOMOTORY APPENDAGES
BT3	ANIMAL APPENDAGES
RT	EXOSKELETON
RT	MERISTIC COUNTS

BONY RAYS
USE	**BONY FINS**

BOOK CATALOGUES
SN	Use only for listings of books, periodicals, etc. issued by publishers and antiquarian dealers
BT1	CATALOGUES
BT2	DOCUMENTS

BOOMERANG CORERS
USE	**FREE-FALL CORERS**

BOOMERS
BT1	SEISMIC ENERGY SOURCES

BOOMS
USE	**FLOATING BARRIERS**

BOOSTER STATIONS
USE	**PUMP STATIONS**

BORA
USE	**LOCAL WINDS**

BORATE MINERALS
UF	borates
BT1	MINERALS
NT1	BORAX
RT	BORON
RT	EVAPORITES

BORATES
USE	**BORATE MINERALS**

BORAX
BT1	BORATE MINERALS
BT2	MINERALS

BORDERLAND
USE	**CONTINENTAL BORDERLAND**

BOREHOLES
UF	drill holes
RT	CORES
RT	DRILLING
RT	HEAT FLOW
RT	HOLE RE-ENTRY
RT	WELL LOGGING

BORERS
USE	**BORING ORGANISMS**

BORES
USE	**TIDAL BORES**

BORES IN ESTUARIES
USE	**TIDAL BORES**

BORIC ACID
SN	Before 1982 search INORGANIC ACIDS
BT1	INORGANIC ACIDS
BT2	HYDROGEN COMPOUNDS
RT	BORON
RT	BORON COMPOUNDS

BORING
USE	**DRILLING**

BORING ORGANISMS
UF	borers
BT1	AQUATIC ORGANISMS
RT	AQUATIC INSECTS
RT	BIOEROSION
RT	BIOLOGICAL DAMAGE
RT	FOULING ORGANISMS

BORON
BT1	CHEMICAL ELEMENTS
RT	BORATE MINERALS
RT	BORIC ACID
RT	BORON COMPOUNDS
RT	BORON ISOTOPES
RT	DISSOLVED CHEMICALS
RT	TRACE ELEMENTS

BORON COMPOUNDS
RT	BORIC ACID
RT	BORON
RT	CHEMICAL COMPOUNDS
RT	ORGANIC COMPOUNDS

BORON ISOTOPES
BT1	ISOTOPES
RT	BORON

BOTANICAL RESOURCES
SN	Added in 1980
UF	algae resources
UF	aquatic botanical resources
UF	aquatic plant resources
UF	seagrass resources
UF	seaweed resources
BT1	LIVING RESOURCES
BT2	NATURAL RESOURCES
BT3	RESOURCES
RT	AQUATIC DRUGS
RT	AQUATIC PLANTS
RT	HARVESTING
RT	SEA GRASS
RT	SEAWEED PRODUCTS
RT	SEAWEED STATISTICS
RT	SEAWEEDS

BOTANISTS
SN	Added in 1980
BT1	BIOLOGISTS
BT2	SCIENTIFIC PERSONNEL
BT3	PERSONNEL
RT	BOTANY
RT	DIRECTORIES
RT	PLANT CULTURE
RT	PLANT PHYSIOLOGISTS
RT	TAXONOMISTS

BOTANY
UF	phytology
BT1	BIOLOGY
NT1	ALGOLOGY
RT	AQUATIC PLANTS
RT	BIOGEOGRAPHY
RT	BOTANISTS
RT	ECOLOGY

BOTANY (cont'd)
RT	GERMINATION
RT	PALAEONTOLOGY
RT	PALYNOLOGY
RT	PHYTOPLANKTON
RT	PHYTOSOCIOLOGY
RT	PLANT PHYSIOLOGY
RT	SPECIES
RT	TAXONOMY

BOTTLE POST
USE	**DRIFT BOTTLES**

BOTTOM BOUNDARY LAYER
USE	**BENTHIC BOUNDARY LAYER**

BOTTOM CAGES
USE	**SUBMERGED CAGES**

BOTTOM CRAWLERS
USE	**SEABED VEHICLES**

BOTTOM CULTURE
UF	seabed farming
BT1	AQUACULTURE TECHNIQUES
RT	CULTURES
RT	MOLLUSC CULTURE
RT	OYSTER CULTURE
RT	PREDATOR CONTROL
RT	SEED COLLECTION
RT	SHELLFISH CULTURE
RT	SUBSTRATA

BOTTOM CURRENTS
SN	Before 1982 search DEEP CURRENTS
UF	near-bottom currents
BT1	WATER CURRENTS
BT2	WATER MOTION
NT1	ABYSSAL CURRENTS
NT1	BENTHIC CURRENTS
RT	BOTTOM EROSION
RT	CURRENT SCOURING
RT	DEEP CURRENTS
RT	DENSITY FLOW
RT	LAKE CURRENTS
RT	OCEAN CURRENTS
RT	SCOURING
RT	SEABED DRIFTERS
RT	SEAMOATS
RT	SEDIMENT DRIFTS
RT	SEDIMENT TRANSPORT
RT	SHELF SEAS
RT	SUBMARINE CANYONS
RT	SUBSURFACE CURRENTS
RT	TURBIDITY CURRENTS

BOTTOM EKMAN LAYER
BT1	EKMAN LAYERS
BT2	BOUNDARY LAYERS
BT3	LAYERS
RT	BENTHIC BOUNDARY LAYER
RT	BENTHIC CURRENTS

BOTTOM EROSION
UF	deep-sea erosion
UF	submarine erosion
UF	underwater erosion
BT1	EROSION
RT	BOTTOM CURRENTS
RT	CONTOUR CURRENTS
RT	CURRENT SCOURING
RT	DEEP-SEA FURROWS
RT	EROSION
RT	EROSION FEATURES
RT	HALMYROLYSIS
RT	HIATUSES
RT	MICROTOPOGRAPHY
RT	SEACHANNELS
RT	SEAMOATS
RT	WAVE SCOURING

BOTTOM FEATURES
USE **SUBMARINE FEATURES**

BOTTOM FRICTION
UF bed friction
BT1 FRICTION
BT2 FORCES (MECHANICS)
RT BED ROUGHNESS
RT BOTTOM STRESS
RT DRAG
RT ENERGY DISSIPATION
RT FORM DRAG
RT RIVER BEDS
RT TIDAL FRICTION
RT WAVE DISSIPATION

BOTTOM LOAD
USE **BED LOAD**

BOTTOM MIXED LAYER
BT1 MIXED LAYER
BT2 WATER COLUMN
BT3 LAYERS
RT BENTHIC BOUNDARY LAYER
RT BOTTOM WATER
RT DEEP LAYER
RT WATER COLUMN

BOTTOM PHOTOGRAPHS
SN Photographs of the seabed
BT1 UNDERWATER PHOTOGRAPHS
BT2 PHOTOGRAPHS
BT3 AUDIOVISUAL MATERIAL
BT4 DOCUMENTS
RT GEOLOGICAL SURVEYS
RT SITE SURVEYS
RT UNDERWATER PHOTOGRAPHY

BOTTOM PRESSURE
BT1 HYDROSTATIC PRESSURE
BT2 PRESSURE
BT3 PHYSICAL PROPERTIES
BT4 PROPERTIES
RT HURRICANES
RT WAVE-SEABED INTERACTION

BOTTOM REVERBERATION
BT1 REVERBERATION
BT2 UNDERWATER NOISE
BT3 NOISE (SOUND)
RT BOTTOM SCATTERING

BOTTOM ROUGHNESS
USE **BED ROUGHNESS**

BOTTOM SAMPLING
USE **SEAFLOOR SAMPLING**

BOTTOM SCATTERING
BT1 SOUND SCATTERING
RT BOTTOM REVERBERATION

BOTTOM STRESS
UF bed shear stress
UF bed stress
BT1 STRESS
BT2 FORCES (MECHANICS)
RT BOTTOM FRICTION
RT DRAG
RT PARTICLE MOTION
RT REYNOLDS STRESSES
RT SEDIMENT DYNAMICS
RT SEDIMENT TRANSPORT
RT SHEAR STRESS
RT VISCOSITY

BOTTOM TEMPERATURE
BT1 WATER TEMPERATURE
BT2 TEMPERATURE
BT3 THERMODYNAMIC PROPERTIES
BT4 PHYSICAL PROPERTIES
RT POTENTIAL TEMPERATURE

BOTTOM TOPOGRAPHY
SN The general configuration of the ocean floor
UF ocean bottom topography
UF ocean floor topography
UF sea floor topography
UF underwater topography
BT1 TOPOGRAPHY (GEOLOGY)
BT2 TOPOGRAPHY
NT1 PALAEOTOPOGRAPHY
RT ATLASES
RT BATHYMETRIC CHARTS
RT BATHYMETRY
RT BOTTOM TOPOGRAPHY EFFECTS
RT ECHOSOUNDING
RT ISOBATHS
RT MORPHOMETRY
RT OCEAN BASINS
RT OCEAN FLOOR
RT PHYSIOGRAPHIC PROVINCES
RT SEDIMENT DISTRIBUTION
RT SUBMARINE FEATURES
RT TOPOGRAPHIC FEATURES
RT WATER DEPTH

BOTTOM TOPOGRAPHY EFFECTS
SN Influence of bottom topography on general ocean circulation, currents and waves
BT1 TOPOGRAPHIC EFFECTS
RT ABYSSAL CIRCULATION
RT BOTTOM TOPOGRAPHY
RT OCEAN CIRCULATION
RT WATER CURRENTS
RT WAVE REFRACTION

BOTTOM TOW
BT1 PIPELINE CONSTRUCTION
BT2 CONSTRUCTION
RT OCEAN FLOOR
RT TOWING

BOTTOM TRAPPED WAVES
USE **TRAPPED WAVES**

BOTTOM TRAWLING
SN Added in 1982
UF dredging (catching methods)
BT1 TRAWLING
BT2 CATCHING METHODS
RT BOTTOM TRAWLS
RT DEMERSAL FISHERIES

BOTTOM TRAWLS
UF beam trawls (bottom)
UF dragging nets
UF otter trawls (bottom)
UF pair trawls (bottom)
BT1 TRAWL NETS
BT2 FISHING NETS
BT3 FISHING GEAR
RT BOTTOM TRAWLING
RT DEMERSAL FISHERIES
RT TRAWLING

BOTTOM WATER
SN The water in the bottom layer of the sea, lakes, reservoirs or other water bodies. For deep water masses such as Antarctic Bottom Water, use DEEP-WATER MASSES
BT1 WATER
RT BOTTOM MIXED LAYER

BOTTOM WATER (cont'd)
RT DEEP-WATER MASSES
RT LAKES
RT RESERVOIRS (WATER)
RT SURFACE WATER

BOTTOM WATER MASSES
USE **DEEP-WATER MASSES**

BOTTOMSET BEDS
BT1 DELTAIC FEATURES
RT DELTAIC DEPOSITS
RT DELTAIC SEDIMENTATION
RT TOPSET BEDS

BOTULISM
SN Bacterial food-born intoxication. Added in 1980
UF botulism hazard
BT1 HUMAN DISEASES
BT2 DISEASES
RT BACTERIAL DISEASES
RT FOOD FISH
RT FOOD POISONING
RT HUMAN FOOD
RT HYGIENE
RT MICROBIAL CONTAMINATION
RT NEUROTOXINS
RT SHELLFISH

BOTULISM HAZARD
USE **BOTULISM**

BOUDINAGE
BT1 SEDIMENTARY STRUCTURES
RT DEFORMATION
RT MELANGES

BOUGUER ANOMALIES
BT1 GRAVITY ANOMALIES
BT2 ANOMALIES
RT BOUGUER GRAVITY CHARTS

BOUGUER CORRECTION
USE **GRAVITY CORRECTIONS**

BOUGUER GRAVITY CHARTS
BT1 GRAVITY CHARTS
BT2 GEOLOGICAL MAPS
BT3 MAPS
BT4 GRAPHICS
RT BOUGUER ANOMALIES

BOULDER CLAY
UF till
BT1 GLACIAL DEPOSITS
RT CLASTICS
RT RUDITES

BOULDERS
BT1 CLASTICS
BT2 SEDIMENTS
RT COBBLESTONE
RT GLACIAL ERRATICS
RT RUDITES

BOUNDARIES
SN Added in 1980
UF boundary line
UF territorial boundaries
NT1 FISHERY BOUNDARIES
NT1 INTERNATIONAL BOUNDARIES
RT CONTIGUOUS ZONES
RT DISPUTES
RT FISHERY DISPUTES
RT INTERFACES
RT LAW OF THE SEA
RT OCEAN SPACE
RT PLATE BOUNDARIES
RT SURFACES

BOUNDARIES (cont'd)
RT	TERRITORIAL WATERS
RT	WATER RIGHTS

BOUNDARY CONDITIONS
SN	Used only as a qualifier
RT	MATHEMATICAL MODELS

BOUNDARY CURRENTS
BT1	WATER CURRENTS
BT2	WATER MOTION
NT1	EASTERN BOUNDARY CURRENTS
NT1	WESTERN BOUNDARY CURRENTS
RT	OCEAN CIRCULATION
RT	OCEAN CURRENTS
RT	WIND-DRIVEN CURRENTS

BOUNDARY LAYERS
BT1	LAYERS
NT1	ATMOSPHERIC BOUNDARY LAYER
NT1	BENTHIC BOUNDARY LAYER
NT1	COASTAL BOUNDARY LAYER
NT1	EKMAN LAYERS
NT2	BOTTOM EKMAN LAYER
NT2	SURFACE EKMAN LAYER
NT1	LAMINAR BOUNDARY LAYER
NT1	OCEANIC BOUNDARY LAYER
NT1	TURBULENT BOUNDARY LAYER
RT	HEAT TRANSFER
RT	HYDRODYNAMICS
RT	INTERFACES

BOUNDARY LINE
USE	**BOUNDARIES**

BOUNDARY VALUE PROBLEMS
UF	initial-value problems
RT	FINITE ELEMENT METHOD
RT	NUMERICAL ANALYSIS

BOUSSINESQ APPROXIMATION
BT1	APPROXIMATION
BT2	NUMERICAL ANALYSIS
BT3	MATHEMATICAL ANALYSIS

BOWEN RATIO
RT	AIR-WATER EXCHANGES
RT	EVAPORATION
RT	HEAT BUDGET
RT	LATENT HEAT TRANSFER
RT	RATIOS
RT	SENSIBLE HEAT TRANSFER
RT	VAPOUR PRESSURE

BOXES
USE	**CONTAINERS**

BRACKISH WATER
BT1	WATER
RT	BRACKISHWATER AQUACULTURE
RT	BRACKISHWATER ENVIRONMENT
RT	BRACKISHWATER POLLUTION
RT	ESTUARIES
RT	LAGOONS
RT	WATER PROPERTIES

BRACKISHWATER AQUACULTURE
SN	Referring to culture of fish and other aquatic organisms in coastal lagoons, deltas, estuaries and mangrove swamps
UF	brackishwater culture
UF	estuarine aquaculture
BT1	AQUACULTURE
RT	ALGAL CULTURE
RT	AQUACULTURE TECHNIQUES
RT	BAIT CULTURE
RT	BRACKISH WATER
RT	BRACKISHWATER ECOLOGY
RT	BRACKISHWATER FISH

BRACKISHWATER AQUACULTURE (cont'd)
RT	BRACKISHWATER MOLLUSCS
RT	CAGE CULTURE
RT	COASTAL LAGOONS
RT	CRUSTACEAN CULTURE
RT	ESTUARINE ORGANISMS
RT	EXTENSIVE CULTURE
RT	FISH CULTURE
RT	FISH PONDS
RT	HATCHERIES
RT	MANGROVE SWAMPS
RT	MOLLUSC CULTURE
RT	MONOSEX CULTURE
RT	OYSTER CULTURE
RT	PEARL CULTURE
RT	POLYCULTURE
RT	SEAWEED CULTURE
RT	SHELLFISH CULTURE
RT	SHRIMP CULTURE
RT	VALLICULTURE

BRACKISHWATER CRAB CULTURE
USE	**CRAB CULTURE**

BRACKISHWATER CULTURE
USE	**BRACKISHWATER AQUACULTURE**

BRACKISHWATER ECOLOGY
SN	Added in 1980
BT1	ECOLOGY
RT	AQUATIC COMMUNITIES
RT	BRACKISHWATER AQUACULTURE
RT	BRACKISHWATER ENVIRONMENT
RT	BRACKISHWATER FISH
RT	BRACKISHWATER POLLUTION
RT	COASTAL LAGOONS
RT	ESTUARIES
RT	ESTUARINE ORGANISMS
RT	MANGROVE SWAMPS

BRACKISHWATER ENVIRONMENT
UF	estuarine environment
BT1	AQUATIC ENVIRONMENT
BT2	ENVIRONMENTS
RT	BRACKISH WATER
RT	BRACKISHWATER ECOLOGY
RT	BRACKISHWATER FISH
RT	COASTAL LAGOONS
RT	DELTAS
RT	ESTUARIES
RT	ESTUARINE SEDIMENTATION
RT	EUTROPHIC WATERS
RT	INLAND WATER ENVIRONMENT
RT	LAGOONAL SEDIMENTATION
RT	LAGOONS
RT	MANGROVE SWAMPS
RT	MARINE ENVIRONMENT
RT	OCEANOGRAPHY
RT	RIVER DISCHARGE

BRACKISHWATER FISH
UF	estuarine fish
BT1	FISH
BT2	AQUATIC ANIMALS
RT	ANADROMOUS MIGRATIONS
RT	BRACKISHWATER AQUACULTURE
RT	BRACKISHWATER ECOLOGY
RT	BRACKISHWATER ENVIRONMENT
RT	CATADROMOUS MIGRATIONS
RT	COMMERCIAL SPECIES
RT	ESTUARINE FISHERIES
RT	ESTUARINE ORGANISMS
RT	FISHERY RESOURCES
RT	LAGOON FISHERIES

BRACKISHWATER MOLLUSCS
SN	Added in 1980
UF	estuarine molluscs
UF	molluscs (brackishwater)
UF	mollusks (brackishwater)

BRACKISHWATER MOLLUSCS (cont'd)
BT1	AQUATIC ANIMALS
RT	BRACKISHWATER AQUACULTURE
RT	COMMERCIAL SPECIES
RT	ESTUARINE ORGANISMS
RT	MOLLUSC CULTURE
RT	OYSTER CULTURE
RT	PEARLS
RT	SHELLS

BRACKISHWATER ORGANISMS
USE	**ESTUARINE ORGANISMS**

BRACKISHWATER POLLUTION
UF	estuarine pollution
UF	pollution (brackishwater)
BT1	WATER POLLUTION
BT2	POLLUTION
RT	BRACKISH WATER
RT	BRACKISHWATER ECOLOGY
RT	CHEMICAL POLLUTION
RT	OIL POLLUTION
RT	POLLUTANTS
RT	POLLUTION EFFECTS
RT	POLLUTION MONITORING
RT	RADIOACTIVE CONTAMINATION
RT	THERMAL POLLUTION
RT	WASTES
RT	WATER POLLUTION TREATMENT

BRAIN
BT1	CENTRAL NERVOUS SYSTEM
BT2	NERVOUS SYSTEM
NT1	HYPOTHALAMUS
NT1	PINEAL ORGAN
RT	GANGLIA
RT	HEAD
RT	NERVES
RT	SKULL

BRANCHED CHAIN SATURATED HYDROCARBONS
USE	**ACYCLIC HYDROCARBONS**

BREADTH
USE	**WIDTH**

BREAK-POINT BARS
BT1	NEARSHORE BARS
BT2	BEACH FEATURES
RT	BEACH PROFILES
RT	BREAKING WAVES
RT	DEPOSITION FEATURES
RT	LONGSHORE BARS

BREAKER ZONE
USE	**SURF ZONE**

BREAKERS
BT1	BREAKING WAVES
BT2	SURFACE WATER WAVES
BT3	WATER WAVES
RT	ROLLERS
RT	UNDERTOW

BREAKING WAVES
BT1	SURFACE WATER WAVES
BT2	WATER WAVES
NT1	BREAKERS
NT1	SPILLING WAVES
NT1	SURF
NT1	WHITECAPS
RT	AERATION
RT	BREAK-POINT BARS
RT	SHOALING WAVES
RT	SURF ZONE
RT	WAVE BREAKING
RT	WAVE CRESTS
RT	WAVE DISSIPATION
RT	WAVES ON BEACHES

ASFIS Thesaurus

BREAKWATERS
BT1	COAST DEFENCES
BT2	COASTAL STRUCTURES
BT3	HYDRAULIC STRUCTURES
NT1	RIPRAP
NT1	RUBBLEMOUND BREAKWATERS
RT	ARTIFICIAL HARBOURS
RT	BARRIERS
RT	BUBBLE BARRIERS
RT	COASTAL EROSION
RT	FLOATING BARRIERS
RT	HARBOURS
RT	ICE BARRIERS
RT	OVERTOPPING
RT	SEA WALLS
RT	WAVE DAMPING
RT	WAVE RUNUP

BREATHING APPARATUS
BT1	LIFE SUPPORT SYSTEMS
RT	BREATHING MIXTURES
RT	DIVING EQUIPMENT
RT	FIRE FIGHTING
RT	SAFETY DEVICES
RT	SCUBA DIVING

BREATHING MIXTURES
BT1	GASES
BT2	FLUIDS
RT	BREATHING APPARATUS
RT	DEEP-SEA DIVING
RT	DIVING EQUIPMENT
RT	DIVING PHYSIOLOGY
RT	LIFE SUPPORT SYSTEMS
RT	SATURATION DIVING
RT	SCUBA DIVING
RT	SPEECH DISTORTION

BRECCIA
BT1	CLASTICS
BT2	SEDIMENTS
RT	CONGLOMERATES
RT	RUDITES
RT	SEDIMENTARY ROCKS
RT	VOLCANIC BRECCIA

BREEDING
UF	natural breeding
NT1	INBREEDING
NT1	INDUCED BREEDING
NT1	SELECTIVE BREEDING
RT	AQUACULTURE
RT	BIOLOGICAL SPECIATION
RT	BREEDING PONDS
RT	BREEDING SEASONS
RT	BREEDING SITES
RT	GENETICS
RT	HYBRIDIZATION
RT	NESTING
RT	PHENOLOGY
RT	PHOTOPERIODICITY
RT	REPRODUCTIVE BEHAVIOUR
RT	REPRODUCTIVE CYCLE
RT	SEXUAL CELLS
RT	SEXUAL MATURITY
RT	SEXUAL REPRODUCTION
RT	SPAWNING

BREEDING CYCLE
USE	**REPRODUCTIVE CYCLE**

BREEDING GROUNDS
USE	**BREEDING SITES**

BREEDING PONDS
BT1	FISH PONDS
BT2	PONDS
BT3	INLAND WATERS
RT	AQUACULTURE FACILITIES
RT	BREEDING

BREEDING PONDS (cont'd)
RT	FRY
RT	SELECTIVE BREEDING

BREEDING SEASONS
SN	Before 1982 use SPAWNING SEASONS
RT	BREEDING
RT	NESTING
RT	SEXUAL ISOLATION

BREEDING SITES
UF	breeding grounds
RT	BREEDING
RT	NESTING
RT	NESTS
RT	SEXUAL REPRODUCTION

BREEDING STOCKS
USE	**BROOD STOCKS**

BREEZES
BT1	LOCAL WINDS
BT2	WINDS
BT3	ATMOSPHERIC MOTION
NT1	LAND AND SEA BREEZES
NT1	LAND BREEZES
NT1	SEA BREEZES
RT	BEAUFORT SCALE
RT	WIND SPEED

BRIDGES
UF	rail bridges
UF	road bridges
RT	INSTRUMENT PLATFORMS
RT	PONTOONS
RT	SCOURING
RT	TRANSPORTATION
RT	TUNNELS

BRIGHT SPOT TECHNOLOGY
BT1	SEISMIC DATA PROCESSING
BT2	DATA PROCESSING
RT	SEISMIC PROFILES

BRIGHTNESS TEMPERATURE
USE	**SURFACE RADIATION TEMPERATURE**

BRIGHTNESS TEMPERATURE (SEA SURFACE)
USE	**SURFACE RADIATION TEMPERATURE**

BRINE
USE	**BRINES**

BRINE SHRIMP CULTURE
SN	Added in 1982
UF	artemia culture
BT1	CRUSTACEAN CULTURE
BT2	SHELLFISH CULTURE
BT3	AQUACULTURE
RT	ARTIFICIAL FEEDING
RT	CULTURE TANKS
RT	FOOD ORGANISMS
RT	LABORATORY CULTURE
RT	MASS CULTURE
RT	ZOOPLANKTON CULTURE

BRINE SHRIMP EGGS
BT1	EGGS
BT2	SEXUAL CELLS
BT3	CELLS
RT	ARTIFICIAL FEEDING
RT	REARING

BRINES
UF	brine
BT1	DISSOLVED SALTS
BT2	SALTS
RT	CHLORINE COMPOUNDS
RT	EVAPORATION
RT	FLUORINE COMPOUNDS

BRINES (cont'd)
RT	HOT BRINES
RT	MINERAL INDUSTRY
RT	SALINE WATER
RT	SEA ICE
RT	SOLUTIONS

BRITTLENESS
BT1	MECHANICAL PROPERTIES
BT2	PHYSICAL PROPERTIES
BT3	PROPERTIES
RT	DETERIORATION
RT	EMBRITTLEMENT

BROCHURES
BT1	DOCUMENTS
RT	EXHIBITIONS
RT	MUSEUMS
RT	PUBLICITY MATERIAL
RT	RESEARCH INSTITUTIONS

BROMIC ACID
BT1	INORGANIC ACIDS
BT2	HYDROGEN COMPOUNDS
RT	BROMINE COMPOUNDS

BROMIDES
BT1	BROMINE COMPOUNDS
BT2	HALOGEN COMPOUNDS
RT	HALIDES

BROMINATED HYDROCARBONS
BT1	HALOGENATED HYDROCARBONS
BT2	HYDROCARBONS
BT3	ORGANIC COMPOUNDS

BROMINE
BT1	CHEMICAL ELEMENTS
RT	BROMINE COMPOUNDS
RT	BROMINE ISOTOPES
RT	CHLORINE
RT	DISSOLVED CHEMICALS
RT	FLUORINE
RT	HALOGENS
RT	IODINE
RT	TRACE ELEMENTS

BROMINE COMPOUNDS
BT1	HALOGEN COMPOUNDS
NT1	BROMIDES
RT	BROMIC ACID
RT	BROMINE
RT	CHEMICAL COMPOUNDS

BROMINE ISOTOPES
BT1	ISOTOPES
RT	BROMINE

BROOD STOCKS
SN	A population of specimens selected for reproduction purposes. Added in 1980
UF	breeding stocks
UF	parent stocks
BT1	STOCKS
RT	AQUACULTURE
RT	FECUNDITY
RT	GENETICS
RT	HYBRIDIZATION
RT	INBREEDING
RT	INDUCED BREEDING
RT	INTENSIVE CULTURE
RT	SELECTIVE BREEDING
RT	SEXUAL REPRODUCTION

BRUCITE
BT1	OXIDE MINERALS
BT2	MINERALS

BRUNT-VAISALA FREQUENCY
UF	buoyancy frequency
UF	stability frequency
BT1	FREQUENCY
RT	VERTICAL STABILITY

BTU
USE	**CALORIMETRY**

BUBBLE BARRIERS
UF	bubble breakwaters
BT1	BARRIERS
RT	BREAKWATERS
RT	CONTAINMENT

BUBBLE BREAKWATERS
USE	**BUBBLE BARRIERS**

BUBBLE BURSTING
RT	AEROSOLS
RT	AIR BUBBLES
RT	AIR-WATER EXCHANGES
RT	BUBBLES
RT	DROPLETS
RT	ELECTRIC CHARGE
RT	SALT NUCLEI
RT	SALT PARTICLES
RT	SURFACE CHEMISTRY

BUBBLE DISEASE
SN	Added in 1980
UF	gas bubble disease
UF	gas embolism
BT1	FISH DISEASES
BT2	ANIMAL DISEASES
BT3	DISEASES
RT	ARTIFICIAL AERATION
RT	DISSOLVED GASES
RT	ENVIRONMENTAL DISEASES
RT	EXOPHTHALMIA
RT	HUSBANDRY DISEASES

BUBBLES
NT1	AIR BUBBLES
RT	AERATION
RT	BUBBLE BURSTING
RT	BUBBLING
RT	CAVITATION
RT	DEBUBBLING

BUBBLING
RT	AERATION
RT	BUBBLES
RT	DEBUBBLING

BUBONIC DISEASE
USE	**BOIL DISEASE**

BUCKET TEMPERATURE
BT1	SURFACE TEMPERATURE
BT2	WATER TEMPERATURE
BT3	TEMPERATURE
BT4	THERMODYNAMIC PROPERTIES
RT	TEMPERATURE MEASUREMENT

BUCKLING
USE	**DEFORMATION**

BUCKLING (PIPE)
USE	**PIPE BUCKLING**

BUDDING
BT1	ASEXUAL REPRODUCTION
BT2	REPRODUCTION
RT	BUDS
RT	GEMMULES
RT	POLYPS
RT	SPORES
RT	VEGETATIVE REPRODUCTION

BUDS
SN	Added in 1980
RT	BUDDING
RT	PLANT MORPHOLOGY
RT	PLANT ORGANS
RT	POLYPS

BUFFER CAPACITY
USE	**BUFFERS**

BUFFER SOLUTION
USE	**BUFFERS**

BUFFERING
USE	**BUFFERS**

BUFFERS
SN	Buffers occurring in natural water or used in laboratory work
UF	buffer capacity
UF	buffer solution
UF	buffering
RT	ACIDITY
RT	ALKALINITY
RT	CHEMICAL REACTIONS
RT	PH
RT	SOLUTIONS

BULK CARRIERS
UF	ore carriers
BT1	MERCHANT SHIPS
BT2	SHIPS
BT3	SURFACE CRAFT
BT4	VEHICLES

BULK MODULUS
BT1	ELASTIC CONSTANTS
RT	COMPRESSIBILITY
RT	DEFORMATION
RT	ELASTICITY
RT	MECHANICAL PROPERTIES
RT	SHEAR MODULUS

BUOY DYNAMICS
USE	**BUOY MOTION**

BUOY HULL SHAPES
USE	**BUOY HULLS**

BUOY HULLS
UF	buoy hull shapes
BT1	HULLS
NT1	DISCUS-SHAPED BUOYS
NT1	SPAR BUOYS
NT2	LARGE SPAR BUOYS
RT	BUOYS

BUOY MOORING SYSTEMS
BT1	MOORING SYSTEMS
RT	BUOY MOTION
RT	BUOY SYSTEMS
RT	BUOYS
RT	MOORING BUOYS
RT	MOORING LINES
RT	MOORING MOTION EFFECTS
RT	MOORING RECOVERY

BUOY MOTION
UF	buoy dynamics
RT	BUOY MOORING SYSTEMS
RT	BUOY MOTION EFFECTS
RT	CABLE DYNAMICS
RT	HEAVING
RT	MOORING MOTION EFFECTS
RT	MOTION
RT	NEAR-SURFACE LAYER
RT	PITCHING
RT	ROLLING
RT	SURGING
RT	SWAYING

BUOY MOTION (cont'd)
RT	WAVE EFFECTS
RT	YAWING

BUOY MOTION EFFECTS
SN	Effect of buoy motion on instruments and on instrument readings
BT1	MOTION EFFECTS
RT	BUOY MOTION
RT	BUOYS
RT	ERRORS
RT	HEAVE RESONANCE
RT	HEAVE RESPONSE
RT	HEAVING
RT	MOORING MOTION EFFECTS
RT	PITCH RESONANCE
RT	PITCH RESPONSE
RT	PITCHING
RT	ROLL RESONANCE
RT	ROLL RESPONSE
RT	ROLLING
RT	SURGE RESPONSE
RT	SURGING
RT	YAW RESPONSE
RT	YAWING

BUOY SYSTEMS
BT1	VEHICLES
RT	ARRAYS
RT	BUOY MOORING SYSTEMS
RT	BUOYS
RT	FLOATING STRUCTURES
RT	INSTRUMENT PLATFORMS

BUOYANCY
SN	Includes mechanisms in organisms for buoyancy
BT1	PHYSICAL PROPERTIES
BT2	PROPERTIES
RT	BALLAST
RT	BUOYANCY FLOATS
RT	BUOYANCY FLUX
RT	BUOYANCY MATERIALS
RT	BUOYS
RT	DENSITY
RT	FLOTATION
RT	HYDROSTATIC BEHAVIOUR
RT	STABILITY
RT	SWIM BLADDER
RT	WATER DENSITY

BUOYANCY FLOATS
UF	buoyancy spheres
UF	floats (buoyancy)
UF	subsurface buoyancy floats
RT	BALLAST
RT	BUOYANCY
RT	BUOYS
RT	IMPLOSIONS

BUOYANCY FLUX
SN	The buoyant or submerged weight of the fluid passing through a cross section in unit time
RT	BUOYANCY
RT	BUOYANT JETS

BUOYANCY FREQUENCY
USE	**BRUNT-VAISALA FREQUENCY**

BUOYANCY MATERIALS
BT1	MATERIALS
RT	BUOYANCY

BUOYANCY SPHERES
USE	**BUOYANCY FLOATS**

ASFIS Thesaurus

BUOYANT JETS
BT1	JETS
BT2	FLUID FLOW
BT3	FLUID MOTION
RT	BUOYANCY FLUX
RT	DENSITY STRATIFICATION
RT	OUTFALLS
RT	PLUMES
RT	RIVER PLUMES
RT	TURBULENT ENTRAINMENT
RT	WATER MIXING

BUOYS
SN	Use of a more specific term is recommended
NT1	DATA BUOYS
NT2	DRIFTING DATA BUOYS
NT2	WAVE BUOYS
NT1	FISHING BUOYS
NT1	MARKER BUOYS
NT1	MOORING BUOYS
NT2	LOADING BUOYS
NT1	NAVIGATIONAL BUOYS
NT1	RADIO BUOYS
NT1	SONOBUOYS
RT	ANCHORING
RT	BUOY HULLS
RT	BUOY MOORING SYSTEMS
RT	BUOY MOTION EFFECTS
RT	BUOY SYSTEMS
RT	BUOYANCY
RT	BUOYANCY FLOATS
RT	DROGUES
RT	MOORING LINES

BURIAL
USE	**BURYING**

BURROWING ORGANISMS
UF	benthic infauna
UF	endofauna
BT1	AQUATIC ORGANISMS
RT	BENTHOS
RT	BIOTURBATION
RT	BURROWS
RT	DAMS
RT	PROTECTIVE BEHAVIOUR

BURROWS
RT	BIOTURBATION
RT	BURROWING ORGANISMS
RT	TRACE FOSSILS

BURYING
UF	burial
RT	ANCHORING
RT	OCEAN FLOOR
RT	PIPELINE CONSTRUCTION
RT	PIPELINE PROTECTION
RT	PIPELINES
RT	TRENCHING

BUSINESS MANAGEMENT
USE	**FINANCIAL MANAGEMENT**

BUTANE
BT1	ACYCLIC HYDROCARBONS
BT2	SATURATED HYDROCARBONS
BT3	HYDROCARBONS
BT4	ORGANIC COMPOUNDS

BWU
USE	**BLUE WHALE UNIT**

BY-CATCH
USE	**BY CATCH**

BY CATCH
SN	The catch taken incidentally during the capture of a species of specific interest to fishermen. Before 1986 search also BY-CATCH
UF	additional catch
UF	by-catch
RT	BYPRODUCTS
RT	CATCH COMPOSITION
RT	CATCH/EFFORT
RT	COMMERCIAL FISHING
RT	FISH CATCH STATISTICS
RT	FISHERY PRODUCTS
RT	SHELLFISH CATCH STATISTICS

BY PRODUCTS
USE	**BYPRODUCTS**

BYPRODUCTS
SN	Added in 1980
UF	by products
BT1	PRODUCTS
RT	BY CATCH
RT	FISH OILS
RT	INDUSTRIAL PRODUCTS
RT	POLLUTANTS
RT	POWDERED PRODUCTS
RT	PROCESSED FISHERY PRODUCTS
RT	STICKWATER
RT	WASTES

BYSSUS
SN	In Mollusca Lamellibranchiata, a tuft of filaments secreted by a gland in the foot and used for attachment. Added in 1980
UF	byssus threads
BT1	ANIMAL APPENDAGES
RT	SECRETION
RT	SUBSTRATA

BYSSUS THREADS
USE	**BYSSUS**

C/N RATIO
USE	**CARBON/NITROGEN RATIO**

CABALING
USE	**CABBELING**

CABBELING
SN	Mixing of two water masses with identical insitu densities but different insitu temperatures and salinities, so that the resulting mixture is denser than its components. Before 1984 search also CABELLING
UF	cabaling
UF	cabelling
BT1	VERTICAL WATER MOVEMENT
BT2	WATER MOTION
RT	MIXING PROCESSES
RT	SALINITY
RT	WATER DENSITY
RT	WATER MASSES
RT	WATER MIXING
RT	WATER TEMPERATURE

CABELLING
USE	**CABBELING**

CABLE BREAKS
USE	**SUBMARINE CABLE BREAKS**

CABLE DEPRESSORS
BT1	DEPRESSORS
RT	OCEANOGRAPHIC EQUIPMENT
RT	TOWED SENSORS
RT	TOWING LINES

CABLE DYNAMICS
BT1	DYNAMICS
BT2	MECHANICS
BT3	PHYSICS
RT	BUOY MOTION
RT	CABLES
RT	CATENARY
RT	MOORING LINES
RT	RISER CABLES
RT	TOWING LINES
RT	WIRE ROPE

CABLE LAYING
RT	CABLE SHIPS
RT	SUBMARINE CABLES

CABLE SHIPS
BT1	SHIPS
BT2	SURFACE CRAFT
BT3	VEHICLES
RT	CABLE LAYING
RT	SUBMARINE CABLES
RT	WORK PLATFORMS

CABLES
NT1	ELECTRIC CABLES
NT2	COAXIAL CABLES
NT2	POWER CABLES
NT2	SUBMARINE CABLES
NT1	GUIDE LINES
NT1	MOORING LINES
NT1	RISER CABLES
NT1	STREAMERS
NT1	TOWING LINES
NT1	UMBILICALS
RT	CABLE DYNAMICS
RT	CATENARY
RT	CHAIN
RT	FAIRINGS
RT	ROPES
RT	TETHERED VEHICLES
RT	TOWED BODY DESIGN
RT	WIRE ROPE

CADMIUM
BT1	CHEMICAL ELEMENTS
RT	CADMIUM COMPOUNDS
RT	CADMIUM ISOTOPES
RT	HEAVY METALS
RT	METALS

CADMIUM COMPOUNDS
RT	ALKALI METAL COMPOUNDS
RT	CADMIUM
RT	CHEMICAL COMPOUNDS

CADMIUM ISOTOPES
BT1	ISOTOPES
RT	CADMIUM

CAENOZOIC
USE	**CENOZOIC**

CAESIUM
UF	cesium
BT1	CHEMICAL ELEMENTS
RT	ALKALI METALS
RT	CAESIUM COMPOUNDS
RT	CAESIUM ISOTOPES

CAESIUM COMPOUNDS
RT	ALKALI METAL COMPOUNDS
RT	CAESIUM
RT	CHEMICAL COMPOUNDS

CAESIUM ISOTOPES
BT1	ISOTOPES
NT1	CAESIUM 137
RT	CAESIUM

CAESIUM 137
BT1	CAESIUM ISOTOPES
BT2	ISOTOPES

CAGE CONSTRUCTION
USE	**GEAR CONSTRUCTION**

CAGE CULTURE
SN	Culture of shellfish species and fish in fixed or floating cages
UF	basket culture
UF	net culture
UF	pen culture
BT1	AQUACULTURE TECHNIQUES
RT	BRACKISHWATER AQUACULTURE
RT	CAGES
RT	CRUSTACEAN CULTURE
RT	FISH CULTURE
RT	FRESHWATER AQUACULTURE
RT	INTENSIVE CULTURE
RT	LOBSTER CULTURE
RT	MARINE AQUACULTURE
RT	MONOCULTURE
RT	OVERWINTERING TECHNIQUES
RT	RAFT CULTURE
RT	SITE SELECTION
RT	STOCKING DENSITY
RT	THERMAL AQUACULTURE

CAGES
SN	Added in 1980
BT1	AQUACULTURE EQUIPMENT
BT2	EQUIPMENT
NT1	FLOATING CAGES
NT1	SUBMERGED CAGES
RT	CAGE CULTURE
RT	DESIGN
RT	GEAR MATERIALS

CAISSONS
BT1	OFFSHORE STRUCTURES
BT2	HYDRAULIC STRUCTURES
RT	SUBMERSIBLE PLATFORMS
RT	UNDERWATER HABITATS
RT	WORKING UNDERWATER

CALCARENITE
BT1	CARBONATE ROCKS
RT	BIOCALCARENITE
RT	LIMESTONE
RT	SEDIMENTARY ROCKS

CALCAREOUS DEPOSITS
USE	**CARBONATE SEDIMENTS**

CALCAREOUS OOZE
UF	ooze (calcareous)
BT1	OOZES
NT1	FORAMINIFERAL OOZE
NT2	GLOBIGERINA OOZE
NT1	PTEROPOD OOZE
RT	CALCIUM CARBONATES
RT	CARBONATE SEDIMENTS
RT	COCCOLITHS
RT	NANNOFOSSIL OOZE

CALCIFEROL
USE	**VITAMIN D**

CALCIFICATION
SN	The formation of calcium salt deposits in a tissue. Added in 1980
UF	physiological calcification
BT1	BIOCHEMICAL PHENOMENA
RT	BONES

CALCIFICATION (cont'd)
RT	DECALCIFICATION
RT	DIAGENESIS
RT	FOSSILS
RT	SHELLS
RT	TISSUES
RT	VITAMIN D

CALCITE
BT1	CARBONATE MINERALS
BT2	MINERALS
RT	CALCITE DISSOLUTION
RT	CALCITIZATION
RT	CALCIUM CARBONATES
RT	LIMESTONE

CALCITE COMPENSATION DEPTH
USE	**CARBONATE COMPENSATION DEPTH**

CALCITE DISSOLUTION
BT1	DISSOLUTION
BT2	SEPARATION PROCESSES
RT	CALCITE
RT	CARBONATE COMPENSATION DEPTH

CALCITIZATION
BT1	DIAGENESIS
BT2	SEDIMENTATION
RT	CALCITE
RT	DOLOMITIZATION

CALCIUM
BT1	CHEMICAL ELEMENTS
RT	ALKALINE EARTH METALS
RT	CALCIUM COMPOUNDS
RT	CALCIUM ISOTOPES
RT	DISSOLVED CHEMICALS
RT	WATER HARDNESS

CALCIUM CARBONATES
BT1	CALCIUM COMPOUNDS
BT2	ALKALINE EARTH METAL COMPOUNDS
RT	ARAGONITE
RT	CALCAREOUS OOZE
RT	CALCITE
RT	CARBONATES
RT	DOLOMITIZATION

CALCIUM COMPOUNDS
SN	Use of a specific compound is recommended
BT1	ALKALINE EARTH METAL COMPOUNDS
NT1	CALCIUM CARBONATES
NT1	CALCIUM PHOSPHATES
NT1	CALCIUM SULPHATES
RT	CALCIUM
RT	CHEMICAL COMPOUNDS
RT	CORAL
RT	WATER HARDNESS

CALCIUM ISOTOPES
BT1	ISOTOPES
RT	CALCIUM

CALCIUM PHOSPHATES
BT1	CALCIUM COMPOUNDS
BT2	ALKALINE EARTH METAL COMPOUNDS
RT	PHOSPHATES

CALCIUM SULPHATES
BT1	CALCIUM COMPOUNDS
BT2	ALKALINE EARTH METAL COMPOUNDS
RT	SULPHATES

CALCRETE
BT1	CARBONATE ROCKS
RT	CONGLOMERATES

CALCULATORS
BT1	ELECTRONIC EQUIPMENT
BT2	EQUIPMENT

CALIBRATION
SN	Methods for calibrating accuracy or reliability of equipment
BT1	STANDARDIZATION
NT1	INTERCALIBRATION
RT	ACCURACY
RT	EFFICIENCY
RT	EQUIPMENT
RT	INTERCOMPARISON
RT	MEASURING DEVICES
RT	OCEANOGRAPHIC EQUIPMENT
RT	TEST EQUIPMENT
RT	TESTING
RT	TESTS
RT	WAVE TANKS

CALIFORNIUM
BT1	CHEMICAL ELEMENTS
RT	ACTINIDES
RT	CALIFORNIUM COMPOUNDS
RT	CALIFORNIUM ISOTOPES
RT	TRANSITION ELEMENTS
RT	TRANSURANIC ELEMENTS

CALIFORNIUM COMPOUNDS
BT1	ACTINIDE COMPOUNDS
RT	CALIFORNIUM
RT	CHEMICAL COMPOUNDS

CALIFORNIUM ISOTOPES
BT1	ISOTOPES
RT	CALIFORNIUM

CALORIES
SN	Before 1982 search NUTRITIVE VALUE
UF	calories (nutrition)
RT	CALORIMETRY
RT	FOOD CONSUMPTION
RT	NUTRITIVE VALUE

CALORIES (NUTRITION)
USE	**CALORIES**

CALORIMETRY
SN	Added in 1980
UF	btu
UF	heat measurement
RT	CALORIES
RT	ENERGY BUDGET
RT	NUTRITIVE VALUE

CALVED ICE
USE	**ICEBERGS**

CALVING
SN	Formation of icebergs
RT	ABLATION
RT	ICE SHELVES
RT	ICEBERGS
RT	WAVE GENERATION

CAMBRIAN
SN	Before 1982 search also CAMBRIAN PERIOD
BT1	PALAEOZOIC
BT2	GEOLOGICAL TIME

CAMERAS
BT1	PHOTOGRAPHIC EQUIPMENT
BT2	EQUIPMENT
NT1	UNDERWATER CAMERAS
RT	OPTICAL FILTERS
RT	PHOTOGRAPHY
RT	REMOTE SENSING EQUIPMENT
RT	SATELLITE PHOTOGRAPHY
RT	TELEVISION SYSTEMS

CAMOUFLAGE
SN	Added in 1980
BT1	ADAPTATIONS
BT2	BIOLOGICAL PHENOMENA
RT	DEFENCE MECHANISMS
RT	MIMICRY
RT	PREDATION
RT	PROTECTIVE BEHAVIOUR

CANALS
SN	Restricted to artificial water courses through a land area used for navigation, irrigation, etc.
UF	irrigation canals
BT1	INLAND WATERS
NT1	INTEROCEAN CANALS
NT1	SHIP CANALS
RT	CHANNELS
RT	DREDGING
RT	HYDRAULIC MODELS
RT	INLETS (WATERWAYS)
RT	IRRIGATION
RT	NAVIGATION

CANGRONID FISHERIES
USE	**SHRIMP FISHERIES**

CANNED PRODUCTS
SN	Fishery products preserved in cans by sterilization process
BT1	PROCESSED FISHERY PRODUCTS
BT2	FISHERY PRODUCTS
BT3	PRODUCTS
RT	CANNING

CANNIBALISM
BT1	FEEDING BEHAVIOUR
BT2	BEHAVIOUR
RT	CARNIVORES
RT	CRUSTACEAN CULTURE
RT	PREDATORS

CANNING
SN	Preservation of fishery products in cans by sterilization process
BT1	PROCESSING FISHERY PRODUCTS
BT2	FISHERY INDUSTRY
BT3	INDUSTRIES
RT	CANNED PRODUCTS

CANOE FISHERIES
BT1	FISHERIES
RT	ARTISANAL FISHING
RT	CANOES

CANOEING
USE	**BOATING**

CANOES
BT1	SURFACE CRAFT
BT2	VEHICLES
RT	ARTISANAL FISHING
RT	BOATS
RT	CANOE FISHERIES

CANS
USE	**CONTAINERS**

CAP ROCKS
RT	DIAPIRS
RT	OIL RESERVOIRS
RT	SALT DOMES

CAPACITANCE
BT1	ELECTRICAL PROPERTIES
BT2	PHYSICAL PROPERTIES
BT3	PROPERTIES
RT	DIELECTRIC CONSTANT
RT	ELECTRIC CHARGE
RT	ELECTRIC IMPEDANCE

CAPACITANCE WIRE WAVE RECORDERS
USE	**WAVE RECORDERS**

CAPACITY
SN	Used only as a qualifier
BT1	DIMENSIONS

CAPACITY (STORAGE)
USE	**STORAGE**

CAPACITY (VOLUME)
USE	**VOLUME**

CAPE ROCK LOBSTER FISHERIES
USE	**LOBSTER FISHERIES**

CAPELIN FISHERIES
USE	**GADOID FISHERIES**

CAPILLARITY
SN	Physical capillary action associated with surface tension
UF	capillary action
UF	capillary phenomena
RT	AIR BUBBLES
RT	CAPILLARY WAVES
RT	DROPLETS
RT	ELECTRICAL PROPERTIES
RT	FOAMS
RT	PERMEABILITY
RT	POROSITY
RT	SURFACE FILMS
RT	SURFACE PROPERTIES
RT	SURFACE TENSION
RT	VISCOSITY

CAPILLARY ACTION
USE	**CAPILLARITY**

CAPILLARY PHENOMENA
USE	**CAPILLARITY**

CAPILLARY WAVES
UF	surface tension waves
BT1	SURFACE WATER WAVES
BT2	WATER WAVES
NT1	WATER RIPPLES
RT	CAPILLARITY
RT	GRAVITY WAVES
RT	NONLINEAR WAVES
RT	SURFACE TENSION
RT	WAVE GAUGES

CAPITAL INVESTMENTS
USE	**INVESTMENTS**

CAPITAL RESOURCES
USE	**FINANCIAL RESOURCES**

CAPSIZING
BT1	SHIP MOTION
RT	ACCIDENTS
RT	EMERGENCIES
RT	FLOATING
RT	FLOATING STRUCTURES
RT	INSTABILITY
RT	RIGHTING
RT	SHIP LOSSES
RT	SHIP STABILITY
RT	SURFACE CRAFT
RT	WAVE EFFECTS

CAPTIVITY
RT	ACCLIMATION
RT	ACCLIMATIZATION
RT	AQUARIA
RT	AQUARIOLOGY
RT	DOMESTICATION
RT	ORNAMENTAL FISH

CAPTURE FISHERIES
USE	**FISHERIES**

CAPTURE FISHERY ECONOMICS
SN	Economics of exploiting wild stocks. Before 1982 search FISHERY ECONOMICS
BT1	FISHERY ECONOMICS
BT2	ECONOMICS
RT	COOPERATIVES
RT	COST ANALYSIS
RT	ECONOMIC FEASIBILITY
RT	ECONOMIC MODELS
RT	EXCLUSIVE ECONOMIC ZONE
RT	FINANCING
RT	FISHERY DEVELOPMENT
RT	FISHERY MANAGEMENT
RT	FISHERY STATISTICS
RT	MARKETING
RT	PRICING
RT	TRADE

CARANGID FISHERIES
SN	Added in 1982
UF	horse mackerel fisheries
UF	jack fisheries
UF	scad fisheries
UF	yellow tail fisheries
BT1	FISHERIES
RT	MARINE FISHERIES
RT	PELAGIC FISHERIES
RT	PERCOID FISHERIES

CARAPACE
SN	An exoskeletal shield covering part or all of the dorsal surface of an animal. Added in 1980
BT1	EXOSKELETON
BT2	SKELETON
BT3	MUSCULOSKELETAL SYSTEM
RT	CEPHALOTHORAX
RT	CHITIN

CARBOHYDRATES
BT1	ORGANIC COMPOUNDS
NT1	GLYCOGEN
NT1	GLYCOSIDES
NT2	PIGMENTS
NT3	CHROMATIC PIGMENTS
NT4	CAROTENOIDS
NT3	PHOTOSYNTHETIC PIGMENTS
NT4	CHLOROPHYLLS
NT4	XANTHOPHYLLS
NT3	RESPIRATORY PIGMENTS
NT4	HAEMOCYANINS
NT4	HAEMOGLOBINS
NT3	VISUAL PIGMENTS
NT2	PORPHYRINS
NT2	SAPONINS
NT1	SACCHARIDES
NT2	MONOSACCHARIDES
NT3	ARABINOSE
NT3	FUCOSE
NT3	GLUCOSE
NT3	MANNOSE
NT3	RIBOSE
NT3	XYLOSE
NT2	POLYSACCHARIDES
NT3	AGAROSE
NT3	ALGINIC ACID
NT3	CELLULOSE
NT3	MUCOPOLYSACCHARIDES
NT4	CHITIN
NT4	HEPARIN
NT3	STARCH
RT	AGAR
RT	ALCOHOLS
RT	BIOCHEMISTRY
RT	CARBON FIXATION

CARBOHYDRATES (cont'd)
RT   CHEMICAL COMPOUNDS
RT   NUTRITIVE VALUE
RT   ORGANIC CONSTITUENTS

CARBON
BT1   CHEMICAL ELEMENTS
NT1   ORGANIC CARBON
NT2   DISSOLVED ORGANIC CARBON
NT2   PARTICULATE ORGANIC CARBON
NT2   TOTAL ORGANIC CARBON
RT   CARBON COMPOUNDS
RT   CARBON CYCLE
RT   CARBON DIOXIDE
RT   CARBON ISOTOPES
RT   CARBON 13
RT   CARBON 14
RT   DIAMONDS
RT   HYDROCARBONS

CARBON ASSIMILATION
    USE   **CARBON FIXATION**

CARBON COMPOUNDS
NT1   BICARBONATES
NT1   CARBON DIOXIDE
NT1   CARBON MONOXIDE
NT1   CARBON SULPHIDES
NT1   CARBONATES
RT   CARBON
RT   CHEMICAL COMPOUNDS
RT   HYDROCARBONS
RT   ORGANIC COMPOUNDS

CARBON CYCLE
BT1   NUTRIENT CYCLES
BT2   BIOGEOCHEMICAL CYCLE
BT3   CYCLES
RT   BIOCHEMISTRY
RT   CARBON
RT   CARBON DIOXIDE
RT   CHEMICAL CYCLES
RT   GEOCHEMICAL CYCLE
RT   TRANSPIRATION

CARBON DIOXIDE
BT1   CARBON COMPOUNDS
RT   ATMOSPHERIC CHEMISTRY
RT   CARBON
RT   CARBON CYCLE
RT   CARBON FIXATION
RT   CHEMICAL COMPOUNDS
RT   CLIMATIC CHANGES
RT   FOSSIL FUELS
RT   GASES
RT   GREENHOUSE EFFECT
RT   HYPERCAPNIA
RT   OXYGEN CONSUMPTION
RT   PHOTOSYNTHESIS
RT   RESPIROMETERS

CARBON DIOXIDE FIXATION
    USE   **CARBON FIXATION**

CARBON DIOXIDE POISONING
    USE   **HYPERCAPNIA**

CARBON FIXATION
SN   Before 1982 search PHOTOSYNTHESIS
UF   carbon assimilation
UF   carbon dioxide fixation
BT1   PHOTOSYNTHESIS
BT2   PHOTOCHEMICAL REACTIONS
BT3   CHEMICAL REACTIONS
RT   CARBOHYDRATES
RT   CARBON DIOXIDE

CARBON ISOTOPE RATIO
RT   CARBON ISOTOPES
RT   GEOCHRONOMETRY

CARBON ISOTOPES
BT1   ISOTOPES
NT1   CARBON 13
NT1   CARBON 14
RT   CARBON
RT   CARBON ISOTOPE RATIO

CARBON MONOXIDE
BT1   CARBON COMPOUNDS
RT   DIVING HAZARDS

CARBON/NITROGEN RATIO
UF   c/n ratio
RT   DISSOLVED ORGANIC CARBON
RT   DISSOLVED ORGANIC NITROGEN
RT .   RATIOS
RT   WATER MASSES

CARBON/PHOSPHORUS RATIO
RT   DISSOLVED ORGANIC CARBON
RT   DISSOLVED ORGANIC PHOSPHORUS
RT   RATIOS

CARBON SULPHIDES
BT1   CARBON COMPOUNDS

CARBON 13
BT1   CARBON ISOTOPES
BT2   ISOTOPES
RT   ABSOLUTE AGE
RT   CARBON
RT   RADIOACTIVE TRACERS
RT   RADIOCARBON DATING
RT   RADIOISOTOPES
RT   RADIOMETRIC DATING

CARBON 14
BT1   CARBON ISOTOPES
BT2   ISOTOPES
RT   ABSOLUTE AGE
RT   CARBON
RT   PRIMARY PRODUCTION
RT   RADIOACTIVE TRACERS
RT   RADIOCARBON DATING
RT   RADIOISOTOPES
RT   RADIOMETRIC DATING

CARBONACEOUS DEPOSITS
    USE   **ORGANIC SEDIMENTS**

CARBONATE BIOGENIC DEPOSITS
    USE   **CARBONATE SEDIMENTS**

CARBONATE COMPENSATION DEPTH
UF   calcite compensation depth
UF   compensation depth (carbonate)
UF   compensation depth (oceans)
BT1   COMPENSATION DEPTH
RT   AEROBIC RESPIRATION
RT   CALCITE DISSOLUTION
RT   DISCONTINUITY LAYERS
RT   DISPHOTIC ZONE
RT   LIGHT PENETRATION
RT   LYSOCLINE

CARBONATE MINERALS
BT1   MINERALS
NT1   ARAGONITE
NT1   CALCITE
NT1   DOLOMITE
NT1   HYDROMAGNESITE
NT1   MAGNESITE
NT1   SIDERITE

CARBONATE ROCKS
NT1   BEACHROCK
NT1   BIOCALCARENITE
NT1   CALCARENITE
NT1   CALCRETE
NT1   CHALK
NT1   DOLOSTONE
NT1   LIMESTONE
RT   CARBONATE SEDIMENTS
RT   CORAL REEFS
RT   SEDIMENTARY ROCKS

CARBONATE SEDIMENTS
UF   calcareous deposits
UF   carbonate biogenic deposits
RT   CALCAREOUS OOZE
RT   CARBONATE ROCKS
RT   CHEMICAL SEDIMENTS
RT   COCCOLITHS
RT   PELAGIC SEDIMENTS
RT   SEDIMENTS

CARBONATES
BT1   CARBON COMPOUNDS
RT   CALCIUM CARBONATES
RT   CARBONIC ACID
RT   CHEMICAL COMPOUNDS
RT   SALTS
RT   WATER HARDNESS

CARBONIC ACID
RT   CARBONATES

CARBONIC ANHYDRASE
BT1   ENZYMES

CARBONIFEROUS
SN   Before 1982 search CARBONIFEROUS
         PERIOD
BT1   PALAEOZOIC
BT2   GEOLOGICAL TIME

CARBOXYLATION
BT1   CHEMICAL REACTIONS
RT   DECARBOXYLATION

CARBOXYLIC ACID SALTS
NT1   ACETATE
NT1   CITRATES

CARBOXYLIC ACIDS
    USE   **ORGANIC ACIDS**

CARCASES
    USE   **CARCASSES**

CARCASSES
SN   Added in 1982
UF   carcases
UF   dead bodies
RT   AQUATIC MAMMALS
RT   STRANDING

CARCINOGENESIS
SN   The production and development of
         cancer. Added in 1980
RT   CARCINOGENS
RT   CHEMICAL POLLUTANTS
RT   CHEMICAL POLLUTION
RT   POLLUTION EFFECTS
RT   RADIOACTIVE POLLUTANTS
RT   TUMOURS

CARCINOGENS
RT   CARCINOGENESIS
RT   CHEMICAL POLLUTANTS
RT   CHEMICAL POLLUTION
RT   DISEASES
RT   RADIOACTIVE POLLUTANTS
RT   TUMOURS

CARCINOLOGISTS
SN	Added in 1980
BT1	ZOOLOGISTS
BT2	BIOLOGISTS
BT3	SCIENTIFIC PERSONNEL
BT4	PERSONNEL
RT	CARCINOLOGY
RT	DIRECTORIES
RT	FISHERY BIOLOGISTS
RT	TAXONOMISTS

CARCINOLOGY
BT1	INVERTEBRATE ZOOLOGY
BT2	ZOOLOGY
BT3	BIOLOGY
RT	CARCINOLOGISTS
RT	FRESHWATER CRUSTACEANS
RT	HYDROBIOLOGY
RT	MARINE CRUSTACEANS

CARCINOMA
USE	**TUMOURS**

CAREERS
RT	EDUCATION
RT	PERSONNEL

CARGO SHIPS
USE	**MERCHANT SHIPS**

CARGOES
RT	AIR TEMPERATURE
RT	HAZARDOUS MATERIALS
RT	HUMIDITY
RT	MARINE TRANSPORTATION
RT	MERCHANT SHIPS
RT	STORAGE CONDITIONS

CARIDEAN SHRIMP FISHERIES
USE	**SHRIMP FISHERIES**

CARNALLITE
BT1	HALIDE MINERALS
BT2	MINERALS

CARNIVORES
BT1	HETEROTROPHIC ORGANISMS
BT2	AQUATIC ORGANISMS
RT	CANNIBALISM
RT	FEEDING BEHAVIOUR
RT	FORAGE FISH
RT	OMNIVORES
RT	PLANKTON FEEDERS
RT	PREDATORS
RT	SECONDARY PRODUCTION
RT	TROPHIC LEVELS

CAROTENES
USE	**VITAMIN A**

CAROTENOIDS
BT1	CHROMATIC PIGMENTS
BT2	PIGMENTS
BT3	GLYCOSIDES
BT4	CARBOHYDRATES
RT	DERIVED LIPIDS
RT	PHOTOSYNTHESIS
RT	PHOTOSYNTHETIC PIGMENTS

CARRAGEENINS
BT1	SEAWEED PRODUCTS
BT2	PROCESSED FISHERY PRODUCTS
BT3	FISHERY PRODUCTS
BT4	PRODUCTS
RT	AGAR
RT	ALGINATES
RT	CHEMICAL EXTRACTION

CARTESIAN COORDINATES
USE	**COORDINATE SYSTEMS**

CARTILAGE
SN	A form of connective tissue of vertebrates. Before 1982 search TISSUES
BT1	CONNECTIVE TISSUES
BT2	TISSUES
RT	BONES
RT	HISTOLOGY
RT	MUSCULOSKELETAL SYSTEM
RT	SKELETON

CARTOGRAPHIC METHODS
USE	**MAPPING**

CARTOGRAPHY
UF	oceanographic cartography
RT	ATLASES
RT	AUTOMATED CARTOGRAPHY
RT	BATHYMETRIC SURVEYS
RT	GEOGRAPHICAL COORDINATES
RT	GEOGRAPHY
RT	GRAPHIC METHODS
RT	HYDROGRAPHIC SURVEYING
RT	HYDROGRAPHIC SURVEYS
RT	MAP GRAPHICS
RT	MAP PROJECTIONS
RT	MAPPING
RT	MAPS
RT	PHOTOGRAMMETRY
RT	SURVEYING

CASCADING
BT1	VERTICAL WATER MOVEMENT
BT2	WATER MOTION
RT	BOLUSES
RT	OVERFLOW
RT	SLOPE PROCESSES

CASSITERITE
BT1	OXIDE MINERALS
BT2	MINERALS
RT	PLACERS
RT	TIN

CAST NETS
UF	falling gear
BT1	FISHING NETS
BT2	FISHING GEAR
RT	COASTAL FISHERIES

CASTRATION
SN	Added in 1980
BT1	ORGAN REMOVAL
RT	OVARIES
RT	PARASITIC CASTRATION
RT	SEXUAL REPRODUCTION
RT	TESTES

CASTRATION BY PARASITES
USE	**PARASITIC CASTRATION**

CAT
USE	**CLEAR AIR TURBULENCE**

CATABOLISM
BT1	METABOLISM
RT	ANABOLISM

CATADROMOUS FISH
USE	**CATADROMOUS SPECIES**

CATADROMOUS MIGRATIONS
UF	downstream migrations
BT1	SPAWNING MIGRATIONS
BT2	MIGRATIONS
RT	AMPHIHALINE SPECIES
RT	ANADROMOUS MIGRATIONS

CATADROMOUS MIGRATIONS (cont'd)
RT	BRACKISHWATER FISH
RT	CATADROMOUS SPECIES
RT	HOMING BEHAVIOUR
RT	POTADROMOUS MIGRATIONS

CATADROMOUS SPECIES
SN	Having the habit to migrate from fresh to salt water to spawn
UF	amphihaline thalassotocous species
UF	catadromous fish
UF	katadromous species
BT1	AMPHIHALINE SPECIES
BT2	SPECIES
BT3	TAXA
RT	CATADROMOUS MIGRATIONS
RT	SPAWNING GROUNDS
RT	SPAWNING MIGRATIONS
RT	SPAWNING SEASONS

CATAGENESIS
RT	DIAGENESIS
RT	SEDIMENTS

CATALOGS
USE	**CATALOGUES**

CATALOGUES
UF	catalogs
UF	equipment catalogues
BT1	DOCUMENTS
NT1	BOOK CATALOGUES
NT1	CHART CATALOGUES
NT1	INVENTORIES
RT	COLLECTIONS
RT	DATA COLLECTIONS
RT	EQUIPMENT
RT	INFORMATION RETRIEVAL
RT	MAPS
RT	PRICING

CATALYSIS
USE	**CATALYSTS**

CATALYSTS
UF	catalysis
RT	CHEMICAL KINETICS
RT	CHEMICAL REACTIONS
RT	ENZYMATIC ACTIVITY
RT	ENZYMES
RT	INHIBITORS

CATAMARANS
BT1	SURFACE CRAFT
BT2	VEHICLES
RT	BOATS
RT	RESEARCH VESSELS
RT	SHIP HULLS

CATASTROPHES
USE	**DISASTERS**

CATASTROPHIC WAVES
RT	FREAK WAVES
RT	STORM SURGES
RT	TSUNAMIS

CATCH COMPOSITION
RT	BY CATCH
RT	CATCH STATISTICS
RT	COMMERCIAL SPECIES
RT	DOMINANT SPECIES
RT	EXPLORATORY FISHING
RT	FISHERY RESOURCES
RT	FISHERY SURVEYS
RT	MULTISPECIES FISHERIES

CATCH/EFFORT
UF	catch per unit effort
UF	catch rate
UF	hook rate
BT1	FISHERY DATA
BT2	DATA
RT	BY CATCH
RT	CATCH STATISTICS
RT	CATCHABILITY
RT	FISHING EFFORT
RT	FISHING POWER
RT	POPULATION DENSITY
RT	POPULATION NUMBER
RT	RESOURCE AVAILABILITY
RT	STOCK ASSESSMENT

CATCH LIMIT
USE	**QUOTA REGULATIONS**

CATCH PER UNIT EFFORT
USE	**CATCH/EFFORT**

CATCH QUOTA
USE	**QUOTA REGULATIONS**

CATCH RATE
USE	**CATCH/EFFORT**

CATCH STATISTICS
BT1	FISHERY STATISTICS
NT1	FISH CATCH STATISTICS
NT1	HUNTING STATISTICS
NT1	SEAWEED STATISTICS
NT1	SHELLFISH CATCH STATISTICS
NT1	WHALING STATISTICS
RT	CATCH COMPOSITION
RT	CATCH/EFFORT
RT	COMMERCIAL FISHING
RT	FISH CONVERSION FACTORS
RT	FISHERY DATA
RT	FISHING EFFORT
RT	FISHING TIME
RT	LANDING STATISTICS
RT	POPULATION DYNAMICS
RT	QUOTA REGULATIONS
RT	STATISTICAL TABLES
RT	STOCK ASSESSMENT
RT	TRADE

CATCHABILITY
SN	Added in 1982
UF	catchability coefficient
RT	AVOIDANCE REACTIONS
RT	CATCH/EFFORT
RT	CATCHING METHODS
RT	ESCAPEMENT
RT	GEAR SELECTIVITY
RT	VULNERABILITY

CATCHABILITY COEFFICIENT
USE	**CATCHABILITY**

CATCHERS
SN	Vessels weaponed with harpoon gun used for hunting whales
BT1	FISHING VESSELS
BT2	SURFACE CRAFT
BT3	VEHICLES
RT	FACTORY SHIPS
RT	WHALING
RT	WHALING STATIONS
RT	WHALING STATISTICS

CATCHING METHODS
UF	fishing methods
NT1	ANGLING
NT2	BAIT FISHING
NT1	AUTOMATED FISHING PLATFORMS
NT1	ELECTRIC FISHING
NT1	EXPLOSIVE FISHING

CATCHING METHODS (cont'd)
NT1	FISH POISONING
NT1	FISHING BY DIVING
NT1	FISHING WITHOUT GEAR
NT1	GRAPPLING
NT1	LIGHT FISHING
NT1	LINE FISHING
NT2	HANDLINING
NT2	JIGGING
NT2	LONGLINING
NT2	POLE-LINE FISHING
NT2	TROLLING
NT1	NET FISHING
NT1	POT FISHING
NT1	PUMP FISHING
NT1	SEINING
NT2	PURSE SEINING
NT1	SPEAR FISHING
NT1	TRAP FISHING
NT1	TRAWLING
NT2	BOTTOM TRAWLING
NT1	WORM FISHING
NT1	WOUNDING
RT	ATTRACTING TECHNIQUES
RT	CATCHABILITY
RT	COMMERCIAL FISHING
RT	EXPERIMENTAL FISHING
RT	FISHERIES
RT	FISHERY DEVELOPMENT
RT	FISHERY ENGINEERING
RT	FISHERY TECHNOLOGY
RT	FISHING GEAR
RT	FISHING OPERATIONS
RT	FISHING TECHNOLOGY
RT	SPORT FISHING
RT	TECHNOLOGY

CATCHMENT AREA
RT	LAKE BASINS
RT	RIVER BASINS
RT	RUNOFF
RT	WATERSHEDS

CATENARY
BT1	DEFLECTION
RT	CABLE DYNAMICS
RT	CABLES
RT	MOORING LINES
RT	RISER CABLES

CATHODES
BT1	ELECTRODES
BT2	ELECTRICAL EQUIPMENT
BT3	EQUIPMENT

CATHODIC PROTECTION
BT1	CORROSION CONTROL
BT2	CONTROL
RT	IMPRESSED CURRENTS
RT	SACRIFICIAL ANODES

CATHODIC STRIPPING VOLTAMMETRY
USE	**STRIPPING ANALYSIS**

CATION EXCHANGE
USE	**ION EXCHANGE**

CATION EXCHANGE CAPACITY
USE	**EXCHANGE CAPACITY**

CATIONS
BT1	IONS
RT	ELECTROLYSIS
RT	EXCHANGE CAPACITY
RT	ION EXCHANGE

CAUSTICITY
USE	**ALKALINITY**

CAUSTICS
RT	ORTHOGONALS
RT	WAVE REFRACTION DIAGRAMS

CAVE FAUNA
USE	**CAVERNICOLOUS SPECIES**

CAVERNICOLOUS SPECIES
UF	cave fauna
BT1	SPECIES
BT2	TAXA
RT	CAVES
RT	SPELAEOLOGY

CAVES
SN	Restricted to marine subterranean environment
UF	sea caves
BT1	COASTAL LANDFORMS
BT2	LANDFORMS
BT3	TOPOGRAPHIC FEATURES
RT	CAVERNICOLOUS SPECIES
RT	CLIFFS
RT	EROSION FEATURES
RT	SPELAEOLOGY

CAVIAR
SN	Sturgeon eggs detached from roe, sorted, washed and salted, or fish roe prepared like caviar. Added in 1980
UF	caviar substitutes
BT1	ROES
BT2	PROCESSED FISHERY PRODUCTS
BT3	FISHERY PRODUCTS
BT4	PRODUCTS

CAVIAR SUBSTITUTES
USE	**CAVIAR**

CAVITATION
UF	acoustic cavitation
BT1	TURBULENT FLOW
BT2	FLUID FLOW
BT3	FLUID MOTION
RT	ACOUSTIC PROPERTIES
RT	AIR BUBBLES
RT	BUBBLES
RT	CORROSION
RT	PROPELLERS
RT	VAPORIZATION
RT	VORTICES

CAVITATION EROSION
USE	**CORROSION**

CAYS
UF	keys (islands)
BT1	ISLANDS
BT2	LANDFORMS
BT3	TOPOGRAPHIC FEATURES
RT	CORAL REEFS

CELESTIAL NAVIGATION
BT1	NAVIGATION
RT	ASTRONOMY
RT	INERTIAL NAVIGATION
RT	NAUTICAL ALMANACS

CELESTITE
BT1	SULPHATE MINERALS
BT2	MINERALS

ASFIS Thesaurus

CELL BIOLOGY
USE **CYTOLOGY**

CELL CONSTITUENTS
NT1   CELL MEMBRANES
NT1   CELL ORGANELLES
NT2   GOLGI APPARATUS
NT1   CELL WALLS
NT1   CHROMOSOMES
NT2   GENES
NT1   CYTOPLASM
NT1   NUCLEI
RT   CELL DIVISION
RT   CELL MORPHOLOGY
RT   CELLS
RT   CYTOLOGY
RT   HISTOCHEMISTRY

CELL COUNTERS
SN   Added in 1980
BT1   COUNTERS
RT   CELLS
RT   PHYTOPLANKTON

CELL CULTURE
BT1   LABORATORY CULTURE
RT   CELLS
RT   CULTURE MEDIA
RT   PHYTOPLANKTON CULTURE
RT   TISSUE CULTURE

CELL DIFFERENTIATION
SN   Added in 1980
UF   differentiation (cells)
RT   CELL MORPHOLOGY
RT   CELLS
RT   CYTOLOGY
RT   GROWTH

CELL DIVISION
UF   nuclear division
BT1   REPRODUCTION
NT1   MEIOSIS
NT1   MITOSIS
RT   CELL CONSTITUENTS
RT   CELL FUSION
RT   CELLS
RT   CYTOLOGY

CELL FLAGELLA
USE   **CELL ORGANELLES**

CELL FUSION
RT   CELL DIVISION

CELL INCLUSIONS
SN   Any non living material present in
        the cytoplasm, whether organic or
        inorganic. Added in 1980
RT   CELLS
RT   CYTOPLASM

CELL MEMBRANES
UF   cytoplasmic membranes
UF   membranes (cells)
UF   nuclear membranes
UF   plasma membranes
UF   plasmalemma
BT1   CELL CONSTITUENTS
RT   BIOLOGICAL MEMBRANES
RT   CELL WALLS
RT   CYTOLOGY

CELL MORPHOLOGY
SN   Added in 1980
BT1   ORGANISM MORPHOLOGY
BT2   BIOLOGY
RT   CELL CONSTITUENTS
RT   CELL DIFFERENTIATION
RT   CYTOLOGY

CELL ORGANELLES
SN   Specialized part of a cell having
        specific functions. Added in 1980
UF   cell flagella
UF   chondriosomes
UF   contractile vacuole
UF   mitochondria
UF   myoneme
UF   organelles
BT1   CELL CONSTITUENTS
NT1   GOLGI APPARATUS
RT   CYTOLOGY

CELL WALLS
SN   Outermost rigid layer of a plant
        cell. Added in 1980
BT1   CELL CONSTITUENTS
RT   CELL MEMBRANES

CELLS
NT1   AMOEBOCYTES
NT1   BLOOD CELLS
NT2   ERYTHROCYTES
NT2   LEUKOCYTES
NT2   LYMPHOCYTES
NT2   MACROPHAGES
NT1   NEURONS
NT1   RECEPTORS
NT2   TARGET CELLS
NT1   SEXUAL CELLS
NT2   EGGS
NT3   BIRD EGGS
NT3   BRINE SHRIMP EGGS
NT3   FISH EGGS
NT3   INSECT EGGS
NT3   RESTING EGGS
NT2   SPERM
RT   ANATOMICAL STRUCTURES
RT   CELL CONSTITUENTS
RT   CELL COUNTERS
RT   CELL CULTURE
RT   CELL DIFFERENTIATION
RT   CELL DIVISION
RT   CELL INCLUSIONS
RT   CHLOROPLASTS
RT   CHROMATOPHORES
RT   CLONES
RT   CYTOLOGY
RT   HISTOCHEMISTRY
RT   NECROSES
RT   PHAGOCYTOSIS
RT   TISSUES
RT   ULTRASTRUCTURE

CELLULAR CONVECTION
UF   thermal convection
BT1   CONVECTION
BT2   ADVECTION
BT3   TRANSPORT PROCESSES
RT   ATMOSPHERIC BOUNDARY LAYER
RT   MANTLE CONVECTION
RT   WINDROWS

CELLULASE
USE   **ENZYMES**

CELLULOSE
SN   Before 1982 use CARBOHYDRATES
BT1   POLYSACCHARIDES
BT2   SACCHARIDES
BT3   CARBOHYDRATES
BT4   ORGANIC COMPOUNDS

CEMENT (BUILDING MATERIAL)
USE   **CONCRETE**

CEMENTATION
BT1   DIAGENESIS
BT2   SEDIMENTATION
RT   CLASTICS
RT   CONSOLIDATION
RT   LITHIFICATION
RT   SUBMARINE CEMENTS

CEMENTS (ADHESIVES)
USE   **ADHESIVES**

CEMENTS (GEOLOGY)
USE   **SUBMARINE CEMENTS**

CENOZOIC
SN   Before 1982 search CENOZOIC ERA
UF   caenozoic
BT1   GEOLOGICAL TIME
NT1   QUATERNARY
NT2   HOLOCENE
NT2   PLEISTOCENE
NT1   TERTIARY
NT2   NEOGENE
NT3   MIOCENE
NT4   MESSINIAN
NT3   PLIOCENE
NT2   PALAEOGENE
NT3   EOCENE
NT3   OLIGOCENE
NT3   PALAEOCENE
RT   PHANEROZOIC

CENSUS
RT   BIOLOGICAL DATA
RT   BIOLOGICAL SAMPLING
RT   DATA COLLECTIONS
RT   SAMPLING
RT   STOCK ASSESSMENT
RT   SURVEYS

CENTRAL NERVOUS SYSTEM
SN   Added in 1980
UF   cns
BT1   NERVOUS SYSTEM
NT1   BRAIN
NT2   HYPOTHALAMUS
NT2   PINEAL ORGAN
NT1   GANGLIA
NT1   SPINAL CORD
RT   SENSE ORGANS

CENTRIFUGAL FORCE
BT1   FORCES
RT   ACCELERATION
RT   CENTRIFUGES
RT   CENTRIPETAL FORCE

CENTRIFUGATION
BT1   SEPARATION
RT   ANALYTICAL TECHNIQUES
RT   CENTRIFUGES
RT   WATER FILTRATION
RT   WATER PURIFICATION

CENTRIFUGES
BT1   LABORATORY EQUIPMENT
BT2   EQUIPMENT
RT   CENTRIFUGAL FORCE
RT   CENTRIFUGATION
RT   CENTRIPETAL FORCE

CENTRIPETAL FORCE
BT1   FORCES
RT   ACCELERATION
RT   CENTRIFUGAL FORCE
RT   CENTRIFUGES
RT   GRADIENT WINDS

CEPHALOPOD FISHERIES
SN	Added in 1982
UF	cuttlefish fisheries
UF	octopus fisheries
UF	squid fisheries
BT1	MOLLUSC FISHERIES
BT2	SHELLFISH FISHERIES
BT3	FISHERIES
RT	JIGGING
RT	LAMPARA NETS
RT	LIGHT FISHING
RT	MARINE FISHERIES
RT	POT FISHING
RT	SQUID CULTURE

CEPHALOTHORAX
SN	Added in 1980
BT1	BODY REGIONS
BT2	ANATOMICAL STRUCTURES
RT	ANIMAL APPENDAGES
RT	CARAPACE
RT	THORAX

CERAMICS
BT1	MATERIALS

CERIUM
BT1	CHEMICAL ELEMENTS
RT	CERIUM COMPOUNDS
RT	CERIUM ISOTOPES
RT	RARE EARTHS
RT	TRANSITION ELEMENTS

CERIUM COMPOUNDS
RT	CERIUM
RT	CHEMICAL COMPOUNDS

CERIUM ISOTOPES
BT1	ISOTOPES
RT	CERIUM

CERTIFICATION
RT	EVALUATION
RT	FLOATING STRUCTURES
RT	PERFORMANCE ASSESSMENT
RT	QUALITY CONTROL
RT	RELIABILITY
RT	SHIPPING
RT	TESTS

CESIUM
USE	**CAESIUM**

CETOLOGISTS
BT1	MAMMALOGISTS
BT2	ZOOLOGISTS
BT3	BIOLOGISTS
BT4	SCIENTIFIC PERSONNEL
RT	CETOLOGY
RT	DIRECTORIES
RT	WHALING

CETOLOGY
SN	Added in 1980
BT1	MAMMALOGY
BT2	VERTEBRATE ZOOLOGY
BT3	ZOOLOGY
BT4	BIOLOGY
RT	AMBERGRIS
RT	AQUATIC MAMMALS
RT	BIPOLAR DISTRIBUTION
RT	CETOLOGISTS
RT	DIVING
RT	ECHOLOCATION
RT	FEEDING MIGRATIONS
RT	LEARNING BEHAVIOUR
RT	MAMMALIAN PHYSIOLOGY
RT	PARTURITION
RT	SOCIAL BEHAVIOUR
RT	VOCALIZATION BEHAVIOUR

CETOLOGY (cont'd)
RT	WHALING
RT	WHALING STATISTICS

CHAIN
RT	ANCHORING
RT	CABLES
RT	MOORING LINES
RT	ROPES

CHALK
BT1	CARBONATE ROCKS
RT	COCCOLITHS
RT	SEDIMENTARY ROCKS

CHAMBERS (ONE-ATMOSPHERE)
USE	**UNDERWATER HABITATS**

CHANDLER WOBBLE
RT	EARTH ROTATION
RT	POLE TIDES

CHANGES (TIME)
USE	**TEMPORAL VARIATIONS**

CHANGES OF STATE
USE	**PHASE CHANGES**

CHANNEL FLOW
SN	Includes flow through pipes and conduits
UF	flow in channels
UF	open channel flow
BT1	FLUID FLOW
BT2	FLUID MOTION
RT	BED ROUGHNESS
RT	FLOWMETERS
RT	FLUVIAL TRANSPORT
RT	LAMINAR FLOW
RT	SEDIMENT DYNAMICS
RT	SEDIMENT TRANSPORT
RT	TRANSVERSE BED FORMS
RT	TURBULENT FLOW
RT	UNIDIRECTIONAL FLOW

CHANNELS
UF	water channels
NT1	NAVIGATIONAL CHANNELS
RT	CANALS
RT	DREDGERS
RT	DREDGING
RT	FLUMES
RT	FLUVIAL FEATURES
RT	HYDRAULIC MODELS
RT	INLETS (WATERWAYS)
RT	RIP CHANNELS
RT	RIVERS
RT	RUNNELS
RT	SEACHANNELS
RT	STRAITS
RT	TIDAL INLETS
RT	TOPOGRAPHIC FEATURES
RT	VALLEYS
RT	WATER BODIES
RT	WATER CURRENTS
RT	WEIRS

CHANNELS (SOUND)
USE	**SOUND CHANNELS**

CHART CATALOGUES
BT1	CATALOGUES
BT2	DOCUMENTS
RT	MAPS
RT	NAVIGATIONAL CHARTS

CHART DATUM
BT1	DATUM LEVELS
BT2	REFERENCE LEVELS
RT	MAPS
RT	NAVIGATIONAL CHARTS

CHARTING (DISTRIBUTIONS)
USE	**MAPPING**

CHARTING (ENVIRONMENTAL CONDITIONS)
USE	**MAPPING**

CHARTING (NAVIGATIONAL HAZARDS)
USE	**HYDROGRAPHIC SURVEYING**

CHARTS (MAPS)
USE	**MAPS**

CHECK LISTS
SN	Any relatively extensive list of a group of organisms by species composition
UF	species composition
RT	COMMUNITY COMPOSITION
RT	IDENTIFICATION KEYS
RT	NEW SPECIES
RT	SPECIES
RT	VERNACULAR NAMES

CHELATES
UF	chelating agents
UF	chelation
RT	CHEMICAL COMPOUNDS
RT	HAEMOGLOBINS
RT	METALS
RT	ORGANIC COMPOUNDS

CHELATING AGENTS
USE	**CHELATES**

CHELATION
USE	**CHELATES**

CHELATOMETRIC TITRATION
USE	**TITRATION**

CHEMICAL ACTIVITY
USE	**THERMODYNAMIC ACTIVITY**

CHEMICAL ANALYSIS
UF	chemical assays
RT	ANALYSIS
RT	ANALYTICAL TECHNIQUES
RT	ASH CONTENT
RT	CHEMICAL COMPOSITION
RT	COMPOSITION
RT	HYDROCARBON ANALYSIS
RT	IDENTIFICATION
RT	MICROSCOPY
RT	PHOTOMETRY
RT	POLLUTION DETECTION
RT	SEDIMENT ANALYSIS
RT	TESTS
RT	WATER ANALYSIS
RT	WATER SAMPLES
RT	X-RAY SPECTROSCOPY

CHEMICAL ASSAYS
USE	**CHEMICAL ANALYSIS**

CHEMICAL COMPOSITION
UF	abundance (chemical)
UF	chemical constituents
BT1	COMPOSITION
RT	CHEMICAL ANALYSIS
RT	CHEMICAL ELEMENTS
RT	CHEMICAL PROPERTIES
RT	CHEMISTRY
RT	CHEMOTAXONOMY
RT	DISSOLVED GASES
RT	DISSOLVED OXYGEN

ASFIS Thesaurus

CHEMICAL COMPOSITION (cont'd)

RT	DISSOLVED SALTS
RT	FEED COMPOSITION
RT	FOOD COMPOSITION
RT	SUSPENDED ORGANIC MATTER
RT	WATER ANALYSIS

CHEMICAL COMPOUNDS

SN	Use of a more specific term is recommended; consult terms listed below
RT	ACTINIUM COMPOUNDS
RT	ADP
RT	ALCOHOLS
RT	ALKALOIDS
RT	ALUMINIUM COMPOUNDS
RT	AMERICIUM COMPOUNDS
RT	AMINO ACIDS
RT	AMMONIA
RT	AMP
RT	ANTIMONY COMPOUNDS
RT	ANTIOXIDANTS
RT	AROMATIC HYDROCARBONS
RT	AROMATICS
RT	ARSENIC COMPOUNDS
RT	ASTATINE COMPOUNDS
RT	ATP
RT	BARIUM COMPOUNDS
RT	BERKELIUM COMPOUNDS
RT	BERYLLIUM COMPOUNDS
RT	BISMUTH COMPOUNDS
RT	BORON COMPOUNDS
RT	BROMINE COMPOUNDS
RT	CADMIUM COMPOUNDS
RT	CAESIUM COMPOUNDS
RT	CALCIUM COMPOUNDS
RT	CALIFORNIUM COMPOUNDS
RT	CARBOHYDRATES
RT	CARBON COMPOUNDS
RT	CARBON DIOXIDE
RT	CARBONATES
RT	CERIUM COMPOUNDS
RT	CHELATES
RT	CHLORINE COMPOUNDS
RT	CHROMIUM COMPOUNDS
RT	COBALT COMPOUNDS
RT	COPPER COMPOUNDS
RT	CURIUM COMPOUNDS
RT	CYANIDES
RT	DISINFECTANTS
RT	DNA
RT	DYSPROSIUM COMPOUNDS
RT	EINSTEINIUM COMPOUNDS
RT	ERBIUM COMPOUNDS
RT	EUROPIUM COMPOUNDS
RT	FATS
RT	FATTY ACIDS
RT	FERMIUM COMPOUNDS
RT	FIXATIVES
RT	FLUORINE COMPOUNDS
RT	FRANCIUM COMPOUNDS
RT	GADOLINIUM COMPOUNDS
RT	GALLIUM COMPOUNDS
RT	GERMANIUM COMPOUNDS
RT	GOLD COMPOUNDS
RT	HAFNIUM COMPOUNDS
RT	HALOGEN COMPOUNDS
RT	HOLMIUM COMPOUNDS
RT	HUMIC ACIDS
RT	HYDROCARBONS
RT	INDIUM COMPOUNDS
RT	INORGANIC ACIDS
RT	INORGANIC COMPOUNDS
RT	IODINE COMPOUNDS
RT	IRIDIUM COMPOUNDS
RT	IRON COMPOUNDS
RT	LANTHANIUM COMPOUNDS
RT	LAWRENCIUM COMPOUNDS

CHEMICAL COMPOUNDS (cont'd)

RT	LEAD COMPOUNDS
RT	LITHIUM COMPOUNDS
RT	LUTETIUM COMPOUNDS
RT	MAGNESIUM COMPOUNDS
RT	MANGANESE COMPOUNDS
RT	MENDELEVIUM COMPOUNDS
RT	MERCURY COMPOUNDS
RT	MOLYBDENUM COMPOUNDS
RT	NEODYMIUM COMPOUNDS
RT	NEPTUNIUM COMPOUNDS
RT	NICKEL COMPOUNDS
RT	NIOBIUM COMPOUNDS
RT	NITRATES
RT	NITRITES
RT	NITROGEN COMPOUNDS
RT	NOBELIUM COMPOUNDS
RT	NUCLEIC ACIDS
RT	NUCLEOTIDES
RT	ORGANIC ACIDS
RT	ORGANIC COMPOUNDS
RT	OSMIUM COMPOUNDS
RT	OXYGEN COMPOUNDS
RT	PALLADIUM COMPOUNDS
RT	PCB
RT	PHENOLS
RT	PHOSPHATES
RT	PHOSPHORUS COMPOUNDS
RT	PLATINUM COMPOUNDS
RT	PLUTONIUM COMPOUNDS
RT	POLONIUM COMPOUNDS
RT	POLYMERS
RT	POTASSIUM COMPOUNDS
RT	PRASEODYMIUM COMPOUNDS
RT	PROMETHIUM COMPOUNDS
RT	PROTACTINIUM COMPOUNDS
RT	PROTEINS
RT	RADIUM COMPOUNDS
RT	RHENIUM COMPOUNDS
RT	RHODIUM COMPOUNDS
RT	RNA
RT	RUBIDIUM COMPOUNDS
RT	RUTHENIUM COMPOUNDS
RT	RUTHERFORDIUM COMPOUNDS
RT	SALTS
RT	SAMARIUM COMPOUNDS
RT	SCANDIUM COMPOUNDS
RT	SELENIUM COMPOUNDS
RT	SILICATES
RT	SILICON COMPOUNDS
RT	SILVER COMPOUNDS
RT	SODIUM COMPOUNDS
RT	STEROIDS
RT	STEROLS
RT	STRONTIUM COMPOUNDS
RT	SULPHUR COMPOUNDS
RT	TANTALUM COMPOUNDS
RT	TECHNETIUM COMPOUNDS
RT	TELLURIUM COMPOUNDS
RT	TERBIUM COMPOUNDS
RT	THALLIUM COMPOUNDS
RT	THORIUM COMPOUNDS
RT	THULIUM COMPOUNDS
RT	TIN COMPOUNDS
RT	TITANIUM COMPOUNDS
RT	TRANSITION ELEMENT COMPOUNDS
RT	TUNGSTEN COMPOUNDS
RT	URANIUM COMPOUNDS
RT	UREA
RT	VANADIUM COMPOUNDS
RT	VOLATILE COMPOUNDS
RT	YTTERBIUM COMPOUNDS
RT	YTTRIUM COMPOUNDS
RT	ZINC COMPOUNDS
RT	ZIRCONIUM COMPOUNDS

CHEMICAL CONSTITUENTS

USE	**CHEMICAL COMPOSITION**

CHEMICAL CONTROL

SN	Use of chemicals to control noxious organisms
UF	chemocontrol
BT1	CONTROL
RT	ANTIFOULING SUBSTANCES
RT	BACTERIOCIDES
RT	BIOLOGICAL DAMAGE
RT	CONTROL RESISTANCE
RT	FOULING ORGANISMS
RT	INSECTICIDES
RT	PEST CONTROL
RT	PESTICIDES
RT	PLANT CONTROL
RT	TOXICANTS

CHEMICAL CYCLES

BT1	CYCLES
RT	BIOCHEMICAL CYCLES
RT	CARBON CYCLE
RT	GEOCHEMICAL CYCLES
RT	NITROGEN CYCLE
RT	NUTRIENT CYCLES
RT	PHOSPHORUS CYCLE
RT	SILICON CYCLE

CHEMICAL DEGRADATION

BT1	DEGRADATION
BT2	CHEMICAL REACTIONS
RT	BIOCHEMICAL CYCLES
RT	BIOGEOCHEMICAL CYCLE
RT	CHEMICAL REACTIONS
RT	CORROSION
RT	ELECTROLYSIS
RT	HYDROLYSIS
RT	SEWAGE TREATMENT
RT	SLUDGE TREATMENT
RT	WATER POLLUTION TREATMENT

CHEMICAL ELEMENTS

SN	Use of a more specific term is recommended
UF	elements (chemical)
NT1	ACTINIUM
NT1	ALUMINIUM
NT1	AMERICIUM
NT1	ANTIMONY
NT1	ARGON
NT1	ARSENIC
NT1	ASTATINE
NT1	BARIUM
NT1	BERKELIUM
NT1	BERYLLIUM
NT1	BISMUTH
NT1	BORON
NT1	BROMINE
NT1	CADMIUM
NT1	CAESIUM
NT1	CALCIUM
NT1	CALIFORNIUM
NT1	CARBON
NT2	ORGANIC CARBON
NT3	DISSOLVED ORGANIC CARBON
NT3	PARTICULATE ORGANIC CARBON
NT3	TOTAL ORGANIC CARBON
NT1	CERIUM
NT1	CHLORINE
NT1	CHROMIUM
NT1	COBALT
NT1	COPPER
NT1	CURIUM
NT1	DYSPROSIUM
NT1	EINSTEINIUM
NT1	ERBIUM
NT1	EUROPIUM

ASFIS Thesaurus

CHEMICAL ELEMENTS (cont'd)

NT1	FERMIUM
NT1	FLUORINE
NT1	FRANCIUM
NT1	GADOLINIUM
NT1	GALLIUM
NT1	GERMANIUM
NT1	GOLD
NT1	HAFNIUM
NT1	HELIUM
NT1	HOLMIUM
NT1	HYDROGEN
NT1	INDIUM
NT1	IODINE
NT1	IRIDIUM
NT1	IRON
NT1	KRYPTON
NT1	LANTHANIUM
NT1	LAWRENCIUM
NT1	LEAD
NT1	LITHIUM
NT1	LUTETIUM
NT1	MAGNESIUM
NT1	MANGANESE
NT1	MENDELEVIUM
NT1	MERCURY
NT1	MOLYBDENUM
NT1	NEODYMIUM
NT1	NEON
NT1	NEPTUNIUM
NT1	NICKEL
NT1	NIOBIUM
NT1	NITROGEN
NT2	ORGANIC NITROGEN
NT3	DISSOLVED ORGANIC NITROGEN
NT3	PARTICULATE ORGANIC NITROGEN
NT1	NOBELIUM
NT1	OSMIUM
NT1	OXYGEN
NT1	PALLADIUM
NT1	PHOSPHORUS
NT2	ORGANIC PHOSPHORUS
NT3	DISSOLVED ORGANIC PHOSPHORUS
NT3	PARTICULATE ORGANIC PHOSPHORUS
NT1	PLATINUM
NT1	PLUTONIUM
NT1	POLONIUM
NT1	POTASSIUM
NT1	PRASEODYMIUM
NT1	PROMETHIUM
NT1	PROTACTINIUM
NT1	RADIUM
NT1	RADON
NT1	RHENIUM
NT1	RHODIUM
NT1	RUBIDIUM
NT1	RUTHENIUM
NT1	RUTHERFORDIUM
NT1	SAMARIUM
NT1	SCANDIUM
NT1	SELENIUM
NT1	SILICON
NT1	SILVER
NT1	SODIUM
NT1	STRONTIUM
NT1	SULPHUR
NT1	TANTALUM
NT1	TECHNETIUM
NT1	TELLURIUM
NT1	TERBIUM
NT1	THALLIUM
NT1	THORIUM
NT1	THULIUM
NT1	TIN
NT1	TITANIUM
NT1	TUNGSTEN
NT1	URANIUM
NT1	VANADIUM
NT1	XENON
NT1	YTTERBIUM

CHEMICAL ELEMENTS (cont'd)

NT1	YTTRIUM
NT1	ZINC
NT1	ZIRCONIUM
RT	ALKALI METALS
RT	ALKALINE EARTH METALS
RT	ALLOYS
RT	CHEMICAL COMPOSITION
RT	CHEMICAL POLLUTANTS
RT	CHEMISTRY
RT	ELECTROANALYSIS
RT	GASES
RT	HALOGENS
RT	HEAVY METALS
RT	ISOTOPES
RT	METALS
RT	RADIOISOTOPES
RT	RESIDENCE TIME
RT	TRACE ELEMENTS

CHEMICAL ENGINEERING

BT1	ENGINEERING
RT	PETROLEUM ENGINEERING
RT	PROCESS PLANTS

CHEMICAL EQUILIBRIUM

UF	equilibrium constants
RT	CHEMICAL KINETICS
RT	CHEMICAL REACTIONS
RT	EQUILIBRIUM
RT	THERMODYNAMIC ACTIVITY
RT	THERMODYNAMIC EQUILIBRIUM

CHEMICAL EXTRACTION

SN	Extraction of fats, enzymes, seaweed products, oils, protein, concentrates, stickwater, etc.
UF	extraction (chemical)
BT1	SEPARATION
RT	AGAR
RT	ALGINATES
RT	ANIMAL OIL EXTRACTION
RT	CARRAGEENINS
RT	CHEMISTRY
RT	FATS
RT	FISH OIL EXTRACTION
RT	LIPIDS
RT	SALTS
RT	SOLVENTS
RT	STICKWATER

CHEMICAL KINETICS

UF	kinetics of chemical reactions
UF	reaction kinetics
RT	CATALYSTS
RT	CHEMICAL EQUILIBRIUM
RT	CHEMICAL REACTIONS
RT	KINETICS

CHEMICAL LIMNOLOGY

SN	Before 1982 search also LIMNOLOGY (CHEMICAL)
UF	limnology (chemical)
BT1	LIMNOLOGY
RT	CHEMICAL PROPERTIES
RT	CHEMISTRY
RT	ESTUARINE CHEMISTRY
RT	WATER ANALYSIS

CHEMICAL MESSENGERS

USE	**HORMONES**

CHEMICAL OCEANOGRAPHY

UF	marine chemistry
UF	oceanography (chemical)
BT1	OCEANOGRAPHY
BT2	EARTH SCIENCES
RT	CHEMICAL PROPERTIES
RT	CHEMISTRY
RT	ESTUARINE CHEMISTRY

CHEMICAL OCEANOGRAPHY (cont'd)

RT	MARINE SCIENCES
RT	WATER ANALYSIS

CHEMICAL OXYGEN DEMAND

UF	cod
BT1	OXYGEN DEMAND
RT	BIOCHEMICAL OXYGEN DEMAND
RT	CHEMICAL PROPERTIES
RT	DISSOLVED OXYGEN
RT	WATER ANALYSIS
RT	WATER POLLUTION
RT	WATER PROPERTIES
RT	WATER QUALITY

CHEMICAL PLUMES

BT1	PLUMES
BT2	FLUID FLOW
BT3	FLUID MOTION
RT	CHEMICAL POLLUTION
RT	CHEMICAL SPILLS

CHEMICAL POLLUTANTS

SN	Any pollutants of chemical origin (organic and inorganic)
BT1	POLLUTANTS
RT	AGRICULTURAL POLLUTION
RT	AGRICULTURAL RUNOFF
RT	ALGICIDES
RT	AROMATIC HYDROCARBONS
RT	BIOACCUMULATION
RT	BIOTESTING
RT	CARCINOGENESIS
RT	CARCINOGENS
RT	CHEMICAL ELEMENTS
RT	CHEMICAL POLLUTION
RT	DDT
RT	DETERGENTS
RT	FERTILIZERS
RT	HAZARD ASSESSMENT
RT	HAZARDOUS MATERIALS
RT	HEAVY METALS
RT	HERBICIDES
RT	INDUSTRIAL WASTES
RT	INSECTICIDES
RT	PAINTS
RT	PCB
RT	PESTICIDES
RT	PHENOLS
RT	PHTHALATE ESTERS
RT	SOAPS
RT	SURFACE MICROLAYER
RT	TOXICITY TESTS

CHEMICAL POLLUTION

SN	pollution (chemical)
BT1	POLLUTION
RT	AGRICULTURAL POLLUTION
RT	AGRICULTURAL RUNOFF
RT	ALGICIDES
RT	AROMATIC HYDROCARBONS
RT	BIOACCUMULATION
RT	BIOTESTING
RT	BRACKISHWATER POLLUTION
RT	CARCINOGENESIS
RT	CARCINOGENS
RT	CHEMICAL PLUMES
RT	CHEMICAL POLLUTANTS
RT	DDT
RT	DETERGENTS
RT	FERTILIZERS
RT	FRESHWATER POLLUTION
RT	HAZARD ASSESSMENT
RT	HAZARDOUS MATERIALS
RT	HEAVY METALS
RT	HERBICIDES
RT	INDUSTRIAL WASTES
RT	INSECTICIDES
RT	MARINE POLLUTION
RT	PAINTS

ASFIS Thesaurus

CHEMICAL POLLUTION (cont'd)
RT	PCB
RT	PESTICIDES
RT	PHENOLS
RT	PHTHALATE ESTERS
RT	POLLUTION CONTROL
RT	SEDIMENT POLLUTION
RT	SEWAGE
RT	SOAPS
RT	SURFACE MICROLAYER
RT	TOXICITY TESTS
RT	WATER POLLUTION

CHEMICAL PRECIPITATION
SN	Before 1982 search PRECIPITATION (CHEMISTRY)
UF	precipitation (chemistry)
BT1	SEPARATION
NT1	COPRECIPITATION
NT1	FLOCCULATION
RT	CHEMICAL PROPERTIES
RT	CHEMICAL REACTIONS
RT	CHEMISTRY
RT	COAGULANTS
RT	COLLOIDS
RT	SEDIMENTATION
RT	SOLUBILITY
RT	SUPERSATURATION

CHEMICAL PROPERTIES
BT1	PROPERTIES
NT1	ACIDITY
NT1	ALKALINITY
NT1	PH
NT1	REDOX POTENTIAL
NT1	SALINITY
NT2	CHLORINITY
NT2	CHLOROSITY
NT2	PALAEOSALINITY
NT2	SURFACE SALINITY
NT1	SOLUBILITY
NT2	GAS SOLUBILITY
RT	ASH CONTENT
RT	CHEMICAL COMPOSITION
RT	CHEMICAL LIMNOLOGY
RT	CHEMICAL OCEANOGRAPHY
RT	CHEMICAL OXYGEN DEMAND
RT	CHEMICAL PRECIPITATION
RT	CHEMICAL REACTIONS
RT	CHEMISTRY
RT	DIFFUSION
RT	ELECTRICAL PROPERTIES
RT	ELECTROCHEMISTRY
RT	ENVIRONMENTAL CHARTS
RT	ENVIRONMENTAL FACTORS
RT	GEOCHEMISTRY
RT	HABITAT IMPROVEMENT (CHEMICAL)
RT	LUMINESCENCE
RT	MOLECULAR WEIGHT
RT	ODOUR
RT	PHOSPHORESCENCE
RT	PHYSICAL PROPERTIES
RT	PHYSICOCHEMICAL PROPERTIES
RT	SEDIMENT CHEMISTRY
RT	THERMODYNAMIC PROPERTIES
RT	WATER
RT	WATER ANALYSIS
RT	WATER HARDNESS
RT	WATER PROPERTIES
RT	WATER QUALITY

CHEMICAL REACTIONS
SN	Use of a more specific term is recommended
UF	reactions (chemical)
NT1	AMINATION
NT1	AUTOLYSIS
NT1	CARBOXYLATION
NT1	COAGULATION
NT1	CORROSION

CHEMICAL REACTIONS (cont'd)
NT2	CRACKING (CORROSION)
NT2	STRESS CORROSION
NT1	DEAMINATION
NT1	DECARBOXYLATION
NT1	DEGRADATION
NT2	BIODEGRADATION
NT3	ANAEROBIC DIGESTION
NT2	CHEMICAL DEGRADATION
NT2	PYROLYSIS
NT2	THERMAL DECOMPOSITION
NT1	DEHYDRATION
NT1	DENITRIFICATION
NT1	DEPOLYMERIZATION
NT1	DISSOCIATION
NT1	ELECTROLYSIS
NT1	FERMENTATION
NT1	HALOGENATION
NT2	CHLORINATION
NT1	HYDROLYSIS
NT2	ENZYMOLYSIS
NT1	ISOMERIZATION
NT1	NITRIFICATION
NT1	NITROGEN FIXATION
NT1	OXIDATION
NT1	PHOTOCHEMICAL REACTIONS
NT2	PHOTOLYSIS
NT2	PHOTOSYNTHESIS
NT3	CARBON FIXATION
NT1	POLYMERIZATION
NT1	REDOX REACTIONS
NT1	REDUCTION
NT2	SULPHATE REDUCTION
RT	BIOCHEMICAL PHENOMENA
RT	BUFFERS
RT	CATALYSTS
RT	CHEMICAL DEGRADATION
RT	CHEMICAL EQUILIBRIUM
RT	CHEMICAL KINETICS
RT	CHEMICAL PRECIPITATION
RT	CHEMICAL PROPERTIES
RT	CHEMILUMINESCENCE
RT	CHEMISTRY
RT	ELECTROCHEMISTRY
RT	FERMENTATION
RT	ION ASSOCIATION
RT	ION EXCHANGE
RT	PHOTOSYNTHESIS
RT	REDOX POTENTIAL
RT	SPECIFICITY
RT	THERMODYNAMIC ACTIVITY
RT	TITRATION

CHEMICAL RECEPTORS
USE	**CHEMORECEPTORS**

CHEMICAL RESISTANCE
USE	**CONTROL RESISTANCE**

CHEMICAL SEDIMENTS
SN	Search also AUTHIGENES before 1983
UF	chemically precipitated sediments
UF	hydrogenous sediments
BT1	SEDIMENTS
NT1	CONCRETIONS
NT1	FERRUGINOUS DEPOSITS
NT1	FLINT
NT1	HYDROTHERMAL DEPOSITS
NT1	MANGANESE DEPOSITS
NT1	METALLIFEROUS SEDIMENTS
NT1	NODULES
NT1	PHOSPHATE ROCKS
NT1	SUBMARINE CEMENTS
NT1	SULPHIDE DEPOSITS
RT	ANHYDRITE
RT	AUTHIGENESIS
RT	AUTHIGENIC MINERALS
RT	AUTOCHTHONOUS DEPOSITS
RT	CARBONATE SEDIMENTS

CHEMICAL SEDIMENTS (cont'd)
RT	CHERTS
RT	EVAPORITES
RT	MINERAL DEPOSITS
RT	ORGANIC SEDIMENTS
RT	PELAGIC SEDIMENTS
RT	SILICEOUS SEDIMENTS

CHEMICAL SPECIATION
RT	CHEMISTRY

CHEMICAL SPILLS
BT1	ACCIDENTS
RT	CHEMICAL PLUMES

CHEMICAL STIMULI
UF	olfactory stimuli
BT1	STIMULI
RT	CHEMORECEPTION
RT	CHEMORECEPTORS
RT	CHEMOTAXIS
RT	CHEMOTROPISM
RT	OLFACTORY ORGANS

CHEMICAL WASTE DISPOSAL
USE	**WASTE DISPOSAL**

CHEMICALLY PRECIPITATED SEDIMENTS
USE	**CHEMICAL SEDIMENTS**

CHEMICALS (FIRE FIGHTING)
USE	**FIRE EXTINGUISHERS**

CHEMILUMINESCENCE
BT1	LUMINESCENCE
RT	AIRGLOW
RT	BIOLUMINESCENCE
RT	CHEMICAL REACTIONS
RT	LIGHT
RT	PHOSPHORESCENCE

CHEMISORPTION
USE	**SORPTION**

CHEMISTRY
SN	Use of a more specific term is recommended
NT1	ATMOSPHERIC CHEMISTRY
NT1	BIOCHEMISTRY
NT2	CYTOCHEMISTRY
NT2	HISTOCHEMISTRY
NT1	ELECTROCHEMISTRY
NT1	GEOCHEMISTRY
NT2	BIOGEOCHEMISTRY
NT2	SEDIMENT CHEMISTRY
NT1	PHOTOCHEMISTRY
NT1	RADIOCHEMISTRY
NT1	SURFACE CHEMISTRY
RT	ANALYTICAL TECHNIQUES
RT	CHEMICAL COMPOSITION
RT	CHEMICAL ELEMENTS
RT	CHEMICAL EXTRACTION
RT	CHEMICAL LIMNOLOGY
RT	CHEMICAL OCEANOGRAPHY
RT	CHEMICAL PRECIPITATION
RT	CHEMICAL PROPERTIES
RT	CHEMICAL REACTIONS
RT	CHEMICAL SPECIATION
RT	WATER ANALYSIS

CHEMOCONTROL
USE	**CHEMICAL CONTROL**

CHEMORECEPTION
SN	Any sensory perception of ions or chemical compounds
RT	ALARM SUBSTANCES
RT	CHEMICAL STIMULI
RT	CHEMORECEPTORS
RT	CHEMOTROPISM

CHEMORECEPTION (cont'd)
RT	IONS
RT	OLFACTORY ORGANS
RT	SENSE FUNCTIONS
RT	TASTE ORGANS

CHEMORECEPTORS
UF	chemical receptors
BT1	SENSE ORGANS
BT2	ANIMAL ORGANS
BT3	BODY ORGANS
RT	CHEMICAL STIMULI
RT	CHEMORECEPTION
RT	OLFACTION
RT	OLFACTORY ORGANS
RT	TASTE FUNCTIONS
RT	TASTE ORGANS

CHEMOSYNTHESIS
RT	BACTERIA
RT	BIOSYNTHESIS
RT	NUTRIENTS (MINERAL)
RT	PHOTOSYNTHESIS

CHEMOTAXIS
BT1	TAXIS
BT2	ORIENTATION BEHAVIOUR
BT3	BEHAVIOUR
RT	CHEMICAL STIMULI
RT	CHEMOTROPISM
RT	OLFACTORY ORGANS

CHEMOTAXONOMY
SN	The classification of organisms on the basis of the distribution and composition of their chemical substances. Added in 1980
UF	molecular taxonomy
BT1	TAXONOMY
RT	BACTERIA
RT	CHEMICAL COMPOSITION
RT	DNA

CHEMOTROPISM
BT1	TROPISM
RT	CHEMICAL STIMULI
RT	CHEMORECEPTION
RT	CHEMOTAXIS

CHENIER PLAINS
BT1	COASTAL LANDFORMS
BT2	LANDFORMS
BT3	TOPOGRAPHIC FEATURES
RT	CHENIERS

CHENIERS
BT1	BEACH RIDGES
BT2	BEACH FEATURES
RT	CHENIER PLAINS
RT	WETLANDS
RT	FLINT

CHERTIFICATION
RT	CHERTS
RT	DIAGENESIS
RT	METASOMATISM
RT	SILICIFICATION

CHERTS
BT1	SILICEOUS ROCKS
RT	CHEMICAL SEDIMENTS
RT	CHERTIFICATION
RT	CONCRETIONS
RT	DIAGENESIS
RT	NODULES
RT	SEDIMENTARY ROCKS
RT	SILICA

CHI SQUARE TEST
USE	**STATISTICAL ANALYSIS**

CHILLED PRODUCTS
BT1	PROCESSED FISHERY PRODUCTS
BT2	FISHERY PRODUCTS
BT3	PRODUCTS
RT	CHILLING STORAGE
RT	FISH HANDLING
RT	FREEZING
RT	FROZEN PRODUCTS
RT	REFRIGERATION

CHILLING STORAGE
BT1	COLD STORAGE
RT	CHILLED PRODUCTS
RT	STORAGE

CHIMAERAS FISHERIES
USE	**SHARK FISHERIES**

CHITIN
BT1	MUCOPOLYSACCHARIDES
BT2	POLYSACCHARIDES
BT3	SACCHARIDES
BT4	CARBOHYDRATES
RT	CARAPACE
RT	CHITOSAN
RT	CUTICLES
RT	EXOSKELETON
RT	GLUCOSAMINE

CHITOSAN
SN	Added in 1980
RT	CHITIN

CHLORIC ACID
BT1	INORGANIC ACIDS
BT2	HYDROGEN COMPOUNDS
RT	CHLORINE COMPOUNDS
RT	FLUORINE COMPOUNDS

CHLORIDES
BT1	CHLORINE COMPOUNDS
BT2	HALOGEN COMPOUNDS
RT	HALIDES
RT	SODIUM CHLORIDE

CHLORINATED HYDROCARBONS
BT1	HALOGENATED HYDROCARBONS
BT2	HYDROCARBONS
BT3	ORGANIC COMPOUNDS
NT1	ALDRIN
NT1	CHLOROFORM
NT1	DDE
NT1	DDT
NT1	DIELDRIN
NT1	TRICHLOROETHYLENE
RT	PESTICIDES

CHLORINATION
SN	Sterilization of water with chlorine or chlorine compounds. Added in 1980
UF	chlorinators
BT1	HALOGENATION
BT2	CHEMICAL REACTIONS
RT	CHLORINE
RT	DECHLORINATION
RT	DISINFECTION
RT	ODOUR
RT	SEWAGE TREATMENT
RT	WATER PURIFICATION

CHLORINATORS
USE	**CHLORINATION**

CHLORINE
BT1	CHEMICAL ELEMENTS
RT	BROMINE
RT	CHLORINATION
RT	CHLORINE COMPOUNDS
RT	CHLORINE ISOTOPES
RT	DECHLORINATION
RT	DISINFECTANTS
RT	FLUORINE
RT	FLUORINE COMPOUNDS
RT	HALOGENS
RT	IODINE

CHLORINE COMPOUNDS
BT1	HALOGEN COMPOUNDS
NT1	CHLORIDES
RT	BRINES
RT	CHEMICAL COMPOUNDS
RT	CHLORIC ACID
RT	CHLORINE
RT	CHLORINITY
RT	DISSOLVED SALTS
RT	FLUORINE COMPOUNDS
RT	ORGANIC COMPOUNDS

CHLORINE ISOTOPES
BT1	ISOTOPES
RT	CHLORINE

CHLORINITY
BT1	SALINITY
BT2	CHEMICAL PROPERTIES
BT3	PROPERTIES
RT	CHLORINE COMPOUNDS
RT	CHLOROSITY
RT	FLUORINE COMPOUNDS
RT	KNUDSEN TABLES
RT	WATER DENSITY
RT	WATER PROPERTIES

CHLORITE
BT1	CLAY MINERALS
BT2	SILICATE MINERALS
BT3	MINERALS
RT	SLATES

CHLOROFORM
BT1	CHLORINATED HYDROCARBONS
BT2	HALOGENATED HYDROCARBONS
BT3	HYDROCARBONS
BT4	ORGANIC COMPOUNDS
RT	METHANE

CHLOROPHYLLS
BT1	PHOTOSYNTHETIC PIGMENTS
BT2	PIGMENTS
BT3	GLYCOSIDES
BT4	CARBOHYDRATES
RT	CHLOROPLASTS
RT	PHOTOSYNTHESIS
RT	PORPHYRINS

CHLOROPLASTS
RT	CELLS
RT	CHLOROPHYLLS
RT	CHROMATOPHORES
RT	PHOTOSYNTHETIC PIGMENTS

CHLOROSITY
SN	Chlorinity in grams/litre
BT1	SALINITY
BT2	CHEMICAL PROPERTIES
BT3	PROPERTIES
RT	CHLORINITY
RT	WATER DENSITY
RT	WATER PROPERTIES

ASFIS Thesaurus

CHOLESTEROL
SN	Added in 1980
BT1	STEROLS
BT2	STEROIDS
BT3	LIPIDS
BT4	ORGANIC COMPOUNDS
RT	BLOOD CELLS

CHOLINE
BT1	ALCOHOLS
BT2	ORGANIC COMPOUNDS
RT	LIPIDS

CHOLINESTERASE INHIBITORS
UF	anticholinesterases
BT1	ENZYME INHIBITORS
BT2	INHIBITORS
RT	DRUGS
RT	ENZYMES
RT	MUSCLES
RT	MUSCULOSKELETAL SYSTEM
RT	PHYSIOLOGY

CHOLOCALCIFEROL
USE	**VITAMIN D**

CHONDRIOSOMES
USE	**CELL ORGANELLES**

CHORDATE ZOOLOGY
USE	**VERTEBRATE ZOOLOGY**

CHOROLOGY
USE	**BIOGEOGRAPHY**

CHRISTMAS TREES
USE	**WELLHEADS**

CHROMATIC ADAPTATIONS
BT1	ADAPTATIONS
BT2	BIOLOGICAL PHENOMENA
RT	CHROMATIC BEHAVIOUR
RT	CHROMATIC PIGMENTS
RT	COLOUR

CHROMATIC BEHAVIOUR
BT1	BEHAVIOUR
RT	CHROMATIC ADAPTATIONS
RT	CHROMATIC PIGMENTS
RT	CHROMATOPHORES
RT	LIGHT EFFECTS
RT	PIGMENTS
RT	PROTECTIVE BEHAVIOUR

CHROMATIC PIGMENTS
BT1	PIGMENTS
BT2	GLYCOSIDES
BT3	CARBOHYDRATES
BT4	ORGANIC COMPOUNDS
NT1	CAROTENOIDS
RT	ALBINISM
RT	CHROMATIC ADAPTATIONS
RT	CHROMATIC BEHAVIOUR
RT	CHROMATOPHORES
RT	COLOUR
RT	DISCOLOURATION

CHROMATOGRAPHIC ANALYSIS
USE	**CHROMATOGRAPHIC TECHNIQUES**

CHROMATOGRAPHIC TECHNIQUES
UF	chromatographic analysis
UF	chromatography
BT1	ANALYTICAL TECHNIQUES
NT1	GAS CHROMATOGRAPHY
RT	ADSORPTION
RT	COLORIMETRIC TECHNIQUES
RT	LIGHT ABSORPTION
RT	SPECTROSCOPIC TECHNIQUES

CHROMATOGRAPHY
USE	**CHROMATOGRAPHIC TECHNIQUES**

CHROMATOPHORES
UF	erytrophores
UF	melanophores
UF	xanthophores
RT	CELLS
RT	CHLOROPLASTS
RT	CHROMATIC BEHAVIOUR
RT	CHROMATIC PIGMENTS
RT	PIGMENTS

CHROMITE
BT1	OXIDE MINERALS
BT2	MINERALS
RT	CHROMIUM
RT	PLACERS

CHROMIUM
BT1	CHEMICAL ELEMENTS
RT	CHROMITE
RT	CHROMIUM COMPOUNDS
RT	CHROMIUM ISOTOPES
RT	HEAVY METALS
RT	HEAVY MINERALS
RT	METALS
RT	TRACE ELEMENTS
RT	TRANSITION ELEMENTS

CHROMIUM COMPOUNDS
RT	CHEMICAL COMPOUNDS
RT	CHROMIUM

CHROMIUM ISOTOPES
BT1	ISOTOPES
RT	CHROMIUM

CHROMOSOME MUTATIONS
USE	**MUTATIONS**

CHROMOSOME NUMBERS
USE	**CHROMOSOMES**

CHROMOSOMES
UF	chromosome numbers
UF	karyomites
BT1	CELL CONSTITUENTS
NT1	GENES
RT	CYTOLOGY
RT	GENETICS
RT	GENOMES
RT	HISTONES
RT	KARYOLOGY
RT	KARYOTYPES
RT	MEIOSIS
RT	MITOSIS
RT	MUTATIONS
RT	POLYPLOIDS
RT	SEX DETERMINATION

CHRONOMETERS
UF	clocks
UF	time measuring equipment
UF	timing devices
BT1	EQUIPMENT
NT1	QUARTZ CLOCKS

CHRONOSTRATIGRAPHY
BT1	STRATIGRAPHY
BT2	GEOLOGY
BT3	EARTH SCIENCES
RT	GEOLOGICAL TIME
RT	PALAEONTOLOGY
RT	STRATIGRAPHIC CORRELATION

CIGUATERA
BT1	HUMAN DISEASES
BT2	DISEASES
RT	CIGUATOXIN
RT	POISONOUS FISH

CIGUATOXIN
BT1	BIOLOGICAL POISONS
RT	CIGUATERA
RT	POISONOUS FISH

CILIA
BT1	ANIMAL APPENDAGES
RT	FLAGELLA
RT	LOCOMOTION

CIRCADIAN RHYTHMS
SN	Pertaining to 24-hour biological cycle
UF	diurnal rhythms
BT1	BIOLOGICAL RHYTHMS
BT2	BIOLOGICAL PHENOMENA
RT	BIOLOGICAL CLOCKS
RT	DIURNAL VARIATIONS
RT	MOON PHASES
RT	PHOTOPERIODS
RT	PHOTOTROPISM

CIRCULATION
SN	Use of a more specific term is recommended. Added in 1982
RT	ADVECTION
RT	ATMOSPHERIC CIRCULATION
RT	BLOOD CIRCULATION
RT	OCEAN CIRCULATION
RT	RECIRCULATING SYSTEMS
RT	UPWELLING
RT	WATER CIRCULATION
RT	WATER CURRENTS
RT	WATER MIXING

CIRCULATION (ATMOSPHERE)
USE	**ATMOSPHERIC CIRCULATION**

CIRCULATION (BLOOD)
USE	**BLOOD CIRCULATION**

CIRCULATION (WATER)
USE	**WATER CIRCULATION**

CIRCULATORY SYSTEM
UF	vascular system
NT1	BLOOD VESSELS
NT1	HEART
RT	ANATOMY
RT	BLOOD
RT	BLOOD CELLS
RT	BLOOD CIRCULATION
RT	BLOOD PRESSURE
RT	BODY FLUIDS
RT	HAEMORRHAGE

CITRATES
BT1	CARBOXYLIC ACID SALTS

CIVIL ENGINEERING
BT1	ENGINEERING
RT	COASTAL ENGINEERING

CLAM CULTURE
SN	Before 1982 search MOLLUSC CULTURE
BT1	MOLLUSC CULTURE
BT2	SHELLFISH CULTURE
BT3	AQUACULTURE
RT	MARINE AQUACULTURE
RT	PREDATOR CONTROL
RT	SEED COLLECTION
RT	SPAT

CLAM FISHERIES
SN	Added in 1982
UF	arkshell fisheries
UF	cockle fisheries
UF	quahog fisheries
BT1	MOLLUSC FISHERIES
BT2	SHELLFISH FISHERIES
BT3	FISHERIES
RT	DREDGING
RT	HARVESTING
RT	MARINE FISHERIES

CLAPOTIS
USE	**STANDING WAVES**

CLASSIFICATION
RT	CLASSIFICATION SYSTEMS

CLASSIFICATION (BIOLOGICAL)
USE	**TAXONOMY**

CLASSIFICATION SYSTEMS
SN	Systems for classification of inanimate objects or ecological or biological attributes of organisms
RT	CLASSIFICATION
RT	NUMERICAL TAXONOMY
RT	TAXONOMY
RT	TERMINOLOGY

CLASSIFIED DOCUMENTS
BT1	REPORT LITERATURE
BT2	DOCUMENTS

CLASTIC DEPOSITS
USE	**CLASTICS**

CLASTIC ROCKS
USE	**CLASTICS**

CLASTIC SEDIMENTS
USE	**CLASTICS**

CLASTICS
SN	Before 1982 search CLASTIC SEDIMENTS
UF	clastic deposits
UF	clastic rocks
UF	clastic sediments
BT1	SEDIMENTS
NT1	ARENITES
NT1	BENTONITE
NT1	BOULDERS
NT1	BRECCIA
NT1	CLAYS
NT2	FULLERS EARTH
NT2	PELAGIC CLAY
NT1	COBBLESTONE
NT1	CONTOURITES
NT1	FLYSCH
NT1	GRAVEL
NT1	MARLSTONE
NT1	MUD
NT2	FLUID MUD
NT1	MUDSTONE
NT1	PEBBLES
NT1	SAND
NT2	QUICKSANDS
NT1	SANDSTONE
NT2	OIL SANDS
NT1	SHALE
NT2	OIL SHALE
NT1	SHINGLE
NT1	SILT
NT1	SILTSTONE
NT1	TURBIDITES
RT	ALLUVIAL DEPOSITS
RT	BOULDER CLAY
RT	CEMENTATION
RT	DETRITAL DEPOSITS
RT	EOLIAN DEPOSITS

CLASTICS (cont'd)
RT	GLACIAL DEPOSITS
RT	RADIOLARITE
RT	TEPHRA
RT	TERRIGENOUS SEDIMENTS

CLAY MINERALS
BT1	SILICATE MINERALS
BT2	MINERALS
NT1	CHLORITE
NT1	ILLITE
NT1	KAOLIN
NT1	KAOLINITE
NT1	MONTMORILLONITE
NT1	NONTRONITE
NT1	PALYGORSKITE
NT1	SAPONITE
NT1	SMECTITE
NT1	VERMICULITE
RT	ARGILLACEOUS DEPOSITS
RT	BAUXITE
RT	CLAYS
RT	FLOCCULATION
RT	PELAGIC CLAY

CLAY SOILS
USE	**CLAYS**

CLAYS
UF	clay soils
BT1	CLASTICS
BT2	SEDIMENTS
NT1	FULLERS EARTH
NT1	PELAGIC CLAY
RT	ARGILLACEOUS DEPOSITS
RT	CLAY MINERALS
RT	KAOLIN
RT	MARL
RT	MUD
RT	SEDIMENT LOAD

CLEAN-UP TECHNIQUES
USE	**OIL REMOVAL**

CLEANING
NT1	TANK CLEANING
RT	PIGGING
RT	SCALING

CLEANING BEHAVIOUR
SN	Added in 1980
BT1	BEHAVIOUR
RT	AQUARIOLOGY
RT	SYMBIOSIS

CLEAR AIR TURBULENCE
UF	cat
BT1	ATMOSPHERIC TURBULENCE
BT2	TURBULENCE
BT3	FLUID MOTION
RT	JET STREAM
RT	KELVIN-HELMHOLTZ INSTABILITY

CLIFFS
BT1	COASTAL LANDFORMS
BT2	LANDFORMS
BT3	TOPOGRAPHIC FEATURES
RT	CAVES
RT	EROSION FEATURES
RT	FAULT SCARPS
RT	ICE FRONTS
RT	LANDSLIDES
RT	WAVE-CUT PLATFORMS

CLIMATE
NT1	HYDROCLIMATE
NT1	PALAEOCLIMATE
NT1	WEATHER
NT2	STORMS
RT	AIR TEMPERATURE

CLIMATE (cont'd)
RT	ATMOSPHERIC PRESSURE
RT	BIOCLIMATOLOGY
RT	CLIMATE PREDICTION
RT	CLIMATIC CHANGES
RT	CLIMATIC DATA
RT	CLIMATIC ZONES
RT	CLIMATOLOGY
RT	DUST CLOUDS
RT	GEOGRAPHY
RT	METEOROLOGICAL DATA
RT	OCEAN-ATMOSPHERE SYSTEM
RT	PHENOLOGY
RT	RAINFALL
RT	SEA LEVEL PRESSURE
RT	SEASONS
RT	SOLAR RADIATION
RT	WAVE CLIMATE
RT	WEATHER FORECASTING
RT	WINDS

CLIMATE PREDICTION
BT1	PREDICTION
RT	CLIMATE
RT	WEATHER FORECASTING

CLIMATIC CHANGES
RT	AIR POLLUTION
RT	ATMOSPHERIC CHEMISTRY
RT	CARBON DIOXIDE
RT	CLIMATE
RT	CLIMATOLOGY
RT	DEGLACIATION
RT	DUST CLOUDS
RT	EARTH ROTATION
RT	EUSTATIC CHANGES
RT	GEOCHRONOMETRY
RT	GLACIATION
RT	GREENHOUSE EFFECT
RT	ICE CAPS
RT	ICE COVER
RT	ICE EDGE
RT	ICE VOLUME
RT	LONG-TERM CHANGES
RT	MASS EXTINCTIONS
RT	PALAEOCLIMATE
RT	PALAEOSALINITY
RT	PALAEOTEMPERATURE
RT	SEA LEVEL CHANGES
RT	SOLAR CONSTANT
RT	SOLAR-TERRESTRIAL ACTIVITY
RT	VOLCANIC ASH

CLIMATIC DATA
UF	climatological data
BT1	METEOROLOGICAL DATA
BT2	DATA
RT	CLIMATE
RT	CLIMATOLOGICAL CHARTS
RT	CLIMATOLOGY

CLIMATIC MAPS
USE	**CLIMATOLOGICAL CHARTS**

CLIMATIC ZONES
SN	Mainly related to hydroclimate
NT1	POLAR ZONES
NT2	ANTARCTIC ZONE
NT2	ARCTIC ZONE
NT1	SUBTROPICAL ZONES
NT1	TEMPERATE ZONES
RT	ARID ENVIRONMENTS
RT	CLIMATE
RT	CLIMATOLOGY
RT	GEOGRAPHY
RT	HYDROCLIMATE
RT	SEASONS

CLIMATOLOGICAL CHARTS
UF	climatic maps
BT1	MAPS
BT2	GRAPHICS
BT3	AUDIOVISUAL MATERIAL
BT4	DOCUMENTS
RT	ATLASES
RT	CLIMATIC DATA
RT	ISOHYETS
RT	OCEANOGRAPHIC ATLASES
RT	WAVE CLIMATE
RT	WIND ROSES

CLIMATOLOGICAL DATA
USE	**CLIMATIC DATA**

CLIMATOLOGISTS
USE	**METEOROLOGISTS**

CLIMATOLOGY
NT1	BIOCLIMATOLOGY
NT1	PALAEOCLIMATOLOGY
RT	AIR TEMPERATURE
RT	ANTICYCLONES
RT	ATMOSPHERIC PRESSURE
RT	ATMOSPHERIC SCIENCES
RT	BIOGEOGRAPHY
RT	CLIMATE
RT	CLIMATIC CHANGES
RT	CLIMATIC DATA
RT	CLIMATIC ZONES
RT	DROUGHTS
RT	EARTH SCIENCES
RT	EVAPORATION
RT	GEOGRAPHY
RT	HUMIDITY
RT	HYDROCLIMATE
RT	LONG-TERM CHANGES
RT	METEOROLOGICAL DATA
RT	METEOROLOGY
RT	PHENOLOGY
RT	SEA LEVEL PRESSURE
RT	SEASONS
RT	WINDS

CLIMAX COMMUNITY
SN	A stable community by climax formation as consequence of a successional series of ecological changes
RT	AQUATIC COMMUNITIES
RT	COMMUNITY COMPOSITION
RT	DOMINANT SPECIES
RT	ECOLOGICAL ASSOCIATIONS
RT	ECOLOGICAL SUCCESSION
RT	SPECIES DIVERSITY

CLINES
SN	Added in 1980
NT1	ECOCLINES
NT1	GEOCLINES
RT	HALOCLINE
RT	THERMOCLINE

CLINOPTILONITE
BT1	ZEOLITES
BT2	SILICATE MINERALS
BT3	MINERALS

CLOCKS
USE	**CHRONOMETERS**

CLONES
SN	Groups of organisms genetically identical. Added in 1980
RT	AQUATIC ORGANISMS
RT	ASEXUAL REPRODUCTION
RT	CELLS
RT	GENETICS
RT	PARTHENOGENESIS

CLOSED RECIRCULATING SYSTEMS
USE	**RECIRCULATING SYSTEMS**

CLOSED SEASONS
USE	**SEASON REGULATIONS**

CLOSURE APPROXIMATION
BT1	APPROXIMATION
BT2	NUMERICAL ANALYSIS
BT3	MATHEMATICAL ANALYSIS

CLOUD COVER
UF	cloudiness
RT	CLOUDS
RT	INSOLATION
RT	SOLAR RADIATION
RT	TERRESTRIAL RADIATION
RT	WEATHER

CLOUD HEIGHT
RT	CLOUDS
RT	HEIGHT

CLOUD PHYSICS
BT1	ATMOSPHERIC PHYSICS
BT2	PHYSICS
RT	CLOUDS

CLOUDINESS
USE	**CLOUD COVER**

CLOUDS
UF	cumulus
BT1	HYDROMETEORS
NT1	FOG
RT	ATMOSPHERIC PRECIPITATIONS
RT	CLOUD COVER
RT	CLOUD HEIGHT
RT	CLOUD PHYSICS
RT	WEATHER

CLUPEOID FISHERIES
SN	Added in 1982
UF	anchovy fisheries
UF	herring fisheries
UF	pilchard fisheries
UF	sardine fisheries
UF	sardinella fisheries
UF	sprat fisheries
BT1	FINFISH FISHERIES
BT2	FISHERIES
RT	BAIT FISH
RT	COASTAL FISHERIES
RT	MARINE FISHERIES
RT	PELAGIC FISHERIES
RT	PURSE SEINING

CLUTCH
SN	Added in 1980
UF	clutch size
RT	BIRD EGGS
RT	HATCHING
RT	NESTING
RT	NESTS

CLUTCH SIZE
USE	**CLUTCH**

CNOIDAL WAVES
BT1	SHALLOW-WATER WAVES
BT2	WATER WAVES
RT	NONLINEAR WAVES
RT	SURFACE GRAVITY WAVES

CNS
USE	**CENTRAL NERVOUS SYSTEM**

COAGULANTS
SN	Added in 1980
RT	ADDITIVES
RT	AGENTS
RT	ANTICOAGULANTS
RT	CHEMICAL PRECIPITATION
RT	COAGULATION
RT	DRUGS

COAGULATION
SN	Added in 1980
UF	coagulators
BT1	CHEMICAL REACTIONS
RT	BIOCHEMICAL OXYGEN DEMAND
RT	BLOOD
RT	COAGULANTS
RT	FLOTATION
RT	WATER POLLUTION TREATMENT
RT	WATER PURIFICATION
RT	WATER TREATMENT

COAGULATORS
USE	**COAGULATION**

COAL
BT1	FOSSIL FUELS
BT2	SUBSURFACE DEPOSITS
BT3	MINERAL DEPOSITS
BT4	MINERAL RESOURCES
RT	MINING
RT	SAPROPELITE

COAMPLITUDE LINES
USE	**CORANGE LINES**

COARSE FISH
SN	Freshwater fish not belonging to the family Salmonidae
BT1	FRESHWATER FISH
BT2	FISH
BT3	AQUATIC ANIMALS

COAST ACCRETION
USE	**PROGRADATION**

COAST DEFENCES
SN	Before 1982 search also COASTAL STRUCTURES
BT1	COASTAL STRUCTURES
BT2	HYDRAULIC STRUCTURES
NT1	BREAKWATERS
NT2	RIPRAP
NT2	RUBBLEMOUND BREAKWATERS
NT1	GROYNES
NT1	SEA WALLS
NT1	STORM SURGE BARRIERS
RT	BEACH EROSION
RT	COASTAL ENGINEERING
RT	COASTAL ZONE
RT	COASTAL ZONE MANAGEMENT
RT	CONCRETE STRUCTURES
RT	SEA LEVEL CHANGES
RT	SEA LEVEL VARIATIONS
RT	SHORE PROTECTION
RT	SPLASH ZONE
RT	STEEL STRUCTURES
RT	STORM SURGES
RT	WAVE SETUP

COAST EFFECT
RT	ELECTRICAL EXPLORATION
RT	GRAVITY EXPLORATION
RT	MAGNETIC EXPLORATION
RT	MAGNETOTELLURIC METHODS
RT	TELLURIC CURRENTS

ASFIS Thesaurus

COAST PROTECTION	
USE	**SHORE PROTECTION**
COASTAL AQUACULTURE	
USE	**MARINE AQUACULTURE**
COASTAL BOUNDARY LAYER	
BT1	BOUNDARY LAYERS
BT2	LAYERS
RT	COASTAL JETS
RT	LAKE DYNAMICS
RT	NEARSHORE DYNAMICS
COASTAL CIRCULATION	
USE	**SHELF DYNAMICS**
COASTAL COUNTERCURRENTS	
BT1	COUNTERCURRENTS
BT2	WATER CURRENTS
BT3	WATER MOTION
RT	COASTAL CURRENTS
RT	COASTAL UPWELLING
RT	OCEAN CURRENTS
RT	SHELF DYNAMICS
RT	UNDERCURRENTS
COASTAL COUNTRIES	
USE	**COASTAL STATES**
COASTAL CURRENTS	
BT1	WATER CURRENTS
BT2	WATER MOTION
RT	COASTAL COUNTERCURRENTS
RT	COASTAL OCEANOGRAPHY
RT	NEARSHORE DYNAMICS
RT	SEDIMENT TRANSPORT
RT	UPWELLING
RT	WIND-DRIVEN CURRENTS
COASTAL CURRENTS (LITTORAL)	
USE	**NEARSHORE CURRENTS**
COASTAL DUNES	
USE	**DUNES**
COASTAL ENGINEERING	
BT1	ENGINEERING
RT	BARRAGES
RT	CIVIL ENGINEERING
RT	COAST DEFENCES
RT	COASTAL STRUCTURES
RT	COASTAL ZONE
RT	COASTAL ZONE MANAGEMENT
RT	GEOTECHNOLOGY
RT	HYDRAULIC MODELS
RT	HYDRAULIC STRUCTURES
RT	MARINE TECHNOLOGY
RT	PORT INSTALLATIONS
RT	RECREATIONAL WATERS
RT	RIVER ENGINEERING
RT	SHORE PROTECTION
RT	STRUCTURAL ENGINEERING
RT	TIDAL BARRAGES
COASTAL ENVIRONMENT	
USE	**COASTAL ZONE**
COASTAL EROSION	
UF	shoreline erosion
BT1	EROSION
NT1	BEACH EROSION
RT	ALLUVIAL DEPOSITS
RT	BEACHES
RT	BREAKWATERS
RT	COASTAL ZONE
RT	COASTS
RT	DELTAS
RT	EROSION CONTROL
RT	LAND RECLAMATION
RT	RETROGRADATION

COASTAL EROSION (cont'd)	
RT	ROCKY SHORES
RT	SEDIMENT TRANSPORT
RT	SHORE PROTECTION
RT	SOIL CONSERVATION
COASTAL EROSION FEATURES	
USE	**EROSION FEATURES**
COASTAL FISHERIES	
BT1	FISHERIES
RT	ARTISANAL FISHING
RT	BARRIERS
RT	BEACH SEINES
RT	BOATS
RT	CAST NETS
RT	CLUPEOID FISHERIES
RT	COASTAL STATES
RT	CRAB FISHERIES
RT	CRUSTACEAN FISHERIES
RT	DREDGES
RT	ECHINODERM FISHERIES
RT	ESTUARINE FISHERIES
RT	FISHING BARRIERS
RT	GILLNETS
RT	GRAPPLING GEAR
RT	HARVESTING MACHINES
RT	LAKE FISHERIES
RT	LIFT-NETS
RT	LINERS
RT	LINES
RT	LOBSTER FISHERIES
RT	MARINE FISH
RT	MARINE FISHERIES
RT	PERCOID FISHERIES
RT	SCALLOP FISHERIES
RT	SEINE NETS
RT	SEINERS
RT	SQUAT LOBSTER FISHERIES
RT	TRAP NETS
RT	TRAWL NETS
COASTAL GEODESY	
BT1	GEODESY
BT2	GEOPHYSICS
BT3	EARTH SCIENCES
RT	MARINE GEODESY
COASTAL INLETS	
UF	voes
BT1	COASTAL WATERS
NT1	BAYS
NT1	DROWNED VALLEYS
NT1	ESTUARIES
NT2	PARTIALLY-MIXED ESTUARIES
NT2	SALT-WEDGE ESTUARIES
NT1	FJORDS
NT1	INLETS (WATERWAYS)
NT1	TIDAL INLETS
RT	COASTAL LAGOONS
RT	COASTAL OCEANOGRAPHY
RT	HARBOURS
RT	PORT INSTALLATIONS
RT	TOPOGRAPHIC FEATURES
RT	WATER BODIES
COASTAL JETS	
BT1	JETS
BT2	FLUID FLOW
BT3	FLUID MOTION
RT	COASTAL BOUNDARY LAYER
RT	LAKE CURRENTS
RT	LAKE DYNAMICS
RT	LONGSHORE CURRENTS
RT	NEARSHORE DYNAMICS
RT	SHELF DYNAMICS

COASTAL LAGOONS	
UF	haff
BT1	LAGOONS
RT	AQUACULTURE
RT	BARRIER ISLANDS
RT	BARRIER SPITS
RT	BRACKISHWATER AQUACULTURE
RT	BRACKISHWATER ECOLOGY
RT	BRACKISHWATER ENVIRONMENT
RT	COASTAL INLETS
RT	COASTAL WATERS
RT	COASTS
RT	CRAB CULTURE
RT	DESALINATION
RT	DESALINATION PLANTS
RT	SABKHAS
RT	SHRIMP CULTURE
RT	TIDAL INLETS
RT	VALLICULTURE
COASTAL LANDFORMS	
UF	coastal topographic features
UF	shoreline features
BT1	LANDFORMS
BT2	TOPOGRAPHIC FEATURES
NT1	BARRIER ISLANDS
NT1	BEACHES
NT2	BARRIER BEACHES
NT2	RAISED BEACHES
NT1	CAVES
NT1	CHENIER PLAINS
NT1	CLIFFS
NT1	DELTAS
NT1	HEADLANDS
NT2	CUSPATE FORELANDS
NT1	PALAEOSHORELINES
NT1	ROCKY SHORES
NT1	STACKS
NT1	TIDAL FLATS
RT	COASTAL MORPHOLOGY
RT	DROWNED VALLEYS
RT	ESTUARIES
RT	FJORDS
RT	LAND AND SEA BREEZES
COASTAL MORPHOLOGY	
UF	morphology (coastal)
BT1	GEOMORPHOLOGY
BT2	GEOLOGY
BT3	EARTH SCIENCES
NT1	BEACH MORPHOLOGY
RT	COASTAL LANDFORMS
RT	ESTUARIES
RT	FJORDS
RT	LAKE SHORES
RT	LANDSLIDES
RT	PALAEOSHORELINES
RT	PROGRADATION
RT	RAISED BEACHES
RT	RETROGRADATION
RT	ROCKY SHORES
COASTAL NATIONS	
USE	**COASTAL STATES**
COASTAL OCEANOGRAPHY	
UF	nearshore oceanography
BT1	OCEANOGRAPHY
BT2	EARTH SCIENCES
RT	COASTAL CURRENTS
RT	COASTAL INLETS
RT	COASTAL WATERS
RT	ESTUARIES
RT	ESTUARINE DYNAMICS
RT	NEARSHORE CURRENTS
RT	NEARSHORE DYNAMICS
RT	SHELF DYNAMICS

ASFIS Thesaurus

COASTAL RECLAMATION
USE   **LAND RECLAMATION**

COASTAL STATES
- SN   Added in 1980
- UF   coastal countries
- UF   coastal nations
- UF   littoral states
- UF   sea states
- BT1   COUNTRIES
- RT   COASTAL FISHERIES
- RT   COASTAL ZONE
- RT   COASTS
- RT   EXCLUSIVE ECONOMIC ZONE
- RT   EXTENDED JURISDICTION
- RT   FISHERY DISPUTES
- RT   FISHING RIGHTS
- RT   FOREIGN FISHING
- RT   JURISDICTION
- RT   LANDLOCKED STATES
- RT   MARINE RESOURCES
- RT   POLITICAL ASPECTS
- RT   SEDENTARY SPECIES
- RT   TERRITORIAL WATERS

COASTAL STRUCTURES
- BT1   HYDRAULIC STRUCTURES
- NT1   ARTIFICIAL HARBOURS
- NT2   MARINAS
- NT2   MILITARY PORTS
- NT1   COAST DEFENCES
- NT2   BREAKWATERS
- NT3   RIPRAP
- NT3   RUBBLEMOUND BREAKWATERS
- NT2   GROYNES
- NT2   SEA WALLS
- NT2   STORM SURGE BARRIERS
- NT1   PIERS
- NT1   PORT INSTALLATIONS
- RT   AIRPORTS
- RT   BARRAGES
- RT   COASTAL ENGINEERING
- RT   COASTAL ZONE MANAGEMENT
- RT   DESIGN WAVE
- RT   HARBOURS
- RT   OVERWASH
- RT   SHORE PROTECTION
- RT   SPLASH ZONE
- RT   STRUCTURES

COASTAL TOPOGRAPHIC FEATURES
USE   **COASTAL LANDFORMS**

COASTAL TRAPPED WAVES
USE   **TRAPPED WAVES**

COASTAL UPWELLING
- BT1   UPWELLING
- BT2   VERTICAL WATER MOVEMENT
- BT3   WATER MOTION
- RT   ARID ENVIRONMENTS
- RT   COASTAL COUNTERCURRENTS
- RT   DIVERGENCE
- RT   EASTERN BOUNDARY CURRENTS
- RT   EKMAN TRANSPORT
- RT   EL NINO PHENOMENA
- RT   SHELF DYNAMICS
- RT   TRADE WINDS

COASTAL WATERS
- NT1   COASTAL INLETS
- NT2   BAYS
- NT2   DROWNED VALLEYS
- NT2   ESTUARIES
- NT3   PARTIALLY-MIXED ESTUARIES
- NT3   SALT-WEDGE ESTUARIES
- NT2   FJORDS
- NT2   INLETS (WATERWAYS)
- NT2   TIDAL INLETS
- NT1   STRAITS

COASTAL WATERS (cont'd)
- RT   COASTAL LAGOONS
- RT   COASTAL OCEANOGRAPHY
- RT   COASTAL ZONE
- RT   COASTS
- RT   HARBOURS
- RT   HYDROSPHERE
- RT   INLAND SEAS
- RT   LITTORAL ZONE
- RT   MARGINAL SEAS
- RT   NEARSHORE DYNAMICS
- RT   SHELF DYNAMICS
- RT   SHOALS
- RT   WATER BODIES

COASTAL ZONE
- SN   The band of dry land and adjacent ocean space in which land ecology and use directly affect ocean space ecology and use, and vice versa
- UF   coastal environment
- UF   nearshore environment
- RT   BARRAGES
- RT   BAYS
- RT   BEACHES
- RT   COAST DEFENCES
- RT   COASTAL ENGINEERING
- RT   COASTAL EROSION
- RT   COASTAL STATES
- RT   COASTAL WATERS
- RT   COASTS
- RT   ESTUARIES
- RT   INLETS (WATERWAYS)
- RT   LITTORAL ZONE
- RT   MARINE ENVIRONMENT
- RT   RANCHING
- RT   TIDAL FLATS
- RT   TIDES

COASTAL ZONE MANAGEMENT
- BT1   MANAGEMENT
- NT1   SHORE PROTECTION
- RT   BARRAGES
- RT   COAST DEFENCES
- RT   COASTAL ENGINEERING
- RT   COASTAL STRUCTURES
- RT   DUNE STABILIZATION
- RT   ENVIRONMENT MANAGEMENT
- RT   LAKE RECLAMATION
- RT   LAND RECLAMATION
- RT   PUBLIC ACCESS
- RT   RECREATIONAL WATERS
- RT   REGIONAL PLANNING
- RT   URBANIZATION

COASTGUARDS
- BT1   PERSONNEL
- RT   HEALTH AND SAFETY
- RT   SURVEILLANCE AND ENFORCEMENT

COASTLINES
USE   **COASTS**

COASTS
- UF   coastlines
- UF   sea coast
- UF   seacoast
- UF   shorelines
- BT1   LANDFORMS
- BT2   TOPOGRAPHIC FEATURES
- NT1   EMERGENT SHORELINES
- NT1   RELICT SHORELINES
- NT1   STRANDLINES
- NT1   SUBMERGED SHORELINES
- NT2   RIA COASTS
- RT   BEACHES
- RT   COASTAL EROSION
- RT   COASTAL LAGOONS
- RT   COASTAL STATES
- RT   COASTAL WATERS

COASTS (cont'd)
- RT   COASTAL ZONE
- RT   DELTAS
- RT   DUNES
- RT   FJORDS
- RT   HARBOURS
- RT   PROGRADATION
- RT   REGRESSIONS
- RT   RETROGRADATION
- RT   RIP CURRENTS
- RT   ROCKY SHORES
- RT   SHOALS
- RT   TRANSGRESSIONS

COATING MATERIALS
- UF   coatings
- UF   protective coatings
- BT1   MATERIALS
- NT1   PAINTS
- NT1   PLASTIC COATINGS
- NT1   PRIMERS
- RT   ANTIFOULING SUBSTANCES
- RT   FILMS
- RT   FOULING CONTROL
- RT   SCALING

COATING PROCESSES
- RT   CORROSION CONTROL
- RT   FOULING CONTROL
- RT   PAINTS
- RT   PIPELINE CONSTRUCTION

COATINGS
USE   **COATING MATERIALS**

COAXIAL CABLES
- BT1   ELECTRIC CABLES
- BT2   CABLES
- RT   SUBMARINE CABLES

COBALT
- BT1   CHEMICAL ELEMENTS
- RT   COBALT COMPOUNDS
- RT   COBALT ISOTOPES
- RT   FERROMANGANESE NODULES
- RT   HEAVY METALS
- RT   METALS
- RT   TRACE ELEMENTS
- RT   TRANSITION ELEMENTS

COBALT COMPOUNDS
- RT   CHEMICAL COMPOUNDS
- RT   COBALT

COBALT ISOTOPES
- BT1   ISOTOPES
- RT   COBALT

COBBLES
USE   **COBBLESTONE**

COBBLESTONE
- UF   cobbles
- BT1   CLASTICS
- BT2   SEDIMENTS
- RT   BOULDERS
- RT   RUDITES
- RT   SEDIMENTARY ROCKS

COCCOLITHS
- SN   Minute calcareous plates of algal, protozoan or protist origin
- RT   CALCAREOUS OOZE
- RT   CARBONATE SEDIMENTS
- RT   CHALK
- RT   NANNOFOSSIL OOZE

COCKLE FISHERIES
USE **CLAM FISHERIES**

COD
USE **CHEMICAL OXYGEN DEMAND**

COD FISHERIES
USE **GADOID FISHERIES**

CODES OF PRACTICE
USE **CODEX STANDARDS**

CODES OF PRACTICE
USE **STANDARDS**

CODEX ALIMENTARIUS
USE **CODEX STANDARDS**

CODEX STANDARDS
SN International standards for fish
and fishery products. Added in 1980
UF codes of practice
UF codex alimentarius
RT ACCEPTABILITY
RT FISH HANDLING
RT FISH INSPECTION REGULATIONS
RT ORGANOLEPTIC PROPERTIES
RT PRESERVATION (FISHERY PRODUCTS)
RT PROCESSING FISHERY PRODUCTS
RT QUALITY CONTROL
RT STORAGE

COEFFICIENT OF EDDY VISCOSITY
USE **EDDY VISCOSITY COEFFICIENT**

COEFFICIENTS
SN Used only as a qualifier
RT CONSTANTS
RT KURTOSIS
RT RATIOS
RT SKEWNESS

COELOM
SN Added in 1980
BT1 BODY CAVITIES
RT AMOEBOCYTES
RT COELOMIC FLUIDS

COELOMIC FLUIDS
SN Added in 1980
BT1 BODY FLUIDS
RT COELOM

COENOBIA
USE **COLONIES**

COENZYMES
SN Added in 1980
UF glutathione
BT1 ENZYMES
NT1 CYTOCHROMES
RT ENZYMATIC ACTIVITY
RT ENZYME INHIBITORS
RT VITAMINS

COHESIONLESS SEDIMENTS
UF non-cohesive sediments
RT COHESIVE SEDIMENTS
RT FLUIDIZED SEDIMENT FLOW
RT GRAIN FLOW
RT GRAVEL
RT QUICKSANDS
RT SEDIMENTS
RT SILT
RT SLOPE STABILITY
RT TURBIDITY CURRENTS

COHESIVE SEDIMENTS
BT1 SEDIMENTS
RT COHESIONLESS SEDIMENTS
RT MUD
RT SHEAR STRENGTH
RT SLOPE STABILITY
RT SOIL MECHANICS
RT VANE SHEAR TESTING

COLD BLOODED ANIMALS
USE **POIKILOTHERMY**

COLD BRANDING
SN Marking fish with liquid nitrogen.
Added in 1982
UF freeze-branding
UF kryogenic marking
BT1 MARKING

COLD FRONTS
USE **ATMOSPHERIC FRONTS**

COLD RESISTANCE
SN Added in 1980
UF frost resistance
BT1 BIOLOGICAL RESISTANCE
BT2 BIOLOGICAL PROPERTIES
BT3 PROPERTIES
RT CRYOBIOLOGY
RT ECOPHYSIOLOGY
RT ENVIRONMENTAL EFFECTS
RT POLAR ZONES
RT TEMPERATURE TOLERANCE

COLD SEASON
SN Added in 1980
BT1 SEASONS
RT AIR TEMPERATURE
RT WATER TEMPERATURE

COLD STORAGE
UF refrigeration storage
NT1 CHILLING STORAGE
RT FISH HANDLING
RT FISH STORAGE
RT FISHERY PRODUCTS
RT FREEZING
RT ICE
RT PROCESSING FISHERY PRODUCTS
RT REFRIGERATION
RT REFRIGERATORS
RT STORAGE
RT STORAGE CONDITIONS

COLD WATER DISEASES
USE **PEDUNCLE DISEASE**

COLLAPSE STRENGTH
BT1 STRENGTH
BT2 MECHANICAL PROPERTIES
BT3 PHYSICAL PROPERTIES
BT4 PROPERTIES
RT DEFORMATION
RT YIELD POINT

COLLECTED PAPERS
BT1 DOCUMENTS
NT1 FESTSCHRIFTEN

COLLECTING DEVICES
SN Devices for collection of aquatic
organisms
NT1 BACTERIA COLLECTING DEVICES
NT1 BENTHOS COLLECTING DEVICES
NT1 NEKTON COLLECTING DEVICES
NT1 PLANKTON COLLECTING DEVICES
RT BIOLOGICAL SAMPLING
RT LIMNOLOGICAL EQUIPMENT
RT OCEANOGRAPHIC EQUIPMENT
RT SAMPLERS

COLLECTING DEVICES (cont'd)
RT SEDIMENT TRAPS
RT STANDARDIZATION

COLLECTIONS
SN Use of a more specific term is
recommended
NT1 BIOLOGICAL COLLECTIONS
NT1 DATA COLLECTIONS
NT1 GEOLOGICAL COLLECTIONS
NT1 MINERAL COLLECTIONS
NT1 MUSEUM COLLECTIONS
NT1 SEDIMENT COLLECTIONS
RT CATALOGUES
RT MUSEUMS

COLLIGATIVE PROPERTIES
BT1 PHYSICAL PROPERTIES
BT2 PROPERTIES
RT BOILING POINT
RT FREEZING POINT
RT OSMOTIC PRESSURE
RT VAPOUR PRESSURE

COLLISION AVOIDANCE
RT COLLISIONS
RT NAVIGATION REGULATIONS
RT NAVIGATIONAL AIDS
RT RADAR NAVIGATION
RT SHIPS
RT SURFACE CRAFT
RT TRAFFIC MANAGEMENT

COLLISIONS
UF impacts
BT1 ACCIDENTS
RT COLLISION AVOIDANCE
RT SHIP LOSSES
RT SINKING

COLLOIDAL CLAY
BT1 SUSPENDED INORGANIC MATTER
BT2 INORGANIC MATTER

COLLOIDS
UF dispersions (chemical)
NT1 AEROSOLS
NT2 RADIOACTIVE AEROSOLS
NT1 GELS
RT AGAR
RT BODY FLUIDS
RT CHEMICAL PRECIPITATION
RT DIALYSIS
RT ELECTROPHORESIS
RT EMULSIONS
RT ENZYMES
RT FLOCCULATION
RT FOAMS
RT SUSPENDED PARTICULATE MATTER
RT TURBIDITY

COLLOQUIA
USE **CONFERENCES**

COLONIES
UF coenobia
RT COLONIZATION
RT ECOLOGICAL ASSOCIATIONS
RT GEMMULES
RT INTRODUCED SPECIES

COLONISATION
USE **COLONIZATION**

COLONIZATION
UF colonisation
RT ALGAL SETTLEMENTS
RT ARTIFICIAL LAKES
RT ARTIFICIAL SUBSTRATA
RT BIOLOGICAL SETTLEMENT

COLONIZATION (cont'd)
RT	COLONIES
RT	ECOSYSTEM RESILIENCE
RT	HABITAT SELECTION
RT	INTRODUCED SPECIES
RT	LARVAL SETTLEMENT
RT	SEEDING (AQUACULTURE)
RT	SETTLING BEHAVIOUR
RT	SUBSTRATE PREFERENCES

COLOR
USE	**COLOUR**

COLORATION
USE	**COLOUR**

COLORIMETRIC TECHNIQUES
UF	colorimetry
BT1	ANALYTICAL TECHNIQUES
RT	CHROMATOGRAPHIC TECHNIQUES
RT	COLOUR
RT	LIGHT MEASURING INSTRUMENTS
RT	LIGHT REFRACTION
RT	OPTICAL PROPERTIES
RT	PHOTOMETRY
RT	SPECTROSCOPIC TECHNIQUES
RT	WATER COLOUR

COLORIMETRY
USE	**COLORIMETRIC TECHNIQUES**

COLOUR
UF	color
UF	coloration
BT1	OPTICAL PROPERTIES
BT2	PHYSICAL PROPERTIES
BT3	PROPERTIES
NT1	WATER COLOUR
RT	BIOLOGICAL PROPERTIES
RT	CHROMATIC ADAPTATIONS
RT	CHROMATIC PIGMENTS
RT	COLORIMETRIC TECHNIQUES
RT	DISCOLOURATION
RT	LIGHT
RT	LIGHT DISPERSION
RT	ORGANOLEPTIC PROPERTIES
RT	SPECTRAL COMPOSITION
RT	VISION

COLUMBIAN
USE	**NIOBIUM**

COMMENSALISM
BT1	INTERSPECIFIC RELATIONSHIPS
RT	COMMENSALS
RT	EPIZOITES
RT	PARASITES
RT	SYMBIOSIS

COMMENSALS
SN	Added in 1980
RT	COMMENSALISM
RT	SYMBIONTS

COMMERCE
RT	ECONOMICS
RT	TRADE

COMMERCIAL AQUACULTURE
USE	**AQUACULTURE ENTERPRISES**

COMMERCIAL AVAILABILITY
SN	Commercial availability of primary and secondary fishery products
BT1	AVAILABILITY
RT	ABUNDANCE
RT	COST ANALYSIS
RT	MARKET RESEARCH
RT	PRICING
RT	TRADE

COMMERCIAL EXPLOITATION
USE	**EXPLOITATION**

COMMERCIAL FISHERIES
USE	**FISHERIES**

COMMERCIAL FISHING
SN	Any activities of fishing or harvesting of aquatic organisms for commercial purposes
UF	fishing industry
BT1	FISHING OPERATIONS
NT1	FOREIGN FISHING
RT	BAIT
RT	BAIT CULTURE
RT	BY CATCH
RT	CATCH STATISTICS
RT	CATCHING METHODS
RT	COST ANALYSIS
RT	EXPLOITATION
RT	FISHERIES
RT	FISHERY INDUSTRY
RT	FISHING GEAR
RT	FISHING VESSELS
RT	LANDING STATISTICS
RT	OVERFISHING

COMMERCIAL LAND USE
USE	**LAND USE**

COMMERCIAL LEGISLATION
SN	Before 1982 search MARKETING LEGISLATION
UF	marketing legislation
BT1	LEGISLATION
NT1	FISH INSPECTION REGULATIONS
RT	CONTROL CHARTS
RT	LEGAL ASPECTS
RT	MARKETING
RT	PRICING
RT	QUALITY CONTROL

COMMERCIAL ORGANIZATIONS
USE	**COMPANIES**

COMMERCIAL SPECIES
SN	Animal or vegetal aquatic species of commercial value
UF	economic species
BT1	SPECIES
BT2	TAXA
NT1	UNDERUTILIZED SPECIES
RT	AQUATIC ANIMALS
RT	AQUATIC MAMMALS
RT	AQUATIC PLANTS
RT	AQUATIC REPTILES
RT	ASSOCIATED SPECIES
RT	BRACKISHWATER FISH
RT	BRACKISHWATER MOLLUSCS
RT	CATCH COMPOSITION
RT	FISH
RT	FISH UTILIZATION
RT	FISHERY RESOURCES
RT	FOOD FISH
RT	FRESHWATER CRUSTACEANS
RT	FRESHWATER MOLLUSCS
RT	LIVING RESOURCES
RT	MARINE CRUSTACEANS
RT	MARINE FISH
RT	MARINE MAMMALS
RT	MARINE MOLLUSCS
RT	SEAFOOD
RT	SEAWEEDS
RT	SHELLFISH
RT	TRASH FISH
RT	VERNACULAR NAMES

COMMERCIALIZATION
USE	**MARKETING**

COMMINUTED PRODUCTS
USE	**MINCED PRODUCTS**

COMMODITY STATISTICS
USE	**INDUSTRIAL PRODUCTS STATISTICS**

COMMON NAMES
USE	**VERNACULAR NAMES**

COMMON PROPERTY RESOURCES
SN	Natural resources held or used by all who choose to do so. Added in 1982
UF	open access resources
BT1	NATURAL RESOURCES
BT2	RESOURCES
RT	FISHERY RESOURCES

COMMON SALT
USE	**SODIUM CHLORIDE**

COMMUNICABLE DISEASES
USE	**INFECTIOUS DISEASES**

COMMUNICATION
RT	COMMUNICATION SATELLITES
RT	COMMUNICATION SYSTEMS
RT	SPEECH DISTORTION
RT	TELEMETRY

COMMUNICATION (BEHAVIOUR)
USE	**ANIMAL COMMUNICATION**

COMMUNICATION SATELLITES
BT1	SATELLITES
BT2	VEHICLES
RT	COMMUNICATION
RT	COMMUNICATION SYSTEMS
RT	SATELLITE COMMUNICATION

COMMUNICATION SYSTEMS
SN	Before 1982 search also COMMUNICATION DEVICES
UF	telecommunications
NT1	RADIO
NT1	SATELLITE COMMUNICATION
NT1	TELEMETRY
NT2	ACOUSTIC TELEMETRY
NT2	BIOTELEMETRY
NT2	RADIO TELEMETRY
NT1	TELEPHONE SYSTEMS
NT1	TELEVISION SYSTEMS
NT2	UNDERWATER TELEVISION
NT1	TELEX
RT	COMMUNICATION
RT	COMMUNICATION SATELLITES
RT	DIVING EQUIPMENT
RT	FISHING OPERATIONS
RT	MICROWAVES
RT	NAVIGATION
RT	RADIO BUOYS
RT	STANDARD SIGNALS
RT	SUBMARINE CABLES

COMMUNITIES (ECOLOGICAL)
USE	**AQUATIC COMMUNITIES**

COMMUNITY COMPOSITION
BT1	COMPOSITION
RT	AQUATIC COMMUNITIES
RT	BIOCOENOSIS
RT	BIOLOGICAL SURVEYS
RT	BIOTA
RT	CHECK LISTS
RT	CLIMAX COMMUNITY
RT	DOMINANT SPECIES
RT	ECOLOGICAL SUCCESSION

COMMUNITY COMPOSITION (cont'd)
RT	POLLUTION EFFECTS
RT	SPECIES DIVERSITY

COMMUNITY DIVERSITY
USE	**SPECIES DIVERSITY**

COMPACTION
BT1	DIAGENESIS
BT2	SEDIMENTATION
RT	BEARING CAPACITY
RT	CONSOLIDATION
RT	LITHIFICATION
RT	POROSITY
RT	SETTLEMENT (STRUCTURAL)
RT	SOIL MECHANICS

COMPANIES
UF	commercial organizations
BT1	ORGANIZATIONS

COMPARATIVE STUDIES
SN	Used only as a qualifier. Added in 1980
RT	ANATOMY
RT	COST ANALYSIS
RT	ORGANISM MORPHOLOGY
RT	PHYSIOLOGY

COMPARTMENTAL MODELS
USE	**MATHEMATICAL MODELS**

COMPASSES
UF	magnetic compasses
BT1	MEASURING DEVICES
NT1	GYROCOMPASSES
RT	DIRECTION INDICATORS
RT	NAVIGATIONAL AIDS
RT	SURVEYING

COMPENSATION DEPTH
SN	Zone in aquatic environment where just enough light penetrates for the rate of photosynthesis to equal the rate of respiration
UF	compensation level
NT1	CARBONATE COMPENSATION DEPTH
RT	AEROBIC RESPIRATION
RT	DISPHOTIC ZONE
RT	EUPHOTIC ZONE
RT	LIGHT PENETRATION
RT	PHOTOSYNTHESIS
RT	PRIMARY PRODUCTION
RT	SOLUBILITY

COMPENSATION DEPTH (CARBONATE)
USE	**CARBONATE COMPENSATION DEPTH**

COMPENSATION DEPTH (ISOSTASY)
USE	**ISOSTASY**

COMPENSATION DEPTH (OCEANS)
USE	**CARBONATE COMPENSATION DEPTH**

COMPENSATION LEVEL
USE	**COMPENSATION DEPTH**

COMPETITION
UF	biological competition
BT1	INTERSPECIFIC RELATIONSHIPS
RT	ASSOCIATED SPECIES
RT	BIOTIC PRESSURE
RT	COMPETITIVE BEHAVIOUR
RT	COMPETITORS
RT	DOMINANCE HIERARCHIES
RT	FOOD AVAILABILITY
RT	INTRASPECIFIC RELATIONSHIPS
RT	NATURAL SELECTION
RT	OVERCROWDING
RT	PREY SELECTION

COMPETITIVE BEHAVIOUR
BT1	BEHAVIOUR
RT	COMPETITION
RT	COMPETITORS
RT	HOME RANGE
RT	TERRITORIALITY

COMPETITORS
RT	COMPETITION
RT	COMPETITIVE BEHAVIOUR
RT	PREDATORS

COMPLETION (WELL)
USE	**WELL COMPLETION**

COMPLEX LIPIDS
SN	Added in 1980
UF	glycolipids
UF	phospholipids
UF	sphingolipids
BT1	LIPIDS
BT2	ORGANIC COMPOUNDS

COMPLIANT PLATFORMS
USE	**GUYED TOWERS**

COMPLIANT TOWERS
USE	**GUYED TOWERS**

COMPONENTS
SN	Used only as a qualifier
RT	EQUIPMENT
RT	MATERIALS

COMPOSITE CULTURES
USE	**POLYCULTURE**

COMPOSITE MATERIALS
BT1	MATERIALS

COMPOSITION
SN	The nature of the elements present in a substance or organism and the proportion in which they occur. Use of a more specific term is recommended
NT1	BIOCHEMICAL COMPOSITION
NT1	CHEMICAL COMPOSITION
NT1	COMMUNITY COMPOSITION
NT1	MINERAL COMPOSITION
NT1	SEDIMENT COMPOSITION
RT	ANALYTICAL TECHNIQUES
RT	BIOCHEMICAL ANALYSIS
RT	CHEMICAL ANALYSIS
RT	MAJOR CONSTITUENTS
RT	SEDIMENT ANALYSIS
RT	WATER ANALYSIS

COMPOUND EYES
BT1	EYES
BT2	PHOTORECEPTORS
BT3	SENSE ORGANS
BT4	ANIMAL ORGANS
RT	AQUATIC INSECTS

COMPOUNDS (ORGANIC)
USE	**ORGANIC COMPOUNDS**

COMPRESSED GAS
BT1	GASES
BT2	FLUIDS

COMPRESSIBILITY
BT1	MECHANICAL PROPERTIES
BT2	PHYSICAL PROPERTIES
BT3	PROPERTIES
RT	BULK MODULUS
RT	COMPRESSION
RT	ELASTICITY

COMPRESSIBILITY (cont'd)
RT	PLASTICITY
RT	POROSITY
RT	SOUND VELOCITY
RT	WATER PROPERTIES

COMPRESSION
BT1	STRESS
BT2	FORCES (MECHANICS)
RT	COMPRESSIBILITY
RT	DECOMPRESSION
RT	DEFORMATION
RT	LITHIFICATION
RT	PRESSURE

COMPRESSION CHAMBERS
USE	**DECOMPRESSION CHAMBERS**

COMPRESSION TABLES
USE	**DECOMPRESSION TABLES**

COMPRESSIONAL WAVE VELOCITIES
BT1	SEISMIC VELOCITIES
BT2	VELOCITY
RT	P-WAVES
RT	SEDIMENT PROPERTIES

COMPRESSIONAL WAVES (SEISMIC)
USE	**P-WAVES**

COMPRESSIVE STRENGTH
BT1	STRENGTH
BT2	MECHANICAL PROPERTIES
BT3	PHYSICAL PROPERTIES
BT4	PROPERTIES
RT	POISSON'S RATIO

COMPRESSORS
UF	air compressors
RT	DIVING EQUIPMENT
RT	LIFE SUPPORT SYSTEMS

COMPUTATION
SN	Used only as a qualifier
RT	COMPUTER PROGRAMS
RT	MODELS

COMPUTER-AIDED CARTOGRAPHY
USE	**AUTOMATED CARTOGRAPHY**

COMPUTER MODELS
USE	**MATHEMATICAL MODELS**

COMPUTER PROGRAMMES
USE	**COMPUTER PROGRAMS**

COMPUTER PROGRAMS
SN	Used only as a qualifier. Before 1986 search also COMPUTER PROGRAMMES
UF	computer programmes
RT	ALGORITHMS
RT	ARTIFICIAL INTELLIGENCE
RT	BATCH PROCESSING
RT	COMPUTATION
RT	COMPUTERS
RT	DATA PROCESSING
RT	DATA RETRIEVAL
RT	LINEAR PROGRAMMING
RT	NUMERICAL ANALYSIS
RT	PROGRAMMES
RT	SYSTEM ANALYSIS

COMPUTERS
SN	Added in 1982. Before 1985 search also MINICOMPUTERS
UF	microcomputers
UF	minicomputers
UF	shipboard computers
BT1	ELECTRONIC EQUIPMENT
BT2	EQUIPMENT

COMPUTERS (cont'd)
RT	AUTOMATION
RT	BATCH PROCESSING
RT	COMPUTER PROGRAMS
RT	DATA PROCESSING
RT	DATA RETRIEVAL
RT	DATA STORAGE
RT	INFORMATION SERVICES
RT	MICROPROCESSORS
RT	ROBOTS
RT	TEST EQUIPMENT

CONCESSIONS
SN	Use only for rights to exploit or explore for mineral resources
BT1	LICENCES
RT	MINERAL EXPLORATION
RT	MINING LEGISLATION
RT	OIL AND GAS EXPLORATION
RT	OIL AND GAS LEGISLATION
RT	RENTAL

CONCH FISHERIES
USE	**GASTROPOD FISHERIES**

CONCHOLOGY
SN	The branch of Zoology dealing with shells of animals (molluscs, brachiopods,etc.). Added in 1980
BT1	ZOOLOGY
BT2	BIOLOGY
RT	MALACOLOGY
RT	SHELLS

CONCRETE
UF	cement (building material)
BT1	CONSTRUCTION MATERIALS
BT2	MATERIALS
NT1	PRESTRESSED CONCRETE
NT1	REINFORCED CONCRETE
RT	CONCRETE STRUCTURES

CONCRETE PLATFORMS
USE	**CONCRETE STRUCTURES**

CONCRETE STRUCTURES
SN	Before 1986 search also CONCRETE PLATFORMS
UF	concrete platforms
RT	COAST DEFENCES
RT	CONCRETE
RT	OFFSHORE STRUCTURES
RT	STEEL STRUCTURES
RT	STRUCTURES

CONCRETIONS
SN	Use only for mineral deposits formed within sediments
UF	crusts (rocks)
UF	encrustations
BT1	CHEMICAL SEDIMENTS
BT2	SEDIMENTS
RT	CHERTS
RT	FLINT
RT	NODULES
RT	OOIDS
RT	OOLITES
RT	SEDIMENTARY STRUCTURES

CONDENSATE FIELDS
USE	**GAS CONDENSATE FIELDS**

CONDENSATION
BT1	PHASE CHANGES
RT	DEW POINT
RT	EVAPORATION
RT	HEAT TRANSFER
RT	HYDROMETEORS
RT	SALT NUCLEI
RT	SALT PARTICLES

CONDENSATION (cont'd)
RT	SATURATION
RT	SATURATION VAPOUR PRESSURE
RT	SUBLIMATION
RT	VAPORIZATION HEAT
RT	VAPOUR PRESSURE
RT	WATER VAPOUR

CONDITION FACTOR
UF	ponderal index
BT1	POPULATION FACTORS
RT	BODY CONDITIONS
RT	GROWTH
RT	LENGTH-WEIGHT RELATIONSHIPS

CONDUCTANCE (ELECTRICAL)
USE	**ELECTRICAL CONDUCTIVITY**

CONDUCTION (HEAT)
USE.	**HEAT CONDUCTION**

CONDUCTIVE HEAT TRANSFER
USE	**HEAT CONDUCTION**

CONDUCTIVITY (ELECTRICAL)
USE	**ELECTRICAL CONDUCTIVITY**

CONDUCTIVITY (THERMAL)
USE	**THERMAL CONDUCTIVITY**

CONDUCTIVITY PROBES
USE	**CONDUCTIVITY SENSORS**

CONDUCTIVITY RATIO
RT	ELECTRICAL CONDUCTIVITY

CONDUCTIVITY SENSORS
UF	conductivity probes
UF	electrical conductivity sensors
RT	CTD PROFILERS
RT	ELECTRICAL CONDUCTIVITY
RT	MEASURING DEVICES
RT	OCEANOGRAPHIC EQUIPMENT
RT	SALINITY MEASUREMENT
RT	SALINITY MEASURING EQUIPMENT
RT	SENSORS
RT	STD PROFILERS

CONFERENCES
SN	Use only to index the monographic entry for bound proceedings, and general reports on meetings; do not use for individual (analytic) conference papers
UF	colloquia
UF	meetings
UF	proceedings
UF	seminars
UF	symposia
UF	workshops
RT	ABSTRACTS
RT	EXHIBITIONS
RT	INTERNATIONAL ORGANIZATIONS
RT	LECTURES
RT	ORGANIZATIONS
RT	PUBLICITY MATERIAL

CONFIGURATION
USE	**SHAPE**

CONFLICT OF INTERESTS
USE	**DISPUTES**

CONFLICTS
USE	**DISPUTES**

CONGLOMERATES
RT	BRECCIA
RT	CALCRETE
RT	KIMBERLITES

CONIDIA
SN	Asexually formed spores produced by fungi
RT	ASEXUAL REPRODUCTION
RT	FUNGI
RT	SPORES

CONNECTING
UF	coupling (joining components)
UF	tie-in
RT	PIPELINE CONSTRUCTION

CONNECTIVE TISSUES
SN	Added in 1980
BT1	TISSUES
NT1	CARTILAGE
RT	BLOOD
RT	BLOOD VESSELS
RT	BONES
RT	HISTOLOGY
RT	MUSCULOSKELETAL SYSTEM
RT	NERVES

CONNECTORS
UF	couplings (components)
UF	underwater connectors
RT	ELECTRIC CABLES
RT	MANIFOLDS

CONSERVATION
SN	Conservation of nature and resources. Use of a more specific term is recommended
UF	conservation (resources)
NT1	NATURE CONSERVATION
NT1	RESOURCE CONSERVATION
NT1	SOIL CONSERVATION
NT1	WATER CONSERVATION
RT	CONTROL
RT	DEPLETION
RT	ECONOMICS
RT	ENVIRONMENTAL LEGISLATION
RT	ENVIRONMENTAL PROTECTION
RT	RECLAMATION
RT	RIVER BASIN MANAGEMENT
RT	SHORE PROTECTION

CONSERVATION (FOOD)
USE	**PRESERVATION (FISHERY PRODUCTS)**

CONSERVATION (ORGANISMS)
USE	**FIXATION**

CONSERVATION (RESOURCES)
USE	**CONSERVATION**

CONSERVATION EQUATIONS
BT1	EQUATIONS
RT	DIFFUSION
RT	EQUATION OF CONTINUITY

CONSERVATION OF ANGULAR MOMENTUM
BT1	CONSERVATION PRINCIPLES
RT	ANGULAR MOMENTUM
RT	CONSERVATION OF VORTICITY

CONSERVATION OF ENERGY
BT1	CONSERVATION PRINCIPLES
RT	ENERGY

CONSERVATION OF HEAT
BT1	CONSERVATION PRINCIPLES
RT	HEAT
RT	HEAT TRANSPORT

CONSERVATION OF MASS
- BT1   CONSERVATION PRINCIPLES
- RT   EQUATION OF CONTINUITY
- RT   MASS

CONSERVATION OF MOMENTUM
- UF   momentum conservation
- BT1   CONSERVATION PRINCIPLES
- RT   MOMENTUM

CONSERVATION OF SALT
- BT1   CONSERVATION PRINCIPLES
- RT   DISSOLVED SALTS
- RT   SALT ADVECTION
- RT   SALT BUDGET
- RT   WATER EXCHANGE

CONSERVATION OF VOLUME
- USE   **EQUATION OF CONTINUITY**

CONSERVATION OF VORTICITY
- BT1   CONSERVATION PRINCIPLES
- RT   ABSOLUTE VORTICITY
- RT   BAROTROPIC MODE
- RT   CONSERVATION OF ANGULAR MOMENTUM
- RT   MESOSCALE EDDIES

CONSERVATION PRINCIPLES
- NT1   CONSERVATION OF ANGULAR MOMENTUM
- NT1   CONSERVATION OF ENERGY
- NT1   CONSERVATION OF HEAT
- NT1   CONSERVATION OF MASS
- NT1   CONSERVATION OF MOMENTUM
- NT1   CONSERVATION OF SALT
- NT1   CONSERVATION OF VORTICITY

CONSERVATIVE PROPERTIES
- BT1   PROPERTIES
- RT   ENTHALPY
- RT   NON-CONSERVATIVE PROPERTIES
- RT   SALINITY
- RT   SEA WATER
- RT   WATER MASSES

CONSOLIDATION
- BT1   DIAGENESIS
- BT2   SEDIMENTATION
- RT   CEMENTATION
- RT   COMPACTION
- RT   LITHIFICATION
- RT   SOIL MECHANICS

CONSTANTS
- SN   Used only as a qualifier
- NT1   STABILITY CONSTANTS
- RT   ASSOCIATION CONSTANTS
- RT   COEFFICIENTS
- RT   ELASTIC CONSTANTS
- RT   RATIOS
- RT   SOLAR CONSTANT

CONSTRUCTION
- UF   assembling
- NT1   INSTALLATION
- NT1   PIPELINE CONSTRUCTION
- NT2   BOTTOM TOW
- NT2   PIPE LAYING
- RT   CONSTRUCTION MATERIALS
- RT   EXCAVATION UNDERWATER
- RT   LAUNCHING

CONSTRUCTION MATERIALS
- BT1   MATERIALS
- NT1   CONCRETE
- NT2   PRESTRESSED CONCRETE
- NT2   REINFORCED CONCRETE
- RT   CONSTRUCTION
- RT   FIBRE GLASS

CONSTRUCTIVE WAVES
- BT1   SURFACE WATER WAVES
- BT2   WATER WAVES
- RT   DESTRUCTIVE WAVES
- RT   PROGRADATION

CONSULTANTS
- SN   Added in 1980
- BT1   PERSONNEL
- RT   DIRECTORIES
- RT   EXPERTS
- RT   SCIENTIFIC PERSONNEL

CONSUMERS
- UF   purchasers
- RT   ECONOMIC ANALYSIS
- RT   MARKET RESEARCH
- RT   MARKETING
- RT   PURCHASING
- RT   TRADE

CONTAGIOUS DISEASES
- USE   **INFECTIOUS DISEASES**

CONTAINER PORTS
- USE   **FERRY TERMINALS**

CONTAINER SHIPS
- BT1   MERCHANT SHIPS
- BT2   SHIPS
- BT3   SURFACE CRAFT
- BT4   VEHICLES
- RT   FERRY TERMINALS

CONTAINERS
- SN   Added in 1980
- UF   boxes
- UF   cans
- UF   packages
- NT1   TANKS
- NT2   CULTURE TANKS
- NT2   DECANTATION TANKS
- NT2   EVAPORATION TANKS
- NT2   OIL TANKS
- NT2   STORAGE TANKS
- NT2   TOWING TANKS
- NT2   WAVE TANKS
- NT2   WIND TUNNELS

CONTAINMENT
- BT1   POLLUTION CONTROL
- BT2   CONTROL
- RT   BARRAGES
- RT   BARRIERS
- RT   BUBBLE BARRIERS
- RT   ENCLOSURES
- RT   FLOATING BARRIERS
- RT   OIL SLICKS
- RT   OIL SPILLS

CONTAMINATION (INTERNAL)
- USE   **RADIONUCLIDE KINETICS**

CONTAMINATION (RADIOACTIVE)
- USE   **RADIOACTIVE CONTAMINATION**

CONTAMINATION OF SAMPLES
- USE   **SAMPLE CONTAMINATION**

CONTIGUOUS FISHING ZONES
- USE   **CONTIGUOUS ZONES**

CONTIGUOUS ZONES
- SN   Offshore area claimed by a nation for exclusive fishing rights. Added in 1980
- UF   contiguous fishing zones
- BT1   OCEAN SPACE
- RT   BOUNDARIES
- RT   EXCLUSIVE ECONOMIC ZONE

CONTIGUOUS ZONES (cont'd)
- RT   FISHERY BOUNDARIES
- RT   FISHING RIGHTS
- RT   INTERNATIONAL AGREEMENTS
- RT   JURISDICTION
- RT   POLLUTION
- RT   TERRITORIAL WATERS

CONTINENTAL AEROSOLS
- USE   **AEROSOLS**

CONTINENTAL BORDERLAND
- UF   borderland
- BT1   SUBMARINE FEATURES
- BT2   TOPOGRAPHIC FEATURES
- RT   CONTINENTAL CRUST
- RT   CONTINENTAL MARGINS
- RT   CONTINENTAL SHELVES
- RT   CONTINENTAL SLOPE
- RT   CONTINENTS
- RT   OCEANIC CRUST

CONTINENTAL CRUST
- BT1   EARTH CRUST
- BT2   EARTH STRUCTURE
- RT   CONTINENTAL BORDERLAND
- RT   CONTINENTS
- RT   CRATONS
- RT   CRUSTAL STRUCTURE
- RT   CRUSTAL THICKNESS
- RT   MICROCONTINENTS
- RT   OBDUCTION
- RT   OCEANIC CRUST
- RT   OCEANIZATION
- RT   SIAL

CONTINENTAL DRIFT
- UF   continental migration
- UF   drift (continental)
- UF   wegener hypothesis
- RT   BIOGEOGRAPHY
- RT   CONTINENTS
- RT   DRIFT
- RT   EARTH MANTLE
- RT   GEOPHYSICS
- RT   MARINE GEOLOGY
- RT   MOHO
- RT   OCEAN BASINS
- RT   PALAEOCLIMATE
- RT   PALAEOCLIMATOLOGY
- RT   PALAEOMAGNETISM
- RT   PALAEONTOLOGY
- RT   PERMANENCE
- RT   PLATE TECTONICS
- RT   POLAR WANDERING
- RT   SEAFLOOR SPREADING
- RT   TECTONOPHYSICS

CONTINENTAL MARGINS
- UF   margins (continental)
- BT1   SUBMARINE FEATURES
- BT2   TOPOGRAPHIC FEATURES
- NT1   ACTIVE MARGINS
- NT1   PASSIVE MARGINS
- RT   CONTINENTAL BORDERLAND
- RT   CONTINENTAL RISE
- RT   CONTINENTAL SHELVES
- RT   CONTINENTAL SLOPE
- RT   CONTINENTS
- RT   CRATONS
- RT   ISLAND ARCS
- RT   OUTER CONTINENTAL SHELF
- RT   TRENCHES (OCEANIC)

CONTINENTAL MIGRATION
- USE   **CONTINENTAL DRIFT**

ASFIS Thesaurus

CONTINENTAL NATIONS
USE **LANDLOCKED STATES**

CONTINENTAL RIDGES
BT1 SUBMARINE FEATURES
BT2 TOPOGRAPHIC FEATURES
RT RELIEF FORMS
RT RIDGES

CONTINENTAL RISE
UF rise (continental)
BT1 SUBMARINE FEATURES
BT2 TOPOGRAPHIC FEATURES
RT ABYSSAL PLAINS
RT CONTINENTAL MARGINS
RT CONTINENTAL SLOPE
RT CONTOUR CURRENTS
RT NEPHELOID LAYER
RT OCEAN FLOOR

CONTINENTAL SHELF
USE **CONTINENTAL SHELVES**

CONTINENTAL SHELF BREAK
USE **SHELF EDGE**

CONTINENTAL SHELF EDGE
USE **SHELF EDGE**

CONTINENTAL SHELVES
SN Before 1982 search also CONTINENTAL
SHELF
UF continental shelf
BT1 SUBMARINE FEATURES
BT2 TOPOGRAPHIC FEATURES
NT1 OUTER CONTINENTAL SHELF
RT CONTINENTAL BORDERLAND
RT CONTINENTAL MARGINS
RT CONTINENTAL SLOPE
RT JURISDICTION
RT LITTORAL ZONE
RT MARINE ENVIRONMENT
RT MARINE GEOLOGY
RT NERITIC PROVINCE
RT OCEAN SPACE
RT OFFSHORE
RT SEDENTARY SPECIES
RT SHALLOW WATER
RT SHELF DYNAMICS
RT SHELF EDGE
RT SHELF EDGE FRONTS
RT SHELF GEOLOGY
RT SHELF SEAS
RT SHELF SEDIMENTATION
RT SUBMARINE CANYONS
RT TERRITORIAL WATERS

CONTINENTAL SLOPE
BT1 SUBMARINE FEATURES
BT2 TOPOGRAPHIC FEATURES
RT CONTINENTAL BORDERLAND
RT CONTINENTAL MARGINS
RT CONTINENTAL RISE
RT CONTINENTAL SHELVES
RT CONTINENTS
RT CONTOUR CURRENTS
RT ISLAND SLOPE
RT JURISDICTION
RT MARGINAL BASINS
RT MARINE ENVIRONMENT
RT MARINE GEOLOGY
RT OCEAN FLOOR
RT OUTER CONTINENTAL SHELF
RT SEDIMENTATION
RT SHELF EDGE
RT SLOPE ENVIRONMENT
RT SLOPES (TOPOGRAPHY)
RT SLUMPING
RT SUBMARINE CANYONS
RT TURBIDITY CURRENTS

CONTINENTS
BT1 LANDFORMS
BT2 TOPOGRAPHIC FEATURES
RT CONTINENTAL BORDERLAND
RT CONTINENTAL CRUST
RT CONTINENTAL DRIFT
RT CONTINENTAL MARGINS
RT CONTINENTAL SLOPE
RT CRATONS
RT EARTH STRUCTURE
RT EPEIROGENY
RT ISLAND ARCS
RT ISOSTASY
RT MARGINAL SEAS
RT PERMANENCE

CONTINUITY EQUATION
USE **EQUATION OF CONTINUITY**

CONTINUOUS CULTURE
SN Added in 1980
BT1 AQUACULTURE SYSTEMS
RT AQUARIA
RT BATCH CULTURE
RT CULTURE TANKS
RT CULTURES
RT LABORATORY CULTURE
RT PHYTOPLANKTON CULTURE
RT ZOOPLANKTON CULTURE

CONTINUOUS PROFILERS
USE **PROFILERS**

CONTINUOUS TRACKING
USE **TRACKING**

CONTOUR CURRENTS
BT1 SURFACE CURRENTS
BT2 WATER CURRENTS
BT3 WATER MOTION
RT BED FORMS
RT BOTTOM EROSION
RT CONTINENTAL RISE
RT CONTINENTAL SLOPE
RT CONTOURITES
RT NEPHELOID LAYER
RT OCEAN CURRENTS
RT SEDIMENT TRANSPORT
RT TOPOGRAPHIC EFFECTS
RT WESTERN BOUNDARY UNDERCURRENTS

CONTOUR FEATHERS
USE **FEATHERS**

CONTOURITES
BT1 CLASTICS
BT2 SEDIMENTS
RT CONTOUR CURRENTS

CONTOURS
BT1 ISOPLETHS
BT2 MAP GRAPHICS
BT3 GRAPHICS
BT4 AUDIOVISUAL MATERIAL
NT1 ISOBATHS
RT DEPTH
RT PROFILES
RT SHAPE
RT TOPOGRAPHY

CONTRACTILE VACUOLE
USE **CELL ORGANELLES**

CONTRACTORS
BT1 PERSONNEL
RT CONTRACTS

CONTRACTS
RT CONTRACTORS

CONTROL
SN Used only as a qualifier. Use of a
more specific term is recommended
UF control systems
UF regulate
NT1 BIOLOGICAL CONTROL
NT1 BLOWOUT CONTROL
NT1 CHEMICAL CONTROL
NT1 CORROSION CONTROL
NT2 CATHODIC PROTECTION
NT1 DEPTH CONTROL
NT1 DISEASE CONTROL
NT1 EROSION CONTROL
NT2 PIPELINE PROTECTION
NT1 FLOOD CONTROL
NT1 FOULING CONTROL
NT1 PARASITE CONTROL
NT1 PEST CONTROL
NT1 PLANT CONTROL
NT1 POLLUTION CONTROL
NT2 CONTAINMENT
NT1 POPULATION CONTROL
NT1 PREDATOR CONTROL
NT1 QUALITY CONTROL
NT1 REMOTE CONTROL
NT1 WATER QUALITY CONTROL
RT AUTOMATION
RT CONSERVATION
RT DAMPING
RT MONITORING

CONTROL CHARTS
BT1 MAPS
BT2 GRAPHICS
BT3 AUDIOVISUAL MATERIAL
BT4 DOCUMENTS
RT COMMERCIAL LEGISLATION
RT CRITICAL PATH METHOD
RT QUALITY CONTROL

CONTROL RESISTANCE
SN Added in 1980
UF antibiotic resistance
UF chemical resistance
UF resistance to chemicals
BT1 BIOLOGICAL RESISTANCE
BT2 BIOLOGICAL PROPERTIES
BT3 PROPERTIES
RT ANTIBIOTICS
RT CHEMICAL CONTROL
RT DRUG RESISTANCE
RT DRUGS
RT PEST CONTROL
RT PESTICIDES

CONTROL SYSTEMS
USE **CONTROL**

CONTROLLED CONDITIONS
SN Used only as a qualifier
UF laboratory conditions
RT ARTIFICIAL FEEDING
RT BEHAVIOURAL RESPONSES
RT DOMESTICATION
RT EXPERIMENTAL DATA
RT EXPERIMENTAL RESEARCH
RT INDUCED BREEDING
RT LABORATORY CULTURE
RT LARVAL DEVELOPMENT
RT PHYTOPLANKTON CULTURE
RT REARING
RT ZOOPLANKTON CULTURE

CONVECTION
UF	convective heat transfer
BT1	ADVECTION
BT2	TRANSPORT PROCESSES
NT1	ATMOSPHERIC CONVECTION
NT1	CELLULAR CONVECTION
NT1	FORCED CONVECTION
NT1	MANTLE CONVECTION
NT1	OCEANIC CONVECTION
RT	HEAT TRANSFER
RT	HEAT TRANSPORT
RT	MASS TRANSFER
RT	SENSIBLE HEAT TRANSFER

CONVECTIVE HEAT TRANSFER
USE	**CONVECTION**

CONVECTIVE OVERTURN
USE	**OVERTURN**

CONVENTIONS
USE	**INTERNATIONAL AGREEMENTS**

CONVERGENCE
RT	ATMOSPHERIC CONVERGENCES
RT	CONVERGENCE ZONES
RT	DIVERGENCE
RT	DOWNWELLING
RT	FRONTAL FEATURES
RT	FRONTOGENESIS
RT	HORIZONTAL MOTION
RT	LANGMUIR CIRCULATION
RT	OCEANIC CONVERGENCES
RT	PLATE CONVERGENCE

CONVERGENCE ZONES
NT1	ATMOSPHERIC CONVERGENCES
NT2	ANTARCTIC FRONT
NT2	INTERTROPICAL CONVERGENCE ZONE
NT2	POLAR FRONTS
NT1	OCEANIC CONVERGENCES
NT2	POLAR CONVERGENCES
NT3	ANTARCTIC CONVERGENCE
NT3	NORTH ATLANTIC POLAR FRONT
NT2	SUBTROPICAL CONVERGENCES
RT	ADVECTION
RT	CONVERGENCE
RT	DIVERGENCE ZONES
RT	FRONTAL FEATURES
RT	FRONTS
RT	WATER MASSES

CONVERGENT EVOLUTION
USE	**EVOLUTION**

CONVERGENT MARGINS
USE	**ACTIVE MARGINS**

CONVERGING PLATE BOUNDARIES
BT1	PLATE BOUNDARIES
RT	ISLAND ARCS
RT	SUBDUCTION ZONES
RT	TRENCHES (OCEANIC)

CONVERSION EFFICIENCY
USE	**FOOD CONVERSION**

CONVERSION FACTORS
SN	Added in 1982
RT	ANIMAL METABOLISM
RT	BIOENERGETICS
RT	CONVERSION TABLES
RT	FEED EFFICIENCY
RT	OXYGEN CONSUMPTION

CONVERSION TABLES
UF	nomograms
BT1	TABLES
BT2	DOCUMENTS
NT1	KNUDSEN TABLES

CONVERSION TABLES (cont'd)
RT	CONVERSION FACTORS
RT	NUMERICAL ANALYSIS
RT	OCEANOGRAPHIC TABLES

CONVERSION TABLES (METEOROLOGY)
USE	**METEOROLOGICAL TABLES**

CONVOLUTION
BT1	MATHEMATICAL ANALYSIS
RT	CROSS CORRELATION
RT	DECONVOLUTION
RT	SEISMIC DATA PROCESSING

COOLING
UF	heat dissipation
BT1	HEAT TRANSFER
RT	COOLING PONDS
RT	COOLING SYSTEMS
RT	COOLING WATER
RT	FREEZING
RT	HEATING

COOLING PONDS
BT1	PONDS
BT2	INLAND WATERS
RT	COOLING
RT	FOSSIL FUELED POWER PLANTS
RT	NUCLEAR POWER PLANTS
RT	POWER PLANTS
RT	THERMAL POLLUTION

COOLING SYSTEMS
RT	COOLING
RT	OPEN SYSTEMS

COOLING WATER
BT1	WATER
RT	COOLING
RT	ENTRAINMENT
RT	FOSSIL FUELED POWER PLANTS
RT	NUCLEAR POWER PLANTS
RT	POWER PLANTS
RT	THERMAL POLLUTION

COOPERATIVES
UF	fishery cooperatives
BT1	FISHERY ORGANIZATIONS
BT2	ORGANIZATIONS
RT	CAPTURE FISHERY ECONOMICS
RT	FINANCING
RT	FISHERMEN
RT	FISHERY ECONOMICS
RT	LABOUR

COORDINATE SYSTEMS
UF	cartesian coordinates
NT1	GEODETIC COORDINATES
NT1	GEOGRAPHICAL COORDINATES
NT2	LATITUDE
NT3	PALAEOLATITUDE
NT2	LONGITUDE

COPOLYMERIZATION
USE	**POLYMERIZATION**

COPPER
BT1	CHEMICAL ELEMENTS
RT	COPPER COMPOUNDS
RT	COPPER ISOTOPES
RT	FERROMANGANESE NODULES
RT	HAEMOCYANINS
RT	HEAVY METALS
RT	HOT BRINES
RT	METALLIFEROUS SEDIMENTS
RT	METALS
RT	TRACE ELEMENTS

COPPER COMPOUNDS
RT	CHEMICAL COMPOUNDS
RT	COPPER

COPPER ISOTOPES
BT1	ISOTOPES
RT	COPPER

COPRECIPITATION
BT1	CHEMICAL PRECIPITATION
BT2	SEPARATION
RT	FLOCCULATION

CORAL
SN	Before 1982 search also CORALS
BT1	ANIMAL PRODUCTS
RT	ATOLLS
RT	CALCIUM COMPOUNDS
RT	CORAL FARMING
RT	CORAL REEFS

CORAL CULTURE
USE	**CORAL FARMING**

CORAL FARMING
SN	Added in 1980
UF	coral culture
BT1	AQUACULTURE
RT	CORAL
RT	CORAL REEFS
RT	CULTURES
RT	MARINE AQUACULTURE

CORAL ISLANDS
USE	**ATOLLS**

CORAL REEFS
UF	reefs (coral)
BT1	BIOGENIC DEPOSITS
NT1	BARRIER REEFS
NT1	FRINGING REEFS
RT	ATOLLS
RT	BIOGENIC SEDIMENTARY STRUCTURES
RT	BIOHERMS
RT	CARBONATE ROCKS
RT	CAYS
RT	CORAL
RT	CORAL FARMING
RT	GEOMORPHOLOGY
RT	LAGOONS
RT	MARINE ENVIRONMENT
RT	POLYPS
RT	REEF FISH
RT	REEF FISHERIES
RT	REEF FORMATION
RT	REEFS
RT	SHOALS
RT	TROPICAL FISH

CORANGE CHARTS
BT1	TIDAL CHARTS
BT2	HYDROGRAPHIC CHARTS
BT3	MAPS
BT4	GRAPHICS
RT	CORANGE LINES
RT	TIDAL AMPLITUDE
RT	TIDAL RANGE

CORANGE LINES
UF	coamplitude lines
BT1	ISOPLETHS
BT2	MAP GRAPHICS
BT3	GRAPHICS
BT4	AUDIOVISUAL MATERIAL
RT	CORANGE CHARTS
RT	TIDAL AMPLITUDE
RT	TIDAL RANGE

CORE (EARTH)
    USE   **EARTH CORE**

CORE ANALYSIS
BT1	SEDIMENT ANALYSIS
RT	ANALYSIS
RT	CORE HANDLING
RT	CORES

CORE HANDLING
RT	CORE ANALYSIS
RT	CORE RECOVERY
RT	CORES
RT	CORING
RT	SAMPLE STORAGE
RT	SEDIMENT SAMPLING

CORE LAYER METHOD
RT	ANALYSIS
RT	CORE LAYERS (WATER)
RT	HYDROGRAPHY
RT	OUTFLOW WATERS
RT	SALINITY MAXIMUM LAYER
RT	SALINITY MINIMUM LAYER
RT	T/S DIAGRAMS
RT	WATER MASSES
RT	WATER MIXING
RT	WATER TYPES

CORE LAYERS (WATER)
BT1	LAYERS
NT1	OXYGEN MAXIMUM LAYER
NT1	OXYGEN MINIMUM LAYER
NT1	SALINITY MAXIMUM LAYER
NT1	SALINITY MINIMUM LAYER
NT1	TEMPERATURE MAXIMUM LAYER
NT1	TEMPERATURE MINIMUM LAYER
RT	CORE LAYER METHOD
RT	HYDROGRAPHY
RT	T/S DIAGRAMS
RT	WATER MASSES
RT	WATER TYPES

CORE ORIENTATION
UF	magnetic core orientation
BT1	ORIENTATION
RT	CORES
RT	REMANENT MAGNETIZATION

CORE RECOVERY
BT1	RECOVERY
RT	CORE HANDLING
RT	CORES
RT	CORING

CORE SAMPLES
    USE   **CORES**

CORE SAMPLING
    USE   **CORING**

CORERS
SN	Before 1982 search CORING DEVICES
UF	coring devices
BT1	SEDIMENT SAMPLERS
BT2	SAMPLERS
NT1	FREE-FALL CORERS
NT1	GRAVITY CORERS
NT1	PISTON CORERS
NT1	VIBRATORY CORERS
RT	CORES
RT	CORING
RT	DRILLING EQUIPMENT
RT	PENETROMETERS
RT	SEDIMENT SAMPLING

CORES
UF	core samples
BT1	SEDIMENT SAMPLES
BT2	GEOLOGICAL SAMPLES
BT3	SAMPLES
RT	BOREHOLES
RT	CORE ANALYSIS
RT	CORE HANDLING
RT	CORE ORIENTATION
RT	CORE RECOVERY
RT	CORERS
RT	CORING
RT	DRILLING
RT	GEOLOGICAL COLLECTIONS
RT	SEAFLOOR SAMPLING
RT	SEDIMENT SAMPLING

CORING
SN	Bottom sampling and core studies
UF	core sampling
BT1	SEDIMENT SAMPLING
BT2	SEAFLOOR SAMPLING
BT3	SAMPLING
RT	CORE HANDLING
RT	CORE RECOVERY
RT	CORERS
RT	CORES
RT	DRILLING
RT	OFFSHORE ENGINEERING
RT	SEAFLOOR SAMPLING
RT	SEDIMENT COLLECTIONS
RT	UNDERWATER EXPLORATION

CORING DEVICES
    USE   **CORERS**

CORIOLIS ACCELERATION
BT1	ACCELERATION
RT	CORIOLIS FORCE
RT	CORIOLIS PARAMETERS

CORIOLIS FORCE
BT1	FORCES (MECHANICS)
RT	ACCELERATION
RT	ATMOSPHERIC CIRCULATION
RT	CORIOLIS ACCELERATION
RT	CORIOLIS PARAMETERS
RT	GEOSTROPHIC EQUILIBRIUM
RT	GEOSTROPHIC FLOW
RT	GRADIENT WINDS
RT	HYDROSTATIC EQUATION
RT	ROSSBY NUMBER
RT	ROTARY CURRENTS
RT	VORTICITY
RT	WATER CIRCULATION
RT	PARAMETERS

CORIOLIS PARAMETERS
RT	ABSOLUTE VORTICITY
RT	BETA SPIRALS
RT	BETA-PLANE
RT	CORIOLIS ACCELERATION
RT	CORIOLIS FORCE
RT	EKMAN SPIRAL
RT	PLANETARY VORTICITY
RT	ROSSBY PARAMETER
RT	STREAM FUNCTIONS

CORRECTIONS
SN	Used only as a qualifier
NT1	GRAVITY CORRECTIONS
RT	ERRORS
RT	REVERSING THERMOMETERS

CORRELATION
SN	Used only as a qualifier
RT	CORRELATION ANALYSIS
RT	STRATIGRAPHIC CORRELATION

CORRELATION ANALYSIS
SN	Used only as a qualifier
UF	correlation functions
BT1	STATISTICAL ANALYSIS
BT2	MATHEMATICAL ANALYSIS
NT1	AUTOCORRELATION
NT1	CROSS CORRELATION
RT	CORRELATION
RT	NUMERICAL TAXONOMY
RT	REGRESSION ANALYSIS
RT	TIME SERIES ANALYSIS
RT	VARIANCE ANALYSIS

CORRELATION FUNCTIONS
    USE   **CORRELATION ANALYSIS**

CORRESPONDENCE (LETTERS)
    USE   **ARCHIVES**

CORROSION
UF	cavitation erosion
UF	crevice corrosion
UF	pitting
UF	rust
BT1	CHEMICAL REACTIONS
NT1	CRACKING (CORROSION)
NT1	STRESS CORROSION
RT	ANTIOXIDANTS
RT	CAVITATION
RT	CHEMICAL DEGRADATION
RT	CORROSION CONTROL
RT	DETERIORATION
RT	ELECTROCHEMISTRY
RT	ELECTROLYSIS
RT	FATIGUE (MATERIALS)
RT	HUMIDITY
RT	MATERIALS TESTING
RT	OXIDATION
RT	SPLASH ZONE
RT	STORAGE LIFE
RT	WEATHERING

CORROSION CONTROL
UF	anticorrosion material
UF	corrosion inhibition
UF	corrosion prevention
UF	corrosion protection
BT1	CONTROL
NT1	CATHODIC PROTECTION
RT	ANTIOXIDANTS
RT	COATING PROCESSES
RT	CORROSION
RT	MAINTENANCE
RT	PROTECTION
RT	STAINLESS STEEL

CORROSION CRACKING
    USE   **CRACKING (CORROSION)**

CORROSION INHIBITION
    USE   **CORROSION CONTROL**

CORROSION PREVENTION
    USE   **CORROSION CONTROL**

CORROSION PROTECTION
    USE   **CORROSION CONTROL**

COSINE COLLECTORS
BT1	LIGHT MEASURING INSTRUMENTS
BT2	MEASURING DEVICES
RT	IRRADIANCE

COSINE RESPONSE
SN	Used only as a qualifier
UF	horizontal cosine response
UF	vertical cosine response
BT1	INSTRUMENT RESPONSES
RT	FLOWMETERS
RT	LIGHT MEASURING INSTRUMENTS

COSMIC DUST
UF	dust (cosmic)
BT1	EXTRATERRESTRIAL MATERIAL
RT	EOLIAN DUST
RT	SEDIMENTS

COSMIC RADIATION
UF	cosmic rays
BT1	IONIZING RADIATION
BT2	RADIATIONS

COSMIC RAYS
USE	**COSMIC RADIATION**

COSMIC SPHERULES
UF	magnetic spherules
BT1	EXTRATERRESTRIAL MATERIAL
RT	MAGNETITE

COSMOPOLITE SPECIES
BT1	SPECIES
BT2	TAXA
RT	BIOGEOGRAPHY
RT	BIPOLAR DISTRIBUTION
RT	GEOGRAPHICAL DISTRIBUTION

COST ANALYSIS
SN	Study of costs related to technical and financial operations in aquaculture, commercial fishing, fishing industry, marketing, trade, etc.
RT	ANALYSIS
RT	AQUACULTURE
RT	AQUACULTURE ECONOMICS
RT	CAPTURE FISHERY ECONOMICS
RT	COMMERCIAL AVAILABILITY
RT	COMMERCIAL FISHING
RT	COMPARATIVE STUDIES
RT	COSTS
RT	ECONOMIC ANALYSIS
RT	ECONOMIC FEASIBILITY
RT	ECONOMICS
RT	FEASIBILITY
RT	FEASIBILITY STUDIES
RT	FINANCIAL MANAGEMENT
RT	FINANCING
RT	FISHERY ECONOMICS
RT	FISHERY INDUSTRY
RT	MARKET RESEARCH
RT	PRICING
RT	PRODUCTION COST
RT	RESOURCE MANAGEMENT

COSTS
SN	Added in 1980
UF	expenditures
UF	expenses
UF	prices
NT1	LABOUR COSTS
NT1	OPERATIONAL COSTS
RT	ACQUISITION
RT	COST ANALYSIS
RT	ECONOMIC FEASIBILITY
RT	ECONOMICS
RT	FINANCING
RT	INDUSTRIAL PRODUCTION
RT	MARKETING
RT	PRICING
RT	PURCHASING
RT	RENTAL
RT	TAXES

COTIDAL CHARTS
BT1	TIDAL CHARTS
BT2	HYDROGRAPHIC CHARTS
BT3	MAPS
BT4	GRAPHICS
RT	COTIDAL LINES
RT	TIDAL PREDICTION

COTIDAL CHARTS (cont'd)
RT	TIDAL PROPAGATION
RT	TIDE TABLES

COTIDAL LINES
BT1	ISOPLETHS
BT2	MAP GRAPHICS
BT3	GRAPHICS
BT4	AUDIOVISUAL MATERIAL
RT	AMPHIDROMIC SYSTEMS
RT	COTIDAL CHARTS
RT	HIGH WATER
RT	ISOCHRONES
RT	TIDAL RANGE

COUETTE FLOW
BT1	LAMINAR FLOW
BT2	FLUID FLOW
BT3	FLUID MOTION
RT	SHEAR STRESS

COUNTERCURRENTS
BT1	WATER CURRENTS
BT2	WATER MOTION
NT1	COASTAL COUNTERCURRENTS
NT1	EQUATORIAL COUNTERCURRENTS

COUNTERS
SN	Automatic devices for biological and physical counting
NT1	BACTERIAL COUNTERS
NT1	CELL COUNTERS
NT1	EGG COUNTERS
NT1	FISH COUNTERS
NT1	GEIGER COUNTERS
NT1	PARTICLE COUNTERS

COUNTRIES
UF	states (political)
NT1	COASTAL STATES
NT1	DEVELOPED COUNTRIES
NT1	DEVELOPING COUNTRIES
NT1	LANDLOCKED STATES
RT	GOVERNMENTS
RT	INTERNATIONAL AGREEMENTS
RT	INTERNATIONAL COOPERATION
RT	INTERNATIONAL ORGANIZATIONS
RT	LAW OF THE SEA

COUPLED BODIES
RT	HYDRODYNAMICS

COUPLING (JOINING COMPONENTS)
USE	**CONNECTING**

COUPLINGS (COMPONENTS)
USE	**CONNECTORS**

COURTSHIP
BT1	REPRODUCTIVE BEHAVIOUR
BT2	BEHAVIOUR
RT	DISPLAY BEHAVIOUR
RT	SEXUAL REPRODUCTION

CRAB CULTURE
SN	Before 1982 search CRUSTACEAN CULTURE
UF	brackishwater crab culture
UF	freshwater crab culture
UF	marine crab culture
BT1	CRUSTACEAN CULTURE
BT2	SHELLFISH CULTURE
BT3	AQUACULTURE
RT	COASTAL LAGOONS
RT	POLYCULTURE
RT	POND CULTURE

CRAB FISHERIES
SN	Added in 1982
UF	dungeness crab fisheries
UF	edible crab fisheries
UF	king crab fisheries
UF	market crab fisheries
UF	snow crab fisheries
UF	tanner crab fisheries
BT1	CRUSTACEAN FISHERIES
BT2	FISHERIES
RT	COASTAL FISHERIES
RT	MARINE FISHERIES
RT	TRAP FISHING

CRACK PROPAGATION
RT	DETERIORATION

CRACKING (CORROSION)
UF	corrosion cracking
BT1	CORROSION
BT2	CHEMICAL REACTIONS
RT	EMBRITTLEMENT

CRACKS
BT1	DEFECTS
RT	FRACTURES
RT	LAMELLAR TEARING

CRANE BARGES
BT1	BARGES
BT2	SURFACE CRAFT
BT3	VEHICLES
RT	CRANES
RT	SUPPORT SHIPS

CRANES
UF	derricks
UF	hoists
BT1	LIFTING TACKLE
BT2	DECK EQUIPMENT
BT3	EQUIPMENT
RT	CRANE BARGES
RT	PONTOONS

CRATONS
RT	CONTINENTAL CRUST
RT	CONTINENTAL MARGINS
RT	CONTINENTS
RT	PLATFORMS (GEOLOGY)

CRAWFISH CULTURE
USE	**CRAYFISH CULTURE**

CRAWLERS
USE	**SEABED VEHICLES**

CRAYFISH CULTURE
SN	Before 1982 search CRUSTACEAN CULTURE
UF	astaciculture
UF	crawfish culture
UF	crayfish farming
BT1	CRUSTACEAN CULTURE
BT2	SHELLFISH CULTURE
BT3	AQUACULTURE
RT	POND CULTURE
RT	RICE FIELD AQUACULTURE
RT	STOCKING (ORGANISMS)

CRAYFISH FARMING
USE	**CRAYFISH CULTURE**

CRAYFISH FISHERIES
USE	**LOBSTER FISHERIES**

CREDIT MANAGEMENT
USE	**FINANCIAL MANAGEMENT**

CREEL CENSUS
USE **SPORT FISHING STATISTICS**

CREEP
UF   solifluction
RT   DEFORMATION
RT   LANDSLIDES
RT   MASS MOVEMENT
RT   SLIDES
RT   SLOPE STABILITY
RT   SLUMPING
RT   SOIL MECHANICS

CRETACEOUS
SN   Before 1982 search CRETACEOUS PERIOD
BT1   MESOZOIC
BT2   GEOLOGICAL TIME
RT   MASS EXTINCTIONS

CREVICE CORROSION
USE   **CORROSION**

CREW
BT1   PERSONNEL

CRISTOBALITE
BT1   OXIDE MINERALS
BT2   MINERALS
RT   SILICA

CRITICAL FLOW
BT1   FLUID FLOW
BT2   FLUID MOTION

CRITICAL PATH METHOD
BT1   OPERATIONS RESEARCH
RT   CONTROL CHARTS
RT   NUMERICAL ANALYSIS
RT   PERT
RT   PREDICTION

CROAKER FISHERIES
USE   **PERCOID FISHERIES**

CROCODILE FARMING
USE   **REPTILE CULTURE**

CROSS BREEDING
USE   **HYBRID CULTURE**

CROSS CORRELATION
BT1   CORRELATION ANALYSIS
BT2   STATISTICAL ANALYSIS
BT3   MATHEMATICAL ANALYSIS
RT   AUTOCORRELATION
RT   CONVOLUTION

CROSS POLLINATION
USE   **POLLINATION**

CROWDING
USE   **STOCKING DENSITY**

CRUDE OIL
BT1   PETROLEUM
BT2   FOSSIL FUELS
BT3   SUBSURFACE DEPOSITS
BT4   MINERAL DEPOSITS
RT   NATURAL GAS
RT   OIL
RT   OIL PRODUCTION
RT   OIL RECOVERY
RT   TANKER TERMINALS

CRUDE OIL PRODUCTION
USE   **OIL PRODUCTION**

CRUDE OIL TREATING
USE   **OIL TREATING**

CRUISE PROGRAMMES
RT   CRUISES
RT   MULTISHIP EXPEDITIONS
RT   PLANNING
RT   RESEARCH PROPOSALS
RT   RESEARCH VESSELS

CRUISE REPORTS
SN   Preliminary report on results
   obtained during a cruise by one
   research vessel
BT1   REPORT LITERATURE
BT2   DOCUMENTS
RT   CRUISES
RT   EXPEDITION REPORTS
RT   TRACK CHARTS

CRUISE STATIONS
UF   anchor stations
UF   expedition stations
BT1   OCEANOGRAPHIC STATIONS
RT   CRUISES
RT   EXPEDITIONS
RT   MULTISHIP EXPEDITIONS
RT   STATION KEEPING
RT   STATION LISTS
RT   TRACK CHARTS

CRUISES
SN   Use only for surveys involving one
   vessel
UF   expeditions (one vessel)
BT1   EXPEDITIONS
RT   CRUISE PROGRAMMES
RT   CRUISE REPORTS
RT   CRUISE STATIONS
RT   DATA REPORTS
RT   DEFENCE CRAFT
RT   EXPEDITION REPORTS
RT   GEOLOGICAL DATA
RT   GEOPHYSICAL DATA
RT   LIMNOLOGICAL DATA
RT   LOGBOOKS
RT   METEOROLOGICAL DATA
RT   MULTISHIP EXPEDITIONS
RT   OCEANOGRAPHIC DATA
RT   OCEANOGRAPHIC INSTITUTIONS
RT   OCEANOGRAPHIC SURVEYS
RT   PLANNING
RT   PROGRAMMES
RT   RESEARCH INSTITUTIONS
RT   RESEARCH VESSELS
RT   STATION LISTS
RT   SURVEYS
RT   TRACK CHARTS

CRUST (EARTH)
USE   **EARTH CRUST**

CRUST (OCEAN)
USE   **OCEANIC CRUST**

CRUST (OCEANIC)
USE   **OCEANIC CRUST**

CRUSTACEAN CULTURE
BT1   SHELLFISH CULTURE
BT2   AQUACULTURE
NT1   BRINE SHRIMP CULTURE
NT1   CRAB CULTURE
NT1   CRAYFISH CULTURE
NT1   LOBSTER CULTURE
NT1   PRAWN CULTURE
NT1   SHRIMP CULTURE
RT   BATCH CULTURE
RT   BRACKISHWATER AQUACULTURE
RT   CAGE CULTURE

CRUSTACEAN CULTURE (cont'd)
RT   CANNIBALISM
RT   CRUSTACEAN LARVAE
RT   CULTURES
RT   FRESHWATER AQUACULTURE
RT   FRESHWATER CRUSTACEANS
RT   GRADING
RT   HATCHERIES
RT   INDUCED BREEDING
RT   MARINE AQUACULTURE
RT   MARINE CRUSTACEANS
RT   MASS CULTURE
RT   METAMORPHOSIS
RT   MONOCULTURE
RT   POND CULTURE
RT   RACEWAY CULTURE
RT   RECIRCULATING SYSTEMS
RT   SEED COLLECTION
RT   SUBMERGED CAGES

CRUSTACEAN FISHERIES
SN   Added in 1982
BT1   FISHERIES
NT1   CRAB FISHERIES
NT1   KRILL FISHERIES
NT1   LOBSTER FISHERIES
NT1   SHRIMP FISHERIES
NT1   SQUAT LOBSTER FISHERIES
RT   COASTAL FISHERIES
RT   DEMERSAL FISHERIES
RT   MARINE FISHERIES
RT   RIVER FISHERIES
RT   TRAP FISHING

CRUSTACEAN LARVAE
SN   Added in 1980
BT1   INVERTEBRATE LARVAE
BT2   LARVAE
BT3   DEVELOPMENTAL STAGES
NT1   MEGALOPS
NT1   NAUPLII
NT1   PHYLLOSOMAE
NT1   ZOEAE
RT   CRUSTACEAN CULTURE
RT   MEROPLANKTON

CRUSTACEANS (FRESHWATER)
USE   **FRESHWATER CRUSTACEANS**

CRUSTACEANS (MARINE)
USE   **MARINE CRUSTACEANS**

CRUSTAL ACCRETION
BT1   ACCRETION
RT   DIVERGING PLATE BOUNDARIES
RT   OCEANIC CRUST
RT   PLATE DIVERGENCE

CRUSTAL ADJUSTMENT
BT1   TECTONICS
BT2   GEOLOGY
BT3   EARTH SCIENCES
NT1   ISOSTASY
RT   EPEIROGENY
RT   PLATE TECTONICS

CRUSTAL SHORTENING
BT1   DIASTROPHISM
RT   EARTH CRUST
RT   EPEIROGENY

CRUSTAL STRUCTURE
RT   CONTINENTAL CRUST
RT   EARTH CRUST
RT   OCEANIC CRUST

ASFIS Thesaurus

CRUSTAL THICKNESS
- BT1 THICKNESS
- BT2 DIMENSIONS
- RT CONTINENTAL CRUST
- RT EARTH CRUST
- RT OCEANIC CRUST

CRUSTS (ROCKS)
- USE **CONCRETIONS**

CRYOBIOLOGY
- SN Low temperature biology. Added in 1980
- BT1 BIOLOGY
- RT COLD RESISTANCE
- RT CRYOPLANKTON
- RT PHYSIOLOGY
- RT POLAR ZONES
- RT TEMPERATURE TOLERANCE

CRYOPLANKTON
- SN Ice- and snow-inhabiting organisms. Added in 1980
- BT1 PLANKTON
- BT2 AQUATIC COMMUNITIES
- RT CRYOBIOLOGY
- RT ICE
- RT POLAR ZONES

CRYOPRESERVATION
- USE **FREEZING STORAGE**

CRYOPROTECTANTS
- USE **FREEZING STORAGE**

CRYOSPHERE
- BT1 HYDROSPHERE
- RT EUSTATIC CHANGES
- RT GLACIERS
- RT ICE
- RT ICE CAPS
- RT ICE VOLUME
- RT PERMAFROST

CTD MEASUREMENTS
- USE **CTD OBSERVATIONS**

CTD OBSERVATIONS
- UF ctd measurements
- BT1 HYDROGRAPHIC DATA
- BT2 DATA
- RT CTD PROFILERS
- RT FINESTRUCTURE
- RT STD OBSERVATIONS
- RT VERTICAL PROFILES

CTD PROBES
- USE **CTD PROFILERS**

CTD PROFILERS
- SN Conductivity-temperature-depth profilers
- UF ctd probes
- UF ctd sensors
- BT1 PROFILERS
- RT CONDUCTIVITY SENSORS
- RT CTD OBSERVATIONS
- RT ELECTRICAL CONDUCTIVITY
- RT FINESTRUCTURE
- RT OCEANOGRAPHIC EQUIPMENT
- RT SALINITY
- RT SALINITY MEASURING EQUIPMENT
- RT SALINITY PROFILES
- RT STD PROFILERS
- RT THERMOMETERS
- RT VERTICAL PROFILES
- RT WATER TEMPERATURE
- RT TEMPERATURE PROFILES

CTD SENSORS
- USE **CTD PROFILERS**

CULCH
- USE **CULTCH**

CULLING
- SN Removal or killing of a certain number of animals to maintain a steady population. Added in 1982
- RT AQUATIC MAMMALS
- RT FISHERY MANAGEMENT

CULTCH
- SN Any substrata placed in the environment to attract the attachment of oyster larvae. Added in 1980
- UF culch
- UF cultch material
- BT1 ARTIFICIAL SUBSTRATA
- RT LARVAL SETTLEMENT
- RT OYSTER CULTURE
- RT SPAT
- RT SUBSTRATE PREFERENCES

CULTCH MATERIAL
- USE **CULTCH**

CULTURE EFFECTS
- SN Effects of aquaculture practice on the ecosystem. Added in 1980
- RT AQUACULTURE ENTERPRISES
- RT BIOLOGICAL POLLUTANTS
- RT EUTROPHICATION

CULTURE MEDIA
- SN Fluid, solid and nutritive media for culture of tissue and organisms
- RT AGAR
- RT BACTERIA
- RT CELL CULTURE
- RT LABORATORY CULTURE
- RT MICROBIOLOGICAL ANALYSIS
- RT MICROBIOLOGICAL CULTURE
- RT STERILIZATION
- RT TISSUE CULTURE
- RT VITAMINS

CULTURE TANKS
- BT1 TANKS
- BT2 CONTAINERS
- RT ALGAL CULTURE
- RT AQUACULTURE
- RT AQUACULTURE EQUIPMENT
- RT AQUACULTURE TECHNIQUES
- RT BATCH CULTURE
- RT BRINE SHRIMP CULTURE
- RT CONTINUOUS CULTURE
- RT EXPERIMENTAL CULTURE
- RT FISH CULTURE
- RT HATCHERIES
- RT LABORATORY CULTURE
- RT LOBSTER CULTURE
- RT MASS CULTURE
- RT REARING
- RT RECIRCULATING SYSTEMS
- RT SEAWEED CULTURE
- RT SHELLFISH CULTURE
- RT SHRIMP CULTURE

CULTURED FISH
- USE **CULTURED ORGANISMS**

CULTURED FOOD
- USE **CULTURED ORGANISMS**

CULTURED ORGANISMS
- UF cultured fish
- UF cultured food
- UF cultured species
- BT1 AQUATIC ORGANISMS
- RT AQUACULTURE
- RT AQUACULTURE PRODUCTS
- RT BALANCED DIETS
- RT BASIC DIETS
- RT DOMESTIC SPECIES
- RT HUMAN FOOD
- RT MICROBIOLOGICAL CULTURE
- RT PHYTOPLANKTON CULTURE
- RT REARING
- RT SUNBURN
- RT TEMPERATURE PREFERENCES
- RT ZOOPLANKTON CULTURE

CULTURED SPECIES
- USE **CULTURED ORGANISMS**

CULTURES
- SN Use of a more specific term is recommended; consult terms listed below
- RT BAIT CULTURE
- RT BATCH CULTURE
- RT BOTTOM CULTURE
- RT CONTINUOUS CULTURE
- RT CORAL FARMING
- RT CRUSTACEAN CULTURE
- RT EXPERIMENTAL CULTURE
- RT EXTENSIVE CULTURE
- RT FISH CULTURE
- RT FROG CULTURE
- RT HYBRID CULTURE
- RT INTENSIVE CULTURE
- RT LABORATORY CULTURE
- RT MOLLUSC CULTURE
- RT MONOSEX CULTURE
- RT OFF-BOTTOM CULTURE
- RT OYSTER CULTURE
- RT PEARL CULTURE
- RT PHYTOPLANKTON CULTURE
- RT PLANT CULTURE
- RT POLYCULTURE
- RT POND CULTURE
- RT RACEWAY CULTURE
- RT RAFT CULTURE
- RT SEAWEED CULTURE
- RT SPONGE CULTURE
- RT TURTLE CULTURE
- RT VALLICULTURE
- RT ZOOPLANKTON CULTURE

CUMULUS
- USE **CLOUDS**

CUP ANEMOMETERS
- USE **ANEMOMETERS**

CURED PRODUCTS
- UF dried salted products
- UF marinated products
- UF smoked products
- BT1 PROCESSED FISHERY PRODUCTS
- BT2 FISHERY PRODUCTS
- BT3 PRODUCTS
- RT CURING
- RT DRIED PRODUCTS

CURING
- SN To preserve by salting, drying, smoking, fermentation or a combination of these methods
- UF salting
- UF smoking
- BT1 PROCESSING FISHERY PRODUCTS
- BT2 FISHERY INDUSTRY
- BT3 INDUSTRIES

CURING (cont'd)
RT	CURED PRODUCTS
RT	DRESSING
RT	DRYING
RT	FREEZE-DRYING

CURIUM
BT1	CHEMICAL ELEMENTS
RT	ACTINIDES
RT	CURIUM COMPOUNDS
RT	CURIUM ISOTOPES
RT	TRANSITION ELEMENTS
RT	TRANSURANIC ELEMENTS

CURIUM COMPOUNDS
BT1	ACTINIDE COMPOUNDS
RT	CHEMICAL COMPOUNDS
RT	CURIUM

CURIUM ISOTOPES
BT1	ISOTOPES
RT	CURIUM

CURL (VECTORS)
BT1	VECTORS
NT1	WIND STRESS CURL
RT	VORTICITY

CURL OF WIND STRESS
USE	**WIND STRESS CURL**

CURRENT CHARTS
UF	tidal current charts
BT1	HYDROGRAPHIC CHARTS
BT2	MAPS
BT3	GRAPHICS
BT4	AUDIOVISUAL MATERIAL
RT	CURRENT DIRECTION
RT	CURRENT ROSES
RT	CURRENT VECTORS
RT	CURRENT VELOCITY
RT	STREAMLINES
RT	TIDAL CHARTS
RT	TIDAL CURRENTS
RT	TIDE TABLES
RT	WATER CURRENTS

CURRENT DATA
SN	Data collections obtained by any method of current measurement
UF	water current data
BT1	HYDROGRAPHIC DATA
BT2	DATA
RT	CURRENT DATA ANALYSIS
RT	CURRENT DIRECTION
RT	CURRENT MEASUREMENT
RT	CURRENT VELOCITY
RT	DATA
RT	LONG-TERM RECORDS
RT	OCEANOGRAPHIC DATA
RT	WATER CURRENTS
RT	CURRENT DATA

CURRENT DENSITY
BT1	DENSITY
BT2	PHYSICAL PROPERTIES
BT3	PROPERTIES
RT	ELECTRIC CURRENTS

CURRENT DIRECTION
RT	CURRENT CHARTS
RT	CURRENT DATA
RT	CURRENT ROSES
RT	STREAMLINES
RT	WATER CURRENTS

CURRENT ELLIPSES
BT1	HODOGRAPHS
BT2	GRAPHS
BT3	GRAPHICS
BT4	AUDIOVISUAL MATERIAL
RT	ROTARY CURRENTS

CURRENT FORCES
BT1	LOADS (FORCES)
BT2	FORCES (MECHANICS)
RT	CURRENT VELOCITY
RT	HYDRODYNAMICS
RT	VORTEX SHEDDING
RT	WATER CURRENTS

CURRENT MARKS
BT1	BEDDING STRUCTURES
BT2	SEDIMENTARY STRUCTURES
NT1	FLUTE CASTS
NT1	SCOUR MARKS
NT1	SOLE MARKS

CURRENT MEANDERING
UF	meandering (currents)
BT1	MEANDERING
BT2	WATER MOTION
RT	CURRENT RINGS
RT	FLUID MOTION
RT	MESOSCALE EDDIES
RT	MESOSCALE FEATURES
RT	WATER CURRENTS

CURRENT MEANDERS
USE	**CURRENT RINGS**

CURRENT MEASUREMENT
SN	Methods for measuring speed and direction of water currents
UF	current measuring
UF	current measuring methods
UF	velocity measurement (water)
BT1	FLOW MEASUREMENT
BT2	MEASUREMENT
NT1	EULERIAN CURRENT MEASUREMENT
NT1	LAGRANGIAN CURRENT MEASUREMENT
RT	CURRENT DATA
RT	CURRENT MEASURING EQUIPMENT
RT	CURRENT METERS
RT	CURRENT OBSERVATIONS
RT	CURRENT VELOCITY
RT	DRIFT BOTTLES
RT	DRIFT CARDS
RT	DRIFTERS
RT	PHOTOGRAMMETRY
RT	SEABED DRIFTERS
RT	SUBSURFACE DRIFTERS
RT	SURFACE DRIFTERS
RT	SWALLOW FLOATS
RT	WATER CURRENTS

CURRENT MEASURING
USE	**CURRENT MEASUREMENT**

CURRENT MEASURING EQUIPMENT
BT1	FLOW MEASURING EQUIPMENT
NT1	CURRENT SENSORS
NT1	DRIFTERS
NT2	SUBSURFACE DRIFTERS
NT3	SEABED DRIFTERS
NT3	SWALLOW FLOATS
NT4	SOFAR FLOATS
NT2	SURFACE DRIFTERS
NT3	DRIFT BOTTLES
NT3	DRIFT CARDS
NT3	DROGUES
NT1	JELLY BOTTLES
RT	CURRENT MEASUREMENT
RT	CURRENT METERS
RT	DROGUES
RT	FLOWMETERS

CURRENT MEASURING EQUIPMENT (cont'd)
RT	GEK
RT	OCEANOGRAPHIC EQUIPMENT
RT	SHEAR PROBES
RT	VELOCITY PROFILERS
RT	WATER CURRENTS

CURRENT MEASURING METHODS
USE	**CURRENT MEASUREMENT**

CURRENT METER ARRAYS
BT1	ARRAYS
RT	DEPLOYMENT
RT	FLOWMETERS
RT	MOORING RECOVERY
RT	RECOVERY

CURRENT METER DATA
BT1	CURRENT OBSERVATIONS
BT2	HYDROGRAPHIC DATA
BT3	DATA
RT	CURRENT METERS
RT	EULERIAN CURRENT MEASUREMENT

CURRENT METER MOORINGS
BT1	MOORING SYSTEMS

CURRENT METER VANES
USE	**VANES**

CURRENT METERS
SN	Restricted to measurement of water speed and direction
BT1	MEASURING DEVICES
NT1	ACOUSTIC CURRENT METERS
RT	CURRENT MEASUREMENT
RT	CURRENT MEASURING EQUIPMENT
RT	CURRENT METER DATA
RT	CURRENT OBSERVATIONS
RT	DOPPLER EFFECT
RT	EULERIAN CURRENT MEASUREMENT
RT	FLOWMETERS
RT	IMPELLERS
RT	OCEANOGRAPHIC EQUIPMENT
RT	WATER CURRENTS

CURRENT OBSERVATIONS
UF	water current data and observations
BT1	HYDROGRAPHIC DATA
BT2	DATA
NT1	CURRENT METER DATA
RT	CURRENT MEASUREMENT
RT	CURRENT METERS
RT	NEAR-SURFACE LAYER

CURRENT POWER
SN	Utilizing the energy of water currents as a source of power
UF	ocean current energy conversion
BT1	POWER FROM THE SEA
BT2	ENERGY RESOURCES
BT3	NATURAL RESOURCES
BT4	RESOURCES
RT	OCEAN CURRENTS
RT	WATER CURRENTS

CURRENT PREDICTION
BT1	PREDICTION
RT	WATER CURRENTS

CURRENT PROFILES
UF	current speed profiles
BT1	VELOCITY PROFILES
BT2	VERTICAL PROFILES
BT3	PROFILES
RT	VELOCITY GRADIENTS
RT	VELOCITY PROFILERS
RT	VELOCITY SECTIONS

ASFIS Thesaurus

CURRENT REVERSAL
RT	MONSOON REVERSAL
RT	WATER CURRENTS

CURRENT RINGS
SN	Oceanic eddies of order 10 kms diameter
UF	anticyclonic eddies
UF	anticyclonic rings
UF	current meanders
UF	cyclonic eddies
UF	cyclonic rings
UF	gulf stream rings
UF	meanders (current)
BT1	OCEANIC EDDIES
BT2	OCEAN CIRCULATION
BT3	WATER CIRCULATION
BT4	WATER MOTION
RT	CURRENT MEANDERING
RT	OCEAN CURRENTS
RT	VORTICES

CURRENT ROSES
BT1	MAP GRAPHICS
BT2	GRAPHICS
BT3	AUDIOVISUAL MATERIAL
BT4	DOCUMENTS
RT	CURRENT CHARTS
RT	CURRENT DIRECTION
RT	CURRENT VELOCITY
RT	WATER CURRENTS
RT	WIND ROSES

CURRENT SCOURING
UF	tidal scour
BT1	SCOURING
BT2	EROSION
RT	ARTIFICIAL SEAWEED
RT	BED FORMS
RT	BOTTOM CURRENTS
RT	BOTTOM EROSION
RT	DETERIORATION
RT	FLOW AROUND OBJECTS
RT	FOUNDATIONS
RT	GEOTECHNOLOGY
RT	LEE EDDIES
RT	SCOUR AND FILL
RT	SCOUR HOLLOWS
RT	SCOUR MARKS
RT	SCOUR PROTECTION
RT	SEDIMENT TRANSPORT
RT	WATER CURRENTS
RT	WAVE SCOURING

CURRENT SENSORS
BT1	CURRENT MEASURING EQUIPMENT
BT2	FLOW MEASURING EQUIPMENT
RT	ACOUSTIC CURRENT METERS
RT	DOPPLER EFFECT
RT	FLOWMETERS

CURRENT SHEAR
BT1	SHEAR
RT	SHEAR PROBES
RT	WIND SHEAR

CURRENT SPECTRA
BT1	SPECTRA

CURRENT SPEED
USE	**CURRENT VELOCITY**

CURRENT SPEED PROFILES
USE	**CURRENT PROFILES**

CURRENT VECTORS
BT1	VECTORS
RT	CURRENT CHARTS
RT	CURRENT VELOCITY
RT	STREAMLINES

CURRENT VECTORS (cont'd)
RT	WATER CURRENTS

CURRENT VELOCITY
UF	current speed
BT1	VELOCITY
NT1	STREAM FLOW RATE
RT	CURRENT CHARTS
RT	CURRENT DATA
RT	CURRENT FORCES
RT	CURRENT MEASUREMENT
RT	CURRENT ROSES
RT	CURRENT VECTORS
RT	ELECTRIC POTENTIAL
RT	FLOWMETERS
RT	ICE DRIFT
RT	TIDE TABLES
RT	VELOCITY GRADIENTS
RT	VELOCITY MICROSTRUCTURE
RT	VELOCITY PROFILERS
RT	VELOCITY SECTIONS
RT	VOLUME TRANSPORT
RT	WESTWARD INTENSIFICATION

CURRENTS (ELECTRIC)
USE	**ELECTRIC CURRENTS**

CURRICULA
SN	Before 1982 search also EDUCATION
UF	syllabuses
UF	training programmes
RT	EDUCATION
RT	EDUCATION ESTABLISHMENTS
RT	TRAINING CENTRES

CURVES (GRAPHS)
USE	**GRAPHS**

CUSPATE FORELANDS
BT1	HEADLANDS
BT2	COASTAL LANDFORMS
BT3	LANDFORMS
BT4	TOPOGRAPHIC FEATURES
RT	BEACH RIDGES

CUSTOMARY FISHING RIGHTS
USE	**FISHING RIGHTS**

CUTICLES
SN	A layer covering and secreted by the epidermis of plants and many invertebrates. Added in 1980
BT1	EXOSKELETON
BT2	SKELETON
BT3	MUSCULOSKELETAL SYSTEM
RT	CHITIN
RT	MOULTING
RT	TRANSPIRATION

CUTTING
RT	WELDING

CUTTING UNDERWATER
RT	WELDING UNDERWATER

CUTTLEFISH FISHERIES
USE	**CEPHALOPOD FISHERIES**

CYANIDES
RT	CHEMICAL COMPOUNDS
RT	NITROGEN COMPOUNDS
RT	SALTS

CYCLES
SN	Use of a more specific term is recommended
UF	rhythms
NT1	BIOCHEMICAL CYCLES
NT1	BIOGEOCHEMICAL CYCLE
NT2	NUTRIENT CYCLES

CYCLES (cont'd)
NT3	CARBON CYCLE
NT3	NITROGEN CYCLE
NT3	PHOSPHORUS CYCLE
NT3	SILICON CYCLE
NT1	CHEMICAL CYCLES
NT1	GEOCHEMICAL CYCLE
NT1	HYDROLOGIC CYCLE
NT1	LIFE CYCLE
NT1	TIDAL CYCLES
NT1	TROPHODYNAMIC CYCLE
RT	ENERGY BUDGET
RT	FOOD CHAINS
RT	FOOD WEBS
RT	HEAT BUDGET
RT	MOON PHASES

CYCLESONDE
BT1	PROFILERS
RT	VELOCITY PROFILERS

CYCLIC LOADING
BT1	LOADS (FORCES)
BT2	FORCES (MECHANICS)
RT	DYNAMIC LOADS
RT	FATIGUE (MATERIALS)
RT	GEOTECHNOLOGY
RT	OCEAN LOADING
RT	PERIODIC VARIATIONS
RT	WAVE-INDUCED LOADING
RT	WAVE-SEABED INTERACTION

CYCLOGENESIS
RT	CYCLONES

CYCLOMORPHOSIS
SN	Seasonal change in morphology displayed by some planktonic animals. Added in 1980
BT1	BIOPOLYMORPHISM
RT	DEFENCE MECHANISMS
RT	PREDATION

CYCLONES
SN	Use of a more specific term is recommended
UF	depressions (meteorology)
UF	midlatitude cyclones
BT1	LOW PRESSURE SYSTEMS
RT	ANTICYCLONES
RT	CYCLOGENESIS
RT	HURRICANES
RT	POLAR FRONTS

CYCLONES (TROPICAL)
USE	**TROPICAL DEPRESSIONS**

CYCLONIC EDDIES
USE	**CURRENT RINGS**

CYCLONIC MOTION
RT	ANTICYCLONIC MOTION
RT	MOTION
RT	ROTATION

CYCLONIC RINGS
USE	**CURRENT RINGS**

CYLINDERS
RT	CYLINDRICAL STRUCTURES
RT	TUBING

CYLINDRICAL BODIES
USE	**CYLINDRICAL STRUCTURES**

CYLINDRICAL STRUCTURES
SN	Before 1986 search also CYLINDRICAL BODIES
UF	cylindrical bodies
RT	CYLINDERS

CYLINDRICAL STRUCTURES (cont'd)
RT	FLOW AROUND OBJECTS
RT	STRUCTURES

CYSTEINE
BT1	AMINO ACIDS
BT2	ORGANIC ACIDS
BT3	ORGANIC COMPOUNDS

CYSTINE
BT1	AMINO ACIDS
BT2	ORGANIC ACIDS
BT3	ORGANIC COMPOUNDS

CYSTS
SN	Resistant resting stages formed by different organisms, as a response to adverse environmental conditions. Added in 1980
UF	dormant stages
RT	DEFENCE MECHANISMS
RT	ENCYSTMENT

CYTOCHEMISTRY
SN	Added in 1982
BT1	BIOCHEMISTRY
BT2	CHEMISTRY
RT	CYTOCHROMES
RT	CYTOLOGY

CYTOCHROMES
SN	Added in 1980
BT1	COENZYMES
BT2	ENZYMES
RT	CYTOCHEMISTRY
RT	OXIDATION
RT	PROTEINS

CYTOGENETICS
USE	**GENETICS**

CYTOKININS
USE	**PHYTOHORMONES**

CYTOLOGY
UF	cell biology
BT1	BIOLOGY
NT1	KARYOLOGY
RT	CELL CONSTITUENTS
RT	CELL DIFFERENTIATION
RT	CELL DIVISION
RT	CELL MEMBRANES
RT	CELL MORPHOLOGY
RT	CELL ORGANELLES
RT	CELLS
RT	CHROMOSOMES
RT	CYTOCHEMISTRY
RT	CYTOPLASM
RT	FIXATIVES
RT	HISTOLOGY
RT	LIGHT MICROSCOPY
RT	MICROSCOPY

CYTOPLASM
UF	bioplasm
UF	protoplasm
BT1	CELL CONSTITUENTS
RT	CELL INCLUSIONS
RT	CYTOLOGY
RT	GOLGI APPARATUS
RT	RIBOSOMES
RT	YOLK

CYTOPLASMIC MEMBRANES
USE	**CELL MEMBRANES**

DAILY
SN	Descriptor to be used only as a qualifier
BT1	PERIODICITY
RT	DIURNAL VARIATIONS

DAILY VARIATION
USE	**DIURNAL VARIATIONS**

DAMAGE
SN	Results of accidents or fires. For biological damage use BIOLOGICAL DAMAGE
RT	ACCIDENTS
RT	DEFECTS
RT	FAILURES
RT	FIRE
RT	HAZARDS
RT	REPAIR

DAMAGE (BIOLOGICAL)
USE	**BIOLOGICAL DAMAGE**

DAMPING
SN	To artificially reduce amplitude or physical processes
UF	suppressing
NT1	EVAPORATION REDUCTION
NT1	NOISE REDUCTION
NT1	WAVE DAMPING
RT	ATTENUATION
RT	CONTROL
RT	INSULATING MATERIALS
RT	VIBRATION

DAMPING (WATER WAVES)
USE	**WAVE DAMPING**

DAMS
SN	Fixed structures for the containment etc. of water in valleys
BT1	BARRAGES
BT2	HYDRAULIC STRUCTURES
RT	ARTIFICIAL LAKES
RT	BACKWATERS
RT	BARRIERS
RT	BURROWING ORGANISMS
RT	FISHWAYS
RT	FLOOD CONTROL
RT	HYDRAULIC ENGINEERING
RT	IMPOUNDMENTS
RT	IRRIGATION WATER
RT	POND CONSTRUCTION
RT	PONDS
RT	RESERVOIRS (WATER)
RT	STRUCTURAL ENGINEERING
RT	WEIRS

DANGER
USE	**HAZARDS**

DANGEROUS MATERIALS
USE	**HAZARDOUS MATERIALS**

DANGEROUS ORGANISMS
SN	Harmful to persons. Added in 1980
BT1	AQUATIC ORGANISMS
RT	BATHING
RT	BIOLOGICAL DAMAGE
RT	DIVING HAZARDS
RT	HAZARDS
RT	INJURIES
RT	RECREATION

DANGERS
USE	**HAZARDS**

DANISH SEINES
USE	**BOAT SEINES**

DATA
SN	Used only as a qualifier. Use of a more specific term is recommended
NT1	BIOLOGICAL DATA
NT1	EXPERIMENTAL DATA
NT1	FISHERY DATA
NT2	CATCH/EFFORT
NT2	FISHING EFFORT
NT2	FISHING POWER
NT2	FISHING TIME
NT1	GEOPHYSICAL DATA
NT2	GEOTHERMAL DATA
NT2	GRAVITY DATA
NT2	MAGNETIC DATA
NT2	SEISMIC DATA
NT1	GEOTECHNICAL DATA
NT1	HYDROGRAPHIC DATA
NT2	CTD OBSERVATIONS
NT2	CURRENT DATA
NT2	CURRENT OBSERVATIONS
NT3	CURRENT METER DATA
NT2	ICE OBSERVATIONS
NT2	SALINITY DATA
NT2	TEMPERATURE DATA
NT1	LIMNOLOGICAL DATA
NT1	METEOROLOGICAL DATA
NT2	CLIMATIC DATA
NT2	METEOROLOGICAL OBSERVATIONS
NT2	WIND DATA
NT1	OCEANOGRAPHIC DATA
NT2	BATHYMETRIC DATA
NT3	SOUNDINGS
NT2	BATHYTHERMOGRAPHIC DATA
NT1	POLLUTION DATA
NT1	WAVE DATA
RT	ACOUSTIC DATA
RT	CURRENT DATA
RT	DATA ACQUISITION
RT	DATA BUOYS
RT	DATA CENTRES
RT	DATA COLLECTIONS
RT	DATA LOGGERS
RT	DATA PROCESSING
RT	DATA REPORTS
RT	DATA RETRIEVAL
RT	DATA STORAGE
RT	INVENTORIES
RT	MAPPING
RT	MAPS
RT	MARSDEN SQUARES
RT	STATION LISTS
RT	STATISTICAL TABLES
RT	TIME SERIES

DATA (BATHYTHERMOGRAPHIC)
USE	**BATHYTHERMOGRAPHIC DATA**

DATA (BIOLOGICAL)
USE	**BIOLOGICAL DATA**

DATA (EXPERIMENTAL)
USE	**EXPERIMENTAL DATA**

DATA (FISHERIES)
USE	**FISHERY DATA**

DATA (LIMNOLOGICAL)
USE	**LIMNOLOGICAL DATA**

DATA (OCEANOGRAPHIC)
USE	**OCEANOGRAPHIC DATA**

DATA ACQUISITION
BT1	ACQUISITION
RT	DATA
RT	DATA LOGGERS
RT	DATA PROCESSING

DATA ACQUISITION (cont'd)
RT	DATA RETRIEVAL
RT	DATA STORAGE
RT	GEOSENSING
RT	REMOTE SENSING

DATA ANALYSIS
USE	**DATA PROCESSING**

DATA BANKS
USE	**DATA COLLECTIONS**

DATA BUOYS
UF	meteorological buoys
UF	oceanographic buoys
UF	rafts (instrument carriers)
BT1	BUOYS
NT1	DRIFTING DATA BUOYS
NT1	WAVE BUOYS
RT	AUTOMATED RECORDING
RT	DATA
RT	DATA COLLECTIONS
RT	INSTRUMENT PLATFORMS
RT	LAGRANGIAN CURRENT MEASUREMENT
RT	MASTS
RT	METEOROLOGICAL DATA
RT	OCEAN STATIONS
RT	OCEANOGRAPHIC DATA
RT	OCEANOGRAPHIC EQUIPMENT
RT	RECORDING EQUIPMENT
RT	WEATHER SHIPS

DATA CATALOGUES
USE	**INVENTORIES**

DATA CENTERS
USE	**DATA CENTRES**

DATA CENTRES
UF	data centers
BT1	INFORMATION CENTRES
BT2	ORGANIZATIONS
RT	DATA
RT	DATA COLLECTIONS
RT	DATA PROCESSING
RT	DATA RETRIEVAL
RT	DATA STORAGE
RT	INVENTORIES
RT	LIBRARIES
RT	SORTING CENTRES

DATA COLLECTIONS
UF	data banks
UF	databases
BT1	COLLECTIONS
RT	CATALOGUES
RT	CENSUS
RT	DATA
RT	DATA BUOYS
RT	DATA CENTRES
RT	DATA PROCESSING
RT	DATA RETRIEVAL
RT	DATA STORAGE
RT	DIRECTORIES
RT	DOCUMENTATION
RT	ENCYCLOPAEDIAS
RT	INFORMATION HANDLING
RT	INFORMATION RETRIEVAL
RT	INVENTORIES
RT	LIBRARIES
RT	LONG-TERM CHANGES
RT	MONITORING
RT	REPORT LITERATURE
RT	STATISTICAL SAMPLING
RT	SURVEYS
RT	TRANSLATIONS

DATA CONVERTERS
SN	Analog/digital converters
RT	ANALOG RECORDS
RT	DIGITAL RECORDS

DATA HANDLING
USE	**DATA PROCESSING**

DATA LOGGERS
RT	DATA
RT	DATA ACQUISITION
RT	EQUIPMENT
RT	RECORDING EQUIPMENT

DATA PRESENTATION
USE	**GRAPHICS**

DATA PRESENTATION (GRAPHICS)
USE	**GRAPHICS**

DATA PROCESSING
UF	automated data processing
UF	data analysis
UF	data handling
NT1	BATCH PROCESSING
NT1	DATA REDUCTION
NT1	DATA RETRIEVAL
NT1	DATA STORAGE
NT1	SEISMIC DATA PROCESSING
NT2	BRIGHT SPOT TECHNOLOGY
NT1	SIGNAL PROCESSING
RT	ANALYSIS
RT	AUTOMATION
RT	COMPUTER PROGRAMS
RT	COMPUTERS
RT	DATA
RT	DATA ACQUISITION
RT	DATA CENTRES
RT	DATA COLLECTIONS
RT	IMAGERY
RT	STATISTICAL ANALYSIS
RT	STATISTICS

DATA REDUCTION
BT1	DATA PROCESSING
RT	REFERENCE LEVELS
RT	SEISMIC DATA PROCESSING
RT	SPECTRAL ANALYSIS

DATA REPORTS
BT1	REPORT LITERATURE
BT2	DOCUMENTS
NT1	STATION LISTS
RT	CRUISES
RT	DATA
RT	INSHORE STATIONS
RT	MULTISHIP EXPEDITIONS
RT	OCEAN STATIONS

DATA RETRIEVAL
BT1	DATA PROCESSING
RT	COMPUTER PROGRAMS
RT	COMPUTERS
RT	DATA
RT	DATA ACQUISITION
RT	DATA CENTRES
RT	DATA COLLECTIONS
RT	DATA STORAGE
RT	INFORMATION RETRIEVAL

DATA STORAGE
BT1	DATA PROCESSING
RT	COMPUTERS
RT	DATA
RT	DATA ACQUISITION
RT	DATA CENTRES
RT	DATA COLLECTIONS
RT	DATA RETRIEVAL
RT	DOCUMENTATION
RT	STORAGE

DATA TRANSMISSION
NT1	FACSIMILE TRANSMISSION
RT	TELEMETRY

DATABASES
USE	**DATA COLLECTIONS**

DATING (BIOLOGICAL)
USE	**AGE DETERMINATION**

DATING (EARTH SCIENCES)
USE	**GEOCHRONOMETRY**

DATUM LEVELS
BT1	REFERENCE LEVELS
NT1	CHART DATUM
NT1	TIDAL DATUM
RT	BENCH MARKS
RT	GEODESY
RT	LEVELLING
RT	SEA LEVEL

DAVITS
BT1	LIFTING TACKLE
BT2	DECK EQUIPMENT
BT3	EQUIPMENT
RT	GEAR HANDLING

DAY LENGTH
USE	**PHOTOPERIODS**

DAYTIME
SN	Descriptor to be used only as a qualifier
RT	DIURNAL VARIATIONS
RT	NIGHTTIME
RT	SEA BREEZES

DDE
UF	dichlorodiphynylethylene
BT1	CHLORINATED HYDROCARBONS
BT2	HALOGENATED HYDROCARBONS
BT3	HYDROCARBONS
BT4	ORGANIC COMPOUNDS

DDT
UF	dichlorodiphenyltrichloroethane
BT1	CHLORINATED HYDROCARBONS
BT2	HALOGENATED HYDROCARBONS
BT3	HYDROCARBONS
BT4	ORGANIC COMPOUNDS
RT	AGRICULTURAL POLLUTION
RT	AGRICULTURAL RUNOFF
RT	CHEMICAL POLLUTANTS
RT	CHEMICAL POLLUTION
RT	INSECTICIDES
RT	PESTICIDES
RT	TOXICANTS

DE-ICING
SN	Preventing and removing rime and glaze from decks, superstructures, equipment, etc. For melting of ice/snow on land and frozen soil, use ICE MELTING. For thawing of frozen fishery products use THAWING.
UF	de-icing equipment
RT	ANTIFREEZES
RT	ICE PREVENTION
RT	ICING

DE-ICING EQUIPMENT
USE	**DE-ICING**

DEAD BODIES
USE	**CARCASSES**

ASFIS Thesaurus

DEAD RECKONING
BT1	NAVIGATION
RT	INERTIAL NAVIGATION
RT	SHIP DRIFT

DEAD WATER
RT	DENSITY STRATIFICATION
RT	FJORDS
RT	FRESH WATER
RT	INTERFACE PHENOMENA
RT	INTERNAL WAVE EFFECTS
RT	SURFACE WAVE-INTERNAL WAVE INTERACTIONS
RT	WATER

DEAMINATION
BT1	CHEMICAL REACTIONS
RT	AMINATION

DEATH RATE
USE	**MORTALITY**

DEBRIS (NUCLEAR)
USE	**FISSION PRODUCTS**

DEBRIS FLOW
UF	mudflows
UF	rock falls
BT1	MASS GRAVITY TRANSPORT (SEDIMENTS)
BT2	SEDIMENT TRANSPORT
RT	MELANGES
RT	OLISTOSTROMES

DEBUBBLING
RT	BUBBLES
RT	BUBBLING

DECALCIFICATION
SN	The process of absorption of lime salts from bones. Added in 1980
BT1	BIOCHEMICAL PHENOMENA
RT	BONES
RT	CALCIFICATION
RT	SHELLS

DECANTATION
SN	Decantation of transported solid pollutants or suspended sediments
BT1	SEPARATION
RT	DECANTATION TANKS
RT	SEDIMENTATION
RT	SLUDGE TREATMENT
RT	WASTE TREATMENT
RT	WATER POLLUTION TREATMENT
RT	WATER TREATMENT

DECANTATION TANKS
BT1	TANKS
BT2	CONTAINERS
RT	DECANTATION
RT	SEWAGE PONDS
RT	WASTE TREATMENT
RT	WATER POLLUTION TREATMENT

DECARBOXYLATION
BT1	CHEMICAL REACTIONS
RT	CARBOXYLATION

DECCA
BT1	RADIO NAVIGATION
BT2	POSITION FIXING
RT	NAVIGATIONAL TABLES

DECHLORINATION
RT	CHLORINATION
RT	CHLORINE
RT	DISINFECTION
RT	ODOUR
RT	SEWAGE TREATMENT
RT	WATER PURIFICATION

DECHLORINATION (cont'd)
RT	WATER TREATMENT

DECK COMPRESSION CHAMBERS
BT1	DECOMPRESSION CHAMBERS
BT2	DIVING EQUIPMENT
BT3	EQUIPMENT
RT	TRANSFER CHAMBERS

DECK EQUIPMENT
UF	deck machinery
UF	handling equipment
BT1	EQUIPMENT
NT1	LIFTING TACKLE
NT2	CRANES
NT2	DAVITS
NT2	WINCHES
RT	ACCIDENT PREVENTION
RT	DECKS
RT	FISHING VESSELS
RT	FLOATING STRUCTURES
RT	GEAR HANDLING
RT	HYDRAULIC SYSTEMS
RT	MECHANIZATION
RT	OCEANOGRAPHIC EQUIPMENT
RT	RESEARCH VESSELS
RT	RIGGING
RT	SAFETY DEVICES

DECK MACHINERY
USE	**DECK EQUIPMENT**

DECK SAFETY EQUIPMENT
USE	**SAFETY DEVICES**

DECKS
NT1	HELIDECKS
RT	DECK EQUIPMENT
RT	FIXED PLATFORMS
RT	MOBILE PLATFORMS

DECOMPOSERS
SN	Micro-organisms returning nutrients to water by biodegradation. Added in 1980
BT1	HETEROTROPHIC ORGANISMS
BT2	AQUATIC ORGANISMS
RT	BACTERIA
RT	BIODEGRADATION
RT	FOOD CHAINS
RT	FUNGI

DECOMPOSITION
USE	**DEGRADATION**

DECOMPRESSION
RT	COMPRESSION
RT	DECOMPRESSION CHAMBERS
RT	DECOMPRESSION SICKNESS
RT	DECOMPRESSION TABLES
RT	HYDROSTATIC PRESSURE
RT	SATURATION DIVING

DECOMPRESSION CHAMBERS
UF	compression chambers
UF	hyperbaric chambers
UF	pressure chambers
BT1	DIVING EQUIPMENT
BT2	EQUIPMENT
NT1	DECK COMPRESSION CHAMBERS
NT1	TRANSFER CHAMBERS
RT	DECOMPRESSION
RT	DECOMPRESSION SICKNESS
RT	DECOMPRESSION TABLES
RT	DIVING BELLS
RT	HIGH PRESSURE EFFECTS
RT	HYPERBARIC
RT	LIFE SUPPORT SYSTEMS
RT	LOCKOUT SUBMERSIBLES
RT	PRESSURE

DECOMPRESSION CHAMBERS (cont'd)
RT	PRESSURE GAUGES

DECOMPRESSION SICKNESS
SN	Before 1986 search also BENDS
UF	bends
BT1	HUMAN DISEASES
BT2	DISEASES
RT	DECOMPRESSION
RT	DECOMPRESSION CHAMBERS
RT	DECOMPRESSION TABLES
RT	DIVING PHYSIOLOGY
RT	NARCOSIS
RT	NITROGEN NARCOSIS
RT	UNDERWATER MEDICINE

DECOMPRESSION TABLES
UF	compression tables
BT1	TABLES
BT2	DOCUMENTS
RT	DECOMPRESSION
RT	DECOMPRESSION CHAMBERS
RT	DECOMPRESSION SICKNESS
RT	DIVING EQUIPMENT

DECONVOLUTION
UF	seismic deconvolution
BT1	MATHEMATICAL ANALYSIS
RT	CONVOLUTION
RT	SEISMIC DATA PROCESSING

DEEP ADJACENT SEAS
USE	**MARGINAL SEAS**

DEEP CURRENTS
SN	Midwater currents in deep ocean
BT1	SUBSURFACE CURRENTS
BT2	WATER CURRENTS
BT3	WATER MOTION
RT	BOTTOM CURRENTS
RT	DEEP WATER
RT	OCEAN CURRENTS
RT	SEDIMENT TRANSPORT
RT	WATER DEPTH

DEEP LAYER
UF	deep layers (water column)
BT1	WATER COLUMN
BT2	LAYERS
RT	BENTHIC BOUNDARY LAYER
RT	BOTTOM MIXED LAYER
RT	HYPOLIMNION
RT	LAYERS

DEEP LAYERS (LAKES)
USE	**HYPOLIMNION**

DEEP LAYERS (WATER COLUMN)
USE	**DEEP LAYER**

DEEP OCEAN MINING
USE	**DEEP-SEA MINING**

DEEP SCATTERING LAYERS
USE	**SCATTERING LAYERS**

DEEP SEA
USE	**DEEP WATER**

DEEP-SEA BED
USE	**OCEAN FLOOR**

DEEP-SEA CHANNELS
BT1	SUBMARINE FEATURES
BT2	TOPOGRAPHIC FEATURES
RT	LEVEES

DEEP-SEA DIVING
- UF   dry diving
- BT1   DIVING
- RT   BREATHING MIXTURES
- RT   DIVING PHYSIOLOGY
- RT   MIXED GAS
- RT   ONE-ATMOSPHERE SYSTEMS
- RT   SUBMERSIBLES
- RT   UNDERWATER EXPLORATION
- RT   UNDERWATER MEDICINE

DEEP-SEA DRILLING
- SN   Drilling operations beyond the continental shelf
- BT1   DRILLING
- RT   DEEP-SEA MINING
- RT   DRILLING VESSELS
- RT   DYNAMIC POSITIONING
- RT   HOLE RE-ENTRY

DEEP-SEA EROSION
- USE   **BOTTOM EROSION**

DEEP-SEA FANS
- UF   abyssal cones
- UF   sea fans
- UF   submarine fans
- BT1   SUBMARINE FEATURES
- BT2   TOPOGRAPHIC FEATURES
- RT   ALLUVIAL FANS
- RT   ARCHIPELAGIC APRONS
- RT   FANS
- RT   SEACHANNELS
- RT   SUBMARINE CANYONS
- RT   TURBIDITES
- RT   TURBIDITY CURRENTS

DEEP-SEA FISHERIES
- SN   Added in 1982
- BT1   MARINE FISHERIES
- BT2   FISHERIES

DEEP-SEA FURROWS
- UF   furrows (deep-sea)
- RT   BOTTOM EROSION
- RT   EROSION FEATURES
- RT   TRENCHES (OCEANIC)
- RT   VALLEYS

DEEP SEA LOBSTER FISHERIES
- USE   **LOBSTER FISHERIES**

DEEP-SEA MINING
- UF   deep ocean mining
- BT1   MINING
- RT   DEEP-SEA DRILLING
- RT   FERROMANGANESE NODULES
- RT   FOSSIL FUELS
- RT   LAW OF THE SEA
- RT   MINERAL DEPOSITS
- RT   MINERAL EXPLORATION
- RT   MINERAL INDUSTRY
- RT   MINERAL RESOURCES
- RT   MINING VESSELS
- RT   OFFSHORE OPERATIONS
- RT   PHOSPHORITE NODULES
- RT   SEABED DEPOSITS
- RT   SITE SURVEYS
- RT   SUBSURFACE DEPOSITS

DEEP-SEA TERRACES
- USE   **TERRACES**

DEEP-SEA THERMOMETERS
- USE   **THERMOMETERS**

DEEP-SEA TIDE GAUGES
- BT1   TIDE GAUGES
- BT2   MEASURING DEVICES
- RT   PRESSURE SENSORS

DEEP SOUND CHANNEL
- USE   **SOFAR CHANNEL**

DEEP TOW
- USE   **TOWED VEHICLES**

DEEP WATER
- UF   deep sea
- RT   APHOTIC ZONE
- RT   BATHYMETRY
- RT   DEEP CURRENTS
- RT   HYPOLIMNION
- RT   SHALLOW WATER
- RT   SOUND PROPAGATION
- RT   WATER DEPTH

DEEP WATER FORMATION
- RT   MISTRAL

DEEP-WATER MASSES
- UF   bottom water masses
- BT1   WATER MASSES
- RT   BOTTOM WATER

DEEP-WATER TERMINALS
- BT1   TANKER TERMINALS
- BT2   HARBOURS
- BT3   ANCHORAGES
- RT   OFFSHORE DOCKING

DEEP-WATER WAVES
- BT1   WATER WAVES

DEFAECATION
- UF   defecation
- BT1   ANIMAL NUTRITION
- BT2   NUTRITION
- RT   FAECAL PELLETS

DEFECATION
- USE   **DEFAECATION**

DEFECTS
- SN   Use for faults of construction or results of damage or deterioration
- UF   faults (defects)
- UF   flaws
- NT1   CRACKS
- NT1   FRACTURES
- NT1   LAMELLAR TEARING
- NT1   SPALLING
- RT   DAMAGE
- RT   DETERIORATION
- RT   FAILURES
- RT   HEAT AFFECTED ZONES
- RT   LEAKS
- RT   NONDESTRUCTIVE TESTING
- RT   QUALITY CONTROL

DEFENCE
- USE   **SECURITY**

DEFENCE CRAFT
- SN   Vessels designed for military/security purposes
- UF   defense craft
- UF   naval craft
- UF   warships
- BT1   VEHICLES
- RT   ARTIFICIAL HARBOURS
- RT   CRUISES
- RT   MILITARY OCEANOGRAPHY
- RT   MILITARY OPERATIONS
- RT   NAVAL BASES
- RT   PROTECTION VESSELS

DEFENCE CRAFT (cont'd)
- RT   SECURITY
- RT   SHIP TECHNOLOGY
- RT   SHIPPING
- RT   SUBMARINES
- RT   SURVEILLANCE AND ENFORCEMENT

DEFENCE MECHANISMS
- SN   Before 1986 search also DEFENSE MECHANISMS
- UF   defense mechanisms
- UF   defensive mechanisms
- UF   defensive secretions
- NT1   PHAGOCYTOSIS
- RT   ANTIBODIES
- RT   BIOELECTRICITY
- RT   CAMOUFLAGE
- RT   CYCLOMORPHOSIS
- RT   CYSTS
- RT   ENCYSTMENT
- RT   IMMUNITY
- RT   IMMUNOLOGY
- RT   MIMICRY
- RT   PROTECTIVE BEHAVIOUR
- RT   RESISTANCE MECHANISMS

DEFENSE CRAFT
- USE   **DEFENCE CRAFT**

DEFENSE MECHANISMS
- USE   **DEFENCE MECHANISMS**

DEFENSIVE MECHANISMS
- USE   **DEFENCE MECHANISMS**

DEFENSIVE SECRETIONS
- USE   **DEFENCE MECHANISMS**

DEFICIENCY DISEASES
- SN   Added in 1980
- UF   deficiency syndromes
- BT1   DISEASES
- RT   ARTIFICIAL FEEDING
- RT   DIETARY DEFICIENCIES
- RT   DIETS
- RT   NUTRIENT DEFICIENCY
- RT   NUTRITIONAL REQUIREMENTS
- RT   VITAMIN DEFICIENCIES

DEFICIENCY SYNDROMES
- USE   **DEFICIENCY DISEASES**

DEFINITIONS
- USE   **TERMINOLOGY**

DEFLECTION
- NT1   CATENARY
- RT   INCLINOMETERS
- RT   PLUMBLINE DEFLECTION

DEFLOCCULATION
- UF   peptization
- RT   DISPERSION
- RT   FLOCCULATION

DEFORMATION
- UF   bending
- UF   buckling
- UF   distortion
- BT1   MECHANICAL PROPERTIES
- BT2   PHYSICAL PROPERTIES
- BT3   PROPERTIES
- NT1   ROCK DEFORMATION
- NT2   DIAPIRISM
- NT1   STRAIN
- RT   ANELASTICITY
- RT   BOUDINAGE
- RT   BULK MODULUS
- RT   COLLAPSE STRENGTH
- RT   COMPRESSION

DEFORMATION (cont'd)
RT	CREEP
RT	ELASTICITY
RT	FLEXIBILITY
RT	MELANGES
RT	PIPE BUCKLING
RT	PLASTIC FLOW
RT	PLASTICITY
RT	RHEOLOGY
RT	SHAPE
RT	STRESS-STRAIN RELATIONS
RT	TENSILE STRENGTH
RT	YIELD POINT

DEFROSTING
USE	**THAWING**

DEGASSIFICATION
USE	**DEGASSING**

DEGASSING
UF	degassification
RT	DESORPTION
RT	EARTH ATMOSPHERE
RT	EARTH MANTLE

DEGENERATION
SN	Added in 1980
UF	evolutionary retrogression
BT1	BIOLOGICAL PHENOMENA
RT	BIODEGRADATION
RT	EVOLUTION
RT	MUTATIONS
RT	REGENERATION

DEGLACIATION
RT	CLIMATIC CHANGES
RT	EMERGENT SHORELINES
RT	EUSTATIC CHANGES
RT	GLACIATION
RT	INTERGLACIAL PERIODS
RT	ISOSTASY
RT	TRANSGRESSIONS

DEGRADATION
UF	decomposition
BT1	CHEMICAL REACTIONS
NT1	BIODEGRADATION
NT2	ANAEROBIC DIGESTION
NT1	CHEMICAL DEGRADATION
NT1	PYROLYSIS
NT1	THERMAL DECOMPOSITION
RT	ANOXIC BASINS
RT	ANOXIC CONDITIONS
RT	AUTOLYSIS
RT	DETERIORATION
RT	DISCOLOURATION
RT	FATE
RT	FOULING
RT	HUMUS
RT	LEACHING
RT	OXIDATION
RT	OXYGEN DEPLETION
RT	WEATHERING

DEHYDRATED PRODUCTS
USE	**DRIED PRODUCTS**

DEHYDRATION
BT1	CHEMICAL REACTIONS
RT	DESICCATION
RT	DRYING
RT	EVAPORATION
RT	FREEZING STORAGE
RT	HYDRATION
RT	SEPARATION
RT	TRANSPIRATION
RT	WATER CONTENT

DEHYDROGENASES
BT1	ENZYMES

DEICING EQUIPMENT
BT1	EQUIPMENT
RT	ICE PREVENTION
RT	ICING

DELTA STRUCTURES
USE	**DELTAIC FEATURES**

DELTAIC DEPOSITS
RT	BOTTOMSET BEDS
RT	FLUVIAL SEDIMENTATION
RT	FORESET BEDS
RT	TOPSET BEDS

DELTAIC FEATURES
UF	delta structures
NT1	BOTTOMSET BEDS
NT1	FORESET BEDS
NT1	TOPSET BEDS

DELTAIC SEDIMENTATION
RT	BOTTOMSET BEDS
RT	FORESET BEDS
RT	SEDIMENTARY ENVIRONMENTS
RT	TOPSET BEDS

DELTAS
BT1	COASTAL LANDFORMS
BT2	LANDFORMS
BT3	TOPOGRAPHIC FEATURES
RT	ALLUVIAL DEPOSITS
RT	BRACKISHWATER ENVIRONMENT
RT	COASTAL EROSION
RT	COASTS
RT	DISTRIBUTARIES
RT	FLOOD PLAINS
RT	FLUVIAL FEATURES
RT	FLUVIAL MORPHOLOGY
RT	GEOMORPHOLOGY
RT	PROGRADATION
RT	RIVER DISCHARGE
RT	RIVERS
RT	SEDIMENTATION
RT	SWAMPS
RT	WETLANDS

DEMERSAL FISHERIES
BT1	FISHERIES
RT	BOTTOM TRAWLING
RT	BOTTOM TRAWLS
RT	CRUSTACEAN FISHERIES
RT	DREDGES
RT	FINFISH FISHERIES
RT	FLATFISH FISHERIES
RT	GADOID FISHERIES
RT	GILLNETS
RT	GILLNETTERS
RT	GRAPPLING GEAR
RT	HARVESTING MACHINES
RT	LAGOON FISHERIES
RT	LAKE FISHERIES
RT	LINERS
RT	LINES
RT	LOBSTER FISHERIES
RT	LONGLINING
RT	MACKEREL FISHERIES
RT	MARINE FISH
RT	MARINE FISHERIES
RT	PERCOID FISHERIES
RT	POLE-LINE FISHING
RT	REDFISH FISHERIES
RT	SEINE NETS
RT	SEINERS
RT	SHRIMP FISHERIES
RT	TRAWL NETS
RT	TRAWLERS

DEMINERALIZATION
UF	salts extraction
BT1	SEPARATION PROCESSES
RT	DISTILLATION
RT	ION EXCHANGE

DENATURATION (PROTEINS)
USE	**PROTEIN DENATURATION**

DENDRITES
USE	**NEURONES**

DENITRIFICATION
SN	Before 1982 search NITROGEN CYCLE
BT1	CHEMICAL REACTIONS
RT	NITRIFICATION
RT	NITROGEN CYCLE

DENSE WATER
BT1	SEA WATER
BT2	WATER

DENSIMETERS
USE	**DENSITOMETERS**

DENSITOMETERS
UF	densimeters
RT	DENSITY MEASUREMENT
RT	DENSITY MEASURING EQUIPMENT

DENSITY
SN	Before 1982 search also DENSITY (PHYSICAL)
UF	density (physical)
BT1	PHYSICAL PROPERTIES
BT2	PROPERTIES
NT1	CURRENT DENSITY
NT1	SEDIMENT DENSITY
NT2	WET BULK DENSITY
NT1	WATER DENSITY
NT2	IN SITU DENSITY
NT2	POTENTIAL DENSITY
NT2	RELATIVE DENSITY
NT2	SIGMA-T
RT	BUOYANCY
RT	DENSITY MEASUREMENT
RT	DENSITY MEASURING EQUIPMENT
RT	DIFFUSION
RT	GRAVIMETRIC TECHNIQUES
RT	POPULATION DENSITY
RT	SIGMA-T
RT	SPECIFIC GRAVITY
RT	WET WEIGHT

DENSITY (PHYSICAL)
USE	**DENSITY**

DENSITY (POPULATION)
USE	**POPULATION DENSITY**

DENSITY (STOCKING)
USE	**STOCKING DENSITY**

DENSITY (WATER)
USE	**WATER DENSITY**

DENSITY (WAVE ACTION)
USE	**WAVE ACTION**

DENSITY CHARTS
SN	Charts showing distribution of water density
BT1	HYDROGRAPHIC CHARTS
BT2	MAPS
BT3	GRAPHICS
BT4	AUDIOVISUAL MATERIAL
RT	DENSITY SECTIONS
RT	ISOPYCNICS
RT	WATER DENSITY

DENSITY CURRENTS
USE **DENSITY FLOW**

DENSITY DEPENDENCE
SN   Added in 1980
UF   density dependent effects
RT   BIOLOGICAL PRODUCTION
RT   BIOTIC FACTORS
RT   POPULATION DENSITY
RT   POPULATION FUNCTIONS
RT   PREDATION
RT   STOCKING (ORGANISMS)
RT   STOCKING DENSITY

DENSITY DEPENDENT EFFECTS
USE   **DENSITY DEPENDENCE**

DENSITY DEPENDENT FACTOR
USE   **POPULATION DENSITY**

DENSITY-DEPENDENT FACTORS
USE   **BIOTIC FACTORS**

DENSITY FIELD
RT   FIELDS
RT   GEOSTROPHIC FLOW
RT   GEOSTROPHIC METHOD
RT   WATER DENSITY

DENSITY FLOW
SN   Before 1982 search TURBIDITY CURRENTS
UF   density currents
UF   gravity-induced flow
BT1   FLUID FLOW
BT2   FLUID MOTION
RT   BOTTOM CURRENTS
RT   STRATIFIED FLOW
RT   TURBIDITY CURRENTS
RT   WATER CURRENTS

DENSITY FRONTS
BT1   OCEANIC FRONTS
BT2   FRONTS
RT   ISOPYCNICS
RT   PYCNOCLINE
RT   WATER DENSITY

DENSITY GRADIENTS
SN   Used only for density gradients in
       water
RT   DENSITY PROFILES
RT   DENSITY STRATIFICATION
RT   GRADIENTS
RT   PYCNOCLINE
RT   WATER DENSITY

DENSITY-INDEPENDENT FACTORS
USE   **ABIOTIC FACTORS**

DENSITY INTERFACES
BT1   INTERFACES
RT   DENSITY STRATIFICATION
RT   WATER DENSITY

DENSITY LAYER
USE   **PYCNOCLINE**

DENSITY MEASUREMENT
UF   hydrometry
UF   specific gravity measurement
BT1   MEASUREMENT
RT   DENSITOMETERS
RT   DENSITY
RT   DENSITY MEASURING EQUIPMENT
RT   HYDROMETERS
RT   SEDIMENT DENSITY
RT   WATER DENSITY

DENSITY MEASURING EQUIPMENT
RT   DENSITOMETERS
RT   DENSITY
RT   DENSITY MEASUREMENT
RT   HYDROMETERS
RT   MEASURING DEVICES

DENSITY PROFILES
BT1   VERTICAL PROFILES
BT2   PROFILES
RT   DENSITY GRADIENTS
RT   DENSITY SECTIONS
RT   DENSITY STRATIFICATION
RT   PYCNOCLINE
RT . WATER DENSITY

DENSITY SECTIONS
BT1   HYDROGRAPHIC SECTIONS
BT2   VERTICAL SECTIONS
BT3   MAP GRAPHICS
BT4   GRAPHICS
RT   DENSITY CHARTS
RT   DENSITY PROFILES
RT   SIGMA-T
RT   WATER DENSITY

DENSITY STRATIFICATION
BT1   STRATIFICATION
RT   BUOYANT JETS
RT   DEAD WATER
RT   DENSITY GRADIENTS
RT   DENSITY INTERFACES
RT   DENSITY PROFILES
RT   GEOSTROPHIC FLOW
RT   MONIN-OBUKHOV LENGTH
RT   PYCNOCLINE
RT   SALINITY STRATIFICATION
RT   SOUND CHANNELS
RT   WATER DENSITY

DENUDATION
SN   Combined effect of erosional
       processes and transportation of
       eroded material.
RT   EROSION
RT   EROSION FEATURES

DEOXYGENATION
RT   DISSOLVED OXYGEN
RT   OXYGEN DEMAND
RT   OXYGEN DEPLETION
RT   OXYGENATION
RT   WATER QUALITY

DEOXYRIBONUCLEIC ACID
USE   **DNA**

DEPENDENT SPECIES
USE   **ASSOCIATED SPECIES**

DEPLETED STOCKS
SN   A stock (or population) suffering
       from recruitment overfishing. Added
       in 1982
UF   stock depletion
BT1   STOCKS
RT   DEPLETION
RT   FISHERY MANAGEMENT
RT   OVERFISHING

DEPLETION
NT1   RESOURCE DEPLETION
RT   CONSERVATION
RT   DEPLETED STOCKS
RT   NATURAL RESOURCES
RT   OXYGEN DEPLETION
RT   RECLAMATION

DEPLOYMENT
SN   Deployment of materials and
       equipment including underwater
       vehicles
UF   deployment of equipment
RT   CURRENT METER ARRAYS
RT   DIVING
RT   GEAR HANDLING
RT   LAUNCHING
RT   OCEANOGRAPHIC EQUIPMENT
RT   RECOVERY
RT   SEAMANSHIP
RT   STATION KEEPING
RT   UNDERWATER VEHICLES

DEPLOYMENT OF EQUIPMENT
USE   **DEPLOYMENT**

DEPOLYMERIZATION
BT1   CHEMICAL REACTIONS
NT1   SILTING

DEPOSITION (GEOLOGY)
USE   **SEDIMENTATION**

DEPOSITION FEATURES
RT   ALLUVIAL FANS
RT   BARRIER ISLANDS
RT   BEACH ACCRETION
RT   BEACH RIDGES
RT   BERMS
RT   BREAK-POINT BARS
RT   EROSION FEATURES
RT   FLUVIAL FEATURES
RT   GLACIAL FEATURES
RT   NEARSHORE BARS
RT   SEDIMENT DRIFTS
RT   SPITS

DEPOSITIONAL ENVIRONMENTS
USE   **SEDIMENTARY ENVIRONMENTS**

DEPRESSIONS (METEOROLOGY)
USE   **CYCLONES**

DEPRESSORS
NT1   CABLE DEPRESSORS
RT   DEPTH CONTROL

DEPTH
BT1   DIMENSIONS
NT1   MIXED LAYER DEPTH
NT1   SILL DEPTH
NT1   STANDARD DEPTHS
NT1   WATER DEPTH
RT   CONTOURS
RT   DEPTH MEASUREMENT
RT   HEIGHT
RT   HYPSOMETRIC CURVES
RT   THICKNESS

DEPTH CONTOURS
USE   **ISOBATHS**

DEPTH CONTROL
BT1   CONTROL
RT   DEPRESSORS

DEPTH FINDERS
USE   **DEPTH RECORDERS**

DEPTH FINDING
USE   **ECHOSOUNDING**

DEPTH MEASUREMENT
SN   Measurement of depth in water only.
       Use of a more specific term is
       recommended
BT1   MEASUREMENT
NT1   BATHYMETRY

ASFIS Thesaurus

DEPTH MEASUREMENT (cont'd)
NT2	LASER BATHYMETRY
NT1	INSTRUMENT DEPTH MEASUREMENT
RT	AIRBORNE SENSING
RT	BATHYMETRIC CHARTS
RT	DEPTH
RT	DEPTH RECORDERS
RT	ICE THICKNESS
RT	LASER BATHYMETERS
RT	SOUNDING LINES
RT	STEREOPHOTOGRAPHY

DEPTH RECORDERS
SN	Added in 1982
UF	depth finders
UF	precision depth recorders
BT1	RECORDING EQUIPMENT
BT2	EQUIPMENT
RT	BATHYTHERMOGRAPHS
RT	DEPTH MEASUREMENT
RT	ELECTRONIC EQUIPMENT
RT	ISOBATHS
RT	OCEANOGRAPHIC EQUIPMENT
RT	WATER DEPTH

DEPTH SOUNDING (WATER)
USE	**BATHYMETRY**

DEPURATION
USE	**SELF PURIFICATION**

DERIVED LIPIDS
SN	Added in 1980
BT1	LIPIDS
BT2	ORGANIC COMPOUNDS
RT	CAROTENOIDS

DERMAL DENTICLES
USE	**SCALES**

DERRICKS
USE	**CRANES**

DESALINATION
SN	Sea water conversion and water desalting
UF	desalination processes
UF	extraction (salts)
UF	sea water conversion
UF	seawater conversion
UF	water desalting
BT1	WATER TREATMENT
RT	COASTAL LAGOONS
RT	DESALINATION PLANTS
RT	DISSOLVED SALTS
RT	DISTILLATION
RT	ELECTRODIALYSIS
RT	EVAPORATION
RT	EVAPORATION TANKS
RT	ION EXCHANGE
RT	ION TRANSPORT
RT	IONS
RT	MEMBRANES
RT	MINERAL INDUSTRY
RT	POWER PLANTS
RT	REVERSE OSMOSIS
RT	SALINE WATER
RT	SALINITY
RT	SALT DEPOSITS
RT	SALT LAKES
RT	SALTS
RT	SEA WATER
RT	SEPARATION
RT	WATER PURIFICATION
RT	WATER RESOURCES

DESALINATION PLANTS
RT	AQUACULTURE FACILITIES
RT	COASTAL LAGOONS
RT	DESALINATION
RT	DISSOLVED SALTS
RT	INDUSTRIAL PRODUCTS
RT	MINERAL INDUSTRY
RT	SALINITY
RT	SALTS
RT	WATER SUPPLY

DESALINATION PROCESSES
USE	**DESALINATION**

DESCRIPTIVE PHYSICAL OCEANOGRAPHY
USE	**HYDROGRAPHY**

DESERTS
RT	ARID ENVIRONMENTS
RT	SABKHAS

DESICCATION
SN	Added in 1980
BT1	SEPARATION
RT	DEHYDRATION
RT	DRYING
RT	EVAPORATION

DESIGN
SN	Limit to design methods. Used only as a qualifier
UF	design engineering
BT1	ENGINEERING
NT1	SHIP DESIGN
NT1	TOWED BODY DESIGN
RT	AQUACULTURE EQUIPMENT
RT	CAGES
RT	ENGINEERING DRAWINGS
RT	HIGH PRESSURE EFFECTS
RT	RESEARCH
RT	SPECIFICATIONS
RT	STRUCTURAL ANALYSIS
RT	TOLERANCES (DIMENSIONAL)

DESIGN ENGINEERING
USE	**DESIGN**

DESIGN WAVE
RT	COASTAL STRUCTURES
RT	OFFSHORE STRUCTURES
RT	SURFACE WATER WAVES
RT	WAVE CLIMATE
RT	WAVE FORCES
RT	WAVE FORECASTING
RT	WAVE HEIGHT
RT	WAVE STATISTICS

DESORPTION
BT1	SORPTION
RT	DEGASSING
RT	SURFACE PROPERTIES

DESTRATIFICATION
RT	STRATIFICATION
RT	WATER MIXING

DESTRUCTIVE WAVES
RT	CONSTRUCTIVE WAVES
RT	NEARSHORE BARS

DETECTION
SN	Used only as a qualifier
NT1	DISEASE DETECTION
NT1	FISH DETECTION
NT1	ICEBERG DETECTION
NT1	POLLUTION DETECTION
NT1	WRECK LOCATION
RT	ACOUSTIC TRACKING SYSTEMS
RT	ALARM SYSTEMS
RT	ECHO RANGING

DETECTION (cont'd)
RT	IDENTIFICATION
RT	INSPECTION
RT	LOCATING
RT	NONDESTRUCTIVE TESTING
RT	RADAR
RT	REMOTE SENSING
RT	SONAR
RT	SONAR DETECTION
RT	SURVEILLANCE AND ENFORCEMENT
RT	TRACKING

DETECTION (DISEASES)
USE	**DISEASE DETECTION**

DETECTION (POLLUTION)
USE	**POLLUTION DETECTION**

DETECTORS
RT	ALARM SYSTEMS

DETERGENTS
NT1	SOAPS
RT	CHEMICAL POLLUTANTS
RT	CHEMICAL POLLUTION
RT	DOMESTIC WASTES
RT	EUTROPHICATION
RT	SEWAGE
RT	SURFACTANTS

DETERIORATION
SN	Gradual decline in quality (of materials). For results of fire and accidents use DAMAGE
RT	BRITTLENESS
RT	CORROSION
RT	CRACK PROPAGATION
RT	CURRENT SCOURING
RT	DEFECTS
RT	DEGRADATION
RT	EMBRITTLEMENT
RT	FAILURES
RT	FATIGUE (MATERIALS)
RT	MAINTENANCE
RT	REPAIR
RT	SCOURING
RT	SPALLING
RT	WEAR

DETONATORS
RT	BLASTING
RT	EXPLOSIVES

DETOXIFICATION
SN	Removal of poison or poison effects
RT	BIOLOGICAL POISONS
RT	DISEASES
RT	HYDROLYSIS
RT	OXIDATION
RT	TOXICANTS
RT	TOXICITY
RT	TOXICOLOGY

DETRITAL DEPOSITS
UF	detrital sediments
RT	CLASTICS
RT	DETRITUS
RT	SEDIMENTS
RT	SUSPENDED PARTICULATE MATTER

DETRITAL SEDIMENTS
USE	**DETRITAL DEPOSITS**

DETRITIVORES
USE	**DETRITUS FEEDERS**

DETRITUS
UF	biodeposition
UF	detritus (organic)
UF	organic detritus
RT	BIOGENIC MATERIAL
RT	BIOGEOCHEMICAL CYCLE
RT	DETRITAL DEPOSITS
RT	DETRITUS FEEDERS
RT	EROSION
RT	FILTER FEEDERS
RT	ORGANIC COMPOUNDS
RT	SAPROPELS
RT	SEDIMENTS
RT	SUSPENDED ORGANIC MATTER
RT	SUSPENDED PARTICULATE MATTER
RT	TURBIDITY
RT	WEATHERING

DETRITUS (ORGANIC)
USE	**DETRITUS**

DETRITUS FEEDERS
UF	detritivores
BT1	HETEROTROPHIC ORGANISMS
BT2	AQUATIC ORGANISMS
RT	DETRITUS
RT	FEEDING BEHAVIOUR
RT	OMNIVORES

DEUTERIUM
SN	Before 1982 search HYDROGEN ISOTOPES
BT1	HYDROGEN ISOTOPES
BT2	ISOTOPES
RT	DEUTERIUM COMPOUNDS

DEUTERIUM COMPOUNDS
BT1	HYDROGEN COMPOUNDS
RT	DEUTERIUM
RT	HEAVY WATER

DEVELOPED COUNTRIES
BT1	COUNTRIES
RT	DEVELOPING COUNTRIES
RT	TECHNOLOGY TRANSFER

DEVELOPING COUNTRIES
UF	developing nations
UF	developing world
UF	underdeveloped countries
BT1	COUNTRIES
RT	DEVELOPED COUNTRIES
RT	EDUCATION
RT	GOVERNMENTS
RT	INTERNATIONAL AGREEMENTS
RT	INTERNATIONAL COOPERATION
RT	INTERNATIONAL ORGANIZATIONS
RT	JOINT VENTURES
RT	RESOURCE DEVELOPMENT
RT	TECHNOLOGY TRANSFER
RT	TRAINING
RT	TRAINING CENTRES

DEVELOPING NATIONS
USE	**DEVELOPING COUNTRIES**

DEVELOPING WORLD
USE	**DEVELOPING COUNTRIES**

DEVELOPMENT (BIOLOGICAL)
USE	**BIOLOGICAL DEVELOPMENT**

DEVELOPMENT (PRODUCTS)
USE	**PRODUCT DEVELOPMENT**

DEVELOPMENT (RESOURCES)
USE	**RESOURCE DEVELOPMENT**

DEVELOPMENT PLANS
USE	**DEVELOPMENT PROJECTS**

DEVELOPMENT POTENTIAL
SN	Added in 1980
RT	DEVELOPMENT PROJECTS
RT	FINANCIAL RESOURCES
RT	HUMAN RESOURCES
RT	NATURAL RESOURCES
RT	RESOURCE AVAILABILITY
RT	RESOURCE DEVELOPMENT
RT	RESOURCE MANAGEMENT

DEVELOPMENT PROJECTS
SN	Added in 1980
UF	development plans
RT	AQUACULTURE DEVELOPMENT
RT	DEVELOPMENT POTENTIAL
RT	FISHERY DEVELOPMENT
RT	INTERNATIONAL COOPERATION
RT	INVESTMENTS
RT	RESOURCE DEVELOPMENT
RT	SOCIOLOGICAL ASPECTS
RT	TECHNOLOGY TRANSFER

DEVELOPMENTAL STAGES
NT1	EMBRYOS
NT2	FOETUS
NT1	JUVENILES
NT1	LARVAE
NT2	FISH LARVAE
NT3	FINGERLINGS
NT3	FRY
NT2	INVERTEBRATE LARVAE
NT3	CRUSTACEAN LARVAE
NT4	MEGALOPS
NT4	NAUPLII
NT4	PHYLLOSOMAE
NT4	ZOEAE
NT3	INSECT LARVAE
NT4	INSTARS
NT4	NYMPHS
NT4	PUPAE
NT3	MOLLUSCAN LARVAE
NT4	SPAT
NT4	VELIGERS
NT1	RESTING STAGES
RT	ADULTS
RT	BIOLOGICAL DEVELOPMENT
RT	EGGS
RT	EMBRYOLOGY
RT	LARVAL DEVELOPMENT
RT	LIFE CYCLE
RT	METAMORPHOSIS
RT	MOULTING
RT	ONTOGENY
RT	POLYPS

DEVITRIFICATION
RT	GLASS
RT	VOLCANIC GLASS

DEVONIAN
SN	Before 1982 search DEVONIAN PERIOD
BT1	PALAEOZOIC
BT2	GEOLOGICAL TIME

DEW POINT
UF	dew point temperature
BT1	TRANSITION TEMPERATURES
BT2	TEMPERATURE
BT3	THERMODYNAMIC PROPERTIES
BT4	PHYSICAL PROPERTIES
RT	CONDENSATION
RT	FOG
RT	HUMIDITY
RT	HYDROMETERS
RT	MIXING RATIO
RT	SATURATION VAPOUR PRESSURE
RT	WATER VAPOUR

DEW POINT TEMPERATURE
USE	**DEW POINT**

DEWATERING
RT	DRYING
RT	PORE WATER
RT	SEDIMENTS
RT	WATER CONTENT

DIAGENESIS
BT1	SEDIMENTATION
NT1	AUTHIGENESIS
NT1	CALCITIZATION
NT1	CEMENTATION
NT1	COMPACTION
NT1	CONSOLIDATION
NT1	DOLOMITIZATION
NT1	LITHIFICATION
RT	BIOTURBATION
RT	CALCIFICATION
RT	CATAGENESIS
RT	CHERTIFICATION
RT	CHERTS
RT	GAS TURBATION
RT	HALMYROLYSIS
RT	METASOMATISM
RT	SEDIMENTOLOGY
RT	SILICIFICATION

DIALYSIS
BT1	SEPARATION PROCESSES
NT1	ELECTRODIALYSIS
RT	COLLOIDS
RT	OSMOSIS

DIAMONDS
BT1	PLACERS
BT2	SEABED DEPOSITS
BT3	MINERAL DEPOSITS
BT4	MINERAL RESOURCES
RT	CARBON
RT	GRAPHITE
RT	KIMBERLITES

DIAPAUSE
SN	The state of suspended development
RT	ANIMAL PHYSIOLOGY
RT	AQUATIC INSECTS
RT	GROWTH
RT	PHOTOPERIODICITY

DIAPIRISM
BT1	ROCK DEFORMATION
BT2	DEFORMATION
BT3	MECHANICAL PROPERTIES
BT4	PHYSICAL PROPERTIES
RT	DIAPIRS
RT	IGNEOUS INTRUSIONS
RT	SALT DOMES

DIAPIRS
RT	CAP ROCKS
RT	DIAPIRISM
RT	SALT DOMES
RT	STRUCTURAL DOMES

DIASTROPHISM
NT1	CRUSTAL SHORTENING

DIATOM CULTURE
USE	**PHYTOPLANKTON CULTURE**

DIATOM OOZE
BT1	SILICEOUS OOZE
BT2	OOZES
RT	DIATOMITES
RT	FOSSIL DIATOMS

DIATOMITES
BT1   SILICEOUS ROCKS
RT   DIATOM OOZE
RT   SEDIMENTARY ROCKS

DIATOMS
SN   Used as descriptor for ASFA-2 only;
   for ASFA-1, use taxonomic
   descriptor BACILLARIOPHYCEAE
BT1   ALGAE

DICHLORODIPHENYLTRICHLOROETHANE
USE   **DDT**

DICHLORODIPHYNYLETHYLENE
USE   **DDE**

DICOTHERMAL LAYER
BT1   TEMPERATURE INVERSIONS
BT2   INVERSIONS
RT   DISCONTINUITY LAYERS
RT   LAYERS
RT   THERMAL STRUCTURE
RT   THERMOCLINE
RT   WATER TEMPERATURE

DICTIONARIES
USE   **GLOSSARIES**

DIELDRIN
BT1   CHLORINATED HYDROCARBONS
BT2   HALOGENATED HYDROCARBONS
BT3   HYDROCARBONS
BT4   ORGANIC COMPOUNDS
RT   INSECTICIDES

DIELECTRIC CONSTANT
BT1   ELECTRICAL PROPERTIES
BT2   PHYSICAL PROPERTIES
BT3   PROPERTIES
RT   CAPACITANCE
RT   ICE PROPERTIES

DIESEL ENGINES
BT1   MOTORS
RT   FUELS
RT   PROPULSION SYSTEMS
RT   SHIPBOARD EQUIPMENT
RT   UNDERWATER PROPULSION

DIESEL FUELS
USE   **FUELS**

DIETARY DEFICIENCIES
SN   Added in 1980
NT1   NUTRIENT DEFICIENCY
NT1   VITAMIN DEFICIENCIES
RT   AQUACULTURE
RT   ARTIFICIAL FEEDING
RT   DEFICIENCY DISEASES
RT   DIETS
RT   FEED COMPOSITION
RT   FEED EFFICIENCY
RT   FEEDING EXPERIMENTS
RT   NUTRITIONAL REQUIREMENTS
RT   NUTRITIVE VALUE
RT   SYMPTOMS

DIETS
NT1   BALANCED DIETS
NT1   BASIC DIETS
RT   ANIMAL NUTRITION
RT   ARTIFICIAL FEEDING
RT   DEFICIENCY DISEASES
RT   DIETARY DEFICIENCIES
RT   DIGESTIBILITY
RT   FEED EFFICIENCY
RT   FOOD ADDITIVES
RT   FOOD ORGANISMS
RT   NUTRITION DISORDERS

DIETS (cont'd)
RT   NUTRITIONAL REQUIREMENTS
RT   NUTRITIVE VALUE
RT   SELECTIVE FEEDING
RT   SINGLE CELL PROTEINS
RT   VITAMIN A
RT   VITAMIN B
RT   VITAMIN C
RT   VITAMIN D
RT   VITAMIN E
RT   VITAMINS

DIFFERENTIAL DISTRIBUTION
SN   Restricted to areal distribution of
   the life history stages of aquatic
   organisms. Used only as a qualifier
BT1   GEOGRAPHICAL DISTRIBUTION
BT2   DISTRIBUTION
RT   LIFE CYCLE

DIFFERENTIAL EQUATIONS
SN   Including integral equations. Used
   only as a qualifier
RT   EIGENFUNCTIONS
RT   EQUATIONS
RT   FINITE ELEMENT METHOD
RT   HARMONIC ANALYSIS
RT   INTEGRAL EQUATIONS
RT   LAPLACE TRANSFORMATION
RT   MATHEMATICS
RT   NONLINEAR EQUATIONS
RT   NUMERICAL ANALYSIS

DIFFERENTIATION (CELLS)
USE   **CELL DIFFERENTIATION**

DIFFRACTION
SN   Use of a more specific term is
   recommended
NT1   LIGHT DIFFRACTION
NT1   SEISMIC DIFFRACTION
NT1   SOUND DIFFRACTION
NT1   WAVE DIFFRACTION
RT   WAVE MOTION
RT   X-RAY DIFFRACTION ANALYSIS

DIFFRACTION (LIGHT)
USE   **LIGHT DIFFRACTION**

DIFFRACTION (SEISMIC)
USE   **SEISMIC DIFFRACTION**

DIFFRACTION (SOUND)
USE   **SOUND DIFFRACTION**

DIFFRACTION (WATER WAVES)
USE   **WAVE DIFFRACTION**

DIFFUSE SKY RADIATION
USE   **SOLAR RADIATION**

DIFFUSION
BT1   TRANSPORT PROCESSES
NT1   ATMOSPHERIC DIFFUSION
NT1   MOLECULAR DIFFUSION
NT2   DOUBLE DIFFUSION
NT1   THERMAL DIFFUSION
NT1   TURBULENT DIFFUSION
RT   ADSORPTION
RT   CHEMICAL PROPERTIES
RT   CONSERVATION EQUATIONS
RT   DENSITY
RT   EQUILIBRIUM
RT   EVAPORATION
RT   HEAT
RT   ION EXCHANGE
RT   ION TRANSPORT
RT   LEACHING
RT   MASS TRANSFER
RT   MIXING PROCESSES

DIFFUSION (cont'd)
RT   MOMENTUM
RT   OSMOSIS
RT   PERMEABILITY
RT   PHYSICAL PROPERTIES
RT   SALTS
RT   SEPARATION
RT   TURBULENCE
RT   WATER CIRCULATION
RT   WATER MIXING

DIFFUSION (DYE PATCH)
USE   **DYE DISPERSION**

DIFFUSION COEFFICIENTS
UF   diffusivity
BT1   EXCHANGE COEFFICIENTS
RT   EDDY DIFFUSIVITY

DIFFUSIVE CONVECTION
USE   **DOUBLE DIFFUSION**

DIFFUSIVITY
USE   **DIFFUSION COEFFICIENTS**

DIGESTIBILITY
SN   Added in 1980
BT1   ORGANOLEPTIC PROPERTIES
BT2   PROPERTIES
RT   ARTIFICIAL FEEDING
RT   DIETS
RT   DIGESTION
RT   FEED
RT   NUTRITIVE VALUE

DIGESTION
BT1   ANIMAL NUTRITION
BT2   NUTRITION
RT   AMOEBOCYTES
RT   ANIMAL METABOLISM
RT   DIGESTIBILITY
RT   DIGESTIVE GLANDS
RT   DIGESTIVE SYSTEM
RT   ENZYMATIC ACTIVITY
RT   ENZYMES
RT   EXCRETORY PRODUCTS
RT   FOOD ABSORPTION
RT   FOOD CONSUMPTION
RT   FOOD CONVERSION
RT   HEPATOPANCREAS
RT   HYDROLYSIS
RT   INTESTINES
RT   METABOLISM
RT   PHYSIOLOGY
RT   PYLORIC CAECA
RT   STOMACH

DIGESTIVE GLANDS
BT1   GLANDS
BT2   SECRETORY ORGANS
NT1   HEPATOPANCREAS
NT1   LIVER
NT1   PANCREAS
RT   ALIMENTARY ORGANS
RT   DIGESTION
RT   DIGESTIVE SYSTEM
RT   EXOCRINE GLANDS
RT   PYLORIC CAECA

DIGESTIVE SYSTEM
UF   gastrointestinal system
RT   ABDOMEN
RT   ALIMENTARY ORGANS
RT   DIGESTION
RT   DIGESTIVE GLANDS
RT   INTESTINES
RT   STOMACH

DIGESTIVE TRACT
BT1   ALIMENTARY ORGANS
BT2   ANIMAL ORGANS
BT3   BODY ORGANS

DIGITAL DATA RECORDS
USE   **DIGITAL RECORDS**

DIGITAL RECORDS
UF   digital data records
BT1   DOCUMENTS
RT   ANALOG RECORDS
RT   DATA CONVERTERS
RT   RECORDS

DIKES (EMBANKMENTS)
USE   **EMBANKMENTS**

DILUTION
SN   Used only as a qualifier
RT   FATE
RT   LIQUIDS
RT   SALINITY
RT   SALTS

DIMENSIONLESS NUMBERS
NT1   MIXING RATIO
RT   FROUDE NUMBER
RT   PRANDTL NUMBER
RT   RATIOS
RT   REYNOLDS NUMBER
RT   ROSSBY NUMBER

DIMENSIONS
SN   Used only as a qualifier
NT1   AMPLITUDE
NT2   WAVE AMPLITUDE
NT3   TIDAL AMPLITUDE
NT1   AREA
NT1   CAPACITY
NT1   DEPTH
NT2   MIXED LAYER DEPTH
NT2   SILL DEPTH
NT2   STANDARD DEPTHS
NT2   WATER DEPTH
NT1   HEIGHT
NT1   LENGTH
NT2   MIXING LENGTH
NT1   SIZE
NT2   PARTICLE SIZE
NT1   THICKNESS
NT2   CRUSTAL THICKNESS
NT2   ICE THICKNESS
NT1   VOLUME
NT2   ICE VOLUME
NT1   WIDTH
RT   GRAIN SIZE
RT   MORPHOMETRY
RT   SHAPE
RT   SPATIAL VARIATIONS

DIMORPHISM (SEXUAL)
USE   **SEXUAL DIMORPHISM**

DIRECTION
SN   Used only as a qualifier
NT1   WAVE DIRECTION
NT1   WIND DIRECTION
RT   AZIMUTH
RT   DIRECTION FINDING
RT   DIRECTION INDICATORS
RT   DIRECTIONAL SPECTRA
RT   ECHO RANGING
RT   HORIZON

DIRECTION FINDING
RT   DIRECTION
RT   NAVIGATION

DIRECTION INDICATORS
RT   COMPASSES
RT   DIRECTION
RT   MEASURING DEVICES
RT   VANES

DIRECTIONAL SPECTRA
UF   directional wave spectra
BT1   SPECTRA
RT   DIRECTION
RT   ENERGY SPECTRA
RT   INTERNAL WAVES
RT   LONG-CRESTED WAVES
RT   SHORT-CRESTED WAVES
RT   SURFACE WATER WAVES
RT   WAVE DIRECTION

DIRECTIONAL WAVE SPECTRA
USE   **DIRECTIONAL SPECTRA**

DIRECTORIES
UF   yearbooks
BT1   DOCUMENTS
RT   ALGOLOGISTS
RT   ANIMAL PHYSIOLOGISTS
RT   AQUACULTURISTS
RT   BACTERIOLOGISTS
RT   BIOLOGISTS
RT   BOTANISTS
RT   CARCINOLOGISTS
RT   CETOLOGISTS
RT   CONSULTANTS
RT   DATA COLLECTIONS
RT   DIVERS
RT   DOCUMENTATION
RT   ECOLOGISTS
RT   ECONOMISTS
RT   ENGINEERS
RT   ENTOMOLOGISTS
RT   EXPERTS
RT   FISHERMEN
RT   FISHERY BIOLOGISTS
RT   FRESHWATER ECOLOGISTS
RT   FRESHWATER SCIENTISTS
RT   GENETICISTS
RT   GEOLOGISTS
RT   GLOSSARIES
RT   ICHTHYOLOGISTS
RT   INFORMATION SCIENTISTS
RT   LIBRARIANS
RT   MALACOLOGISTS
RT   MAMMALOGISTS
RT   MARINE ECOLOGISTS
RT   MARINE SCIENTISTS
RT   METEOROLOGISTS
RT   MICROBIOLOGISTS
RT   MYCOLOGISTS
RT   ORGANIZATIONS
RT   ORNITHOLOGISTS
RT   PHYSIOLOGISTS
RT   PLANT PHYSIOLOGISTS
RT   RESEARCH INSTITUTIONS
RT   SCIENTIFIC PERSONNEL
RT   STATISTICIANS
RT   TAXONOMISTS
RT   TECHNICIANS
RT   VIROLOGISTS
RT   ZOOLOGISTS

DISASTERS
UF   catastrophes
UF   disasters (natural)
UF   natural disasters
RT   ACCIDENTS
RT   DROUGHTS
RT   EARTHQUAKES
RT   EL NINO PHENOMENA
RT   EMERGENCIES
RT   EMERGENCY VESSELS
RT   FLOODS

DISASTERS (cont'd)
RT   HAZARDS
RT   HURRICANES
RT   STORM SURGES
RT   TSUNAMIS
RT   VOLCANIC ERUPTIONS
RT   WARNING SERVICES

DISASTERS (MAN-MADE)
USE   **ACCIDENTS**

DISASTERS (NATURAL)
USE   **DISASTERS**

DISCOLORATION
USE   **DISCOLOURATION**

DISCOLORED WATER
USE   **DISCOLOURED WATER**

DISCOLOURATION
UF   discoloration
RT   CHROMATIC PIGMENTS
RT   COLOUR
RT   DEGRADATION
RT   PIGMENTS
RT   STAINING

DISCOLOURED WATER
SN   Before 1982 search also RED TIDES
UF   discolored water
BT1   WATER
RT   EOLIAN DUST
RT   RED TIDES
RT   VOLCANIC ASH
RT   WATER COLOUR

DISCONTINUITY LAYERS
BT1   LAYERS
NT1   HALOCLINE
NT1   LYSOCLINE
NT1   NEPHELOID LAYER
NT1   PYCNOCLINE
NT1   SCATTERING LAYERS
NT1   THERMOCLINE
NT2   DIURNAL THERMOCLINE
NT2   PERMANENT THERMOCLINE
NT2   SEASONAL THERMOCLINE
RT   CARBONATE COMPENSATION DEPTH
RT   DICOTHERMAL LAYER
RT   ENVIRONMENTAL FACTORS
RT   INTERFACES
RT   INVERSIONS
RT   THERMAL STRATIFICATION

DISCUS-SHAPED BUOYS
BT1   BUOY HULLS
BT2   HULLS

DISEASE CONTROL
BT1   CONTROL
RT   AETIOLOGY
RT   ANIMAL DISEASES
RT   ANTIHELMINTHIC AGENTS
RT   ANTIPARASITIC AGENTS
RT   ANTIPROTOZOAL AGENTS
RT   DISEASE DETECTION
RT   DISEASE RESISTANCE
RT   DISEASES
RT   DRUGS
RT   EPIDEMIOLOGY
RT   FISH DISEASES
RT   MACROPHAGES
RT   PATHOGENS
RT   PEST CONTROL
RT   PROPHYLAXIS
RT   PROTOZOAN DISEASES
RT   THERAPY

DISEASE DETECTION
SN	Added in 1980
UF	detection (diseases)
BT1	DETECTION
RT	AETIOLOGY
RT	DISEASE CONTROL
RT	DISEASES
RT	SYMPTOMS
RT	THERAPY

DISEASE PREVENTIVE TREATMENT
USE	**PROPHYLAXIS**

DISEASE RESISTANCE
SN	Added in 1980
UF	disease susceptibility
UF	pathogen resistance
UF	resistance to disease
BT1	BIOLOGICAL RESISTANCE
BT2	BIOLOGICAL PROPERTIES
BT3	PROPERTIES
RT	DISEASE CONTROL
RT	DISEASES
RT	DRUG RESISTANCE
RT	ECOPHYSIOLOGY
RT	ENVIRONMENTAL EFFECTS
RT	FISH DISEASES
RT	IMMUNITY
RT	NUTRITIONAL REQUIREMENTS
RT	VACCINATION

DISEASE SUSCEPTIBILITY
USE	**DISEASE RESISTANCE**

DISEASE TRANSMISSION
SN	Added in 1982
UF	transmission diseases
RT	DISEASES
RT	INFECTIOUS DISEASES

DISEASE TREATMENT
USE	**THERAPY**

DISEASES
UF	disorders (biological)
UF	morbidity
NT1	ANIMAL DISEASES
NT2	FISH DISEASES
NT3	BOIL DISEASE
NT3	BUBBLE DISEASE
NT3	GILL DISEASE
NT3	PEDUNCLE DISEASE
NT3	REDMOUTH DISEASE
NT3	SUNBURN
NT3	ULCERATIVE DERMAL NECROSIS
NT3	WHIRLING DISEASE
NT1	DEFICIENCY DISEASES
NT1	ENVIRONMENTAL DISEASES
NT1	HAEMATOLOGICAL DISEASES
NT2	ANAEMIA
NT1	HUMAN DISEASES
NT2	BOTULISM
NT2	CIGUATERA
NT2	DECOMPRESSION SICKNESS
NT2	HYPERCAPNIA
NT2	HYPOTHERMIA
NT2	HYPOXIA
NT2	MALARIA
NT2	SEA SICKNESS
NT1	HUSBANDRY DISEASES
NT1	INFECTIOUS DISEASES
NT2	BACTERIAL DISEASES
NT3	TUBERCULOSIS
NT3	VIBRIOSIS
NT2	FUNGAL DISEASES
NT2	PARASITIC DISEASES
NT2	PROTOZOAN DISEASES
NT2	SEPTICAEMIA
NT2	VIRAL DISEASES
NT1	METABOLIC DISORDERS

DISEASES (cont'd)
NT1	NUTRITION DISORDERS
NT2	PROTEIN DEFICIENCY
NT1	PLANT DISEASES
NT1	TUMOURS
RT	AETIOLOGY
RT	ANTIBIOTICS
RT	CARCINOGENS
RT	DETOXIFICATION
RT	DISEASE CONTROL
RT	DISEASE DETECTION
RT	DISEASE RESISTANCE
RT	DISEASE TRANSMISSION
RT	EPIDEMIOLOGY
RT	HAEMORRHAGE
RT	HISTOPATHOLOGY
RT	HOSTS
RT	HYGIENE
RT	IMMUNOLOGY
RT	INCUBATION
RT	INTERSPECIFIC RELATIONSHIPS
RT	LETHAL EFFECTS
RT	MICROBIAL CONTAMINATION
RT	MORTALITY CAUSES
RT	NATURAL MORTALITY
RT	NECROSES
RT	PATHOGENS
RT	PATHOLOGY
RT	POLLUTION EFFECTS
RT	POPULATION CONTROL
RT	PROPHYLAXIS
RT	SUBLETHAL EFFECTS
RT	SYMPTOMS
RT	THERAPY
RT	UNDERWATER MEDICINE
RT	VACCINATION

DISINFECTANTS
SN	Added in 1980
UF	antiseptic agents
UF	antiseptic chemicals
UF	antiseptics
RT	CHEMICAL COMPOUNDS
RT	CHLORINE
RT	DISINFECTION
RT	PESTICIDES
RT	WATER PURIFICATION

DISINFECTION
SN	Added in 1980
RT	BACTERIAL DISEASES
RT	CHLORINATION
RT	DECHLORINATION
RT	DISINFECTANTS
RT	INJURIES
RT	MICROBIAL CONTAMINATION
RT	PATHOGENS
RT	WATER PURIFICATION

DISORDERS
USE	**HUMAN DISEASES**

DISORDERS (BIOLOGICAL)
USE	**DISEASES**

DISPERSAL PHENOMENA
USE	**DISPERSION**

DISPERSANTS
SN	Chemicals used to contribute to the break-up of an oil spill at sea
UF	dispersing agents
RT	AGENTS
RT	ANTICOAGULANTS
RT	DISPERSION
RT	OIL POLLUTION
RT	OIL REMOVAL
RT	OIL SPILLS
RT	SOLVENTS
RT	SURFACTANTS

DISPERSING
USE	**DISPERSION**

DISPERSING AGENTS
USE	**DISPERSANTS**

DISPERSION
UF	dispersal phenomena
UF	dispersing
UF	spreading
NT1	BIOLOGICAL DRIFT
NT1	DYE DISPERSION
NT1	LIGHT DISPERSION
NT1	LONGITUDINAL DISPERSION
NT1	SOUND DISPERSION
NT1	WAVE DISPERSION
RT	DEFLOCCULATION
RT	DISPERSANTS
RT	EMULSIONS
RT	FATE
RT	MIGRATIONS
RT	MIXING PROCESSES
RT	SEPARATION
RT	SUSPENDED PARTICULATE MATTER
RT	WATER MIXING

DISPERSION (WATER WAVES)
USE	**WAVE DISPERSION**

DISPERSIONS (CHEMICAL)
USE	**COLLOIDS**

DISPHOTIC ZONE
RT	APHOTIC ZONE
RT	CARBONATE COMPENSATION DEPTH
RT	COMPENSATION DEPTH
RT	EPIPELAGIC ZONE
RT	EUPHOTIC ZONE
RT	INLAND WATER ENVIRONMENT
RT	LENITIC ENVIRONMENT
RT	LIGHT PENETRATION
RT	MARINE ENVIRONMENT
RT	MESOPELAGIC ZONE
RT	PHOTOSYNTHESIS

DISPLACEMENT
SN	Weight of water displaced by vehicle; weight in water
RT	FLOTATION
RT	MOTION
RT	SURFACE CRAFT
RT	WEIGHT

DISPLAY BEHAVIOUR
SN	Added in 1980
BT1	BEHAVIOUR
RT	AGONISTIC BEHAVIOUR
RT	COURTSHIP

DISPOSAL (WASTE)
USE	**WASTE DISPOSAL**

DISPUTES
SN	Added in 1980
UF	conflict of interests
UF	conflicts
NT1	FISHERY DISPUTES
RT	BOUNDARIES
RT	INTERNATIONAL LAW
RT	LEGAL ASPECTS
RT	OCEAN SPACE

DISSIPATION (WATER WAVES)
USE	**WAVE DISSIPATION**

DISSOCIATION
BT1	CHEMICAL REACTIONS
RT	PYROLYSIS

DISSOLUTION
UF	solution
BT1	SEPARATION PROCESSES
NT1	CALCITE DISSOLUTION
RT	EXCHANGE CAPACITY
RT	LEACHING
RT	SOLUBILITY
RT	SOLUTIONS
RT	SOLVENT EXTRACTION
RT	SOLVENTS
RT	SUPERSATURATION

DISSOLVED CHEMICALS
UF	dissolved mineral resources
BT1	MINERAL RESOURCES
BT2	NATURAL RESOURCES
BT3	RESOURCES
RT	BORON
RT	BROMINE
RT	CALCIUM
RT	HOT BRINES
RT	MAGNESIUM
RT	POTASSIUM
RT	RENEWABLE RESOURCES
RT	SODIUM CHLORIDE
RT	STRONTIUM
RT	SULPHUR
RT	URANIUM

DISSOLVED GASES
BT1	GASES
BT2	FLUIDS
NT1	DISSOLVED OXYGEN
RT	BUBBLE DISEASE
RT	CHEMICAL COMPOSITION
RT	SOLUBILITY
RT	WATER ANALYSIS

DISSOLVED INORGANIC MATTER
BT1	INORGANIC MATTER

DISSOLVED MINERAL RESOURCES
USE	**DISSOLVED CHEMICALS**

DISSOLVED ORGANIC CARBON
BT1	ORGANIC CARBON
BT2	CARBON
BT3	CHEMICAL ELEMENTS
RT	CARBON/NITROGEN RATIO
RT	CARBON/PHOSPHORUS RATIO
RT	DISSOLVED ORGANIC MATTER
RT	TOTAL ORGANIC CARBON

DISSOLVED ORGANIC MATTER
SN	Before 1982 search ORGANIC SUSPENDED MATTER
BT1	ORGANIC MATTER
RT	DISSOLVED ORGANIC CARBON
RT	DISSOLVED ORGANIC NITROGEN
RT	DISSOLVED ORGANIC PHOSPHORUS

DISSOLVED ORGANIC NITROGEN
BT1	ORGANIC NITROGEN
BT2	NITROGEN
BT3	CHEMICAL ELEMENTS
RT	CARBON/NITROGEN RATIO
RT	DISSOLVED ORGANIC MATTER

DISSOLVED ORGANIC PHOSPHORUS
BT1	ORGANIC PHOSPHORUS
BT2	PHOSPHORUS
BT3	CHEMICAL ELEMENTS
RT	CARBON/PHOSPHORUS RATIO
RT	DISSOLVED ORGANIC MATTER

DISSOLVED OXYGEN
UF	do
UF	oxygen content
BT1	DISSOLVED GASES
BT2	GASES
BT3	FLUIDS
RT	ABIOTIC FACTORS
RT	AERATION
RT	AEROBIC RESPIRATION
RT	ANOXIC CONDITIONS
RT	BIOCHEMICAL OXYGEN DEMAND
RT	CHEMICAL COMPOSITION
RT	CHEMICAL OXYGEN DEMAND
RT	DEOXYGENATION
RT	EUTROPHICATION
RT	HABITAT IMPROVEMENT (CHEMICAL)
RT	HYDROGRAPHIC SECTIONS
RT	HYDROGRAPHY
RT	NON-CONSERVATIVE PROPERTIES
RT	OXYGEN
RT	OXYGEN DEMAND
RT	OXYGEN DEPLETION
RT	OXYGEN MINIMUM LAYER
RT	OXYGEN PROFILES
RT	OXYGENATION
RT	SOLUBILITY
RT	SOLUTIONS
RT	WATER PROPERTIES
RT	WINKLER METHOD

DISSOLVED SALTS
BT1	SALTS
NT1	BRINES
RT	CHEMICAL COMPOSITION
RT	CHLORINE COMPOUNDS
RT	CONSERVATION OF SALT
RT	DESALINATION
RT	DESALINATION PLANTS
RT	FLUORINE COMPOUNDS
RT	SALINITY
RT	SALT BUDGET
RT	SALT FINGERS
RT	SALT FLUX
RT	SALT LAKES
RT	SODIUM COMPOUNDS
RT	SOLUTIONS
RT	WATER PROPERTIES

DISTANCE
SN	Used only as a qualifier

DISTANT WATER FISHERIES
USE	**HIGH SEAS FISHERIES**

DISTILLATION
BT1	SEPARATION PROCESSES
RT	DEMINERALIZATION
RT	DESALINATION

DISTILLED WATER
BT1	WATER

DISTORTION
USE	**DEFORMATION**

DISTRESS SIGNALS
UF	beacons (distress)
BT1	ALARM SYSTEMS

DISTRIBUTARIES
BT1	RIVERS
BT2	INLAND WATERS
RT	DELTAS
RT	FLUVIAL MORPHOLOGY
RT	TRIBUTARIES

DISTRIBUTION
SN	Used only as a qualifier. Use of a narrower term is recommended
NT1	ECOLOGICAL DISTRIBUTION
NT1	GAUSSIAN DISTRIBUTION
NT1	GEOGRAPHICAL DISTRIBUTION
NT2	DIFFERENTIAL DISTRIBUTION
NT2	HORIZONTAL DISTRIBUTION
NT3	BIPOLAR DISTRIBUTION
NT2	MERIDIONAL DISTRIBUTION
NT2	VERTICAL DISTRIBUTION
NT2	ZONAL DISTRIBUTION
NT1	GEOLOGICAL DISTRIBUTION
NT1	NEW RECORDS
NT1	QUANTITATIVE DISTRIBUTION
NT1	SEDIMENT DISTRIBUTION
NT1	TEMPORAL DISTRIBUTION
NT2	MONTHLY DISTRIBUTION
NT2	SEASONAL DISTRIBUTION
RT	DISTRIBUTION RECORDS

DISTRIBUTION RECORDS
SN	Added in 1980
RT	BIOGEOGRAPHY
RT	BIOLOGICAL CHARTS
RT	DISTRIBUTION
RT	GEOGRAPHICAL DISTRIBUTION
RT	TYPE LOCALITIES

DISTURBANCE (ECOSYSTEM)
USE	**ECOSYSTEM DISTURBANCE**

DITCHING
USE	**TRENCHING**

DIURNAL RHYTHMS
USE	**CIRCADIAN RHYTHMS**

DIURNAL THERMOCLINE
BT1	THERMOCLINE
BT2	DISCONTINUITY LAYERS
BT3	LAYERS
RT	DIURNAL VARIATIONS

DIURNAL TIDES
BT1	TIDES
BT2	TIDAL MOTION

DIURNAL VARIATIONS
UF	daily variation
BT1	PERIODIC VARIATIONS
BT2	TEMPORAL VARIATIONS
RT	CIRCADIAN RHYTHMS
RT	DAILY
RT	DAYTIME
RT	DIURNAL THERMOCLINE
RT	NIGHTTIME
RT	NYCTIMERAL RHYTHMS
RT	PHOTOPERIODICITY
RT	PHOTOPERIODS
RT	TEMPORAL DISTRIBUTION
RT	VERTICAL DISTRIBUTION
RT	VERTICAL MIGRATIONS

DIVERGENCE
RT	COASTAL UPWELLING
RT	CONVERGENCE
RT	DIVERGENCE ZONES
RT	EQUATORIAL UPWELLING
RT	HORIZONTAL MOTION
RT	LANGMUIR CIRCULATION
RT	PLATE DIVERGENCE
RT	UPWELLING

DIVERGENCE ZONES
NT1	OCEANIC DIVERGENCES
RT	CONVERGENCE ZONES
RT	DIVERGENCE
RT	UPWELLING
RT	WATER MASSES

DIVERGENT MARGINS
USE **PASSIVE MARGINS**

DIVERGING PLATE BOUNDARIES
UF accreting plate boundaries
BT1 PLATE BOUNDARIES
RT CRUSTAL ACCRETION
RT MANTLE PLUMES
RT MID-OCEAN RIDGES
RT PLATE DIVERGENCE
RT RIFT ZONES
RT SPREADING CENTRES

DIVERS
BT1 EXPERTS
BT2 PERSONNEL
RT DIRECTORIES
RT DIVING INDUSTRY
RT SPEECH DISTORTION

DIVERS PHYSIOLOGY
USE **DIVING PHYSIOLOGY**

DIVERS SAFETY
USE **DIVING REGULATIONS**

DIVERS WORK
USE **WORKING UNDERWATER**

DIVERSITY INDEX
USE **SPECIES DIVERSITY**

DIVING
NT1 DEEP-SEA DIVING
NT1 SATURATION DIVING
NT1 SCUBA DIVING
RT AQUATIC MAMMALS
RT ARTIFICIAL AERATION
RT CETOLOGY
RT DEPLOYMENT
RT DIVING ACCIDENTS
RT DIVING BELLS
RT DIVING EQUIPMENT
RT DIVING HAZARDS
RT DIVING PHYSIOLOGY
RT DIVING REGULATIONS
RT FISHING BY DIVING
RT HUMAN PHYSIOLOGY
RT LIFE SUPPORT SYSTEMS
RT MANNED VEHICLES
RT PRESSURE EFFECTS
RT RECOVERY
RT RECREATIONAL WATERS
RT SEARCH AND RESCUE
RT SHARK ATTACKS
RT SPEAR FISHING
RT SURVEYING UNDERWATER
RT UNDERWATER EXPLORATION
RT UNDERWATER MEDICINE
RT UNDERWATER PHOTOGRAPHS
RT UNDERWATER PHOTOGRAPHY
RT UNDERWATER TELEVISION
RT VISIBILITY UNDERWATER
RT WORKING UNDERWATER

DIVING ACCIDENTS
BT1 ACCIDENTS
RT DIVING
RT DIVING HAZARDS
RT DIVING REGULATIONS
RT DROWNING
RT MORTALITY CAUSES

DIVING BELLS
BT1 MANNED VEHICLES
BT2 UNDERWATER VEHICLES
BT3 VEHICLES
RT DECOMPRESSION CHAMBERS
RT DIVING
RT ONE-ATMOSPHERE SYSTEMS

DIVING BELLS (cont'd)
RT SATURATION DIVING
RT SUBMERSIBLES
RT SUPPORT SHIPS
RT TETHERED VEHICLES
RT TRANSFER CHAMBERS
RT UNDERWATER HABITATS
RT WORKING UNDERWATER

DIVING CHAMBERS
USE **MANNED VEHICLES**

DIVING EQUIPMENT
UF diving gear
UF diving systems
BT1 EQUIPMENT
NT1 DECOMPRESSION CHAMBERS
NT2 DECK COMPRESSION CHAMBERS
NT2 TRANSFER CHAMBERS
NT1 DIVING SUITS
NT1 DIVING TOOLS
RT BREATHING APPARATUS
RT BREATHING MIXTURES
RT COMMUNICATION SYSTEMS
RT COMPRESSORS
RT DECOMPRESSION TABLES
RT DIVING
RT DIVING INDUSTRY
RT LIFE SUPPORT SYSTEMS
RT PROTECTIVE CLOTHING
RT SUBMERSIBLES
RT SUPPORT SHIPS
RT SURVEYING EQUIPMENT

DIVING GEAR
USE **DIVING EQUIPMENT**

DIVING HAZARDS
BT1 HAZARDS
NT1 SHARK ATTACKS
RT CARBON MONOXIDE
RT DANGEROUS ORGANISMS
RT DIVING
RT DIVING ACCIDENTS
RT DIVING HAZARDS
RT DROWNING
RT HYPERTHERMIA

DIVING INDUSTRY
BT1 INDUSTRIES
RT DIVERS
RT DIVING EQUIPMENT
RT OFFSHORE ENGINEERING
RT OIL AND GAS INDUSTRY
RT RECREATION
RT WORKING UNDERWATER

DIVING MEDICINE
USE **UNDERWATER MEDICINE**

DIVING PHYSIOLOGY
SN All physiological and medical
aspects of diving in man, mammals,
and other animals, including
experimental laboratory studies
UF divers physiology
BT1 PHYSIOLOGY
BT2 BIOLOGY
RT ANIMAL PHYSIOLOGY
RT AQUATIC MAMMALS
RT BONE NECROSIS
RT BREATHING MIXTURES
RT DECOMPRESSION SICKNESS
RT DEEP-SEA DIVING
RT DIVING
RT HIGH PRESSURE EFFECTS
RT HUMAN PHYSIOLOGY
RT HYPERBARIC
RT HYPERTHERMIA
RT HYPOTHERMIA

DIVING PHYSIOLOGY (cont'd)
RT MAMMALIAN PHYSIOLOGY
RT MEDICINE
RT MIXED GAS
RT PRESSURE EFFECTS
RT SPEECH DISTORTION
RT UNDERWATER MEDICINE
RT UNDERWATER VEHICLES
RT WORKING UNDERWATER

DIVING REGULATIONS
UF divers safety
BT1 SAFETY REGULATIONS
BT2 LEGISLATION
RT ACCIDENT PREVENTION
RT DIVING
RT DIVING ACCIDENTS

DIVING SUITS
SN Use for one-man equipment with
articulated limbs
BT1 DIVING EQUIPMENT
BT2 EQUIPMENT
RT LIFE SUPPORT SYSTEMS
RT MANIPULATORS
RT ONE-ATMOSPHERE SYSTEMS
RT SATURATION DIVING
RT SUBMERSIBLES
RT UMBILICALS

DIVING SURVEYS
BT1 SURVEYS
RT SURVEYING UNDERWATER
RT UNDERWATER EXPLORATION
RT WORKING UNDERWATER

DIVING SYSTEMS
USE **DIVING EQUIPMENT**

DIVING TOOLS
SN Pertains to tools operated by divers
UF tools (underwater)
UF underwater tools
BT1 DIVING EQUIPMENT
BT2 EQUIPMENT
RT UNDERWATER EQUIPMENT
RT WORKING UNDERWATER

DIVING VEHICLES
USE **MANNED VEHICLES**

DNA
SN Before 1982 search DEOXYRIBONUCLEIC
ACID
UF deoxyribonucleic acid
BT1 NUCLEIC ACIDS
BT2 ORGANIC ACIDS
BT3 ORGANIC COMPOUNDS
RT CHEMICAL COMPOUNDS
RT CHEMOTAXONOMY
RT GENES
RT POLYMERIZATION

DO
USE **DISSOLVED OXYGEN**

DOCKING
USE **BERTHING**

DOCKS
USE **PORT INSTALLATIONS**

DOCUMENTATION
UF information sciences
NT1 INFORMATION HANDLING
NT1 INFORMATION RETRIEVAL
RT BIBLIOGRAPHIC INFORMATION
RT BIBLIOGRAPHIES
RT BIOGRAPHIES
RT DATA COLLECTIONS

DOCUMENTATION (cont'd)	
RT	DATA STORAGE
RT	DIRECTORIES
RT	DOCUMENTS
RT	ENCYCLOPAEDIAS
RT	GLOSSARIES
RT	INFORMATION SERVICES
RT	LIBRARIANS
RT	LIBRARIES
RT	LITERATURE REVIEWS
RT	THESAURUS
DOCUMENTATION SERVICES	
USE	**INFORMATION SERVICES**
DOCUMENTS	
SN	Before 1982 search also PUBLICATIONS
UF	publications
NT1	ABSTRACTS
NT1	ARCHIVES
NT1	ATLASES
NT2	OCEANOGRAPHIC ATLASES
NT1	AUDIOVISUAL MATERIAL
NT2	AUDIO RECORDINGS
NT2	FILMS
NT2	FILMSTRIPS
NT2	GRAPHICS
NT3	ANALOG RECORDS
NT4	BATHYTHERMOGRAMS
NT4	ECHOSOUNDER PROFILES
NT4	SEISMIC PROFILES
NT4	SEISMOGRAMS
NT4	TIDAL CURVES
NT4	TIDAL RECORDS
NT3	ENGINEERING DRAWINGS
NT3	GRAPHS
NT4	GROWTH CURVES
NT4	HODOGRAPHS
NT4	HYPSOMETRIC CURVES
NT4	T/S DIAGRAMS
NT4	WAVE REFRACTION DIAGRAMS
NT3	MAP GRAPHICS
NT4	CURRENT ROSES
NT4	ISOPLETHS
NT4	STREAMLINES
NT4	VERTICAL SECTIONS
NT4	WIND ROSES
NT4	WIND VECTORS
NT3	MAPS
NT4	BIOLOGICAL CHARTS
NT4	CLIMATOLOGICAL CHARTS
NT4	CONTROL CHARTS
NT4	ENVIRONMENTAL CHARTS
NT4	FISHERY CHARTS
NT4	GEOLOGICAL MAPS
NT4	HYDROGRAPHIC CHARTS
NT4	METEOROLOGICAL CHARTS
NT4	NAVIGATIONAL CHARTS
NT4	POLLUTION MAPS
NT4	TOPOGRAPHIC MAPS
NT4	TRACK CHARTS
NT2	MICROFORMS
NT2	PHOTOGRAPHS
NT3	AERIAL PHOTOGRAPHS
NT3	UNDERWATER PHOTOGRAPHS
NT4	BOTTOM PHOTOGRAPHS
NT2	SATELLITE MOSAICS
NT2	SLIDES (PHOTOGRAPHIC)
NT2	VIDEOTAPE RECORDINGS
NT1	BIBLIOGRAPHIES
NT2	PERSONAL BIBLIOGRAPHIES
NT1	BIOGRAPHIES
NT1	BROCHURES
NT1	CATALOGUES
NT2	BOOK CATALOGUES
NT2	CHART CATALOGUES
NT2	INVENTORIES
NT1	COLLECTED PAPERS
NT2	FESTSCHRIFTEN
NT1	DIGITAL RECORDS

DOCUMENTS (cont'd)	
NT1	DIRECTORIES
NT1	ENCYCLOPAEDIAS
NT1	EXPEDITION REPORTS
NT1	GAZETEERS
NT1	GLOSSARIES
NT1	ILLUSTRATIONS
NT1	LOGBOOKS
NT1	MANUALS
NT2	INSTRUMENT HANDBOOKS
NT1	PATENTS
NT1	PUBLICITY MATERIAL
NT1	REPORT LITERATURE
NT2	ANNUAL REPORTS
NT2	CLASSIFIED DOCUMENTS
NT2	CRUISE REPORTS
NT2	DATA REPORTS
NT3	STATION LISTS
NT2	PROGRESS REPORTS
NT1	SAILING DIRECTIONS
NT1	SYNOPSIS
NT1	TABLES
NT2	ALMANACS
NT3	NAUTICAL ALMANACS
NT3	TIDE TABLES
NT2	CONVERSION TABLES
NT3	KNUDSEN TABLES
NT2	DECOMPRESSION TABLES
NT2	METEOROLOGICAL TABLES
NT2	NAVIGATIONAL TABLES
NT2	OCEANOGRAPHIC TABLES
NT3	SALINITY TABLES
NT2	STATISTICAL TABLES
NT3	SCATTER DIAGRAMS
NT2	TRAVERSE TABLES
NT1	THESAURUS
NT1	TRANSLATIONS
RT	BIBLIOGRAPHIC INFORMATION
RT	DOCUMENTATION
RT	INFORMATION HANDLING
RT	INFORMATION RETRIEVAL
RT	LIBRARIES
RT	LITERATURE REVIEWS
RT	RECORDS
RT	STANDARDS
DODECANE	
BT1	ACYCLIC HYDROCARBONS
BT2	SATURATED HYDROCARBONS
BT3	HYDROCARBONS
BT4	ORGANIC COMPOUNDS
DOLDRUMS	
USE	**EQUATORIAL TROUGH**
DOLOMITE	
SN	Use only for mineral dolomite
BT1	CARBONATE MINERALS
BT2	MINERALS
RT	DOLOSTONE
RT	EVAPORITES
DOLOMITE (ROCK)	
USE	**DOLOSTONE**
DOLOMITIZATION	
BT1	DIAGENESIS
BT2	SEDIMENTATION
RT	CALCITIZATION
RT	CALCIUM CARBONATES
RT	DOLOSTONE
RT	LIMESTONE
DOLOSTONE	
UF	dolomite (rock)
BT1	CARBONATE ROCKS
RT	DOLOMITE
RT	DOLOMITIZATION
RT	SEDIMENTARY ROCKS

DOMES	
BT1	ANTICLINES
BT2	FOLDS
BT3	GEOLOGICAL STRUCTURES
RT	SALT DOMES
RT	STRUCTURAL DOMES
DOMESTIC SPECIES	
SN	Species kept by man from the wild.
	Added in 1980
UF	domesticated species
BT1	SPECIES
BT2	TAXA
RT	CULTURED ORGANISMS
RT	DOMESTICATION
RT	INTRODUCED SPECIES
RT	SELECTIVE BREEDING
DOMESTIC WASTES	
BT1	WASTES
RT	DETERGENTS
RT	INDUSTRIAL WASTES
RT	ORGANIC WASTES
RT	SEWAGE
RT	SEWAGE TREATMENT
RT	SOAPS
RT	WASTE TREATMENT
RT	WASTEWATER AQUACULTURE
DOMESTICATED SPECIES	
USE	**DOMESTIC SPECIES**
DOMESTICATION	
SN	Added in 1980
RT	CAPTIVITY
RT	CONTROLLED CONDITIONS
RT	DOMESTIC SPECIES
DOMINANCE HIERARCHIES	
SN	Before 1982 search SOCIAL BEHAVIOUR
UF	hierarchies (social)
UF	social hierarchy
BT1	SOCIAL BEHAVIOUR
BT2	BEHAVIOUR
NT1	PECKING ORDER
RT	COMPETITION
RT	STOCKING DENSITY
RT	TERRITORIALITY
RT	VISUAL STIMULI
DOMINANT SPECIES	
BT1	SPECIES
BT2	TAXA
RT	CATCH COMPOSITION
RT	CLIMAX COMMUNITY
RT	COMMUNITY COMPOSITION
RT	ECOLOGICAL ASSOCIATIONS
RT	ECOLOGICAL SUCCESSION
RT	MULTISPECIES FISHERIES
RT	SPECIES DIVERSITY
DOPPLER EFFECT	
UF	doppler shift
RT	CURRENT METERS
RT	CURRENT SENSORS
RT	DOPPLER NAVIGATION
RT	DOPPLER SONAR
RT	ELECTROMAGNETIC RADIATION
RT	FLOWMETERS
RT	RADAR
RT	SOUND PROPAGATION
DOPPLER NAVIGATION	
BT1	NAVIGATION
RT	DOPPLER EFFECT

ASFIS Thesaurus

DOPPLER SHIFT
USE **DOPPLER EFFECT**

DOPPLER SONAR
UF acoustic doppler sonar
BT1 ACTIVE SONAR
BT2 SONAR
BT3 REMOTE SENSING EQUIPMENT
BT4 EQUIPMENT
RT ACOUSTIC EQUIPMENT
RT ACOUSTIC NAVIGATION
RT DOPPLER EFFECT

DOPPLER SONAR NAVIGATION
USE **ACOUSTIC NAVIGATION**

DORMANCY
RT AESTIVATION
RT HIBERNATION
RT METABOLISM
RT RESTING EGGS
RT THERMOREGULATION

DORMANT STAGES
USE **CYSTS**

DOUBLE DIFFUSION
UF diffusive convection
UF double diffusive convection
UF salt finger convection
UF salt fingering
BT1 MOLECULAR DIFFUSION
BT2 DIFFUSION
BT3 TRANSPORT PROCESSES
RT DOUBLE DIFFUSIVE INSTABILITY
RT HEAT
RT MICROSTRUCTURE
RT SALINITY GRADIENTS
RT SALT FINGERS
RT SALTS
RT TEMPERATURE GRADIENTS
RT VERTICAL MIXING

DOUBLE DIFFUSIVE CONVECTION
USE **DOUBLE DIFFUSION**

DOUBLE DIFFUSIVE INSTABILITY
BT1 INSTABILITY
RT DOUBLE DIFFUSION
RT TRANS-ISOPYCNAL MIXING

DOUBLE KELVIN WAVES
USE **KELVIN WAVES**

DOUGLAS SCALE
USE **SEA STATE SCALES**

DOWNSTREAM MIGRATIONS
USE **CATADROMOUS MIGRATIONS**

DOWNWARD IRRADIANCE
BT1 IRRADIANCE

DOWNWARD LONG WAVE RADIATION
UF atmospheric radiation
BT1 TERRESTRIAL RADIATION
BT2 ELECTROMAGNETIC RADIATION
BT3 RADIATIONS
RT EXTRATERRESTRIAL RADIATION

DOWNWELLING
BT1 VERTICAL WATER MOVEMENT
BT2 WATER MOTION
RT CONVERGENCE
RT MIXING PROCESSES
RT OCEANIC CONVERGENCES
RT UPWELLING
RT WATER MIXING

DRAG
NT1 FORM DRAG
RT AIR-WATER EXCHANGES
RT BOTTOM FRICTION
RT BOTTOM STRESS
RT DRAG COEFFICIENT
RT FRICTION
RT WIND STRESS
RT WIND WAVE GENERATION

DRAG COEFFICIENT
RT BED ROUGHNESS
RT DRAG
RT KINETIC ENERGY
RT REYNOLDS NUMBER
RT SURFACE ROUGHNESS
RT WIND STRESS
RT WIND WAVE GENERATION

DRAGGING NETS
USE **BOTTOM TRAWLS**

DRAINAGE BASINS
USE **RIVER BASINS**

DRAINAGE WATER
SN Drainage water of artificial or natural origin
BT1 WATER
NT1 RUNOFF
NT2 AGRICULTURAL RUNOFF
NT2 STORMWATER RUNOFF
NT2 URBAN RUNOFF
RT HYDROLOGY
RT SEWAGE
RT URBANIZATION
RT WASTE WATER
RT WATER TABLE
RT WATERSHEDS

DRAWING COLLECTIONS
USE **ILLUSTRATIONS**

DRAWINGS
USE **ILLUSTRATIONS**

DREDGE SPOIL
BT1 WASTES
RT DREDGERS
RT DREDGING
RT SPOIL

DREDGED SAMPLES
BT1 SEDIMENT SAMPLES
BT2 GEOLOGICAL SAMPLES
BT3 SAMPLES
RT DREDGES (GEOLOGY)

DREDGERS
UF dredging vessels
BT1 SURFACE CRAFT
BT2 VEHICLES
RT CHANNELS
RT DREDGE SPOIL
RT DREDGES
RT DREDGING
RT WORK PLATFORMS

DREDGES
SN Refers to fishing dredges only. For sediment dredges use DREDGES (GEOLOGY)
UF boat dredges
UF hand dredges
BT1 FISHING GEAR
RT BOATS
RT COASTAL FISHERIES
RT DEMERSAL FISHERIES
RT DREDGERS

DREDGES (GEOLOGY)
BT1 SEDIMENT SAMPLERS
BT2 SAMPLERS
RT DREDGED SAMPLES
RT SEAFLOOR SAMPLING

DREDGING
UF dredging (excavation)
UF excavating
RT AGGREGATES
RT CANALS
RT CHANNELS
RT CLAM FISHERIES
RT DREDGE SPOIL
RT DREDGERS
RT ECOSYSTEM DISTURBANCE
RT EXCAVATION UNDERWATER
RT NAVIGATIONAL CHANNELS
RT OCEAN FLOOR
RT SPOIL
RT TRENCHING

DREDGING (CATCHING METHODS)
USE **BOTTOM TRAWLING**

DREDGING (EXCAVATION)
USE **DREDGING**

DREDGING VESSELS
USE **DREDGERS**

DRESSING
SN To remove scales, head and tail from fish. Added in 1982
UF fish dressing
BT1 FISH HANDLING
BT2 FISHERY INDUSTRY
BT3 INDUSTRIES
NT1 GUTTING
RT CURING
RT PROCESSED FISHERY PRODUCTS

DRIED FISH
USE **DRIED PRODUCTS**

DRIED PRODUCTS
SN Added in 1980
UF dehydrated products
UF dried fish
UF sun dried products
BT1 PROCESSED FISHERY PRODUCTS
BT2 FISHERY PRODUCTS
BT3 PRODUCTS
RT CURED PRODUCTS
RT DRYING
RT FREEZE-DRYING

DRIED SALTED PRODUCTS
USE **CURED PRODUCTS**

DRIFT
NT1 ICE DRIFT
NT1 SHIP DRIFT
RT ANCHORING
RT CONTINENTAL DRIFT
RT DRIFTERS
RT MOTION

DRIFT (BIOLOGICAL)
USE **BIOLOGICAL DRIFT**

DRIFT (CONTINENTAL)
USE **CONTINENTAL DRIFT**

DRIFT (GENETIC)
USE **GENETIC DRIFT**

DRIFT (ICE)
USE **ICE DRIFT**

DRIFT (SEDIMENTS)
USE **GLACIAL DEPOSITS**

DRIFT (SHIPS)
USE **SHIP DRIFT**

DRIFT BOTTLES
SN   Before 1982 search DRIFTERS
UF   bottle post
BT1   SURFACE DRIFTERS
BT2   DRIFTERS
BT3   CURRENT MEASURING EQUIPMENT
BT4   FLOW MEASURING EQUIPMENT
RT   CURRENT MEASUREMENT
RT   DRIFT CARDS

DRIFT BUOYS
USE **DRIFTING DATA BUOYS**

DRIFT CARDS
SN   Before 1982 search DRIFTERS
BT1   SURFACE DRIFTERS
BT2   DRIFTERS
BT3   CURRENT MEASURING EQUIPMENT
BT4   FLOW MEASURING EQUIPMENT
RT   CURRENT MEASUREMENT
RT   DRIFT BOTTLES

DRIFT CURRENTS
USE **WIND-DRIVEN CURRENTS**

DRIFT-LINES
USE **LINES**

DRIFT NETS
USE **GILLNETS**

DRIFTERS
UF   floats (current measurement)
UF   lagrangian drifters
BT1   CURRENT MEASURING EQUIPMENT
BT2   FLOW MEASURING EQUIPMENT
NT1   SUBSURFACE DRIFTERS
NT2   SEABED DRIFTERS
NT2   SWALLOW FLOATS
NT3   SOFAR FLOATS
NT1   SURFACE DRIFTERS
NT2   DRIFT BOTTLES
NT2   DRIFT CARDS
NT2   DROGUES
RT   CURRENT MEASUREMENT
RT   DRIFT
RT   LAGRANGIAN CURRENT MEASUREMENT

DRIFTING BUOYS
USE **DRIFTING DATA BUOYS**

DRIFTING DATA BUOYS
SN   Before 1985 search also DRIFT BUOYS
UF   drift buoys
UF   drifting buoys
UF   expendable drifting buoys
UF   lagrangian drifting buoys
UF   satellite-tracked buoys
BT1   DATA BUOYS
BT2   BUOYS
RT   DRIFTING STATIONS
RT   SURFACE DRIFTERS

DRIFTING STATIONS
BT1   OCEANOGRAPHIC STATIONS
RT   DRIFTING DATA BUOYS
RT   ICE ISLANDS

DRILL BITS
USE **DRILLS**

DRILL HOLES
USE **BOREHOLES**

DRILL PIPE
RT   DRILL STRING
RT   DRILLING EQUIPMENT
RT   DRILLING FLUIDS
RT   DRILLING RIGS
RT   DRILLS

DRILL STEM
USE **DRILL STRING**

DRILL STRING
UF   drill stem
RT   DRILL PIPE
RT   DRILLING EQUIPMENT
RT   DRILLS
RT   HEAVE COMPENSATORS

DRILLING
SN   Before 1986 search also OFFSHORE
       DRILLING
UF   boring
UF   offshore drilling
NT1   DEEP-SEA DRILLING
RT   BOREHOLES
RT   CORES
RT   CORING
RT   DRILLING EQUIPMENT
RT   DRILLING PLATFORMS
RT   FOSSIL FUELS
RT   HEAVE COMPENSATORS
RT   MARINE GEOLOGY
RT   OFFSHORE OPERATIONS
RT   OIL AND GAS EXPLORATION
RT   OIL SPILLS
RT   OIL WELLS
RT   PERMITS
RT   PRODUCTION PLATFORMS
RT   SEAFLOOR SAMPLING
RT   SEDIMENT SAMPLING
RT   SITE SELECTION
RT   SITE SURVEYS
RT   TEMPLATES
RT   UNDERWATER EXPLORATION
RT   WELL COMPLETION

DRILLING DEVICES
USE **DRILLING EQUIPMENT**

DRILLING EQUIPMENT
SN   Before 1982 search DRILLING DEVICES
UF   drilling devices
BT1   EQUIPMENT
NT1   DRILLING RIGS
RT   CORERS
RT   DRILL PIPE
RT   DRILL STRING
RT   DRILLING
RT   DRILLING FLUIDS
RT   DRILLING PLATFORMS
RT   OFFSHORE ENGINEERING
RT   PRODUCTION PLATFORMS

DRILLING FLUIDS
UF   drilling muds
UF   muds (drilling)
UF   sludge (drilling fluids)
RT   DRILL PIPE
RT   DRILLING EQUIPMENT
RT   FLUIDS

DRILLING MUDS
USE **DRILLING FLUIDS**

DRILLING PLATFORMS
SN   Use with type of offshore structures
BT1   WORK PLATFORMS
BT2   VEHICLES
RT   DRILLING
RT   DRILLING EQUIPMENT
RT   DRILLING RIGS
RT   DRILLING VESSELS
RT   FIXED PLATFORMS
RT   OFFSHORE STRUCTURES
RT   PRODUCTION PLATFORMS

DRILLING RIGS
UF   oil rigs
UF   rigs
BT1   DRILLING EQUIPMENT
BT2   EQUIPMENT
RT   DRILL PIPE
RT   DRILLING PLATFORMS
RT   PRODUCTION PLATFORMS

DRILLING SHIPS
USE **DRILLING VESSELS**

DRILLING VESSELS
UF   drilling ships
BT1   SURFACE CRAFT
BT2   VEHICLES
RT   DEEP-SEA DRILLING
RT   DRILLING PLATFORMS
RT   POSITIONING SYSTEMS
RT   PRODUCTION PLATFORMS
RT   WORK PLATFORMS

DRILLS
UF   drill bits
BT1   SEDIMENT SAMPLERS
BT2   SAMPLERS
RT   DRILL PIPE
RT   DRILL STRING

DROGUES
BT1   SURFACE DRIFTERS
BT2   DRIFTERS
BT3   CURRENT MEASURING EQUIPMENT
BT4   FLOW MEASURING EQUIPMENT
RT   ANCHORS
RT   BUOYS
RT   CURRENT MEASURING EQUIPMENT
RT   LAGRANGIAN CURRENT MEASUREMENT

DROPLETS
UF   drops
UF   rain drops
BT1   HYDROMETEORS
RT   BUBBLE BURSTING
RT   CAPILLARITY
RT   SPRAY

DROPS
USE **DROPLETS**

DROPSONDE
BT1   PROFILERS
RT   VELOCITY PROFILERS

DROPWINDSONDES
USE **RADIOSONDES**

DROUGHT RESISTANCE
SN   Added in 1980
BT1   BIOLOGICAL RESISTANCE
BT2   BIOLOGICAL PROPERTIES
BT3   PROPERTIES
RT   DROUGHTS
RT   ECOPHYSIOLOGY
RT   ENVIRONMENTAL EFFECTS

ASFIS Thesaurus

DROUGHT RESISTANCE (cont'd)
RT	PLANT PHYSIOLOGY
RT	TEMPORARY PONDS

DROUGHTS
SN	Added in 1980
UF	drouths
BT1	HAZARDS
RT	ARID ENVIRONMENTS
RT	CLIMATOLOGY
RT	DISASTERS
RT	DROUGHT RESISTANCE
RT	DRY SEASON
RT	HYDROLOGY
RT	RAIN
RT	RAINFALL
RT	TEMPORARY PONDS
RT	WATER LEVELS
RT	WATER RESOURCES
RT	WEATHER HAZARDS

DROUTHS
USE	**DROUGHTS**

DROWNED VALLEYS
UF	rias
BT1	COASTAL INLETS
BT2	COASTAL WATERS
RT	COASTAL LANDFORMS
RT	FJORDS
RT	RELIEF FORMS
RT	RIA COASTS
RT	SUBMARINE VALLEYS
RT	SUBMERGED SHORELINES
RT	VALLEYS

DROWNING
RT	ACCIDENTS
RT	BATHING
RT	DIVING ACCIDENTS
RT	DIVING HAZARDS
RT	HEALTH AND SAFETY
RT	MORTALITY CAUSES

DRUG RESISTANCE
SN	Added in 1982
UF	resistance to drugs
BT1	BIOLOGICAL RESISTANCE
BT2	BIOLOGICAL PROPERTIES
BT3	PROPERTIES
RT	CONTROL RESISTANCE
RT	DISEASE RESISTANCE
RT	DRUGS
RT	TOXICOLOGY

DRUG TOXICOLOGY
USE	**TOXICOLOGY**

DRUGS
UF	pharmaceutical products
NT1	ANAESTHETICS
NT1	ANTIBIOTICS
NT1	AQUATIC DRUGS
NT1	NARCOTICS
NT1	VACCINES
NT2	BACTERINS
RT	AGENTS
RT	ALKALOIDS
RT	ANAESTHESIA
RT	BACTERIAL DISEASES
RT	BIOASSAYS
RT	CHOLINESTERASE INHIBITORS
RT	COAGULANTS
RT	CONTROL RESISTANCE
RT	DISEASE CONTROL
RT	DRUG RESISTANCE
RT	FUNGAL DISEASES
RT	HORMONES
RT	INHIBITORS
RT	MEDICINE

DRUGS (cont'd)
RT	PHARMACOLOGY
RT	PROTOZOAN DISEASES
RT	STEROIDS
RT	THERAPY
RT	VIRAL DISEASES
RT	VITAMINS

DRY
SN	Used only as a qualifier
RT	WET

DRY BULB TEMPERATURE
USE	**AIR TEMPERATURE**

DRY DIVING
USE	**DEEP-SEA DIVING**

DRY SEASON
BT1	SEASONS
RT	DROUGHTS
RT	RAINY SEASON
RT	TROPICAL ENVIRONMENT
RT	TROPICAL LAKES

DRY WEIGHT
BT1	WEIGHT
BT2	PHYSICAL PROPERTIES
BT3	PROPERTIES
RT	DRYING
RT	SPECIFIC GRAVITY
RT	WET WEIGHT

DRYING
UF	drying of fish
UF	fish drying
BT1	PROCESSING FISHERY PRODUCTS
BT2	FISHERY INDUSTRY
BT3	INDUSTRIES
NT1	FREEZE-DRYING
RT	ADSORPTION
RT	CURING
RT	DEHYDRATION
RT	DESICCATION
RT	DEWATERING
RT	DRIED PRODUCTS
RT	DRY WEIGHT
RT	EVAPORATION
RT	FOOD TECHNOLOGY
RT	SEPARATION
RT	WATER CONTENT

DRYING OF FISH
USE	**DRYING**

DUCTED IMPELLERS
USE	**IMPELLERS**

DUCTED PROPELLERS
USE	**IMPELLERS**

DUCTLESS GLANDS
USE	**ENDOCRINE GLANDS**

DUMPING
USE	**OCEAN DUMPING**

DUMPING GROUNDS
USE	**WASTE DISPOSAL SITES**

DUNE STABILIZATION
RT	BEACH EROSION
RT	COASTAL ZONE MANAGEMENT
RT	DUNES
RT	EROSION CONTROL
RT	VEGETATION COVER

DUNES
UF	coastal dunes
UF	sand dunes (subaerial)
BT1	BEACH FEATURES
RT	BEACHES
RT	BED FORMS
RT	COASTS
RT	DUNE STABILIZATION
RT	EOLIAN TRANSPORT
RT	SAND
RT	SAND WAVES
RT	WIND ABRASION
RT	WIND EROSION

DUNG
USE	**MANURE**

DUNGENESS CRAB FISHERIES
USE	**CRAB FISHERIES**

DURABILITY
USE	**TOUGHNESS**

DURATION
RT	WATER WAVE PARAMETERS
RT	WIND WAVE GENERATION
RT	WIND WAVE PARAMETERS
RT	WINDS

DUST
RT	AEROSOLS
RT	AIR POLLUTION
RT	ATMOSPHERIC CHEMISTRY
RT	ATMOSPHERIC PARTICULATES
RT	DUST CLOUDS
RT	EOLIAN DUST
RT	FALLOUT
RT	HAZE
RT	RADIOACTIVE CONTAMINATION

DUST (ATMOSPHERIC)
USE	**ATMOSPHERIC PARTICULATES**

DUST (COSMIC)
USE	**COSMIC DUST**

DUST (VOLCANIC)
USE	**VOLCANIC ASH**

DUST CLOUDS
UF	dust falls
UF	dust storms
RT	ATMOSPHERIC CHEMISTRY
RT	CLIMATE
RT	CLIMATIC CHANGES
RT	DUST
RT	EOLIAN TRANSPORT
RT	HAZE
RT	VOLCANIC ASH
RT	VOLCANIC ERUPTIONS

DUST FALLS
USE	**DUST CLOUDS**

DUST STORMS
USE	**DUST CLOUDS**

DWARFISM
USE	**SEXUAL DIMORPHISM**

DYE DISPERSION
UF	diffusion (dye patch)
BT1	DISPERSION
RT	DYES
RT	OCEANIC TURBULENCE
RT	RHODAMINE B-DYE
RT	TURBULENT DIFFUSION
RT	WATER CURRENTS

DYES
BT1	TRACERS
NT1	RHODAMINE B-DYE
RT	DYE DISPERSION
RT	PIGMENTS
RT	STAINING

DYNAMIC ANALYSIS
RT	ANALYSIS

DYNAMIC HEIGHT
UF	geopotential
BT1	POTENTIAL ENERGY
BT2	ENERGY
RT	DYNAMIC HEIGHT ANOMALY
RT	DYNAMIC TOPOGRAPHY
RT	HEIGHT
RT	STREAM FUNCTIONS

DYNAMIC HEIGHT ANOMALY
UF	geopotential anomaly
BT1	ANOMALIES
RT	DYNAMIC HEIGHT
RT	ISOBARIC SURFACES
RT	SPECIFIC VOLUME ANOMALIES

DYNAMIC INSTABILITY
USE	**INSTABILITY**

DYNAMIC LOADS
BT1	LOADS (FORCES)
BT2	FORCES (MECHANICS)
RT	CYCLIC LOADING
RT	STRUCTURAL DYNAMICS

DYNAMIC POSITIONING
BT1	POSITIONING SYSTEMS
RT	ACOUSTIC BEACONS
RT	ACOUSTIC NAVIGATION
RT	DEEP-SEA DRILLING
RT	HOLE RE-ENTRY
RT	LOCATING
RT	NAVIGATION
RT	SEMISUBMERSIBLE PLATFORMS
RT	THRUSTERS

DYNAMIC RESPONSE
SN	Used only as a qualifier
BT1	INSTRUMENT RESPONSES
NT1	HEAVE RESPONSE
NT1	PITCH RESPONSE
NT1	ROLL RESPONSE
NT1	SURGE RESPONSE
NT1	YAW RESPONSE
RT	FREQUENCY
RT	HEAVING
RT	PITCHING
RT	RESONANT FREQUENCY
RT	ROLLING
RT	SURGING
RT	YAWING

DYNAMIC TOPOGRAPHY
UF	geopotential topography
BT1	TOPOGRAPHY
RT	DYNAMIC HEIGHT
RT	GEOSTROPHIC FLOW
RT	GEOSTROPHIC METHOD
RT	ISOBARIC SURFACES
RT	STREAMLINES
RT	SURFACE SLOPE
RT	SURFACE TOPOGRAPHY

DYNAMIC VISCOSITY
BT1	VISCOSITY
BT2	MECHANICAL PROPERTIES
BT3	PHYSICAL PROPERTIES
BT4	PROPERTIES
RT	EDDY VISCOSITY
RT	KINEMATIC VISCOSITY

DYNAMIC VISCOSITY (cont'd)
RT	MOLECULAR VISCOSITY COEFFICIENTS
RT	MOMENTUM TRANSFER
RT	SHEAR
RT	SHEAR FLOW
RT	SHEAR STRESS

DYNAMICAL OCEANOGRAPHY
UF	oceanography (dynamic)
BT1	OCEANOGRAPHY
BT2	EARTH SCIENCES
RT	EQUATORIAL DYNAMICS
RT	ESTUARINE DYNAMICS
RT	FLUID MECHANICS
RT	FLUID MOTION
RT	HYDRODYNAMIC EQUATIONS
RT	MARINE GEODESY
RT	NEARSHORE DYNAMICS
RT	OCEAN CURRENTS
RT	OCEAN-ATMOSPHERE SYSTEM
RT	SEICHES
RT	SHELF DYNAMICS
RT	TIDES
RT	WATER WAVE MOTION

DYNAMICS
BT1	MECHANICS
BT2	PHYSICS
NT1	CABLE DYNAMICS
NT1	SEDIMENT DYNAMICS
NT1	STRUCTURAL DYNAMICS

DYSPROSIUM
BT1	CHEMICAL ELEMENTS
RT	DYSPROSIUM COMPOUNDS
RT	DYSPROSIUM ISOTOPES
RT	RARE EARTHS
RT	TRANSITION ELEMENTS

DYSPROSIUM COMPOUNDS
RT	CHEMICAL COMPOUNDS
RT	DYSPROSIUM

DYSPROSIUM ISOTOPES
BT1	ISOTOPES
RT	DYSPROSIUM

DYSTROPHIC LAKES
UF	dystrophic waters
BT1	LAKES
BT2	INLAND WATERS
RT	EUTROPHIC LAKES
RT	HUMIC ACIDS
RT	OLIGOTROPHIC LAKES
RT	STAGNANT WATER

DYSTROPHIC WATERS
USE	**DYSTROPHIC LAKES**

EAGRE
USE	**TIDAL BORES**

EARS
USE	**AUDITORY ORGANS**

EARTH
RT	ATMOSPHERE EVOLUTION
RT	EARTH AGE
RT	EARTH ATMOSPHERE
RT	EARTH CORE
RT	EARTH CRUST
RT	EARTH CURVATURE
RT	EARTH HISTORY
RT	EARTH ORBIT
RT	EARTH ROTATION
RT	EARTH SCIENCES
RT	EARTH STRUCTURE
RT	EARTH TIDES
RT	EARTH TILT
RT	EARTHQUAKES

EARTH (cont'd)
RT	EQUATOR
RT	GEOID
RT	GEOMAGNETISM
RT	GEOPHYSICS
RT	HYDROSPHERE
RT	LITHOSPHERE
RT	SEAWATER EVOLUTION

EARTH (SOIL)
USE	**SOILS**

EARTH AGE
UF	age of earth
BT1	AGE
RT	ABSOLUTE AGE
RT	EARTH
RT	GEOCHRONOMETRY
RT	GEOLOGICAL TIME

EARTH ATMOSPHERE
SN	Before 1982 search also ATMOSPHERE (EARTH)
UF	atmosphere (earth)
UF	terrestrial atmosphere
BT1	PLANETARY ATMOSPHERES
NT1	STRATOSPHERE
NT1	TROPOPAUSE
NT1	TROPOSPHERE
NT1	UPPER ATMOSPHERE
NT2	IONOSPHERE
RT	AIR
RT	ATMOSPHERE EVOLUTION
RT	ATMOSPHERIC CHEMISTRY
RT	ATMOSPHERIC MOTION
RT	ATMOSPHERIC PHYSICS
RT	ATMOSPHERIC PRESSURE
RT	ATMOSPHERIC SCIENCES
RT	DEGASSING
RT	EARTH
RT	GREENHOUSE EFFECT
RT	HEAT BUDGET
RT	HYGROMETRY
RT	METEOROLOGY
RT	OCEAN-ATMOSPHERE SYSTEM
RT	OZONE

EARTH CORE
UF	core (earth)
BT1	EARTH STRUCTURE
RT	EARTH
RT	EARTH MANTLE
RT	MESOSPHERE (EARTH)

EARTH CRUST
UF	crust (earth)
BT1	EARTH STRUCTURE
NT1	CONTINENTAL CRUST
NT1	OCEANIC CRUST
NT1	SIAL
NT1	SIMA
RT	BASEMENT ROCK
RT	CRUSTAL SHORTENING
RT	CRUSTAL STRUCTURE
RT	CRUSTAL THICKNESS
RT	EARTH
RT	EARTH MANTLE
RT	EPEIROGENY
RT	ISOSTASY
RT	LITHOSPHERE
RT	TECTONOPHYSICS

EARTH CURRENTS
USE	**TELLURIC CURRENTS**

EARTH CURVATURE
RT	EARTH

EARTH HISTORY
RT   ATMOSPHERE EVOLUTION
RT   EARTH
RT   SEDIMENT CHEMISTRY

EARTH MAGNETIC FIELD
USE   **GEOMAGNETIC FIELD**

EARTH MAGNETISM
USE   **GEOMAGNETISM**

EARTH MANTLE
SN   Before 1986 search also MANTLE
UF   mantle (earth)
BT1   EARTH STRUCTURE
NT1   LOWER MANTLE
NT1   UPPER MANTLE
RT   CONTINENTAL DRIFT
RT   DEGASSING
RT   EARTH CORE
RT   EARTH CRUST
RT   MANTLE CONVECTION
RT   MOHO
RT   PERIDOTITE

EARTH MEASUREMENT
USE   **GEODESY**

EARTH ORBIT
RT   ASTRONOMY
RT   EARTH

EARTH REMOTE SENSING
USE   **GEOSENSING**

EARTH ROTATION
BT1   ROTATION
RT   CHANDLER WOBBLE
RT   CLIMATIC CHANGES
RT   EARTH
RT   MOTION
RT   POLAR WANDERING
RT   TIDAL FRICTION
RT   VORTICITY

EARTH SCIENCES
NT1   GEOLOGY
NT2   GEOMORPHOLOGY
NT3   COASTAL MORPHOLOGY
NT4   BEACH MORPHOLOGY
NT3   FLUVIAL MORPHOLOGY
NT3   LAKE MORPHOLOGY
NT2   HYDROLOGY
NT2   LITHOLOGY
NT2   MARINE GEOLOGY
NT3   SHELF GEOLOGY
NT2   PETROGENESIS
NT2   PETROLEUM GEOLOGY
NT2   PETROLOGY
NT2   SEDIMENTOLOGY
NT2   STRATIGRAPHY
NT3   BIOSTRATIGRAPHY
NT3   CHRONOSTRATIGRAPHY
NT3   MAGNETOSTRATIGRAPHY
NT3   OXYGEN ISOTOPE STRATIGRAPHY
NT3   SEISMIC STRATIGRAPHY
NT2   STRUCTURAL GEOLOGY
NT2   TECTONICS
NT3   CRUSTAL ADJUSTMENT
NT4   ISOSTASY
NT3   EPEIROGENY
NT4   SUBSIDENCE
NT4   UPLIFT
NT3   OROGENY
NT3   PLATE TECTONICS
NT3   VERTICAL TECTONICS
NT1   GEOPHYSICS
NT2   GEODESY
NT3   COASTAL GEODESY
NT3   MARINE GEODESY

EARTH SCIENCES (cont'd)
NT2   GEOMAGNETISM
NT2   PALAEOMAGNETISM
NT2   SEISMOLOGY
NT2   TECTONOPHYSICS
NT1   OCEANOGRAPHY
NT2   CHEMICAL OCEANOGRAPHY
NT2   COASTAL OCEANOGRAPHY
NT2   DYNAMICAL OCEANOGRAPHY
NT2   FISHERY OCEANOGRAPHY
NT2   MILITARY OCEANOGRAPHY
NT2   PALAEOCEANOGRAPHY
NT2   PHYSICAL OCEANOGRAPHY
NT3   HYDROGRAPHY
NT2   POLAR OCEANOGRAPHY
NT2   RADIO OCEANOGRAPHY
NT2   TROPICAL OCEANOGRAPHY
RT   AQUATIC SCIENCES
RT   ATMOSPHERIC SCIENCES
RT   CLIMATOLOGY
RT   EARTH
RT   GEOCHEMISTRY

EARTH STRUCTURE
NT1   ASEISMIC ZONES
NT1   ASTHENOSPHERE
NT1   BASEMENT ROCK
NT1   BENIOFF ZONE
NT1   EARTH CORE
NT1   EARTH CRUST
NT2   CONTINENTAL CRUST
NT2   OCEANIC CRUST
NT2   SIAL
NT2   SIMA
NT1   EARTH MANTLE
NT2   LOWER MANTLE
NT2   UPPER MANTLE
NT1   LITHOSPHERE
NT1   MESOSPHERE (EARTH)
NT1   PLATES
NT1   SEISMIC LAYERS
NT2   LOW-VELOCITY LAYER
NT1   SEISMIC ZONES
RT   CONTINENTS
RT   EARTH
RT   MOHO
RT   OCEAN BASINS

EARTH TIDES
UF   tides (earth)
BT1   TIDAL MOTION
RT   ATMOSPHERIC TIDES
RT   EARTH
RT   GEODESY
RT   OCEAN LOADING
RT   TIDES
RT   TILTMETERS

EARTH TILT
RT   EARTH

EARTH WAVES
USE   **SEISMIC WAVES**

EARTHQUAKE LOADING
BT1   LOADS (FORCES)
BT2   FORCES (MECHANICS)
RT   EARTHQUAKES
RT   GROUND MOTION
RT   OFFSHORE STRUCTURES
RT   SEISMIC ACTIVITY

EARTHQUAKE PREDICTION
BT1   PREDICTION
RT   EARTHQUAKES
RT   WARNING SERVICES

EARTHQUAKE WAVES
USE   **SEISMIC WAVES**

EARTHQUAKES
UF   seismic events
NT1   MICROEARTHQUAKES
RT   ACTIVE MARGINS
RT   DISASTERS
RT   EARTH
RT   EARTHQUAKE LOADING
RT   EARTHQUAKE PREDICTION
RT   EPICENTRES
RT   GEOLOGICAL HAZARDS
RT   GROUND MOTION
RT   RICHTER SCALE
RT   SEAQUAKES
RT   SEISMIC ACTIVITY
RT   SEISMOLOGY
RT   SLUMPING
RT   TSUNAMI GENERATION
RT   TSUNAMIS
RT   TURBIDITY CURRENTS

EASTERLY WAVES
RT   EQUATORIAL EASTERLIES
RT   EQUATORIAL TROUGH
RT   TROPICAL DEPRESSIONS
RT   TROPICAL METEOROLOGY

EASTERN BOUNDARY CURRENTS
BT1   BOUNDARY CURRENTS
BT2   WATER CURRENTS
BT3   WATER MOTION
RT   COASTAL UPWELLING
RT   EKMAN TRANSPORT
RT   OCEAN CURRENTS
RT   TIDAL CYCLES

EBB CURRENTS
BT1   TIDAL CURRENTS
BT2   WATER CURRENTS
BT3   WATER MOTION
RT   LOW TIDE
RT   TIDAL CYCLES

ECDYSIS
USE   **MOULTING**

ECDYSONES
USE   **ECDYSONS**

ECDYSONS
SN   Before 1982 search HORMONES
UF   ecdysones
UF   moulting hormones
BT1   HORMONES
BT2   SECRETORY PRODUCTS
RT   AQUATIC INSECTS
RT   FRESHWATER CRUSTACEANS
RT   MARINE CRUSTACEANS
RT   MOULTING

ECHINODERM FISHERIES
SN   Added in 1982
UF   sea cucumber fisheries
UF   sea urchin fisheries
BT1   SHELLFISH FISHERIES
BT2   FISHERIES
RT   COASTAL FISHERIES
RT   MARINE FISHERIES

ECHO COUNTING SYSTEMS
USE   **FISH COUNTERS**

ECHO INTEGRATION
USE   **ECHO INTEGRATORS**

ECHO INTEGRATORS
UF	echo integration
RT	ACOUSTIC EQUIPMENT
RT	ECHOES
RT	FISH COUNTERS
RT	SONAR DETECTION

ECHO RANGING
UF	acoustic direction finding
UF	acoustic distance measurement
UF	sound ranging
RT	ACOUSTIC TRACKING SYSTEMS
RT	ACTIVE SONAR
RT	DETECTION
RT	DIRECTION
RT	ECHOES
RT	ECHOLOCATION
RT	SONAR DETECTION

ECHO SURVEYS
UF	acoustic surveys
BT1	SURVEYS
RT	ACOUSTIC EQUIPMENT
RT	ACOUSTICS
RT	ACTIVE SONAR
RT	ECHOES
RT	ECHOSOUNDERS
RT	ECHOSOUNDING
RT	EXPLORATORY FISHING
RT	FISH COUNTERS
RT	FISH SIZING
RT	FISHERY SURVEYS
RT	SONAR
RT	SOUND RECORDERS
RT	STOCK ASSESSMENT
RT	TRACKING

ECHOES
RT	ACOUSTICS
RT	ECHO INTEGRATORS
RT	ECHO RANGING
RT	ECHO SURVEYS
RT	ECHOLOCATION
RT	ECHOSOUNDER PROFILES
RT	ECHOSOUNDERS
RT	ECHOSOUNDING

ECHOLOCATION
SN	Added in 1980
RT	AQUATIC MAMMALS
RT	AUDITORY ORGANS
RT	BEHAVIOUR
RT	CETOLOGY
RT	ECHO RANGING
RT	ECHOES
RT	SONAR DETECTION
RT	SOUND PRODUCTION

ECHOSOUNDER PROFILES
BT1	ANALOG RECORDS
BT2	GRAPHICS
BT3	AUDIOVISUAL MATERIAL
BT4	DOCUMENTS
RT	BATHYMETRIC PROFILES
RT	ECHOES
RT	GEOLOGICAL SECTIONS
RT	VERTICAL SECTIONS

ECHOSOUNDERS
UF	precision depth recorders
UF	precision echosounders
BT1	ACTIVE SONAR
BT2	SONAR
BT3	REMOTE SENSING EQUIPMENT
BT4	EQUIPMENT
RT	ECHO SURVEYS
RT	ECHOES
RT	ECHOSOUNDING
RT	FISH COUNTERS
RT	FISH DETECTION

ECHOSOUNDERS (cont'd)
RT	FISHING OPERATIONS
RT	WAVE MEASURING EQUIPMENT

ECHOSOUNDING
SN	For detection of organisms and abundance estimation, depth and bottom structure
UF	depth finding
RT	ACOUSTIC EQUIPMENT
RT	BATHYMETRIC CHARTS
RT	BATHYMETRY
RT	BOTTOM TOPOGRAPHY
RT	ECHO SURVEYS
RT	ECHOES
RT	ECHOSOUNDERS
RT	FISHERY ENGINEERING
RT	FISHING OPERATIONS
RT	REMOTE SENSING
RT	SCATTERING LAYERS
RT	SEAFLOOR MAPPING
RT	SOUND RECORDERS
RT	SOUND WAVES
RT	SUB-BOTTOM PROFILING

ECLIPSE (SOLAR)
USE	**SOLAR ECLIPSE**

ECOCLINES
SN	Added in 1980
BT1	CLINES
RT	ECOLOGICAL DISTRIBUTION
RT	ECOLOGICAL ZONATION
RT	THERMOCLINE

ECOLOGICAL AGGREGATIONS
SN	Added in 1980
UF	aggregations (ecological)
RT	ENVIRONMENTAL EFFECTS
RT	SOCIAL BEHAVIOUR
RT	STIMULI

ECOLOGICAL ASSOCIATIONS
SN	A characteristic association of animals and/or plants belonging to a particular habitat. Before 1982 search ASSOCIATIONS (ECOLOGICAL)
UF	animal associations
UF	associations (animal)
UF	associations (ecological)
UF	organism associations
RT	AQUATIC COMMUNITIES
RT	BIOCOENOSIS
RT	BIOTOPES
RT	CLIMAX COMMUNITY
RT	COLONIES
RT	DOMINANT SPECIES
RT	ECOLOGICAL SUCCESSION
RT	FOSSIL ASSEMBLAGES
RT	HABITAT
RT	SYNECOLOGY

ECOLOGICAL BALANCE
SN	The state of dynamic equilibrium of a biotic community or ecosystem. Added in 1980
UF	balance (ecological)
UF	balance of nature
UF	biological balance
UF	biological equilibrium
UF	ecosystem stability
UF	stability (ecological)
RT	ECOLOGICAL CRISIS
RT	ECOLOGY
RT	ECOSYSTEMS
RT	ENVIRONMENT MANAGEMENT
RT	ENVIRONMENTAL LEGISLATION

ECOLOGICAL BALANCE DISRUPTION
USE	**ECOLOGICAL CRISIS**

ECOLOGICAL BASELINE STUDIES
USE	**BASELINE STUDIES**

ECOLOGICAL CRISIS
SN	Added in 1980
UF	ecological balance disruption
RT	ECOLOGICAL BALANCE
RT	ECOLOGY
RT	ENVIRONMENTAL EFFECTS
RT	POLLUTION

ECOLOGICAL DISTRIBUTION
BT1	DISTRIBUTION
RT	BIOGEOGRAPHY
RT	BIOLOGICAL RHYTHMS
RT	ECOCLINES
RT	ECOLOGICAL ZONATION
RT	ECOLOGY
RT	ECOSYSTEMS
RT	ENDEMIC SPECIES
RT	ENVIRONMENTAL EFFECTS
RT	EURYHALINITY
RT	EURYTHERMY
RT	GEOGRAPHICAL DISTRIBUTION
RT	LIMITING FACTORS
RT	MIGRATIONS
RT	RELICT SPECIES
RT	STENOHALINITY
RT	STENOTHERMY

ECOLOGICAL DIVERSITY
USE	**SPECIES DIVERSITY**

ECOLOGICAL EFFICIENCY
SN	Ratio of production to food ingestion. Added in 1980
UF	efficiency (ecological)
RT	ENERGY BUDGET
RT	FOOD CONSUMPTION
RT	NUTRITIONAL REQUIREMENTS
RT	STOMACH CONTENT

ECOLOGICAL NICHES
USE	**NICHES**

ECOLOGICAL PHYSIOLOGY
USE	**ECOPHYSIOLOGY**

ECOLOGICAL SCIENCES
USE	**ECOLOGY**

ECOLOGICAL SUCCESSION
SN	Before 1982 search SUCCESSION (ECOLOGICAL)
UF	succession (ecological)
RT	AQUATIC COMMUNITIES
RT	CLIMAX COMMUNITY
RT	COMMUNITY COMPOSITION
RT	DOMINANT SPECIES
RT	ECOLOGICAL ASSOCIATIONS
RT	HABITAT
RT	MULTISPECIES FISHERIES
RT	SPECIES DIVERSITY

ECOLOGICAL ZONATION
UF	intertidal zonation
UF	littoral zonation
UF	zonation (ecological)
RT	BENTHOS
RT	ECOCLINES
RT	ECOLOGICAL DISTRIBUTION
RT	EXPOSED HABITATS
RT	INTERTIDAL ENVIRONMENT
RT	LITTORAL ZONE
RT	PHYTOBENTHOS
RT	SHELTERED HABITATS
RT	SUBSTRATA

ECOLOGICAL ZONATION (cont'd)
RT	TIDES
RT	VERTICAL DISTRIBUTION
RT	ZOOBENTHOS

ECOLOGISTS
SN	Added in 1980
BT1	SCIENTIFIC PERSONNEL
BT2	PERSONNEL
NT1	FRESHWATER ECOLOGISTS
NT1	MARINE ECOLOGISTS
RT	DIRECTORIES
RT	ECOLOGY
RT	PLANKTONOLOGY
RT	SYNECOLOGY

ECOLOGY
UF	aquatic ecology
UF	bionomics
UF	ecological sciences
NT1	AUTECOLOGY
NT1	BRACKISHWATER ECOLOGY
NT1	ETHOLOGY
NT1	FRESHWATER ECOLOGY
NT1	GENECOLOGY
NT1	MARINE ECOLOGY
NT1	PALAEOECOLOGY
NT1	PARASITOLOGY
NT1	PHYTOSOCIOLOGY
NT1	PLANKTONOLOGY
NT1	RADIOECOLOGY
NT1	SYNECOLOGY
RT	BASELINE STUDIES
RT	BEHAVIOUR
RT	BIOFACIES
RT	BIOGEOGRAPHY
RT	BIOLOGY
RT	BIOTELEMETRY
RT	BOTANY
RT	ECOLOGICAL BALANCE
RT	ECOLOGICAL CRISIS
RT	ECOLOGICAL DISTRIBUTION
RT	ECOLOGISTS
RT	ECOPHYSIOLOGY
RT	ECOSYSTEMS
RT	ENVIRONMENT MANAGEMENT
RT	ENVIRONMENTAL CONDITIONS
RT	FISHERY BIOLOGY
RT	ORGANISM AGGREGATIONS
RT	PHENOLOGY
RT	PHOTOPERIODICITY
RT	SPECIES
RT	ZOOLOGY

ECONOMETRIC MODELS
USE	**ECONOMIC MODELS**

ECONOMETRICS
SN	Statistical analysis of economic data with the aid of electronic computers. Added in 1982
BT1	ECONOMICS
RT	ECONOMIC ANALYSIS
RT	LINEAR PROGRAMMING

ECONOMIC ANALYSIS
UF	economic evaluations
RT	ANALYSIS
RT	CONSUMERS
RT	COST ANALYSIS
RT	ECONOMETRICS
RT	ECONOMIC MODELS
RT	FINANCING
RT	FISHERY ECONOMICS
RT	MARKET RESEARCH
RT	MARKETING
RT	MATHEMATICAL MODELS
RT	PRICING
RT	STATISTICAL ANALYSIS

ECONOMIC EVALUATIONS
USE	**ECONOMIC ANALYSIS**

ECONOMIC FEASIBILITY
SN	Before 1982 search FEASIBILITY
UF	feasibility (economics)
BT1	FEASIBILITY
RT	AQUACULTURE ECONOMICS
RT	CAPTURE FISHERY ECONOMICS
RT	COST ANALYSIS
RT	COSTS
RT	ECONOMICS
RT	FEASIBILITY STUDIES
RT	FINANCIAL INSTITUTIONS
RT	FINANCIAL MANAGEMENT
RT	FINANCING
RT	FISHERY ECONOMICS
RT	MARGINAL FIELDS
RT	SITE SELECTION

ECONOMIC MODELS
UF	econometric models
BT1	MATHEMATICAL MODELS
BT2	MODELS
RT	AQUACULTURE ECONOMICS
RT	CAPTURE FISHERY ECONOMICS
RT	ECONOMIC ANALYSIS
RT	ECONOMICS
RT	FISHERY ECONOMICS
RT	LINEAR PROGRAMMING
RT	OPERATIONS RESEARCH

ECONOMIC RESOURCES
USE	**RESOURCES**

ECONOMIC SPECIES
USE	**COMMERCIAL SPECIES**

ECONOMICS
NT1	ECONOMETRICS
NT1	FISHERY ECONOMICS
NT2	AQUACULTURE ECONOMICS
NT2	CAPTURE FISHERY ECONOMICS
RT	BILATERAL AGREEMENTS
RT	COMMERCE
RT	CONSERVATION
RT	COST ANALYSIS
RT	COSTS
RT	ECONOMIC FEASIBILITY
RT	ECONOMIC MODELS
RT	ECONOMISTS
RT	EVALUATION
RT	FEASIBILITY
RT	FEASIBILITY STUDIES
RT	FINANCING
RT	GOVERNMENTS
RT	JOINT VENTURES
RT	MANAGEMENT
RT	MARKET RESEARCH
RT	MARKETING
RT	NATURAL RESOURCES
RT	PLANNING
RT	POLITICAL ASPECTS
RT	PRICING
RT	RECLAMATION
RT	RESOURCE DEVELOPMENT
RT	RESOURCE MANAGEMENT
RT	RISKS
RT	SOCIOLOGICAL ASPECTS
RT	TRADE
RT	WORLD

ECONOMISTS
SN	Added in 1980
BT1	SCIENTIFIC PERSONNEL
BT2	PERSONNEL
RT	DIRECTORIES
RT	ECONOMICS
RT	FISHERY ECONOMICS
RT	MANAGEMENT

ECOPHENE
SN	A type of individual developing as a result of a physiological, as opposed to genetic, response to habitat factors. Added in 1980
RT	ECOPHYSIOLOGY
RT	PHENOTYPES

ECOPHYSIOLOGY
SN	Added in 1980
UF	ecological physiology
UF	physiological ecology
BT1	PHYSIOLOGY
BT2	BIOLOGY
RT	AESTIVATION
RT	BIOLOGICAL RESISTANCE
RT	COLD RESISTANCE
RT	DISEASE RESISTANCE
RT	DROUGHT RESISTANCE
RT	ECOLOGY
RT	ECOPHENE
RT	ENVIRONMENTAL EFFECTS
RT	PHOTOPERIODS
RT	SURVIVAL
RT	TOLERANCE

ECOSYSTEM DISTURBANCE
SN	Added in 1982
UF	disturbance (ecosystem)
RT	AQUATIC COMMUNITIES
RT	DREDGING
RT	ECOSYSTEMS

ECOSYSTEM MANAGEMENT
SN	Management of aquatic ecosystems. Added in 1980
BT1	MANAGEMENT
NT1	ENVIRONMENT MANAGEMENT
RT	AQUATIC COMMUNITIES
RT	ECOSYSTEMS
RT	NATURAL POPULATIONS
RT	NATURAL RESOURCES

ECOSYSTEM RESILIENCE
SN	Added in 1982
UF	resilience (ecosystem)
RT	AQUATIC COMMUNITIES
RT	COLONIZATION
RT	ECOSYSTEMS

ECOSYSTEM STABILITY
USE	**ECOLOGICAL BALANCE**

ECOSYSTEMS
RT	AQUATIC COMMUNITIES
RT	AQUATIC ENVIRONMENT
RT	BIOENERGETICS
RT	BIOLOGICAL PRODUCTION
RT	ECOLOGICAL BALANCE
RT	ECOLOGICAL DISTRIBUTION
RT	ECOLOGY
RT	ECOSYSTEM DISTURBANCE
RT	ECOSYSTEM MANAGEMENT
RT	ECOSYSTEM RESILIENCE
RT	ENERGY FLOW
RT	FOOD CHAINS
RT	FOOD WEBS
RT	NICHES
RT	POLLUTION EFFECTS
RT	TROPHIC LEVELS
RT	TROPHIC STRUCTURE

ECOTYPES
SN	A biotype resulting from selection in a particular habitat. Added in 1980
UF	habitat types
RT	ADAPTATIONS
RT	BIOLOGICAL SPECIATION

ECOTYPES (cont'd)
RT   HABITAT
RT   TYPOLOGY

ECTOCRINES
RT   BEHAVIOUR
RT   HORMONES
RT   METABOLITES

ECTODERM
USE   **SKIN**

ECTOPARASITES
BT1   PARASITES
RT   ECTOPARASITISM
RT   EPIZOITES
RT   LAMPREY ATTACHMENT
RT   LESIONS

ECTOPARASITISM
BT1   PARASITISM
BT2   INTERSPECIFIC RELATIONSHIPS
RT   ECTOPARASITES

ECTOSYMBIONTS
USE   **SYMBIONTS**

EDDIES (LEE)
USE   **LEE EDDIES**

EDDIES (OCEANIC)
USE   **OCEANIC EDDIES**

EDDY COEFFICIENTS
USE   **EXCHANGE COEFFICIENTS**

EDDY CONDUCTION
UF   eddy heat conduction
UF   eddy heat flux
UF   turbulent heat transfer
BT1   HEAT TRANSFER
RT   EDDY CONDUCTIVITY
RT   HEAT CONDUCTION
RT   TURBULENT DIFFUSION

EDDY CONDUCTION COEFFICIENT
USE   **EDDY CONDUCTIVITY**

EDDY CONDUCTIVITY
UF   eddy conduction coefficient
BT1   EDDY DIFFUSIVITY
RT   EDDY CONDUCTION
RT   THERMAL CONDUCTIVITY
RT   TURBULENCE

EDDY DIFFUSION
USE   **TURBULENT DIFFUSION**

EDDY DIFFUSION COEFFICIENT
USE   **EDDY DIFFUSIVITY**

EDDY DIFFUSIVITY
UF   eddy diffusion coefficient
NT1   EDDY CONDUCTIVITY
RT   DIFFUSION COEFFICIENTS
RT   THERMAL DIFFUSIVITY
RT   TURBULENCE
RT   TURBULENT DIFFUSION

EDDY FLUX
UF   turbulent exchange
RT   EXCHANGE COEFFICIENTS
RT   MIXING LENGTH

EDDY HEAT CONDUCTION
USE   **EDDY CONDUCTION**

EDDY HEAT FLUX
USE   **EDDY CONDUCTION**

EDDY KINETIC ENERGY
UF   turbulent energy
BT1   KINETIC ENERGY
BT2   ENERGY
RT   MESOSCALE EDDIES

EDDY STRESSES
USE   **REYNOLDS STRESSES**

EDDY VISCOSITY
BT1   VISCOSITY
BT2   MECHANICAL PROPERTIES
BT3   PHYSICAL PROPERTIES
BT4   PROPERTIES
RT   DYNAMIC VISCOSITY
RT   EDDY VISCOSITY COEFFICIENT
RT   EXCHANGE COEFFICIENTS
RT   KINEMATIC VISCOSITY
RT   MIXING LENGTH
RT   MOMENTUM TRANSFER
RT   REYNOLDS STRESSES
RT   TURBULENCE
RT   TURBULENT DIFFUSION
RT   TURBULENT FLOW
RT   VISCOSITY COEFFICIENTS

EDDY VISCOSITY COEFFICIENT
UF   coefficient of eddy viscosity
BT1   VISCOSITY COEFFICIENTS
BT2   EXCHANGE COEFFICIENTS
RT   EDDY VISCOSITY

EDGE WAVES
BT1   TRAPPED WAVES
BT2   WATER WAVES
RT   BEACH CUSPS
RT   NONLINEAR WAVES
RT   RIP CURRENTS
RT   TSUNAMIS
RT   WAVES ON BEACHES

EDIBLE CRAB FISHERIES
USE   **CRAB FISHERIES**

EDIBLE FISH
USE   **FOOD FISH**

EDUCATION
UF   teaching
RT   AUDIOVISUAL MATERIAL
RT   CAREERS
RT   CURRICULA
RT   DEVELOPING COUNTRIES
RT   EDUCATION ESTABLISHMENTS
RT   FELLOWSHIPS
RT   FISHERY INSTITUTIONS
RT   GEAR HANDLING
RT   PERSONNEL
RT   RESEARCH INSTITUTIONS
RT   SEAMANSHIP
RT   SOCIOLOGICAL ASPECTS
RT   TRAINING
RT   TRAINING AIDS
RT   TRAINING CENTRES

EDUCATION ESTABLISHMENTS
UF   schools
UF   universities
BT1   ORGANIZATIONS
RT   CURRICULA
RT   EDUCATION
RT   RESEARCH PROGRAMMES
RT   TRAINING CENTRES

EEZ
USE   **EXCLUSIVE ECONOMIC ZONE**

EFFERENT NERVES
USE   **NERVES**

EFFICIENCY
SN   Descriptor to be used only as a qualifier
RT   CALIBRATION
RT   EQUIPMENT
RT   INSTRUMENTS
RT   PERFORMANCE ASSESSMENT

EFFICIENCY (ECOLOGICAL)
USE   **ECOLOGICAL EFFICIENCY**

EFFLUENTS
USE   **WASTES**

EFFLUENTS (AQUACULTURE)
USE   **AQUACULTURE EFFLUENTS**

EGG COUNTERS
BT1   COUNTERS
RT   EGGS
RT   FECUNDITY

EGGS
UF   ova
BT1   SEXUAL CELLS
BT2   CELLS
NT1   BIRD EGGS
NT1   BRINE SHRIMP EGGS
NT1   FISH EGGS
NT1   INSECT EGGS
NT1   RESTING EGGS
RT   DEVELOPMENTAL STAGES
RT   EGG COUNTERS
RT   EMBRYOLOGY
RT   EMBRYONIC DEVELOPMENT
RT   EMBRYOS
RT   FECUNDITY
RT   FEMALES
RT   HATCHING
RT   INCUBATION
RT   OOGENESIS
RT   OVARIES
RT   OVIPARITY
RT   OVOVIVIPARITY
RT   OVULATION
RT   VITELLOGENESIS
RT   YOLK

EH
USE   **REDOX POTENTIAL**

EIGENFUNCTIONS
SN   Solutions of differential equations satisfying specific conditions. Used only as a qualifier
RT   DIFFERENTIAL EQUATIONS
RT   MATHEMATICS

EINSTEINIUM
BT1   CHEMICAL ELEMENTS
RT   EINSTEINIUM COMPOUNDS
RT   EINSTEINIUM ISOTOPES
RT   TRANSURANIC ELEMENTS

EINSTEINIUM COMPOUNDS
RT   CHEMICAL COMPOUNDS
RT   EINSTEINIUM

EINSTEINIUM ISOTOPES
BT1   ISOTOPES
RT   EINSTEINIUM

ASFIS Thesaurus

EKMAN BOUNDARY LAYERS
USE **EKMAN LAYERS**

EKMAN CIRCULATION
USE **EKMAN TRANSPORT**

EKMAN CURRENT
USE **EKMAN TRANSPORT**

EKMAN LAYERS
UF   ekman boundary layers
BT1   BOUNDARY LAYERS
BT2   LAYERS
NT1   BOTTOM EKMAN LAYER
NT1   SURFACE EKMAN LAYER
RT   EKMAN SPIRAL
RT   LAYERS
RT   VERTICAL SHEAR

EKMAN PUMPING
UF   ekman suction
RT   UPWELLING

EKMAN SPIRAL
BT1   HODOGRAPHS
BT2   GRAPHS
BT3   GRAPHICS
BT4   AUDIOVISUAL MATERIAL
RT   CORIOLIS PARAMETERS
RT   EKMAN LAYERS
RT   WIND-DRIVEN CURRENTS

EKMAN SUCTION
USE **EKMAN PUMPING**

EKMAN TRANSPORT
UF   ekman circulation
UF   ekman current
RT   COASTAL UPWELLING
RT   EASTERN BOUNDARY CURRENTS
RT   EL NINO PHENOMENA
RT   EQUATORIAL UPWELLING
RT   TRANSPORT
RT   UPWELLING

EL NINO PHENOMENA
RT   COASTAL UPWELLING
RT   DISASTERS
RT   EKMAN TRANSPORT
RT   SOUTHERN OSCILLATION
RT   TELECONNECTIONS

ELASTIC CONSTANTS
NT1   BULK MODULUS
NT1   SHEAR MODULUS
RT   CONSTANTS
RT   ELASTICITY
RT   MECHANICAL PROPERTIES
RT   POISSON'S RATIO
RT   SOIL MECHANICS

ELASTIC WAVES
UF   pressure waves
NT1   SEISMIC WAVES
NT2   BODY WAVES
NT3   P-WAVES
NT3   S-WAVES
NT2   MICROSEISMS
NT2   SURFACE SEISMIC WAVES
NT3   LOVE WAVES
NT3   RAYLEIGH WAVES
NT3   STONELEY WAVES
NT1   SOUND WAVES
RT   SOUND
RT   VIBRATION

ELASTICITY
BT1   MECHANICAL PROPERTIES
BT2   PHYSICAL PROPERTIES
BT3   PROPERTIES
RT   ANELASTICITY
RT   BULK MODULUS
RT   COMPRESSIBILITY
RT   DEFORMATION
RT   ELASTIC CONSTANTS
RT   FLEXIBILITY
RT   PLASTICITY
RT   POISSON'S RATIO
RT   ROCK MECHANICS
RT   SHEAR MODULUS
RT   SOIL MECHANICS
RT   STRAIN
RT   STRESS
RT   TENSILE STRENGTH

ELECTRIC ARC WELDING
BT1   WELDING
RT   ELECTRODES

ELECTRIC BATTERIES
USE **BATTERIES**

ELECTRIC CABLES
BT1   CABLES
NT1   COAXIAL CABLES
NT1   POWER CABLES
NT1   SUBMARINE CABLES
RT   CONNECTORS
RT   ELECTRICAL EQUIPMENT
RT   UMBILICALS

ELECTRIC CHARGE
BT1   ELECTRICITY
RT   BUBBLE BURSTING
RT   CAPACITANCE
RT   ELECTRICAL PROPERTIES

ELECTRIC CURRENTS
UF   currents (electric)
NT1   IMPRESSED CURRENTS
NT1   TELLURIC CURRENTS
RT   AIR-WATER EXCHANGES
RT   CURRENT DENSITY
RT   ELECTRIC FIELDS
RT   ELECTRICITY

ELECTRIC FENCES
BT1   GUIDING DEVICES
RT   ELECTRIC FISHING
RT   ELECTRIC STIMULI
RT   ELECTRIFIED GEAR

ELECTRIC FIELDS
RT   ELECTRIC CURRENTS
RT   ELECTRIC POTENTIAL
RT   ELECTRICAL CONDUCTIVITY
RT   ELECTROMAGNETIC RADIATION
RT   FIELDS

ELECTRIC FISHING
UF   electro-fishing
BT1   CATCHING METHODS
RT   ATTRACTING TECHNIQUES
RT   AUTOMATED FISHING PLATFORMS
RT   ELECTRIC FENCES
RT   ELECTRIC STIMULI
RT   ELECTRIFIED GEAR
RT   FISHING
RT   PUMP FISHING
RT   STUPEFYING METHODS

ELECTRIC GENERATORS
UF   generators
BT1   ELECTRIC POWER SOURCES
RT   ELECTRICAL EQUIPMENT
RT   MOTORS

ELECTRIC IMPEDANCE
UF   impedance (electrical)
BT1   ELECTRICAL PROPERTIES
BT2   PHYSICAL PROPERTIES
BT3   PROPERTIES
RT   CAPACITANCE
RT   ELECTRICAL CONDUCTIVITY
RT   ELECTRICAL RESISTIVITY
RT   IMPEDANCE

ELECTRIC ORGANS
UF   electroreceptors
RT   BIOELECTRICITY
RT   ELECTRIC STIMULI
RT   STINGING ORGANS

ELECTRIC POTENTIAL
UF   electric potential difference
RT   CURRENT VELOCITY
RT   ELECTRIC FIELDS
RT   ELECTRICAL PROPERTIES
RT   ELECTRODES
RT   ELECTROMAGNETISM
RT   GEK
RT   SUBMARINE CABLES

ELECTRIC POTENTIAL DIFFERENCE
USE **ELECTRIC POTENTIAL**

ELECTRIC POWER PLANTS
USE **POWER PLANTS**

ELECTRIC POWER SOURCES
UF   power supplies
UF   power systems
NT1   BATTERIES
NT1   ELECTRIC GENERATORS
NT1   SOLAR CELLS
NT1   WAVE POWER DEVICES
RT   ELECTRICITY
RT   MOTORS
RT   OTEC PLANTS
RT   POWER CABLES
RT   POWER CONSUMPTION
RT   POWER PLANTS

ELECTRIC SHOCKING GEAR
USE **ELECTRIFIED GEAR**

ELECTRIC STIMULI
BT1   STIMULI
RT   ATTRACTING TECHNIQUES
RT   ELECTRIC FENCES
RT   ELECTRIC FISHING
RT   ELECTRIC ORGANS
RT   ELECTROPHYSIOLOGY
RT   RISER CABLES

ELECTRICAL CONDUCTANCE
USE **ELECTRICAL CONDUCTIVITY**

ELECTRICAL CONDUCTIVITY
SN   Before 1982 search also ELECTRICAL
        CONDUCTANCE
UF   conductance (electrical)
UF   conductivity (electrical)
UF   electrical conductance
BT1   ELECTRICAL PROPERTIES
BT2   PHYSICAL PROPERTIES
BT3   PROPERTIES
RT   CONDUCTIVITY RATIO
RT   CONDUCTIVITY SENSORS
RT   CTD PROFILERS
RT   ELECTRIC FIELDS
RT   ELECTRIC IMPEDANCE
RT   ELECTRICAL RESISTIVITY
RT   HYDROSTATIC PRESSURE
RT   REFRACTIVE INDEX
RT   SALINITY

ASFIS Thesaurus

ELECTRICAL CONDUCTIVITY (cont'd)
RT   SALINITY MEASUREMENT
RT   WATER TEMPERATURE

ELECTRICAL CONDUCTIVITY SENSORS
USE   **CONDUCTIVITY SENSORS**

ELECTRICAL ENGINEERING
BT1   ENGINEERING

ELECTRICAL EQUIPMENT
BT1   EQUIPMENT
NT1   ELECTRODES
NT2   ANODES
NT3   SACRIFICIAL ANODES
NT2   CATHODES
RT   BATTERIES
RT   ELECTRIC CABLES
RT   ELECTRIC GENERATORS
RT   ELECTRONIC EQUIPMENT

ELECTRICAL EXPLORATION
BT1   GEOPHYSICAL EXPLORATION
BT2   EXPLORATION
RT   COAST EFFECT
RT   ELECTRICAL RESISTIVITY

ELECTRICAL INSULATION
BT1   INSULATING MATERIALS
BT2   MATERIALS

ELECTRICAL PROPERTIES
BT1   PHYSICAL PROPERTIES
BT2   PROPERTIES
NT1   CAPACITANCE
NT1   DIELECTRIC CONSTANT
NT1   ELECTRIC IMPEDANCE
NT1   ELECTRICAL CONDUCTIVITY
NT1   ELECTRICAL RESISTIVITY
RT   CAPILLARITY
RT   CHEMICAL PROPERTIES
RT   ELECTRIC CHARGE
RT   ELECTRIC POTENTIAL
RT   ELECTRICITY
RT   ELECTROANALYSIS
RT   ELECTROCHEMISTRY
RT   ELECTRODIALYSIS
RT   ELECTROLYSIS
RT   ELECTROPHORESIS
RT   LUMINESCENCE
RT   THERMODYNAMIC PROPERTIES

ELECTRICAL RESISTIVITY
UF   resistivity (electrical)
BT1   ELECTRICAL PROPERTIES
BT2   PHYSICAL PROPERTIES
BT3   PROPERTIES
RT   ELECTRIC IMPEDANCE
RT   ELECTRICAL CONDUCTIVITY
RT   ELECTRICAL EXPLORATION
RT   MAGNETOTELLURIC METHODS
RT   PERMEABILITY
RT   POROSITY
RT   RESISTIVITY PROBES
RT   SEDIMENT PROPERTIES

ELECTRICITY
NT1   ATMOSPHERIC ELECTRICITY
NT2   AURORA
NT2   LIGHTNING
NT1   ELECTRIC CHARGE
RT   ELECTRIC CURRENTS
RT   ELECTRIC POWER SOURCES
RT   ELECTRICAL PROPERTIES
RT   ELECTROMAGNETISM
RT   POWER CONSUMPTION

ELECTRIFIED GEAR
UF   electric shocking gear
UF   electrified nets
BT1   FISHING GEAR
RT   ELECTRIC FENCES
RT   ELECTRIC FISHING
RT   STUPEFYING METHODS

ELECTRIFIED NETS
USE   **ELECTRIFIED GEAR**

ELECTRO-FISHING
USE   **ELECTRIC FISHING**

ELECTROACOUSTIC DEVICES
RT   ACOUSTIC EQUIPMENT
RT   ACOUSTIC TRANSDUCERS
RT   ACOUSTICS
RT   ELECTRONIC EQUIPMENT
RT   PINGERS

ELECTROANAESTHESIA
USE   **ANAESTHESIA**

ELECTROANALYSIS
UF   electrolytic analysis
RT   ANALYSIS
RT   CHEMICAL ELEMENTS
RT   ELECTRICAL PROPERTIES
RT   ELECTROCHEMISTRY
RT   POLAROGRAPHY
RT   SOLUTIONS
RT   VOLTAMMETRY

ELECTROCHEMISTRY
BT1   CHEMISTRY
RT   CHEMICAL PROPERTIES
RT   CHEMICAL REACTIONS
RT   CORROSION
RT   ELECTRICAL PROPERTIES
RT   ELECTROANALYSIS
RT   ELECTRODIALYSIS
RT   ELECTROLYSIS
RT   ELECTROPHORESIS

ELECTRODES
BT1   ELECTRICAL EQUIPMENT
BT2   EQUIPMENT
NT1   ANODES
NT2   SACRIFICIAL ANODES
NT1   CATHODES
RT   ELECTRIC ARC WELDING
RT   ELECTRIC POTENTIAL

ELECTRODIALYSIS
BT1   DIALYSIS
BT2   SEPARATION PROCESSES
RT   DESALINATION
RT   ELECTRICAL PROPERTIES
RT   ELECTROCHEMISTRY
RT   ELECTROPHORESIS

ELECTROLYSIS
BT1   CHEMICAL REACTIONS
RT   ANALYSIS
RT   ANIONS
RT   CATIONS
RT   CHEMICAL DEGRADATION
RT   CORROSION
RT   ELECTRICAL PROPERTIES
RT   ELECTROCHEMISTRY
RT   ELECTROLYTES
RT   ION TRANSPORT
RT   OXIDATION
RT   POLARIZATION
RT   POLAROGRAPHY
RT   VOLTAMMETRY

ELECTROLYTES
RT   ELECTROLYSIS

ELECTROLYTIC ANALYSIS
USE   **ELECTROANALYSIS**

ELECTROMAGNETIC EXPLORATION
UF   electromagnetic survey
BT1   GEOPHYSICAL EXPLORATION
BT2   EXPLORATION
RT   MAGNETOTELLURIC METHODS

ELECTROMAGNETIC POWER
BT1   POWER FROM THE SEA
BT2   ENERGY RESOURCES
BT3   NATURAL RESOURCES
BT4   RESOURCES
RT   BATTERIES

ELECTROMAGNETIC RADIATION
UF   electromagnetic waves
UF   waves (electromagnetic)
BT1   RADIATIONS
NT1   GAMMA RADIATION
NT1   INFRARED RADIATION
NT1   LIGHT
NT1   MICROWAVES
NT1   RADIO WAVES
NT1   SOLAR RADIATION
NT2   EXTRATERRESTRIAL RADIATION
NT2   REFLECTED GLOBAL RADIATION
NT1   TERRESTRIAL RADIATION
NT2   DOWNWARD LONG WAVE RADIATION
NT2   UPWARD LONG WAVE RADIATION
NT1   ULTRAVIOLET RADIATION
NT1   X-RAYS
RT   DOPPLER EFFECT
RT   ELECTRIC FIELDS
RT   ELECTROMAGNETISM
RT   GEOSENSING
RT   LASERS
RT   LIGHT DIFFRACTION
RT   LUMINESCENCE
RT   MAGNETIC FIELDS
RT   MICROWAVE IMAGERY
RT   NUCLEAR RADIATIONS
RT   POLARIZATION
RT   RADAR IMAGERY
RT   RADIATIVE TRANSFER
RT   RADIOMETERS
RT   REMOTE SENSING
RT   THERMAL RADIATION

ELECTROMAGNETIC SURVEY
USE   **ELECTROMAGNETIC EXPLORATION**

ELECTROMAGNETIC WAVES
USE   **ELECTROMAGNETIC RADIATION**

ELECTROMAGNETISM
BT1   MAGNETISM
RT   ELECTRIC POTENTIAL
RT   ELECTRICITY
RT   ELECTROMAGNETIC RADIATION
RT   MAGNETIC FIELDS
RT   PHYSICS

ELECTRON MICROSCOPES
USE   **ELECTRON MICROSCOPY**

ELECTRON MICROSCOPY
UF   electron microscopes
UF   scanning electron microscopy
BT1   MICROSCOPY
BT2   ANALYTICAL TECHNIQUES
RT   ELECTRONIC EQUIPMENT
RT   LABORATORY EQUIPMENT
RT   MICROSCOPES
RT   ULTRASTRUCTURE

ASFIS Thesaurus

ELECTRONIC EQUIPMENT
SN	Excluding computer systems
BT1	EQUIPMENT
NT1	CALCULATORS
NT1	COMPUTERS
NT1	ROBOTS
NT1	SENSORS
NT2	TOWED SENSORS
RT	ACOUSTIC EQUIPMENT
RT	ACOUSTIC TRANSPONDERS
RT	AERIAL SURVEYS
RT	AIRBORNE EQUIPMENT
RT	AIRCRAFT
RT	DEPTH RECORDERS
RT	ELECTRICAL EQUIPMENT
RT	ELECTROACOUSTIC DEVICES
RT	ELECTRON MICROSCOPY
RT	ELECTRONIC NOISE
RT	FISH COUNTERS
RT	MICROPROCESSORS
RT	POWER CONSUMPTION
RT	RADAR
RT	RECORDING EQUIPMENT
RT	REMOTE CONTROL
RT	REMOTE SENSING
RT	REMOTE SENSING EQUIPMENT
RT	SATELLITES
RT	SONAR
RT	SONIC TAGS
RT	TELEMETRY
RT	TEST EQUIPMENT
RT	THERMISTORS
RT	THERMOCOUPLE ARRAYS
RT	THERMOCOUPLES
RT	TRANSPONDERS

ELECTRONIC MODELS
USE	**ANALOG MODELS**

ELECTRONIC NOISE
UF	noise (electronics)
RT	ELECTRONIC EQUIPMENT
RT	SIGNAL-TO-NOISE RATIO

ELECTROPHORESIS
UF	electrophoretic analysis
BT1	ANALYTICAL TECHNIQUES
RT	BIOCHEMICAL ANALYSIS
RT	BLOOD
RT	BLOOD CELLS
RT	BODY FLUIDS
RT	COLLOIDS
RT	ELECTRICAL PROPERTIES
RT	ELECTROCHEMISTRY
RT	ELECTRODIALYSIS
RT	ISOENZYMES
RT	PROTEINS
RT	RACIAL STUDIES
RT	SEPARATION
RT	SEROLOGICAL STUDIES
RT	SEROLOGICAL TAXONOMY
RT	STOCK IDENTIFICATION
RT	TAXONOMY

ELECTROPHORETIC ANALYSIS
USE	**ELECTROPHORESIS**

ELECTROPHORETIC MARKING
USE	**MARKING**

ELECTROPHYSIOLOGY
SN	Added in 1980
BT1	PHYSIOLOGY
BT2	BIOLOGY
RT	ELECTRIC STIMULI

ELECTRORECEPTORS
USE	**ELECTRIC ORGANS**

ELEMENTS (CHEMICAL)
USE	**CHEMICAL ELEMENTS**

ELVERS
USE	**JUVENILES**

EMBANKMENTS
UF	dikes (embankments)
NT1	LEVEES
RT	BANKS (TOPOGRAPHY)
RT	FLOOD CONTROL
RT	IRRIGATION
RT	POLDERS
RT	RIVER BANKS
RT	RIVER ENGINEERING
RT	SEMI-ENCLOSED SEAS

EMBRITTLEMENT
RT	BRITTLENESS
RT	CRACKING (CORROSION)
RT	DETERIORATION
RT	STRESS CORROSION

EMBRYOLOGY
BT1	BIOLOGY
RT	BIOLOGICAL DEVELOPMENT
RT	DEVELOPMENTAL STAGES
RT	EGGS
RT	EMBRYONIC DEVELOPMENT
RT	EMBRYOS
RT	FOETUS
RT	LIFE CYCLE
RT	MORPHOGENESIS
RT	ONTOGENY
RT	ORGANOGENESIS
RT	SEXUAL REPRODUCTION
RT	VITELLOGENESIS
RT	ZOOLOGY

EMBRYONIC DEVELOPMENT
BT1	BIOLOGICAL DEVELOPMENT
RT	EGGS
RT	EMBRYOLOGY
RT	EMBRYOS
RT	MORPHOGENESIS
RT	VITELLOGENESIS

EMBRYOS
BT1	DEVELOPMENTAL STAGES
NT1	FOETUS
RT	EGGS
RT	EMBRYOLOGY
RT	EMBRYONIC DEVELOPMENT
RT	LARVAE

EMERGENCE
SN	Appearance of the imago from the pupa-case or pupal integument. Added in 1980
RT	AQUATIC INSECTS
RT	ENTOMOLOGY
RT	NYMPHS

EMERGENCIES
RT	ACCIDENTS
RT	CAPSIZING
RT	DISASTERS
RT	EVACUATION

EMERGENCY VESSELS
UF	standby vessels
BT1	SURFACE CRAFT
BT2	VEHICLES
RT	ACCIDENTS
RT	DISASTERS
RT	FIRE FIGHTING
RT	HEALTH AND SAFETY

EMERGENCY VESSELS (cont'd)
RT	SAFETY DEVICES
RT	SEARCH AND RESCUE
RT	SUPPORT SHIPS

EMERGENT COASTS
USE	**EMERGENT SHORELINES**

EMERGENT SHORELINES
UF	emergent coasts
BT1	COASTS
BT2	LANDFORMS
BT3	TOPOGRAPHIC FEATURES
RT	DEGLACIATION
RT	EPEIROGENY
RT	EUSTATIC CHANGES
RT	ICE AGES
RT	ISOSTASY
RT	PROGRADATION
RT	RAISED BEACHES
RT	REGRESSIONS
RT	SUBMERGED SHORELINES
RT	UPLIFT

EMISSION SPECTROSCOPY
BT1	SPECTROSCOPIC TECHNIQUES
BT2	ANALYTICAL TECHNIQUES

EMISSIVITY
RT	ABSORPTION COEFFICIENT
RT	OPTICAL PROPERTIES
RT	RADIANCE
RT	SURFACE PROPERTIES

EMPLOYEES
USE	**PERSONNEL**

EMULSIONS
RT	COLLOIDS
RT	DISPERSION
RT	OIL IN WATER CONTENT

ENCLOSURES
BT1	BARRAGES
BT2	HYDRAULIC STRUCTURES
RT	CONTAINMENT
RT	FISH PONDS
RT	HABITAT IMPROVEMENT (PHYSICAL)
RT	HYDRAULIC ENGINEERING
RT	HYDRAULIC STRUCTURES
RT	MARINE AQUACULTURE
RT	SITE SELECTION

ENCRUSTATIONS
USE	**CONCRETIONS**

ENCYCLOPAEDIAS
UF	encyclopedias
BT1	DOCUMENTS
RT	DATA COLLECTIONS
RT	DOCUMENTATION

ENCYCLOPEDIAS
USE	**ENCYCLOPAEDIAS**

ENCYSTMENT
SN	The formation by an organism of a protective capsule surrounding itself. Added in 1980
RT	BIOLOGICAL PHENOMENA
RT	CYSTS
RT	DEFENCE MECHANISMS
RT	SPORES

ENDANGERED ORGANISMS
USE	**RARE SPECIES**

ASFIS Thesaurus

ENDANGERED SPECIES
USE **RARE SPECIES**

ENDEMIC SPECIES
SN A species confined naturally to a certain limited area or region
UF indigenous species
BT1 SPECIES
BT2 TAXA
RT BIOGEOGRAPHY
RT ECOLOGICAL DISTRIBUTION
RT ENDEMISM
RT GEOGRAPHICAL DISTRIBUTION
RT INTRODUCED SPECIES
RT MIGRATORY SPECIES

ENDEMICITY
USE **ENDEMISM**

ENDEMISM
UF endemicity
RT BIOGEOGRAPHY
RT ENDEMIC SPECIES
RT GEOGRAPHICAL DISTRIBUTION

ENDOCRINE GLANDS
UF ductless glands
UF endocrine systems
BT1 GLANDS
BT2 SECRETORY ORGANS
NT1 ADRENAL GLANDS
NT1 PITUITARY GLAND
NT1 THYMUS
NT1 THYROID
RT HORMONES
RT PHEROMONES

ENDOCRINE SYSTEMS
USE **ENDOCRINE GLANDS**

ENDOCRINOLOGY
BT1 PHYSIOLOGY
BT2 BIOLOGY
RT ANIMAL METABOLISM
RT ANIMAL PHYSIOLOGY
RT ENZYMES
RT GLANDS
RT HORMONES
RT METABOLISM
RT PHEROMONES

ENDOFAUNA
USE **BURROWING ORGANISMS**

ENDOGENOUS RHYTHMS
USE **BIOLOGICAL RHYTHMS**

ENDOPARASITES
BT1 PARASITES
RT ENDOPARASITISM
RT PHAGOCYTOSIS
RT TOXICITY

ENDOPARASITISM
BT1 PARASITISM
BT2 INTERSPECIFIC RELATIONSHIPS
RT ENDOPARASITES
RT PHAGOCYTOSIS

ENDOSKELETON
BT1 SKELETON
BT2 MUSCULOSKELETAL SYSTEM
NT1 BONES
NT2 SKULL
NT2 VERTEBRAE
RT ANATOMY
RT OTOLITHS
RT VERTEBRAE COUNTS

ENDOSYMBIONTS
USE **SYMBIONTS**

ENDOTHELIUM
USE **EPITHELIA**

ENDOTOXINS
SN Poisonous substances produced and retained within a cell, and released only after death of the cell. Added in 1980
BT1 BIOLOGICAL POISONS
RT BACTERIA
RT BACTERIAL DISEASES
RT BACTERIOLOGY

ENERGY
SN Use does not include energy resources
NT1 HEAT
NT2 SENSIBLE HEAT
NT2 WASTE HEAT
NT1 KINETIC ENERGY
NT2 EDDY KINETIC ENERGY
NT1 NUCLEAR ENERGY
NT1 POTENTIAL ENERGY
NT2 DYNAMIC HEIGHT
NT1 WAVE ENERGY
NT2 TIDAL ENERGY
RT AIR-WATER EXCHANGES
RT CONSERVATION OF ENERGY
RT ENERGY BALANCE
RT ENERGY BUDGET
RT ENERGY DISSIPATION
RT ENERGY FLOW
RT ENERGY TRANSFER
RT ENTROPY
RT FREE ENERGY
RT PHYSICS
RT THERMODYNAMICS

ENERGY BALANCE
RT ENERGY
RT ENERGY BUDGET
RT ENERGY FLOW
RT EVAPORATION
RT EVAPOTRANSPIRATION
RT HEAT
RT HEAT BUDGET
RT HEAT TRANSFER
RT TEMPERATURE
RT THERMODYNAMICS

ENERGY BUDGET
NT1 HEAT BUDGET
RT BIOENERGETICS
RT CALORIMETRY
RT CYCLES
RT ECOLOGICAL EFFICIENCY
RT ENERGY
RT ENERGY BALANCE
RT ENERGY DISSIPATION
RT ENERGY FLOW
RT ENTROPY
RT EVAPORATION
RT EVAPOTRANSPIRATION
RT HYDROLOGIC CYCLE
RT INTERFACE PHENOMENA
RT NUTRIENTS (MINERAL)

ENERGY DISSIPATION
BT1 ENERGY TRANSFER
NT1 WAVE DISSIPATION
NT2 TIDAL DISSIPATION
NT2 WAVE ATTENUATION
NT3 SOUND ATTENUATION
NT2 WAVE BREAKING
NT3 WHITECAPPING
RT BOTTOM FRICTION
RT ENERGY
RT ENERGY BUDGET

ENERGY DISSIPATION (cont'd)
RT FRICTION
RT WAVE ENERGY

ENERGY FLOW
RT ECOSYSTEMS
RT ENERGY
RT ENERGY BALANCE
RT ENERGY BUDGET
RT FOOD CHAINS
RT FOOD WEBS
RT METABOLISM
RT SOLAR RADIATION
RT TROPHIC LEVELS
RT TROPHODYNAMIC CYCLE

ENERGY FLUX
USE **ENERGY TRANSFER**

ENERGY RESOURCES
UF energy sources
BT1 NATURAL RESOURCES
BT2 RESOURCES
NT1 GEOTHERMAL POWER
NT1 HYDROELECTRIC POWER
NT1 POWER FROM THE SEA
NT2 CURRENT POWER
NT2 ELECTROMAGNETIC POWER
NT2 SALINITY POWER
NT2 THERMAL POWER
NT3 OTEC
NT2 TIDAL POWER
NT2 WAVE POWER
NT1 SOLAR POWER
NT1 WIND POWER
RT ALGAL CULTURE
RT FOSSIL FUELS
RT MARINE RESOURCES
RT NUCLEAR POWER PLANTS
RT OIL RESERVES
RT SEAWEED CULTURE

ENERGY SOURCES
USE **ENERGY RESOURCES**

ENERGY SPECTRA
UF power spectra
BT1 SPECTRA
RT DIRECTIONAL SPECTRA
RT FREQUENCY SPECTRA
RT WATER CURRENTS
RT WATER WAVES

ENERGY TRANSFER
UF energy flux
UF transfer of properties
NT1 ENERGY DISSIPATION
NT2 WAVE DISSIPATION
NT3 TIDAL DISSIPATION
NT3 WAVE ATTENUATION
NT4 SOUND ATTENUATION
NT3 WAVE BREAKING
NT4 WHITECAPPING
NT1 RADIATIVE TRANSFER
RT AIR-WATER EXCHANGES
RT AIR-WATER INTERFACE
RT BAROCLINIC INSTABILITY
RT BAROTROPIC INSTABILITY
RT ENERGY
RT HEAT
RT HEAT EXCHANGE
RT HEAT TRANSFER
RT MASS TRANSFER
RT MOISTURE TRANSFER
RT MOMENTUM TRANSFER
RT WAVE ENERGY
RT WAVE GENERATION
RT WAVE INTERACTIONS

ENGINEERING
SN		Use of a more specific term is recommended
NT1	BIOTECHNOLOGY	
NT1	CHEMICAL ENGINEERING	
NT1	CIVIL ENGINEERING	
NT1	COASTAL ENGINEERING	
NT1	DESIGN	
NT2	SHIP DESIGN	
NT2	TOWED BODY DESIGN	
NT1	ELECTRICAL ENGINEERING	
NT1	FISHERY ENGINEERING	
NT1	GEOTECHNOLOGY	
NT1	HYDRAULIC ENGINEERING	
NT1	OFFSHORE ENGINEERING	
NT1	PETROLEUM ENGINEERING	
NT1	RIVER ENGINEERING	
NT1	SANITARY ENGINEERING	
NT1	STRUCTURAL ENGINEERING	
NT2	STRUCTURAL ANALYSIS	
RT	ENGINEERING DRAWINGS	
RT	ENGINEERS	
RT	SHIP TECHNOLOGY	
RT	TECHNICAL FEASIBILITY	
RT	TECHNICIANS	
RT	TECHNOLOGY	

ENGINEERING DRAWINGS
SN		Descriptor to be used only as a qualifier
UF	blueprints	
BT1	GRAPHICS	
BT2	AUDIOVISUAL MATERIAL	
BT3	DOCUMENTS	
RT	DESIGN	
RT	ENGINEERING	
RT	INSTRUMENTS	
RT	PATENTS	
RT	SHIP TECHNOLOGY	

ENGINEERS
SN	Added in 1980
BT1	EXPERTS
BT2	PERSONNEL
RT	DIRECTORIES
RT	ENGINEERING

ENGINES
USE	**MOTORS**

ENMESHING NETS
USE	**GILLNETS**

ENSTROPHY
SN	Total squared vorticity
BT1	VORTICITY

ENTANGLING NETS
UF	trammels
BT1	FISHING NETS
BT2	FISHING GEAR
RT	GILLNETS

ENTERIC REDMOUTH
USE	**REDMOUTH DISEASE**

ENTHALPY
BT1	THERMODYNAMIC PROPERTIES
BT2	PHYSICAL PROPERTIES
BT3	PROPERTIES
NT1	FUSION HEAT
NT1	SUBLIMATION HEAT
NT1	VAPORIZATION HEAT
RT	CONSERVATIVE PROPERTIES
RT	ENTROPY
RT	FREE ENERGY
RT	SPECIFIC HEAT
RT	THERMODYNAMICS

ENTOMOLOGISTS
SN	Added in 1980
BT1	ZOOLOGISTS
BT2	BIOLOGISTS
BT3	SCIENTIFIC PERSONNEL
BT4	PERSONNEL
RT	AQUATIC INSECTS
RT	DIRECTORIES
RT	ENTOMOLOGY
RT	TAXONOMISTS

ENTOMOLOGY
BT1	INVERTEBRATE ZOOLOGY
BT2	ZOOLOGY
BT3	BIOLOGY
RT	AQUATIC INSECTS
RT	EMERGENCE
RT	ENTOMOLOGISTS
RT	HYDROBIOLOGY
RT	INSECT EGGS

ENTRAINMENT
SN		Intaking of free-floating organisms from surrounding waters through power plant screens. For entrainment as a hydrodynamic process use TURBULENT ENTRAINMENT
UF	plankton entrainment	
UF	power plant entrainment	
RT	COOLING WATER	
RT	IMPINGEMENT	
RT	PLANKTON	
RT	POWER PLANTS	

ENTROPY
BT1	THERMODYNAMIC PROPERTIES
BT2	PHYSICAL PROPERTIES
BT3	PROPERTIES
RT	ENERGY
RT	ENERGY BUDGET
RT	ENTHALPY
RT	HEAT
RT	HEAT TRANSFER
RT	ISENTROPIC ANALYSIS
RT	ISENTROPIC PROCESSES
RT	ISENTROPIC SURFACES
RT	THERMODYNAMICS

ENVIRONMENT (AQUATIC)
USE	**AQUATIC ENVIRONMENT**

ENVIRONMENT MANAGEMENT
SN		Management of the aquatic environment. Added in 1980
BT1	ECOSYSTEM MANAGEMENT	
BT2	MANAGEMENT	
RT	AQUATIC ENVIRONMENT	
RT	COASTAL ZONE MANAGEMENT	
RT	ECOLOGICAL BALANCE	
RT	ECOLOGY	
RT	ENVIRONMENTAL LEGISLATION	
RT	NATURAL RESOURCES	
RT	NATURE CONSERVATION	
RT	POLLUTION	
RT	POLLUTION CONTROL	
RT	POLLUTION LEGISLATION	
RT	POLLUTION MONITORING	
RT	POLLUTION SURVEYS	
RT	RESOURCE CONSERVATION	
RT	RESOURCE MANAGEMENT	
RT	WASTE TREATMENT	

ENVIRONMENTAL CHARTS
SN		Distributional charts of physico-chemical factors in aquatic environment
BT1	MAPS	
BT2	GRAPHICS	
BT3	AUDIOVISUAL MATERIAL	
BT4	DOCUMENTS	

ENVIRONMENTAL CHARTS (cont'd)
RT	CHEMICAL PROPERTIES
RT	ENVIRONMENTAL CONDITIONS
RT	ENVIRONMENTAL FACTORS
RT	ENVIRONMENTAL SURVEYS
RT	ENVIRONMENTS
RT	HYDROGRAPHIC CHARTS
RT	ISOHALINES
RT	ISOTHERMS
RT	PHYSICAL PROPERTIES
RT	SALINITY
RT	WATER PROPERTIES
RT	WATER TEMPERATURE
RT	WAVE CLIMATE

ENVIRONMENTAL CHEMISTRY
USE	**GEOCHEMISTRY**

ENVIRONMENTAL CONDITIONS
RT	AIR TEMPERATURE
RT	ANTHROPOGENIC FACTORS
RT	AQUATIC ENVIRONMENT
RT	AUTECOLOGY
RT	ECOLOGY
RT	ENVIRONMENTAL CHARTS
RT	ENVIRONMENTAL DISEASES
RT	ENVIRONMENTAL EFFECTS
RT	ENVIRONMENTAL FACTORS
RT	ENVIRONMENTAL SURVEYS
RT	ENVIRONMENTS
RT	FISHERY CHARTS
RT	LIMITING FACTORS
RT	LIMNOLOGICAL DATA
RT	LIMNOLOGICAL SURVEYS
RT	OCEANOGRAPHIC DATA
RT	OCEANOGRAPHIC SURVEYS
RT	SEA STATE
RT	SITE SELECTION
RT	SYNECOLOGY
RT	WAVE CLIMATE

ENVIRONMENTAL CONTAMINATION
USE	**POLLUTION**

ENVIRONMENTAL DISEASES
SN		Diseases associated with physical or physico-chemical abnormalities of water. Added in 1980
UF	abiotic diseases	
BT1	DISEASES	
RT	ANIMAL DISEASES	
RT	BUBBLE DISEASE	
RT	ENVIRONMENTAL CONDITIONS	
RT	FISH DISEASES	
RT	HUSBANDRY DISEASES	
RT	PEDUNCLE DISEASE	
RT	SUNBURN	

ENVIRONMENTAL EFFECTS
SN		Effects of environmental conditions on living organisms and fisheries
NT1	GRAVITY EFFECTS	
NT1	GROUP EFFECTS	
NT1	LIGHT EFFECTS	
NT1	PH EFFECTS	
NT1	PRESSURE EFFECTS	
NT2	HIGH PRESSURE EFFECTS	
NT1	SALINITY EFFECTS	
NT1	TEMPERATURE EFFECTS	
NT1	TIDAL EFFECTS	
RT	ABIOTIC FACTORS	
RT	AESTIVATION	
RT	AQUATIC ENVIRONMENT	
RT	AUTECOLOGY	
RT	BEHAVIOUR	
RT	BIOLOGICAL PRODUCTION	
RT	BIOLOGICAL RESISTANCE	
RT	COLD RESISTANCE	
RT	DISEASE RESISTANCE	
RT	DROUGHT RESISTANCE	

ENVIRONMENTAL EFFECTS (cont'd)

RT	ECOLOGICAL AGGREGATIONS
RT	ECOLOGICAL CRISIS
RT	ECOLOGICAL DISTRIBUTION
RT	ECOPHYSIOLOGY
RT	ENVIRONMENTAL CONDITIONS
RT	ENVIRONMENTAL FACTORS
RT	ENVIRONMENTS
RT	EVAPOTRANSPIRATION
RT	HIBERNATION
RT	LIMITING FACTORS
RT	NATURAL SELECTION
RT	PHENOTYPES
RT	PHENOTYPIC VARIATIONS
RT	PHYSICAL PROPERTIES
RT	RESTING EGGS
RT	RESTING STAGES
RT	SUBSTRATA
RT	SYNECOLOGY
RT	TOLERANCE
RT	VERTICAL MIGRATIONS
RT	WEATHERING

ENVIRONMENTAL FACTORS

NT1	ABIOTIC FACTORS
NT1	ANTHROPOGENIC FACTORS
NT1	BIOTIC FACTORS
RT	AQUATIC ENVIRONMENT
RT	CHEMICAL PROPERTIES
RT	DISCONTINUITY LAYERS
RT	ENVIRONMENTAL CHARTS
RT	ENVIRONMENTAL CONDITIONS
RT	ENVIRONMENTAL EFFECTS
RT	ENVIRONMENTAL SURVEYS
RT	ENVIRONMENTS
RT	FOOD AVAILABILITY
RT	HABITAT
RT	LIMITING FACTORS
RT	LIMNOLOGICAL DATA
RT	MARINE ECOLOGY
RT	PHYSICAL PROPERTIES
RT	SEISMIC ACTIVITY
RT	THERMOCLINE
RT	WATER MASSES
RT	WATER PROPERTIES

ENVIRONMENTAL IMPACT

SN	The change in well-being of the ecosystems, that results from a process set in motion or accelerated by man's actions. Added in 1980
RT	AQUATIC ENVIRONMENT
RT	ENVIRONMENTAL LEGISLATION
RT	HAZARD ASSESSMENT
RT	MAN-INDUCED EFFECTS
RT	POLLUTION EFFECTS

ENVIRONMENTAL LEGISLATION

SN	Legislation for protection of aquatic environment and organisms
BT1	LEGISLATION
NT1	POLLUTION LEGISLATION
RT	AQUACULTURE EFFLUENTS
RT	CONSERVATION
RT	ECOLOGICAL BALANCE
RT	ENVIRONMENT MANAGEMENT
RT	ENVIRONMENTAL IMPACT
RT	ENVIRONMENTAL PROTECTION
RT	HAZARD ASSESSMENT
RT	LAW OF THE SEA
RT	MARINE PARKS
RT	NATURAL RESOURCES
RT	NATURE CONSERVATION
RT	OCEAN SPACE
RT	POLLUTION
RT	POLLUTION CONTROL
RT	POLLUTION CONVENTION
RT	POLLUTION MONITORING
RT	RESOURCE CONSERVATION

ENVIRONMENTAL LEGISLATION (cont'd)

RT	RESOURCE MANAGEMENT
RT	RIVER BASIN MANAGEMENT
RT	WATER POLLUTION

ENVIRONMENTAL MONITORING

BT1	MONITORING
RT	ENVIRONMENTAL PROTECTION
RT	WARNING SERVICES
RT	WASTE DISPOSAL SITES

ENVIRONMENTAL POLLUTION

USE	**POLLUTION**

ENVIRONMENTAL PROTECTION

BT1	PROTECTION
RT	CONSERVATION
RT	ENVIRONMENTAL LEGISLATION
RT	ENVIRONMENTAL MONITORING
RT	POLLUTION CONTROL
RT	POLLUTION LEGISLATION

ENVIRONMENTAL SURVEYS

BT1	SURVEYS
NT1	LIMNOLOGICAL SURVEYS
NT1	OCEANOGRAPHIC SURVEYS
RT	AQUATIC ENVIRONMENT
RT	ENVIRONMENTAL CHARTS
RT	ENVIRONMENTAL CONDITIONS
RT	ENVIRONMENTAL FACTORS
RT	FISHERY OCEANOGRAPHY
RT	ICHTHYOPLANKTON SURVEYS
RT	LIMNOLOGICAL DATA
RT	LIMNOLOGY
RT	OCEANOGRAPHIC DATA
RT	OCEANOGRAPHIC EQUIPMENT
RT	OCEANOGRAPHY
RT	POLLUTION SURVEYS
RT	SITE SELECTION
RT	WATER SAMPLING

ENVIRONMENTS

SN	Use of a more specific term is recommended
NT1	AQUATIC ENVIRONMENT
NT2	BENTHIC ENVIRONMENT
NT3	ABYSSOBENTHIC ZONE
NT3	BATHYAL-BENTHIC ZONE
NT3	LITTORAL ZONE
NT4	EULITTORAL ZONE
NT4	SUBLITTORAL ZONE
NT4	SUPRALITTORAL ZONE
NT2	BRACKISHWATER ENVIRONMENT
NT2	INLAND WATER ENVIRONMENT
NT3	LENITIC ENVIRONMENT
NT3	LOTIC ENVIRONMENT
NT2	INTERSTITIAL ENVIRONMENT
NT2	MARINE ENVIRONMENT
NT3	INTERTIDAL ENVIRONMENT
NT2	PELAGIC ENVIRONMENT
NT3	NERITIC PROVINCE
NT3	OCEANIC PROVINCE
NT4	ABYSSOPELAGIC ZONE
NT4	BATHYPELAGIC ZONE
NT4	EPIPELAGIC ZONE
NT4	MESOPELAGIC ZONE
NT1	PALAEOENVIRONMENTS
NT1	SEDIMENTARY ENVIRONMENTS
NT1	TROPICAL ENVIRONMENT
RT	ENVIRONMENTAL CHARTS
RT	ENVIRONMENTAL CONDITIONS
RT	ENVIRONMENTAL EFFECTS
RT	ENVIRONMENTAL FACTORS

ENZYMATIC ACTIVITY

SN	Added in 1980
UF	enzyme activity
UF	enzymic activity
RT	BIOSYNTHESIS
RT	CATALYSTS

ENZYMATIC ACTIVITY (cont'd)

RT	COENZYMES
RT	DIGESTION
RT	ENZYMES
RT	METABOLISM

ENZYMATIC HYDROLYSIS

USE	**ENZYMOLYSIS**

ENZYME ACTIVITY

USE	**ENZYMATIC ACTIVITY**

ENZYME INHIBITORS

SN	Before 1982 search INHIBITORS
BT1	INHIBITORS
NT1	CHOLINESTERASE INHIBITORS
RT	ADDITIVES
RT	ANIMAL PHYSIOLOGY
RT	BIOCHEMISTRY
RT	COENZYMES
RT	ENZYMES
RT	METABOLISM

ENZYMES

UF	cellulase
UF	heteroenzymes
UF	isodynamic enzymes
UF	proteinase
NT1	CARBONIC ANHYDRASE
NT1	COENZYMES
NT2	CYTOCHROMES
NT1	DEHYDROGENASES
NT1	HYDROLASES
NT1	ISOMERASES
NT1	LIGASES
NT1	LYASES
NT1	OXIDOREDUCTASES
NT1	PERMEASES
NT1	TRANSFERASES
RT	AUTOLYSIS
RT	BIOCHEMISTRY
RT	CATALYSTS
RT	CHOLINESTERASE INHIBITORS
RT	COLLOIDS
RT	DIGESTION
RT	ENDOCRINOLOGY
RT	ENZYMATIC ACTIVITY
RT	ENZYME INHIBITORS
RT	ENZYMOLYSIS
RT	FERMENTATION
RT	GLYCOPROTEINS
RT	HORMONES
RT	ISOENZYMES
RT	PROTEINS

ENZYMIC ACTIVITY

USE	**ENZYMATIC ACTIVITY**

ENZYMOLYSIS

SN	Hydrolysis by means of enzymes. Added in 1980
UF	enzymatic hydrolysis
BT1	HYDROLYSIS
BT2	CHEMICAL REACTIONS
RT	ENZYMES

EOCENE

SN	Before 1982 search EOCENE EPOCH
BT1	PALAEOGENE
BT2	TERTIARY
BT3	CENOZOIC
BT4	GEOLOGICAL TIME

EOLIAN DEPOSITS

SN	Consolidated wind-blown deposits
UF	aeolian deposits
RT	ALLOCHTHONOUS DEPOSITS
RT	CLASTICS
RT	EOLIAN PROCESSES
RT	EOLIAN TRANSPORT

ASFIS Thesaurus

EOLIAN DEPOSITS (cont'd)
RT	SABKHAS
RT	SANDSTONE
RT	SEDIMENTS
RT	TERRIGENOUS SEDIMENTS
RT	VOLCANIC ASH

EOLIAN DUST
SN	Restrict use to dust of terrigenous origin found in sediments, suspended particulate matter or at sea surface
UF	aeolian dust
RT	AIR-WATER INTERFACE
RT	COSMIC DUST
RT	DISCOLOURED WATER
RT	DUST
RT	EOLIAN PROCESSES
RT	EOLIAN TRANSPORT
RT	PALAEOCLIMATOLOGY
RT	SUSPENDED PARTICULATE MATTER
RT	TERRIGENOUS SEDIMENTS
RT	VOLCANIC ASH
RT	WINDS

EOLIAN PROCESSES
UF	aeolian processes
RT	EOLIAN DEPOSITS
RT	EOLIAN DUST
RT	EOLIAN TRANSPORT
RT	WINDS

EOLIAN TRANSPORT
UF	aeolian-transport
BT1	SEDIMENT TRANSPORT
RT	DUNES
RT	DUST CLOUDS
RT	EOLIAN DEPOSITS
RT	EOLIAN DUST
RT	EOLIAN PROCESSES
RT	SANDSTONE
RT	VOLCANIC ASH
RT	WIND ABRASION
RT	WINDS

EOTVOS CORRECTION
USE	**GRAVITY CORRECTIONS**

EPEIROGENY
UF	bathygenesis
UF	vertical movements (geology)
BT1	TECTONICS
BT2	GEOLOGY
BT3	EARTH SCIENCES
NT1	SUBSIDENCE
NT1	UPLIFT
RT	CONTINENTS
RT	CRUSTAL ADJUSTMENT
RT	CRUSTAL SHORTENING
RT	EARTH CRUST
RT	EMERGENT SHORELINES
RT	EUSTATIC CHANGES
RT	ISOSTASY
RT	OCEAN BASINS
RT	OROGENY
RT	SUBMERGED SHORELINES
RT	SUBMERGENCE
RT	VERTICAL TECTONICS

EPHEMERAL LAKES
USE	**TEMPORARY PONDS**

EPHEMERIS
USE	**NAUTICAL ALMANACS**

EPIBENTHOS
USE	**BENTHOS**

EPIBIONTS
SN	Added in 1980
UF	epibiota
NT1	EPIPHYTES
NT1	EPIZOITES
RT	EPIBIOSIS

EPIBIOSIS
BT1	INTERSPECIFIC RELATIONSHIPS
RT	EPIBIONTS
RT	EPIPHYTES
RT	EPIZOITES
RT	SYMBIOSIS

EPIBIOTA
USE	**EPIBIONTS**

EPICENTRES
UF	seismic epicentres
RT	EARTHQUAKES
RT	SEISMOLOGY

EPIDEMICS
RT	EPIDEMIOLOGY
RT	HUMAN DISEASES
RT	MICROBIAL CONTAMINATION
RT	MORTALITY
RT	PATHOLOGY
RT	POLLUTION EFFECTS
RT	PUBLIC HEALTH

EPIDEMIOLOGY
RT	BACTERIOLOGY
RT	DISEASE CONTROL
RT	DISEASES
RT	EPIDEMICS
RT	HUMAN DISEASES
RT	INFECTIOUS DISEASES
RT	MORTALITY CAUSES
RT	NATURAL MORTALITY
RT	PARASITOLOGY

EPIDERMIS
USE	**SKIN**

EPILIMNION
UF	upper layers (lakes)
RT	HYPOLIMNION
RT	METALIMNION
RT	OVERTURN
RT	RESERVOIRS (WATER)
RT	SURFACE LAYERS
RT	SURFACE MIXED LAYER
RT	SURFACE WATER
RT	THERMAL STRATIFICATION
RT	THERMOCLINE
RT	WATER COLUMN

EPIPELAGIC ZONE
SN	Waters above 200 m depth
UF	photic environment
BT1	OCEANIC PROVINCE
BT2	PELAGIC ENVIRONMENT
BT3	AQUATIC ENVIRONMENT
BT4	ENVIRONMENTS
RT	DISPHOTIC ZONE
RT	EUPHOTIC ZONE
RT	LITTORAL ZONE
RT	NERITIC PROVINCE

EPIPHYTES
BT1	EPIBIONTS
RT	EPIBIOSIS
RT	PERIPHYTON
RT	SYMBIONTS

EPIPSAMMIC SPECIES
USE	**EPIPSAMMON**

EPIPSAMMON
SN	Organisms living attached to sand grain. Added in 1980
UF	epipsammic species
BT1	AQUATIC COMMUNITIES
RT	MICROORGANISMS
RT	PSAMMON
RT	SAND

EPITHELIA
SN	Added in 1980
UF	endothelium
UF	epithelium
BT1	TISSUES
RT	INTEGUMENTARY SYSTEM
RT	SKIN

EPITHELIUM
USE	**EPITHELIA**

EPIZOITES
BT1	EPIBIONTS
RT	COMMENSALISM
RT	ECTOPARASITES
RT	EPIBIOSIS

EPONTIC ENVIRONMENT
UF	under-ice environment
RT	EPONTIC ORGANISMS

EPONTIC ORGANISMS
UF	under-ice organisms
RT	EPONTIC ENVIRONMENT

EPOXY RESINS
SN	Synthetic resins used for protective coatings and adhesives
RT	ADHESIVES
RT	PLASTIC COATINGS

EPSOMITE
BT1	SULPHATE MINERALS
BT2	MINERALS

EQUATION OF CONTINUITY
UF	conservation of volume
UF	continuity equation
RT	CONSERVATION EQUATIONS
RT	CONSERVATION OF MASS
RT	EQUATIONS
RT	EQUATIONS OF STATE
RT	FLUID DYNAMICS

EQUATIONS
SN	Used only as a qualifier
NT1	CONSERVATION EQUATIONS
NT1	EQUATIONS OF MOTION
NT1	EQUATIONS OF STATE
NT1	INTEGRAL EQUATIONS
NT1	KORTWEG DEVRIES EQUATION
NT1	LAPLACE EQUATION
NT1	MORISON'S EQUATION
NT1	NONLINEAR EQUATIONS
NT1	POISSON'S EQUATION
RT	DIFFERENTIAL EQUATIONS
RT	EQUATION OF CONTINUITY
RT	HYDRODYNAMIC EQUATIONS
RT	MATHEMATICS
RT	NAVIER-STOKES EQUATIONS
RT	TIDAL EQUATIONS

EQUATIONS OF MOTION
UF	euler equations of motion
BT1	EQUATIONS
RT	HYDROSTATIC EQUATION

EQUATIONS OF STATE
BT1	EQUATIONS
RT	EQUATION OF CONTINUITY
RT	THERMODYNAMICS

EQUATOR
RT	EARTH
RT	LATITUDE

EQUATORIAL CALMS
USE	**EQUATORIAL TROUGH**

EQUATORIAL CIRCULATION
SN	Before 1982 search EQUATORIAL CURRENTS
UF	equatorial current system
UF	equatorial currents
BT1	OCEAN CIRCULATION
BT2	WATER CIRCULATION
BT3	WATER MOTION
RT	EQUATORIAL COUNTERCURRENTS
RT	EQUATORIAL DYNAMICS
RT	EQUATORIAL UNDERCURRENTS
RT	EQUATORIAL UPWELLING
RT	MONSOON REVERSAL
RT	TROPICAL OCEANOGRAPHY

EQUATORIAL COUNTERCURRENTS
BT1	COUNTERCURRENTS
BT2	WATER CURRENTS
BT3	WATER MOTION
RT	EQUATORIAL CIRCULATION
RT	EQUATORIAL DYNAMICS
RT	OCEAN CURRENTS

EQUATORIAL CURRENT SYSTEM
USE	**EQUATORIAL CIRCULATION**

EQUATORIAL CURRENTS
USE	**EQUATORIAL CIRCULATION**

EQUATORIAL DYNAMICS
RT	BETA-PLANE
RT	DYNAMICAL OCEANOGRAPHY
RT	EQUATORIAL CIRCULATION
RT	EQUATORIAL COUNTERCURRENTS
RT	EQUATORIAL TRAPPED WAVES
RT	EQUATORIAL UNDERCURRENTS
RT	EQUATORIAL UPWELLING
RT	KELVIN WAVES
RT	MONSOON REVERSAL
RT	PLANETARY WAVES
RT	TROPICAL METEOROLOGY
RT	TROPICAL OCEANOGRAPHY

EQUATORIAL EASTERLIES
BT1	TRADE WINDS
BT2	PLANETARY WINDS
BT3	WINDS
BT4	ATMOSPHERIC MOTION
RT	EASTERLY WAVES
RT	EQUATORIAL WAVES

EQUATORIAL TRAPPED WAVES
BT1	KELVIN WAVES
BT2	TRAPPED WAVES
BT3	WATER WAVES
RT	EQUATORIAL DYNAMICS

EQUATORIAL TROUGH
UF	doldrums
UF	equatorial calms
BT1	LOW PRESSURE TROUGHS
BT2	LOW PRESSURE SYSTEMS
RT	EASTERLY WAVES
RT	EQUATORIAL WESTERLIES
RT	INTERTROPICAL CONVERGENCE ZONE
RT	TROPICAL METEOROLOGY

EQUATORIAL UNDERCURRENTS
BT1	UNDERCURRENTS
BT2	WATER CURRENTS
BT3	WATER MOTION
RT	EQUATORIAL CIRCULATION
RT	EQUATORIAL DYNAMICS
RT	OCEAN CURRENTS

EQUATORIAL UPWELLING
BT1	UPWELLING
BT2	VERTICAL WATER MOVEMENT
BT3	WATER MOTION
RT	DIVERGENCE
RT	EKMAN TRANSPORT
RT	EQUATORIAL CIRCULATION
RT	EQUATORIAL DYNAMICS

EQUATORIAL WAVES
RT	EQUATORIAL EASTERLIES

EQUATORIAL WESTERLIES
BT1	WESTERLIES
BT2	PLANETARY WINDS
BT3	WINDS
BT4	ATMOSPHERIC MOTION
RT	EQUATORIAL TROUGH

EQUILIBRIUM
SN	Used only as a qualifier
RT	CHEMICAL EQUILIBRIUM
RT	DIFFUSION
RT	GEOSTROPHIC EQUILIBRIUM
RT	ISOSTASY
RT	STABILITY
RT	STEADY STATE
RT	THERMODYNAMIC EQUILIBRIUM
RT	UNSTEADY STATE
RT	VARIABILITY

EQUILIBRIUM CONSTANTS
USE	**CHEMICAL EQUILIBRIUM**

EQUILIBRIUM TIDES
BT1	TIDES
BT2	TIDAL MOTION
NT1	ORTHOTIDES
RT	ATMOSPHERIC TIDES
RT	GRAVITY
RT	MEAN SEA LEVEL
RT	TIDAL ANALYSIS
RT	TIDE GENERATING POTENTIAL

EQUIPMENT
SN	Only for papers in which the description, use, performance, or fabrication of equipment is the main topic. Use of a more specific term is recommended
UF	plant (equipment)
NT1	ACOUSTIC EQUIPMENT
NT2	SOUND GENERATORS
NT3	PINGERS
NT1	AIRBORNE EQUIPMENT
NT1	AQUACULTURE EQUIPMENT
NT2	CAGES
NT3	FLOATING CAGES
NT3	SUBMERGED CAGES
NT2	FEEDING EQUIPMENT
NT1	CHRONOMETERS
NT2	QUARTZ CLOCKS
NT1	DECK EQUIPMENT
NT2	LIFTING TACKLE
NT3	CRANES
NT3	DAVITS
NT3	WINCHES
NT1	DEICING EQUIPMENT
NT1	DIVING EQUIPMENT
NT2	DECOMPRESSION CHAMBERS
NT3	DECK COMPRESSION CHAMBERS
NT3	TRANSFER CHAMBERS

EQUIPMENT (cont'd)
NT2	DIVING SUITS
NT2	DIVING TOOLS
NT1	DRILLING EQUIPMENT
NT2	DRILLING RIGS
NT1	ELECTRICAL EQUIPMENT
NT2	ELECTRODES
NT3	ANODES
NT4	SACRIFICIAL ANODES
NT3	CATHODES
NT1	ELECTRONIC EQUIPMENT
NT2	CALCULATORS
NT2	COMPUTERS
NT2	ROBOTS
NT2	SENSORS
NT3	TOWED SENSORS
NT1	FISHERY INDUSTRY EQUIPMENT
NT2	REFRIGERATORS
NT1	GEOLOGICAL EQUIPMENT
NT1	GEOPHYSICAL EQUIPMENT
NT2	GEOTHERMAL EQUIPMENT
NT3	HEAT PROBES
NT2	SEISMIC EQUIPMENT
NT1	LABORATORY EQUIPMENT
NT2	CENTRIFUGES
NT2	FLUMES
NT2	MICROSCOPES
NT1	LIMNOLOGICAL EQUIPMENT
NT1	MACHINERY
NT1	MINING EQUIPMENT
NT1	MONITORING SYSTEMS
NT1	OCEANOGRAPHIC EQUIPMENT
NT1	OFFSHORE EQUIPMENT
NT1	PHOTOGRAPHIC EQUIPMENT
NT2	CAMERAS
NT3	UNDERWATER CAMERAS
NT1	RECORDING EQUIPMENT
NT2	DEPTH RECORDERS
NT2	SOUND RECORDERS
NT2	WAVE RECORDERS
NT1	REMOTE SENSING EQUIPMENT
NT2	RADAR
NT3	MICROWAVE RADAR
NT4	RADAR ALTIMETERS
NT4	SCATTEROMETERS
NT4	SYNTHETIC APERTURE RADAR
NT2	RADIOMETERS
NT3	ACTINOMETERS
NT4	PYRANOMETERS
NT4	PYRGEOMETERS
NT4	PYRHELIOMETERS
NT3	INFRARED DETECTORS
NT3	MICROWAVE RADIOMETERS
NT2	SONAR
NT3	ACTIVE SONAR
NT4	DOPPLER SONAR
NT4	ECHOSOUNDERS
NT4	MULTIBEAM SONAR
NT4	SIDE SCAN SONAR
NT3	PASSIVE SONAR
NT1	SAFETY DEVICES
NT1	SALVAGE EQUIPMENT
NT1	SHIPBOARD EQUIPMENT
NT1	SURVEYING EQUIPMENT
NT1	TEST EQUIPMENT
NT1	UNDERWATER EQUIPMENT
RT	ACCURACY
RT	ACRONYMS
RT	ARRAYS
RT	CALIBRATION
RT	CATALOGUES
RT	COMPONENTS
RT	DATA LOGGERS
RT	EFFICIENCY
RT	FISHING GEAR
RT	MAINTENANCE
RT	MEASURING DEVICES
RT	METHODOLOGY
RT	MODULES
RT	NAVIGATIONAL AIDS

ASFIS Thesaurus

EQUIPMENT (cont'd)
RT	PATENTS
RT	PERFORMANCE ASSESSMENT
RT	RADIO AIDS
RT	RELIABILITY
RT	SPECIFICATIONS
RT	STANDARDIZATION

EQUIPMENT CATALOGUES
USE	**CATALOGUES**

ERBIUM
BT1	CHEMICAL ELEMENTS
RT	ERBIUM COMPOUNDS
RT	ERBIUM ISOTOPES
RT	RARE EARTHS
RT	TRANSITION ELEMENTS

ERBIUM COMPOUNDS
RT	CHEMICAL COMPOUNDS
RT	ERBIUM

ERBIUM ISOTOPES
BT1	ISOTOPES
RT	ERBIUM

EROSION
UF	erosion (geology)
NT1	BOTTOM EROSION
NT1	COASTAL EROSION
NT2	BEACH EROSION
NT1	GLACIAL EROSION
NT1	SCOURING
NT2	CURRENT SCOURING
NT2	ICEBERG SCOURING
NT2	WAVE SCOURING
NT1	SOIL EROSION
NT1	WIND EROSION
RT	ALLUVIAL DEPOSITS
RT	BIOEROSION
RT	BOTTOM EROSION
RT	DENUDATION
RT	DETRITUS
RT	EROSION CONTROL
RT	FLUVIAL MORPHOLOGY
RT	GEOMORPHOLOGY
RT	LANDFORMS
RT	RIP CHANNELS
RT	RIVER VALLEYS
RT	SEDIMENT TRANSPORT
RT	SEDIMENTATION
RT	SEDIMENTOLOGY
RT	SLUMPING
RT	SOIL CONSERVATION
RT	SOILS
RT	TOPOGRAPHIC FEATURES
RT	VALLEYS
RT	WEATHERING

EROSION (BIOLOGICAL)
USE	**BIOEROSION**

EROSION (GEOLOGY)
USE	**EROSION**

EROSION (THERMOCLINE)
USE	**THERMOCLINE DECAY**

EROSION CONTROL
UF	erosion prevention
UF	erosion protection
BT1	CONTROL
NT1	PIPELINE PROTECTION
RT	COASTAL EROSION
RT	DUNE STABILIZATION
RT	EROSION
RT	FLOOD CONTROL
RT	SOIL CONSERVATION
RT	SOIL EROSION
RT	WIND EROSION

EROSION FEATURES
UF	coastal erosion features
RT	BEACH EROSION
RT	BED FORMS
RT	BOTTOM EROSION
RT	CAVES
RT	CLIFFS
RT	DEEP-SEA FURROWS
RT	DENUDATION
RT	DEPOSITION FEATURES
RT	EROSION SURFACES
RT	GEOMORPHOLOGY
RT	GLACIAL EROSION
RT	GLACIAL FEATURES
RT	LANDFORMS
RT	RAISED BEACHES
RT	RIP CHANNELS
RT	SEACHANNELS
RT	SEAMOATS
RT	STACKS
RT	SUBMARINE CANYONS
RT	SUBMARINE FEATURES
RT	TERRACES
RT	TOPOGRAPHIC FEATURES
RT	WAVE-CUT PLATFORMS

EROSION PLATFORMS
USE	**WAVE-CUT PLATFORMS**

EROSION PREVENTION
USE	**EROSION CONTROL**

EROSION PROTECTION
USE	**EROSION CONTROL**

EROSION SURFACES
UF	planation surfaces
RT	EROSION FEATURES
RT	SURFACES
RT	WAVE-CUT PLATFORMS

ERRATICS
USE	**GLACIAL ERRATICS**

ERRORS
SN	Used only as a qualifier
NT1	ANALYTICAL ERRORS
RT	APPROXIMATION
RT	BUOY MOTION EFFECTS
RT	CORRECTIONS
RT	RESOLUTION

ERYTHROCYTES
UF	red blood cells
UF	red blood corpuscles
BT1	BLOOD CELLS
BT2	CELLS
RT	ANAEMIA
RT	ERYTHROPOIESIS
RT	NECROSES

ERYTHROPOIESIS
RT	ERYTHROCYTES
RT	HAEMATOLOGY
RT	HAEMOPOIESIS

ERYTROPHORES
USE	**CHROMATOPHORES**

ESCAPE OF WATER
USE	**FLOODS**

ESCAPEMENT
UF	escapement rate
RT	AVOIDANCE REACTIONS
RT	BIOLOGICAL SAMPLING
RT	CATCHABILITY
RT	FISHING GEAR
RT	GEAR SELECTIVITY

ESCAPEMENT (cont'd)
RT	MESH SELECTIVITY
RT	NEKTON COLLECTING DEVICES
RT	PLANKTON COLLECTING DEVICES
RT	SURVIVAL

ESCAPEMENT RATE
USE	**ESCAPEMENT**

ESCARPMENTS
UF	scarps
NT1	FAULT SCARPS
RT	FRACTURE ZONES
RT	MEDIAN VALLEYS
RT	RELIEF FORMS
RT	SUBMARINE SCARPS
RT	TOPOGRAPHIC FEATURES

ESKERS
RT	GLACIAL FEATURES

ESTERS
BT1	ORGANIC COMPOUNDS
NT1	PHTHALATE ESTERS
RT	LIPIDS

ESTIMATION
USE	**APPROXIMATION**

ESTROGENS
USE	**SEX HORMONES**

ESTUARIES
UF	estuarine oceanography
BT1	COASTAL INLETS
BT2	COASTAL WATERS
NT1	PARTIALLY-MIXED ESTUARIES
NT1	SALT-WEDGE ESTUARIES
RT	BAYS
RT	BRACKISH WATER
RT	BRACKISHWATER ECOLOGY
RT	BRACKISHWATER ENVIRONMENT
RT	COASTAL LANDFORMS
RT	COASTAL MORPHOLOGY
RT	COASTAL OCEANOGRAPHY
RT	COASTAL ZONE
RT	ESTUARINE CHEMISTRY
RT	ESTUARINE DYNAMICS
RT	ESTUARINE FRONT
RT	ESTUARINE SEDIMENTATION
RT	ESTUARINE TIDES
RT	FJORDS
RT	FLUSHING TIME
RT	FLUVIAL MORPHOLOGY
RT	INLETS (WATERWAYS)
RT	MUD FLATS
RT	RIVER DISCHARGE
RT	RIVERS
RT	SALINE INTRUSION
RT	SALT MARSHES
RT	SALT WEDGES
RT	SEA WATER
RT	TIDAL FLATS
RT	TIDAL INLETS
RT	WATER BODIES

ESTUARINE AQUACULTURE
USE	**BRACKISHWATER AQUACULTURE**

ESTUARINE CHEMISTRY
RT	CHEMICAL LIMNOLOGY
RT	CHEMICAL OCEANOGRAPHY
RT	ESTUARIES
RT	RIVER DISCHARGE
RT	SALT WEDGES

ESTUARINE CIRCULATION
USE   **ESTUARINE DYNAMICS**

ESTUARINE DYNAMICS
SN   Before 1982 search also ESTUARINE CIRCULATION
UF   estuarine circulation
BT1   SHELF DYNAMICS
BT2   WATER CIRCULATION
BT3   WATER MOTION
RT   BAY DYNAMICS
RT   COASTAL OCEANOGRAPHY
RT   DYNAMICAL OCEANOGRAPHY
RT   ESTUARIES
RT   ESTUARINE FRONT
RT   ESTUARINE TIDES
RT   FLUSHING TIME
RT   LONGITUDINAL DISPERSION
RT   LONGSHORE CURRENTS
RT   NEARSHORE CURRENTS
RT   NEARSHORE DYNAMICS
RT   PARTIALLY-MIXED ESTUARIES
RT   SALT WEDGES
RT   SALT-WEDGE ESTUARIES
RT   TIDAL CURRENTS
RT   TIDAL MIXING
RT   TRANSVERSE MIXING
RT   WATER MIXING

ESTUARINE ENVIRONMENT
USE   **BRACKISHWATER ENVIRONMENT**

ESTUARINE FISH
USE   **BRACKISHWATER FISH**

ESTUARINE FISHERIES
SN   Fisheries in estuaries and coastal lagoons
BT1   FISHERIES
RT   ARTISANAL FISHING
RT   BRACKISHWATER FISH
RT   COASTAL FISHERIES
RT   ESTUARINE ORGANISMS
RT   FINFISH FISHERIES
RT   MARINE FISHERIES
RT   MULLET FISHERIES
RT   OYSTER FISHERIES
RT   RIVER FISHERIES

ESTUARINE FRONT
UF   estuarine interface
UF   freshwater-seawater interface
BT1   OCEANIC FRONTS
BT2   FRONTS
RT   ESTUARIES
RT   ESTUARINE DYNAMICS
RT   RIVER PLUMES

ESTUARINE INTERFACE
USE   **ESTUARINE FRONT**

ESTUARINE MOLLUSCS
USE   **BRACKISHWATER MOLLUSCS**

ESTUARINE OCEANOGRAPHY
USE   **ESTUARIES**

ESTUARINE ORGANISMS
SN   Added in 1980
UF   brackishwater organisms
BT1   AQUATIC ORGANISMS
RT   BRACKISHWATER AQUACULTURE
RT   BRACKISHWATER ECOLOGY
RT   BRACKISHWATER FISH
RT   BRACKISHWATER MOLLUSCS
RT   ESTUARINE FISHERIES
RT   EURYHALINITY
RT   SALINITY TOLERANCE

ESTUARINE POLLUTION
USE   **BRACKISHWATER POLLUTION**

ESTUARINE SEDIMENTATION
BT1   SEDIMENTATION
RT   BRACKISHWATER ENVIRONMENT
RT   ESTUARIES
RT   INTERTIDAL SEDIMENTATION
RT   SALT MARSHES
RT   SEDIMENTARY ENVIRONMENTS
RT   TIDAL DEPOSITS
RT   TIDAL FLATS

ESTUARINE TIDES
BT1   TIDES
BT2   TIDAL MOTION
RT   ESTUARIES
RT   ESTUARINE DYNAMICS
RT   SHALLOW-WATER TIDES

ETHANE
BT1   ACYCLIC HYDROCARBONS
BT2   SATURATED HYDROCARBONS
BT3   HYDROCARBONS
BT4   ORGANIC COMPOUNDS

ETHENE
UF   ethylene
BT1   ALKENES
BT2   UNSATURATED HYDROCARBONS
BT3   HYDROCARBONS
BT4   ORGANIC COMPOUNDS

ETHOLOGY
SN   Study of all aspects of behaviour using biological methods. Before 1982 search BEHAVIOUR
BT1   ECOLOGY
RT   BEHAVIOUR

ETHYLENE
USE   **ETHENE**

ETHYNE
UF   acetylene
BT1   ALKYNES
BT2   UNSATURATED HYDROCARBONS
BT3   HYDROCARBONS
BT4   ORGANIC COMPOUNDS

ETIOLOGY
USE   **AETIOLOGY**

EULER EQUATIONS OF MOTION
USE   **EQUATIONS OF MOTION**

EULERIAN CURRENT MEASUREMENT
SN   Before 1982 search also EULERIAN METHODS (CURRENT MEASUREMENT)
UF   eulerian methods (current measurement)
BT1   CURRENT MEASUREMENT
BT2   FLOW MEASUREMENT
BT3   MEASUREMENT
RT   ACOUSTIC CURRENT METERS
RT   CURRENT METER DATA
RT   CURRENT METERS

EULERIAN METHODS (CURRENT MEASUREMENT)
USE   **EULERIAN CURRENT MEASUREMENT**

EULITTORAL ZONE
BT1   LITTORAL ZONE
BT2   BENTHIC ENVIRONMENT
BT3   AQUATIC ENVIRONMENT
BT4   ENVIRONMENTS
RT   INTERTIDAL ENVIRONMENT
RT   INTERTIDAL SEDIMENTATION

EUPHOTIC ZONE
RT   APHOTIC ZONE
RT   COMPENSATION DEPTH
RT   DISPHOTIC ZONE
RT   EPIPELAGIC ZONE
RT   LENITIC ENVIRONMENT
RT   LIGHT PENETRATION
RT   MARINE ENVIRONMENT
RT   MESOPELAGIC ZONE
RT   PHOTOSYNTHESIS
RT   PHYTOPLANKTON
RT   PRIMARY PRODUCTION

EUROPIUM
BT1   CHEMICAL ELEMENTS
RT   EUROPIUM COMPOUNDS
RT   EUROPIUM ISOTOPES
RT   METALS
RT   RADIOISOTOPES
RT   RARE EARTHS
RT   TRACE METALS
RT   TRANSITION ELEMENTS

EUROPIUM COMPOUNDS
RT   CHEMICAL COMPOUNDS
RT   EUROPIUM

EUROPIUM ISOTOPES
BT1   ISOTOPES
RT   EUROPIUM

EURYHALINE ORGANISMS
USE   **EURYHALINITY**

EURYHALINE SPECIES
USE   **EURYHALINITY**

EURYHALINITY
SN   Added in 1980
UF   euryhaline organisms
UF   euryhaline species
BT1   BIOLOGICAL PROPERTIES
BT2   PROPERTIES
RT   ECOLOGICAL DISTRIBUTION
RT   ESTUARINE ORGANISMS
RT   OSMOREGULATION
RT   OSMOTIC ADAPTATIONS
RT   SALINITY TOLERANCE
RT   STENOHALINITY

EURYTHERMAL ORGANISMS
USE   **EURYTHERMY**

EURYTHERMY
SN   Added in 1980
UF   eurythermal organisms
BT1   BIOLOGICAL PROPERTIES
BT2   PROPERTIES
RT   ECOLOGICAL DISTRIBUTION
RT   STENOTHERMY
RT   TEMPERATURE TOLERANCE

EUSTASY
USE   **EUSTATIC CHANGES**

EUSTATIC CHANGES
SN   World-wide sea level changes resulting from change in absolute volume of seawater due mainly to climatic change
UF   eustasy
RT   CLIMATIC CHANGES
RT   CRYOSPHERE
RT   DEGLACIATION
RT   EMERGENT SHORELINES
RT   EPEIROGENY
RT   GLACIATION
RT   HYDROSPHERE
RT   ICE AGES
RT   ICE CAPS

EUSTATIC CHANGES (cont'd)
RT	ICE VOLUME
RT	INTERGLACIAL PERIODS
RT	ISOSTASY
RT	LAND BRIDGES
RT	PROGRADATION
RT	RAISED BEACHES
RT	REGRESSIONS
RT	RETROGRADATION
RT	SEA LEVEL
RT	SUBMERGED SHORELINES
RT	SUBMERGENCE
RT	TRANSGRESSIONS
RT	WATER BUDGET

EUTROPHIC LAKES
BT1	LAKES
BT2	INLAND WATERS
RT	DYSTROPHIC LAKES
RT	EUTROPHIC WATERS
RT	EUTROPHICATION
RT	OLIGOTROPHIC LAKES

EUTROPHIC WATERS
RT	BRACKISHWATER ENVIRONMENT
RT	EUTROPHIC LAKES
RT	EUTROPHICATION
RT	INLAND WATER ENVIRONMENT
RT	MARINE ENVIRONMENT

EUTROPHICATION
SN	The continuing process of increasing fertility of water
RT	AGRICULTURAL POLLUTION
RT	ALGAL BLOOMS
RT	AQUACULTURE EFFLUENTS
RT	CULTURE EFFECTS
RT	DETERGENTS
RT	DISSOLVED OXYGEN
RT	EUTROPHIC LAKES
RT	EUTROPHIC WATERS
RT	FISH KILL
RT	FRESHWATER LAKES
RT	HYPERTROPHY
RT	INDUSTRIAL WASTES
RT	LAKES
RT	LIMNOLOGY
RT	MORTALITY CAUSES
RT	NUTRIENTS (MINERAL)
RT	POLLUTION EFFECTS
RT	PRIMARY PRODUCTION
RT	RED TIDES
RT	STAGNANT WATER
RT	WASTEWATER AQUACULTURE
RT	WATER PROPERTIES
RT	WATER QUALITY

EVACUATION
RT	ACCOMMODATION
RT	EMERGENCIES
RT	HEALTH AND SAFETY
RT	OFFSHORE STRUCTURES
RT	VEHICLES

EVALUATION
SN	Used only as a qualifier
UF	appraisal
NT1	PERFORMANCE ASSESSMENT
NT1	SITE SELECTION
RT	ACCEPTABILITY
RT	CERTIFICATION
RT	ECONOMICS
RT	FEASIBILITY
RT	RELIABILITY
RT	STOCK ASSESSMENT

EVAPORATION
BT1	VAPORIZATION
BT2	PHASE CHANGES
NT1	EVAPOTRANSPIRATION
RT	ABLATION
RT	AIR TEMPERATURE
RT	AIR-ICE INTERFACE
RT	AIR-WATER EXCHANGES
RT	AIR-WATER INTERFACE
RT	BOWEN RATIO
RT	BRINES
RT	CLIMATOLOGY
RT	CONDENSATION
RT	DEHYDRATION
RT	DESALINATION
RT	DESICCATION
RT	DIFFUSION
RT	DRYING
RT	ENERGY BALANCE
RT	ENERGY BUDGET
RT	EVAPORATION REDUCTION
RT	EVAPORATION TANKS
RT	HEAT BALANCE
RT	HEAT BUDGET
RT	HEAT EXCHANGE
RT	HYDROLOGIC CYCLE
RT	LATENT HEAT TRANSFER
RT	METEOROLOGY
RT	MOISTURE
RT	MOISTURE TRANSFER
RT	SALINITY
RT	SALTS
RT	SATURATION
RT	SOLAR RADIATION
RT	SUBLIMATION
RT	SURFACE WATER
RT	TRANSPIRATION
RT	VAPORIZATION HEAT
RT	WATER BUDGET
RT	WATER PROPERTIES
RT	WATER TEMPERATURE

EVAPORATION CONTROL
USE	**EVAPORATION REDUCTION**

EVAPORATION FOG
USE	**FOG**

EVAPORATION PONDS
USE	**EVAPORATION TANKS**

EVAPORATION REDUCTION
UF	evaporation control
BT1	DAMPING
RT	EVAPORATION
RT	MONOMOLECULAR FILMS
RT	WATER CONSERVATION

EVAPORATION TANKS
UF	evaporation ponds
BT1	TANKS
BT2	CONTAINERS
RT	DESALINATION
RT	EVAPORATION

EVAPORITES
BT1	AUTHIGENIC MINERALS
BT2	SEDIMENTS
RT	ANHYDRITE
RT	BORATE MINERALS
RT	CHEMICAL SEDIMENTS
RT	DOLOMITE
RT	GYPSUM
RT	HALITE
RT	SABKHAS
RT	SALT DEPOSITS
RT	SEDIMENTARY ROCKS
RT	SODIUM CHLORIDE

EVAPOTRANSPIRATION
SN	Loss of water vapour from soil surface and vegetation combined. Added in 1980
BT1	EVAPORATION
BT2	VAPORIZATION
BT3	PHASE CHANGES
RT	ENERGY BALANCE
RT	ENERGY BUDGET
RT	ENVIRONMENTAL EFFECTS
RT	HYDROLOGIC CYCLE
RT	STOMATA
RT	TRANSPIRATION
RT	WATER BALANCE
RT	WATER CONTENT

EVISCERATION
USE	**GUTTING**

EVOLUTION
SN	Use of a more specific term is recommended
UF	bioevolution
UF	convergent evolution
UF	evolution (organisms)
BT1	BIOLOGICAL PHENOMENA
RT	BIOGENESIS
RT	BIOGENY
RT	BIOLOGICAL SPECIATION
RT	BIOSELECTION
RT	DEGENERATION
RT	GENETIC DRIFT
RT	GENETICS
RT	MORPHOGENESIS
RT	MUTATIONS
RT	NATURAL SELECTION
RT	NEW GENERA
RT	NEW SPECIES
RT	PHYLOGENETICS
RT	PHYLOGENY
RT	POPULATION GENETICS
RT	PROTISTS
RT	SEXUAL SELECTION
RT	SIBLING SPECIES
RT	TAXONOMY
RT	TYPOLOGY

EVOLUTION (ATMOSPHERE)
USE	**ATMOSPHERE EVOLUTION**

EVOLUTION (ORGANISMS)
USE	**EVOLUTION**

EVOLUTION (SEAWATER)
USE	**SEAWATER EVOLUTION**

EVOLUTIONARY RETROGRESSION
USE	**DEGENERATION**

EXAMINATIONS
USE	**INSPECTION**

EXCAVATING
USE	**DREDGING**

EXCAVATION (ARCHAEOLOGY)
USE	**ARCHAEOLOGY**

EXCAVATION UNDERWATER
RT	CONSTRUCTION
RT	DREDGING

EXCHANGE CAPACITY
UF	cation exchange capacity
RT	ADSORPTION
RT	CATIONS
RT	DISSOLUTION
RT	IONS
RT	SOLUTIONS

EXCHANGE COEFFICIENTS
UF	austausch coefficients
UF	eddy coefficients
NT1	DIFFUSION COEFFICIENTS
NT1	VISCOSITY COEFFICIENTS
NT2	EDDY VISCOSITY COEFFICIENT
NT2	MOLECULAR VISCOSITY COEFFICIENTS
RT	EDDY FLUX
RT	EDDY VISCOSITY
RT	MIXING LENGTH

EXCLUSIVE ECONOMIC ZONE
UF	eez
UF	exclusive fishery zone
UF	exclusive fishing zone
BT1	OCEAN SPACE
RT	ALLOCATION SYSTEMS
RT	CAPTURE FISHERY ECONOMICS
RT	COASTAL STATES
RT	CONTIGUOUS ZONES
RT	EXPLOITATION
RT	EXPLORATION RIGHTS
RT	FISHERY BOUNDARIES
RT	FISHERY ECONOMICS
RT	FISHERY PROTECTION
RT	FISHERY REGULATIONS
RT	FISHING RIGHTS
RT	FOREIGN FISHING
RT	ILLEGAL FISHING
RT	RESOURCE CONSERVATION
RT	RESOURCE MANAGEMENT
RT	SHARED STOCKS
RT	SURVEILLANCE AND ENFORCEMENT
RT	TERRITORIAL WATERS
RT	UNDERWATER EXPLOITATION

EXCLUSIVE FISHERY ZONE
USE	**EXCLUSIVE ECONOMIC ZONE**

EXCLUSIVE FISHING RIGHTS
USE	**FISHING RIGHTS**

EXCLUSIVE FISHING ZONE
USE	**EXCLUSIVE ECONOMIC ZONE**

EXCLUSIVE RIGHTS
SN	Added in 1980
BT1	RIGHTS
RT	EXPLOITATION
RT	FISHING RIGHTS
RT	NATURAL RESOURCES
RT	UNDERWATER EXPLORATION
RT	WATER RIGHTS

EXCRETION
RT	AMOEBOCYTES
RT	BIOACCUMULATION
RT	EXCRETORY ORGANS
RT	EXCRETORY PRODUCTS
RT	RADIONUCLIDE KINETICS
RT	SECRETION
RT	WATER BALANCE

EXCRETORY ORGANS
BT1	ANIMAL ORGANS
BT2	BODY ORGANS
NT1	KIDNEYS
NT1	SPLEEN
RT	ANATOMY
RT	BLADDERS
RT	EXCRETION
RT	EXCRETORY PRODUCTS
RT	LACTATION

EXCRETORY PRODUCTS
NT1	FAECAL PELLETS
NT1	URINE
RT	DIGESTION
RT	EXCRETION
RT	EXCRETORY ORGANS

EXCRETORY PRODUCTS (cont'd)
RT	LYMPHOCYTES
RT	WATER BALANCE

EXHIBITIONS
UF	trade shows
RT	BROCHURES
RT	CONFERENCES
RT	MUSEUMS

EXOCRINE GLANDS
BT1	GLANDS
BT2	SECRETORY ORGANS
RT	DIGESTIVE GLANDS
RT	MUCINS
RT	MUCUS

EXOPHTHALMIA
SN	Protruding of fish eyeballs as a result of accumulation of fluid or gases at the back of the eye socket. Added in 1980
UF	popeye
BT1	SYMPTOMS
RT	BUBBLE DISEASE

EXOSKELETON
BT1	SKELETON
BT2	MUSCULOSKELETAL SYSTEM
NT1	CARAPACE
NT1	CUTICLES
NT1	SCALES
RT	BONY FINS
RT	CHITIN
RT	SHELLS

EXPEDITION REPORTS
SN	Final published reports containing results etc. of both cruises and multiship expeditions
BT1	DOCUMENTS
RT	ATLASES
RT	CRUISE REPORTS
RT	CRUISES
RT	EXPEDITIONS
RT	HISTORICAL ACCOUNT
RT	MULTISHIP EXPEDITIONS

EXPEDITION STATIONS
USE	**CRUISE STATIONS**

EXPEDITIONS
SN	Use only for international projects involving simultaneous surveys of land, sea and air, e.g. IGY. For oceanographic surveys use narrower term. Before 1982 search also CRUISES
NT1	CRUISES
NT1	MULTISHIP EXPEDITIONS
RT	ACRONYMS
RT	CRUISE STATIONS
RT	EXPEDITION REPORTS
RT	EXPLORATION
RT	GEOGRAPHICAL EXPLORATION
RT	OCEANOGRAPHIC SURVEYS
RT	SURVEYS

EXPEDITIONS (MULTISHIP)
USE	**MULTISHIP EXPEDITIONS**

EXPEDITIONS (ONE VESSEL)
USE	**CRUISES**

EXPENDABLE BATHYTHERMOGRAPHS
USE	**XBTS**

EXPENDABLE DRIFTING BUOYS
USE	**DRIFTING DATA BUOYS**

EXPENDITURES
USE	**COSTS**

EXPENSES
USE	**COSTS**

EXPERIMENTAL CULTURE
UF	pilot-scale culture
BT1	AQUACULTURE SYSTEMS
RT	AQUACULTURE
RT	AQUACULTURE DEVELOPMENT
RT	AQUACULTURE TECHNIQUES
RT	CULTURE TANKS
RT	CULTURES
RT	EXPERIMENTAL RESEARCH
RT	LABORATORY CULTURE
RT	REARING
RT	RECIRCULATING SYSTEMS

EXPERIMENTAL DATA
SN	Used only as a qualifier
UF	data (experimental)
BT1	DATA
RT	CONTROLLED CONDITIONS
RT	EXPERIMENTAL RESEARCH
RT	GEAR RESEARCH
RT	TEST EQUIPMENT
RT	TESTS

EXPERIMENTAL FISHERIES
USE	**EXPERIMENTAL FISHING**

EXPERIMENTAL FISHING
UF	experimental fisheries
UF	test fishing
BT1	FISHING OPERATIONS
RT	CATCHING METHODS
RT	EXPLORATORY FISHING
RT	FISHING
RT	FISHING GEAR
RT	FISHING TECHNOLOGY
RT	FISHING VESSELS
RT	GEAR RESEARCH
RT	GEAR SELECTIVITY
RT	KRILL FISHERIES

EXPERIMENTAL REARING
USE	**REARING**

EXPERIMENTAL RESEARCH
SN	Research done in experimental/laboratory conditions. Used only as a qualifier
UF	laboratory research
UF	research (experimental)
BT1	RESEARCH
RT	CONTROLLED CONDITIONS
RT	EXPERIMENTAL CULTURE
RT	EXPERIMENTAL DATA
RT	LABORATORIES
RT	ORGAN REMOVAL
RT	REARING
RT	SCIENTIFIC PERSONNEL

EXPERT SYSTEMS
USE	**ARTIFICIAL INTELLIGENCE**

EXPERTS
SN	Restricted to professionals involved with aquatic sciences and technology. Added in 1980
UF	professionals
UF	specialists
BT1	PERSONNEL
NT1	DIVERS
NT1	ENGINEERS
NT1	TECHNICIANS

EXPERTS (cont'd)
NT2	AQUACULTURISTS
RT	CONSULTANTS
RT	DIRECTORIES
RT	SCIENTIFIC PERSONNEL

EXPLODING WIRE
BT1	SEISMIC ENERGY SOURCES

EXPLOITATION
UF	commercial exploitation
UF	exploitation rate
UF	resource exploitation
NT1	UNDERWATER EXPLOITATION
RT	AQUATIC SCIENCES
RT	COMMERCIAL FISHING
RT	EXCLUSIVE ECONOMIC ZONE
RT	EXCLUSIVE RIGHTS
RT	INTERNATIONAL WATERS
RT	MARINE TECHNOLOGY
RT	MINERAL RESOURCES
RT	MULTIPLE USE OF RESOURCES
RT	NATURAL RESOURCES
RT	OCEAN SPACE
RT	OFFSHORE ENGINEERING
RT	OFFSHORE OPERATIONS
RT	OIL AND GAS INDUSTRY
RT	OIL WELLS
RT	PIPELINES
RT	PLANNING
RT	PRODUCTION COST
RT	RENTAL
RT	RESOURCE AVAILABILITY
RT	RESOURCE CONSERVATION
RT	RESOURCE DEVELOPMENT
RT	RESOURCE MANAGEMENT
RT	RESOURCES
RT	SURVEILLANCE AND ENFORCEMENT
RT	TECHNOLOGY
RT	TERRITORIAL WATERS

EXPLOITATION (MINERALS)
USE **MINING**

EXPLOITATION (OIL AND GAS)
USE **OIL AND GAS PRODUCTION**

EXPLOITATION RATE
USE **EXPLOITATION**

EXPLORATION
SN	Use of a specific term is recommended
NT1	GEOGRAPHICAL EXPLORATION
NT1	GEOPHYSICAL EXPLORATION
NT2	ELECTRICAL EXPLORATION
NT2	ELECTROMAGNETIC EXPLORATION
NT2	GEOTHERMAL EXPLORATION
NT2	GRAVITY EXPLORATION
NT2	MAGNETIC EXPLORATION
NT2	SEISMIC EXPLORATION
NT3	SEISMIC REFLECTION PROFILING
NT3	SEISMIC REFRACTION PROFILING
NT3	SUB-BOTTOM PROFILING
NT1	POLAR EXPLORATION
NT1	RESOURCE EXPLORATION
NT2	MINERAL EXPLORATION
NT2	OIL AND GAS EXPLORATION
NT1	UNDERWATER EXPLORATION
RT	EXPEDITIONS
RT	MARINE TECHNOLOGY
RT	SURVEYS

EXPLORATION (MINERALS)
USE **MINERAL EXPLORATION**

EXPLORATION RIGHTS
SN	Added in 1980
BT1	RIGHTS
RT	EXCLUSIVE ECONOMIC ZONE
RT	LEGAL ASPECTS

EXPLORATORY BEHAVIOUR
SN	Added in 1980
BT1	BEHAVIOUR
RT	AQUATIC ENVIRONMENT
RT	HABITAT

EXPLORATORY DRILLING
USE **OIL AND GAS EXPLORATION**

EXPLORATORY FISHING
BT1	FISHING OPERATIONS
RT	CATCH COMPOSITION
RT	ECHO SURVEYS
RT	EXPERIMENTAL FISHING
RT	FISHERY RESOURCES
RT	FISHING GROUNDS
RT	POTENTIAL RESOURCES
RT	STOCK ASSESSMENT
RT	UNCONVENTIONAL RESOURCES

EXPLORATORY MINING
USE **MINERAL EXPLORATION**

EXPLOSIONS
NT1	NUCLEAR EXPLOSIONS
NT1	UNDERWATER EXPLOSIONS
RT	BLASTING
RT	EXPLOSIVES
RT	FIRE
RT	FIRE HAZARDS
RT	IMPLOSIONS

EXPLOSIVE FISHING
SN	Handling of explosives for capture of aquatic animals, mainly fish
BT1	CATCHING METHODS
RT	FISHERY REGULATIONS
RT	FISHING
RT	STUPEFYING METHODS

EXPLOSIVE WELDING
BT1	WELDING

EXPLOSIVES
NT1	SHAPED CHARGES
RT	BLASTING
RT	DETONATORS
RT	EXPLOSIONS
RT	HAZARDOUS MATERIALS
RT	HEALTH AND SAFETY
RT	SAFETY REGULATIONS
RT	SEISMIC ENERGY SOURCES

EXPORTS
USE **TRADE**

EXPOSED ENVIRONMENT
USE **EXPOSED HABITATS**

EXPOSED HABITATS
SN	Added in 1980
UF	exposed environment
BT1	HABITAT
RT	ECOLOGICAL ZONATION
RT	EXPOSURE TOLERANCE
RT	INTERTIDAL ENVIRONMENT
RT	SURF
RT	WAVE ACTION

EXPOSURE (TO AIR)
USE **AIR EXPOSURE**

EXPOSURE TOLERANCE
SN	Added in 1980
BT1	TOLERANCE
BT2	BIOLOGICAL PROPERTIES
BT3	PROPERTIES
RT	AIR EXPOSURE
RT	EXPOSED HABITATS

EXPOSURE TOLERANCE (cont'd)
RT	SHELTERED HABITATS

EXTENDED JURISDICTION
SN	Added in 1980
UF	extraterritoriality
BT1	JURISDICTION
RT	COASTAL STATES
RT	FISHING RIGHTS
RT	LEGISLATION
RT	OCEAN SPACE
RT	POLITICAL ASPECTS

EXTENSIVE AQUACULTURE
USE **EXTENSIVE CULTURE**

EXTENSIVE CULTURE
SN	Added in 1980
UF	extensive aquaculture
BT1	AQUACULTURE SYSTEMS
RT	BRACKISHWATER AQUACULTURE
RT	CULTURES
RT	FISH CULTURE
RT	FRESHWATER AQUACULTURE
RT	POND CULTURE
RT	SEED COLLECTION
RT	VALLICULTURE

EXTERNAL ANATOMY
USE **ORGANISM MORPHOLOGY**

EXTERNAL FERTILIZATION
USE **BIOLOGICAL FERTILIZATION**

EXTEROCEPTORS
USE **RECEPTORS**

EXTINCTION COEFFICIENT
SN	Before 1982 search ABSORPTIVITY
UF	attenuation coefficient
BT1	OPTICAL PROPERTIES
BT2	PHYSICAL PROPERTIES
BT3	PROPERTIES
RT	ABSORPTION COEFFICIENT
RT	ATTENUANCE
RT	LIGHT ABSORPTION
RT	LIGHT ATTENUATION
RT	OPTICAL CLASSIFICATION
RT	SECCHI DISCS
RT	VISIBILITY UNDERWATER
RT	WATER TRANSPARENCY

EXTINCTION OF SPECIES
USE **SPECIES EXTINCTION**

EXTRACTION (ANIMAL OIL)
USE **ANIMAL OIL EXTRACTION**

EXTRACTION (CHEMICAL)
USE **CHEMICAL EXTRACTION**

EXTRACTION (SALTS)
USE **DESALINATION**

EXTRATERRESTRIAL INTERACTIONS
USE **SOLAR-TERRESTRIAL ACTIVITY**

EXTRATERRESTRIAL MATERIAL
SN	Material of cosmic origin found in sediments
UF	tektites
NT1	COSMIC DUST
NT1	COSMIC SPHERULES
RT	ALLOCHTHONOUS DEPOSITS
RT	ASTRONOMY
RT	PELAGIC SEDIMENTS
RT	SEDIMENTS

ASFIS Thesaurus

EXTRATERRESTRIAL RADIATION
SN	Solar radiation received at outer limit of earth's atmosphere
BT1	SOLAR RADIATION
BT2	ELECTROMAGNETIC RADIATION
BT3	RADIATIONS
RT	DOWNWARD LONG WAVE RADIATION
RT	SOLAR CONSTANT

EXTRATERRITORIALITY
USE	**EXTENDED JURISDICTION**

EXTREME VALUES
SN	Used only as a qualifier. Use with property or phenomenon
UF	extremes
NT1	ANNUAL RANGE
RT	ASTRONOMICAL TIDES
RT	EXTREME WAVES
RT	HIGHEST ASTRONOMICAL TIDES
RT	LOWEST ASTRONOMICAL TIDES

EXTREME WAVES
RT	EXTREME VALUES
RT	SURFACE WATER WAVES
RT	WAVE HEIGHT

EXTREMES
USE	**EXTREME VALUES**

EYES
BT1	PHOTORECEPTORS
BT2	SENSE ORGANS
BT3	ANIMAL ORGANS
BT4	BODY ORGANS
NT1	COMPOUND EYES
NT1	EYESTALKS
NT1	RETINAS
RT	HEAD
RT	VISION
RT	VISUAL STIMULI

EYESTALK ABLATION
USE	**EYESTALK EXTIRPATION**

EYESTALK EXTIRPATION
SN	Before 1982 search ORGAN REMOVAL
UF	eyestalk ablation
BT1	ORGAN REMOVAL
RT	EYESTALKS
RT	MARINE CRUSTACEANS
RT	MOULTING
RT	SEXUAL MATURITY

EYESTALKS
BT1	EYES
BT2	PHOTORECEPTORS
BT3	SENSE ORGANS
BT4	ANIMAL ORGANS
RT	EYESTALK EXTIRPATION

FACIES
NT1	BIOFACIES
NT1	LITHOFACIES
NT1	METAMORPHIC FACIES
NT2	AMPHIBOLITE FACIES
NT2	GREENSCHIST FACIES
NT2	ZEOLITE FACIES
NT1	SHELF FACIES

FACILITIES
USE	**RESOURCES**

FACSIMILE TRANSMISSION
BT1	DATA TRANSMISSION
RT	WEATHER MAPS

FACTORY SHIPS
BT1	SUPPORT SHIPS
BT2	SHIPS
BT3	SURFACE CRAFT
BT4	VEHICLES
RT	CATCHERS
RT	FISHERY INDUSTRY EQUIPMENT
RT	FISHERY INDUSTRY PLANTS
RT	FISHING VESSELS
RT	HIGH SEAS FISHERIES
RT	WHALING
RT	WORK PLATFORMS

FAECAL PELLETS
UF	fecal pellets
BT1	EXCRETORY PRODUCTS
RT	DEFAECATION
RT	TRACE FOSSILS

FAILURES
SN	Significant result of damage, defects or deterioration
RT	DAMAGE
RT	DEFECTS
RT	DETERIORATION
RT	RELIABILITY
RT	REPLACING
RT	SCOURING
RT	SETTLEMENT (STRUCTURAL)
RT	SLOPE STABILITY

FAIRINGS
RT	CABLES

FALL
USE	**AUTUMN**

FALL SEASON
USE	**AUTUMN**

FALLING GEAR
USE	**CAST NETS**

FALLOUT
UF	atmospheric fallout
UF	radioactive fallout
RT	AEROSOLS
RT	AIR POLLUTION
RT	ATMOSPHERIC CHEMISTRY
RT	ATMOSPHERIC PARTICULATES
RT	DUST
RT	FISSION PRODUCTS
RT	NUCLEAR RADIATIONS
RT	RADIOACTIVE AEROSOLS
RT	RADIOACTIVE CONTAMINATION
RT	RADIOACTIVE POLLUTANTS
RT	RADIOACTIVE WASTES
RT	RADIOACTIVITY
RT	RADIOISOTOPES

FANS
RT	ALLUVIAL FANS
RT	DEEP-SEA FANS
RT	TURBIDITY CURRENTS

FARM PONDS
USE	**FISH PONDS**

FARMED FISH ECONOMICS
USE	**AQUACULTURE ECONOMICS**

FAST ICE
BT1	FLOATING ICE
BT2	ICE
RT	ICE FOOT
RT	ICE SHELVES
RT	LAKE ICE
RT	SEA ICE

FAT CONTENT
USE	**BODY CONDITIONS**

FATE
SN	Fate of substances in the environment. Used only as a qualifier
RT	ACCUMULATION
RT	BIOACCUMULATION
RT	DEGRADATION
RT	DILUTION
RT	DISPERSION
RT	PERSISTENCE
RT	POLLUTANT PERSISTENCE
RT	POLLUTANTS
RT	POLLUTION EFFECTS
RT	WEATHERING

FATIGUE (BIOLOGICAL)
USE	**BIOLOGICAL STRESS**

FATIGUE (MATERIALS)
SN	Before 1982 search STRESS
NT1	METAL FATIGUE
RT	CORROSION
RT	CYCLIC LOADING
RT	DETERIORATION
RT	STRESS
RT	STRESS CORROSION

FATS
BT1	LIPIDS
BT2	ORGANIC COMPOUNDS
RT	BILE
RT	CHEMICAL COMPOUNDS
RT	CHEMICAL EXTRACTION
RT	FATTY ACIDS
RT	NUTRITION
RT	NUTRITIVE VALUE
RT	ORGANIC CONSTITUENTS
RT	VITAMINS
RT	YOLK

FATTENING PONDS
USE	**GROWING PONDS**

FATTY ACIDS
BT1	ORGANIC ACIDS
BT2	ORGANIC COMPOUNDS
NT1	POLYUNSATURATED FATTY ACIDS
RT	CHEMICAL COMPOUNDS
RT	FATS
RT	HYDROCARBONS

FAULT ESCARPMENTS
USE	**FAULT SCARPS**

FAULT SCARPS
UF	fault escarpments
BT1	ESCARPMENTS
RT	CLIFFS
RT	FAULTS
RT	RELIEF FORMS
RT	SUBMARINE SCARPS

FAULT ZONES
RT	FAULTS
RT	FRACTURE ZONES
RT	MEDIAN VALLEYS
RT	RIFT VALLEYS
RT	RIFT ZONES
RT	RIFTING

FAULTS
UF	faults (geology)
UF	geological faults
BT1	GEOLOGICAL STRUCTURES
NT1	TRANSFORM FAULTS
RT	FAULT SCARPS
RT	FAULT ZONES
RT	FRACTURE ZONES

ASFIS Thesaurus

FAULTS (cont'd)
RT	GRABEN
RT	MEDIAN VALLEYS
RT	RIFT VALLEYS
RT	RIFT ZONES
RT	ROCK DEFORMATION
RT	SHEAR ZONE

FAULTS (DEFECTS)
USE	**DEFECTS**

FAULTS (GEOLOGY)
USE	**FAULTS**

FAUNAL PROVINCES
RT	BIOGEOGRAPHY

FEASIBILITY
SN	Use only as a qualifier. More specific term is recommended. Added in 1980
NT1	ECONOMIC FEASIBILITY
NT1	TECHNICAL FEASIBILITY
RT	COST ANALYSIS
RT	ECONOMICS
RT	EVALUATION
RT	FEASIBILITY STUDIES
RT	FINANCING
RT	OPERATIONS RESEARCH
RT	PREDICTION
RT	PRODUCTION COST
RT	RESOURCE MANAGEMENT
RT	RISKS

FEASIBILITY (ECONOMICS)
USE	**ECONOMIC FEASIBILITY**

FEASIBILITY (TECHNICAL)
USE	**TECHNICAL FEASIBILITY**

FEASIBILITY STUDIES
SN	Use only as a qualifier. Before 1982 search FEASIBILITY
RT	COST ANALYSIS
RT	ECONOMIC FEASIBILITY
RT	ECONOMICS
RT	FEASIBILITY
RT	FINANCING
RT	OPERATIONS RESEARCH
RT	PRODUCTION COST
RT	SITE SELECTION
RT	TECHNICAL FEASIBILITY

FEATHERS
SN	Added in 1980
UF	contour feathers
UF	filoplumes
UF	plumulae
BT1	INTEGUMENTARY SYSTEM
BT2	ANATOMICAL STRUCTURES
RT	AQUATIC BIRDS

FECAL PELLETS
USE	**FAECAL PELLETS**

FECUNDITY
SN	An organism's capacity to produce offspring
UF	fertility (reproductive)
UF	natality
BT1	BIOLOGICAL PROPERTIES
BT2	PROPERTIES
RT	BROOD STOCKS
RT	EGG COUNTERS
RT	EGGS
RT	LARVAE
RT	OVARIES
RT	RECRUITMENT
RT	SPERM
RT	TESTES

FEDERAL GOVERNMENTS
USE	**GOVERNMENTS**

FEDERAL JURISDICTION
USE	**JURISDICTION**

FEE FISHING
SN	An enterprise in which catchable organisms are stocked into ponds or lakes and customers pay for the privilege of fishing. Added in 1980
RT	FISHING
RT	LAKE FISHERIES
RT	SPORT FISHING
RT	STOCKING (ORGANISMS)
RT	STOCKING PONDS

FEED
SN	Substances used for animal feeding by man
UF	animal feed
UF	artificial feed
NT1	PELLET FEEDS
RT	ARTIFICIAL FEEDING
RT	DIGESTIBILITY
RT	FEED EFFICIENCY
RT	FEED PREPARATION
RT	FEEDING EXPERIMENTS
RT	FISH MEAL
RT	FOOD TECHNOLOGY
RT	NUTRITIVE VALUE
RT	POWDERED PRODUCTS
RT	SEAWEED PRODUCTS
RT	SELECTIVE FEEDING
RT	SINGLE CELL PROTEINS
RT	UREA

FEED COMPOSITION
SN	Constituents and chemical composition of artificial feeds
RT	ARTIFICIAL FEEDING
RT	BODY CONDITIONS
RT	CHEMICAL COMPOSITION
RT	DIETARY DEFICIENCIES
RT	FEED EFFICIENCY
RT	FEED PREPARATION
RT	FEEDING EXPERIMENTS
RT	VITAMIN A
RT	VITAMIN C

FEED CONVERSION RATE
USE	**FEED EFFICIENCY**

FEED EFFICIENCY
SN	Added in 1982
UF	feed conversion rate
RT	ARTIFICIAL FEEDING
RT	CONVERSION FACTORS
RT	DIETARY DEFICIENCIES
RT	DIETS
RT	FEED
RT	FEED COMPOSITION
RT	FEEDING EXPERIMENTS
RT	NUTRITIVE VALUE

FEED PREPARATION
RT	ARTIFICIAL FEEDING
RT	FEED
RT	FEED COMPOSITION
RT	FEEDING EQUIPMENT
RT	FEEDING EXPERIMENTS

FEEDING
NT1	ARTIFICIAL FEEDING
NT2	SELECTIVE FEEDING
RT	ACTIVITY PATTERNS
RT	BALEENS
RT	FEEDING BEHAVIOUR
RT	FEEDING EQUIPMENT

FEEDING (cont'd)
RT	FEEDING MIGRATIONS
RT	FOOD AVAILABILITY
RT	FOOD CONVERSION
RT	NUTRITION

FEEDING BEHAVIOUR
BT1	BEHAVIOUR
NT1	CANNIBALISM
RT	ANIMAL NUTRITION
RT	CARNIVORES
RT	DETRITUS FEEDERS
RT	FEEDING
RT	FEEDING MIGRATIONS
RT	FILTER FEEDERS
RT	FOOD CHAINS
RT	FOOD PREFERENCES
RT	GRAZING
RT	HERBIVORES
RT	HETEROTROPHIC ORGANISMS
RT	MOUTH PARTS
RT	OMNIVORES
RT	PLANKTON FEEDERS
RT	POLYCULTURE
RT	PREDATION
RT	PREDATORS
RT	PREY SELECTION
RT	SCAVENGERS
RT	SCHOOLING BEHAVIOUR
RT	STOMACH CONTENT
RT	TROPHIC LEVELS
RT	TROPHODYNAMIC CYCLE

FEEDING EQUIPMENT
BT1	AQUACULTURE EQUIPMENT
BT2	EQUIPMENT
RT	ARTIFICIAL FEEDING
RT	FEED PREPARATION
RT	FEEDING

FEEDING EXPERIMENTS
SN	Added in 1980
RT	AQUACULTURE
RT	ARTIFICIAL FEEDING
RT	DIETARY DEFICIENCIES
RT	FEED
RT	FEED COMPOSITION
RT	FEED EFFICIENCY
RT	FEED PREPARATION
RT	NUTRITIONAL REQUIREMENTS

FEEDING GROUND
USE	**NURSERY GROUNDS**

FEEDING MIGRATIONS
BT1	MIGRATIONS
RT	CETOLOGY
RT	FEEDING
RT	FEEDING BEHAVIOUR
RT	NURSERY GROUNDS
RT	OCEANODROMOUS MIGRATIONS
RT	RANCHING

FELDSPARS
BT1	SILICATE MINERALS
BT2	MINERALS
NT1	ANORTHITE
NT1	ANORTHOCLASE
NT1	ORTHOCLASE
NT1	PLAGIOCLASE

FELLOWSHIPS
UF	scholarships
RT	EDUCATION
RT	GRANTS
RT	RESEARCH PROGRAMMES
RT	SCIENTIFIC PERSONNEL

FEMALES
SN   Added in 1980
BT1   SEX
RT   EGGS
RT   PARTURITION
RT   SEX CHARACTERS
RT   SEX RATIO
RT   SEXUAL MATURITY

FENDERS
RT   SHIP MOORING SYSTEMS

FERMENTATION
BT1   CHEMICAL REACTIONS
RT   ANAEROBIC BACTERIA
RT   ANAEROBIC RESPIRATION
RT   BIOCHEMICAL PHENOMENA
RT   BIOTECHNOLOGY
RT   CHEMICAL REACTIONS
RT   ENZYMES
RT   FERMENTED PRODUCTS
RT   FISH SILAGE
RT   YEASTS

FERMENTED FISH PASTE
USE   **FERMENTED PRODUCTS**

FERMENTED FISH SAUCE
USE   **FERMENTED PRODUCTS**

FERMENTED PRODUCTS
SN   Before 1982 search CURED PRODUCTS
UF   fermented fish paste
UF   fermented fish sauce
BT1   PROCESSED FISHERY PRODUCTS
BT2   FISHERY PRODUCTS
BT3   PRODUCTS
RT   FERMENTATION
RT   HUMAN FOOD
RT   MINCED PRODUCTS

FERMIUM
BT1   CHEMICAL ELEMENTS
RT   ACTINIDES
RT   FERMIUM COMPOUNDS
RT   FERMIUM ISOTOPES
RT   TRANSITION ELEMENTS
RT   TRANSURANIC ELEMENTS

FERMIUM COMPOUNDS
RT   CHEMICAL COMPOUNDS
RT   FERMIUM

FERMIUM ISOTOPES
BT1   ISOTOPES
RT   FERMIUM

FERRIC COMPOUNDS
USE   **IRON COMPOUNDS**

FERRIC PHOSPHATE
USE   **IRON PHOSPHATES**

FERRIES
USE   **PASSENGER SHIPS**

FERROMANGANESE NODULES
SN   Nodules rich in Mn, Fe, Ni, Co, and
     Cu. Before 1982 search NODULES
UF   manganese nodules
UF   polymetallic nodules
BT1   SEABED DEPOSITS
BT2   MINERAL DEPOSITS
BT3   MINERAL RESOURCES
BT4   NATURAL RESOURCES
RT   ALUMINIUM
RT   COBALT
RT   COPPER
RT   DEEP-SEA MINING
RT   FERROMANGANESE OXIDES

FERROMANGANESE NODULES (cont'd)
RT   GALLIUM
RT   IRON
RT   LEAD
RT   MAGNESIUM
RT   MANGANESE
RT   MANGANESE DEPOSITS
RT   MINERAL INDUSTRY
RT   MOLYBDENUM
RT   NICKEL
RT   NODULES
RT   SILVER
RT   TITANIUM
RT   VANADIUM
RT   ZINC
RT   ZIRCONIUM

FERROMANGANESE OXIDES
RT   FERROMANGANESE NODULES
RT   IRON
RT   MANGANESE
RT   OXIDES

FERROUS ALLOYS
BT1   ALLOYS
BT2   MATERIALS
NT1   STEEL
NT2   STAINLESS STEEL

FERROUS COMPOUNDS
USE   **IRON COMPOUNDS**

FERRUGINOUS DEPOSITS
BT1   CHEMICAL SEDIMENTS
BT2   SEDIMENTS
RT   IRONSTONE
RT   JASPILLITE

FERRY TERMINALS
UF   container ports
BT1   HARBOURS
BT2   ANCHORAGES
RT   CONTAINER SHIPS
RT   PORT INSTALLATIONS

FERTILITY
SN   Restricted to environmental quality
RT   BIOLOGICAL PRODUCTION
RT   FERTILIZERS
RT   NUTRIENTS (MINERAL)
RT   OCEANIC DESERTS
RT   PLANT NUTRITION
RT   PRIMARY PRODUCTION
RT   UPWELLING

FERTILITY (REPRODUCTIVE)
USE   **FECUNDITY**

FERTILITY VITAMIN
USE   **VITAMIN E**

FERTILIZATION (BIOLOGICAL)
USE   **BIOLOGICAL FERTILIZATION**

FERTILIZERS
SN   Chemical products used for
     artificial fertilization of soils
     or aquatic environment
RT   AGRICULTURAL POLLUTION
RT   AGRICULTURAL RUNOFF
RT   ALGAL CULTURE
RT   ASHES
RT   CHEMICAL POLLUTANTS
RT   CHEMICAL POLLUTION
RT   FERTILITY
RT   FISH MEAL
RT   GUANO
RT   HABITAT IMPROVEMENT (FERTILIZATION)
RT   LEACHING
RT   MANURE

FERTILIZERS (cont'd)
RT   NITRATES
RT   NITROGEN COMPOUNDS
RT   NUTRIENTS (MINERAL)
RT   PHOSPHATES
RT   PHOSPHORUS COMPOUNDS
RT   PLANT UTILIZATION
RT   SEAWEED CULTURE
RT   SEWAGE
RT   UREA

FESTSCHRIFTEN
UF   honour volumes
BT1   COLLECTED PAPERS
BT2   DOCUMENTS
RT   PERSONAL BIBLIOGRAPHIES
RT   SCIENTIFIC PERSONNEL

FETCH
UF   wave fetch
RT   WATER WAVE PARAMETERS
RT   WIND WAVE GENERATION
RT   WIND WAVE PARAMETERS
RT   WINDS

FETUS
USE   **FOETUS**

FIBER GLASS
USE   **FIBRE GLASS**

FIBER OPTICS
USE   **FIBRE OPTICS**

FIBER ROPE (NATURAL)
USE   **FIBRE ROPE (NATURAL)**

FIBER ROPE (SYNTHETIC)
USE   **FIBRE ROPE (SYNTHETIC)**

FIBRE GLASS
UF   fiber glass
BT1   MATERIALS
RT   CONSTRUCTION MATERIALS
RT   FIBRE OPTICS
RT   GLASS
RT   GLASS-REINFORCED PLASTICS

FIBRE OPTICS
UF   fiber optics
BT1   TECHNOLOGY
RT   FIBRE GLASS
RT   OPTICS

FIBRE ROPE (NATURAL)
UF   fiber rope (natural)
UF   natural fibre rope
BT1   ROPES

FIBRE ROPE (SYNTHETIC)
UF   fiber rope (synthetic)
UF   synthetic fibre rope
BT1   ROPES

FIELDS
SN   Used only as a qualifier. Use of a
     specific term is recommended
RT   BAROCLINIC FIELD
RT   BAROTROPIC FIELD
RT   DENSITY FIELD
RT   ELECTRIC FIELDS
RT   GRAVITY FIELD
RT   HYDROTHERMAL FIELDS
RT   ICE FIELDS
RT   LIGHT FIELDS
RT   PRESSURE FIELD
RT   TEMPERATURE FIELD
RT   VELOCITY FIELD

FILLETS (FISH)		
USE	**FISH FILLETS**	

FILLETTING
SN	Added in 1982
BT1	FISH HANDLING
BT2	FISHERY INDUSTRY
BT3	INDUSTRIES
RT	FISH FILLETS
RT	PROCESSING FISHERY PRODUCTS

FILM STRIPS
| USE | **FILMSTRIPS** |

FILMS
SN	Use only for cinema films
BT1	AUDIOVISUAL MATERIAL
BT2	DOCUMENTS
RT	COATING MATERIALS
RT	FILMSTRIPS
RT	PHOTOGRAPHIC EQUIPMENT
RT	PHOTOGRAPHY
RT	VIDEOTAPE RECORDINGS

FILMS (SURFACE)
| USE | **SURFACE FILMS** |

FILMSTRIPS
UF	film strips
BT1	AUDIOVISUAL MATERIAL
BT2	DOCUMENTS
RT	FILMS
RT	SLIDES (PHOTOGRAPHIC)

FILOPLUMES
| USE | **FEATHERS** |

FILTER FEEDERS
UF	suspension feeders
BT1	HETEROTROPHIC ORGANISMS
BT2	AQUATIC ORGANISMS
RT	BACTERIA
RT	DETRITUS
RT	FEEDING BEHAVIOUR
RT	LOPHOPHORES
RT	NANNOPLANKTON
RT	PLANKTON FEEDERS

FILTERS
SN	Use of a more specific term is
	recommended
NT1	KALMAN FILTERS
NT1	OPTICAL FILTERS
NT1	WATER FILTERS

FILTERS (BIOLOGICAL)
| USE | **BIOFILTERS** |

FILTRATION
| NT1 | WATER FILTRATION |

FILTRATION (WATER)
| USE | **WATER FILTRATION** |

FIN RAY COUNTS
| BT1 | MERISTIC COUNTS |
| RT | FINS |

FIN RAYS
| USE | **FINS** |

FIN SPINES
| USE | **FINS** |

FINANCIAL INSTITUTIONS
SN	Added in 1980
UF	banks
UF	institutions (financial)
BT1	ORGANIZATIONS
RT	ECONOMIC FEASIBILITY

FINANCIAL INSTITUTIONS (cont'd)
RT	FINANCIAL RESOURCES
RT	FINANCING
RT	INSTITUTIONAL RESOURCES
RT	RESOURCE DEVELOPMENT

FINANCIAL MANAGEMENT
SN	Added in 1980
UF	business management
UF	credit management
UF	investment management
BT1	MANAGEMENT
RT	COST ANALYSIS
RT	ECONOMIC FEASIBILITY
RT	FINANCIAL RESOURCES
RT	FINANCING

FINANCIAL MEANS
| USE | **FINANCIAL RESOURCES** |

FINANCIAL RESOURCES
SN	Added in 1980
UF	capital resources
UF	financial means
BT1	RESOURCES
RT	DEVELOPMENT POTENTIAL
RT	FINANCIAL INSTITUTIONS
RT	FINANCIAL MANAGEMENT
RT	FINANCING
RT	RESOURCE DEVELOPMENT

FINANCING
UF	funding
RT	AQUACULTURE ECONOMICS
RT	AQUACULTURE ENTERPRISES
RT	CAPTURE FISHERY ECONOMICS
RT	COOPERATIVES
RT	COST ANALYSIS
RT	COSTS
RT	ECONOMIC ANALYSIS
RT	ECONOMIC FEASIBILITY
RT	ECONOMICS
RT	FEASIBILITY
RT	FEASIBILITY STUDIES
RT	FINANCIAL INSTITUTIONS
RT	FINANCIAL MANAGEMENT
RT	FINANCIAL RESOURCES
RT	FISHERY ECONOMICS
RT	GRANTS
RT	INSURANCE
RT	INVESTMENTS
RT	MANAGEMENT
RT	MARKETING
RT	PLANNING
RT	PRICING
RT	RESEARCH PROGRAMMES
RT	RESOURCE DEVELOPMENT

FINE STRUCTURE (BIOLOGY)
| USE | **ULTRASTRUCTURE** |

FINE STRUCTURE (OCEAN)
| USE | **FINESTRUCTURE** |

FINESTRUCTURE
SN	Variations in the vertical
	distribution of temperature,
	salinity and velocity with layer
	scales ranging from 1-100 cm
UF	fine structure (ocean)
UF	finestructure (ocean)
BT1	SPATIAL VARIATIONS
RT	CTD OBSERVATIONS
RT	CTD PROFILERS
RT	MICROSTRUCTURE
RT	VERTICAL DISTRIBUTION
RT	VERTICAL PROFILES

FINESTRUCTURE (BIOLOGY)
| USE | **ULTRASTRUCTURE** |

FINESTRUCTURE (OCEAN)
| USE | **FINESTRUCTURE** |

FINFISH FISHERIES
SN	Added in 1982
BT1	FISHERIES
NT1	CLUPEOID FISHERIES
NT1	FLATFISH FISHERIES
NT1	GADOID FISHERIES
NT1	MACKEREL FISHERIES
NT1	MULLET FISHERIES
NT1	PERCOID FISHERIES
NT1	REDFISH FISHERIES
NT1	SALMON FISHERIES
NT1	SHARK FISHERIES
NT1	TUNA FISHERIES
RT	DEMERSAL FISHERIES
RT	ESTUARINE FISHERIES
RT	INLAND FISHERIES
RT	MARINE FISHERIES
RT	PELAGIC FISHERIES

FINFISH NUTRITION
| USE | **ANIMAL NUTRITION** |

FINGER BARS
| USE | **TRANSVERSE BARS** |

FINGERLINGS
BT1	FISH LARVAE
BT2	LARVAE
BT3	DEVELOPMENTAL STAGES
RT	FRY
RT	HATCHERIES
RT	LIFE CYCLE
RT	NURSERY PONDS
RT	SEED (AQUACULTURE)

FINITE AMPLITUDE WAVES
| BT1 | NONLINEAR WAVES |
| BT2 | WATER WAVES |

FINITE DIFFERENCE METHOD
SN	Used only as a qualifier
BT1	NUMERICAL ANALYSIS
BT2	MATHEMATICAL ANALYSIS
RT	APPROXIMATION

FINITE ELEMENT METHOD
SN	Used only as a qualifier
BT1	NUMERICAL ANALYSIS
BT2	MATHEMATICAL ANALYSIS
RT	BOUNDARY VALUE PROBLEMS
RT	DIFFERENTIAL EQUATIONS
RT	FUNCTIONAL ANALYSIS

FINS
UF	fin rays
UF	fin spines
BT1	LOCOMOTORY APPENDAGES
BT2	ANIMAL APPENDAGES
NT1	BONY FINS
RT	FIN RAY COUNTS
RT	LOCOMOTION
RT	SWIMMING

FIORD DYNAMICS
| USE | **FJORD DYNAMICS** |

FIORDS
| USE | **FJORDS** |

FIRE
BT1	HAZARDS
RT	ACCIDENTS
RT	BLOWOUTS
RT	DAMAGE

FIRE (cont'd)
RT	EXPLOSIONS
RT	FIRE FIGHTING
RT	FIRE HAZARDS
RT	FIRE PREVENTION
RT	OIL SPILLS
RT	SHIP LOSSES
RT	SMOKE

FIRE CONTROL
USE	**FIRE FIGHTING**

FIRE EXTINGUISHERS
UF	chemicals (fire fighting)
RT	FIRE FIGHTING
RT	SAFETY DEVICES

FIRE FIGHTING
UF	fire control
RT	ACCIDENTS
RT	ASBESTOS
RT	BREATHING APPARATUS
RT	EMERGENCY VESSELS
RT	FIRE
RT	FIRE EXTINGUISHERS

FIRE HAZARDS
BT1	HAZARDS
RT	BLOWOUTS
RT	EXPLOSIONS
RT	FIRE
RT	FIRE PREVENTION
RT	OIL SPILLS

FIRE PREVENTION
UF	fire protection
UF	fire safety
RT	ASBESTOS
RT	FIRE
RT	FIRE HAZARDS
RT	SAFETY REGULATIONS

FIRE PROTECTION
USE	**FIRE PREVENTION**

FIRE SAFETY
USE	**FIRE PREVENTION**

FISH
SN	Use of a more specific term is recommended. Used only for general papers dealing with fish of all kinds; always use taxonomic name where given
UF	fishes
BT1	AQUATIC ANIMALS
NT1	AIR-BREATHING FISH
NT1	BAIT FISH
NT1	BRACKISHWATER FISH
NT1	FOOD FISH
NT1	FORAGE FISH
NT1	FRESHWATER FISH
NT2	COARSE FISH
NT1	GAME FISH
NT1	HERBIVOROUS FISH
NT1	MARINE FISH
NT2	REEF FISH
NT1	ORNAMENTAL FISH
NT1	POISONOUS FISH
NT1	TRASH FISH
NT1	TROPICAL FISH
RT	BARBELS
RT	COMMERCIAL SPECIES
RT	FISH DISEASES
RT	FISH HANDLING
RT	FISH KILL
RT	FISH OILS
RT	FISH PHYSIOLOGY
RT	FISH POISONING
RT	FISH REPELLENTS

FISH (cont'd)
RT	FISH WASTES
RT	FISHERIES
RT	ICHTHYOLOGY
RT	LATERAL LINE
RT	NEKTON
RT	NESTING
RT	PHOTOPHORES
RT	VERNACULAR NAMES

FISH (TOWED SENSORS)
USE	**TOWED SENSORS**

FISH ATTRACTING
USE	**ATTRACTING TECHNIQUES**

FISH BALLS
USE	**MINCED PRODUCTS**

FISH CATCH STATISTICS
SN	Catch tabulation of fish by number or weight
BT1	CATCH STATISTICS
BT2	FISHERY STATISTICS
RT	BY CATCH
RT	FISH CONVERSION FACTORS
RT	FISHERY DATA

FISH CONSUMPTION
SN	Added in 1980
UF	fish consumption statistics
RT	HUMAN FOOD
RT	PROCESSED FISHERY PRODUCTS

FISH CONSUMPTION STATISTICS
USE	**FISH CONSUMPTION**

FISH CONVERSION
USE	**FISH HANDLING**

FISH CONVERSION FACTORS
BT1	POPULATION FACTORS
RT	CATCH STATISTICS
RT	FISH CATCH STATISTICS
RT	FISH HANDLING

FISH COUNTERS
SN	Added in 1982
UF	echo counting systems
UF	fish counting devices
BT1	COUNTERS
RT	ACOUSTIC EQUIPMENT
RT	ECHO INTEGRATORS
RT	ECHO SURVEYS
RT	ECHOSOUNDERS
RT	ELECTRONIC EQUIPMENT
RT	FISHERY SURVEYS
RT	STOCK ASSESSMENT

FISH COUNTING DEVICES
USE	**FISH COUNTERS**

FISH CULTURE
SN	Methods and techniques for fish culture
UF	fish farms
UF	pisciculture
BT1	AQUACULTURE
NT1	BAIT CULTURE
RT	AGROPISCICULTURE
RT	AIR-BREATHING FISH
RT	AQUARIUM CULTURE
RT	ARTIFICIAL SPAWNING GROUNDS
RT	BRACKISHWATER AQUACULTURE
RT	CAGE CULTURE
RT	CULTURE TANKS
RT	CULTURES
RT	EXTENSIVE CULTURE
RT	FISHING BUOYS
RT	FLOATING CAGES

FISH CULTURE (cont'd)
RT	FRESHWATER AQUACULTURE
RT	GRADING
RT	HATCHERIES
RT	HUSBANDRY DISEASES
RT	HYBRID CULTURE
RT	INDUCED BREEDING
RT	INTENSIVE CULTURE
RT	INTERMEDIATE FISHING
RT	LIVE STORAGE
RT	MARINE AQUACULTURE
RT	MONOCULTURE
RT	MONOSEX CULTURE
RT	MULLET FISHERIES
RT	OVERWINTERING TECHNIQUES
RT	PEDUNCLE DISEASE
RT	POLYCULTURE
RT	POND CULTURE
RT	RACEWAY CULTURE
RT	RECIRCULATING SYSTEMS
RT	RICE FIELD AQUACULTURE
RT	SALMON FISHERIES
RT	SEED COLLECTION
RT	SELECTIVE BREEDING
RT	SILO CULTURE
RT	SINGLE CELL PROTEINS
RT	SUBMERGED CAGES
RT	SUNBURN
RT	THERMAL AQUACULTURE
RT	WASTEWATER AQUACULTURE
RT	WHIRLING DISEASE
RT	WILD SPAWNING

FISH CULTURE DISEASES
USE	**HUSBANDRY DISEASES**

FISH CULTURE ECONOMICS
USE	**AQUACULTURE ECONOMICS**

FISH-CUM-CHICKEN CULTURE
USE	**AGROPISCICULTURE**

FISH-CUM-DUCK CULTURE
USE	**AGROPISCICULTURE**

FISH-CUM-PIG CULTURE
USE	**AGROPISCICULTURE**

FISH DETECTION
UF	fish location
BT1	DETECTION
RT	ACTIVE SONAR
RT	ECHOSOUNDERS
RT	FISHING OPERATIONS
RT	SONAR
RT	SONAR DETECTION
RT	TARGET STRENGTH

FISH DISEASES
SN	Added in 1980
UF	shellfish diseases
BT1	ANIMAL DISEASES
BT2	DISEASES
NT1	BOIL DISEASE
NT1	BUBBLE DISEASE
NT1	GILL DISEASE
NT1	PEDUNCLE DISEASE
NT1	REDMOUTH DISEASE
NT1	SUNBURN
NT1	ULCERATIVE DERMAL NECROSIS
NT1	WHIRLING DISEASE
RT	DISEASE CONTROL
RT	DISEASE RESISTANCE
RT	ENVIRONMENTAL DISEASES
RT	FISH
RT	FISH KILL
RT	FISH PHYSIOLOGY
RT	FUNGAL DISEASES
RT	HUSBANDRY DISEASES
RT	INFECTIOUS DISEASES

ASFIS Thesaurus

FISH DISEASES (cont'd)

RT	NATURAL MORTALITY
RT	NECROSES
RT	NUTRITION DISORDERS
RT	PARASITIC DISEASES
RT	PEST CONTROL
RT	PROTOZOAN DISEASES
RT	SEPTICAEMIA
RT	TUBERCULOSIS
RT	TUMOURS
RT	VIBRIOSIS
RT	VIRAL DISEASES

FISH DRESSING

USE	**DRESSING**

FISH DRYING

USE	**DRYING**

FISH EGGS

BT1	EGGS
BT2	SEXUAL CELLS
BT3	CELLS
RT	FISH LARVAE
RT	HATCHING
RT	ICHTHYOPLANKTON
RT	ICHTHYOPLANKTON SURVEYS
RT	NESTS

FISH FARMS

USE	**FISH CULTURE**

FISH FILLETS

SN	Added in 1980
UF	block fillets
UF	fillets (fish)
UF	side fillets
BT1	PROCESSED FISHERY PRODUCTS
BT2	FISHERY PRODUCTS
BT3	PRODUCTS
RT	FILLETTING
RT	GUTTING

FISH FLOUR

SN	Fish meal prepared for human consumption. Before 1982 search POWDERED PRODUCTS
UF	fish protein concentrate
BT1	FISH MEAL
BT2	POWDERED PRODUCTS
BT3	PROCESSED FISHERY PRODUCTS
BT4	FISHERY PRODUCTS
RT	FISH MEAL
RT	HUMAN FOOD
RT	ORGANOLEPTIC PROPERTIES

FISH FOOD ORGANISMS

USE	**FOOD ORGANISMS**

FISH FRY COLLECTION

USE	**SEED COLLECTION**

FISH FURUNCOLOSIS

USE	**BOIL DISEASE**

FISH GLUE

SN	Gelatinous liquid glue from fish waste. Added in 1980
BT1	PROCESSED FISHERY PRODUCTS
BT2	FISHERY PRODUCTS
BT3	PRODUCTS
RT	ADHESIVES
RT	FISH WASTES

FISH GRADING

USE	**GRADING**

FISH HANDLING

UF	fish conversion
UF	unloading
BT1	FISHERY INDUSTRY
BT2	INDUSTRIES
NT1	DRESSING
NT2	GUTTING
NT1	FILLETTING
NT1	HEADING
RT	CHILLED PRODUCTS
RT	CODEX STANDARDS
RT	COLD STORAGE
RT	FISH
RT	FISH CONVERSION FACTORS
RT	FISH INSPECTION
RT	FISH INSPECTION REGULATIONS
RT	FISH PUMPS
RT	FISH WASTES
RT	FISHERY PRODUCTS
RT	HANDLING
RT	MARKETING
RT	PRESERVATION (FISHERY PRODUCTS)
RT	PROCESSED FISHERY PRODUCTS
RT	QUALITY CONTROL

FISH HOOKS

USE	**HOOKS**

FISH IMPINGEMENT

USE	**IMPINGEMENT**

FISH INSPECTION

SN	Monitoring of fish and fishery products quality control. Added in 1980
UF	inspection (fish)
BT1	INSPECTION
RT	ACCEPTANCE TESTS
RT	FISH HANDLING
RT	FISH INSPECTION REGULATIONS
RT	HUMAN FOOD
RT	PROCESSED FISHERY PRODUCTS
RT	PROCESSING FISHERY PRODUCTS
RT	QUALITY CONTROL
RT	STORAGE EFFECTS

FISH INSPECTION REGULATIONS

BT1	COMMERCIAL LEGISLATION
BT2	LEGISLATION
RT	CODEX STANDARDS
RT	FISH HANDLING
RT	FISH INSPECTION
RT	FISHERY INDUSTRY
RT	FISHERY PRODUCTS
RT	HUMAN FOOD
RT	INSPECTION
RT	PROCESSED FISHERY PRODUCTS
RT	PROCESSING FISHERY PRODUCTS
RT	QUALITY CONTROL
RT	STORAGE EFFECTS

FISH KILL

SN	Excessive or conspicuous mortalities of fish due to several causes. Added in 1980
UF	mass mortality
NT1	WINTERKILL
RT	ANOXIC CONDITIONS
RT	EUTROPHICATION
RT	FISH
RT	FISH DISEASES
RT	INFECTIOUS DISEASES
RT	MORTALITY CAUSES
RT	OXYGEN DEPLETION
RT	POLLUTION EFFECTS
RT	PREDATION

FISH LARVAE

UF	ammocetes
UF	leptocephalus
BT1	LARVAE
BT2	DEVELOPMENTAL STAGES
NT1	FINGERLINGS
NT1	FRY
RT	BIOLOGICAL DRIFT
RT	FISH EGGS
RT	ICHTHYOPLANKTON
RT	ICHTHYOPLANKTON SURVEYS
RT	NURSERY GROUNDS

FISH LOCATION

USE	**FISH DETECTION**

FISH MEAL

SN	Before 1982 search POWDERED PRODUCTS
BT1	POWDERED PRODUCTS
BT2	PROCESSED FISHERY PRODUCTS
BT3	FISHERY PRODUCTS
BT4	PRODUCTS
NT1	FISH FLOUR
RT	FEED
RT	FERTILIZERS
RT	FISH FLOUR
RT	FISH MEAL PROCESSING
RT	FISH WASTES
RT	SHARK UTILIZATION

FISH MEAL PROCESSING

BT1	PROCESSING FISHERY PRODUCTS
BT2	FISHERY INDUSTRY
BT3	INDUSTRIES
RT	FISH MEAL
RT	FISH WASTES
RT	POWDERED PRODUCTS
RT	TRASH FISH

FISH MINCE

USE	**MINCED PRODUCTS**

FISH NUTRITION

USE	**ANIMAL NUTRITION**

FISH OIL EXTRACTION

BT1	ANIMAL OIL EXTRACTION
BT2	PROCESSING FISHERY PRODUCTS
BT3	FISHERY INDUSTRY
BT4	INDUSTRIES
RT	CHEMICAL EXTRACTION
RT	FISH OILS
RT	FISH WASTES
RT	HYDROCARBONS
RT	SOLVENTS

FISH OILS

SN	Oils extracted from fish, fish liver, fish wastes and marine mammals
UF	oils (fish)
UF	sperm oils
BT1	PROCESSED FISHERY PRODUCTS
BT2	FISHERY PRODUCTS
BT3	PRODUCTS
RT	BYPRODUCTS
RT	FISH
RT	FISH OIL EXTRACTION
RT	FISH WASTES
RT	HYDROCARBONS
RT	POWDERED PRODUCTS
RT	SHARK UTILIZATION
RT	STICKWATER
RT	TRASH FISH

FISH PASTE

USE	**MINCED PRODUCTS**

ASFIS Thesaurus

FISH PATHOLOGY
USE **PATHOLOGY**

FISH PHYSIOLOGY
SN Before 1982 search PHYSIOLOGY
UF physiology (fish)
BT1 ANIMAL PHYSIOLOGY
BT2 PHYSIOLOGY
BT3 BIOLOGY
RT FISH
RT FISH DISEASES
RT ICHTHYOLOGY
RT SWIMMING

FISH PLANTS
USE **FISHERY INDUSTRY PLANTS**

FISH POISONING
SN Capture of fish or other aquatic
animals by use of poisons of
different origin
UF poison fishing
UF poisoning
UF shellfish poisoning
BT1 CATCHING METHODS
RT FISH
RT FISHING
RT ROTENONE
RT STUPEFYING METHODS

FISH POND CULTURE
USE **POND CULTURE**

FISH PONDS
UF farm ponds
BT1 PONDS
BT2 INLAND WATERS
NT1 BREEDING PONDS
NT1 GROWING PONDS
NT1 NURSERY PONDS
NT1 STOCKING PONDS
RT AGROPISCICULTURE
RT AQUACULTURE
RT AQUACULTURE FACILITIES
RT BRACKISHWATER AQUACULTURE
RT ENCLOSURES
RT FRESHWATER AQUACULTURE
RT HATCHERIES
RT INTERMEDIATE FISHING
RT IRRIGATION
RT MARINE AQUACULTURE
RT MONOSEX CULTURE
RT OVERWINTERING TECHNIQUES
RT POLYCULTURE
RT POND CONSTRUCTION
RT POND CULTURE
RT SMALL SCALE AQUACULTURE

FISH PRODUCTS
USE **FISHERY PRODUCTS**

FISH PROTEIN CONCENTRATE
USE **FISH FLOUR**

FISH PUMPS
SN Used for unloading small fish.
Before 1982 search HARVESTING
MACHINES
BT1 PUMPS
RT FISH HANDLING

FISH REARING PONDS
USE **NURSERY PONDS**

FISH REPELLENTS
UF shark repellents
BT1 REPELLENTS
RT FISH
RT SHARK ATTACKS

FISH RESOURCES
USE **FISHERY RESOURCES**

FISH ROE
USE **ROES**

FISH SCALES
USE **SCALES**

FISH SCIENTISTS
USE **ICHTHYOLOGISTS**

FISH SCREENS
USE **SCREENS**

FISH SEED
USE **SEED (AQUACULTURE)**

FISH SILAGE
SN Added in 1982
UF liquid fish products
UF silage from fish
RT ACIDIFICATION
RT FERMENTATION

FISH SIZING
SN Added in 1982
UF acoustic sizing techniques
RT ECHO SURVEYS
RT SWIM BLADDER
RT TARGET STRENGTH

FISH SOLUBLES
USE **STICKWATER**

FISH SOUNDS
USE **BIOLOGICAL NOISE**

FISH SPOILAGE
SN Added in 1982
UF spoilage (fish)
RT ORGANOLEPTIC PROPERTIES
RT PRESERVATION (FISHERY PRODUCTS)
RT QUALITY CONTROL
RT VOLATILE COMPOUNDS

FISH STOCKS
USE **STOCKS**

FISH STORAGE
SN Before 1982 search STORAGE
UF storage (fish)
RT COLD STORAGE
RT FISHERY PRODUCTS
RT ICE
RT LIVE STORAGE
RT PRESERVATION (FISHERY PRODUCTS)
RT STORAGE
RT STORAGE CONDITIONS
RT STORAGE EFFECTS
RT STORAGE TANKS

FISH TRACKING
USE **TRACKING**

FISH TRAPS
USE **TRAP NETS**

FISH UTILIZATION
SN Added in 1982
RT COMMERCIAL SPECIES
RT FISHERY PRODUCTS
RT PROCESSING FISHERY PRODUCTS

FISH WASTE UTILIZATION
USE **WASTE UTILIZATION**

FISH WASTES
BT1 WASTES
RT FISH
RT FISH GLUE
RT FISH HANDLING
RT FISH MEAL
RT FISH MEAL PROCESSING
RT FISH OIL EXTRACTION
RT FISH OILS
RT GUTTING
RT LIVESTOCK FOOD
RT ODOUR
RT ORGANIC WASTES
RT PROCESSING FISHERY PRODUCTS
RT STICKWATER
RT TRASH FISH
RT WASTE UTILIZATION

FISHERIES
UF capture fisheries
UF commercial fisheries
NT1 CANOE FISHERIES
NT1 CARANGID FISHERIES
NT1 COASTAL FISHERIES
NT1 CRUSTACEAN FISHERIES
NT2 CRAB FISHERIES
NT2 KRILL FISHERIES
NT2 LOBSTER FISHERIES
NT2 SHRIMP FISHERIES
NT2 SQUAT LOBSTER FISHERIES
NT1 DEMERSAL FISHERIES
NT1 ESTUARINE FISHERIES
NT1 FINFISH FISHERIES
NT2 CLUPEOID FISHERIES
NT2 FLATFISH FISHERIES
NT2 GADOID FISHERIES
NT2 MACKEREL FISHERIES
NT2 MULLET FISHERIES
NT2 PERCOID FISHERIES
NT2 REDFISH FISHERIES
NT2 SALMON FISHERIES
NT2 SHARK FISHERIES
NT2 TUNA FISHERIES
NT1 INLAND FISHERIES
NT2 LAGOON FISHERIES
NT2 LAKE FISHERIES
NT2 RESERVOIR FISHERIES
NT2 RIVER FISHERIES
NT2 SWAMP FISHERIES
NT1 MARINE FISHERIES
NT2 DEEP-SEA FISHERIES
NT2 HIGH SEAS FISHERIES
NT2 REEF FISHERIES
NT2 SEAWEED HARVESTING
NT1 MULTISPECIES FISHERIES
NT1 PEARL FISHERIES
NT1 PELAGIC FISHERIES
NT1 ROE FISHERIES
NT1 SHELLFISH FISHERIES
NT2 ECHINODERM FISHERIES
NT2 MOLLUSC FISHERIES
NT3 CEPHALOPOD FISHERIES
NT3 CLAM FISHERIES
NT3 GASTROPOD FISHERIES
NT3 MUSSEL FISHERIES
NT3 OYSTER FISHERIES
NT3 SCALLOP FISHERIES
NT1 SPONGE FISHERIES
NT1 TURTLE FISHERIES
RT AQUATIC SCIENCES
RT ARTISANAL FISHING
RT CATCHING METHODS
RT COMMERCIAL FISHING
RT FISH
RT FISHERY DEVELOPMENT
RT FISHERY MANAGEMENT
RT FISHERY RESOURCES
RT FISHERY STATISTICS

FISHERIES (cont'd)
RT   FISHING GEAR
RT   FISHING GROUNDS
RT   FISHING OPERATIONS
RT   FISHING VESSELS
RT   WATER USE

FISHERIES BIOLOGY
USE   **FISHERY BIOLOGY**

FISHERIES DATA
USE   **FISHERY DATA**

FISHERIES HYDROGRAPHY
USE   **FISHERY OCEANOGRAPHY**

FISHERIES INSTITUTIONS
USE   **FISHERY INSTITUTIONS**

FISHERIES MANAGEMENT
USE   **FISHERY MANAGEMENT**

FISHERIES ORGANIZATIONS
USE   **FISHERY ORGANIZATIONS**

FISHERIES REGULATIONS
USE   **FISHERY REGULATIONS**

FISHERIES RESOURCES
USE   **FISHERY RESOURCES**

FISHERIES SCIENCES
USE   **FISHERY SCIENCES**

FISHERIES STATISTICS
USE   **FISHERY STATISTICS**

FISHERMEN
BT1   PERSONNEL
RT   COOPERATIVES
RT   DIRECTORIES
RT   FISHERMEN STATISTICS
RT   FISHERY POLICY
RT   LABOUR
RT   LABOUR LEGISLATION
RT   WOMEN

FISHERMEN STATISTICS
BT1   FISHERY STATISTICS
RT   FISHERMEN
RT   LABOUR

FISHERY BIOLOGISTS
SN   Added in 1980
BT1   BIOLOGISTS
BT2   SCIENTIFIC PERSONNEL
BT3   PERSONNEL
RT   ALGOLOGISTS
RT   CARCINOLOGISTS
RT   DIRECTORIES
RT   FISHERY BIOLOGY
RT   ICHTHYOLOGISTS
RT   MALACOLOGISTS

FISHERY BIOLOGY
SN   Scientific complex of different disciplines applied to biological research in fisheries
UF   fisheries biology
BT1   BIOLOGY
RT   BIOMETRICS
RT   ECOLOGY
RT   FISHERY BIOLOGISTS
RT   FISHERY DATA
RT   FISHERY LIMNOLOGY
RT   FISHERY OCEANOGRAPHY
RT   FISHERY RESOURCES
RT   FISHERY SCIENCES
RT   HYDROBIOLOGY
RT   ICHTHYOLOGY

FISHERY BIOLOGY (cont'd)
RT   POPULATION DYNAMICS

FISHERY BOUNDARIES
SN   Added in 1982
BT1   BOUNDARIES
RT   CONTIGUOUS ZONES
RT   EXCLUSIVE ECONOMIC ZONE
RT   FISHERY DISPUTES

FISHERY CHARTS
SN   Charts for use in fishery operations including graphical descriptions of fishing grounds
BT1   MAPS
BT2   GRAPHICS
BT3   AUDIOVISUAL MATERIAL
BT4   DOCUMENTS
RT   ENVIRONMENTAL CONDITIONS
RT   FISHERY SURVEYS
RT   FISHING GROUNDS
RT   FISHING HARBOURS
RT   FISHING OPERATIONS
RT   QUANTITATIVE DISTRIBUTION

FISHERY CONFLICTS
USE   **FISHERY DISPUTES**

FISHERY COOPERATIVES
USE   **COOPERATIVES**

FISHERY DATA
SN   Restricted to fishery operation data
UF   data (fisheries)
UF   fisheries data
BT1   DATA
NT1   CATCH/EFFORT
NT1   FISHING EFFORT
NT1   FISHING POWER
NT1   FISHING TIME
RT   CATCH STATISTICS
RT   FISH CATCH STATISTICS
RT   FISHERY BIOLOGY
RT   FISHERY STATISTICS
RT   FISHING OPERATIONS
RT   LANDING STATISTICS
RT   STOCK ASSESSMENT

FISHERY DEVELOPMENT
BT1   RESOURCE DEVELOPMENT
RT   CAPTURE FISHERY ECONOMICS
RT   CATCHING METHODS
RT   DEVELOPMENT PROJECTS
RT   FISHERIES
RT   FISHERY ECONOMICS
RT   FISHERY ENGINEERING
RT   FISHERY INDUSTRY
RT   FISHERY INSTITUTIONS
RT   FISHERY ORGANIZATIONS
RT   FISHERY POLICY
RT   FISHERY SURVEYS
RT   FISHERY TECHNOLOGY
RT   INTERNATIONAL COOPERATION
RT   LIVING RESOURCES
RT   POTENTIAL RESOURCES
RT   UNCONVENTIONAL RESOURCES
RT   WOMEN

FISHERY DISPUTES
SN   Added in 1980
UF   fishery conflicts
UF   fishery litigation
BT1   DISPUTES
RT   BOUNDARIES
RT   COASTAL STATES
RT   FISHERY BOUNDARIES
RT   FISHERY POLICY
RT   FISHERY PROTECTION
RT   FISHERY REGULATIONS
RT   FISHING RIGHTS

FISHERY DISPUTES (cont'd)
RT   FOREIGN FISHING
RT   ILLEGAL FISHING
RT   LEGAL ASPECTS
RT   OCEAN SPACE
RT   SURVEILLANCE AND ENFORCEMENT

FISHERY ECONOMICS
SN   Economics of all aspects of fisheries, exploitation, production, processing, marketing, distribution, trade etc.
BT1   ECONOMICS
NT1   AQUACULTURE ECONOMICS
NT1   CAPTURE FISHERY ECONOMICS
RT   COOPERATIVES
RT   COST ANALYSIS
RT   ECONOMIC ANALYSIS
RT   ECONOMIC FEASIBILITY
RT   ECONOMIC MODELS
RT   ECONOMISTS
RT   EXCLUSIVE ECONOMIC ZONE
RT   FINANCING
RT   FISHERY DEVELOPMENT
RT   FISHERY MANAGEMENT
RT   FISHERY POLICY
RT   FISHERY SCIENCES
RT   FISHERY STATISTICS
RT   FUEL ECONOMY
RT   MARKET RESEARCH
RT   MARKETING
RT   PRICING
RT   PROCESSED FISHERY PRODUCTS
RT   RESOURCE DEVELOPMENT
RT   TRADE

FISHERY ENGINEERING
BT1   ENGINEERING
RT   CATCHING METHODS
RT   ECHOSOUNDING
RT   FISHERY DEVELOPMENT
RT   FISHERY SCIENCES
RT   FISHING GEAR
RT   FISHING OPERATIONS
RT   GEAR RESEARCH

FISHERY INDUSTRY
SN   Including any industries of fishery products obtained by handling or processing methods
BT1   INDUSTRIES
NT1   FISH HANDLING
NT2   DRESSING
NT3   GUTTING
NT2   FILLETTING
NT2   HEADING
NT1   PROCESSING FISHERY PRODUCTS
NT2   ANIMAL OIL EXTRACTION
NT3   FISH OIL EXTRACTION
NT2   CANNING
NT2   CURING
NT2   DRYING
NT3   FREEZE-DRYING
NT2   FISH MEAL PROCESSING
NT2   REFRIGERATION
NT1   SEAWEED PROCESSING
RT   COMMERCIAL FISHING
RT   COST ANALYSIS
RT   FISH INSPECTION REGULATIONS
RT   FISHERY DEVELOPMENT
RT   FISHERY INDUSTRY EQUIPMENT
RT   FISHERY INDUSTRY LEGISLATION
RT   FISHERY INDUSTRY PLANTS
RT   FISHERY POLICY
RT   FISHERY PRODUCTS
RT   FISHERY TECHNOLOGY
RT   INDUSTRIAL PRODUCTS STATISTICS
RT   PACKING FISHERY PRODUCTS
RT   PRESERVATION (FISHERY PRODUCTS)
RT   PROCESSED FISHERY PRODUCTS

ASFIS Thesaurus

FISHERY INDUSTRY EQUIPMENT
SN	Industrial equipment used for handling and processing fishery products
BT1	EQUIPMENT
NT1	REFRIGERATORS
RT	FACTORY SHIPS
RT	FISHERY INDUSTRY
RT	FISHERY INDUSTRY PLANTS
RT	FISHING VESSELS

FISHERY INDUSTRY LEGISLATION
BT1	LEGISLATION
RT	FISHERY INDUSTRY
RT	FISHERY ORGANIZATIONS

FISHERY INDUSTRY PLANTS
UF	fish plants
RT	FACTORY SHIPS
RT	FISHERY INDUSTRY
RT	FISHERY INDUSTRY EQUIPMENT
RT	FISHERY TECHNOLOGY
RT	ODOUR
RT	REFRIGERATORS

FISHERY INSTITUTIONS
UF	fisheries institutions
UF	fishery research institutions
BT1	RESEARCH INSTITUTIONS
BT2	ORGANIZATIONS
RT	EDUCATION
RT	FISHERY DEVELOPMENT
RT	FISHERY ORGANIZATIONS
RT	FISHERY POLICY
RT	FISHERY RESOURCES
RT	FISHERY SCIENCES
RT	FISHERY SURVEYS
RT	LIMNOLOGICAL INSTITUTIONS
RT	OCEANOGRAPHIC INSTITUTIONS
RT	RESEARCH PROGRAMMES

FISHERY LAWS
USE	**FISHERY REGULATIONS**

FISHERY LEGISLATION
USE	**FISHERY REGULATIONS**

FISHERY LIMNOLOGY
SN	Added in 1980
BT1	LIMNOLOGY
RT	FISHERY BIOLOGY
RT	FISHERY SCIENCES
RT	FISHERY SURVEYS
RT	FRESHWATER ECOLOGY
RT	LAKE FISHERIES

FISHERY LITIGATION
USE	**FISHERY DISPUTES**

FISHERY MANAGEMENT
UF	fisheries management
BT1	RESOURCE MANAGEMENT
BT2	MANAGEMENT
RT	CAPTURE FISHERY ECONOMICS
RT	CULLING
RT	DEPLETED STOCKS
RT	FISHERIES
RT	FISHERY ECONOMICS
RT	FISHERY ORGANIZATIONS
RT	FISHERY POLICY
RT	FISHERY RESOURCES
RT	FISHERY STATISTICS
RT	LIVING RESOURCES
RT	RIVER BASIN MANAGEMENT
RT	SPORT FISHING

FISHERY OCEANOGRAPHY
SN	Applied investigations on oceanic conditions of fishing regions or grounds
UF	fisheries hydrography
UF	oceanography (fisheries)
BT1	OCEANOGRAPHY
BT2	EARTH SCIENCES
RT	ENVIRONMENTAL SURVEYS
RT	FISHERY BIOLOGY
RT	FISHERY SCIENCES
RT	FISHING GROUNDS
RT	HYDROGRAPHY
RT	MARINE SCIENCES
RT	METEOROLOGY
RT	PREDICTION

FISHERY ORGANIZATIONS
UF	fisheries organizations
BT1	ORGANIZATIONS
NT1	COOPERATIVES
RT	AQUACULTURE DEVELOPMENT
RT	FISHERY DEVELOPMENT
RT	FISHERY INDUSTRY LEGISLATION
RT	FISHERY INSTITUTIONS
RT	FISHERY MANAGEMENT
RT	FISHERY POLICY
RT	FISHERY REGULATIONS
RT	LIVING RESOURCES
RT	RESOURCE CONSERVATION
RT	RESOURCE DEVELOPMENT
RT	SOCIOLOGICAL ASPECTS

FISHERY POLICY
SN	Added in 1980
UF	fishing policy
BT1	POLICIES
RT	ALLOCATION SYSTEMS
RT	FISHERMEN
RT	FISHERY DEVELOPMENT
RT	FISHERY DISPUTES
RT	FISHERY ECONOMICS
RT	FISHERY INDUSTRY
RT	FISHERY INSTITUTIONS
RT	FISHERY MANAGEMENT
RT	FISHERY ORGANIZATIONS
RT	FISHERY PROTECTION
RT	FISHERY REGULATIONS
RT	FISHERY RESOURCES
RT	FISHING RIGHTS
RT	FOREIGN FISHING
RT	SHARED STOCKS

FISHERY PRODUCTS
UF	fish products
UF	primary fishery products
UF	seafood products
BT1	PRODUCTS
NT1	PROCESSED FISHERY PRODUCTS
NT2	CANNED PRODUCTS
NT2	CHILLED PRODUCTS
NT2	CURED PRODUCTS
NT2	DRIED PRODUCTS
NT2	FERMENTED PRODUCTS
NT2	FISH FILLETS
NT2	FISH GLUE
NT2	FISH OILS
NT2	FREEZE-DRIED PRODUCTS
NT2	FROZEN PRODUCTS
NT2	KRILL PRODUCTS
NT2	MINCED PRODUCTS
NT2	POWDERED PRODUCTS
NT3	FISH MEAL
NT4	FISH FLOUR
NT2	ROES
NT3	CAVIAR
NT2	SEAWEED PRODUCTS
NT3	AGAR
NT3	ALGINATES
NT3	CARRAGEENINS

FISHERY PRODUCTS (cont'd)
NT2	STICKWATER
RT	AQUACULTURE PRODUCTS
RT	BY CATCH
RT	COLD STORAGE
RT	FISH HANDLING
RT	FISH INSPECTION REGULATIONS
RT	FISH STORAGE
RT	FISH UTILIZATION
RT	FISHERY INDUSTRY
RT	HUMAN FOOD
RT	PACKING FISHERY PRODUCTS
RT	PROCESSING FISHERY PRODUCTS
RT	QUALITY CONTROL
RT	STORAGE CONDITIONS
RT	STORAGE EFFECTS

FISHERY PRODUCTS STATISTICS
USE	**INDUSTRIAL PRODUCTS STATISTICS**

FISHERY PROTECTION
SN	Measures against illegal fishing by foreign vessels in EEZ, territorial waters or protected fisheries
BT1	PROTECTION
RT	EXCLUSIVE ECONOMIC ZONE
RT	FISHERY DISPUTES
RT	FISHERY POLICY
RT	FISHERY REGULATIONS
RT	FISHING RIGHTS
RT	FOREIGN FISHING
RT	PROTECTION VESSELS
RT	SECURITY
RT	SURVEILLANCE AND ENFORCEMENT
RT	TERRITORIAL WATERS

FISHERY PROTECTION VESSELS
USE	**PROTECTION VESSELS**

FISHERY REGULATIONS
SN	Regulations on national rights to fisheries and legislative management of fisheries resources
UF	fisheries regulations
UF	fishery laws
UF	fishery legislation
BT1	LEGISLATION
NT1	MESH REGULATIONS
NT1	QUOTA REGULATIONS
NT1	SEASON REGULATIONS
NT1	SIZE-LIMIT REGULATIONS
NT1	WHALING REGULATIONS
RT	EXCLUSIVE ECONOMIC ZONE
RT	EXPLOSIVE FISHING
RT	FISHERY DISPUTES
RT	FISHERY ORGANIZATIONS
RT	FISHERY POLICY
RT	FISHERY PROTECTION
RT	FISHING RIGHTS
RT	GEAR SELECTIVITY
RT	INTERNATIONAL AGREEMENTS
RT	LEGAL ASPECTS
RT	MARITIME LEGISLATION
RT	MIGRATORY SPECIES
RT	MONITORING
RT	OCEAN SPACE
RT	PROTECTION VESSELS
RT	RENTAL
RT	RESOURCE CONSERVATION

FISHERY RESEARCH INSTITUTIONS
USE	**FISHERY INSTITUTIONS**

FISHERY RESOURCES
UF	fish resources
UF	fisheries resources
BT1	LIVING RESOURCES
BT2	NATURAL RESOURCES
BT3	RESOURCES
RT	ANIMAL PRODUCTS

ASFIS Thesaurus

FISHERY RESOURCES (cont'd)
RT	AQUATIC MAMMALS
RT	AQUATIC PLANTS
RT	AQUATIC REPTILES
RT	BIOLOGICAL CHARTS
RT	BRACKISHWATER FISH
RT	CATCH COMPOSITION
RT	COMMERCIAL SPECIES
RT	COMMON PROPERTY RESOURCES
RT	EXPLORATORY FISHING
RT	FISHERIES
RT	FISHERY BIOLOGY
RT	FISHERY INSTITUTIONS
RT	FISHERY MANAGEMENT
RT	FISHERY POLICY
RT	FISHERY SURVEYS
RT	FISHING RIGHTS
RT	FRESHWATER FISH
RT	HIGH SEAS FISHERIES
RT	HUMAN FOOD
RT	MARINE FISH
RT	MIGRATORY SPECIES
RT	POLLUTION EFFECTS
RT	POTENTIAL RESOURCES
RT	RARE SPECIES
RT	RENEWABLE RESOURCES
RT	RESOURCE CONSERVATION
RT	SEAWEEDS
RT	SHARED STOCKS
RT	SHELLFISH
RT	STOCKS
RT	VERNACULAR NAMES

FISHERY SCIENCES
UF	fisheries sciences
RT	FISHERY BIOLOGY
RT	FISHERY ECONOMICS
RT	FISHERY ENGINEERING
RT	FISHERY INSTITUTIONS
RT	FISHERY LIMNOLOGY
RT	FISHERY OCEANOGRAPHY
RT	FISHERY TECHNOLOGY
RT	TRAINING

FISHERY STATISTICS
SN	Including statistical tabulation of data
UF	fisheries statistics
NT1	AQUACULTURE STATISTICS
NT1	CATCH STATISTICS
NT2	FISH CATCH STATISTICS
NT2	HUNTING STATISTICS
NT2	SEAWEED STATISTICS
NT2	SHELLFISH CATCH STATISTICS
NT2	WHALING STATISTICS
NT1	FISHERMEN STATISTICS
NT1	FISHING VESSELS STATISTICS
NT1	INDUSTRIAL PRODUCTS STATISTICS
NT1	LANDING STATISTICS
NT1	SPORT FISHING STATISTICS
RT	CAPTURE FISHERY ECONOMICS
RT	FISHERIES
RT	FISHERY DATA
RT	FISHERY ECONOMICS
RT	FISHERY MANAGEMENT
RT	STATISTICIANS
RT	TRADE

FISHERY SURVEYS
BT1	SURVEYS
RT	AERIAL SURVEYS
RT	AGE GROUPS
RT	CATCH COMPOSITION
RT	ECHO SURVEYS
RT	FISH COUNTERS
RT	FISHERY CHARTS
RT	FISHERY DEVELOPMENT
RT	FISHERY INSTITUTIONS
RT	FISHERY LIMNOLOGY
RT	FISHERY RESOURCES

FISHERY SURVEYS (cont'd)
RT	ICHTHYOPLANKTON
RT	ICHTHYOPLANKTON SURVEYS
RT	STOCK ASSESSMENT

FISHERY TECHNOLOGY
SN	Scientific research and industrial techniques applied to fishery industry
BT1	TECHNOLOGY
RT	CATCHING METHODS
RT	FISHERY DEVELOPMENT
RT	FISHERY INDUSTRY
RT	FISHERY INDUSTRY PLANTS
RT	FISHERY SCIENCES
RT	FOOD TECHNOLOGY
RT	PROCESSED FISHERY PRODUCTS

FISHES
USE	**FISH**

FISHING
SN	Use of a more specific term is recommended; consult terms listed below. Added in 1980
RT	ANGLING
RT	ARTISANAL FISHING
RT	BAIT FISHING
RT	ELECTRIC FISHING
RT	EXPERIMENTAL FISHING
RT	EXPLOSIVE FISHING
RT	FEE FISHING
RT	FISH POISONING
RT	FISHING BARRIERS
RT	FISHING BY DIVING
RT	FISHING WITHOUT GEAR
RT	GRAPPLING
RT	ICE FISHING
RT	INTERMEDIATE FISHING
RT	LIGHT FISHING
RT	MOTOR BOATS
RT	NET FISHING
RT	OVERFISHING
RT	POLE-LINE FISHING
RT	SEINING
RT	SPEAR FISHING
RT	SPORT FISHING
RT	TRAP FISHING
RT	TRAWLING
RT	WORM FISHING
RT	WOUNDING

FISHING BAIT
USE	**BAIT**

FISHING BARRIERS
SN	Before 1982 search BARRIERS
UF	barriers (fishing)
BT1	BARRIERS
RT	COASTAL FISHERIES
RT	FISHING
RT	FISHING GEAR
RT	INLAND FISHERIES
RT	LAGOON FISHERIES
RT	POTS

FISHING BUOYS
BT1	BUOYS
RT	FISH CULTURE
RT	FISHING GEAR
RT	RADIO BUOYS

FISHING BY DIVING
BT1	CATCHING METHODS
RT	DIVING
RT	FISHING
RT	PEARL FISHERIES
RT	SPONGE FISHERIES

FISHING CRAFT
USE	**FISHING VESSELS**

FISHING EFFORT
UF	fishing effort statistics
BT1	FISHERY DATA
BT2	DATA
RT	CATCH STATISTICS
RT	CATCH/EFFORT
RT	FISHING MORTALITY
RT	FISHING POWER
RT	FISHING TIME
RT	FISHING VESSELS
RT	FISHING VESSELS STATISTICS
RT	STOCK ASSESSMENT

FISHING EFFORT STATISTICS
USE	**FISHING EFFORT**

FISHING GEAR
SN	Technical description of gear used mainly for commercial fishing purposes
UF	gear
NT1	DREDGES
NT1	ELECTRIFIED GEAR
NT1	FISHING NETS
NT2	CAST NETS
NT2	ENTANGLING NETS
NT2	GILLNETS
NT2	LIFT-NETS
NT2	SEINE NETS
NT3	BEACH SEINES
NT3	BOAT SEINES
NT2	SURROUNDING NETS
NT3	LAMPARA NETS
NT3	PURSE SEINES
NT2	TRAP NETS
NT2	TRAWL NETS
NT3	BOTTOM TRAWLS
NT3	MIDWATER TRAWLS
NT1	GRAPPLING GEAR
NT1	HARVESTING MACHINES
NT1	LINES
NT2	HOOKS
NT1	POTS
NT1	WOUNDING GEAR
RT	ATTRACTING TECHNIQUES
RT	AVOIDANCE REACTIONS
RT	BAIT FISHING
RT	CATCHING METHODS
RT	COMMERCIAL FISHING
RT	EQUIPMENT
RT	ESCAPEMENT
RT	EXPERIMENTAL FISHING
RT	FISHERIES
RT	FISHERY ENGINEERING
RT	FISHING BARRIERS
RT	FISHING BUOYS
RT	FISHING OPERATIONS
RT	FISHING POWER
RT	FISHING TECHNOLOGY
RT	FISHING VESSELS
RT	GEAR CONSTRUCTION
RT	GEAR MATERIALS
RT	GEAR RESEARCH
RT	GEAR SELECTIVITY
RT	MECHANIZATION
RT	SPORT FISHING
RT	STUPEFYING METHODS
RT	VULNERABILITY
RT	WINCHES

FISHING GROUNDS
RT	EXPLORATORY FISHING
RT	FISHERIES
RT	FISHERY CHARTS
RT	FISHERY OCEANOGRAPHY
RT	FISHING OPERATIONS
RT	FISHING RIGHTS

FISHING GROUNDS (cont'd)
RT	SPAWNING GROUNDS
RT	SUBMARINE BANKS

FISHING HARBOURS
BT1	HARBOURS
BT2	ANCHORAGES
RT	FISHERY CHARTS
RT	SITE SELECTION

FISHING INDUSTRY
USE	**COMMERCIAL FISHING**

FISHING INJURIES
USE	**INJURIES**

FISHING LICENSES
USE	**FISHING RIGHTS**

FISHING METHODS
USE	**CATCHING METHODS**

FISHING MORTALITY
UF	fishing mortality coefficient
BT1	MORTALITY
BT2	POPULATION FUNCTIONS
RT	FISHING EFFORT
RT	OVERFISHING
RT	TOTAL MORTALITY
RT	VULNERABILITY
RT	YIELD

FISHING MORTALITY COEFFICIENT
USE	**FISHING MORTALITY**

FISHING NETS
BT1	FISHING GEAR
NT1	CAST NETS
NT1	ENTANGLING NETS
NT1	GILLNETS
NT1	LIFT-NETS
NT1	SEINE NETS
NT2	BEACH SEINES
NT2	BOAT SEINES
NT1	SURROUNDING NETS
NT2	LAMPARA NETS
NT2	PURSE SEINES
NT1	TRAP NETS
NT1	TRAWL NETS
NT2	BOTTOM TRAWLS
NT2	MIDWATER TRAWLS
RT	AVOIDANCE REACTIONS
RT	FISHING OPERATIONS
RT	FISHING TECHNOLOGY
RT	NEKTON COLLECTING DEVICES
RT	NET FISHING
RT	NETS
RT	NETTING MATERIALS
RT	PLANKTON COLLECTING DEVICES
RT	YARNS

FISHING OPERATIONS
NT1	ARTISANAL FISHING
NT1	COMMERCIAL FISHING
NT2	FOREIGN FISHING
NT1	EXPERIMENTAL FISHING
NT1	EXPLORATORY FISHING
NT1	ICE FISHING
NT1	INTERMEDIATE FISHING
RT	ACOUSTIC EQUIPMENT
RT	CATCHING METHODS
RT	COMMUNICATION SYSTEMS
RT	ECHOSOUNDERS
RT	ECHOSOUNDING
RT	FISH DETECTION
RT	FISHERIES
RT	FISHERY CHARTS
RT	FISHERY DATA
RT	FISHERY ENGINEERING
RT	FISHING GEAR

FISHING OPERATIONS (cont'd)
RT	FISHING GROUNDS
RT	FISHING NETS
RT	FISHING TECHNOLOGY
RT	FISHING VESSELS
RT	NAVIGATION
RT	RADIO AIDS
RT	RADIO NAVIGATION
RT	SONAR
RT	SPEEDOMETERS
RT	STANDARD SIGNALS
RT	SUPPORT SHIPS

FISHING OVEREXPLOITATION
USE	**OVERFISHING**

FISHING POLICY
USE	**FISHERY POLICY**

FISHING POWER
BT1	FISHERY DATA
BT2	DATA
RT	CATCH/EFFORT
RT	FISHING EFFORT
RT	FISHING GEAR
RT	FISHING TIME
RT	FISHING VESSELS

FISHING RIGHTS
SN	The legal right of fishing in a given place at a given time. Added in 1980
UF	customary fishing rights
UF	exclusive fishing rights
UF	fishing licenses
BT1	RIGHTS
RT	COASTAL STATES
RT	CONTIGUOUS ZONES
RT	EXCLUSIVE ECONOMIC ZONE
RT	EXCLUSIVE RIGHTS
RT	EXTENDED JURISDICTION
RT	FISHERY DISPUTES
RT	FISHERY POLICY
RT	FISHERY PROTECTION
RT	FISHERY REGULATIONS
RT	FISHERY RESOURCES
RT	FISHING GROUNDS
RT	FOREIGN FISHING
RT	INTERNATIONAL AGREEMENTS
RT	JOINT VENTURES
RT	JURISDICTION
RT	LAW OF THE SEA
RT	LEGAL ASPECTS
RT	MIGRATORY SPECIES
RT	RENTAL
RT	RIPARIAN RIGHTS
RT	SEDENTARY SPECIES
RT	TERRITORIAL WATERS

FISHING SEASONS
USE	**SEASON REGULATIONS**

FISHING TECHNOLOGY
SN	Before 1982 search CATCHING METHODS
BT1	TECHNOLOGY
RT	CATCHING METHODS
RT	EXPERIMENTAL FISHING
RT	FISHING GEAR
RT	FISHING NETS
RT	FISHING OPERATIONS
RT	FISHING VESSELS

FISHING TIME
BT1	FISHERY DATA
BT2	DATA
RT	CATCH STATISTICS
RT	FISHING EFFORT
RT	FISHING POWER
RT	LANDING STATISTICS

FISHING VESSELS
UF	fishing craft
BT1	SURFACE CRAFT
BT2	VEHICLES
NT1	CATCHERS
NT1	GILLNETTERS
NT1	LINERS
NT1	SEINERS
NT1	TRAWLERS
RT	ACCOMMODATION
RT	BOATS
RT	COMMERCIAL FISHING
RT	DECK EQUIPMENT
RT	EXPERIMENTAL FISHING
RT	FACTORY SHIPS
RT	FISHERIES
RT	FISHERY INDUSTRY EQUIPMENT
RT	FISHING EFFORT
RT	FISHING GEAR
RT	FISHING OPERATIONS
RT	FISHING POWER
RT	FISHING TECHNOLOGY
RT	FISHING VESSELS STATISTICS
RT	FUEL ECONOMY
RT	MOTHER SHIPS
RT	SHIP TECHNOLOGY
RT	SUPPORT SHIPS
RT	WORK PLATFORMS

FISHING VESSELS STATISTICS
SN	Statistical data tabulated by types of vessels and size categories
BT1	FISHERY STATISTICS
RT	FISHING EFFORT
RT	FISHING VESSELS

FISHING WITHOUT GEAR
SN	Includes collecting by hand and use of trained hunting animals
BT1	CATCHING METHODS
RT	FISHING

FISHWAYS
BT1	GUIDING DEVICES
RT	ANADROMOUS MIGRATIONS
RT	DAMS
RT	HABITAT IMPROVEMENT (PHYSICAL)
RT	HYDRAULIC STRUCTURES
RT	RESERVOIRS (WATER)
RT	SCREENS

FISSION PRODUCTS
UF	debris (nuclear)
BT1	RADIOACTIVE MATERIALS
BT2	MATERIALS
RT	ACCIDENTS
RT	FALLOUT
RT	ISOTOPES
RT	NUCLEAR EXPLOSIONS
RT	RADIOACTIVE WASTES

FIXATION
SN	Fixation methods used to kill and preserve aquatic animal and vegetal organisms for laboratory purposes
UF	conservation (organisms)
UF	preservation (organisms)
RT	ANAESTHETICS
RT	FIXATIVES
RT	PRESERVATION (FISHERY PRODUCTS)
RT	PRESERVATIVES

FIXATIVES
SN	Added in 1980
UF	fixing agents
RT	CHEMICAL COMPOUNDS
RT	CYTOLOGY
RT	FIXATION
RT	HISTOLOGY
RT	TISSUES

ASFIS Thesaurus

FIXED PLATFORMS
SN	Membered structures, permanently attached to the sea floor, with the working level above water
UF	fixed structures
BT1	OFFSHORE STRUCTURES
BT2	HYDRAULIC STRUCTURES
NT1	GRAVITY PLATFORMS
NT1	GUYED TOWERS
NT1	PILED PLATFORMS
NT1	TENSION LEG PLATFORMS
RT	DECKS
RT	DRILLING PLATFORMS
RT	LEGS (STRUCTURAL)
RT	MOBILE PLATFORMS
RT	MODULES
RT	PRODUCTION PLATFORMS
RT	TOWERS
RT	WORK PLATFORMS

FIXED STATIONS
BT1	OCEANOGRAPHIC STATIONS
NT1	INSHORE STATIONS
NT1	OCEAN STATIONS
RT	MONITORING SYSTEMS
RT	STANDARD OCEAN SECTIONS
RT	TIME SERIES

FIXED STRUCTURES
USE	**FIXED PLATFORMS**

FIXING AGENTS
USE	**FIXATIVES**

FIXING POSITION
USE	**POSITION FIXING**

FJORD DYNAMICS
SN	Water motion in fjords
UF	fiord dynamics
BT1	SHELF DYNAMICS
BT2	WATER CIRCULATION
BT3	WATER MOTION

FJORDS
UF	fiords
UF	fyords
BT1	COASTAL INLETS
BT2	COASTAL WATERS
RT	ANOXIC CONDITIONS
RT	ANOXIC SEDIMENTS
RT	COASTAL LANDFORMS
RT	COASTAL MORPHOLOGY
RT	COASTS
RT	DEAD WATER
RT	DROWNED VALLEYS
RT	ESTUARIES
RT	FOSSIL SEA WATER
RT	GEOMORPHOLOGY
RT	GLACIAL EROSION
RT	GLACIAL FEATURES
RT	INLETS (WATERWAYS)
RT	MARINE ENVIRONMENT
RT	OVERTURN
RT	SILL DEPTH
RT	SILLS
RT	SUBMERGED SHORELINES
RT	SUBMERGENCE
RT	WATER BODIES

FLAGELLA
SN	Before 1982 search CILIA
UF	flagellum
RT	ANIMAL APPENDAGES
RT	CILIA
RT	LOCOMOTORY APPENDAGES

FLAGELLUM
USE	**FLAGELLA**

FLARING
USE	**GAS FLARING**

FLATFISH FISHERIES
SN	Added in 1982
UF	flounder fisheries
UF	halibut fisheries
UF	plaice fisheries
UF	sole fisheries
BT1	FINFISH FISHERIES
BT2	FISHERIES
RT	DEMERSAL FISHERIES
RT	LONGLINING
RT	MARINE FISHERIES
RT	TRAWLING

FLAVOR
USE	**TASTE**

FLAVOUR
USE	**TASTE**

FLAVOUR TESTS
USE	**TASTE TESTS**

FLAW DETECTION
USE	**NONDESTRUCTIVE TESTING**

FLAW LEADS
BT1	LEADS
RT	NAVIGATION IN ICE

FLAWS
USE	**DEFECTS**

FLEXIBILITY
UF	flexible
UF	rigidity
BT1	MECHANICAL PROPERTIES
BT2	PHYSICAL PROPERTIES
BT3	PROPERTIES
RT	DEFORMATION
RT	ELASTICITY
RT	POISSON'S RATIO

FLEXIBLE
USE	**FLEXIBILITY**

FLIGHT BEHAVIOUR
SN	Added in 1980
UF	bird flight behaviour
BT1	BEHAVIOUR
RT	AQUATIC BIRDS
RT	AVIAN PHYSIOLOGY
RT	FLYING

FLINT
BT1	CHEMICAL SEDIMENTS
BT2	SEDIMENTS
RT	CHERT
RT	CONCRETIONS
RT	SEDIMENTARY ROCKS
RT	SILICEOUS SEDIMENTS

FLIP SPAR BUOYS
USE	**LARGE SPAR BUOYS**

FLOATING
RT	BALLAST
RT	CAPSIZING

FLOATING BARRIERS
UF	booms
UF	oil booms
BT1	BARRIERS
RT	BREAKWATERS
RT	CONTAINMENT

FLOATING BARRIERS (cont'd)
RT	OIL REMOVAL

FLOATING CAGES
SN	Added in 1980
BT1	CAGES
BT2	AQUACULTURE EQUIPMENT
BT3	EQUIPMENT
RT	FISH CULTURE

FLOATING HOSES
BT1	HOSES
RT	LOADING BUOYS
RT	TANKER LOADING

FLOATING ICE
BT1	ICE
NT1	FAST ICE
NT1	ICE ISLANDS
NT1	ICE SHELVES
NT1	ICEBERGS
NT2	TABULAR BERGS
NT1	PACK ICE
RT	ICE BREAKUP
RT	ICE CAPS
RT	ICE JAMS
RT	ICE VOLUME
RT	LAKE ICE
RT	LEADS
RT	POLYNYAS
RT	SEA ICE
RT	WAVE-ICE INTERACTION

FLOATING STRUCTURES
BT1	OFFSHORE STRUCTURES
BT2	HYDRAULIC STRUCTURES
NT1	MOBILE PLATFORMS
NT2	JACKUP PLATFORMS
NT2	SEMISUBMERSIBLE PLATFORMS
NT2	SUBMERSIBLE PLATFORMS
NT2	WORKOVER BARGES
NT1	PONTOONS
RT	BARGES
RT	BUOY SYSTEMS
RT	CAPSIZING
RT	CERTIFICATION
RT	DECK EQUIPMENT
RT	ICE RAFTS
RT	STRUCTURES
RT	SURFACE CRAFT
RT	TENSION LEG PLATFORMS

FLOATING TRAWLS
USE	**MIDWATER TRAWLS**

FLOATS (BUOYANCY)
USE	**BUOYANCY FLOATS**

FLOATS (CURRENT MEASUREMENT)
USE	**DRIFTERS**

FLOATS (SUBSURFACE)
USE	**SUBSURFACE DRIFTERS**

FLOCCULATION
BT1	CHEMICAL PRECIPITATION
BT2	SEPARATION
RT	CLAY MINERALS
RT	COLLOIDS
RT	COPRECIPITATION
RT	DEFLOCCULATION
RT	SEWAGE TREATMENT
RT	SUSPENDED PARTICULATE MATTER
RT	SUSPENSION

FLOOD CONTROL
UF	flood prevention
BT1	CONTROL
RT	AQUACULTURE EQUIPMENT
RT	AQUACULTURE FACILITIES

FLOOD CONTROL (cont'd)
RT	DAMS
RT	EMBANKMENTS
RT	EROSION CONTROL
RT	FLOOD FORECASTING
RT	FLOOD PLAINS
RT	FLOODS
RT	HABITAT IMPROVEMENT (PHYSICAL)
RT	HYDRAULIC ENGINEERING
RT	HYDRAULIC STRUCTURES
RT	HYDROLOGY
RT	PONDS
RT	RESERVOIRS (WATER)
RT	RIVER BASIN MANAGEMENT
RT	RIVER DISCHARGE
RT	RUNOFF
RT	STREAM FLOW
RT	WATER MANAGEMENT
RT	WATER POLICY
RT	WATERSHEDS

FLOOD CURRENTS
BT1	TIDAL CURRENTS
BT2	WATER CURRENTS
BT3	WATER MOTION
RT	HIGH WATER
RT	TIDAL CYCLES

FLOOD FORECASTING
SN	Added in 1980
UF	flood predictions
BT1	PREDICTION
RT	FLOOD CONTROL
RT	FLOOD PLAINS
RT	FLOODS
RT	WATERSHEDS

FLOOD PLAINS
UF	floodplains
BT1	LANDFORMS
BT2	TOPOGRAPHIC FEATURES
RT	ALLUVIAL DEPOSITS
RT	DELTAS
RT	FLOOD CONTROL
RT	FLOOD FORECASTING
RT	FLOODS
RT	FLUVIAL FEATURES
RT	FLUVIAL MORPHOLOGY
RT	GEOMORPHOLOGY
RT	LEVEES
RT	OXBOW LAKES
RT	PLAINS
RT	RIVER DISCHARGE
RT	RIVER MEANDERS
RT	RIVER VALLEYS
RT	RIVERS
RT	SEDIMENTATION

FLOOD PREDICTIONS
USE	**FLOOD FORECASTING**

FLOOD PREVENTION
USE	**FLOOD CONTROL**

FLOODING
SN	Added in 1980
UF	intentional inundation
UF	inundation
RT	FLOODS
RT	PEST CONTROL
RT	RICE FIELDS
RT	STORM SURGES
RT	TSUNAMIS
RT	WAVE EFFECTS
RT	WETLANDS

FLOODING (DISASTERS)
USE	**FLOODS**

FLOODING (IRRIGATION)
USE	**IRRIGATION**

FLOODPLAINS
USE	**FLOOD PLAINS**

FLOODS
UF	escape of water
UF	flooding (disasters)
RT	BACKWATERS
RT	DISASTERS
RT	FLOOD CONTROL
RT	FLOOD FORECASTING
RT	FLOOD PLAINS
RT	FLOODING
RT	GEOLOGICAL HAZARDS
RT	HYDRAULIC ENGINEERING
RT	HYDROLOGY
RT	RIVER DISCHARGE
RT	RUNOFF
RT	SEA WALLS
RT	STORM SURGE BARRIERS
RT	STORMS
RT	TSUNAMIS
RT	WATER LEVELS
RT	WEATHER HAZARDS

FLOOR (OCEAN)
USE	**OCEAN FLOOR**

FLOTATION
SN	Including flotation mechanisms
BT1	SEPARATION
RT	BUOYANCY
RT	COAGULATION
RT	DISPLACEMENT
RT	HYDROSTATIC BEHAVIOUR
RT	PLANKTON
RT	SURFACE PROPERTIES
RT	SURFACE TENSION
RT	SWIM BLADDER

FLOTSAM
SN	Floating wreckage
UF	jetsam
RT	SOLID IMPURITIES
RT	SURFACE DRIFTERS
RT	WRECKS

FLOUNDER FISHERIES
USE	**FLATFISH FISHERIES**

FLOW AROUND IMMERSED STRUCTURE
USE	**FLOW AROUND OBJECTS**

FLOW AROUND OBJECTS
UF	flow around immersed structure
BT1	FLUID FLOW
BT2	FLUID MOTION
RT	CURRENT SCOURING
RT	CYLINDRICAL STRUCTURES
RT	LEE EDDIES
RT	MOORING SYSTEMS
RT	OFFSHORE STRUCTURES
RT	WAVE FORCES

FLOW IN CHANNELS
USE	**CHANNEL FLOW**

FLOW MEASUREMENT
SN	Before 1984 search also FLUID FLOW MEASUREMENT
BT1	MEASUREMENT
NT1	CURRENT MEASUREMENT
NT2	EULERIAN CURRENT MEASUREMENT
NT2	LAGRANGIAN CURRENT MEASUREMENT
NT1	TURBULENCE MEASUREMENT

FLOW MEASUREMENT (cont'd)
NT1	WIND MEASUREMENT
RT	FLOW MEASURING EQUIPMENT
RT	FLOWMETERS
RT	FLUID FLOW
RT	FLUID MOTION

FLOW MEASURING EQUIPMENT
NT1	CURRENT MEASURING EQUIPMENT
NT2	CURRENT SENSORS
NT2	DRIFTERS
NT3	SUBSURFACE DRIFTERS
NT4	SEABED DRIFTERS
NT4	SWALLOW FLOATS
NT3	SURFACE DRIFTERS
NT4	DRIFT BOTTLES
NT4	DRIFT CARDS
NT4	DROGUES
NT2	JELLY BOTTLES
NT1	WIND MEASURING EQUIPMENT
RT	FLOW MEASUREMENT
RT	FLOWMETERS
RT	FLUID MOTION
RT	MEASURING DEVICES

FLOW OVER SURFACES
SN	Use of a more specific term is recommended
BT1	FLUID FLOW
BT2	FLUID MOTION
NT1	AIR FLOW OVER LAND
NT1	AIR FLOW OVER WATER
RT	TOPOGRAPHIC EFFECTS

FLOW OVER WATER SURFACE
USE	**AIR FLOW OVER WATER**

FLOW SENSORS
USE	**FLOWMETERS**

FLOW STRUCTURES
BT1	SEDIMENTARY STRUCTURES
RT	SLUMPING
RT	TURBIDITY CURRENT STRUCTURES

FLOWLINES
SN	Pipelines from underwater wellheads to manifolds or riser pipes
BT1	PIPELINES
BT2	UNDERWATER STRUCTURES
BT3	OFFSHORE STRUCTURES
BT4	HYDRAULIC STRUCTURES
RT	GATHERING LINES
RT	MANIFOLDS
RT	RISER PIPES
RT	WELLHEADS

FLOWMETERS
UF	flow sensors
BT1	MEASURING DEVICES
RT	ANEMOMETERS
RT	CHANNEL FLOW
RT	COSINE RESPONSE
RT	CURRENT MEASURING EQUIPMENT
RT	CURRENT METER ARRAYS
RT	CURRENT METERS
RT	CURRENT SENSORS
RT	CURRENT VELOCITY
RT	DOPPLER EFFECT
RT	FLOW MEASUREMENT
RT	FLOW MEASURING EQUIPMENT
RT	OCEANOGRAPHIC EQUIPMENT
RT	SENSORS
RT	SHEAR PROBES
RT	STREAM FLOW RATE
RT	THERMISTORS
RT	WEIRS
RT	WIND MEASURING EQUIPMENT
RT	WIND SPEED

FLUID DYNAMICS
BT1	FLUID MECHANICS
BT2	MECHANICS
BT3	PHYSICS
NT1	AERODYNAMICS
RT	ATMOSPHERIC MOTION
RT	EQUATION OF CONTINUITY
RT	FLUID FLOW
RT	FLUID MOTION
RT	WATER MOTION

FLUID FLOW
BT1	FLUID MOTION
NT1	AGEOSTROPHIC FLOW
NT1	CHANNEL FLOW
NT1	CRITICAL FLOW
NT1	DENSITY FLOW
NT1	FLOW AROUND OBJECTS
NT1	FLOW OVER SURFACES
NT2	AIR FLOW OVER LAND
NT2	AIR FLOW OVER WATER
NT1	GEOSTROPHIC FLOW
NT2	QUASI-GEOSTROPHIC MOTION
NT1	HORIZONTAL MOTION
NT1	HYDROTHERMAL FLOW
NT1	JETS
NT2	BUOYANT JETS
NT2	COASTAL JETS
NT1	LAMINAR FLOW
NT2	COUETTE FLOW
NT1	MULTIPHASE FLOW
NT1	PERCOLATION
NT1	PLUMES
NT2	CHEMICAL PLUMES
NT2	MANTLE PLUMES
NT2	RIVER PLUMES
NT2	THERMAL PLUMES
NT1	POTENTIAL FLOW
NT1	SHEAR FLOW
NT2	STRATIFIED SHEAR FLOW
NT2	TURBULENT SHEAR FLOW
NT1	STRATIFIED FLOW
NT1	TURBULENT FLOW
NT2	CAVITATION
RT	FLOW MEASUREMENT
RT	FLUID DYNAMICS
RT	FLUIDS
RT	FROUDE NUMBER
RT	OSCILLATORY FLOW
RT	WATER CURRENTS
RT	WINDS

FLUID MECHANICS
SN	Before 1982 search HYDRODYNAMICS
BT1	MECHANICS
BT2	PHYSICS
NT1	FLUID DYNAMICS
NT2	AERODYNAMICS
NT1	HYDRODYNAMICS
NT1	HYDROSTATICS
RT	DYNAMICAL OCEANOGRAPHY
RT	FLUID MOTION
RT	FLUIDS

FLUID MOTION
SN	Before 1982 search HYDRODYNAMICS
NT1	BAROCLINIC MOTION
NT1	BAROTROPIC MOTION
NT1	BILLOWS
NT1	FLUID FLOW
NT2	AGEOSTROPHIC FLOW
NT2	CHANNEL FLOW
NT2	CRITICAL FLOW
NT2	DENSITY FLOW
NT2	FLOW AROUND OBJECTS
NT2	FLOW OVER SURFACES
NT3	AIR FLOW OVER LAND
NT3	AIR FLOW OVER WATER
NT2	GEOSTROPHIC FLOW
NT3	QUASI-GEOSTROPHIC MOTION

FLUID MOTION (cont'd)
NT2	HORIZONTAL MOTION
NT2	HYDROTHERMAL FLOW
NT2	JETS
NT3	BUOYANT JETS
NT3	COASTAL JETS
NT2	LAMINAR FLOW
NT3	COUETTE FLOW
NT2	MULTIPHASE FLOW
NT2	PERCOLATION
NT2	PLUMES
NT3	CHEMICAL PLUMES
NT3	MANTLE PLUMES
NT3	RIVER PLUMES
NT3	THERMAL PLUMES
NT2	POTENTIAL FLOW
NT2	SHEAR FLOW
NT3	STRATIFIED SHEAR FLOW
NT3	TURBULENT SHEAR FLOW
NT2	STRATIFIED FLOW
NT2	TURBULENT FLOW
NT3	CAVITATION
NT1	LANGMUIR CIRCULATION
NT1	TURBULENCE
NT2	ATMOSPHERIC TURBULENCE
NT3	CLEAR AIR TURBULENCE
NT3	GUSTS
NT2	OCEANIC TURBULENCE
NT1	TURBULENT ENTRAINMENT
NT1	UNIDIRECTIONAL FLOW
NT1	UNSTEADY FLOW
RT	ANTICYCLONIC MOTION
RT	BAROCLINIC MODE
RT	BAROTROPIC MODE
RT	CURRENT MEANDERING
RT	DYNAMICAL OCEANOGRAPHY
RT	FLOW MEASUREMENT
RT	FLOW MEASURING EQUIPMENT
RT	FLUID DYNAMICS
RT	FLUID MECHANICS
RT	MEANDERING
RT	MOTION
RT	PLANETARY WAVES
RT	RESIDUAL FLOW
RT	ROTATING FLUIDS
RT	STREAM FLOW
RT	TIDAL MOTION
RT	VERTICAL MOTION
RT	VORTICES
RT	WATER CIRCULATION
RT	WATER CURRENTS
RT	WATER WAVE MOTION

FLUID MUD
BT1	MUD
BT2	CLASTICS
BT3	SEDIMENTS
RT	FLUIDIZATION

FLUIDIZATION
BT1	PHASE CHANGES
RT	FLUID MUD
RT	FLUIDIZED SEDIMENT FLOW
RT	FLUIDS
RT	GRAIN FLOW
RT	LIQUEFACTION
RT	LIQUEFIED SEDIMENT FLOW
RT	SHEAR STRENGTH
RT	SLUMPING

FLUIDIZED SEDIMENT FLOW
UF	liquefied sediment flow
BT1	SEDIMENT GRAVITY FLOWS
BT2	SEDIMENT MOVEMENT
RT	COHESIONLESS SEDIMENTS
RT	FLUIDIZATION
RT	PORE PRESSURE
RT	PORE WATER
RT	SILT

FLUIDS
SN	Use of a more specific term is recommended
NT1	GASES
NT2	AIR
NT2	ATMOSPHERIC GASES
NT2	BREATHING MIXTURES
NT2	COMPRESSED GAS
NT2	DISSOLVED GASES
NT3	DISSOLVED OXYGEN
NT2	OZONE
NT2	RARE GASES
NT2	WATER VAPOUR
NT1	LIQUIDS
NT1	NON-NEWTONIAN FLUIDS
NT1	ROTATING FLUIDS
RT	BODY FLUIDS
RT	DRILLING FLUIDS
RT	FLUID FLOW
RT	FLUID MECHANICS
RT	FLUIDIZATION
RT	WATER

FLUMES
BT1	LABORATORY EQUIPMENT
BT2	EQUIPMENT
RT	CHANNELS
RT	SCALE MODELS
RT	WAVE TANKS

FLUORESCENCE
BT1	LUMINESCENCE
RT	ANALYTICAL TECHNIQUES
RT	BIOLOGICAL PROPERTIES
RT	BIOLUMINESCENCE
RT	FLUORESCENCE MICROSCOPY
RT	FLUORIMETERS
RT	LIGHT
RT	LIGHT SCATTERING
RT	PHOSPHORESCENCE
RT	SPECTROSCOPIC TECHNIQUES

FLUORESCENCE MICROSCOPY
BT1	MICROSCOPY
BT2	ANALYTICAL TECHNIQUES
RT	FLUORESCENCE
RT	RADIOGRAPHY

FLUORESCENCE SPECTROSCOPY
UF	atomic fluorescence spectroscopy
BT1	SPECTROSCOPIC TECHNIQUES
BT2	ANALYTICAL TECHNIQUES

FLUORIDES
BT1	FLUORINE COMPOUNDS
BT2	HALOGEN COMPOUNDS
RT	HALIDES
RT	MAGNESIUM FLUORIDES

FLUORIMETERS
UF	fluorometers
RT	FLUORESCENCE
RT	LIGHT MEASURING INSTRUMENTS

FLUORINATED HYDROCARBONS
BT1	HALOGENATED HYDROCARBONS
BT2	HYDROCARBONS
BT3	ORGANIC COMPOUNDS
NT1	FREONS

FLUORINE
BT1	CHEMICAL ELEMENTS
RT	BROMINE
RT	CHLORINE
RT	FLUORINE COMPOUNDS
RT	FLUORINE ISOTOPES
RT	FLUORITE
RT	HALOGENS
RT	IODINE
RT	TRACE ELEMENTS

FLUORINE COMPOUNDS

BT1	HALOGEN COMPOUNDS
NT1	FLUORIDES
RT	BRINES
RT	CHEMICAL COMPOUNDS
RT	CHLORIC ACID
RT	CHLORINE
RT	CHLORINE COMPOUNDS
RT	CHLORINITY
RT	DISSOLVED SALTS
RT	FLUORINE
RT	ORGANIC COMPOUNDS

FLUORINE ISOTOPES

BT1	ISOTOPES
RT	FLUORINE

FLUORITE

BT1	HALIDE MINERALS
BT2	MINERALS
RT	FLUORINE

FLUOROMETERS

USE	**FLUORIMETERS**

FLUSHING

RT	FLUSHING TIME
RT	TIDAL INLETS

FLUSHING TIME

RT	ESTUARIES
RT	ESTUARINE DYNAMICS
RT	FLUSHING
RT	HARBOURS
RT	LAKE DYNAMICS
RT	PERSISTENCE
RT	POLLUTANTS
RT	RENEWAL
RT	RESERVOIRS (WATER)
RT	RESIDENCE TIME
RT	TIDAL INLETS

FLUTE CASTS

BT1	CURRENT MARKS
BT2	BEDDING STRUCTURES
BT3	SEDIMENTARY STRUCTURES
RT	SOLE MARKS

FLUVIAL DEPOSITION FEATURES

USE	**FLUVIAL FEATURES**

FLUVIAL DEPOSITS

RT	FLUVIAL FEATURES
RT	FLUVIAL SEDIMENTATION
RT	FLUVIAL TRANSPORT

FLUVIAL FEATURES

UF	fluvial deposition features
RT	ALLUVIAL FANS
RT	BED FORMS
RT	CHANNELS
RT	DELTAS
RT	DEPOSITION FEATURES
RT	FLOOD PLAINS
RT	FLUVIAL DEPOSITS
RT	FLUVIAL MORPHOLOGY
RT	LEVEES
RT	RIVER BASINS
RT	RIVER MEANDERS
RT	RIVER PLUMES
RT	RIVER VALLEYS
RT	RIVERS

FLUVIAL MORPHOLOGY

UF	river morphology
BT1	GEOMORPHOLOGY
BT2	GEOLOGY
BT3	EARTH SCIENCES
RT	ALLUVIAL DEPOSITS
RT	DELTAS

FLUVIAL MORPHOLOGY (cont'd)

RT	DISTRIBUTARIES
RT	EROSION
RT	ESTUARIES
RT	FLOOD PLAINS
RT	FLUVIAL FEATURES
RT	FLUVIAL TRANSPORT
RT	RIVER BANKS
RT	RIVER BEDS
RT	RIVER ENGINEERING
RT	RIVER MEANDERS
RT	RIVER VALLEYS
RT	RIVERS
RT	TERRACES
RT	TRIBUTARIES

FLUVIAL SEDIMENTATION

BT1	SEDIMENTATION
RT	ALLUVIAL DEPOSITS
RT	DELTAIC DEPOSITS
RT	FLUVIAL DEPOSITS
RT	FLUVIAL TRANSPORT
RT	RIVERS
RT	SEDIMENTARY ENVIRONMENTS

FLUVIAL TRANSPORT

BT1	SEDIMENT TRANSPORT
RT	ALLUVIAL DEPOSITS
RT	CHANNEL FLOW
RT	FLUVIAL DEPOSITS
RT	FLUVIAL MORPHOLOGY
RT	FLUVIAL SEDIMENTATION
RT	LEVEES
RT	RIVER DISCHARGE
RT	RIVERS

FLY ASH

BT1	ASHES
RT	AIR POLLUTION
RT	ATMOSPHERIC PARTICULATES

FLYFISHING

USE	**SPORT FISHING**

FLYING

SN	Added in 1980
UF	bird flying
BT1	LOCOMOTION
RT	AQUATIC BIRDS
RT	FLIGHT BEHAVIOUR

FLYSCH

BT1	CLASTICS
BT2	SEDIMENTS
RT	TERRIGENOUS SEDIMENTS

FOAMS

SN	Including foaming phenomena on the surface of water bodies
RT	AIR BUBBLES
RT	CAPILLARITY
RT	COLLOIDS
RT	SEA SURFACE
RT	SURFACE CHEMISTRY
RT	SURFACE MICROLAYER
RT	WHITECAPS

FOETUS

SN	Added in 1980
UF	fetus
BT1	EMBRYOS
BT2	DEVELOPMENTAL STAGES
RT	AQUATIC MAMMALS
RT	EMBRYOLOGY
RT	PARTURITION
RT	PLACENTA

FOG

UF	advection fog
UF	arctic sea smoke
UF	evaporation fog
UF	mist
UF	radiation fog
UF	sea fog
UF	sea mist
UF	sea smoke
UF	steam fog
BT1	CLOUDS
BT2	HYDROMETEORS
RT	DEW POINT
RT	HAZE
RT	UPWELLING
RT	VISIBILITY
RT	WEATHER

FOLDS

UF	folds (geology)
BT1	GEOLOGICAL STRUCTURES
NT1	ANTICLINES
NT2	DOMES
NT1	ANTICLINORIA
NT1	GEOSYNCLINES
NT1	STRUCTURAL DOMES
NT2	SALT DOMES
NT1	SYNCLINES
NT1	SYNCLINORIA
RT	ROCK DEFORMATION

FOLDS (GEOLOGY)

USE	**FOLDS**

FOOD

SN	Use of a more specific term is recommended; consult terms listed below
RT	FOOD ABSORPTION
RT	FOOD ADDITIVES
RT	FOOD AVAILABILITY
RT	FOOD CHAINS
RT	FOOD COMPOSITION
RT	FOOD CONSUMPTION
RT	FOOD CONVERSION
RT	FOOD FISH
RT	FOOD POISONING
RT	FOOD TECHNOLOGY
RT	FOOD WEBS
RT	HUMAN FOOD
RT	LIVESTOCK FOOD
RT	NUTRITION
RT	NUTRITIONAL REQUIREMENTS

FOOD ABSORPTION

UF	absorption (food)
BT1	ANIMAL NUTRITION
BT2	NUTRITION
RT	DIGESTION
RT	FOOD
RT	INTESTINES
RT	PYLORIC CAECA

FOOD ADDITIVES

UF	food colours
UF	food stabilizers
BT1	ADDITIVES
RT	ANTIOXIDANTS
RT	DIETS
RT	FOOD
RT	FOOD COMPOSITION
RT	FOOD TECHNOLOGY
RT	PALATABILITY
RT	PRESERVATION (FISHERY PRODUCTS)
RT	QUALITY CONTROL
RT	VITAMIN A
RT	VITAMIN B
RT	VITAMIN C
RT	VITAMIN D
RT	VITAMIN E

ASFIS Thesaurus

FOOD ADDITIVES (cont'd)
RT	VITAMINS

FOOD AVAILABILITY
BT1	AVAILABILITY
RT	ABUNDANCE
RT	BIOTIC FACTORS
RT	BIOTIC PRESSURE
RT	COMPETITION
RT	ENVIRONMENTAL FACTORS
RT	FEEDING
RT	FOOD
RT	FOOD CHAINS
RT	FOOD CONSUMPTION
RT	FOOD ORGANISMS
RT	STARVATION

FOOD CHAINS
BT1	FOOD WEBS
RT	BIOACCUMULATION
RT	BIOENERGETICS
RT	BIOLOGICAL PRODUCTION
RT	CYCLES
RT	DECOMPOSERS
RT	ECOSYSTEMS
RT	ENERGY FLOW
RT	FEEDING BEHAVIOUR
RT	FOOD
RT	FOOD AVAILABILITY
RT	FOOD ORGANISMS
RT	GRAZING
RT	HETEROTROPHIC ORGANISMS
RT	INTERSPECIFIC RELATIONSHIPS
RT	PLANKTONOLOGY
RT	POISONOUS FISH
RT	POISONOUS ORGANISMS
RT	PRIMARY PRODUCTION
RT	SAPROPHYTES
RT	SECONDARY PRODUCTION
RT	STOMACH CONTENT
RT	TROPHIC LEVELS
RT	TROPHIC RELATIONSHIPS

FOOD COLOURS
USE	**FOOD ADDITIVES**

FOOD COMPOSITION
SN	Chemical composition of industrial aquatic products for human and animal consumption
RT	CHEMICAL COMPOSITION
RT	FOOD
RT	FOOD ADDITIVES
RT	FOOD CONVERSION
RT	FOOD TECHNOLOGY
RT	NUTRITIVE VALUE
RT	POWDERED PRODUCTS
RT	PROCESSED FISHERY PRODUCTS
RT	QUALITY CONTROL

FOOD CONSUMPTION
UF	food consumption rate
BT1	ANIMAL NUTRITION
BT2	NUTRITION
RT	BIOENERGETICS
RT	CALORIES
RT	DIGESTION
RT	ECOLOGICAL EFFICIENCY
RT	FOOD
RT	FOOD AVAILABILITY
RT	NUTRITIONAL REQUIREMENTS
RT	STOMACH CONTENT

FOOD CONSUMPTION RATE
USE	**FOOD CONSUMPTION**

FOOD CONVERSION
SN	Efficiency of food conversion by organisms
UF	assimilation (food)
UF	conversion efficiency
UF	food conversion rate
BT1	ANIMAL NUTRITION
BT2	NUTRITION
RT	DIGESTION
RT	FEEDING
RT	FOOD
RT	FOOD COMPOSITION
RT	GROWTH

FOOD CONVERSION RATE
USE	**FOOD CONVERSION**

FOOD CYCLE
USE	**TROPHODYNAMIC CYCLE**

FOOD FISH
UF	edible fish
BT1	FISH
BT2	AQUATIC ANIMALS
RT	BOTULISM
RT	COMMERCIAL SPECIES
RT	FOOD
RT	FOOD ORGANISMS
RT	HUMAN FOOD
RT	NUTRITIVE VALUE
RT	ORGANOLEPTIC PROPERTIES
RT	PALATABILITY
RT	QUALITY CONTROL
RT	TASTE
RT	TASTE TESTS

FOOD FOR HUMAN CONSUMPTION
USE	**HUMAN FOOD**

FOOD ORGANISMS
UF	fish food organisms
UF	live feed
UF	live food
UF	natural food
BT1	AQUATIC ORGANISMS
RT	AQUACULTURE
RT	AQUATIC INSECTS
RT	ARTIFICIAL FEEDING
RT	BRINE SHRIMP CULTURE
RT	DIETS
RT	FOOD AVAILABILITY
RT	FOOD CHAINS
RT	FOOD FISH
RT	FORAGE FISH
RT	HABITAT IMPROVEMENT (BIOLOGICAL)
RT	OFF-BOTTOM CULTURE
RT	PHYTOPLANKTON
RT	SELECTIVE FEEDING
RT	STOMACH CONTENT
RT	WORM CULTURE
RT	ZOOPLANKTON

FOOD POISONING
RT	ALLERGIC REACTIONS
RT	BACTERIA
RT	BOTULISM
RT	FOOD
RT	HUMAN FOOD
RT	MICROBIAL CONTAMINATION
RT	QUALITY CONTROL
RT	TOXICITY

FOOD PREFERENCES
SN	Added in 1982
RT	ARTIFICIAL FEEDING
RT	FEEDING BEHAVIOUR
RT	GRAZING

FOOD PROCESSING
USE	**FOOD TECHNOLOGY**

FOOD REQUIREMENTS
USE	**NUTRITIONAL REQUIREMENTS**

FOOD RESOURCES
SN	For human consumption only. Added in 1980
BT1	NATURAL RESOURCES
BT2	RESOURCES
RT	HUMAN FOOD
RT	LIVING RESOURCES
RT	MARINE RESOURCES
RT	RENEWABLE RESOURCES
RT	UNCONVENTIONAL RESOURCES

FOOD STABILIZERS
USE	**FOOD ADDITIVES**

FOOD TECHNOLOGY
SN	Restricted to industrial aquatic products for human and animal consumption
UF	food processing
BT1	TECHNOLOGY
RT	ACCEPTANCE TESTS
RT	DRYING
RT	FEED
RT	FISHERY TECHNOLOGY
RT	FOOD
RT	FOOD ADDITIVES
RT	FOOD COMPOSITION
RT	HUMAN FOOD
RT	MICROBIOLOGY
RT	MINCED PRODUCTS
RT	NUTRITIVE VALUE
RT	PALATABILITY
RT	POWDERED PRODUCTS
RT	PROCESSED FISHERY PRODUCTS
RT	QUALITY CONTROL

FOOD WEBS
NT1	FOOD CHAINS
RT	BIOLOGICAL PRODUCTION
RT	CYCLES
RT	ECOSYSTEMS
RT	ENERGY FLOW
RT	FOOD
RT	HETEROTROPHIC ORGANISMS
RT	INTERSPECIFIC RELATIONSHIPS
RT	TROPHIC RELATIONSHIPS
RT	TROPHODYNAMIC CYCLE

FORAGE FISH
SN	The prey of predatory fish
BT1	FISH
BT2	AQUATIC ANIMALS
RT	AQUACULTURE
RT	CARNIVORES
RT	FOOD ORGANISMS

FORAMINIFERA
SN	Used as subject descriptor in ASFA-2 only; in ASFA-1, used as taxonomic descriptor
RT	FORAMINIFERAL OOZE
RT	FOSSIL FORAMINIFERA
RT	MICROPALAEONTOLOGY

FORAMINIFERAL OOZE
BT1	CALCAREOUS OOZE
BT2	OOZES
NT1	GLOBIGERINA OOZE
RT	FORAMINIFERA
RT	FOSSIL FORAMINIFERA

FORCED CONVECTION
BT1	CONVECTION
BT2	ADVECTION
BT3	TRANSPORT PROCESSES
RT	HEAT TRANSFER
RT	LAMINAR FLOW
RT	PRANDTL NUMBER

FORCED OSCILLATIONS
BT1	OSCILLATIONS

FORCES
NT1	CENTRIFUGAL FORCE
NT1	CENTRIPETAL FORCE
RT	GRAVITATION
RT	INERTIA

FORCES (MECHANICS)
NT1	CORIOLIS FORCE
NT1	FRICTION
NT2	BOTTOM FRICTION
NT2	TIDAL FRICTION
NT1	GRAVITY
NT1	LOADS (FORCES)
NT2	CURRENT FORCES
NT2	CYCLIC LOADING
NT2	DYNAMIC LOADS
NT2	EARTHQUAKE LOADING
NT2	ICE LOADS
NT2	OCEAN LOADING
NT2	WAVE FORCES
NT2	WAVE-INDUCED LOADING
NT2	WIND PRESSURE
NT1	STRESS
NT2	BOTTOM STRESS
NT2	COMPRESSION
NT2	REYNOLDS STRESSES
NT2	SHEAR STRESS
NT2	TENSION
NT3	SURFACE TENSION
NT2	TORQUE
NT2	WIND STRESS

FOREARC BASINS
BT1	STRUCTURAL BASINS
RT	ACTIVE MARGINS
RT	BASINS
RT	ISLAND ARCS
RT	MARGINAL BASINS
RT	OCEAN BASINS
RT	SUBDUCTION
RT	TRENCHES (OCEANIC)

FORECASTING
USE	**PREDICTION**

FORECASTS
USE	**PREDICTION**

FOREIGN FISHING
SN	Refers to commercial fishing by foreign vessels. Added in 1980
BT1	COMMERCIAL FISHING
BT2	FISHING OPERATIONS
RT	BILATERAL AGREEMENTS
RT	COASTAL STATES
RT	EXCLUSIVE ECONOMIC ZONE
RT	FISHERY DISPUTES
RT	FISHERY POLICY
RT	FISHERY PROTECTION
RT	FISHING RIGHTS
RT	INTERNATIONAL AGREEMENTS
RT	JOINT VENTURES
RT	MIGRATORY SPECIES

FOREIGN TRADE
USE	**TRADE**

FORESET BEDS
BT1	DELTAIC FEATURES
RT	DELTAIC DEPOSITS
RT	DELTAIC SEDIMENTATION

FORESHORE
UF	beach face
BT1	BEACH FEATURES
RT	BACKSHORE

FOREST INDUSTRY
SN	Added in 1980
BT1	INDUSTRIES
RT	INDUSTRIAL WASTES
RT	PULP WASTES

FORM DRAG
BT1	DRAG
RT	BED ROUGHNESS
RT	BOTTOM FRICTION

FORMULAE
SN	Used only as a qualifier
RT	MATHEMATICAL MODELS

FORWARD SCATTERING
SN	Forward scattering of sound waves
BT1	SOUND SCATTERING
RT	BACKSCATTER

FOSSIL ASSEMBLAGES
RT	BIOSTRATIGRAPHY
RT	ECOLOGICAL ASSOCIATIONS
RT	FOSSILS

FOSSIL DIATOMS
BT1	VEGETAL FOSSILS
BT2	FOSSILS
RT	DIATOM OOZE
RT	OOZES

FOSSIL FORAMINIFERA
BT1	ANIMAL FOSSILS
BT2	FOSSILS
RT	FORAMINIFERA
RT	FORAMINIFERAL OOZE
RT	OOZES

FOSSIL FUELED POWER PLANTS
BT1	POWER PLANTS
RT	COOLING PONDS
RT	COOLING WATER
RT	FOSSIL FUELS
RT	THERMAL AQUACULTURE
RT	THERMAL PLUMES
RT	THERMAL POLLUTION
RT	WASTE HEAT

FOSSIL FUELS
UF	fuel resources
BT1	SUBSURFACE DEPOSITS
BT2	MINERAL DEPOSITS
BT3	MINERAL RESOURCES
BT4	NATURAL RESOURCES
NT1	COAL
NT1	PETROLEUM
NT2	CRUDE OIL
NT2	GAS CONDENSATES
NT2	NATURAL GAS
NT3	LIQUEFIED NATURAL GAS
NT2	PETROLEUM RESIDUES
RT	AIR POLLUTION
RT	CARBON DIOXIDE
RT	DEEP-SEA MINING
RT	DRILLING
RT	ENERGY RESOURCES
RT	FOSSIL FUELED POWER PLANTS
RT	HYDROCARBONS
RT	MINING
RT	NONRENEWABLE RESOURCES

FOSSIL POLLEN
BT1	VEGETAL FOSSILS
BT2	FOSSILS
RT	PALAEONTOLOGY
RT	PALYNOLOGY
RT	POLLEN

FOSSIL PTEROPODS
BT1	ANIMAL FOSSILS
BT2	FOSSILS
RT	PTEROPOD OOZE

FOSSIL RADIOLARIA
BT1	ANIMAL FOSSILS
BT2	FOSSILS
RT	RADIOLARIAN OOZE

FOSSIL SEA WATER
BT1	SEA WATER
BT2	WATER
RT	FJORDS
RT	LAKES
RT	PALAEOCEANOGRAPHY
RT	RELICT LAKES

FOSSIL SPORES
BT1	VEGETAL FOSSILS
BT2	FOSSILS
RT	PALYNOLOGY
RT	SPORES

FOSSILIZED TRACKS
BT1	TRACE FOSSILS
BT2	BIOGENIC SEDIMENTARY STRUCTURES
BT3	SEDIMENTARY STRUCTURES

FOSSILS
NT1	ANIMAL FOSSILS
NT2	FOSSIL FORAMINIFERA
NT2	FOSSIL PTEROPODS
NT2	FOSSIL RADIOLARIA
NT1	VEGETAL FOSSILS
NT2	FOSSIL DIATOMS
NT2	FOSSIL POLLEN
NT2	FOSSIL SPORES
RT	AGE DETERMINATION
RT	ARCHAEOLOGY
RT	BIOFACIES
RT	BIOSTRATIGRAPHY
RT	CALCIFICATION
RT	FOSSIL ASSEMBLAGES
RT	GEOLOGICAL DISTRIBUTION
RT	GEOLOGY
RT	LIVING FOSSILS
RT	MICROPALAEONTOLOGY
RT	PALAEOCLIMATE
RT	PALAEOECOLOGY
RT	PALAEONTOLOGY
RT	STRATIGRAPHY
RT	TRACE FOSSILS

FOULERS
USE	**FOULING ORGANISMS**

FOULING
SN	Added in 1980
RT	ANTIFOULING SUBSTANCES
RT	AQUATIC PLANTS
RT	DEGRADATION
RT	FOULING CONTROL
RT	FOULING ORGANISMS
RT	SCALING

FOULING CONTROL
UF	fouling prevention
BT1	CONTROL
RT	ANTIFOULING SUBSTANCES
RT	BIOLOGICAL CONTROL
RT	COATING MATERIALS

FOULING CONTROL (cont'd)
RT	COATING PROCESSES
RT	FOULING
RT	FOULING ORGANISMS
RT	HEAT EXCHANGERS
RT	MAINTENANCE
RT	PROTECTION
RT	SHIP HULLS

FOULING ORGANISMS
UF	foulers
BT1	AQUATIC ORGANISMS
RT	ANTIFOULING SUBSTANCES
RT	BIODEGRADATION
RT	BIOLOGICAL DAMAGE
RT	BORING ORGANISMS
RT	CHEMICAL CONTROL
RT	FOULING
RT	FOULING CONTROL

FOULING PREVENTION
USE	**FOULING CONTROL**

FOUNDATIONS
UF	marine foundations
UF	seabed foundations
NT1	PILES
RT	CURRENT SCOURING
RT	GEOTECHNOLOGY
RT	GROUTING
RT	HYDRAULIC STRUCTURES
RT	SCOURING
RT	SETTLEMENT (STRUCTURAL)

FOURIER ANALYSIS
SN	Before 1982 search HARMONIC ANALYSIS
BT1	MATHEMATICAL ANALYSIS
RT	FOURIER TRANSFORMS
RT	HARMONIC ANALYSIS
RT	SIGNAL PROCESSING
RT	TIDAL ANALYSIS
RT	TIME SERIES ANALYSIS
RT	WAVEFORM ANALYSIS

FOURIER TRANSFORMS
BT1	FUNCTIONAL ANALYSIS
BT2	NUMERICAL ANALYSIS
BT3	MATHEMATICAL ANALYSIS
RT	FOURIER ANALYSIS

FOVEA
USE	**RETINAS**

FRACTURE ZONES
BT1	SUBMARINE FEATURES
BT2	TOPOGRAPHIC FEATURES
RT	ESCARPMENTS
RT	FAULT ZONES
RT	FAULTS
RT	MID-OCEAN RIDGES
RT	PLATE TECTONICS
RT	RELIEF FORMS
RT	SEAFLOOR SPREADING
RT	SUBMARINE SCARPS
RT	TRANSFORM FAULTS
RT	VALLEYS

FRACTURES
BT1	DEFECTS
RT	CRACKS

FRANCIUM
BT1	CHEMICAL ELEMENTS
RT	ALKALI METALS
RT	FRANCIUM COMPOUNDS
RT	FRANCIUM ISOTOPES

FRANCIUM COMPOUNDS
RT	CHEMICAL COMPOUNDS
RT	FRANCIUM

FRANCIUM ISOTOPES
BT1	ISOTOPES
RT	FRANCIUM

FRANCOLITE
BT1	PHOSPHATE MINERALS
BT2	MINERALS

FREAK WAVES
RT	CATASTROPHIC WAVES

FREE AIR ANOMALIES
BT1	GRAVITY ANOMALIES
BT2	ANOMALIES
RT	FREE AIR GRAVITY CHARTS

FREE AIR CORRECTION
USE	**GRAVITY CORRECTIONS**

FREE AIR GRAVITY CHARTS
BT1	GRAVITY CHARTS
BT2	GEOLOGICAL MAPS
BT3	MAPS
BT4	GRAPHICS
RT	FREE AIR ANOMALIES

FREE ENERGY
BT1	THERMODYNAMIC PROPERTIES
BT2	PHYSICAL PROPERTIES
BT3	PROPERTIES
RT	ENERGY
RT	ENTHALPY

FREE-FALL CORERS
UF	boomerang corers
BT1	CORERS
BT2	SEDIMENT SAMPLERS
BT3	SAMPLERS
RT	FREE-FALL INSTRUMENTS

FREE-FALL EQUIPMENT
USE	**FREE-FALL INSTRUMENTS**

FREE-FALL INSTRUMENTS
UF	free-fall equipment
BT1	INSTRUMENTS
RT	FREE-FALL CORERS
RT	FREE-FALL PROFILERS
RT	OCEANOGRAPHIC EQUIPMENT

FREE-FALL PROFILERS
BT1	PROFILERS
RT	FREE-FALL INSTRUMENTS
RT	VELOCITY PROFILERS

FREE-SWIMMING VEHICLES
SN	Underwater vehicles with 3-D manoeuvrability
BT1	UNDERWATER VEHICLES
BT2	VEHICLES
RT	SELF-PROPELLED VEHICLES
RT	SUBMERSIBLES
RT	TETHERED FREE-SWIMMING VEHICLES
RT	UNTETHERED VEHICLES

FREEZE-BRANDING
USE	**COLD BRANDING**

FREEZE-DRIED PRODUCTS
SN	Added in 1980
BT1	PROCESSED FISHERY PRODUCTS
BT2	FISHERY PRODUCTS
BT3	PRODUCTS
RT	FREEZE-DRYING

FREEZE-DRYING
SN	To dry in frozen state water vacuum. Added in 1980
BT1	DRYING
BT2	PROCESSING FISHERY PRODUCTS
BT3	FISHERY INDUSTRY
BT4	INDUSTRIES
RT	CURING
RT	DRIED PRODUCTS
RT	FREEZE-DRIED PRODUCTS

FREEZING
UF	freezing (physics)
BT1	PHASE CHANGES
RT	ANTIFREEZES
RT	CHILLED PRODUCTS
RT	COLD STORAGE
RT	COOLING
RT	FREEZING POINT
RT	FREEZING STORAGE
RT	FUSION HEAT
RT	HEAT TRANSFER
RT	ICE FORMATION
RT	ICE MELTING
RT	ICE NUCLEI
RT	ICING
RT	MELTING
RT	PERMAFROST
RT	PROCESSING FISHERY PRODUCTS
RT	REFRIGERATION
RT	SOLIDIFICATION
RT	SUBLIMATION
RT	THAWING

FREEZING (FISHERY PRODUCTS)
USE	**REFRIGERATION**

FREEZING (PHYSICS)
USE	**FREEZING**

FREEZING POINT
BT1	TRANSITION TEMPERATURES
BT2	TEMPERATURE
BT3	THERMODYNAMIC PROPERTIES
BT4	PHYSICAL PROPERTIES
RT	COLLIGATIVE PROPERTIES
RT	FREEZING
RT	ICE MELTING
RT	PHASE CHANGES
RT	SEA WATER
RT	WATER DENSITY

FREEZING POINT DEPRESSANTS
USE	**ANTIFREEZES**

FREEZING STORAGE
UF	cryopreservation
UF	cryoprotectants
UF	frozen storage
RT	DEHYDRATION
RT	FREEZING
RT	FROZEN PRODUCTS
RT	ICE
RT	SPERM
RT	STORAGE

FREONS
BT1	FLUORINATED HYDROCARBONS
BT2	HALOGENATED HYDROCARBONS
BT3	HYDROCARBONS
BT4	ORGANIC COMPOUNDS

FREQUENCY
NT1	BRUNT-VAISALA FREQUENCY
NT1	HIGH FREQUENCY
NT1	LOW FREQUENCY
NT1	RESONANT FREQUENCY
NT1	WAVE FREQUENCY
RT	DYNAMIC RESPONSE
RT	FREQUENCY ANALYSIS

FREQUENCY (cont'd)
RT	FREQUENCY SPECTRA
RT	PERIODICITY

FREQUENCY (TIME)
USE	**PERIODICITY**

FREQUENCY ANALYSIS
SN	Used only as a qualifier
BT1	STATISTICAL ANALYSIS
BT2	MATHEMATICAL ANALYSIS
RT	FREQUENCY
RT	SPECTRAL ANALYSIS

FREQUENCY SPECTRA
BT1	SPECTRA
RT	ENERGY SPECTRA
RT	FREQUENCY

FRESH WATER
SN	Including any type of surface and subsurface waters. Before 1982 search also FRESHWATER
BT1	WATER
RT	DEAD WATER
RT	FRESHWATER AQUACULTURE
RT	FRESHWATER ECOLOGY
RT	FRESHWATER POLLUTION
RT	GLACIERS
RT	LAKES
RT	LIMNOLOGY
RT	MELT WATER
RT	PONDS
RT	RIVER DISCHARGE
RT	RIVERS
RT	SALT-WEDGE ESTUARIES
RT	SPRING STREAMS
RT	SUBMARINE SPRINGS
RT	WATER PROPERTIES
RT	WATER SPRINGS
RT	WETLANDS

FRESHWATER AQUACULTURE
UF	inland water aquaculture
BT1	AQUACULTURE
RT	AGROPISCICULTURE
RT	AIR-BREATHING FISH
RT	ALGAL CULTURE
RT	AQUACULTURE EFFLUENTS
RT	AQUACULTURE TECHNIQUES
RT	BAIT CULTURE
RT	CAGE CULTURE
RT	CRUSTACEAN CULTURE
RT	EXTENSIVE CULTURE
RT	FISH CULTURE
RT	FISH PONDS
RT	FRESH WATER
RT	FRESHWATER FISH
RT	FRESHWATER ORGANISMS
RT	FROG CULTURE
RT	HATCHERIES
RT	HYBRID CULTURE
RT	LAKE RECLAMATION
RT	MONOCULTURE
RT	MONOSEX CULTURE
RT	OVERWINTERING TECHNIQUES
RT	PEARL CULTURE
RT	POLYCULTURE
RT	PRAWN CULTURE
RT	RACEWAY CULTURE
RT	RECIRCULATING SYSTEMS
RT	RICE FIELD AQUACULTURE
RT	SHELLFISH CULTURE
RT	THERMAL AQUACULTURE
RT	WHIRLING DISEASE

FRESHWATER CRAB CULTURE
USE	**CRAB CULTURE**

FRESHWATER CRUSTACEANS
UF	crustaceans (freshwater)
BT1	AQUATIC ANIMALS
RT	CARCINOLOGY
RT	COMMERCIAL SPECIES
RT	CRUSTACEAN CULTURE
RT	ECDYSONS
RT	FRESHWATER ORGANISMS
RT	MOULTING
RT	SHELLFISH
RT	SHELLFISH CATCH STATISTICS
RT	SHELLFISH FISHERIES
RT	VERNACULAR NAMES

FRESHWATER ECOLOGISTS
SN	Added in 1980
BT1	ECOLOGISTS
BT2	SCIENTIFIC PERSONNEL
BT3	PERSONNEL
RT	DIRECTORIES
RT	FRESHWATER ECOLOGY

FRESHWATER ECOLOGY
UF	biological limnology
UF	limnology (biological)
BT1	ECOLOGY
RT	AQUATIC ANIMALS
RT	AQUATIC COMMUNITIES
RT	AQUATIC PLANTS
RT	FISHERY LIMNOLOGY
RT	FRESH WATER
RT	FRESHWATER ECOLOGISTS
RT	FRESHWATER SCIENCES
RT	HYDROBIOLOGY
RT	INLAND WATER ENVIRONMENT
RT	LIMNOLOGY
RT	WATER ANALYSIS

FRESHWATER ENVIRONMENT
USE	**INLAND WATER ENVIRONMENT**

FRESHWATER FISH
BT1	FISH
BT2	AQUATIC ANIMALS
NT1	COARSE FISH
RT	AGROPISCICULTURE
RT	BAIT FISHING
RT	FISHERY RESOURCES
RT	FRESHWATER AQUACULTURE
RT	FRESHWATER ORGANISMS
RT	HERBIVOROUS FISH
RT	INLAND FISHERIES
RT	INLAND WATER ENVIRONMENT
RT	LAKE FISHERIES
RT	POTADROMOUS MIGRATIONS

FRESHWATER ICE
BT1	ICE
RT	GLACIERS
RT	ICE PROPERTIES
RT	ICE-WATER INTERFACE
RT	LAKE ICE
RT	LAND ICE

FRESHWATER LAGOONS
USE	**INLAND LAGOONS**

FRESHWATER LAKES
BT1	LAKES
BT2	INLAND WATERS
RT	EUTROPHICATION
RT	LAKE ICE
RT	WATER RESOURCES

FRESHWATER MOLLUSCS
UF	molluscs (freshwater)
UF	mollusks (freshwater)
BT1	AQUATIC ANIMALS
RT	COMMERCIAL SPECIES
RT	FRESHWATER ORGANISMS
RT	MALACOLOGY
RT	MOLLUSC CULTURE
RT	PEARLS
RT	RADULAE
RT	SHELLFISH
RT	SHELLFISH CATCH STATISTICS
RT	SHELLFISH CULTURE
RT	SHELLFISH FISHERIES
RT	SHELLS
RT	VERNACULAR NAMES

FRESHWATER ORGANISMS
SN	Added in 1980
BT1	AQUATIC ORGANISMS
RT	FRESHWATER AQUACULTURE
RT	FRESHWATER CRUSTACEANS
RT	FRESHWATER FISH
RT	FRESHWATER MOLLUSCS
RT	FRESHWATER WEEDS

FRESHWATER POLLUTION
UF	pollution (freshwater)
BT1	WATER POLLUTION
BT2	POLLUTION
RT	ACID RAIN
RT	CHEMICAL POLLUTION
RT	FRESH WATER
RT	GROUNDWATER POLLUTION
RT	OIL POLLUTION
RT	POLLUTANTS
RT	POLLUTION EFFECTS
RT	POLLUTION MONITORING
RT	THERMAL POLLUTION
RT	WASTES
RT	WATER POLLUTION TREATMENT

FRESHWATER SCIENCES
BT1	AQUATIC SCIENCES
RT	FRESHWATER ECOLOGY
RT	HYDROLOGY
RT	LIMNOLOGY

FRESHWATER SCIENTISTS
UF	limnologists
BT1	SCIENTIFIC PERSONNEL
BT2	PERSONNEL
RT	DIRECTORIES
RT	LIMNOLOGY

FRESHWATER-SEAWATER INTERFACE
USE	**ESTUARINE FRONT**

FRESHWATER SEDIMENTATION
USE	**SEDIMENTATION**

FRESHWATER SPRINGS
USE	**WATER SPRINGS**

FRESHWATER WEEDS
UF	pond weeds
BT1	WEEDS
RT	FRESHWATER ORGANISMS
RT	LIVESTOCK FOOD
RT	PLANT CONTROL
RT	PLANT UTILIZATION
RT	VEGETATION COVER

FRICTION
BT1	FORCES (MECHANICS)
NT1	BOTTOM FRICTION
NT1	TIDAL FRICTION
RT	DRAG
RT	ENERGY DISSIPATION
RT	ROUGHNESS

FRICTION (cont'd)
RT   WEAR

FRINGING REEFS
BT1   CORAL REEFS
BT2   BIOGENIC DEPOSITS
RT   BARRIER REEFS

FROG CULTURE
UF   amphibian culture
UF   frog farms
BT1   AQUACULTURE
RT   AGROPISCICULTURE
RT   CULTURES
RT   FRESHWATER AQUACULTURE
RT   POLYCULTURE
RT   POND CULTURE
RT   TERRITORIALITY
RT   WORM CULTURE

FROG FARMS
USE   **FROG CULTURE**

FRONTAL FEATURES
SN   Mesoscale features of convergence in atmosphere and oceans
BT1   MESOSCALE FEATURES
RT   ATMOSPHERIC FRONTS
RT   CONVERGENCE
RT   CONVERGENCE ZONES
RT   FRONTOGENESIS
RT   FRONTS
RT   OCEANIC FRONTS

FRONTIERS (NATIONAL)
USE   **INTERNATIONAL BOUNDARIES**

FRONTOGENESIS
BT1   INTERFACE PHENOMENA
RT   AIR MASSES
RT   ATMOSPHERIC FRONTS
RT   CONVERGENCE
RT   FRONTAL FEATURES
RT   FRONTS
RT   OCEANIC FRONTS
RT   THERMAL FRONTS
RT   WATER MASSES

FRONTS
SN   Use of a more specific term is recommended
NT1   ATMOSPHERIC FRONTS
NT1   OCEANIC FRONTS
NT2   BENTHIC FRONTS
NT2   DENSITY FRONTS
NT2   ESTUARINE FRONT
NT2   SHELF FRONTS
NT3   SHELF EDGE FRONTS
NT1   THERMAL FRONTS
RT   ANTARCTIC CONVERGENCE
RT   ANTARCTIC FRONT
RT   ATMOSPHERIC CONVERGENCES
RT   CONVERGENCE ZONES
RT   FRONTAL FEATURES
RT   FRONTOGENESIS
RT   INTERFACES
RT   INTERTROPICAL CONVERGENCE ZONE
RT   OCEANIC CONVERGENCES
RT   POLAR FRONTS

FRONTS (METEOROLOGY)
USE   **ATMOSPHERIC FRONTS**

FROST RESISTANCE
USE   **COLD RESISTANCE**

FROUDE NUMBER
RT   DIMENSIONLESS NUMBERS
RT   FLUID FLOW
RT   INERTIA
RT   KINETIC ENERGY
RT   POTENTIAL ENERGY
RT   REYNOLDS NUMBER

FROZEN PRODUCTS
BT1   PROCESSED FISHERY PRODUCTS
BT2   FISHERY PRODUCTS
BT3   PRODUCTS
RT   CHILLED PRODUCTS
RT   FREEZING STORAGE
RT   REFRIGERATION
RT   THAWING

FROZEN STORAGE
USE   **FREEZING STORAGE**

FRY
BT1   FISH LARVAE
BT2   LARVAE
BT3   DEVELOPMENTAL STAGES
RT   BREEDING PONDS
RT   FINGERLINGS
RT   GRADING
RT   HATCHERIES
RT   HATCHING
RT   JUVENILES
RT   NURSERY PONDS
RT   SEED (AQUACULTURE)
RT   SEED COLLECTION

FUCOSE
BT1   MONOSACCHARIDES
BT2   SACCHARIDES
BT3   CARBOHYDRATES
BT4   ORGANIC COMPOUNDS

FUCOSTEROL
BT1   STEROLS
BT2   STEROIDS
BT3   LIPIDS
BT4   ORGANIC COMPOUNDS

FUEL ECONOMY
SN   Energy-saving measures, including equipment and methods
RT   FISHERY ECONOMICS
RT   FISHING VESSELS
RT   FUELS
RT   HULLS
RT   PROPULSION SYSTEMS
RT   SAILING SHIPS
RT   SHIP TECHNOLOGY

FUEL RESOURCES
USE   **FOSSIL FUELS**

FUELS
UF   diesel fuels
UF   heating fuels
UF   motor fuels
NT1   LIQUEFIED PETROLEUM GAS
RT   ADDITIVES
RT   DIESEL ENGINES
RT   FUEL ECONOMY
RT   LUBRICANTS
RT   MOTORS
RT   OIL AND GAS INDUSTRY
RT   OIL WASTES
RT   PETROLEUM

FULLERS EARTH
BT1   CLAYS
BT2   CLASTICS
BT3   SEDIMENTS

FULVIC ACIDS
BT1   ORGANIC ACIDS
BT2   ORGANIC COMPOUNDS
RT   HUMIC ACIDS
RT   HUMUS

FUMARIC ACID
BT1   ORGANIC ACIDS
BT2   ORGANIC COMPOUNDS

FUNCTIONAL ANALYSIS
BT1   NUMERICAL ANALYSIS
BT2   MATHEMATICAL ANALYSIS
NT1   FOURIER TRANSFORMS
NT1   HARMONIC ANALYSIS
NT1   LAPLACE TRANSFORMATION
RT   FINITE ELEMENT METHOD
RT   INTEGRAL EQUATIONS

FUNCTIONAL MORPHOLOGY
BT1   BIOLOGY
RT   ORGANISM MORPHOLOGY

FUNDING
USE   **FINANCING**

FUNGAL DISEASES
UF   fungous diseases
UF   fungus diseases
UF   mycoses
UF   mycotic diseases
BT1   INFECTIOUS DISEASES
BT2   DISEASES
RT   ANTIBIOTICS
RT   DRUGS
RT   FISH DISEASES
RT   FUNGI
RT   FUNGICIDES
RT   GILL DISEASE
RT   MYCOLOGY
RT   PARASITIC DISEASES

FUNGAL GILL DISEASE
USE   **GILL DISEASE**

FUNGAL VACCINES
USE   **VACCINES**

FUNGI
SN   In ASFA-1, use as taxonomic descriptor; in ASFA-2, use as subject descriptor
RT   AQUATIC PLANTS
RT   BIOEROSION
RT   CONIDIA
RT   DECOMPOSERS
RT   FUNGAL DISEASES
RT   FUNGICIDES
RT   MICROBIAL CONTAMINATION
RT   MICROBIOLOGICAL ANALYSIS
RT   MICROBIOLOGICAL CULTURE
RT   MICROORGANISMS
RT   MYCOLOGY
RT   SAPROPHYTES
RT   SPORES

FUNGICIDES
SN   Before 1982 search PESTICIDES
UF   antifungals
UF   slimicides
BT1   PESTICIDES
RT   ANTIBIOTICS
RT   FUNGAL DISEASES
RT   FUNGI
RT   MYCOLOGY

FUNGOUS DISEASES
  USE   **FUNGAL DISEASES**

FUNGUS DISEASES
  USE   **FUNGAL DISEASES**

FURROWS (DEEP-SEA)
  USE   **DEEP-SEA FURROWS**

FURUNCOLOSIS
  USE   **BOIL DISEASE**

FUSION HEAT
  UF   latent heat of fusion
  BT1   ENTHALPY
  BT2   THERMODYNAMIC PROPERTIES
  BT3   PHYSICAL PROPERTIES
  BT4   PROPERTIES
  RT   FREEZING
  RT   ICE MELTING
  RT   MELTING

FYKE NETS
  USE   **TRAP NETS**

FYORDS
  USE   **FJORDS**

GABBROS
  BT1   IGNEOUS ROCKS
  BT2   ROCKS
  RT   ANORTHOSITE

GADOID FISHERIES
  SN   Added in 1982
  UF   capelin fisheries
  UF   cod fisheries
  UF   haddock fisheries
  UF   hake fisheries
  UF   pollack fisheries .
  UF   whiting fisheries
  BT1   FINFISH FISHERIES
  BT2   FISHERIES
  RT   DEMERSAL FISHERIES
  RT   MARINE FISHERIES
  RT   TRAWLING

GADOLINIUM
  BT1   CHEMICAL ELEMENTS
  RT   GADOLINIUM COMPOUNDS
  RT   GADOLINIUM ISOTOPES
  RT   RARE EARTHS
  RT   TRANSITION ELEMENTS

GADOLINIUM COMPOUNDS
  RT   CHEMICAL COMPOUNDS
  RT   GADOLINIUM

GADOLINIUM ISOTOPES
  BT1   ISOTOPES
  RT   GADOLINIUM

GALATHEID FISHERIES
  USE   **SQUAT LOBSTER FISHERIES**

GALE FORCE WINDS
  SN   Winds of 28-55 knots
  BT1   WINDS
  BT2   ATMOSPHERIC MOTION
  RT   BEAUFORT SCALE
  RT   GUSTS
  RT   HURRICANES
  RT   STORMS
  RT   WIND SPEED

GALES
  USE   **STORMS**

GALL BLADDER
  BT1   BLADDERS
  BT2   ANIMAL ORGANS
  BT3   BODY ORGANS
  RT   BILE

GALLIUM
  BT1   CHEMICAL ELEMENTS
  RT   FERROMANGANESE NODULES
  RT   GALLIUM COMPOUNDS
  RT   GALLIUM ISOTOPES
  RT   METALS
  RT   TRACE METALS

GALLIUM COMPOUNDS
  RT   CHEMICAL COMPOUNDS
  RT   GALLIUM

GALLIUM ISOTOPES
  BT1   ISOTOPES
  RT   GALLIUM

GAME FISH
  UF   sport fish
  BT1   FISH
  BT2   AQUATIC ANIMALS
  RT   SPORT FISHING
  RT   SPORT FISHING STATISTICS

GAME THEORY
  SN   Used only as a qualifier
  BT1   OPERATIONS RESEARCH
  RT   LINEAR PROGRAMMING
  RT   MATHEMATICAL MODELS
  RT   MATHEMATICAL PROGRAMMING
  RT   NUMERICAL ANALYSIS
  RT   PROBABILITY THEORY
  RT   SIMULATION
  RT   STATISTICAL MODELS

GAMETES
  USE   **SEXUAL CELLS**

GAMETOGENESIS
  BT1   MORPHOGENESIS
  NT1   OOGENESIS
  NT1   SPERMATOGENESIS
  RT   SEXUAL MATURITY

GAMMA RADIATION
  UF   gamma rays
  BT1   ELECTROMAGNETIC RADIATION
  BT2   RADIATIONS
  RT   GAMMA SPECTROSCOPY

GAMMA-RAY TRANSMISSION
  USE   **GAMMA SPECTROSCOPY**

GAMMA RAYS
  USE   **GAMMA RADIATION**

GAMMA SPECTROSCOPY
  UF   gamma-ray transmission
  BT1   SPECTROSCOPIC TECHNIQUES
  BT2   ANALYTICAL TECHNIQUES
  RT   GAMMA RADIATION
  RT   RADIOACTIVITY

GAMMAGLOBULINS
  USE   **GLOBULINS**

GANGLIA
  SN   Added in 1980
  UF   ganglion
  UF   nerve ganglia
  BT1   CENTRAL NERVOUS SYSTEM
  BT2   NERVOUS SYSTEM
  RT   BRAIN
  RT   NERVES
  RT   NERVOUS TISSUES

GANGLION
  USE   **GANGLIA**

GANGRENES
  USE   **NECROSES**

GARNET
  BT1   SILICATE MINERALS
  BT2   MINERALS
  RT   PLACERS

GAS
  USE   **GASES**

GAS BLADDERS
  USE   **SWIM BLADDER**

GAS BUBBLE DISEASE
  USE   **BUBBLE DISEASE**

GAS CHROMATOGRAPHY
  BT1   CHROMATOGRAPHIC TECHNIQUES
  BT2   ANALYTICAL TECHNIQUES

GAS CONDENSATE FIELDS
  UF   condensate fields
  BT1   OIL AND GAS FIELDS
  RT   GAS CONDENSATES

GAS CONDENSATES
  BT1   PETROLEUM
  BT2   FOSSIL FUELS
  BT3   SUBSURFACE DEPOSITS
  BT4   MINERAL DEPOSITS
  RT   GAS CONDENSATE FIELDS
  RT   NATURAL GAS

GAS EMBOLISM
  USE   **BUBBLE DISEASE**

GAS EXCHANGE
  UF   gas transfer
  RT   AIR-WATER EXCHANGES
  RT   AIR-WATER INTERFACE
  RT   GASES
  RT   SEDIMENT-WATER EXCHANGES
  RT   SEDIMENT-WATER INTERFACE

GAS EXPLODERS
  BT1   SEISMIC ENERGY SOURCES

GAS FIELDS
  BT1   OIL AND GAS FIELDS
  RT   NATURAL GAS

GAS FLARING
  UF   flaring
  RT   ARTICULATED COLUMNS
  RT   OIL TREATING
  RT   WASTE DISPOSAL

GAS GATHERING
  USE   **GATHERING LINES**

GAS HYDRATES
  UF   solid gas hydrates
  BT1   HYDROCARBONS
  BT2   ORGANIC COMPOUNDS
  RT   METHANE
  RT   SEDIMENT PROPERTIES
  RT   SHEAR STRENGTH

GAS INDUSTRY
  USE   **OIL AND GAS INDUSTRY**

GAS-OIL INTERFACE
USE **OIL-GAS INTERFACE**

GAS OIL SEPARATION
UF	oil gas separation
UF	oil-gas separation
BT1	SEPARATION
RT	OIL AND GAS PRODUCTION

GAS PROCESSING
SN	For field operations
RT	LIQUEFIED NATURAL GAS
RT	OIL AND GAS PRODUCTION
RT	SEPARATION

GAS PRODUCTION
SN	Pertains to surface equipment and methods used to produce natural gas from underground reservoirs
BT1	OIL AND GAS PRODUCTION
RT	NATURAL GAS

GAS SEEPAGES
BT1	SEEPAGES
RT	GAS TURBATION
RT	NATURAL GAS

GAS SOLUBILITY
BT1	SOLUBILITY
BT2	CHEMICAL PROPERTIES
BT3	PROPERTIES
RT	GASES

GAS TERMINALS
RT	LIQUEFIED NATURAL GAS
RT	LIQUEFIED PETROLEUM GAS
RT	NATURAL GAS
RT	OIL AND GAS INDUSTRY
RT	PIPELINES
RT	PORT INSTALLATIONS
RT	STORAGE TANKS
RT	TANKER TERMINALS

GAS TRANSFER
USE **GAS EXCHANGE**

GAS TURBATION
BT1	SEDIMENT MIXING
RT	DIAGENESIS
RT	GAS SEEPAGES
RT	MIXING PROCESSES
RT	POCK MARKS

GAS WATER SEPARATION
BT1	SEPARATION

GASES
UF	gas
BT1	FLUIDS
NT1	AIR
NT1	ATMOSPHERIC GASES
NT1	BREATHING MIXTURES
NT1	COMPRESSED GAS
NT1	DISSOLVED GASES
NT2	DISSOLVED OXYGEN
NT1	OZONE
NT1	RARE GASES
NT1	WATER VAPOUR
RT	AIR BUBBLES
RT	AIR-WATER EXCHANGES
RT	AMMONIA
RT	ARTIFICIAL AERATION
RT	CARBON DIOXIDE
RT	CHEMICAL ELEMENTS
RT	GAS EXCHANGE
RT	GAS SOLUBILITY
RT	HYDROGEN
RT	LIQUIDS
RT	NATURAL GAS
RT	NITROGEN

GASES (cont'd)
RT	OIL-GAS INTERFACE
RT	OXYGEN

GASTROINTESTINAL SYSTEM
USE **DIGESTIVE SYSTEM**

GASTROPOD FISHERIES
SN	Added in 1982
UF	abalone fisheries
UF	conch fisheries
UF	ormer fisheries
UF	sea snail fisheries
UF	whelk fisheries
UF	winkle fisheries
BT1	MOLLUSC FISHERIES
BT2	SHELLFISH FISHERIES
BT3	FISHERIES
RT	MARINE FISHERIES
RT	TRAP FISHING

GATHERING LINES
UF	gas gathering
BT1	PIPELINES
BT2	UNDERWATER STRUCTURES
BT3	OFFSHORE STRUCTURES
BT4	HYDRAULIC STRUCTURES
RT	FLOWLINES

GAUGES
BT1	MEASURING DEVICES
RT	STRAIN GAUGES
RT	TIDE GAUGES

GAUSSIAN DISTRIBUTION
BT1	DISTRIBUTION
RT	STATISTICAL ANALYSIS

GAZETEERS
BT1	DOCUMENTS
RT	ATLASES
RT	GEOGRAPHY
RT	SUBMARINE FEATURES

GEAR
USE **FISHING GEAR**

GEAR CONSTRUCTION
UF	cage construction
UF	net construction
RT	FISHING GEAR
RT	GEAR MATERIALS
RT	GEAR RESEARCH

GEAR EFFICIENCY
USE **GEAR SELECTIVITY**

GEAR HANDLING
RT	ACCIDENT PREVENTION
RT	DAVITS
RT	DECK EQUIPMENT
RT	DEPLOYMENT
RT	EDUCATION
RT	RECOVERY
RT	SEAMANSHIP
RT	TRAINING AIDS
RT	WINCHES

GEAR MATERIALS
SN	Description and different types of synthetic material used in construction of gear, fishing nets, aquaculture equipment
BT1	MATERIALS
NT1	NETTING MATERIALS
NT1	YARNS
RT	AQUACULTURE EQUIPMENT
RT	CAGES
RT	FISHING GEAR
RT	GEAR CONSTRUCTION

GEAR MATERIALS (cont'd)
RT	GEAR RESEARCH
RT	SYNTHETIC FIBRES

GEAR RESEARCH
RT	EXPERIMENTAL DATA
RT	EXPERIMENTAL FISHING
RT	FISHERY ENGINEERING
RT	FISHING GEAR
RT	GEAR CONSTRUCTION
RT	GEAR MATERIALS
RT	GEAR SELECTIVITY
RT	TELEMETRY

GEAR SELECTIVITY
SN	Restricted to biological sampling and fishing gear
UF	gear efficiency
RT	AVOIDANCE REACTIONS
RT	CATCHABILITY
RT	ESCAPEMENT
RT	EXPERIMENTAL FISHING
RT	FISHERY REGULATIONS
RT	FISHING GEAR
RT	GEAR RESEARCH
RT	HOOKS
RT	MESH SELECTIVITY
RT	TEST EQUIPMENT

GEIGER COUNTERS
BT1	COUNTERS
RT	RADIOACTIVITY

GEK
UF	geomagnetic electrokinetograph
RT	CURRENT MEASURING EQUIPMENT
RT	ELECTRIC POTENTIAL
RT	OCEANOGRAPHIC EQUIPMENT

GELBSTOFF
UF	yellow substance
RT	WATER COLOUR

GELS
BT1	COLLOIDS
RT	THIXOTROPY

GEMMULES
RT	ASEXUAL REPRODUCTION
RT	BUDDING
RT	COLONIES

GENE MUTATIONS
USE **MUTATIONS**

GENECOLOGY
SN	Added in 1980
BT1	ECOLOGY
RT	GENETIC DRIFT
RT	GENETICS
RT	POPULATION GENETICS

GENERAL CIRCULATION (ATMOSPHERIC)
USE **ATMOSPHERIC CIRCULATION**

GENERAL CIRCULATION (OCEANS)
USE **OCEAN CIRCULATION**

GENERATION (SOUND WAVES)
USE **SOUND GENERATION**

GENERATION (WATER WAVES)
USE **WAVE GENERATION**

GENERATORS
USE **ELECTRIC GENERATORS**

GENES
SN	Added in 1980
BT1	CHROMOSOMES
BT2	CELL CONSTITUENTS
RT	DNA
RT	GENETICS
RT	GENOTYPES
RT	MUTATIONS

GENETIC ABNORMALITIES
BT1	ABNORMALITIES
RT	ALBINISM
RT	GENETICS
RT	MUTATIONS
RT	TERATOGENS
RT	TERATOLOGY

GENETIC DRIFT
SN	Added in 1980
UF	drift (genetic)
UF	genetic selection
UF	seawall wright effect
BT1	BIOSELECTION
RT	EVOLUTION
RT	GENECOLOGY
RT	GENETIC ISOLATION
RT	MUTATIONS
RT	POPULATION GENETICS

GENETIC FACTORS
USE	**GENOMES**

GENETIC ISOLATION
SN	Added in 1980
UF	isolation (genetics)
BT1	ISOLATING MECHANISMS
RT	GENETIC DRIFT

GENETIC POLYMORPHISM
USE	**BIOPOLYMORPHISM**

GENETIC SELECTION
USE	**GENETIC DRIFT**

GENETICISTS
SN	Added in 1980
BT1	BIOLOGISTS
BT2	SCIENTIFIC PERSONNEL
BT3	PERSONNEL
RT	DIRECTORIES
RT	GENETICS

GENETICS
UF	cytogenetics
UF	heredity
BT1	BIOLOGY
NT1	POPULATION GENETICS
RT	BIOLOGICAL SPECIATION
RT	BREEDING
RT	BROOD STOCKS
RT	CHROMOSOMES
RT	CLONES
RT	EVOLUTION
RT	GENECOLOGY
RT	GENES
RT	GENETIC ABNORMALITIES
RT	GENETICISTS
RT	GENOMES
RT	GENOTYPES
RT	HYBRIDIZATION
RT	HYBRIDS
RT	MORPHOGENESIS
RT	MUTAGENS
RT	MUTATIONS
RT	NUCLEIC ACIDS
RT	POLYPLOIDS
RT	RACIAL STUDIES
RT	SELECTIVE BREEDING
RT	SIBLING SPECIES

GENOM
USE	**GENOMES**

GENOMES
SN	Added in 1980
UF	genetic factors
UF	genom
RT	CHROMOSOMES
RT	GENETICS
RT	GENOTYPES
RT	KARYOTYPES
RT	NUCLEI
RT	SEXUAL CELLS

GENOTYPES
RT	GENES
RT	GENETICS
RT	GENOMES
RT	HYBRIDIZATION
RT	KARYOTYPES
RT	MUTATIONS
RT	PHENOTYPES
RT	SUBPOPULATIONS
RT	TYPOLOGY

GEOCHEMICAL CYCLE
BT1	CYCLES
RT	BIOGEOCHEMICAL CYCLE
RT	CARBON CYCLE
RT	GEOCHEMISTRY
RT	SEDIMENT CHEMISTRY
RT	CHEMICAL CYCLES

GEOCHEMICAL SURVEYS
BT1	SURVEYS
RT	GEOCHEMISTRY

GEOCHEMISTRY
UF	environmental chemistry
BT1	CHEMISTRY
NT1	BIOGEOCHEMISTRY
NT1	SEDIMENT CHEMISTRY
RT	ATMOSPHERE EVOLUTION
RT	CHEMICAL PROPERTIES
RT	EARTH SCIENCES
RT	GEOCHEMICAL CYCLE
RT	GEOCHEMICAL SURVEYS
RT	GEOLOGY
RT	GEOPHYSICS
RT	HALMYROLYSIS
RT	HYDROLOGY
RT	LEACHING
RT	MARINE GEOLOGY
RT	MINERALOGY
RT	PETROLOGY
RT	PORE WATER
RT	PORE WATER SAMPLERS
RT	RADIOMETRIC DATING
RT	SEA WATER
RT	SEAWATER EVOLUTION
RT	SEDIMENT ANALYSIS
RT	TRACE ELEMENTS
RT	WEATHERING

GEOCHRONOLOGY
USE	**GEOCHRONOMETRY**

GEOCHRONOMETRY
SN	Measurement of geologic time.
	Before 1982 search also
	GEOCHRONOLOGY and RADIOACTIVE DATING
UF	age determination (earth sciences)
UF	dating (earth sciences)
UF	geochronology
NT1	RADIOMETRIC DATING
NT2	OXYGEN ISOTOPE DATING
NT2	POTASSIUM-ARGON DATING
NT2	RADIOCARBON DATING
NT2	RUBIDIUM-STRONTIUM DATING
NT2	THORIUM-230/THORIUM-232 DATING

GEOCHRONOMETRY (cont'd)
NT2	URANIUM-HELIUM DATING
RT	ABSOLUTE AGE
RT	AGE
RT	CARBON ISOTOPE RATIO
RT	CLIMATIC CHANGES
RT	EARTH AGE
RT	GEOLOGICAL TIME
RT	STRATIGRAPHIC CORRELATION
RT	STRATIGRAPHY
RT	VARVES

GEOCLINES
SN	Added in 1980
BT1	CLINES
RT	GEOGRAPHICAL DISTRIBUTION

GEODESY
UF	earth measurement
BT1	GEOPHYSICS
BT2	EARTH SCIENCES
NT1	COASTAL GEODESY
NT1	MARINE GEODESY
RT	DATUM LEVELS
RT	EARTH TIDES
RT	GEODETIC COORDINATES
RT	GEOID
RT	HORIZON
RT	ISOSTASY
RT	LEVELLING
RT	MEAN SEA LEVEL
RT	PLUMBLINE DEFLECTION

GEODETIC COORDINATES
BT1	COORDINATE SYSTEMS
RT	GEODESY

GEODYNAMICS
USE	**TECTONOPHYSICS**

GEOGRAPHICAL COORDINATES
BT1	COORDINATE SYSTEMS
NT1	LATITUDE
NT2	PALAEOLATITUDE
NT1	LONGITUDE
RT	CARTOGRAPHY
RT	MAP PROJECTIONS
RT	MARSDEN SQUARES
RT	POSITION FIXING

GEOGRAPHICAL DISTRIBUTION
SN	Distributional studies of organisms and abiotic factors in aquatic environment. Used only as a qualifier
UF	spatial distribution
BT1	DISTRIBUTION
NT1	DIFFERENTIAL DISTRIBUTION
NT1	HORIZONTAL DISTRIBUTION
NT2	BIPOLAR DISTRIBUTION
NT1	MERIDIONAL DISTRIBUTION
NT1	VERTICAL DISTRIBUTION
NT1	ZONAL DISTRIBUTION
RT	ALLOPATRIC POPULATIONS
RT	BIOGEOGRAPHY
RT	BIOLOGICAL CHARTS
RT	COSMOPOLITE SPECIES
RT	DISTRIBUTION RECORDS
RT	ECOLOGICAL DISTRIBUTION
RT	ENDEMIC SPECIES
RT	ENDEMISM
RT	GEOCLINES
RT	GEOGRAPHICAL ISOLATION
RT	IMMIGRATIONS
RT	MIGRATIONS
RT	NEW RECORDS
RT	QUANTITATIVE DISTRIBUTION
RT	REFUGES
RT	RELICT SPECIES
RT	SEDIMENT DISTRIBUTION
RT	STRANDING

ASFIS Thesaurus

GEOGRAPHICAL DISTRIBUTION (cont'd)
RT   SYMPATRIC POPULATIONS

GEOGRAPHICAL EXPLORATION
SN   Geographical discovery - history
BT1   EXPLORATION
RT   EXPEDITIONS
RT   POLAR EXPLORATION
RT   UNDERWATER EXPLORATION

GEOGRAPHICAL ISOLATION
SN   Added in 1980
UF   isolation (geographical)
UF   spatial isolation
BT1   ISOLATING MECHANISMS
RT   GEOGRAPHICAL DISTRIBUTION

GEOGRAPHICAL REFERENCE SYSTEMS
NT1   MARSDEN SQUARES

GEOGRAPHY
NT1   BIOGEOGRAPHY
RT   ATLASES
RT   CARTOGRAPHY
RT   CLIMATE
RT   CLIMATIC ZONES
RT   CLIMATOLOGY
RT   GAZETEERS
RT   GEOMORPHOLOGY
RT   LANDFORMS
RT   MAPPING
RT   TOPOGRAPHIC FEATURES

GEOID
RT   EARTH
RT   GEODESY
RT   GEOID ANOMALIES
RT   LEVELLING
RT   MARINE GEODESY
RT   MEAN SEA LEVEL
RT   MICROPALAEONTOLOGY
RT   SATELLITE ALTIMETRY
RT   SURFACE TOPOGRAPHY

GEOID ANOMALIES
BT1   ANOMALIES
RT   GEOID
RT   GRAVITY ANOMALIES
RT   SURFACE TOPOGRAPHY

GEOLOGICAL AGES
USE   **GEOLOGICAL TIME**

GEOLOGICAL CHARTS
USE   **GEOLOGICAL MAPS**

GEOLOGICAL COLLECTIONS
SN   Collections in museums, data banks etc.
BT1   COLLECTIONS
RT   CORES
RT   GEOLOGICAL SAMPLES
RT   MINERAL SAMPLES
RT   SAMPLES
RT   SEDIMENT SAMPLES

GEOLOGICAL COLUMN
USE   **GEOLOGICAL TIME**

GEOLOGICAL CORRELATION
NT1   STRATIGRAPHIC CORRELATION

GEOLOGICAL DATA
RT   BATHYMETRIC DATA
RT   CRUISES
RT   MINERAL SAMPLES
RT   MULTISHIP EXPEDITIONS
RT   SEDIMENT SAMPLES

GEOLOGICAL DEPOSITION
USE   **SEDIMENTATION**

GEOLOGICAL DISTRIBUTION
SN   Distribution of biota through geological time
BT1   DISTRIBUTION
RT   FOSSILS
RT   GEOLOGICAL MAPS
RT   GEOLOGICAL SURVEYS
RT   GEOLOGY
RT   MARINE GEOLOGY

GEOLOGICAL DOMES
USE   **STRUCTURAL DOMES**

GEOLOGICAL EQUIPMENT
BT1   EQUIPMENT
RT   GEOPHYSICAL EQUIPMENT
RT   PENETROMETERS
RT   PORE WATER SAMPLERS
RT   SEDIMENT SAMPLERS
RT   SEDIMENT TRAPS
RT   STRATIGRAPHIC TRAPS
RT   VANE DEVICES

GEOLOGICAL EXPLORATION
USE   **GEOLOGICAL SURVEYS**

GEOLOGICAL FAULTS
USE   **FAULTS**

GEOLOGICAL HAZARDS
BT1   HAZARDS
RT   EARTHQUAKES
RT   FLOODS
RT   GROUND MOTION
RT   LANDSLIDES
RT   SEDIMENT STABILITY
RT   SETTLEMENT (STRUCTURAL)
RT   SITE SURVEYS
RT   SLOPE STABILITY
RT   SLUMPING
RT   VOLCANIC ERUPTIONS

GEOLOGICAL HISTORY
RT   GEOLOGICAL TIME
RT   GEOLOGY

GEOLOGICAL INSTITUTIONS
UF   geophysical institutions
BT1   RESEARCH INSTITUTIONS
BT2   ORGANIZATIONS
RT   GEOLOGY
RT   GEOPHYSICS
RT   OCEANOGRAPHIC INSTITUTIONS

GEOLOGICAL MAPPING
USE   **GEOLOGICAL SURVEYS**

GEOLOGICAL MAPS
SN   Before 1982 search GEOLOGICAL CHARTS
UF   geological charts
UF   geophysical charts
UF   geophysical maps
BT1   MAPS
BT2   GRAPHICS
BT3   AUDIOVISUAL MATERIAL
BT4   DOCUMENTS
NT1   GRAVITY CHARTS
NT2   BOUGUER GRAVITY CHARTS
NT2   FREE AIR GRAVITY CHARTS
NT1   ISOPACH MAPS
NT1   MAGNETIC CHARTS
NT2   MAGNETIC ANOMALY CHARTS
RT   ATLASES
RT   BATHYMETRIC CHARTS
RT   GEOLOGICAL DISTRIBUTION
RT   GEOLOGICAL SECTIONS
RT   GEOLOGICAL SURVEYS

GEOLOGICAL MAPS (cont'd)
RT   GEOLOGY
RT   GEOPHYSICS
RT   MINERAL DEPOSITS
RT   OCEANOGRAPHIC ATLASES
RT   SEDIMENT DISTRIBUTION
RT   SEDIMENT TRANSPORT
RT   SEDIMENTOLOGY
RT   TOPOGRAPHIC MAPS

GEOLOGICAL OCEANOGRAPHY
USE   **MARINE GEOLOGY**

GEOLOGICAL RECORD
USE   **GEOLOGICAL TIME**

GEOLOGICAL SAMPLES
BT1   SAMPLES
NT1   MINERAL SAMPLES
NT1   SEDIMENT SAMPLES
NT2   CORES
NT2   DREDGED SAMPLES
RT   GEOLOGICAL COLLECTIONS
RT   GEOLOGICAL SURVEYS

GEOLOGICAL SECTIONS
BT1   VERTICAL SECTIONS
BT2   MAP GRAPHICS
BT3   GRAPHICS
BT4   AUDIOVISUAL MATERIAL
RT   ECHOSOUNDER PROFILES
RT   GEOLOGICAL MAPS
RT   SEISMIC PROFILES

GEOLOGICAL STRUCTURES
NT1   FAULTS
NT2   TRANSFORM FAULTS
NT1   FOLDS
NT2   ANTICLINES
NT3   DOMES
NT2   ANTICLINORIA
NT2   GEOSYNCLINES
NT2   STRUCTURAL DOMES
NT3   SALT DOMES
NT2   SYNCLINES
NT2   SYNCLINORIA
NT1   GRABEN
RT   SEDIMENTARY STRUCTURES
RT   STRUCTURAL GEOLOGY

GEOLOGICAL SURVEYS
UF   geological exploration
UF   geological mapping
BT1   SURVEYS
NT1   GEOPHYSICAL SURVEYS
NT2   GRAVITY SURVEYS
RT   BOTTOM PHOTOGRAPHS
RT   GEOLOGICAL DISTRIBUTION
RT   GEOLOGICAL MAPS
RT   GEOLOGICAL SAMPLES
RT   GEOLOGY
RT   GEOMORPHOLOGY
RT   MINERAL COLLECTIONS
RT   MINERAL RESOURCES
RT   OCEANIC CRUST
RT   OCEANOGRAPHIC SURVEYS
RT   SEAFLOOR MAPPING
RT   SEAFLOOR SAMPLING
RT   SEISMIC EXPLORATION
RT   SITE SURVEYS
RT   SURVEYING UNDERWATER
RT   UNDERWATER EXPLORATION

GEOLOGICAL SYSTEMS
USE   **GEOLOGICAL TIME**

ASFIS Thesaurus

GEOLOGICAL TIME
UF	geological ages
UF	geological column
UF	geological record
UF	geological systems
UF	geological time divisions
UF	geological time scale
UF	stratigraphic systems
NT1	CENOZOIC
NT2	QUATERNARY
NT3	HOLOCENE
NT3	PLEISTOCENE
NT2	TERTIARY
NT3	NEOGENE
NT4	MIOCENE
NT4	PLIOCENE
NT3	PALAEOGENE
NT4	EOCENE
NT4	OLIGOCENE
NT4	PALAEOCENE
NT1	MESOZOIC
NT2	CRETACEOUS
NT2	JURASSIC
NT2	TRIASSIC
NT1	PALAEOZOIC
NT2	CAMBRIAN
NT2	CARBONIFEROUS
NT2	DEVONIAN
NT2	ORDOVICIAN
NT2	PERMIAN
NT2	SILURIAN
NT1	PHANEROZOIC
NT1	PRECAMBRIAN
RT	CHRONOSTRATIGRAPHY
RT	EARTH AGE
RT	GEOCHRONOMETRY
RT	GEOLOGICAL HISTORY
RT	GEOLOGY
RT	PALAEOCLIMATE
RT	PALAEOECOLOGY
RT	RADIOMETRIC DATING
RT	STRATIGRAPHY
RT	TEMPORAL DISTRIBUTION

GEOLOGICAL TIME DIVISIONS
USE	**GEOLOGICAL TIME**

GEOLOGICAL TIME SCALE
USE	**GEOLOGICAL TIME**

GEOLOGISTS
BT1	SCIENTIFIC PERSONNEL
BT2	PERSONNEL
RT	DIRECTORIES
RT	GEOLOGY

GEOLOGY
BT1	EARTH SCIENCES
NT1	GEOMORPHOLOGY
NT2	COASTAL MORPHOLOGY
NT3	BEACH MORPHOLOGY
NT2	FLUVIAL MORPHOLOGY
NT2	LAKE MORPHOLOGY
NT1	HYDROLOGY
NT1	LITHOLOGY
NT1	MARINE GEOLOGY
NT2	SHELF GEOLOGY
NT1	PETROGENESIS
NT1	PETROLEUM GEOLOGY
NT1	PETROLOGY
NT1	SEDIMENTOLOGY
NT1	STRATIGRAPHY
NT2	BIOSTRATIGRAPHY
NT2	CHRONOSTRATIGRAPHY
NT2	MAGNETOSTRATIGRAPHY
NT2	OXYGEN ISOTOPE STRATIGRAPHY
NT2	SEISMIC STRATIGRAPHY
NT1	STRUCTURAL GEOLOGY
NT1	TECTONICS
NT2	CRUSTAL ADJUSTMENT

GEOLOGY (cont'd)
NT3	ISOSTASY
NT2	EPEIROGENY
NT3	SUBSIDENCE
NT3	UPLIFT
NT2	OROGENY
NT2	PLATE TECTONICS
NT2	VERTICAL TECTONICS
RT	FOSSILS
RT	GEOCHEMISTRY
RT	GEOLOGICAL DISTRIBUTION
RT	GEOLOGICAL HISTORY
RT	GEOLOGICAL INSTITUTIONS
RT	GEOLOGICAL MAPS
RT	GEOLOGICAL SURVEYS
RT	GEOLOGICAL TIME
RT	GEOLOGISTS
RT	GEOPHYSICS
RT	GLACIERS
RT	MINERALOGY
RT	PALAEONTOLOGY
RT	PALYNOLOGY
RT	SEDIMENT CHEMISTRY
RT	SEDIMENTATION
RT	SEISMOLOGY
RT	SOILS
RT	TECTONOPHYSICS

GEOMAGNETIC ELECTROKINETOGRAPH
USE	**GEK**

GEOMAGNETIC FIELD
UF	earth magnetic field
UF	magnetic field (earth)
BT1	MAGNETIC FIELDS
RT	AEROMAGNETIC SURVEYS
RT	GEOMAGNETISM
RT	MAGNETIC ANOMALIES
RT	MAGNETIC FIELD ELEMENTS
RT	MAGNETIC INCLINATION
RT	MAGNETIC INTENSITY
RT	MAGNETIC REVERSALS
RT	MAGNETIC SUSCEPTIBILITY
RT	MAGNETIC VARIATIONS
RT	MAGNETOTELLURIC METHODS
RT	POLE POSITIONS
RT	REMANENT MAGNETIZATION
RT	TELLURIC CURRENTS

GEOMAGNETIC REVERSALS
USE	**MAGNETIC REVERSALS**

GEOMAGNETIC SURVEYS
USE	**MAGNETIC EXPLORATION**

GEOMAGNETISM
UF	earth magnetism
UF	terrestrial magnetism
BT1	GEOPHYSICS
BT2	EARTH SCIENCES
RT	EARTH
RT	GEOMAGNETIC FIELD
RT	MAGNETIC PROPERTIES
RT	MAGNETISM
RT	MAGNETOMETERS
RT	MAGNETOTELLURIC METHODS
RT	PALAEOMAGNETISM

GEOMORPHOLOGY
UF	physiography
BT1	GEOLOGY
BT2	EARTH SCIENCES
NT1	COASTAL MORPHOLOGY
NT2	BEACH MORPHOLOGY
NT1	FLUVIAL MORPHOLOGY
NT1	LAKE MORPHOLOGY
RT	BEACHES
RT	CORAL REEFS
RT	DELTAS
RT	EROSION

GEOMORPHOLOGY (cont'd)
RT	EROSION FEATURES
RT	FJORDS
RT	FLOOD PLAINS
RT	GEOGRAPHY
RT	GEOLOGICAL SURVEYS
RT	GLACIAL EROSION
RT	GLACIAL GEOLOGY
RT	GLACIAL LAKES
RT	GLACIERS
RT	HYDROLOGY
RT	LANDFORMS
RT	PALAEOCLIMATOLOGY
RT	QUATERNARY
RT	REEFS
RT	SEDIMENTATION
RT	SEDIMENTOLOGY
RT	SEISMOLOGY
RT	SPELAEOLOGY
RT	TOPOGRAPHIC FEATURES
RT	VALLEYS
RT	WEATHERING

GEOPHONES
USE	**SEISMOMETERS**

GEOPHYSICAL CHARTS
USE	**GEOLOGICAL MAPS**

GEOPHYSICAL DATA
BT1	DATA
NT1	GEOTHERMAL DATA
NT1	GRAVITY DATA
NT1	MAGNETIC DATA
NT1	SEISMIC DATA
RT	CRUISES
RT	GEOPHYSICAL EXPLORATION
RT	GEOPHYSICAL SURVEYS
RT	GEOPHYSICS
RT	MULTISHIP EXPEDITIONS
RT	OIL AND GAS EXPLORATION
RT	SEISMIC DATA PROCESSING

GEOPHYSICAL EQUIPMENT
BT1	EQUIPMENT
NT1	GEOTHERMAL EQUIPMENT
NT2	HEAT PROBES
NT1	SEISMIC EQUIPMENT
RT	GEOLOGICAL EQUIPMENT
RT	GEOPHYSICAL EXPLORATION
RT	GEOPHYSICAL SURVEYS
RT	GEOPHYSICS
RT	GRAVITY METERS
RT	MAGNETOMETERS
RT	OCEANOGRAPHIC EQUIPMENT
RT	RESISTIVITY PROBES
RT	SEISMIC ARRAYS
RT	SEISMIC ENERGY SOURCES
RT	SEISMOMETERS
RT	TILTMETERS

GEOPHYSICAL EXPLORATION
UF	geophysical methods
BT1	EXPLORATION
NT1	ELECTRICAL EXPLORATION
NT1	ELECTROMAGNETIC EXPLORATION
NT1	GEOTHERMAL EXPLORATION
NT1	GRAVITY EXPLORATION
NT1	MAGNETIC EXPLORATION
NT1	SEISMIC EXPLORATION
NT2	SEISMIC REFLECTION PROFILING
NT2	SEISMIC REFRACTION PROFILING
NT2	SUB-BOTTOM PROFILING
RT	GEOPHYSICAL DATA
RT	GEOPHYSICAL EQUIPMENT
RT	GEOPHYSICAL SURVEYS
RT	GEOPHYSICS
RT	MINERAL EXPLORATION
RT	OIL AND GAS EXPLORATION

ASFIS Thesaurus

GEOPHYSICAL INSTITUTIONS
USE **GEOLOGICAL INSTITUTIONS**

GEOPHYSICAL MAPS
USE **GEOLOGICAL MAPS**

GEOPHYSICAL METHODS
USE **GEOPHYSICAL EXPLORATION**

GEOPHYSICAL SURVEYS
SN Used for surveys of specific regions using geophysical methods
BT1 GEOLOGICAL SURVEYS
BT2 SURVEYS
NT1 GRAVITY SURVEYS
RT GEOPHYSICAL DATA
RT GEOPHYSICAL EQUIPMENT
RT GEOPHYSICAL EXPLORATION
RT GEOPHYSICS
RT MAGNETIC EXPLORATION
RT SITE SURVEYS

GEOPHYSICS
BT1 EARTH SCIENCES
NT1 GEODESY
NT2 COASTAL GEODESY
NT2 MARINE GEODESY
NT1 GEOMAGNETISM
NT1 PALAEOMAGNETISM
NT1 SEISMOLOGY
NT1 TECTONOPHYSICS
RT CONTINENTAL DRIFT
RT EARTH
RT GEOCHEMISTRY
RT GEOLOGICAL INSTITUTIONS
RT GEOLOGICAL MAPS
RT GEOLOGY
RT GEOPHYSICAL DATA
RT GEOPHYSICAL EQUIPMENT
RT GEOPHYSICAL EXPLORATION
RT GEOPHYSICAL SURVEYS
RT GRAVITY
RT MARINE GEOLOGY
RT RADIOACTIVITY
RT SEDIMENT CHEMISTRY
RT TECTONICS

GEOPOTENTIAL
USE **DYNAMIC HEIGHT**

GEOPOTENTIAL ANOMALY
USE **DYNAMIC HEIGHT ANOMALY**

GEOPOTENTIAL TOPOGRAPHY
USE **DYNAMIC TOPOGRAPHY**

GEOSENSING
SN Use for remote sensing of earth surface from space. Before 1986 search also REMOTE SENSING
UF earth remote sensing
UF remote sensing (earth)
UF teledetection
NT1 AIRBORNE SENSING
NT1 SATELLITE SENSING
RT AERIAL PHOTOGRAPHY
RT DATA ACQUISITION
RT ELECTROMAGNETIC RADIATION
RT INFRARED IMAGERY
RT MICROWAVE IMAGERY
RT RADAR IMAGERY
RT REMOTE SENSING
RT SCIENTIFIC SATELLITES

GEOSTROPHIC CURRENTS
USE **GEOSTROPHIC FLOW**

GEOSTROPHIC EQUILIBRIUM
RT CORIOLIS FORCE
RT EQUILIBRIUM
RT GEOSTROPHIC FLOW
RT STREAM FUNCTIONS

GEOSTROPHIC FLOW
SN Before 1982 search GEOSTROPHIC CURRENTS
UF geostrophic currents
BT1 FLUID FLOW
BT2 FLUID MOTION
NT1 QUASI-GEOSTROPHIC MOTION
RT AGEOSTROPHIC FLOW
RT CORIOLIS FORCE
RT DENSITY FIELD
RT DENSITY STRATIFICATION
RT DYNAMIC TOPOGRAPHY
RT GEOSTROPHIC EQUILIBRIUM
RT GEOSTROPHIC METHOD
RT GEOSTROPHIC TRANSPORT
RT GEOSTROPHY
RT LEVEL OF NO MOTION
RT SURFACE SLOPE

GEOSTROPHIC FLOW CALCULATION
USE **GEOSTROPHIC METHOD**

GEOSTROPHIC METHOD
UF geostrophic flow calculation
RT DENSITY FIELD
RT DYNAMIC TOPOGRAPHY
RT GEOSTROPHIC FLOW
RT LEVEL OF NO MOTION

GEOSTROPHIC TRANSPORT
UF geostrophic volume transport
RT GEOSTROPHIC FLOW

GEOSTROPHIC VOLUME TRANSPORT
USE **GEOSTROPHIC TRANSPORT**

GEOSTROPHIC WINDS
BT1 WINDS
BT2 ATMOSPHERIC MOTION
RT GRADIENT CURRENTS
RT GRADIENT WINDS

GEOSTROPHY
RT AGEOSTROPHIC FLOW
RT GEOSTROPHIC FLOW

GEOSYNCLINES
BT1 FOLDS
BT2 GEOLOGICAL STRUCTURES
RT ANTICLINORIA
RT OPHIOLITES
RT OROGENY
RT SYNCLINES

GEOTECHNICAL DATA
SN Data on engineering properties of sediments and rocks
BT1 DATA
RT BEARING CAPACITY
RT GEOTECHNOLOGY
RT IN SITU MEASUREMENTS
RT PENETROMETERS
RT PERMEABILITY
RT PORE PRESSURE
RT POROSITY
RT SEAFLOOR SAMPLING
RT SEDIMENT PROPERTIES
RT SEDIMENT SAMPLING
RT SHEAR STRENGTH
RT VANE DEVICES
RT VOID RATIO
RT WATER CONTENT
RT WET BULK DENSITY

GEOTECHNICAL PROPERTIES
USE **SEDIMENT PROPERTIES**

GEOTECHNICS
USE **GEOTECHNOLOGY**

GEOTECHNOLOGY
SN Before 1986 search also SOIL MECHANICS
UF geotechnics
BT1 ENGINEERING
RT ANCHORING
RT COASTAL ENGINEERING
RT CURRENT SCOURING
RT CYCLIC LOADING
RT FOUNDATIONS
RT GEOTECHNICAL DATA
RT GROUTING
RT OCEAN FLOOR
RT OFFSHORE ENGINEERING
RT PENETRATION DEPTH
RT PILE DRIVING
RT PILES
RT SAND STRUCTURES
RT SCOURING
RT SEDIMENTS
RT SOIL MECHANICS
RT STRUCTURAL ENGINEERING
RT TECHNOLOGY

GEOTECTONICS
USE **TECTONICS**

GEOTHERMAL ALTERATION
USE **HYDROTHERMAL ALTERATION**

GEOTHERMAL DATA
BT1 GEOPHYSICAL DATA
BT2 DATA
RT GEOTHERMAL EXPLORATION
RT HEAT FLOW

GEOTHERMAL ENERGY
RT GEOTHERMAL POWER
RT HEAT FLOW
RT HOT SPRINGS
RT HYDROTHERMAL ACTIVITY

GEOTHERMAL EQUIPMENT
BT1 GEOPHYSICAL EQUIPMENT
BT2 EQUIPMENT
NT1 HEAT PROBES

GEOTHERMAL EXPLORATION
BT1 GEOPHYSICAL EXPLORATION
BT2 EXPLORATION
RT GEOTHERMAL DATA
RT HEAT FLOW

GEOTHERMAL FIELDS
USE **HYDROTHERMAL FIELDS**

GEOTHERMAL FLUIDS
USE **HYDROTHERMAL SOLUTIONS**

GEOTHERMAL GRADIENT
BT1 TEMPERATURE GRADIENTS
RT HEAT FLOW
RT THERMAL CONDUCTIVITY

GEOTHERMAL MEASUREMENT
UF sediment temperature measurement
BT1 TEMPERATURE MEASUREMENT
BT2 MEASUREMENT
RT HEAT FLOW
RT HEAT PROBES
RT SEDIMENT TEMPERATURE

ASFIS Thesaurus

GEOTHERMAL POWER
SN	Utilizing geothermal energy as a source of power
UF	hydrothermal energy
BT1	ENERGY RESOURCES
BT2	NATURAL RESOURCES
BT3	RESOURCES
RT	GEOTHERMAL ENERGY
RT	POWER FROM THE SEA
RT	RENEWABLE RESOURCES
RT	THERMAL POWER

GEOTHERMAL PROPERTIES
BT1	PHYSICAL PROPERTIES
BT2	PROPERTIES
RT	GEOTHERMAL SPRINGS

GEOTHERMAL SPRINGS
SN	Before 1982 search THERMAL SPRINGS
UF	thermal springs (geothermal)
BT1	WATER SPRINGS
NT1	HYDROTHERMAL SPRINGS
RT	GEOTHERMAL PROPERTIES
RT	SEEPAGES
RT	WATER TEMPERATURE

GEOTROPISM
BT1	TROPISM
RT	GRAVITY
RT	GRAVITY EFFECTS

GER
USE	**PRODUCTION COST**

GERMANIUM
BT1	CHEMICAL ELEMENTS
RT	GERMANIUM COMPOUNDS
RT	GERMANIUM ISOTOPES
RT	METALS
RT	TRACE METALS

GERMANIUM COMPOUNDS
RT	CHEMICAL COMPOUNDS
RT	GERMANIUM

GERMANIUM ISOTOPES
BT1	ISOTOPES
RT	GERMANIUM

GERMINATION
RT	AQUATIC PLANTS
RT	BOTANY
RT	SPORES

GESTATION
USE	**PREGNANCY**

GEYSERS
USE	**HOT SPRINGS**

GIANT WAVES
RT	WAVE HEIGHT
RT	WAVE-CURRENT INTERACTION

GIBBERELLINS
USE	**PHYTOHORMONES**

GIBBING
USE	**GUTTING**

GIBBSITE
BT1	OXIDE MINERALS
BT2	MINERALS

GILL ARCHES
USE	**GILLS**

GILL DISEASE
SN	Added in 1980
UF	bacterial gill disease
UF	fungal gill disease
BT1	FISH DISEASES
BT2	ANIMAL DISEASES
BT3	DISEASES
RT	FUNGAL DISEASES
RT	GILLS
RT	HUSBANDRY DISEASES
RT	NUTRITION DISORDERS
RT	TUMOURS

GILL RAKERS
USE	**GILLS**

GILLNETS
UF	drift nets
UF	enmeshing nets
UF	set nets
UF	tangle nets
BT1	FISHING NETS
BT2	FISHING GEAR
RT	COASTAL FISHERIES
RT	DEMERSAL FISHERIES
RT	ENTANGLING NETS
RT	GILLNETTERS
RT	PELAGIC FISHERIES
RT	SPORT FISHING

GILLNETTERS
BT1	FISHING VESSELS
BT2	SURFACE CRAFT
BT3	VEHICLES
RT	DEMERSAL FISHERIES
RT	GILLNETS
RT	PELAGIC FISHERIES

GILLRAKER COUNTS
BT1	MERISTIC COUNTS

GILLS
SN	Respiratory organs usually specialized for gaseous exchange in water. Before1982 search RESPIRATORY ORGANS
UF	gill arches
UF	gill rakers
BT1	RESPIRATORY ORGANS
BT2	ANIMAL ORGANS
BT3	BODY ORGANS
RT	AEROBIC RESPIRATION
RT	AQUATIC ANIMALS
RT	GILL DISEASE
RT	MANTLE
RT	MANTLE CAVITY

GLACIAL DEPOSITION
USE	**GLACIAL SEDIMENTATION**

GLACIAL DEPOSITS
UF	drift (sediments)
UF	glacial drift
UF	glacial-marine sediments
NT1	BOULDER CLAY
NT1	GLACIAL ERRATICS
RT	ALLOCHTHONOUS DEPOSITS
RT	CLASTICS
RT	GLACIAL EROSION
RT	GLACIAL FEATURES
RT	GLACIAL SEDIMENTATION
RT	GLACIAL TRANSPORT
RT	ICE DRIFT
RT	LAKE DEPOSITS
RT	MORAINES
RT	RAFTING
RT	TERRIGENOUS SEDIMENTS
RT	VARVES

GLACIAL DRIFT
USE	**GLACIAL DEPOSITS**

GLACIAL EPOCH
USE	**PLEISTOCENE**

GLACIAL EROSION
BT1	EROSION
RT	EROSION FEATURES
RT	FJORDS
RT	GEOMORPHOLOGY
RT	GLACIAL DEPOSITS
RT	GLACIAL FEATURES
RT	GLACIAL LAKES
RT	ICEBERG SCOURING
RT	PLOUGHMARKS
RT	RIVER VALLEYS

GLACIAL ERRATICS
UF	erratics
UF	ice-rafted detritus
BT1	GLACIAL DEPOSITS
RT	BOULDERS
RT	ICE AGES
RT	ICE RAFTING

GLACIAL FEATURES
NT1	MORAINES
RT	DEPOSITION FEATURES
RT	EROSION FEATURES
RT	ESKERS
RT	FJORDS
RT	GLACIAL DEPOSITS
RT	GLACIAL EROSION
RT	GLACIAL LAKES
RT	GLACIAL TRANSPORT
RT	GLACIERS
RT	LANDFORMS
RT	PLOUGHMARKS
RT	TOPOGRAPHIC FEATURES

GLACIAL GEOLOGY
RT	GEOMORPHOLOGY
RT	GLACIERS

GLACIAL LAKES
SN	Lakes occupying basins formed as a result of glaciation
UF	kettle lakes
UF	tarns
BT1	LAKES
BT2	INLAND WATERS
RT	GEOMORPHOLOGY
RT	GLACIAL EROSION
RT	GLACIAL FEATURES
RT	GLACIATION
RT	STRANDLINES

GLACIAL-MARINE SEDIMENTS
USE	**GLACIAL DEPOSITS**

GLACIAL PERIODS
USE	**ICE AGES**

GLACIAL SEDIMENTATION
UF	glacial deposition
BT1	SEDIMENTATION
RT	GLACIAL DEPOSITS
RT	GLACIERS
RT	LAKE DEPOSITS
RT	SEDIMENTARY ENVIRONMENTS

GLACIAL TRANSPORT
BT1	SEDIMENT TRANSPORT
RT	GLACIAL DEPOSITS
RT	GLACIAL FEATURES
RT	GLACIERS
RT	ICE RAFTING

GLACIATION
RT	CLIMATIC CHANGES
RT	DEGLACIATION
RT	EUSTATIC CHANGES
RT	GLACIAL LAKES
RT	GLACIERS
RT	ICE AGES
RT	ISOSTASY
RT	REGRESSIONS

GLACIER ICE
USE	**GLACIERS**

GLACIERS
SN	Glaciers and their influence on aquatic environment
UF	glacier ice
BT1	ICE
RT	ABLATION
RT	ATMOSPHERIC PRECIPITATIONS
RT	CRYOSPHERE
RT	FRESH WATER
RT	FRESHWATER ICE
RT	GEOLOGY
RT	GEOMORPHOLOGY
RT	GLACIAL FEATURES
RT	GLACIAL GEOLOGY
RT	GLACIAL SEDIMENTATION
RT	GLACIAL TRANSPORT
RT	GLACIATION
RT	HYDROLOGY
RT	ICE VOLUME
RT	ICEBERGS
RT	RIVER VALLEYS
RT	VALLEYS
RT	WATER RESOURCES

GLANDS
BT1	SECRETORY ORGANS
NT1	DIGESTIVE GLANDS
NT2	HEPATOPANCREAS
NT2	LIVER
NT2	PANCREAS
NT1	ENDOCRINE GLANDS
NT2	ADRENAL GLANDS
NT2	PITUITARY GLAND
NT2	THYMUS
NT2	THYROID
NT1	EXOCRINE GLANDS
RT	ENDOCRINOLOGY
RT	GRAFTING
RT	METABOLISM
RT	MUCUS
RT	SECRETION
RT	SECRETORY PRODUCTS

GLASS
NT1	OBSIDIAN
RT	DEVITRIFICATION
RT	FIBRE GLASS
RT	PALAGONITE
RT	VOLCANIC GLASS

GLASS-REINFORCED PLASTICS
BT1	PLASTICS
BT2	MATERIALS
RT	FIBRE GLASS

GLAUCONITE
BT1	MICAS
BT2	SILICATE MINERALS
BT3	MINERALS

GLITTER
RT	LIGHT REFLECTION
RT	REFLECTANCE
RT	WAVE MEASUREMENT

GLOBAL RADIATION
USE	**SOLAR RADIATION**

GLOBAL TECTONICS
USE	**PLATE TECTONICS**

GLOBIGERINA OOZE
BT1	FORAMINIFERAL OOZE
BT2	CALCAREOUS OOZE
BT3	OOZES

GLOBULINS
SN	Before 1982 search PROTEINS
UF	gammaglobulins
UF	serum globulins
BT1	PROTEINS
BT2	ORGANIC COMPOUNDS

GLORIA
SN	Geological Long Range Inclined Asdic
BT1	TOWED VEHICLES
BT2	UNMANNED VEHICLES
BT3	UNDERWATER VEHICLES
BT4	VEHICLES
RT	SIDE SCAN SONAR
RT	SONOGRAPHS

GLOSSARIES
UF	dictionaries
UF	lexicons
BT1	DOCUMENTS
RT	DIRECTORIES
RT	DOCUMENTATION
RT	TERMINOLOGY

GLUCOSAMINE
BT1	HEXOSAMINES
BT2	AMINES
BT3	ORGANIC COMPOUNDS
RT	CHITIN

GLUCOSE
BT1	MONOSACCHARIDES
BT2	SACCHARIDES
BT3	CARBOHYDRATES
BT4	ORGANIC COMPOUNDS
RT	ALDEHYDES

GLUTAMIC ACID
BT1	AMINO ACIDS
BT2	ORGANIC ACIDS
BT3	ORGANIC COMPOUNDS

GLUTATHIONE
USE	**COENZYMES**

GLYCEROL
BT1	ALCOHOLS
BT2	ORGANIC COMPOUNDS

GLYCINE
BT1	AMINO ACIDS
BT2	ORGANIC ACIDS
BT3	ORGANIC COMPOUNDS

GLYCOGEN
SN	Added in 1980
BT1	CARBOHYDRATES
BT2	ORGANIC COMPOUNDS
RT	LIVER
RT	MUSCLES

GLYCOLIC ACID
BT1	ORGANIC ACIDS
BT2	ORGANIC COMPOUNDS

GLYCOLIPIDS
USE	**COMPLEX LIPIDS**

GLYCOPROTEINS
SN	Before 1982 search PROTEINS
BT1	PROTEINS
BT2	ORGANIC COMPOUNDS
RT	ANTIGENS
RT	ENZYMES
RT	HORMONES

GLYCOSIDES
BT1	CARBOHYDRATES
BT2	ORGANIC COMPOUNDS
NT1	PIGMENTS
NT2	CHROMATIC PIGMENTS
NT3	CAROTENOIDS
NT2	PHOTOSYNTHETIC PIGMENTS
NT3	CHLOROPHYLLS
NT3	XANTHOPHYLLS
NT2	RESPIRATORY PIGMENTS
NT3	HAEMOCYANINS
NT3	HAEMOGLOBINS
NT2	VISUAL PIGMENTS
NT1	PORPHYRINS
NT1	SAPONINS

GOETHITE
BT1	OXIDE MINERALS
BT2	MINERALS

GOLD
BT1	CHEMICAL ELEMENTS
RT	GOLD COMPOUNDS
RT	GOLD ISOTOPES
RT	METALS
RT	PLACERS
RT	TRACE METALS

GOLD COMPOUNDS
RT	CHEMICAL COMPOUNDS
RT	GOLD

GOLD ISOTOPES
BT1	ISOTOPES
RT	GOLD

GOLGI APPARATUS
SN	Added in 1980
UF	golgi bodies
UF	golgi complex
BT1	CELL ORGANELLES
BT2	CELL CONSTITUENTS
RT	CYTOPLASM

GOLGI BODIES
USE	**GOLGI APPARATUS**

GOLGI COMPLEX
USE	**GOLGI APPARATUS**

GONAD HORMONES
USE	**SEX HORMONES**

GONADOTROPIC HORMONES
USE	**SEX HORMONES**

GONADS
USE	**ANIMAL REPRODUCTIVE ORGANS**

GOODS
USE	**PRODUCTS**

GOVERNMENT POLICY
RT	GOVERNMENTS

ASFIS Thesaurus

GOVERNMENTS
SN	Added in 1980
UF	federal governments
UF	state governments
RT	COUNTRIES
RT	DEVELOPING COUNTRIES
RT	ECONOMICS
RT	GOVERNMENT POLICY
RT	LEGISLATION
RT	POLICIES
RT	POLITICAL ASPECTS
RT	WATER POLICY

GRABEN
SN	Structural rock feature downthrown between two parallel faults relative to the surrounding area
BT1	GEOLOGICAL STRUCTURES
RT	FAULTS
RT	RIFT VALLEYS

GRABS
BT1	SEDIMENT SAMPLERS
BT2	SAMPLERS

GRADES
USE	QUALITY

GRADIENT CURRENTS
BT1	WATER CURRENTS
BT2	WATER MOTION
RT	GEOSTROPHIC WINDS

GRADIENT WINDS
BT1	WINDS
BT2	ATMOSPHERIC MOTION
RT	CENTRIPETAL FORCE
RT	CORIOLIS FORCE
RT	GEOSTROPHIC WINDS

GRADIENTS
SN	Used only as a qualifier
RT	BEACH SLOPE
RT	DENSITY GRADIENTS
RT	HORIZONTAL PROFILES
RT	PROFILES
RT	SALINITY GRADIENTS
RT	SLOPE INDICATORS
RT	SLOPES (TOPOGRAPHY)
RT	VELOCITY GRADIENTS
RT	VERTICAL PROFILES
RT	WAVE STEEPNESS
RT	WIRE ANGLE

GRADING
UF	fish grading
UF	grading devices
UF	size grading
RT	AQUACULTURE EQUIPMENT
RT	CRUSTACEAN CULTURE
RT	FISH CULTURE
RT	FRY
RT	HATCHERIES
RT	MOLLUSC CULTURE
RT	OYSTER CULTURE
RT	SHELLFISH CULTURE
RT	SPAT

GRADING DEVICES
USE	GRADING

GRAFTING
SN	Transplantation, implantation or removal of tissue or organs
RT	GLANDS
RT	HISTOLOGY
RT	TISSUES

GRAFTS
USE	TRANSPLANTS

GRAIN FLOW
BT1	SEDIMENT GRAVITY FLOWS
BT2	SEDIMENT MOVEMENT
RT	COHESIONLESS SEDIMENTS
RT	FLUIDIZATION
RT	LIQUEFIED SEDIMENT FLOW

GRAIN MOTION
USE	PARTICLE MOTION

GRAIN ORIENTATION
BT1	ORIENTATION
RT	GRAIN PROPERTIES
RT	SEDIMENT TEXTURE

GRAIN PACKING
RT	GRAIN PROPERTIES
RT	SEDIMENT TEXTURE

GRAIN PROPERTIES
BT1	SEDIMENT PROPERTIES
BT2	PROPERTIES
RT	GRAIN ORIENTATION
RT	GRAIN PACKING
RT	GRAIN SHAPE
RT	GRAIN SIZE

GRAIN SHAPE
BT1	SHAPE
RT	GRAIN PROPERTIES
RT	SEDIMENT TEXTURE

GRAIN SIZE
UF	grain size distribution
UF	sediment size
RT	DIMENSIONS
RT	GRAIN PROPERTIES
RT	GRANULOMETRY
RT	PERMEABILITY
RT	POROSITY
RT	SEDIMENT PROPERTIES
RT	SEDIMENT SORTING
RT	SEDIMENT TEXTURE
RT	WATER CONTENT
RT	WET BULK DENSITY

GRAIN SIZE DISTRIBUTION
USE	GRAIN SIZE

GRAMOPHONE RECORDS
USE	AUDIO RECORDINGS

GRANITE
BT1	IGNEOUS ROCKS
BT2	ROCKS

GRANITIC LAYER
USE	SIAL

GRANTS
RT	FELLOWSHIPS
RT	FINANCING
RT	ORGANIZATIONS
RT	RESEARCH PROGRAMMES
RT	RESEARCH PROPOSALS

GRANULOMETRY
BT1	MEASUREMENT
RT	GRAIN SIZE

GRAPHIC DATA PRESENTATIONS
USE	GRAPHICS

GRAPHIC METHODS
SN	Used only as a qualifier
NT1	GRAPHICAL ANALYSIS
NT1	MAPPING
NT2	AUTOMATED CARTOGRAPHY
NT2	SEAFLOOR MAPPING
RT	ATLASES
RT	CARTOGRAPHY
RT	GRAPHICS
RT	GRAPHS
RT	MAPS
RT	METHODOLOGY
RT	STATISTICAL ANALYSIS
RT	STATISTICAL TABLES

GRAPHICAL ANALYSIS
SN	Before 1982 search GRAPHIC METHODS
BT1	GRAPHIC METHODS
RT	STATISTICAL ANALYSIS
RT	STATISTICAL TABLES

GRAPHICS
UF	data presentation
UF	data presentation (graphics)
UF	graphic data presentations
BT1	AUDIOVISUAL MATERIAL
BT2	DOCUMENTS
NT1	ANALOG RECORDS
NT2	BATHYTHERMOGRAMS
NT2	ECHOSOUNDER PROFILES
NT2	SEISMIC PROFILES
NT3	SEISMIC REFLECTION PROFILES
NT3	SEISMIC REFRACTION PROFILES
NT2	SEISMOGRAMS
NT2	TIDAL CURVES
NT2	TIDAL RECORDS
NT1	ENGINEERING DRAWINGS
NT1	GRAPHS
NT2	GROWTH CURVES
NT2	HODOGRAPHS
NT3	CURRENT ELLIPSES
NT3	EKMAN SPIRAL
NT2	HYPSOMETRIC CURVES
NT2	T/S DIAGRAMS
NT2	WAVE REFRACTION DIAGRAMS
NT1	MAP GRAPHICS
NT2	CURRENT ROSES
NT2	ISOPLETHS
NT3	CONTOURS
NT4	ISOBATHS
NT3	CORANGE LINES
NT3	COTIDAL LINES
NT3	ISOBARS
NT3	ISOCHRONES
NT3	ISOHALINES
NT3	ISOHYETS
NT3	ISOMAGNETIC LINES
NT3	ISOPACHS
NT3	ISOPYCNICS
NT3	ISOSTERES
NT3	ISOTHERMS
NT2	STREAMLINES
NT2	VERTICAL SECTIONS
NT3	GEOLOGICAL SECTIONS
NT3	HYDROGRAPHIC SECTIONS
NT4	BATHYMETRIC PROFILES
NT4	DENSITY SECTIONS
NT4	OXYGEN SECTIONS
NT4	SALINITY SECTIONS
NT4	TEMPERATURE SECTIONS
NT4	VELOCITY SECTIONS
NT2	WIND ROSES
NT2	WIND VECTORS
NT1	MAPS
NT2	BIOLOGICAL CHARTS
NT2	CLIMATOLOGICAL CHARTS
NT2	CONTROL CHARTS
NT2	ENVIRONMENTAL CHARTS
NT2	FISHERY CHARTS
NT2	GEOLOGICAL MAPS

GRAPHICS (cont'd)
NT3	GRAVITY CHARTS	
NT4	BOUGUER GRAVITY CHARTS	
NT4	FREE AIR GRAVITY CHARTS	
NT3	ISOPACH MAPS	
NT3	MAGNETIC CHARTS	
NT4	MAGNETIC ANOMALY CHARTS	
NT2	HYDROGRAPHIC CHARTS	
NT3	BATHYMETRIC CHARTS	
NT3	CURRENT CHARTS	
NT3	DENSITY CHARTS	
NT3	ICE CHARTS	
NT3	SALINITY CHARTS	
NT3	TEMPERATURE CHARTS	
NT3	TIDAL CHARTS	
NT4	CORANGE CHARTS	
NT4	COTIDAL CHARTS	
NT2	METEOROLOGICAL CHARTS	
NT3	WEATHER MAPS	
NT2	NAVIGATIONAL CHARTS	
NT3	LATTICE CHARTS	
NT3	PILOT CHARTS	
NT2	POLLUTION MAPS	
NT2	TOPOGRAPHIC MAPS	
NT2	TRACK CHARTS	
RT	GRAPHIC METHODS	
RT	SLIDES (PHOTOGRAPHIC)	

GRAPHITE
BT1	MINERALS
RT	DIAMONDS

GRAPHS
SN	Descriptor to be used only as a qualifier
UF	curves (graphs)
BT1	GRAPHICS
BT2	AUDIOVISUAL MATERIAL
BT3	DOCUMENTS
NT1	GROWTH CURVES
NT1	HODOGRAPHS
NT2	CURRENT ELLIPSES
NT2	EKMAN SPIRAL
NT1	HYPSOMETRIC CURVES
NT1	T/S DIAGRAMS
NT1	WAVE REFRACTION DIAGRAMS
RT	GRAPHIC METHODS
RT	ISOPLETHS
RT	PROFILES

GRAPPLING
BT1	CATCHING METHODS
RT	FISHING
RT	GRAPPLING GEAR

GRAPPLING GEAR
UF	rakes
BT1	FISHING GEAR
RT	COASTAL FISHERIES
RT	DEMERSAL FISHERIES
RT	GRAPPLING

GRAVEL
BT1	CLASTICS
BT2	SEDIMENTS
RT	AGGREGATES
RT	ALLUVIAL DEPOSITS
RT	COHESIONLESS SEDIMENTS
RT	SAND
RT	SEDIMENT LOAD
RT	SEDIMENT TEXTURE
RT	SOILS

GRAVEL PITS
USE	**PITS**

GRAVEL WAVES
BT1	BED FORMS
BT2	SEDIMENTARY STRUCTURES
RT	TRANSVERSE BED FORMS

GRAVIMETERS
USE	**GRAVITY METERS**

GRAVIMETRIC TECHNIQUES
BT1	ANALYTICAL TECHNIQUES
RT	DENSITY
RT	PARTICLE CONCENTRATION
RT	SEDIMENT ANALYSIS

GRAVIMETRY
BT1	MEASUREMENT
RT	GRAVITY
RT	GRAVITY EXPLORATION
RT	GRAVITY METERS
RT	GRAVITY SURVEYS

GRAVITATION
RT	FORCES
RT	GRAVITY
RT	GRAVITY METERS

GRAVITATIONAL FIELD
USE	**GRAVITY FIELD**

GRAVITY
BT1	FORCES (MECHANICS)
RT	EQUILIBRIUM TIDES
RT	GEOPHYSICS
RT	GEOTROPISM
RT	GRAVIMETRY
RT	GRAVITATION
RT	GRAVITY ANOMALIES
RT	GRAVITY EFFECTS
RT	GRAVITY FIELD
RT	GRAVITY WAVES
RT	PLUMBLINE DEFLECTION
RT	WEIGHT

GRAVITY ANOMALIES
BT1	ANOMALIES
NT1	BOUGUER ANOMALIES
NT1	FREE AIR ANOMALIES
RT	GEOID ANOMALIES
RT	GRAVITY
RT	GRAVITY CHARTS
RT	GRAVITY DATA
RT	GRAVITY EXPLORATION
RT	GRAVITY FIELD
RT	MAGNETIC ANOMALIES

GRAVITY ANOMALY CHARTS
USE	**GRAVITY CHARTS**

GRAVITY CHARTS
UF	gravity anomaly charts
BT1	GEOLOGICAL MAPS
BT2	MAPS
BT3	GRAPHICS
BT4	AUDIOVISUAL MATERIAL
NT1	BOUGUER GRAVITY CHARTS
NT1	FREE AIR GRAVITY CHARTS
RT	GRAVITY ANOMALIES
RT	GRAVITY EXPLORATION

GRAVITY CORERS
BT1	CORERS
BT2	SEDIMENT SAMPLERS
BT3	SAMPLERS

GRAVITY CORRECTIONS
UF	bouguer correction
UF	eotvos correction
UF	free air correction
UF	latitude correction
BT1	CORRECTIONS

GRAVITY CORRECTIONS (cont'd)
RT	GRAVITY EXPLORATION
RT	GRAVITY SURVEYS

GRAVITY DATA
BT1	GEOPHYSICAL DATA
BT2	DATA
RT	GRAVITY ANOMALIES
RT	GRAVITY EXPLORATION

GRAVITY EFFECTS
BT1	ENVIRONMENTAL EFFECTS
RT	BEHAVIOUR
RT	GEOTROPISM
RT	GRAVITY

GRAVITY EXPLORATION
UF	gravity methods
BT1	GEOPHYSICAL EXPLORATION
BT2	EXPLORATION
RT	COAST EFFECT
RT	GRAVIMETRY
RT	GRAVITY ANOMALIES
RT	GRAVITY CHARTS
RT	GRAVITY CORRECTIONS
RT	GRAVITY DATA

GRAVITY FIELD
SN	Before 1982 search also GRAVITATIONAL FIELD
UF	gravitational field
RT	FIELDS
RT	GRAVITY
RT	GRAVITY ANOMALIES

GRAVITY-INDUCED FLOW
USE	**DENSITY FLOW**

GRAVITY METERS
UF	gravimeters
BT1	MEASURING DEVICES
RT	ACCELEROMETERS
RT	GEOPHYSICAL EQUIPMENT
RT	GRAVIMETRY
RT	GRAVITATION

GRAVITY METHODS
USE	**GRAVITY EXPLORATION**

GRAVITY PLATFORMS
BT1	FIXED PLATFORMS
BT2	OFFSHORE STRUCTURES
BT3	HYDRAULIC STRUCTURES

GRAVITY SURVEYS
BT1	GEOPHYSICAL SURVEYS
BT2	GEOLOGICAL SURVEYS
BT3	SURVEYS
RT	GRAVIMETRY
RT	GRAVITY CORRECTIONS

GRAVITY WAVES
BT1	WATER WAVES
RT	CAPILLARY WAVES
RT	GRAVITY

GRAYWACKE
RT	ARENITES
RT	SANDSTONE
RT	SEDIMENTARY ROCKS

GRAZING
RT	BIOLOGICAL PRODUCTION
RT	FEEDING BEHAVIOUR
RT	FOOD CHAINS
RT	FOOD PREFERENCES
RT	HERBIVORES

GREEN'S FUNCTION
RT   MATHEMATICAL ANALYSIS

GREENFLASH
RT   ATMOSPHERIC OPTICAL PHENOMENA

GREENHOUSE EFFECT
RT   CARBON DIOXIDE
RT   CLIMATIC CHANGES
RT   EARTH ATMOSPHERE
RT   HEAT BUDGET
RT   TERRESTRIAL RADIATION
RT   WATER VAPOUR

GREENSCHIST FACIES
BT1   METAMORPHIC FACIES
BT2   FACIES
RT   GREENSCHISTS

GREENSCHISTS
BT1   SCHISTS
BT2   METAMORPHIC ROCKS
BT3   ROCKS
RT   GREENSCHIST FACIES

GREIGITE
BT1   SULPHIDE MINERALS
BT2   MINERALS

GROINS
USE   **GROYNES**

GROSS ENERGY REQUIREMENT
USE   **PRODUCTION COST**

GROUND MOTION
UF   motion (ground)
RT   EARTHQUAKE LOADING
RT   EARTHQUAKES
RT   GEOLOGICAL HAZARDS
RT   MOTION
RT   SEISMIC ACTIVITY
RT   SEISMOLOGY
RT   SURFACE SEISMIC WAVES

GROUND SWELL
USE   **SWELL**

GROUND WATER
UF   phreatic water
UF   underground water
BT1   WATER
RT   GROUNDWATER POLLUTION
RT   HYDROLOGY
RT   PERCOLATION
RT   SALINE INTRUSION
RT   SPRING STREAMS
RT   WATER RESOURCES
RT   WATER SPRINGS
RT   WATER TABLE
RT   WATERSHEDS

GROUNDINGS
RT   ACCIDENTS
RT   KEEL CLEARANCE
RT   SHIP LOSSES
RT   SHIPS
RT   SHOALS

GROUNDWATER POLLUTION
SN   Added in 1980
UF   pollution (groundwater)
BT1   WATER POLLUTION
BT2   POLLUTION
RT   FRESHWATER POLLUTION
RT   GROUND WATER
RT   MARINE POLLUTION
RT   SALINE WATER
RT   SEDIMENT POLLUTION

GROUP EFFECTS
SN   Collective sensorial or chemical stimulation within organisms. Added in 1980
BT1   ENVIRONMENTAL EFFECTS
RT   BIOTIC FACTORS
RT   GROWTH REGULATORS
RT   SOCIAL BEHAVIOUR

GROUP VELOCITY
BT1   VELOCITY
RT   PHASE VELOCITY
RT   WATER WAVES
RT   WAVE DISPERSION
RT   WAVE GROUPS
RT   WAVE VELOCITY

GROUPER FISHERIES
USE   **PERCOID FISHERIES**

GROUTING
RT   FOUNDATIONS
RT   GEOTECHNOLOGY

GROWING PONDS
UF   fattening ponds
BT1   FISH PONDS
BT2   PONDS
BT3   INLAND WATERS
RT   JUVENILES
RT   STOCKING DENSITY

GROWTH
UF   animal growth
UF   growth rate
UF   plant growth
BT1   POPULATION FUNCTIONS
RT   AGE COMPOSITION
RT   AGE DETERMINATION
RT   BIOLOGICAL AGE
RT   BIOLOGICAL AGING
RT   BIOLOGICAL DEVELOPMENT
RT   CELL DIFFERENTIATION
RT   CONDITION FACTOR
RT   DIAPAUSE
RT   FOOD CONVERSION
RT   GROWTH CURVES
RT   GROWTH REGULATORS
RT   JUVENILES
RT   METABOLISM
RT   OTOLITH READING
RT   REGENERATION
RT   SCALE READING
RT   VITAMIN E

GROWTH CURVES
UF   age-length relationships
BT1   GRAPHS
BT2   GRAPHICS
BT3   AUDIOVISUAL MATERIAL
BT4   DOCUMENTS
RT   GROWTH
RT   LENGTH-WEIGHT RELATIONSHIPS
RT   POPULATION DYNAMICS

GROWTH RATE
USE   **GROWTH**

GROWTH REGULATORS
SN   Chemical and biochemical products affecting growth of organisms
UF   stimulants (growth)
NT1   AUXINS
RT   GROUP EFFECTS
RT   GROWTH
RT   HORMONES
RT   INHIBITORS
RT   VITAMIN B
RT   VITAMINS

GROYNES
UF   groins
BT1   COAST DEFENCES
BT2   COASTAL STRUCTURES
BT3   HYDRAULIC STRUCTURES
RT   BEACH EROSION
RT   LONGSHORE CURRENTS
RT   LONGSHORE SEDIMENT TRANSPORT

GUANO
BT1   ANIMAL PRODUCTS
RT   FERTILIZERS
RT   GUANO BIRDS
RT   MINERAL INDUSTRY
RT   MINERAL RESOURCES
RT   PHOSPHATE DEPOSITS

GUANO BIRDS
BT1   MARINE BIRDS
BT2   AQUATIC BIRDS
BT3   AQUATIC ANIMALS
RT   GUANO

GUIDE LINES
BT1   CABLES
RT   UNDERWATER STRUCTURES
RT   WIRE ROPE

GUIDING (ORGANISMS)
USE   **GUIDING DEVICES**

GUIDING DEVICES
UF   guiding (organisms)
UF   organism guiding
NT1   ELECTRIC FENCES
NT1   FISHWAYS

GULF STREAM RINGS
USE   **CURRENT RINGS**

GUSTATION
USE   **TASTE**

GUSTS
BT1   ATMOSPHERIC TURBULENCE
BT2   TURBULENCE
BT3   FLUID MOTION
RT   GALE FORCE WINDS
RT   WIND SPEED
RT   WINDS

GUTTING
SN   Removal of gut from fish. Added in 1980
UF   evisceration
UF   gibbing
UF   nobbing
BT1   DRESSING
BT2   FISH HANDLING
BT3   FISHERY INDUSTRY
BT4   INDUSTRIES
RT   FISH FILLETS
RT   FISH WASTES

GUYED TOWERS
UF   compliant platforms
UF   compliant towers
BT1   FIXED PLATFORMS
BT2   OFFSHORE STRUCTURES
BT3   HYDRAULIC STRUCTURES
RT   PILED PLATFORMS

GUYOTS
UF   tablemounts
BT1   SEAMOUNTS
BT2   SUBMARINE FEATURES
BT3   TOPOGRAPHIC FEATURES
RT   RELIEF FORMS

GYPSUM
BT1	SULPHATE MINERALS
BT2	MINERALS
RT	AUTHIGENIC MINERALS
RT	EVAPORITES
RT	POLYHALITE
RT	SEDIMENTARY ROCKS

GYRES
UF	anticyclonic gyres
UF	subtropical gyres
BT1	OCEAN CIRCULATION
BT2	WATER CIRCULATION
BT3	WATER MOTION
RT	OCEANIC DESERTS
RT	SUBTROPICAL CONVERGENCES
RT	SURFACE CIRCULATION
RT	WATER CIRCULATION

GYROCOMPASSES
BT1	COMPASSES
BT2	MEASURING DEVICES
RT	NAVIGATIONAL AIDS

GYROSCOPES
UF	precision gyroscopes
BT1	INSTRUMENTS
RT	STABILIZED PLATFORMS

GYROSCOPIC WAVES
USE	**INERTIAL WAVES**

HABITAT
SN	A specific place with its environmental conditions occupied by an organism, a population or a community
UF	aquatic habitat
UF	habitat (natural)
UF	natural habitat
NT1	BIOTOPES
NT1	EXPOSED HABITATS
NT1	MICROHABITATS
NT1	SHELTERED HABITATS
RT	AQUATIC COMMUNITIES
RT	AQUATIC ENVIRONMENT
RT	BIOCOENOSIS
RT	BIOTA
RT	ECOLOGICAL ASSOCIATIONS
RT	ECOLOGICAL SUCCESSION
RT	ECOTYPES
RT	ENVIRONMENTAL FACTORS
RT	EXPLORATORY BEHAVIOUR
RT	HABITAT IMPROVEMENT
RT	HABITAT SELECTION
RT	HOME RANGE
RT	NICHES
RT	SUBSTRATA
RT	UNDERWATER HABITATS

HABITAT (NATURAL)
USE	**HABITAT**

HABITAT IMPROVEMENT
SN	Man-made changes in aquatic natural habitat mainly for aquaculture purposes
NT1	HABITAT IMPROVEMENT (BIOLOGICAL)
NT1	HABITAT IMPROVEMENT (CHEMICAL)
NT1	HABITAT IMPROVEMENT (FERTILIZATION)
NT1	HABITAT IMPROVEMENT (PHYSICAL)
RT	AQUACULTURE
RT	AQUACULTURE TECHNIQUES
RT	HABITAT
RT	ICHTHYOCIDES
RT	LAKES
RT	POND CULTURE
RT	RESERVOIRS (WATER)

HABITAT IMPROVEMENT (BIOLOGICAL)
SN	Improvement of habitat by increasing food organisms and/or introduction of forage by man
BT1	HABITAT IMPROVEMENT
RT	FOOD ORGANISMS
RT	ICHTHYOCIDES
RT	MOLLUSCICIDES
RT	PLANT CONTROL
RT	VEGETATION COVER

HABITAT IMPROVEMENT (CHEMICAL)
SN	Chemical improvement of the water properties by pH adjustment, and/or by reducing unfavourable elements
BT1	HABITAT IMPROVEMENT
RT	ARTIFICIAL AERATION
RT	CHEMICAL PROPERTIES
RT	DISSOLVED OXYGEN
RT	HABITAT IMPROVEMENT (FERTILIZATION)
RT	PH

HABITAT IMPROVEMENT (FERTILIZATION)
SN	Habitat improvement by fertilizers or other elements
BT1	HABITAT IMPROVEMENT
RT	FERTILIZERS
RT	HABITAT IMPROVEMENT (CHEMICAL)
RT	MANURE

HABITAT IMPROVEMENT (PHYSICAL)
SN	Change of water depth, volume, flow by construction of dams, ripple, removal of rubble and other hydraulic techniques
BT1	HABITAT IMPROVEMENT
RT	ARTIFICIAL REEFS
RT	ENCLOSURES
RT	FISHWAYS
RT	FLOOD CONTROL
RT	HYDRAULIC ENGINEERING
RT	HYDRAULIC STRUCTURES
RT	PHYSICAL PROPERTIES
RT	SHELTERS

HABITAT SELECTION
SN	Added in 1982
RT	COLONIZATION
RT	HABITAT

HABITAT TYPES
USE	**ECOTYPES**

HABITATS (ARTIFICIAL)
USE	**UNDERWATER HABITATS**

HADDOCK FISHERIES
USE	**GADOID FISHERIES**

HAEMAGGLUTININS
USE	**AGGLUTININS**

HAEMATITE
UF	hematite
BT1	OXIDE MINERALS
BT2	MINERALS
RT	IRON OXIDES

HAEMATOBLASTS
USE	**BLOOD CELLS**

HAEMATOLOGICAL DISEASES
SN	Before 1982 search HAEMATOLOGY
UF	blood diseases
UF	hematological diseases
UF	hemic diseases
BT1	DISEASES
NT1	ANAEMIA
RT	HAEMATOLOGY
RT	SEPTICAEMIA

HAEMATOLOGY
UF	blood chemistry
UF	hematology
BT1	BIOLOGY
RT	BLOOD
RT	BLOOD GROUPS
RT	BODY FLUIDS
RT	ERYTHROPOIESIS
RT	HAEMATOLOGICAL DISEASES
RT	HAEMOPOIESIS
RT	SEROLOGICAL STUDIES
RT	SERUM

HAEMATOPOIESIS
USE	**HAEMOPOIESIS**

HAEMOCYANINS
SN	Added in 1980
UF	hemocyanins
BT1	RESPIRATORY PIGMENTS
BT2	PIGMENTS
BT3	GLYCOSIDES
BT4	CARBOHYDRATES
RT	ANAEMIA
RT	BLOOD
RT	COPPER
RT	PROTEINS

HAEMOGLOBINS
UF	hemoglobins
BT1	RESPIRATORY PIGMENTS
BT2	PIGMENTS
BT3	GLYCOSIDES
BT4	CARBOHYDRATES
RT	ANAEMIA
RT	BLOOD CELLS
RT	CHELATES

HAEMOLYMPH
BT1	BODY FLUIDS
RT	BODY CAVITIES
RT	LEUKOCYTES

HAEMOPOIESIS
SN	Formation of blood or blood cells
UF	haematopoiesis
UF	hematopoiesis
UF	hemopoiesis
RT	BLOOD CELLS
RT	ERYTHROPOIESIS
RT	HAEMATOLOGY

HAEMORRHAGE
SN	Added in 1980
UF	hemorrhage
BT1	SYMPTOMS
RT	BLOOD VESSELS
RT	CIRCULATORY SYSTEM
RT	DISEASES

HAFF
USE	**COASTAL LAGOONS**

HAFNIUM
BT1	CHEMICAL ELEMENTS
RT	HAFNIUM COMPOUNDS
RT	HAFNIUM ISOTOPES
RT	METALS
RT	TRACE METALS

HAFNIUM COMPOUNDS
RT	CHEMICAL COMPOUNDS
RT	HAFNIUM

HAFNIUM ISOTOPES
BT1	ISOTOPES
RT	HAFNIUM

HAGERMON REDMOUTH
USE **REDMOUTH DISEASE**

HAIL
UF hailstones
BT1 ATMOSPHERIC PRECIPITATIONS
BT2 HYDROMETEORS
RT RAINFALL
RT SNOW

HAILSTONES
USE **HAIL**

HAKE FISHERIES
USE **GADOID FISHERIES**

HALF LIFE (BIOLOGICAL)
USE **BIOLOGICAL HALF LIFE**

HALF-LIFE (EFFECTIVE)
USE **BIOLOGICAL HALF LIFE**

HALF-TIDE LEVEL
USE **SEA LEVEL**

HALIBUT FISHERIES
USE **FLATFISH FISHERIES**

HALIDE MINERALS
BT1 MINERALS
NT1 CARNALLITE
NT1 FLUORITE
NT1 HALITE

HALIDES
BT1 HALOGEN COMPOUNDS
RT BROMIDES
RT CHLORIDES
RT FLUORIDES
RT IODIDES

HALINE CIRCULATION
BT1 THERMOHALINE CIRCULATION
BT2 OCEAN CIRCULATION
BT3 WATER CIRCULATION
BT4 WATER MOTION

HALITE
BT1 HALIDE MINERALS
BT2 MINERALS
RT AUTHIGENIC MINERALS
RT EVAPORITES

HALMYROLYSIS
UF low temperature weathering
UF submarine weathering
RT BASALT-SEAWATER INTERACTION
RT BOTTOM EROSION
RT DIAGENESIS
RT GEOCHEMISTRY
RT SEDIMENT-WATER INTERFACE

HALOCLINE
BT1 DISCONTINUITY LAYERS
BT2 LAYERS
RT CLINES
RT ISOHALINES
RT SALINITY
RT SALINITY STRATIFICATION
RT SALT-WEDGE ESTUARIES

HALOGEN COMPOUNDS
NT1 ASTATINE COMPOUNDS
NT1 BROMINE COMPOUNDS
NT2 BROMIDES
NT1 CHLORINE COMPOUNDS
NT2 CHLORIDES
NT1 FLUORINE COMPOUNDS
NT2 FLUORIDES
NT1 HALIDES

HALOGEN COMPOUNDS (cont'd)
NT1 IODINE COMPOUNDS
NT2 IODATES
NT2 IODIDES
NT2 IODINATED HYDROCARBONS
NT3 IODOMETHANE
RT CHEMICAL COMPOUNDS
RT HALOGENATED HYDROCARBONS
RT ORGANIC COMPOUNDS
RT SALTS

HALOGENATED HYDROCARBONS
BT1 HYDROCARBONS
BT2 ORGANIC COMPOUNDS
NT1 BROMINATED HYDROCARBONS
NT1 CHLORINATED HYDROCARBONS
NT2 ALDRIN
NT2 CHLOROFORM
NT2 DDE
NT2 DDT
NT2 DIELDRIN
NT2 TRICHLOROETHYLENE
NT1 FLUORINATED HYDROCARBONS
NT2 FREONS
RT HALOGEN COMPOUNDS

HALOGENATION
BT1 CHEMICAL REACTIONS
NT1 CHLORINATION

HALOGENS
RT ASTATINE
RT BROMINE
RT CHEMICAL ELEMENTS
RT CHLORINE
RT FLUORINE
RT IODINE

HAND DREDGES
USE **DREDGES**

HAND-LINES
USE **LINES**

HANDLING
SN Descriptor used only as a qualifier
RT FISH HANDLING
RT SHIP HANDLING

HANDLING EQUIPMENT
USE **DECK EQUIPMENT**

HANDLINING
BT1 LINE FISHING
BT2 CATCHING METHODS
RT ARTISANAL FISHING
RT JIGGING

HANGING CULTURE
USE **OFF-BOTTOM CULTURE**

HARBOR MODELS
USE **HARBOUR MODELS**

HARBOR REGULATIONS
USE **HARBOUR REGULATIONS**

HARBORS
USE **HARBOURS**

HARBOUR INSTALLATIONS
USE **PORT INSTALLATIONS**

HARBOUR MODELS
UF harbor models
BT1 HYDRAULIC MODELS
BT2 SCALE MODELS
BT3 MODELS
RT HARBOURS

HARBOUR OSCILLATIONS
UF range action
BT1 SEICHES
BT2 SURFACE WATER WAVES
BT3 WATER WAVES

HARBOUR REGULATIONS
UF harbor regulations
BT1 NAVIGATION REGULATIONS
BT2 LEGISLATION
RT HARBOURS
RT NAVIGATION REGULATIONS

HARBOUR STRUCTURES
USE **PORT INSTALLATIONS**

HARBOURS
UF harbors
UF ports
BT1 ANCHORAGES
NT1 FERRY TERMINALS
NT1 FISHING HARBOURS
NT1 NAVAL BASES
NT1 TANKER TERMINALS
NT2 DEEP-WATER TERMINALS
NT2 OFFSHORE TERMINALS
RT ARTIFICIAL HARBOURS
RT BREAKWATERS
RT COASTAL INLETS
RT COASTAL STRUCTURES
RT COASTAL WATERS
RT COASTS
RT FLUSHING TIME
RT HARBOUR MODELS
RT HARBOUR REGULATIONS
RT MARINE TRANSPORTATION
RT MOORING BUOYS
RT PORT INSTALLATIONS
RT SHIP CANALS
RT TIDAL INLETS
RT WATER POLLUTION TREATMENT

HARD ROE
USE **ROES**

HARDNESS (WATER)
USE **WATER HARDNESS**

HARMONIC ANALYSIS
BT1 FUNCTIONAL ANALYSIS
BT2 NUMERICAL ANALYSIS
BT3 MATHEMATICAL ANALYSIS
RT ANALYSIS
RT DIFFERENTIAL EQUATIONS
RT FOURIER ANALYSIS
RT HARMONIC FUNCTIONS
RT TIDAL ANALYSIS
RT TIME SERIES ANALYSIS
RT WAVEFORM ANALYSIS

HARMONIC FUNCTIONS
RT HARMONIC ANALYSIS
RT LAPLACE EQUATION
RT POISSON'S EQUATION
RT TIDAL CONSTANTS
RT TIDAL CONSTITUENTS

HARMONIC TIDAL CONSTANTS
USE **TIDAL CONSTANTS**

HARMONIC TIDAL CONSTITUENTS
USE **TIDAL CONSTITUENTS**

HARPOONS
USE **WOUNDING GEAR**

ASFIS Thesaurus

HARVESTING
SN Harvesting methods for biological purposes
RT BOTANICAL RESOURCES
RT CLAM FISHERIES
RT HARVESTING MACHINES
RT MINING
RT PLANT CONTROL
RT PLANT UTILIZATION
RT SEA GRASS
RT SEAWEEDS
RT SHELLFISH

HARVESTING EQUIPMENT
USE **HARVESTING MACHINES**

HARVESTING MACHINES
SN Harvesting equipment for biological purposes only
UF harvesting equipment
BT1 FISHING GEAR
RT AQUACULTURE EQUIPMENT
RT AUTOMATED FISHING PLATFORMS
RT COASTAL FISHERIES
RT DEMERSAL FISHERIES
RT HARVESTING
RT MECHANIZATION
RT SEAWEED HARVESTING
RT WATER PUMPS

HATCHERIES
BT1 AQUACULTURE FACILITIES
RT AQUACULTURE
RT AQUACULTURE EQUIPMENT
RT AQUACULTURE TECHNIQUES
RT AQUACULTURISTS
RT BAIT CULTURE
RT BATCH CULTURE
RT BRACKISHWATER AQUACULTURE
RT CRUSTACEAN CULTURE
RT CULTURE TANKS
RT FINGERLINGS
RT FISH CULTURE
RT FISH PONDS
RT FRESHWATER AQUACULTURE
RT FRY
RT GRADING
RT HATCHING
RT HYBRID CULTURE
RT INCUBATION
RT INTENSIVE CULTURE
RT MARINE AQUACULTURE
RT MASS CULTURE
RT MECHANIZATION
RT MOLLUSC CULTURE
RT PRAWN CULTURE
RT REDMOUTH DISEASE
RT SEED COLLECTION
RT SEED PRODUCTION
RT SELECTIVE BREEDING
RT SHELLFISH CULTURE
RT SHRIMP CULTURE
RT STOCKING (ORGANISMS)

HATCHING
RT BIRD EGGS
RT CLUTCH
RT EGGS
RT FISH EGGS
RT FRY
RT HATCHERIES
RT INCUBATION
RT INSECT EGGS
RT NESTING
RT NESTS
RT REARING

HAZARD ASSESSMENT
SN Evaluation of hazards to aquatic life associated with the use of chemical substances. Added in 1982
UF hazard evaluation
RT BIODEGRADABLE SUBSTANCES
RT CHEMICAL POLLUTANTS
RT CHEMICAL POLLUTION
RT ENVIRONMENTAL IMPACT
RT ENVIRONMENTAL LEGISLATION
RT HAZARDS
RT LETHAL LIMITS
RT POLLUTION EFFECTS
RT TOXICITY TESTS
RT TOXICOLOGY
RT WATER QUALITY

HAZARD EVALUATION
USE **HAZARD ASSESSMENT**

HAZARDOUS MATERIALS
UF dangerous materials
BT1 MATERIALS
RT BIOLOGICAL POISONS
RT CARGOES
RT CHEMICAL POLLUTANTS
RT CHEMICAL POLLUTION
RT EXPLOSIVES
RT HAZARDS
RT INDUSTRIAL WASTES
RT PESTICIDES
RT RADIOACTIVE WASTES
RT TOXICANTS

HAZARDS
UF danger
UF dangers
NT1 DIVING HAZARDS
NT2 SHARK ATTACKS
NT1 DROUGHTS
NT1 FIRE
NT1 FIRE HAZARDS
NT1 GEOLOGICAL HAZARDS
NT1 NAVIGATIONAL HAZARDS
NT1 RADIATION HAZARDS
NT1 WEATHER HAZARDS
RT ACCIDENT PREVENTION
RT ACCIDENTS
RT DAMAGE
RT DANGEROUS ORGANISMS
RT DISASTERS
RT HAZARD ASSESSMENT
RT HAZARDOUS MATERIALS
RT INJURIES
RT RISKS
RT SAFETY DEVICES
RT SITE SURVEYS

HAZE
UF atmospheric turbidity
RT AIR POLLUTION
RT ATMOSPHERIC OPTICAL PHENOMENA
RT DUST
RT DUST CLOUDS
RT FOG
RT SALT PARTICLES
RT TURBIDITY
RT VISIBILITY

HEAD
SN Added in 1980
UF animal head
BT1 BODY REGIONS
BT2 ANATOMICAL STRUCTURES
RT AUDITORY ORGANS
RT BRAIN
RT EYES
RT SKULL

HEADED FISH
USE **HEADING**

HEADING
SN Added in 1980
UF headed fish
BT1 FISH HANDLING
BT2 FISHERY INDUSTRY
BT3 INDUSTRIES
RT PROCESSING FISHERY PRODUCTS

HEADLANDS
UF promontories
BT1 COASTAL LANDFORMS
BT2 LANDFORMS
BT3 TOPOGRAPHIC FEATURES
NT1 CUSPATE FORELANDS
RT BAYS
RT BEACH FEATURES

HEALTH
USE **PUBLIC HEALTH**

HEALTH AND SAFETY
SN Before 1986 search also SAFETY
UF protection (human)
UF safety
NT1 ACCIDENT PREVENTION
NT1 MEDICINE
NT2 AETIOLOGY
NT2 UNDERWATER MEDICINE
NT1 PUBLIC HEALTH
NT1 RADIATION PROTECTION
RT COASTGUARDS
RT DROWNING
RT EMERGENCY VESSELS
RT EVACUATION
RT EXPLOSIVES
RT PROTECTION
RT SAFETY DEVICES
RT SAFETY REGULATIONS
RT SHARK ATTACKS

HEART
BT1 CIRCULATORY SYSTEM
RT BLOOD CIRCULATION
RT BLOOD VESSELS

HEAT
BT1 ENERGY
NT1 SENSIBLE HEAT
NT1 WASTE HEAT
RT AIR TEMPERATURE
RT CONSERVATION OF HEAT
RT DIFFUSION
RT DOUBLE DIFFUSION
RT ENERGY BALANCE
RT ENERGY TRANSFER
RT ENTROPY
RT HEAT BALANCE
RT HEAT BUDGET
RT HEAT TRANSFER
RT MOLECULAR DIFFUSION
RT SPECIFIC HEAT
RT TEMPERATURE
RT THERMAL POLLUTION
RT THERMAL RADIATION
RT THERMODYNAMIC PROPERTIES
RT THERMODYNAMICS

HEAT ADVECTION
USE **HEAT TRANSPORT**

HEAT AFFECTED ZONES
RT DEFECTS
RT WELDING

HEAT BALANCE
SN	Restricted to heat balance studies	
	of organisms	
UF	heat loss	
RT	AESTIVATION	
RT	BODY TEMPERATURE	
RT	EVAPORATION	
RT	HEAT	
RT	HEAT TRANSFER	

HEAT BUDGET
SN	Use only for heat budget of water	
	bodies and atmosphere. For studies	
	in organisms use HEAT BALANCE	
UF	heat gain	
UF	heat loss	
BT1	ENERGY BUDGET	
RT	BOWEN RATIO	
RT	CYCLES	
RT	EARTH ATMOSPHERE	
RT	ENERGY BALANCE	
RT	EVAPORATION	
RT	GREENHOUSE EFFECT	
RT	HEAT	
RT	HEAT CONTENT	
RT	HEAT EXCHANGE	
RT	HEAT FLOW	
RT	HEAT STORAGE	
RT	HEAT TRANSPORT	
RT	RADIATION BALANCE	
RT	TEMPERATURE	
RT	THERMAL STRATIFICATION	
RT	WATER BUDGET	
RT	WATER COLUMN	

HEAT CAPACITY
USE	**SPECIFIC HEAT**	

HEAT CONDUCTION
UF	conduction (heat)	
UF	conductive heat transfer	
UF	molecular heat conduction	
BT1	HEAT TRANSFER	
RT	EDDY CONDUCTION	
RT	HEAT FLOW	
RT	SENSIBLE HEAT	
RT	THERMAL CONDUCTIVITY	

HEAT CONTENT
RT	HEAT BUDGET	
RT	WATER BODIES	
RT	WATER TEMPERATURE	

HEAT DISSIPATION
USE	**COOLING**	

HEAT EXCHANGE
SN	Heat transfer at air-water,	
	air-ice, ice-water, or	
	sediment-water interface	
BT1	HEAT TRANSFER	
NT1	LATENT HEAT TRANSFER	
NT1	SENSIBLE HEAT TRANSFER	
RT	AIR-ICE INTERFACE	
RT	AIR-WATER EXCHANGES	
RT	AIR-WATER INTERFACE	
RT	ENERGY TRANSFER	
RT	EVAPORATION	
RT	HEAT BUDGET	
RT	RADIATION BALANCE	

HEAT EXCHANGERS
RT	FOULING CONTROL	
RT	OTEC PLANTS	

HEAT FLOW
SN	Use only for heat flow measurements	
	and amounts on the ocean floor. Use	
	GEOTHERMAL ENERGY for land areas	
UF	heat flow flux	

HEAT FLOW (cont'd)
BT1	HEAT TRANSFER	
RT	BOREHOLES	
RT	GEOTHERMAL DATA	
RT	GEOTHERMAL ENERGY	
RT	GEOTHERMAL EXPLORATION	
RT	GEOTHERMAL GRADIENT	
RT	GEOTHERMAL MEASUREMENT	
RT	HEAT BUDGET	
RT	HEAT CONDUCTION	
RT	HEAT PROBES	
RT	HOT SPOTS	
RT	HOT SPRINGS	
RT	MANTLE CONVECTION	
RT	PLATE TECTONICS	
RT	SEAFLOOR SPREADING	
RT	SEDIMENT TEMPERATURE	
RT	SEDIMENT-WATER EXCHANGES	
RT	SEDIMENT-WATER INTERFACE	
RT	THERMAL CONDUCTIVITY	
RT	TRENCHES (OCEANIC)	

HEAT FLOW FLUX
USE	**HEAT FLOW**	

HEAT FLUX
USE	**HEAT TRANSFER**	

HEAT GAIN
USE	**HEAT BUDGET**	

HEAT LOSS
USE	**HEAT BALANCE**	

HEAT LOSS
USE	**HEAT BUDGET**	

HEAT MEASUREMENT
USE	**CALORIMETRY**	

HEAT PROBES
BT1	GEOTHERMAL EQUIPMENT	
BT2	GEOPHYSICAL EQUIPMENT	
BT3	EQUIPMENT	
RT	GEOTHERMAL MEASUREMENT	
RT	HEAT FLOW	
RT	SEDIMENT TEMPERATURE	

HEAT PROPERTIES
USE	**THERMODYNAMIC PROPERTIES**	

HEAT RADIATION
USE	**THERMAL RADIATION**	

HEAT SINKS
RT	THERMODYNAMICS	

HEAT STORAGE
SN	Amount of heat used in changing the	
	temperature of a body of water in a	
	given time interval. A component of	
	the heat budget	
RT	HEAT BUDGET	

HEAT TRANSFER
UF	heat flux	
NT1	COOLING	
NT1	EDDY CONDUCTION	
NT1	HEAT CONDUCTION	
NT1	HEAT EXCHANGE	
NT2	LATENT HEAT TRANSFER	
NT2	SENSIBLE HEAT TRANSFER	
NT1	HEAT FLOW	
NT1	HEAT TRANSPORT	
RT	ATMOSPHERIC BOUNDARY LAYER	
RT	BOUNDARY LAYERS	
RT	CONDENSATION	
RT	CONVECTION	
RT	ENERGY BALANCE	
RT	ENERGY TRANSFER	

HEAT TRANSFER (cont'd)
RT	ENTROPY	
RT	FORCED CONVECTION	
RT	FREEZING	
RT	HEAT	
RT	HEAT BALANCE	
RT	ICE MELTING	
RT	MASS TRANSFER	
RT	PRANDTL NUMBER	
RT	RADIATIVE TRANSFER	
RT	TEMPERATURE	
RT	TEMPERATURE DIFFERENCES	
RT	THERMAL RADIATION	
RT	THERMODYNAMICS	
RT	WASTE HEAT	

HEAT TRANSPORT
SN	Heat advected by oceanic or	
	atmospheric circulation into or out	
	of a region	
UF	heat advection	
UF	poleward heat flux	
BT1	HEAT TRANSFER	
RT	ADVECTION	
RT	ATMOSPHERIC CIRCULATION	
RT	ATMOSPHERIC MOTION	
RT	CONSERVATION OF HEAT	
RT	CONVECTION	
RT	HEAT BUDGET	
RT	OCEAN CIRCULATION	
RT	OCEAN CURRENTS	
RT	TRANSPORT	
RT	WATER CURRENTS	
RT	WATER EXCHANGE	

HEATED EFFLUENT SYSTEMS
USE	**THERMAL AQUACULTURE**	

HEATING
SN	Includes heating equipment	
RT	COOLING	
RT	ICE PREVENTION	
RT	LIFE SUPPORT SYSTEMS	

HEATING FUELS
USE	**FUELS**	

HEAVE
USE	**HEAVING**	

HEAVE COMPENSATORS
RT	DRILL STRING	
RT	DRILLING	
RT	SHIP MOTION	
RT	STABILIZING	

HEAVE RESONANCE
BT1	RESONANCE	
RT	BUOY MOTION EFFECTS	
RT	HEAVING	

HEAVE RESPONSE
BT1	DYNAMIC RESPONSE	
BT2	INSTRUMENT RESPONSES	
RT	BUOY MOTION EFFECTS	
RT	HEAVING	

HEAVING
UF	heave	
BT1	SHIP MOTION	
RT	BUOY MOTION	
RT	BUOY MOTION EFFECTS	
RT	DYNAMIC RESPONSE	
RT	HEAVE RESONANCE	
RT	HEAVE RESPONSE	
RT	WAVE BUOYS	

ASFIS Thesaurus

HEAVY METALS
SN	Metallic elements with a specific gravity greater than four
BT1	METALS
RT	BIOACCUMULATION
RT	BISMUTH
RT	CADMIUM
RT	CHEMICAL ELEMENTS
RT	CHEMICAL POLLUTANTS
RT	CHEMICAL POLLUTION
RT	CHROMIUM
RT	COBALT
RT	COPPER
RT	IRON
RT	LEAD
RT	MANGANESE
RT	MERCURY
RT	MOLYBDENUM
RT	NICKEL
RT	PLATINUM
RT	SEDIMENT POLLUTION
RT	SILVER
RT	TANTALUM
RT	TELLURIUM
RT	THORIUM
RT	TIN
RT	TOXICANTS
RT	TOXICITY
RT	ZINC

HEAVY MINERALS
BT1	MINERALS
RT	CHROMIUM
RT	RUTILE

HEAVY WATER
BT1	WATER
RT	DEUTERIUM COMPOUNDS
RT	HYDROGEN ISOTOPES

HEIGHT
SN	Used only as a qualifier
UF	altitude
BT1	DIMENSIONS
RT	ALTIMETERS
RT	ALTIMETRY
RT	CLOUD HEIGHT
RT	DEPTH
RT	DYNAMIC HEIGHT
RT	HYPSOMETRIC CURVES
RT	SATELLITE ALTIMETRY

HELICOPTERS
BT1	AIRCRAFT
BT2	VEHICLES
RT	AERIAL PHOTOGRAPHY
RT	AERIAL SURVEYS
RT	AIR TRANSPORTATION
RT	AIRBORNE SENSING
RT	HELIDECKS
RT	INSTRUMENT PLATFORMS
RT	RADAR ALTIMETRY
RT	WATER SAMPLING

HELIDECKS
SN	Helicopter landing deck
BT1	DECKS
RT	AIR TRANSPORTATION
RT	HELICOPTERS

HELIUM
BT1	CHEMICAL ELEMENTS
RT	RARE GASES

HELIUM ISOTOPES
BT1	ISOTOPES
RT	URANIUM-HELIUM DATING

HELIUM OXYGEN MIXTURE
USE	**MIXED GAS**

HELMHOLTZ INSTABILITY
USE	**KELVIN-HELMHOLTZ INSTABILITY**

HEMATITE
USE	**HAEMATITE**

HEMATOLOGICAL DISEASES
USE	**HAEMATOLOGICAL DISEASES**

HEMATOLOGY
USE	**HAEMATOLOGY**

HEMATOPOIESIS
USE	**HAEMOPOIESIS**

HEMIC DISEASES
USE	**HAEMATOLOGICAL DISEASES**

HEMOCYANINS
USE	**HAEMOCYANINS**

HEMOGLOBINS
USE	**HAEMOGLOBINS**

HEMOPOIESIS
USE	**HAEMOPOIESIS**

HEMORRHAGE
USE	**HAEMORRHAGE**

HEPARIN
BT1	MUCOPOLYSACCHARIDES
BT2	POLYSACCHARIDES
BT3	SACCHARIDES
BT4	CARBOHYDRATES

HEPATOMA
USE	**TUMOURS**

HEPATOPANCREAS
SN	Added in 1980
BT1	DIGESTIVE GLANDS
BT2	GLANDS
BT3	SECRETORY ORGANS
RT	DIGESTION

HERBICIDES
BT1	PESTICIDES
RT	ALGICIDES
RT	CHEMICAL POLLUTANTS
RT	CHEMICAL POLLUTION
RT	PLANT CONTROL
RT	TOXICANTS

HERBIVORES
BT1	HETEROTROPHIC ORGANISMS
BT2	AQUATIC ORGANISMS
RT	FEEDING BEHAVIOUR
RT	GRAZING
RT	HERBIVOROUS FISH
RT	OMNIVORES
RT	PLANKTON FEEDERS
RT	SECONDARY PRODUCTION
RT	TROPHIC LEVELS

HERBIVOROUS FISH
UF	phytophagous fishes
BT1	FISH
BT2	AQUATIC ANIMALS
RT	AGROPISCICULTURE
RT	BIOLOGICAL CONTROL
RT	FRESHWATER FISH
RT	HERBIVORES
RT	PLANT CONTROL
RT	POLYCULTURE
RT	STOCKING (ORGANISMS)
RT	TRANSPLANTATION

HERBIVOROUS FISH (cont'd)
RT	TROPICAL FISH

HEREDITY
USE	**GENETICS**

HERMAPHRODITISM
UF	bisexuality
NT1	SELF FERTILIZATION
RT	ANIMAL REPRODUCTIVE ORGANS
RT	PROTANDRY
RT	SEX DETERMINATION
RT	SEXUAL REPRODUCTION

HERPETOLOGY
SN	Added in 1980
BT1	VERTEBRATE ZOOLOGY
BT2	ZOOLOGY
BT3	BIOLOGY
RT	AQUATIC REPTILES

HERRING FISHERIES
USE	**CLUPEOID FISHERIES**

HETEROENZYMES
USE	**ENZYMES**

HETEROSIS
SN	Added in 1980
UF	hybrid vigor
BT1	BIOLOGICAL PROPERTIES
BT2	PROPERTIES
RT	HYBRID CULTURE
RT	HYBRIDIZATION
RT	HYBRIDS

HETEROTROPHIC ORGANISMS
SN	Use of a more specific term is recommended
UF	heterotrophs
BT1	AQUATIC ORGANISMS
NT1	CARNIVORES
NT1	DECOMPOSERS
NT1	DETRITUS FEEDERS
NT1	FILTER FEEDERS
NT1	HERBIVORES
NT1	OMNIVORES
NT1	PLANKTON FEEDERS
NT1	PREDATORS
NT1	SCAVENGERS
RT	FEEDING BEHAVIOUR
RT	FOOD CHAINS
RT	FOOD WEBS
RT	HETEROTROPHY
RT	NUTRITIONAL TYPES
RT	TROPHODYNAMIC CYCLE

HETEROTROPHS
USE	**HETEROTROPHIC ORGANISMS**

HETEROTROPHY
BT1	NUTRITIONAL TYPES
RT	ANIMAL NUTRITION
RT	HETEROTROPHIC ORGANISMS

HEULANDITE
BT1	ZEOLITES
BT2	SILICATE MINERALS
BT3	MINERALS

HEXOSAMINES
BT1	AMINES
BT2	ORGANIC COMPOUNDS
NT1	GLUCOSAMINE

HIATUSES
RT	BOTTOM EROSION

HIBERNATION
SN	Dormancy or resting state during winter period
RT	AESTIVATION
RT	BODY TEMPERATURE
RT	DORMANCY
RT	ENVIRONMENTAL EFFECTS
RT	METABOLISM
RT	THERMOREGULATION

HIERARCHIES (SOCIAL)
USE	**DOMINANCE HIERARCHIES**

HIGH FREQUENCY
SN	Used only as a qualifier
BT1	FREQUENCY

HIGH PRESSURE EFFECTS
BT1	PRESSURE EFFECTS
BT2	ENVIRONMENTAL EFFECTS
RT	DECOMPRESSION CHAMBERS
RT	DESIGN
RT	DIVING PHYSIOLOGY
RT	HYDROSTATIC PRESSURE
RT	HYPERBARIC
RT	IMPLOSIONS
RT	OCEANOGRAPHIC EQUIPMENT
RT	PRESSURE VESSELS

HIGH PRESSURE RIDGES
RT	ATMOSPHERIC DISTURBANCES

HIGH PRESSURE SYSTEMS
RT	ATMOSPHERIC DISTURBANCES
RT	SEA LEVEL PRESSURE

HIGH SEAS
SN	Added in 1980
BT1	OCEAN SPACE
RT	HIGH SEAS FISHERIES
RT	INTERNATIONAL WATERS

HIGH SEAS FISHERIES
SN	Added in 1980
UF	distant water fisheries
BT1	MARINE FISHERIES
BT2	FISHERIES
RT	FACTORY SHIPS
RT	FISHERY RESOURCES
RT	HIGH SEAS
RT	INTERNATIONAL WATERS

HIGH TIDE
USE	**HIGH WATER**

HIGH WATER
UF	high tide
BT1	TIDES
BT2	TIDAL MOTION
RT	COTIDAL LINES
RT	FLOOD CURRENTS
RT	LOW TIDE
RT	TIDAL CYCLES

HIGHEST ASTRONOMICAL TIDES
BT1	ASTRONOMICAL TIDES
BT2	TIDES
BT3	TIDAL MOTION
RT	EXTREME VALUES
RT	LOWEST ASTRONOMICAL TIDES

HIGHLY MIGRATORY SPECIES
USE	**MIGRATORY SPECIES**

HINDCASTING (WAVES)
USE	**WAVE HINDCASTING**

HISTAMINES
SN	Added in 1980
BT1	ORGANIC COMPOUNDS
RT	ALLERGIC REACTIONS

HISTOCHEMISTRY
BT1	BIOCHEMISTRY
BT2	CHEMISTRY
RT	CELL CONSTITUENTS
RT	CELLS
RT	HISTOLOGY
RT	STAINING
RT	TISSUES

HISTOLOGY
UF	tissue morphology
BT1	BIOLOGY
RT	ANATOMY
RT	CARTILAGE
RT	CONNECTIVE TISSUES
RT	CYTOLOGY
RT	FIXATIVES
RT	GRAFTING
RT	HISTOCHEMISTRY
RT	HISTOPATHOLOGY
RT	LIGHT MICROSCOPY
RT	MICROSCOPY
RT	STAINING
RT	TISSUES

HISTONES
SN	Added in 1980
BT1	PROTEINS
BT2	ORGANIC COMPOUNDS
RT	CHROMOSOMES

HISTOPATHOLOGY
SN	Added in 1980
BT1	PATHOLOGY
RT	DISEASES
RT	HISTOLOGY
RT	TISSUES

HISTORICAL ACCOUNT
SN	History/development of aquatic sciences or research institutions. Used only as a qualifier
UF	history
RT	ARCHIVES
RT	EXPEDITION REPORTS
RT	RESEARCH INSTITUTIONS

HISTORY
USE	**HISTORICAL ACCOUNT**

HISTORY OF SEA WATER
USE	**SEAWATER EVOLUTION**

HODOGRAPHS
BT1	GRAPHS
BT2	GRAPHICS
BT3	AUDIOVISUAL MATERIAL
BT4	DOCUMENTS
NT1	CURRENT ELLIPSES
NT1	EKMAN SPIRAL
RT	MAP GRAPHICS
RT	VECTORS

HOISTING
USE	**LIFTING**

HOISTS
USE	**CRANES**

HOLDFASTS
BT1	PLANT ORGANS
BT2	BODY ORGANS
RT	KELPS
RT	SEAWEEDS

HOLE RE-ENTRY
UF	re-entry (deep-sea drilling)
RT	BOREHOLES
RT	DEEP-SEA DRILLING
RT	DYNAMIC POSITIONING
RT	LOCATING

HOLMIUM
BT1	CHEMICAL ELEMENTS
RT	HOLMIUM COMPOUNDS
RT	HOLMIUM ISOTOPES
RT	RARE EARTHS
RT	TRANSITION ELEMENTS

HOLMIUM COMPOUNDS
RT	CHEMICAL COMPOUNDS
RT	HOLMIUM

HOLMIUM ISOTOPES
BT1	ISOTOPES
RT	HOLMIUM

HOLOCENE
SN	Before 1982 search HOLOCENE EPOCH
UF	recent epoch
BT1	QUATERNARY
BT2	CENOZOIC
BT3	GEOLOGICAL TIME

HOLOGRAPHY
NT1	ACOUSTIC HOLOGRAPHY
RT	LASERS
RT	LIGHT DIFFRACTION
RT	PHOTOGRAPHY

HOLOPLANKTON
UF	permanent plankton
BT1	ZOOPLANKTON
BT2	PLANKTON
BT3	AQUATIC COMMUNITIES

HOLOTYPES
SN	Single designated plant or animal specimen that serves as the basis for the original name and description of any taxon. Added in 1980
UF	type specimens
RT	MUSEUM COLLECTIONS
RT	NEW CLASSES
RT	NEW FAMILIES
RT	NEW GENERA
RT	NEW ORDERS
RT	NEW SPECIES
RT	NEW TAXA
RT	TAXONOMY
RT	TYPE LOCALITIES
RT	TYPOLOGY

HOME RANGE
UF	territory
RT	COMPETITIVE BEHAVIOUR
RT	HABITAT
RT	HOMING BEHAVIOUR
RT	LOCAL MOVEMENTS
RT	TERRITORIALITY

HOMEOTHERMY
USE	**HOMOIOTHERMY**

HOMING BEHAVIOUR
BT1	BEHAVIOUR
RT	ANADROMOUS MIGRATIONS
RT	ANIMAL NAVIGATION
RT	CATADROMOUS MIGRATIONS
RT	HOME RANGE
RT	LOCAL MOVEMENTS

HOMOIOTHERMIC ANIMALS	
USE	**HOMOIOTHERMY**

HOMOIOTHERMY
SN	Added in 1980
UF	homeothermy
UF	homoiothermic animals
UF	warm-blooded animals
BT1	BIOLOGICAL PROPERTIES
BT2	PROPERTIES
RT	BODY TEMPERATURE
RT	POIKILOTHERMY
RT	TEMPERATURE TOLERANCE
RT	THERMOREGULATION

HONOUR VOLUMES	
USE	**FESTSCHRIFTEN**

HOOK RATE	
USE	**CATCH/EFFORT**

HOOKS
UF	fish hooks
BT1	LINES
BT2	FISHING GEAR
RT	ANGLING
RT	BAIT
RT	GEAR SELECTIVITY
RT	SPORT FISHING

HORIZON
RT	DIRECTION
RT	GEODESY

HORIZONTAL
SN	Used only as a qualifier
RT	HORIZONTAL ADVECTION
RT	HORIZONTAL DISTRIBUTION
RT	HORIZONTAL MOTION
RT	HORIZONTAL PROFILES

HORIZONTAL ADVECTION
BT1	ADVECTION
BT2	TRANSPORT PROCESSES
RT	HORIZONTAL
RT	HORIZONTAL MOTION

HORIZONTAL COSINE RESPONSE	
USE	**COSINE RESPONSE**

HORIZONTAL DISTRIBUTION
SN	Used only as a qualifier
BT1	GEOGRAPHICAL DISTRIBUTION
BT2	DISTRIBUTION
NT1	BIPOLAR DISTRIBUTION
RT	ANNUAL VARIATIONS
RT	HORIZONTAL
RT	MIGRATIONS
RT	REGIONAL VARIATIONS
RT	SEASONAL VARIATIONS
RT	SPATIAL VARIATIONS

HORIZONTAL MOTION
BT1	FLUID FLOW
BT2	FLUID MOTION
RT	ATMOSPHERIC MOTION
RT	CONVERGENCE
RT	DIVERGENCE
RT	HORIZONTAL
RT	HORIZONTAL ADVECTION
RT	WATER CURRENTS

HORIZONTAL PROFILES
BT1	PROFILES
NT1	BEACH PROFILES
NT1	THALWEG
RT	BATHYMETRIC PROFILES
RT	GRADIENTS
RT	HORIZONTAL
RT	PROFILERS

HORIZONTAL PROFILES (cont'd)
RT	VERTICAL PROFILES

HORMONES
UF	chemical messengers
UF	messengers (chemicals)
BT1	SECRETORY PRODUCTS
NT1	ECDYSONS
NT1	INSULIN
NT1	NEUROTRANSMITTERS
NT1	PHEROMONES
NT1	PHYTOHORMONES
NT1	SEX HORMONES
RT	ADRENAL GLANDS
RT	DRUGS
RT	ECTOCRINES
RT	ENDOCRINE GLANDS
RT	ENDOCRINOLOGY
RT	ENZYMES
RT	GLYCOPROTEINS
RT	GROWTH REGULATORS
RT	INDUCED BREEDING
RT	LACTATION
RT	METABOLISM
RT	NEUROSECRETION
RT	PHYSIOLOGY
RT	PITUITARY GLAND
RT	SECRETION
RT	STEROIDS
RT	TARGET CELLS
RT	THYMUS
RT	THYROID

HORNBLENDE
BT1	AMPHIBOLITES
BT2	METAMORPHIC ROCKS
BT3	ROCKS

HORSE MACKEREL FISHERIES	
USE	**CARANGID FISHERIES**

HOSES
NT1	FLOATING HOSES
RT	PIPES

HOST PREFERENCES
RT	HOSTS
RT	PARASITISM
RT	SPECIFICITY

HOSTS
SN	Added in 1980
UF	intermediate hosts
RT	BIOLOGICAL VECTORS
RT	DISEASES
RT	HOST PREFERENCES
RT	PARASITES
RT	PARASITISM

HOT BRINES
UF	hot salty water
UF	metalliferous brines
BT1	HYDROTHERMAL SOLUTIONS
BT2	SOLUTIONS
RT	BRINES
RT	COPPER
RT	DISSOLVED CHEMICALS
RT	LEAD
RT	METALLIFEROUS SEDIMENTS
RT	SILVER
RT	ZINC

HOT SALTY WATER	
USE	**HOT BRINES**

HOT SPOTS
RT	HEAT FLOW
RT	MAGMA
RT	MANTLE PLUMES
RT	PLATE TECTONICS

HOT SPOTS (cont'd)
RT	SEAMOUNT CHAINS
RT	VOLCANISM

HOT SPRINGS
SN	Before 1982 search THERMAL SPRINGS
UF	geysers
UF	thermal springs (hot)
BT1	WATER SPRINGS
RT	GEOTHERMAL ENERGY
RT	HEAT FLOW
RT	HYDROTHERMAL SPRINGS
RT	SEEPAGES

HOURLY
SN	Descriptor to be used only as a qualifier
BT1	PERIODICITY

HOVERCRAFT
UF	air cushion vehicles
BT1	SURFACE CRAFT
BT2	VEHICLES
RT	AIR TRANSPORTATION
RT	AMPHIBIOUS VEHICLES

HULLS
NT1	BUOY HULLS
NT2	DISCUS-SHAPED BUOYS
NT2	SPAR BUOYS
NT3	LARGE SPAR BUOYS
NT1	SHIP HULLS
RT	FUEL ECONOMY
RT	SHIP DESIGN

HUMAN DISEASES
SN	Added in 1980
UF	disorders
UF	sickness
BT1	DISEASES
NT1	BOTULISM
NT1	CIGUATERA
NT1	DECOMPRESSION SICKNESS
NT1	HYPERCAPNIA
NT1	HYPOTHERMIA
NT1	HYPOXIA
NT1	MALARIA
NT1	SEA SICKNESS
RT	EPIDEMICS
RT	EPIDEMIOLOGY
RT	HUMAN PHYSIOLOGY
RT	PATHOLOGY
RT	PUBLIC HEALTH

HUMAN FOOD
UF	food for human consumption
NT1	SEAFOOD
RT	BOTULISM
RT	CULTURED ORGANISMS
RT	FERMENTED PRODUCTS
RT	FISH CONSUMPTION
RT	FISH FLOUR
RT	FISH INSPECTION
RT	FISH INSPECTION REGULATIONS
RT	FISHERY PRODUCTS
RT	FISHERY RESOURCES
RT	FOOD
RT	FOOD FISH
RT	FOOD POISONING
RT	FOOD RESOURCES
RT	FOOD TECHNOLOGY
RT	NUTRITIVE VALUE
RT	ORGANOLEPTIC PROPERTIES
RT	PALATABILITY
RT	PLANT UTILIZATION
RT	POISONOUS FISH
RT	POWDERED PRODUCTS
RT	PROCESSED FISHERY PRODUCTS
RT	QUALITY CONTROL
RT	ROES

HUMAN FOOD (cont'd)
RT	SEAWEED PRODUCTS
RT	SHARK UTILIZATION
RT	TASTE
RT	TASTE TESTS
RT	VITAMIN A
RT	VITAMIN B
RT	VITAMIN C
RT	VITAMIN D
RT	VITAMIN E
RT	VITAMINS

HUMAN HABITATS
USE	**UNDERWATER HABITATS**

HUMAN HEALTH
USE	**PUBLIC HEALTH**

HUMAN IMPACT
USE	**MAN-INDUCED EFFECTS**

HUMAN PHYSIOLOGY
SN	Added in 1980
BT1	PHYSIOLOGY
BT2	BIOLOGY
RT	DIVING
RT	DIVING PHYSIOLOGY
RT	HUMAN DISEASES
RT	MEDICINE

HUMAN RESOURCES
SN	Added in 1980
UF	manpower resources
BT1	RESOURCES
NT1	WOMEN
RT	DEVELOPMENT POTENTIAL
RT	PERSONNEL
RT	SCIENTIFIC PERSONNEL

HUMIC ACIDS
BT1	ORGANIC ACIDS
BT2	ORGANIC COMPOUNDS
RT	CHEMICAL COMPOUNDS
RT	DYSTROPHIC LAKES
RT	FULVIC ACIDS
RT	HUMUS

HUMIDITY
SN	Use of a more specific term is recommended
NT1	ABSOLUTE HUMIDITY
NT1	RELATIVE HUMIDITY
NT1	SPECIFIC HUMIDITY
RT	CARGOES
RT	CLIMATOLOGY
RT	CORROSION
RT	DEW POINT
RT	HYGROMETERS
RT	HYGROMETRY
RT	METEOROLOGICAL DATA
RT	MIXING RATIO
RT	RADIOSONDES
RT	SATURATION VAPOUR PRESSURE
RT	STORAGE CONDITIONS
RT	VAPOUR PRESSURE
RT	WATER CONTENT
RT	WATER VAPOUR
RT	WEATHER

HUMIDITY MEASUREMENT
USE	**HYGROMETRY**

HUMIDITY SENSORS
USE	**HYGROMETERS**

HUMUS
SN	Added in 1980
BT1	ORGANIC MATTER
RT	DEGRADATION
RT	FULVIC ACIDS

HUMUS (cont'd)
RT	HUMIC ACIDS
RT	LEAVES
RT	ORGANIC MATTER
RT	PEAT
RT	SOILS

HUNTING
RT	AQUATIC MAMMALS
RT	HUNTING STATISTICS
RT	MARINE MAMMALS
RT	WHALING
RT	WOUNDING
RT	WOUNDING GEAR

HUNTING STATISTICS
SN	Tabulation of hunted pinnipeds and allied species, including derived industrial products
BT1	CATCH STATISTICS
BT2	FISHERY STATISTICS
RT	HUNTING

HURRICANE SURGES
USE	**HURRICANE WAVES**

HURRICANE TIDES
USE	**HURRICANE WAVES**

HURRICANE TRACKING
BT1	TRACKING
RT	HURRICANES

HURRICANE WAVES
UF	hurricane surges
UF	hurricane tides
BT1	STORM SURGES
BT2	SURFACE WATER WAVES
BT3	WATER WAVES
RT	HURRICANES
RT	TROPICAL OCEANOGRAPHY

HURRICANES
SN	Mature tropical depressions with wind speeds of 65 knots and over
UF	tropical cyclones
UF	typhoons
BT1	TROPICAL DEPRESSIONS
BT2	ATMOSPHERIC DEPRESSIONS
RT	ATMOSPHERIC FORCING
RT	BOTTOM PRESSURE
RT	CYCLONES
RT	DISASTERS
RT	GALE FORCE WINDS
RT	HURRICANE TRACKING
RT	HURRICANE WAVES
RT	MIXED LAYER DEPTH
RT	OCEANIC RESPONSE
RT	SHIP ROUTEING
RT	STORM SURGES
RT	STORMS
RT	TEMPERATURE (AIR-SEA)
RT	THERMAL STRUCTURE
RT	TROPICAL METEOROLOGY
RT	WATERSPOUTS
RT	WEATHER HAZARDS
RT	WINDS

HUSBANDRY DISEASES
SN	Added in 1980
UF	fish culture diseases
BT1	DISEASES
RT	BUBBLE DISEASE
RT	ENVIRONMENTAL DISEASES
RT	FISH CULTURE
RT	FISH DISEASES
RT	GILL DISEASE
RT	NUTRITION DISORDERS
RT	PEDUNCLE DISEASE
RT	REDMOUTH DISEASE

HUSBANDRY DISEASES (cont'd)
RT	SHELLFISH CULTURE
RT	SUNBURN
RT	WHIRLING DISEASE

HYBRID CULTURE
UF	cross breeding
BT1	AQUACULTURE TECHNIQUES
RT	CULTURES
RT	FISH CULTURE
RT	FRESHWATER AQUACULTURE
RT	HATCHERIES
RT	HETEROSIS
RT	HYBRIDIZATION
RT	HYBRIDS
RT	INTENSIVE CULTURE
RT	SEED (AQUACULTURE)
RT	SELECTIVE BREEDING

HYBRID VIGOR
USE	**HETEROSIS**

HYBRIDIZATION
UF	hybridizing
UF	interbreeding
RT	BREEDING
RT	BROOD STOCKS
RT	GENETICS
RT	GENOTYPES
RT	HETEROSIS
RT	HYBRID CULTURE
RT	HYBRIDS

HYBRIDIZING
USE	**HYBRIDIZATION**

HYBRIDS
SN	Occurring in nature or cultured form
RT	GENETICS
RT	HETEROSIS
RT	HYBRID CULTURE
RT	HYBRIDIZATION
RT	SELECTIVE BREEDING

HYDRATES
RT	HYDRATION
RT	IONS

HYDRATION
BT1	SOLVATION
RT	DEHYDRATION
RT	HYDRATES

HYDRAULIC ENGINEERING
BT1	ENGINEERING
RT	DAMS
RT	ENCLOSURES
RT	FLOOD CONTROL
RT	FLOODS
RT	HABITAT IMPROVEMENT (PHYSICAL)
RT	HYDRAULIC MODELS
RT	HYDRAULIC STRUCTURES
RT	HYDRAULICS
RT	POND CONSTRUCTION
RT	RESERVOIRS (WATER)
RT	WEIRS

HYDRAULIC JUMP
RT	STANDING WAVES
RT	TIDAL BORES

HYDRAULIC MODELS
BT1	SCALE MODELS
BT2	MODELS
NT1	HARBOUR MODELS
RT	CANALS
RT	CHANNELS
RT	COASTAL ENGINEERING
RT	HYDRAULIC ENGINEERING
RT	HYDRAULIC STRUCTURES

HYDRAULIC MODELS (cont'd)
RT	TEST EQUIPMENT
RT	WAVE TANKS

HYDRAULIC POWER TRANSMISSION SYSTEMS
USE	**HYDRAULIC SYSTEMS**

HYDRAULIC STRUCTURES
SN	Use of a more specific term is recommended. Before 1982 search also COASTAL STRUCTURES and MARINE STRUCTURES
UF	maritime structures
NT1	BARRAGES
NT2	DAMS
NT2	ENCLOSURES
NT2	TIDAL BARRAGES
NT2	WEIRS
NT1	COASTAL STRUCTURES
NT2	ARTIFICIAL HARBOURS
NT3	MARINAS
NT3	MILITARY PORTS
NT2	COAST DEFENCES
NT3	BREAKWATERS
NT4	RIPRAP
NT4	RUBBLEMOUND BREAKWATERS
NT3	GROYNES
NT3	SEA WALLS
NT3	STORM SURGE BARRIERS
NT2	PIERS
NT2	PORT INSTALLATIONS
NT1	OFFSHORE STRUCTURES
NT2	ARTICULATED COLUMNS
NT2	ARTIFICIAL ISLANDS
NT3	ICE RAFTS
NT3	SAND STRUCTURES
NT2	ARTIFICIAL REEFS
NT2	CAISSONS
NT2	FIXED PLATFORMS
NT3	GRAVITY PLATFORMS
NT3	GUYED TOWERS
NT3	PILED PLATFORMS
NT3	TENSION LEG PLATFORMS
NT2	FLOATING STRUCTURES
NT3	MOBILE PLATFORMS
NT4	JACKUP PLATFORMS
NT4	SEMISUBMERSIBLE PLATFORMS
NT4	SUBMERSIBLE PLATFORMS
NT4	WORKOVER BARGES
NT3	PONTOONS
NT2	UNDERWATER STRUCTURES
NT3	PIPELINES
NT4	FLOWLINES
NT4	GATHERING LINES
NT3	UNDERWATER HABITATS
NT3	WELLHEADS
NT1	OUTFALLS
RT	COASTAL ENGINEERING
RT	ENCLOSURES
RT	FISHWAYS
RT	FLOOD CONTROL
RT	FOUNDATIONS
RT	HABITAT IMPROVEMENT (PHYSICAL)
RT	HYDRAULIC ENGINEERING
RT	HYDRAULIC MODELS
RT	POND CONSTRUCTION
RT	POWER PLANTS
RT	RESERVOIRS (WATER)
RT	SCREENS
RT	STRUCTURAL ENGINEERING
RT	STRUCTURES

HYDRAULIC SYSTEMS
UF	hydraulic power transmission systems
UF	hydraulically operated devices
RT	DECK EQUIPMENT
RT	HYDROSTATIC PRESSURE
RT	MINING EQUIPMENT

HYDRAULICALLY OPERATED DEVICES
USE	**HYDRAULIC SYSTEMS**

HYDRAULICS
BT1	MECHANICS
BT2	PHYSICS
RT	HYDRAULIC ENGINEERING

HYDROBIOLOGISTS
USE	**BIOLOGISTS**

HYDROBIOLOGY
UF	aquatic biology
BT1	BIOLOGY
RT	ALGOLOGY
RT	AQUATIC ANIMALS
RT	AQUATIC ORGANISMS
RT	AQUATIC PLANTS
RT	CARCINOLOGY
RT	ENTOMOLOGY
RT	FISHERY BIOLOGY
RT	FRESHWATER ECOLOGY
RT	ICHTHYOLOGY
RT	MALACOLOGY
RT	MARINE ECOLOGY
RT	MARINE SCIENCES

HYDROBIOTITE
BT1	MICAS
BT2	SILICATE MINERALS
BT3	MINERALS

HYDROCARBON ANALYSIS
RT	ANALYTICAL TECHNIQUES
RT	CHEMICAL ANALYSIS
RT	HYDROCARBONS
RT	PETROLEUM
RT	SEDIMENT ANALYSIS
RT	WATER ANALYSIS

HYDROCARBON COMPOUNDS
USE	**HYDROCARBONS**

HYDROCARBONS
UF	hydrocarbon compounds
UF	solid hydrocarbons
BT1	ORGANIC COMPOUNDS
NT1	GAS HYDRATES
NT1	HALOGENATED HYDROCARBONS
NT2	BROMINATED HYDROCARBONS
NT2	CHLORINATED HYDROCARBONS
NT3	ALDRIN
NT3	CHLOROFORM
NT3	DDE
NT3	DDT
NT3	DIELDRIN
NT3	TRICHLOROETHYLENE
NT2	FLUORINATED HYDROCARBONS
NT3	FREONS
NT1	PETROLEUM HYDROCARBONS
NT2	ASPHALT
NT2	BITUMENS
NT2	KEROGEN
NT2	TAR
NT2	VOLATILE HYDROCARBONS
NT1	SATURATED HYDROCARBONS
NT2	ACYCLIC HYDROCARBONS
NT3	BUTANE
NT3	DODECANE
NT3	ETHANE
NT3	METHANE
NT3	PROPANE
NT2	ALICYCLIC HYDROCARBONS
NT1	UNSATURATED HYDROCARBONS
NT2	ALKENES
NT3	ETHENE
NT2	ALKYNES
NT3	ETHYNE
NT2	AROMATIC HYDROCARBONS
NT3	BENZENE

HYDROCARBONS (cont'd)
NT3	NAPHTHALENE
NT3	PCB
NT3	XYLENE
NT2	POLYUNSATURATED HYDROCARBONS
NT3	SQUALENE
NT3	TERPENES
RT	CARBON
RT	CARBON COMPOUNDS
RT	CHEMICAL COMPOUNDS
RT	FATTY ACIDS
RT	FISH OIL EXTRACTION
RT	FISH OILS
RT	FOSSIL FUELS
RT	HYDROCARBON ANALYSIS
RT	HYDROGEN
RT	OIL
RT	OIL AND GAS
RT	OIL SANDS
RT	OIL SHALE
RT	SAPROPELS

HYDROCLIMATE
BT1	CLIMATE
RT	BIOCLIMATOLOGY
RT	BIOGEOGRAPHY
RT	CLIMATIC ZONES
RT	CLIMATOLOGY
RT	PHENOLOGY
RT	SEASONS
RT	WATER TEMPERATURE

HYDRODYNAMIC EQUATIONS
RT	DYNAMICAL OCEANOGRAPHY
RT	EQUATIONS
RT	HYDRODYNAMICS
RT	HYDROSTATIC EQUATION

HYDRODYNAMICS
BT1	FLUID MECHANICS
BT2	MECHANICS
BT3	PHYSICS
RT	BOUNDARY LAYERS
RT	COUPLED BODIES
RT	CURRENT FORCES
RT	HYDRODYNAMIC EQUATIONS
RT	HYDROSTATICS
RT	NAVIER-STOKES EQUATIONS
RT	PHYSICAL LIMNOLOGY
RT	PHYSICAL OCEANOGRAPHY
RT	SPHERES
RT	STREAM FLOW
RT	VORTICITY
RT	WAKES
RT	WATER CIRCULATION
RT	WAVE FORCES

HYDROELECTRIC POWER
BT1	ENERGY RESOURCES
BT2	NATURAL RESOURCES
BT3	RESOURCES
RT	HYDROELECTRIC POWER PLANTS
RT	RENEWABLE RESOURCES
RT	TIDAL POWER
RT	WATER RESOURCES
RT	WAVE POWER

HYDROELECTRIC POWER PLANTS
BT1	POWER PLANTS
NT1	TIDAL POWER PLANTS
RT	HYDROELECTRIC POWER
RT	WAVE POWER DEVICES

HYDROFOILS
BT1	SURFACE CRAFT
BT2	VEHICLES
RT	MARINE TRANSPORTATION
RT	SHIP TECHNOLOGY

HYDROGEN

BT1	CHEMICAL ELEMENTS
RT	GASES
RT	HYDROCARBONS
RT	HYDROGEN COMPOUNDS
RT	HYDROGEN IONS
RT	HYDROGEN ISOTOPES
RT	PH

HYDROGEN COMPOUNDS

NT1	DEUTERIUM COMPOUNDS
NT1	HYDROGEN SULPHIDE
NT1	HYDROXIDES
NT1	INORGANIC ACIDS
NT2	BORIC ACID
NT2	BROMIC ACID
NT2	CHLORIC ACID
NT2	NITRIC ACIDS
NT2	PHOSPHORIC ACID
NT2	SILICIC ACID
NT2	SULPHURIC ACID
RT	HYDROGEN
RT	WATER

HYDROGEN ION CONCENTRATION

USE	**PH**

HYDROGEN IONS

BT1	IONS
RT	HYDROGEN

HYDROGEN ISOTOPES

BT1	ISOTOPES
NT1	DEUTERIUM
NT1	TRITIUM
RT	HEAVY WATER
RT	HYDROGEN

HYDROGEN SULPHIDE

BT1	HYDROGEN COMPOUNDS
RT	ANOXIC BASINS
RT	ANOXIC SEDIMENTS
RT	SULPHIDES

HYDROGENOUS SEDIMENTS

USE	**CHEMICAL SEDIMENTS**

HYDROGRAPHIC CHARTS

UF	oceanographic charts
BT1	MAPS
BT2	GRAPHICS
BT3	AUDIOVISUAL MATERIAL
BT4	DOCUMENTS
NT1	BATHYMETRIC CHARTS
NT1	CURRENT CHARTS
NT1	DENSITY CHARTS
NT1	ICE CHARTS
NT1	SALINITY CHARTS
NT1	TEMPERATURE CHARTS
NT1	TIDAL CHARTS
NT2	CORANGE CHARTS
NT2	COTIDAL CHARTS
RT	ATLASES
RT	ENVIRONMENTAL CHARTS
RT	HYDROGRAPHIC SECTIONS
RT	OCEANOGRAPHIC ATLASES

HYDROGRAPHIC DATA

BT1	DATA
NT1	CTD OBSERVATIONS
NT1	CURRENT DATA
NT1	CURRENT OBSERVATIONS
NT2	CURRENT METER DATA
NT1	ICE OBSERVATIONS
NT1	SALINITY DATA
NT1	TEMPERATURE DATA
RT	HYDROGRAPHY
RT	STD OBSERVATIONS
RT	STD PROFILES
RT	SURVEYING EQUIPMENT

HYDROGRAPHIC SECTIONS

SN	Use of a more specific term is recommended
BT1	VERTICAL SECTIONS
BT2	MAP GRAPHICS
BT3	GRAPHICS
BT4	AUDIOVISUAL MATERIAL
NT1	BATHYMETRIC PROFILES
NT1	DENSITY SECTIONS
NT1	OXYGEN SECTIONS
NT1	SALINITY SECTIONS
NT1	TEMPERATURE SECTIONS
NT1	VELOCITY SECTIONS
RT	DISSOLVED OXYGEN
RT	HYDROGRAPHIC CHARTS
RT	HYDROGRAPHY
RT	MERIDIONAL DISTRIBUTION
RT	OCEANOGRAPHIC ATLASES
RT	STANDARD OCEAN SECTIONS
RT	VERTICAL PROFILES
RT	ZONAL DISTRIBUTION

HYDROGRAPHIC SURVEYING

SN	Surveying for data required for the compilation of navigational charts, principally the determination of water depth, nature of the seabed, currents and tides, and the location of fixed objects
UF	charting (navigational hazards)
BT1	SURVEYING
NT1	SURVEYING UNDERWATER
RT	BATHYMETRIC CHARTS
RT	BATHYMETRY
RT	CARTOGRAPHY
RT	NAVIGATION
RT	NAVIGATIONAL CHARTS
RT	RESEARCH VESSELS
RT	SOUNDINGS
RT	SURVEY VESSELS
RT	WATER DEPTH

HYDROGRAPHIC SURVEYS

SN	Hydrographic, archaeological, cartographic, navigational, bathymetric and other seabed surveys. For TSD distribution use HYDROGRAPHY
BT1	SURVEYS
NT1	BATHYMETRIC SURVEYS
RT	ARCHAEOLOGY
RT	BATHYMETRIC CHARTS
RT	BATHYMETRY
RT	CARTOGRAPHY
RT	NAVIGATION
RT	NAVIGATIONAL CHARTS
RT	RESEARCH VESSELS
RT	SITE SURVEYS
RT	SURVEY VESSELS
RT	WATER DEPTH

HYDROGRAPHIC WIRE

BT1	WIRE ROPE
BT2	ROPES
RT	LIMNOLOGICAL EQUIPMENT
RT	MESSENGERS
RT	OCEANOGRAPHIC EQUIPMENT
RT	WATER SAMPLERS
RT	WINCHES
RT	WIRE ANGLE
RT	WIRE ANGLE INDICATORS

HYDROGRAPHY

SN	Use only for general studies of the distribution of the common physico-chemical properties (temperature, salinity, oxygen, etc.) of the oceans and inland waters
UF	descriptive physical oceanography

HYDROGRAPHY (cont'd)

BT1	PHYSICAL OCEANOGRAPHY
BT2	OCEANOGRAPHY
BT3	EARTH SCIENCES
RT	BATHYMETRIC CHARTS
RT	BATHYMETRY
RT	CORE LAYER METHOD
RT	CORE LAYERS (WATER)
RT	DISSOLVED OXYGEN
RT	FISHERY OCEANOGRAPHY
RT	HYDROGRAPHIC DATA
RT	HYDROGRAPHIC SECTIONS
RT	LIMNOLOGY
RT	OCEANOGRAPHIC ATLASES
RT	OCEANOGRAPHIC SURVEYS
RT	PHYSICAL LIMNOLOGY
RT	SALINITY
RT	STRATIFICATION
RT	THERMAL STRATIFICATION
RT	THERMAL STRUCTURE
RT	WATER
RT	WATER CIRCULATION
RT	WATER MASSES
RT	WATER TEMPERATURE
RT	WATER TYPES

HYDROLASES

SN	Before 1982 search ENZYMES
BT1	ENZYMES
RT	HYDROLYSIS

HYDROLOGIC CYCLE

UF	water cycle
BT1	CYCLES
RT	ENERGY BUDGET
RT	EVAPORATION
RT	EVAPOTRANSPIRATION
RT	HYDROLOGY
RT	HYDROSPHERE
RT	ICE
RT	METEOROLOGY
RT	RAINFALL
RT	RIVER DISCHARGE
RT	RIVER OUTFLOW
RT	SEA WATER
RT	TRANSPIRATION
RT	WATER
RT	WATER BUDGET
RT	WATER CIRCULATION
RT	WATER RESOURCES

HYDROLOGY

SN	Use for studies of continental surface water and hydrogeology
BT1	GEOLOGY
BT2	EARTH SCIENCES
RT	BED FORMS
RT	DRAINAGE WATER
RT	DROUGHTS
RT	FLOOD CONTROL
RT	FLOODS
RT	FRESHWATER SCIENCES
RT	GEOCHEMISTRY
RT	GEOMORPHOLOGY
RT	GLACIERS
RT	GROUND WATER
RT	HYDROLOGIC CYCLE
RT	HYDROSPHERE
RT	INLAND WATERS
RT	LAKES
RT	LIMNOLOGICAL SURVEYS
RT	LIMNOLOGY
RT	PONDS
RT	RESERVOIRS (WATER)
RT	RIVERS
RT	RUNOFF
RT	SEDIMENT CHEMISTRY
RT	STORMWATER RUNOFF
RT	WATER
RT	WATER BUDGET

HYDROLOGY (cont'd)
RT	WATER USE
RT	WATERSHEDS

HYDROLYSIS
BT1	CHEMICAL REACTIONS
NT1	ENZYMOLYSIS
RT	CHEMICAL DEGRADATION
RT	DETOXIFICATION
RT	DIGESTION
RT	HYDROLASES

HYDROMAGNESITE
BT1	CARBONATE MINERALS
BT2	MINERALS

HYDROMETEORS
SN	Products of condensation or sublimation of atmospheric water vapour and of water particles blown by the wind from the earth's surface. Use of a more specific term is recommended
NT1	ATMOSPHERIC PRECIPITATIONS
NT2	ACID RAIN
NT2	HAIL
NT2	SNOW
NT1	CLOUDS
NT2	FOG
NT1	DROPLETS
NT1	SPRAY
RT	ATMOSPHERIC CHEMISTRY
RT	CONDENSATION
RT	SALT NUCLEI
RT	SALT PARTICLES
RT	SUBLIMATION
RT	WATER
RT	WATER VAPOUR

HYDROMETERS
BT1	MEASURING DEVICES
RT	DENSITY MEASUREMENT
RT	DENSITY MEASURING EQUIPMENT
RT	DEW POINT

HYDROMETRY
USE	**DENSITY MEASUREMENT**

HYDROPHONES
BT1	ACOUSTIC TRANSDUCERS
BT2	TRANSDUCERS
RT	ACOUSTIC ARRAYS
RT	MICROPHONES
RT	PIEZOELECTRIC TRANSDUCERS
RT	SONOBUOYS
RT	SOUND RECORDERS
RT	STREAMERS
RT	TRANSDUCER ARRAYS

HYDROPHOTOMETERS
USE	**PHOTOMETERS**

HYDROPHYTES
USE	**AQUATIC PLANTS**

HYDROSPHERE
NT1	CRYOSPHERE
RT	AQUATIC SCIENCES
RT	COASTAL WATERS
RT	EARTH
RT	EUSTATIC CHANGES
RT	HYDROLOGIC CYCLE
RT	HYDROLOGY
RT	INLAND WATERS
RT	MARGINAL SEAS
RT	OCEAN-ATMOSPHERE SYSTEM
RT	WATER
RT	WATER BODIES
RT	WATER BUDGET
RT	WATER COLUMN

HYDROSTATIC BEHAVIOUR
SN	Added 1980
UF	hydrostatic reactions
BT1	BEHAVIOUR
RT	BUOYANCY
RT	FLOTATION
RT	SWIM BLADDER

HYDROSTATIC EQUATION
RT	CORIOLIS FORCE
RT	EQUATIONS OF MOTION
RT	HYDRODYNAMIC EQUATIONS
RT	HYDROSTATICS

HYDROSTATIC PRESSURE
SN	Before 1982 search WATER PRESSURE
UF	pressure (water)
UF	water pressure
BT1	PRESSURE
BT2	PHYSICAL PROPERTIES
BT3	PROPERTIES
NT1	BOTTOM PRESSURE
RT	DECOMPRESSION
RT	ELECTRICAL CONDUCTIVITY
RT	HIGH PRESSURE EFFECTS
RT	HYDRAULIC SYSTEMS
RT	HYDROSTATICS
RT	HYPERBARIC
RT	ISOBARIC SURFACES
RT	ISOBARS
RT	PORE PRESSURE
RT	PRESSURE EFFECTS
RT	PRESSURE FIELD
RT	SOUND VELOCITY
RT	WATER
RT	WATER DENSITY

HYDROSTATIC REACTIONS
USE	**HYDROSTATIC BEHAVIOUR**

HYDROSTATICS
BT1	FLUID MECHANICS
BT2	MECHANICS
BT3	PHYSICS
RT	HYDRODYNAMICS
RT	HYDROSTATIC EQUATION
RT	HYDROSTATIC PRESSURE
RT	PRESSURE GRADIENTS

HYDROTHERMAL ACTIVITY
SN	Before 1982 search also HYDROTHERMAL SYSTEMS
UF	hydrothermal processes
UF	hydrothermal systems
NT1	BASALT-SEAWATER INTERACTION
RT	GEOTHERMAL ENERGY
RT	HYDROTHERMAL ALTERATION
RT	HYDROTHERMAL DEPOSITS
RT	HYDROTHERMAL FIELDS
RT	HYDROTHERMAL FLOW
RT	HYDROTHERMAL SOLUTIONS
RT	HYDROTHERMAL SPRINGS
RT	MID-OCEAN RIDGES

HYDROTHERMAL ALTERATION
SN	Changes in the mineralogic composition of rock brought about by the action of hydrothermal solutions
UF	geothermal alteration
UF	hydrothermal metamorphism
BT1	METAMORPHISM
RT	BASALT-SEAWATER INTERACTION
RT	HYDROTHERMAL ACTIVITY
RT	HYDROTHERMAL SOLUTIONS
RT	METASOMATISM
RT	MINERAL COMPOSITION
RT	SERPENTINITIZATION

HYDROTHERMAL AREAS
USE	**HYDROTHERMAL FIELDS**

HYDROTHERMAL CIRCULATION
USE	**HYDROTHERMAL FLOW**

HYDROTHERMAL DEPOSITS
UF	hydrothermal sediments
BT1	CHEMICAL SEDIMENTS
BT2	SEDIMENTS
RT	HYDROTHERMAL ACTIVITY
RT	HYDROTHERMAL FIELDS
RT	HYDROTHERMAL SOLUTIONS
RT	HYDROTHERMAL SPRINGS
RT	METALLIFEROUS SEDIMENTS
RT	SULPHIDE DEPOSITS

HYDROTHERMAL ENERGY
USE	**GEOTHERMAL POWER**

HYDROTHERMAL FIELDS
UF	geothermal fields
UF	hydrothermal areas
RT	FIELDS
RT	HYDROTHERMAL ACTIVITY
RT	HYDROTHERMAL DEPOSITS
RT	HYDROTHERMAL SPRINGS

HYDROTHERMAL FLOW
SN	Before 1982 search HYDROTHERMAL CIRCULATION
UF	hydrothermal circulation
BT1	FLUID FLOW
BT2	FLUID MOTION
RT	HYDROTHERMAL ACTIVITY
RT	HYDROTHERMAL SPRINGS

HYDROTHERMAL FLUIDS
USE	**HYDROTHERMAL SOLUTIONS**

HYDROTHERMAL METAMORPHISM
USE	**HYDROTHERMAL ALTERATION**

HYDROTHERMAL PROCESSES
USE	**HYDROTHERMAL ACTIVITY**

HYDROTHERMAL SEDIMENTS
USE	**HYDROTHERMAL DEPOSITS**

HYDROTHERMAL SOLUTIONS
UF	geothermal fluids
UF	hydrothermal fluids
UF	hydrothermal waters
BT1	SOLUTIONS
NT1	HOT BRINES
RT	HYDROTHERMAL ACTIVITY
RT	HYDROTHERMAL ALTERATION
RT	HYDROTHERMAL DEPOSITS
RT	HYDROTHERMAL SPRINGS
RT	JUVENILE WATER
RT	PORE WATER

HYDROTHERMAL SPRINGS
UF	hydrothermal vents
UF	thermal springs (hydrothermal)
UF	vents (hydrothermal)
BT1	GEOTHERMAL SPRINGS
BT2	WATER SPRINGS
RT	HOT SPRINGS
RT	HYDROTHERMAL ACTIVITY
RT	HYDROTHERMAL DEPOSITS
RT	HYDROTHERMAL FIELDS
RT	HYDROTHERMAL FLOW
RT	HYDROTHERMAL SOLUTIONS
RT	SEEPAGES

HYDROTHERMAL SYSTEMS
USE **HYDROTHERMAL ACTIVITY**

HYDROTHERMAL VENTS
USE **HYDROTHERMAL SPRINGS**

HYDROTHERMAL WATERS
USE **HYDROTHERMAL SOLUTIONS**

HYDROXIDES
BT1 HYDROGEN COMPOUNDS

HYDROXYLAMINES
BT1 AMINES
BT2 ORGANIC COMPOUNDS

HYGIENE
SN Hygienic practices and precautions
for public health
RT BIOLOGICAL VECTORS
RT BOTULISM
RT DISEASES
RT LEGISLATION
RT PUBLIC HEALTH
RT SANITARY ENGINEERING
RT WATER POLLUTION TREATMENT
RT WATER QUALITY

HYGROMETERS
UF humidity sensors
BT1 MEASURING DEVICES
NT1 PSYCHROMETERS
RT HUMIDITY
RT HYGROMETRY
RT RELATIVE HUMIDITY
RT WATER VAPOUR

HYGROMETRY
UF humidity measurement
RT EARTH ATMOSPHERE
RT HUMIDITY
RT HYGROMETERS
RT LIDAR
RT MEASUREMENT
RT PSYCHROMETERS
RT WATER CONTENT
RT WATER VAPOUR

HYPERBARIC
SN Used only as qualifier
RT DECOMPRESSION CHAMBERS
RT DIVING PHYSIOLOGY
RT HIGH PRESSURE EFFECTS
RT HYDROSTATIC PRESSURE

HYPERBARIC CHAMBERS
USE **DECOMPRESSION CHAMBERS**

HYPERCAPNIA
UF carbon dioxide poisoning
BT1 HUMAN DISEASES
BT2 DISEASES
RT ASPHYXIA
RT BLOOD
RT CARBON DIOXIDE
RT MORTALITY CAUSES
RT UNDERWATER MEDICINE

HYPERTHERMIA
RT BODY TEMPERATURE
RT DIVING HAZARDS
RT DIVING PHYSIOLOGY
RT HYPOTHERMIA
RT MANNED VEHICLES
RT UNDERWATER MEDICINE

HYPERTROPHY
RT EUTROPHICATION
RT NUTRIENTS (MINERAL)

HYPOLIMNION
UF deep layers (lakes)
RT DEEP LAYER
RT DEEP WATER
RT EPILIMNION
RT METALIMNION
RT RESERVOIRS (WATER)
RT STAGNANT WATER
RT THERMAL STRATIFICATION
RT THERMOCLINE
RT WATER COLUMN

HYPOPHYSATION
USE **INDUCED BREEDING**

HYPOPHYSECTOMY
SN Added in 1980
BT1 ORGAN REMOVAL
RT PITUITARY GLAND

HYPOPHYSIS
USE **PITUITARY GLAND**

HYPOTHALAMUS
BT1 BRAIN
BT2 CENTRAL NERVOUS SYSTEM
BT3 NERVOUS SYSTEM

HYPOTHERMIA
BT1 HUMAN DISEASES
BT2 DISEASES
RT BODY TEMPERATURE
RT DIVING PHYSIOLOGY
RT HYPERTHERMIA
RT MEDICINE
RT MORTALITY CAUSES
RT SURVIVAL AT SEA
RT UNDERWATER MEDICINE

HYPOXIA
UF oxygen poisoning
BT1 HUMAN DISEASES
BT2 DISEASES
RT ANOXIA
RT OXYGEN CONSUMPTION
RT OXYGEN DEPLETION
RT UNDERWATER MEDICINE

HYPSOGRAPHIC CURVES
USE **HYPSOMETRIC CURVES**

HYPSOMETRIC CURVES
UF hypsographic curves
BT1 GRAPHS
BT2 GRAPHICS
BT3 AUDIOVISUAL MATERIAL
BT4 DOCUMENTS
RT AREA
RT DEPTH
RT HEIGHT
RT MORPHOMETRY

HYPSOMETRY
RT ATMOSPHERIC PRESSURE
RT SEA LEVEL

ICE
SN Use for ice in the environment or
as a preservative
UF sludge (ice)
NT1 FLOATING ICE
NT2 FAST ICE
NT2 ICE ISLANDS
NT2 ICE SHELVES
NT2 ICEBERGS
NT3 TABULAR BERGS

ICE (cont'd)
NT2 PACK ICE
NT1 FRESHWATER ICE
NT1 GLACIERS
NT1 LAKE ICE
NT1 LAND ICE
NT2 ICE CAPS
NT1 SEA ICE
RT ABLATION
RT AIR-ICE INTERFACE
RT COLD STORAGE
RT CRYOPLANKTON
RT CRYOSPHERE
RT FISH STORAGE
RT FREEZING STORAGE
RT HYDROLOGIC CYCLE
RT ICE BREAKUP
RT ICE COVER
RT ICE FISHING
RT ICE JAMS
RT ICE PREVENTION
RT ICE PROPERTIES
RT ICE RIDGES
RT ICE THICKNESS
RT ICE VOLUME
RT ICE-OIL INTERFACE
RT ICE-WATER INTERFACE
RT ICING
RT MELTING POINT
RT NAVIGATION IN ICE
RT POLAR EXPLORATION
RT PRESERVATION (FISHERY PRODUCTS)
RT SNOW
RT WATER

ICE ACCRETION
BT1 ACCRETION
NT1 ICING
RT ABLATION
RT ICE VOLUME

ICE AGES
UF glacial periods
RT EMERGENT SHORELINES
RT EUSTATIC CHANGES
RT GLACIAL ERRATICS
RT GLACIATION
RT ICE VOLUME
RT PALAEOCLIMATE
RT PLEISTOCENE

ICE-AIR INTERFACE
USE **AIR-ICE INTERFACE**

ICE BARRIERS
SN Protection for offshore structures
subject to floating ice
BT1 BARRIERS
RT BREAKWATERS
RT ICE LOADS
RT OFFSHORE STRUCTURES
RT PACK ICE

ICE BREAKERS
BT1 SURFACE CRAFT
BT2 VEHICLES
RT ICE BREAKING
RT ICE BREAKUP
RT NAVIGATION IN ICE

ICE BREAKING
RT ICE BREAKERS
RT ICE BREAKUP
RT NAVIGATION IN ICE
RT SEA ICE

ASFIS Thesaurus

ICE BREAKUP
RT	FLOATING ICE
RT	ICE
RT	ICE BREAKERS
RT	ICE BREAKING
RT	ICE FORMATION
RT	ICE JAMS
RT	ICE MELTING
RT	ICE-FREE PERIODS
RT	MELTING
RT	NAVIGATION IN ICE
RT	RIVERS

ICE CANOPY
UF	submarine ice profiles
UF	underwater ice profiles
RT	ICE-WATER INTERFACE
RT	NAVIGATION UNDER ICE
RT	PACK ICE
RT	POLYNYAS

ICE CAPS
UF	ice mantle
UF	ice sheets
BT1	LAND ICE
BT2	ICE
RT	ABLATION
RT	AIR-ICE INTERFACE
RT	CLIMATIC CHANGES
RT	CRYOSPHERE
RT	EUSTATIC CHANGES
RT	FLOATING ICE
RT	ICE COVER
RT	ICE THICKNESS
RT	ICE VOLUME

ICE CHARTS
BT1	HYDROGRAPHIC CHARTS
BT2	MAPS
BT3	GRAPHICS
BT4	AUDIOVISUAL MATERIAL
RT	ICE CONDITIONS
RT	ICE COVER
RT	ICE EDGE
RT	ICE OBSERVATIONS
RT	ICE ROUTEING

ICE CLEARINGS
USE	**POLYNYAS**

ICE CONDITIONS
RT	ICE CHARTS
RT	ICE COVER
RT	WEATHER

ICE CONTROL
USE	**ICE PREVENTION**

ICE COVER
RT	AERIAL SURVEYS
RT	CLIMATIC CHANGES
RT	ICE
RT	ICE CAPS
RT	ICE CHARTS
RT	ICE CONDITIONS
RT	ICE EDGE
RT	ICE OBSERVATIONS
RT	ICE VOLUME
RT	ICE-FREE PERIODS
RT	PALAEOCLIMATE
RT	WINTERKILL

ICE DRIFT
UF	drift (ice)
UF	ice movement
BT1	DRIFT
RT	CURRENT VELOCITY
RT	GLACIAL DEPOSITS
RT	ICE ISLANDS
RT	ICEBERGS

ICE DRIFT (cont'd)
RT	PACK ICE
RT	RAFTING
RT	WIND STRESS

ICE EDGE
UF	ice limit
RT	CLIMATIC CHANGES
RT	ICE CHARTS
RT	ICE COVER
RT	POLAR OCEANOGRAPHY

ICE FIELDS
RT	FIELDS
RT	PACK ICE
RT	SEA ICE

ICE FISHING
SN	Fishing through holes cut in the ice. Added in 1980
BT1	FISHING OPERATIONS
RT	BAIT FISHING
RT	FISHING
RT	ICE
RT	INLAND FISHERIES
RT	LAKE FISHERIES
RT	POLAR ZONES
RT	RECREATION
RT	SPORT FISHING

ICE FLOES
USE	**PACK ICE**

ICE FOOT
RT	FAST ICE

ICE FORCES
USE	**ICE LOADS**

ICE FORECASTING
BT1	PREDICTION
RT	NAVIGATION IN ICE

ICE FORMATION
RT	FREEZING
RT	ICE BREAKUP
RT	ICE NUCLEI
RT	ICE-WATER INTERFACE
RT	ICING
RT	NAVIGATION IN ICE
RT	SUBLIMATION

ICE-FREE PERIODS
RT	ICE BREAKUP
RT	ICE COVER
RT	NAVIGATION IN ICE

ICE FRONTS
RT	CLIFFS
RT	ICE SHELVES

ICE ISLANDS
BT1	FLOATING ICE
BT2	ICE
RT	ABLATION
RT	ARTIFICIAL ISLANDS
RT	DRIFTING STATIONS
RT	ICE DRIFT
RT	ICE RAFTS
RT	ICE SHELVES
RT	INSTRUMENT PLATFORMS
RT	ISLANDS

ICE JAMS
RT	FLOATING ICE
RT	ICE
RT	ICE BREAKUP
RT	ICE LOADS
RT	ICE PRESSURE
RT	NAVIGATION IN ICE

ICE JAMS (cont'd)
RT	RIVERS

ICE KEELS
RT	NAVIGATION UNDER ICE

ICE LEADS
USE	**LEADS**

ICE LIMIT
USE	**ICE EDGE**

ICE LOADS
UF	ice forces
BT1	LOADS (FORCES)
BT2	FORCES (MECHANICS)
RT	ICE BARRIERS
RT	ICE JAMS
RT	ICE PRESSURE
RT	ICE PREVENTION
RT	SEA WALLS
RT	SHORE PROTECTION

ICE MANTLE
USE	**ICE CAPS**

ICE MELTING
SN	Used for melting of ice/snow on land and in frozen soil. For thawing of frozen fishery products, use THAWING. For preventing and removing rime and glaze from decks, superstructures, equipment, etc. use DE-ICING
BT1	MELTING
BT2	PHASE CHANGES
RT	ABLATION
RT	FREEZING
RT	FREEZING POINT
RT	FUSION HEAT
RT	HEAT TRANSFER
RT	ICE BREAKUP
RT	MELT WATER
RT	MELTING POINT
RT	POLAR OCEANOGRAPHY
RT	SUBLIMATION

ICE MOVEMENT
USE	**ICE DRIFT**

ICE NAVIGATION
USE	**NAVIGATION IN ICE**

ICE NUCLEI
RT	FREEZING
RT	ICE FORMATION
RT	NUCLEI

ICE OBSERVATIONS
UF	ice reporting
BT1	HYDROGRAPHIC DATA
BT2	DATA
RT	AIRBORNE SENSING
RT	ICE CHARTS
RT	ICE COVER
RT	ICEBERG DETECTION
RT	SATELLITE SENSING

ICE-OIL INTERFACE
UF	oil-ice interface
BT1	INTERFACES
RT	ICE
RT	OIL POLLUTION
RT	OIL SPILLS

ICE PRESSURE
RT	ICE JAMS
RT	ICE LOADS

ICE PREVENTION
UF	ice control
RT	AIR BUBBLES
RT	DE-ICING
RT	DEICING EQUIPMENT
RT	HEATING
RT	ICE
RT	ICE LOADS
RT	NAVIGATION IN ICE
RT	NAVIGATION UNDER ICE

ICE PROPERTIES
BT1	PROPERTIES
RT	DIELECTRIC CONSTANT
RT	FRESHWATER ICE
RT	ICE
RT	SEA ICE
RT	THERMAL CONDUCTIVITY

ICE-RAFTED DETRITUS
USE	**GLACIAL ERRATICS**

ICE RAFTING
SN	Transport of sediments by ice
BT1	RAFTING
BT2	SEDIMENT TRANSPORT
RT	GLACIAL ERRATICS
RT	GLACIAL TRANSPORT
RT	PALAEOCURRENTS
RT	SEA ICE

ICE RAFTS
BT1	ARTIFICIAL ISLANDS
BT2	OFFSHORE STRUCTURES
BT3	HYDRAULIC STRUCTURES
RT	FLOATING STRUCTURES
RT	ICE ISLANDS

ICE REPORTING
USE	**ICE OBSERVATIONS**

ICE RIDGES
RT	ICE
RT	ICE THICKNESS

ICE ROUTEING
BT1	SHIP ROUTEING
RT	AERIAL SURVEYS
RT	ICE CHARTS
RT	NAVIGATION IN ICE

ICE SCOURING
USE	**ICEBERG SCOURING**

ICE SHEETS
USE	**ICE CAPS**

ICE SHELVES
BT1	FLOATING ICE
BT2	ICE
RT	ABLATION
RT	CALVING
RT	FAST ICE
RT	ICE FRONTS
RT	ICE ISLANDS
RT	ICE THICKNESS

ICE THICKNESS
BT1	THICKNESS
BT2	DIMENSIONS
RT	DEPTH MEASUREMENT
RT	ICE
RT	ICE CAPS
RT	ICE RIDGES
RT	ICE SHELVES

ICE VOLUME
SN	Estimates of total volume of ice caps, glaciers, sea ice, etc. in the cryosphere
BT1	VOLUME
BT2	DIMENSIONS
RT	ABLATION
RT	CLIMATIC CHANGES
RT	CRYOSPHERE
RT	EUSTATIC CHANGES
RT	FLOATING ICE
RT	GLACIERS
RT	ICE
RT	ICE ACCRETION
RT	ICE AGES
RT	ICE CAPS
RT	ICE COVER
RT	ISOSTASY
RT	LAND ICE
RT	WATER BUDGET

ICE-WATER INTERFACE
BT1	INTERFACES
RT	FRESHWATER ICE
RT	ICE
RT	ICE CANOPY
RT	ICE FORMATION
RT	LAKE ICE
RT	SEA ICE
RT	WAVE-ICE INTERACTION

ICEBERG DETECTION
BT1	DETECTION
RT	ICE OBSERVATIONS
RT	ICEBERGS
RT	RADAR
RT	WARNING SERVICES

ICEBERG SCOUR MARKS
USE	**PLOUGHMARKS**

ICEBERG SCOURING
UF	ice scouring
BT1	SCOURING
BT2	EROSION
RT	BED FORMS
RT	GLACIAL EROSION
RT	PLOUGHMARKS

ICEBERGS
UF	calved ice
BT1	FLOATING ICE
BT2	ICE
NT1	TABULAR BERGS
RT	ABLATION
RT	CALVING
RT	GLACIERS
RT	ICE DRIFT
RT	ICEBERG DETECTION
RT	MARINE ENVIRONMENT
RT	MELT WATER
RT	WATER RESOURCES

ICHTHYOCIDES
UF	piscicides
UF	polychloropinene
BT1	PESTICIDES
RT	HABITAT IMPROVEMENT
RT	HABITAT IMPROVEMENT (BIOLOGICAL)
RT	STOCKING (ORGANISMS)

ICHTHYOLOGISTS
SN	Added in 1980
UF	fish scientists
BT1	ZOOLOGISTS
BT2	BIOLOGISTS
BT3	SCIENTIFIC PERSONNEL
BT4	PERSONNEL
RT	DIRECTORIES
RT	FISHERY BIOLOGISTS

ICHTHYOLOGISTS (cont'd)
RT	ICHTHYOLOGY
RT	TAXONOMISTS
RT	ZOOLOGY

ICHTHYOLOGY
BT1	VERTEBRATE ZOOLOGY
BT2	ZOOLOGY
BT3	BIOLOGY
RT	BIOGEOGRAPHY
RT	FISH
RT	FISH PHYSIOLOGY
RT	FISHERY BIOLOGY
RT	HYDROBIOLOGY
RT	ICHTHYOLOGISTS

ICHTHYOPLANKTON
BT1	ZOOPLANKTON
BT2	PLANKTON
BT3	AQUATIC COMMUNITIES
RT	FISH EGGS
RT	FISH LARVAE
RT	FISHERY SURVEYS
RT	ICHTHYOPLANKTON SURVEYS
RT	MEROPLANKTON
RT	NEKTON COLLECTING DEVICES
RT	PLANKTON COLLECTING DEVICES
RT	PLANKTONOLOGY
RT	SPAWNING GROUNDS
RT	SPAWNING SEASONS

ICHTHYOPLANKTON SURVEYS
BT1	PLANKTON SURVEYS
BT2	BIOLOGICAL SURVEYS
BT3	SURVEYS
RT	ENVIRONMENTAL SURVEYS
RT	FISH EGGS
RT	FISH LARVAE
RT	FISHERY SURVEYS
RT	ICHTHYOPLANKTON
RT	PLANKTONOLOGY
RT	SPAWNING GROUNDS
RT	SPAWNING SEASONS
RT	ZOOPLANKTON

ICING
SN	Formation of ice on ships and offshore structures by freezing of spray on impact
BT1	ICE ACCRETION
BT2	ACCRETION
RT	DE-ICING
RT	DEICING EQUIPMENT
RT	FREEZING
RT	ICE
RT	ICE FORMATION
RT	OFFSHORE STRUCTURES
RT	SHIP STABILITY
RT	SHIPS
RT	SPLASH ZONE
RT	SPRAY
RT	SURFACE CRAFT
RT	WEATHER
RT	WEATHER HAZARDS

IDENTIFICATION
SN	Use only as a qualifier
NT1	POLLUTANT IDENTIFICATION
RT	CHEMICAL ANALYSIS
RT	DETECTION
RT	IDENTIFICATION KEYS
RT	INSPECTION
RT	POLLUTANTS
RT	TERMINOLOGY
RT	TOXICANTS
RT	TRACKING

IDENTIFICATION KEYS
UF	keys
UF	taxonomic keys
RT	CHECK LISTS
RT	IDENTIFICATION
RT	NEW GENERA
RT	SPECIES
RT	TAXONOMY

IGNEOUS DIKES
BT1	IGNEOUS INTRUSIONS
RT	BATHOLITHS
RT	IGNEOUS ROCKS
RT	LACCOLITHS

IGNEOUS INTRUSIONS
UF	intrusions (igneous)
NT1	BATHOLITHS
NT1	IGNEOUS DIKES
NT1	LACCOLITHS
RT	DIAPIRISM
RT	MAGMA CHAMBERS
RT	PLUTONS

IGNEOUS ROCKS
UF	rocks (igneous)
BT1	ROCKS
NT1	GABBROS
NT1	GRANITE
NT1	PLUTONS
NT1	ULTRAMAFIC ROCKS
NT2	OPHIOLITES
NT2	PERIDOTITE
NT1	VOLCANIC ROCKS
NT2	ANDESITE
NT2	BASALTS
NT3	ALKALI BASALTS
NT3	OCEANITE
NT3	THOLEIITE
NT3	THOLEIITIC BASALT
NT2	LAVA
NT3	PILLOW LAVA
NT2	PALAGONITE
NT2	PUMICE
NT2	RHYOLITES
NT2	TEPHRA
NT3	IGNIMBRITES
NT3	VOLCANIC BRECCIA
NT3	VOLCANIC LAPILLI
NT2	VOLCANIC ASH
NT2	VOLCANIC GLASS
RT	BASEMENT ROCK
RT	BATHOLITHS
RT	IGNEOUS DIKES
RT	LACCOLITHS
RT	MAGMA

IGNIMBRITES
BT1	TEPHRA
BT2	VOLCANIC ROCKS
BT3	IGNEOUS ROCKS
BT4	ROCKS
RT	VOLCANIC GLASS

ILLEGAL FISHING
SN	Added in 1980
RT	EXCLUSIVE ECONOMIC ZONE
RT	FISHERY DISPUTES
RT	SURVEILLANCE AND ENFORCEMENT

ILLITE
BT1	CLAY MINERALS
BT2	SILICATE MINERALS
BT3	MINERALS

ILLUMINATION
USE	**LIGHTING SYSTEMS**

ILLUSTRATIONS
SN	Added in 1980
UF	drawing collections
UF	drawings
UF	zoological drawings
BT1	DOCUMENTS
RT	ORGANISM MORPHOLOGY

ILMENITE
BT1	OXIDE MINERALS
BT2	MINERALS
RT	PLACERS
RT	TITANIUM

IMAGE ENHANCEMENT
BT1	IMAGING TECHNIQUES
RT	IMAGERY
RT	MICROWAVE IMAGERY
RT	PATTERN RECOGNITION
RT	RESOLUTION
RT	SIGNAL-TO-NOISE RATIO

IMAGE PROCESSING
RT	IMAGERY
RT	IMAGING TECHNIQUES

IMAGE SENSORS
USE	**REMOTE SENSING EQUIPMENT**

IMAGERY
UF	images
BT1	REMOTE SENSING
NT1	ACOUSTIC IMAGERY
NT2	ACOUSTIC TOMOGRAPHY
NT2	SONAR IMAGERY
NT1	INFRARED IMAGERY
NT1	MICROWAVE IMAGERY
NT2	RADAR IMAGERY
NT1	PHOTOGRAPHY
NT2	AERIAL PHOTOGRAPHY
NT3	SATELLITE PHOTOGRAPHY
NT2	MICROPHOTOGRAPHY
NT2	STEREOPHOTOGRAPHY
NT2	UNDERWATER PHOTOGRAPHY
RT	DATA PROCESSING
RT	IMAGE ENHANCEMENT
RT	IMAGE PROCESSING
RT	IMAGING TECHNIQUES
RT	RESOLUTION

IMAGES
USE	**IMAGERY**

IMAGING
USE	**IMAGING TECHNIQUES**

IMAGING TECHNIQUES
UF	imaging
NT1	IMAGE ENHANCEMENT
RT	ACOUSTIC HOLOGRAPHY
RT	IMAGE PROCESSING
RT	IMAGERY
RT	REMOTE SENSING

IMMERSION EFFECTS
RT	LIGHT MEASUREMENT
RT	LIGHT MEASURING INSTRUMENTS

IMMIGRATIONS
SN	Added in 1980
RT	GEOGRAPHICAL DISTRIBUTION
RT	MIGRATIONS

IMMUNE RESPONSE
USE	**IMMUNITY**

IMMUNITY
SN	The ability of an animal or plant to resist and/or overcome harmful infection or agents. Added in 1980
UF	immune response
UF	innate immunity
UF	natural immunity
BT2	PROPERTIES
BT1	BIOLOGICAL PROPERTIES
RT	ANTIBODIES
RT	DEFENCE MECHANISMS
RT	DISEASE RESISTANCE
RT	IMMUNIZATION
RT	IMMUNOLOGY
RT	THYMUS
RT	VACCINATION
RT	VACCINES

IMMUNIZATION
SN	The process of rendering an animal resistant to infection or harmful agents. Added in 1980
NT1	VACCINATION
RT	BACTERIAL DISEASES
RT	IMMUNITY
RT	IMMUNOLOGY
RT	PROTOZOAN DISEASES
RT	VACCINES
RT	VIRAL DISEASES

IMMUNOLOGY
RT	ALLERGIC REACTIONS
RT	ANTIBODIES
RT	DEFENCE MECHANISMS
RT	DISEASES
RT	IMMUNITY
RT	IMMUNIZATION
RT	IMMUNOPRECIPITATION
RT	INFECTIOUS DISEASES
RT	MEDICINE
RT	SEROLOGICAL STUDIES
RT	THERAPY
RT	TOXICITY
RT	VACCINATION
RT	VACCINES

IMMUNOPRECIPITATION
SN	Added in 1980
RT	ANTIBODIES
RT	ANTIGENS
RT	IMMUNOLOGY
RT	VACCINATION
RT	VACCINES

IMPACT (WAVES)
USE	**WAVE FORCES**

IMPACTS
USE	**COLLISIONS**

IMPALING GEAR
USE	**WOUNDING GEAR**

IMPEDANCE
NT1	ACOUSTIC IMPEDANCE
RT	ELECTRIC IMPEDANCE

IMPEDANCE (ELECTRICAL)
USE	**ELECTRIC IMPEDANCE**

IMPELLERS
UF	ducted impellers
UF	ducted propellers
RT	CURRENT METERS

IMPINGEMENT
SN	Trapping of aquatic organisms by power plant screens
UF	fish impingement
RT	ENTRAINMENT

IMPINGEMENT (cont'd)
RT	OTEC PLANTS
RT	POWER PLANTS

IMPLOSIONS
RT	BUOYANCY FLOATS
RT	EXPLOSIONS
RT	HIGH PRESSURE EFFECTS

IMPORTS
USE	**TRADE**

IMPOUNDING LAKES
USE	**RESERVOIRS (WATER)**

IMPOUNDMENTS
SN	Added in 1982
RT	DAMS
RT	LAKES

IMPRESSED CURRENTS
BT1	ELECTRIC CURRENTS
RT	CATHODIC PROTECTION

IMPRINTING
SN	A learning process in animals, especially birds. Added in 1980
UF	odour imprinting
BT1	LEARNING BEHAVIOUR
BT2	BEHAVIOUR
RT	AQUATIC BIRDS
RT	ARTIFICIAL FEEDING

IMPROVED PRODUCTS
USE	**NEW PRODUCTS**

IN SITU DENSITY
BT1	WATER DENSITY
BT2	DENSITY
BT3	PHYSICAL PROPERTIES
BT4	PROPERTIES
RT	IN SITU MEASUREMENTS
RT	IN SITU TEMPERATURE
RT	KNUDSEN TABLES
RT	POTENTIAL DENSITY
RT	SALINITY
RT	SIGMA-T
RT	THERMOSTERIC ANOMALIES
RT	WATER MASSES
RT	WATER TEMPERATURE

IN SITU INSTRUMENTATION
USE	**IN SITU MEASUREMENTS**

IN SITU MEASUREMENTS
UF	in situ instrumentation
RT	GEOTECHNICAL DATA
RT	IN SITU DENSITY
RT	IN SITU TEMPERATURE
RT	SALINITY MEASUREMENT
RT	VANE SHEAR TESTING

IN SITU TEMPERATURE
BT1	WATER TEMPERATURE
BT2	TEMPERATURE
BT3	THERMODYNAMIC PROPERTIES
BT4	PHYSICAL PROPERTIES
RT	IN SITU DENSITY
RT	IN SITU MEASUREMENTS
RT	REVERSING THERMOMETERS
RT	SIGMA-T

INBREEDING
SN	Breeding within the descendants of a foundation stock of related animals. Added in 1982
BT1	BREEDING
RT	AQUACULTURE
RT	BROOD STOCKS

INCINERATION
UF	incinerators
RT	WASTE DISPOSAL

INCINERATORS
USE	**INCINERATION**

INCLINOMETERS
BT1	SLOPE INDICATORS
BT2	MEASURING DEVICES
RT	DEFLECTION
RT	TILTMETERS

INCUBATION
UF	incubation time
RT	DISEASES
RT	EGGS
RT	HATCHERIES
RT	HATCHING

INCUBATION TIME
USE	**INCUBATION**

INDICATOR ORGANISMS
USE	**INDICATOR SPECIES**

INDICATOR SPECIES
SN	Organisms or species used to indicate current patterns, water masses or environmental changes
UF	bioindicator organisms
UF	bioindicators
UF	indicator organisms
BT1	SPECIES
BT2	TAXA
RT	BIOCHEMICAL OXYGEN DEMAND
RT	INDICATORS
RT	PLANKTON
RT	POLLUTION INDICATORS
RT	SALINITY TOLERANCE
RT	TEMPERATURE TOLERANCE
RT	TEST ORGANISMS
RT	WATER ANALYSIS
RT	WATER MASSES
RT	WATER QUALITY

INDICATORS
RT	INDICATOR SPECIES
RT	POLLUTION INDICATORS
RT	WATER MASSES
RT	WATER PROPERTIES

INDIGENOUS SPECIES
USE	**ENDEMIC SPECIES**

INDIUM
BT1	CHEMICAL ELEMENTS
RT	INDIUM COMPOUNDS
RT	INDIUM ISOTOPES
RT	METALS
RT	TRACE METALS

INDIUM COMPOUNDS
RT	CHEMICAL COMPOUNDS
RT	INDIUM

INDIUM ISOTOPES
BT1	ISOTOPES
RT	INDIUM

INDUCED BREEDING
SN	Spawning or breeding under artificial conditions using physiological techniques and/or biological products
UF	artificial fecundation
UF	artificial spawning
UF	hypophysation
UF	induced ovulation
UF	induced spawning

INDUCED BREEDING (cont'd)
BT1	BREEDING
RT	AQUACULTURE TECHNIQUES
RT	BROOD STOCKS
RT	CONTROLLED CONDITIONS
RT	CRUSTACEAN CULTURE
RT	FISH CULTURE
RT	HORMONES
RT	INTENSIVE CULTURE
RT	REARING
RT	SEXUAL CELLS

INDUCED OVULATION
USE	**INDUCED BREEDING**

INDUCED SPAWNING
USE	**INDUCED BREEDING**

INDUSTRIAL EFFLUENTS
USE	**INDUSTRIAL WASTES**

INDUSTRIAL FISH
USE	**TRASH FISH**

INDUSTRIAL LAND USE
USE	**LAND USE**

INDUSTRIAL PRODUCTION
SN	Added in 1980
UF	production (industrial)
RT	AQUACULTURE
RT	COSTS
RT	INDUSTRIAL PRODUCTS
RT	INDUSTRIAL WASTES
RT	INDUSTRIES
RT	MANAGEMENT
RT	MARKETING
RT	PROCESS PLANTS
RT	PRODUCTION MANAGEMENT
RT	PRODUCTS

INDUSTRIAL PRODUCTS
RT	BYPRODUCTS
RT	DESALINATION PLANTS
RT	INDUSTRIAL PRODUCTION
RT	INDUSTRIES
RT	NEW PRODUCTS
RT	PETROLEUM
RT	PROCESS PLANTS
RT	PROCESSED FISHERY PRODUCTS
RT	PRODUCTION COST
RT	PRODUCTION MANAGEMENT
RT	SALTS

INDUSTRIAL PRODUCTS STATISTICS
SN	Restricted to statistics of processed products derived from fishery industry
UF	commodity statistics
UF	fishery products statistics
BT1	FISHERY STATISTICS
RT	FISHERY INDUSTRY
RT	PROCESSED FISHERY PRODUCTS
RT	TRADE
RT	WORLD

INDUSTRIAL WASTES
SN	Before 1982 for non-organic domestic wastes search also DOMESTIC WASTES
UF	industrial effluents
BT1	WASTES
RT	CHEMICAL POLLUTANTS
RT	CHEMICAL POLLUTION
RT	DOMESTIC WASTES
RT	EUTROPHICATION
RT	FOREST INDUSTRY
RT	HAZARDOUS MATERIALS
RT	INDUSTRIAL PRODUCTION
RT	MARINE POLLUTION

INDUSTRIAL WASTES (cont'd)
RT	OIL WASTES
RT	PHENOLS
RT	SEWAGE
RT	SEWAGE DISPOSAL
RT	WASTE WATER
RT	WATER POLLUTION

INDUSTRIES
SN	Use of a more specific term is recommended
UF	industry
NT1	AQUACULTURE ENTERPRISES
NT1	DIVING INDUSTRY
NT1	FISHERY INDUSTRY
NT2	FISH HANDLING
NT3	DRESSING
NT4	GUTTING
NT3	FILLETTING
NT3	HEADING
NT2	PROCESSING FISHERY PRODUCTS
NT3	ANIMAL OIL EXTRACTION
NT4	FISH OIL EXTRACTION
NT3	CANNING
NT3	CURING
NT3	DRYING
NT4	FREEZE-DRYING
NT3	FISH MEAL PROCESSING
NT3	REFRIGERATION
NT2	SEAWEED PROCESSING
NT1	FOREST INDUSTRY
NT1	MINERAL INDUSTRY
NT1	OIL AND GAS INDUSTRY
RT	INDUSTRIAL PRODUCTION
RT	INDUSTRIAL PRODUCTS
RT	PRODUCTS
RT	RESOURCE DEVELOPMENT

INDUSTRY
USE	**INDUSTRIES**

INERT GASES
USE	**RARE GASES**

INERTIA
UF	inertial forces
RT	FORCES
RT	FROUDE NUMBER
RT	INERTIAL OSCILLATIONS
RT	INERTIAL WAVES
RT	MOTION
RT	ROSSBY NUMBER

INERTIAL CURRENTS
BT1	WATER CURRENTS
BT2	WATER MOTION

INERTIAL FORCES
USE	**INERTIA**

INERTIAL GUIDANCE
RT	INERTIAL NAVIGATION
RT	STABILIZED PLATFORMS

INERTIAL NAVIGATION
BT1	POSITION FIXING
RT	CELESTIAL NAVIGATION
RT	DEAD RECKONING
RT	INERTIAL GUIDANCE
RT	NAVIGATION UNDER ICE
RT	NAVIGATION UNDERWATER

INERTIAL OSCILLATIONS
RT	INERTIA
RT	INERTIAL WAVES

INERTIAL WAVES
UF	gyroscopic waves
BT1	WATER WAVES
RT	INERTIA
RT	INERTIAL OSCILLATIONS

INFECTIONS
USE	**INFECTIOUS DISEASES**

INFECTIOUS DISEASES
SN	Added in 1980
UF	biotic diseases
UF	communicable diseases
UF	contagious diseases
UF	infections
BT1	DISEASES
NT1	BACTERIAL DISEASES
NT2	TUBERCULOSIS
NT2	VIBRIOSIS
NT1	FUNGAL DISEASES
NT1	PARASITIC DISEASES
NT1	PROTOZOAN DISEASES
NT1	SEPTICAEMIA
NT1	VIRAL DISEASES
RT	ANIMAL DISEASES
RT	DISEASE TRANSMISSION
RT	EPIDEMIOLOGY
RT	FISH DISEASES
RT	FISH KILL
RT	IMMUNOLOGY
RT	MALARIA
RT	MICROBIOLOGY
RT	PARASITOLOGY
RT	TUBERCULOSIS
RT	VACCINATION

INFESTATION
RT	AQUATIC INSECTS
RT	PEST CONTROL
RT	PESTICIDES

INFINITESIMAL WAVES
USE	**LINEAR WAVES**

INFLATABLE CRAFT
BT1	SURFACE CRAFT
BT2	VEHICLES
RT	LIFEBOATS

INFLOW
SN	Component of water budget of a body of water
NT1	RIVER DISCHARGE
RT	OUTFLOW
RT	WATER BUDGET
RT	WATER EXCHANGE

INFLUENTS
RT	WASTES

INFORMATION ANALYSIS SERVICES
USE	**INFORMATION SERVICES**

INFORMATION CENTRES
BT1	ORGANIZATIONS
NT1	DATA CENTRES
NT1	LIBRARIES
NT1	MUSEUMS
NT1	WARNING SERVICES
NT2	STORM TIDE WARNING SERVICES
RT	INFORMATION HANDLING
RT	INFORMATION RETRIEVAL
RT	INFORMATION SCIENTISTS
RT	INFORMATION SERVICES
RT	SORTING CENTRES

INFORMATION HANDLING
SN	Control of literature and information
BT1	DOCUMENTATION
RT	BIBLIOGRAPHIC INFORMATION
RT	DATA COLLECTIONS
RT	DOCUMENTS
RT	INFORMATION CENTRES
RT	LIBRARIES
RT	THESAURUS
RT	TRANSLATIONS

INFORMATION RETRIEVAL
SN	Location of required information previously classified and stored
BT1	DOCUMENTATION
RT	BIBLIOGRAPHIC INFORMATION
RT	BIBLIOGRAPHIES
RT	CATALOGUES
RT	DATA COLLECTIONS
RT	DATA RETRIEVAL
RT	DOCUMENTS
RT	INFORMATION CENTRES
RT	LIBRARIES
RT	THESAURUS

INFORMATION SCIENCES
USE	**DOCUMENTATION**

INFORMATION SCIENTISTS
SN	Added in 1980
UF	information specialists
BT1	SCIENTIFIC PERSONNEL
BT2	PERSONNEL
RT	DIRECTORIES
RT	INFORMATION CENTRES
RT	INFORMATION SERVICES
RT	LIBRARIANS

INFORMATION SERVICES
SN	Added in 1980
UF	documentation services
UF	information analysis services
RT	COMPUTERS
RT	DOCUMENTATION
RT	INFORMATION CENTRES
RT	INFORMATION SCIENTISTS

INFORMATION SPECIALISTS
USE	**INFORMATION SCIENTISTS**

INFRARED DETECTORS
BT1	RADIOMETERS
BT2	REMOTE SENSING EQUIPMENT
BT3	EQUIPMENT
RT	AERIAL SURVEYS
RT	AIRBORNE EQUIPMENT
RT	INFRARED IMAGERY
RT	INFRARED RADIATION
RT	LASERS
RT	REMOTE SENSING
RT	SURFACE TEMPERATURE
RT	TEMPERATURE MEASUREMENT

INFRARED IMAGERY
UF	infrared sensing
UF	ir imagery
UF	thermal imagery
UF	thermal infrared imagery
UF	thermal ir imagery
BT1	IMAGERY
BT2	REMOTE SENSING
RT	AIRBORNE SENSING
RT	GEOSENSING
RT	INFRARED DETECTORS
RT	INFRARED RADIATION
RT	SATELLITE MOSAICS
RT	SATELLITE SENSING
RT	SURFACE RADIATION TEMPERATURE

INFRARED RADIATION
BT1	ELECTROMAGNETIC RADIATION
BT2	RADIATIONS
RT	INFRARED DETECTORS
RT	INFRARED IMAGERY
RT	SOLAR RADIATION
RT	TERRESTRIAL RADIATION

INFRARED SENSING
USE	**INFRARED IMAGERY**

INFRARED SPECTROSCOPY
BT1	SPECTROSCOPIC TECHNIQUES
BT2	ANALYTICAL TECHNIQUES

INGESTION
BT1	ANIMAL NUTRITION
BT2	NUTRITION
RT	MOUTH PARTS

INHIBITORS
SN	Chemicals used to slow down reactions
NT1	ENZYME INHIBITORS
NT2	CHOLINESTERASE INHIBITORS
RT	AGENTS
RT	ANAESTHETICS
RT	CATALYSTS
RT	DRUGS
RT	GROWTH REGULATORS
RT	NARCOTICS

INITIAL-VALUE PROBLEMS
USE	**BOUNDARY VALUE PROBLEMS**

INJECTION TEMPERATURE
USE	**INTAKE TEMPERATURE**

INJURIES
SN	Used for injuries to man or animals. Added in 1980. Before 1986 search also WOUNDS
UF	fishing injuries
UF	wounds
RT	ACCIDENTS
RT	DANGEROUS ORGANISMS
RT	DISINFECTION
RT	HAZARDS
RT	LESIONS
RT	MEDICINE
RT	NECROSES
RT	PARASITES

INJURIOUS ORGANISMS
USE	**NOXIOUS ORGANISMS**

INLAND FISHERIES
BT1	FISHERIES
NT1	LAGOON FISHERIES
NT1	LAKE FISHERIES
NT1	RESERVOIR FISHERIES
NT1	RIVER FISHERIES
NT1	SWAMP FISHERIES
RT	BARRIERS
RT	BEACH SEINES
RT	BOATS
RT	FINFISH FISHERIES
RT	FISHING BARRIERS
RT	FRESHWATER FISH
RT	ICE FISHING
RT	INLAND LAGOONS
RT	LANDLOCKED STATES
RT	LIFT-NETS
RT	LINES
RT	MOLLUSC FISHERIES
RT	TRAP NETS

INLAND LAGOONS
UF	freshwater lagoons
BT1	LAGOONS
RT	AQUACULTURE
RT	INLAND FISHERIES
RT	INLAND WATERS
RT	LENITIC ENVIRONMENT

INLAND SEAS
SN	Use for Great Lakes, Caspian, Aral Sea and other large inland bodies of water
BT1	INLAND WATERS
RT	COASTAL WATERS
RT	LAKE SHORES
RT	LAKES
RT	WATER BODIES

INLAND WATER AQUACULTURE
USE	**FRESHWATER AQUACULTURE**

INLAND WATER ENVIRONMENT
UF	freshwater environment
BT1	AQUATIC ENVIRONMENT
BT2	ENVIRONMENTS
NT1	LENITIC ENVIRONMENT
NT1	LOTIC ENVIRONMENT
RT	ACID RAIN
RT	APHOTIC ZONE
RT	BRACKISHWATER ENVIRONMENT
RT	DISPHOTIC ZONE
RT	EUTROPHIC WATERS
RT	FRESHWATER ECOLOGY
RT	FRESHWATER FISH
RT	LIMNOLOGY
RT	PROPERTY RIGHTS
RT	RUNOFF
RT	SPRING STREAMS
RT	WATER RESOURCES
RT	WATER SPRINGS

INLAND WATERS
SN	Use of a more specific term is recommended
UF	inland waterways
NT1	CANALS
NT2	INTEROCEAN CANALS
NT2	SHIP CANALS
NT1	INLAND SEAS
NT1	LAKES
NT2	ARTIFICIAL LAKES
NT2	DYSTROPHIC LAKES
NT2	EUTROPHIC LAKES
NT2	FRESHWATER LAKES
NT2	GLACIAL LAKES
NT2	MEROMICTIC LAKES
NT2	OLIGOTROPHIC LAKES
NT2	OXBOW LAKES
NT2	RELICT LAKES
NT2	SALT LAKES
NT2	STRIP MINE LAKES
NT2	TROPICAL LAKES
NT1	PONDS
NT2	COOLING PONDS
NT2	FISH PONDS
NT3	BREEDING PONDS
NT3	GROWING PONDS
NT3	NURSERY PONDS
NT3	STOCKING PONDS
NT2	SEWAGE PONDS
NT2	TEMPORARY PONDS
NT1	RESERVOIRS (WATER)
NT1	RIVERS
NT2	DISTRIBUTARIES
NT2	TRIBUTARIES
RT	HYDROLOGY
RT	HYDROSPHERE
RT	INLAND LAGOONS
RT	LANDLOCKED STATES
RT	WATER BODIES

INLAND WATERS (cont'd)
RT	WATER BUDGET

INLAND WATERWAYS
USE	**INLAND WATERS**

INLETS (WATERWAYS)
BT1	COASTAL INLETS
BT2	COASTAL WATERS
RT	BAYS
RT	CANALS
RT	CHANNELS
RT	COASTAL ZONE
RT	ESTUARIES
RT	FJORDS
RT	TIDES
RT	TOPOGRAPHIC FEATURES

INNATE IMMUNITY
USE	**IMMUNITY**

INNOVATION PROCESSES
USE	**TECHNOLOGY TRANSFER**

INORGANIC ACIDS
UF	acids (inorganic)
BT1	HYDROGEN COMPOUNDS
NT1	BORIC ACID
NT1	BROMIC ACID
NT1	CHLORIC ACID
NT1	NITRIC ACIDS
NT1	PHOSPHORIC ACID
NT1	SILICIC ACID
NT1	SULPHURIC ACID
RT	ACIDITY
RT	CHEMICAL COMPOUNDS
RT	INORGANIC COMPOUNDS
RT	ORGANIC ACIDS
RT	PH

INORGANIC COMPOUNDS
RT	CHEMICAL COMPOUNDS
RT	INORGANIC ACIDS
RT	INORGANIC MATTER

INORGANIC MATTER
NT1	DISSOLVED INORGANIC MATTER
NT1	SUSPENDED INORGANIC MATTER
NT2	COLLOIDAL CLAY
RT	INORGANIC COMPOUNDS

INORGANIC SUSPENDED MATTER
USE	**SUSPENDED INORGANIC MATTER**

INSECT EGGS
SN	Added in 1980
BT1	EGGS
BT2	SEXUAL CELLS
BT3	CELLS
RT	AQUATIC INSECTS
RT	ENTOMOLOGY
RT	HATCHING
RT	INSECT LARVAE
RT	NYMPHS

INSECT LARVAE
SN	Added in 1980
BT1	INVERTEBRATE LARVAE
BT2	LARVAE
BT3	DEVELOPMENTAL STAGES
NT1	INSTARS
NT1	NYMPHS
NT1	PUPAE
RT	AQUATIC INSECTS
RT	INSECT EGGS
RT	MALARIA
RT	METAMORPHOSIS

ASFIS Thesaurus

INSECTICIDES
- BT1 PESTICIDES
- RT ALDRIN
- RT CHEMICAL CONTROL
- RT CHEMICAL POLLUTANTS
- RT CHEMICAL POLLUTION
- RT DDT
- RT DIELDRIN
- RT PCB
- RT REPELLENTS
- RT TOXICANTS

INSECTS (AQUATIC)
- USE **AQUATIC INSECTS**

INSHORE CURRENTS
- USE **NEARSHORE CURRENTS**

INSHORE STATIONS
- UF shore stations
- BT1 FIXED STATIONS
- BT2 OCEANOGRAPHIC STATIONS
- RT DATA REPORTS
- RT LIGHTSHIPS
- RT OCEANOGRAPHIC DATA

INSOLATION
- RT CLOUD COVER
- RT SOLAR RADIATION

INSONIFICATION
- SN Irradiation by acoustic waves
- UF irradiation (acoustic waves)
- RT ACTIVE SONAR
- RT SONAR IMAGERY
- RT SONOGRAPHS
- RT SOUND

INSPECTION
- SN Added in 1980
- UF examinations
- UF inspectors
- NT1 FISH INSPECTION
- NT1 UNDERWATER INSPECTION
- NT1 VISUAL INSPECTION
- NT1 X-RAY INSPECTION
- RT ACCEPTABILITY
- RT ACCEPTANCE TESTS
- RT ACCESS
- RT DETECTION
- RT FISH INSPECTION REGULATIONS
- RT IDENTIFICATION
- RT MAINTENANCE
- RT MATERIALS TESTING
- RT MONITORING
- RT QUALITY CONTROL
- RT SPECIFICATIONS
- RT TESTS

INSPECTION (FISH)
- USE **FISH INSPECTION**

INSPECTORS
- USE **INSPECTION**

INSTABILITY
- UF dynamic instability
- NT1 BAROCLINIC INSTABILITY
- NT1 BAROTROPIC INSTABILITY
- NT1 BENJAMIN FEIR INSTABILITY
- NT1 DOUBLE DIFFUSIVE INSTABILITY
- NT1 KELVIN-HELMHOLTZ INSTABILITY
- NT1 STATIC INSTABILITY
- RT CAPSIZING
- RT RICHARDSON NUMBER
- RT STABILITY
- RT UNSTEADY STATE
- RT VERTICAL STABILITY

INSTALLATION
- SN Before 1984 search also INSTALLING
- UF installing
- BT1 CONSTRUCTION
- RT LAUNCHING
- RT LIFTING
- RT MODULES

INSTALLING
- USE **INSTALLATION**

INSTARS
- SN Added in 1980
- BT1 INSECT LARVAE
- BT2 INVERTEBRATE LARVAE
- BT3 LARVAE
- BT4 DEVELOPMENTAL STAGES
- RT MOULTING

INSTINCT
- SN Added in 1980
- RT BEHAVIOUR
- RT BIOLOGICAL PROPERTIES
- RT ZOOLOGY

INSTITUTIONAL RESOURCES
- SN Added in 1980
- BT1 RESOURCES
- RT FINANCIAL INSTITUTIONS
- RT ORGANIZATIONS
- RT RESEARCH INSTITUTIONS

INSTITUTIONS (FINANCIAL)
- USE **FINANCIAL INSTITUTIONS**

INSTITUTIONS (RESEARCH)
- USE **RESEARCH INSTITUTIONS**

INSTRUMENT CARRIERS
- USE **INSTRUMENT PLATFORMS**

INSTRUMENT DEPTH MEASUREMENT
- BT1 DEPTH MEASUREMENT
- BT2 MEASUREMENT
- RT NET SOUNDERS

INSTRUMENT HANDBOOKS
- SN Use with instrument or equipment specified
- BT1 MANUALS
- BT2 DOCUMENTS

INSTRUMENT PLATFORMS
- UF instrument carriers
- UF observation platforms
- UF platforms (instrument)
- BT1 VEHICLES
- NT1 STABILIZED PLATFORMS
- NT2 TOWERS
- NT1 WAVE FOLLOWERS
- RT AIRCRAFT
- RT BALLOONS
- RT BRIDGES
- RT BUOY SYSTEMS
- RT DATA BUOYS
- RT HELICOPTERS
- RT ICE ISLANDS
- RT LARGE SPAR BUOYS
- RT MASTS
- RT RADIOSONDES
- RT RESEARCH VESSELS
- RT SCIENTIFIC SATELLITES
- RT SELECTED SHIPS
- RT SURFACE CRAFT
- RT SURVEY VESSELS
- RT UNDERWATER VEHICLES
- RT WEATHER SHIPS

INSTRUMENT RESOLUTION
- USE **RESOLUTION**

INSTRUMENT RESPONSES
- NT1 COSINE RESPONSE
- NT1 DYNAMIC RESPONSE
- NT2 HEAVE RESPONSE
- NT2 PITCH RESPONSE
- NT2 ROLL RESPONSE
- NT2 SURGE RESPONSE
- NT2 YAW RESPONSE
- RT MEASURING DEVICES

INSTRUMENTS
- NT1 ACCELEROMETERS
- NT1 FREE-FALL INSTRUMENTS
- NT1 GYROSCOPES
- NT1 STRAIN GAUGES
- RT ACCURACY
- RT EFFICIENCY
- RT ENGINEERING DRAWINGS
- RT RESOLUTION

INSTRUMENTS (ACOUSTIC)
- USE **ACOUSTIC EQUIPMENT**

INSULAR SLOPE
- USE **ISLAND SLOPE**

INSULATING MATERIALS
- UF insulation
- UF lagging
- BT1 MATERIALS
- NT1 ACOUSTIC INSULATION
- NT1 ELECTRICAL INSULATION
- NT1 THERMAL INSULATION
- RT DAMPING

INSULATION
- USE **INSULATING MATERIALS**

INSULIN
- SN Before 1982 search HORMONES
- BT1 HORMONES
- BT2 SECRETORY PRODUCTS
- RT PANCREAS
- RT PROTEINS

INSURANCE
- UF marine insurance
- RT FINANCING
- RT INVESTMENTS
- RT LIABILITY
- RT RISKS

INTAKE TEMPERATURE
- UF injection temperature
- BT1 SURFACE TEMPERATURE
- BT2 WATER TEMPERATURE
- BT3 TEMPERATURE
- BT4 THERMODYNAMIC PROPERTIES
- RT TEMPERATURE MEASUREMENT

INTEGRAL EQUATIONS
- BT1 EQUATIONS
- RT DIFFERENTIAL EQUATIONS
- RT FUNCTIONAL ANALYSIS
- RT NONLINEAR EQUATIONS
- RT NUMERICAL ANALYSIS

INTEGRATED AGRICULTURE
- USE **AGROPISCICULTURE**

INTEGUMENTARY SYSTEM
- SN Added in 1980
- BT1 ANATOMICAL STRUCTURES
- NT1 FEATHERS
- RT ANIMAL MORPHOLOGY
- RT EPITHELIA
- RT SCALES

INTENSIVE AQUACULTURE
USE **INTENSIVE CULTURE**

INTENSIVE CULTURE
SN   Added in 1980
UF   intensive aquaculture
BT1   AQUACULTURE SYSTEMS
RT   AIR-BREATHING FISH
RT   AQUACULTURE EFFLUENTS
RT   ARTIFICIAL FEEDING
RT   BROOD STOCKS
RT   CAGE CULTURE
RT   CULTURES
RT   FISH CULTURE
RT   HATCHERIES
RT   HYBRID CULTURE
RT   INDUCED BREEDING
RT   MONOSEX CULTURE
RT   POLYCULTURE
RT   RACEWAY CULTURE
RT   SELECTIVE BREEDING
RT   SHELLFISH CULTURE
RT   SILO CULTURE

INTENTIONAL INUNDATION
USE **FLOODING**

INTER-ARC BASINS
USE **MARGINAL BASINS**

INTERACTIONS
SN   Used only as a qualifier
RT   AIR-SEA INTERACTION
RT   TIDE-SURGE INTERACTION
RT   WAVE-CURRENT INTERACTION
RT   WAVE-ICE INTERACTION
RT   WAVE-SEABED INTERACTION
RT   WAVE-WAVE INTERACTION

INTERBREEDING
USE **HYBRIDIZATION**

INTERCALIBRATION
BT1   CALIBRATION
BT2   STANDARDIZATION
RT   INTERCOMPARISON
RT   PERFORMANCE ASSESSMENT

INTERCOMPARISON
RT   CALIBRATION
RT   INTERCALIBRATION
RT   PERFORMANCE ASSESSMENT
RT   STANDARDIZATION
RT   TESTING

INTERDEPENDENT SPECIES
USE **ASSOCIATED SPECIES**

INTERFACE PHENOMENA
SN   Interface strata and their phenomena
NT1   FRONTOGENESIS
RT   DEAD WATER
RT   ENERGY BUDGET
RT   INTERFACIAL WAVES
RT   SALT FINGERS
RT   SURFACE PROPERTIES
RT   SURFACE TENSION

INTERFACES
NT1   AIR-ICE INTERFACE
NT1   AIR-WATER INTERFACE
NT1   DENSITY INTERFACES
NT1   ICE-OIL INTERFACE
NT1   ICE-WATER INTERFACE
NT1   OIL-GAS INTERFACE
NT1   OIL-WATER INTERFACE
NT1   SEDIMENT-WATER INTERFACE
RT   BOUNDARIES
RT   BOUNDARY LAYERS
RT   DISCONTINUITY LAYERS

INTERFACES (cont'd)
RT   FRONTS
RT   MIXING PROCESSES
RT   SURFACES

INTERFACIAL TENSION
USE **SURFACE TENSION**

INTERFACIAL WAVES
RT   INTERFACE PHENOMENA
RT   INTERNAL WAVES
RT   LEE WAVES
RT   SURFACE WATER WAVES

INTERFEROMETRY
BT1   ANALYTICAL TECHNIQUES

INTERGLACIAL PERIODS
RT   DEGLACIATION
RT   EUSTATIC CHANGES
RT   PALAEOCLIMATE
RT   PLEISTOCENE
RT   SUBMERGED SHORELINES
RT   SUBMERGENCE

INTERMEDIATE FISHING
SN   Fishing carried out in a fish pond
        during growing season to decrease
        the density of a stock or to obtain
        marketable fish. Added in 1980
BT1   FISHING OPERATIONS
RT   FISH CULTURE
RT   FISH PONDS
RT   FISHING
RT   POND CULTURE

INTERMEDIATE HOSTS
USE **HOSTS**

INTERMEDIATE WATER MASSES
BT1   WATER MASSES
RT   METALIMNION
RT   THERMAL STRATIFICATION

INTERNAL FERTILIZATION
USE **BIOLOGICAL FERTILIZATION**

INTERNAL GRAVITY WAVES
USE **INTERNAL WAVES**

INTERNAL TIDES
UF   baroclinic tides
BT1   INTERNAL WAVES
BT2   WATER WAVES
RT   BAROCLINIC MODE
RT   BAROCLINIC MOTION

INTERNAL WAVE BREAKING
RT   INTERNAL WAVES
RT   TRANS-ISOPYCNAL MIXING
RT   WAVE BREAKING

INTERNAL WAVE EFFECTS
RT   DEAD WATER
RT   SOUND PROPAGATION

INTERNAL WAVE GENERATION
BT1   WAVE GENERATION
RT   INTERNAL WAVES
RT   LEE WAVES
RT   SURFACE WAVE-INTERNAL WAVE
        INTERACTIONS

INTERNAL WAVES
UF   internal gravity waves
BT1   WATER WAVES
NT1   INTERNAL TIDES
NT1   LEE WAVES
RT   BILLOWS
RT   DIRECTIONAL SPECTRA

INTERNAL WAVES (cont'd)
RT   INTERFACIAL WAVES
RT   INTERNAL WAVE BREAKING
RT   INTERNAL WAVE GENERATION
RT   MICROSTRUCTURE
RT   NONLINEAR WAVES
RT   RESONANT WAVE INTERACTION
RT   SOUND PROPAGATION
RT   SURFACE WAVE-INTERNAL WAVE
        INTERACTIONS

INTERNATIONAL AGENCIES
USE **INTERNATIONAL ORGANIZATIONS**

INTERNATIONAL AGREEMENTS
UF   agreements
UF   conventions
UF   treaties
BT1   LEGISLATION
NT1   POLLUTION CONVENTION
NT1   SEABED CONVENTIONS
RT   BILATERAL AGREEMENTS
RT   CONTIGUOUS ZONES
RT   COUNTRIES
RT   DEVELOPING COUNTRIES
RT   FISHERY REGULATIONS
RT   FISHING RIGHTS
RT   FOREIGN FISHING
RT   INTERNATIONAL LAW
RT   INTERNATIONAL ORGANIZATIONS
RT   INTERNATIONAL POLICY
RT   INTERNATIONAL WATERS
RT   LEGAL ASPECTS
RT   MARINE RESOURCES
RT   OCEAN DUMPING
RT   OCEAN POLICY
RT   OCEAN SPACE
RT   POLITICAL ASPECTS
RT   SHARED STOCKS
RT   TERRITORIAL WATERS
RT   WHALING REGULATIONS

INTERNATIONAL ALLOCATION
USE **ALLOCATION SYSTEMS**

INTERNATIONAL BOUNDARIES
UF   frontiers (national)
UF   national boundaries
BT1   BOUNDARIES
RT   LAW OF THE SEA
RT   MEDIAN LINES
RT   TERRITORIAL WATERS

INTERNATIONAL CASE LAW
USE **INTERNATIONAL LAW**

INTERNATIONAL COOPERATION
SN   Including exchange of information
        and technical aid
UF   international exchange
UF   international relation
RT   AQUACULTURE DEVELOPMENT
RT   COUNTRIES
RT   DEVELOPING COUNTRIES
RT   DEVELOPMENT PROJECTS
RT   FISHERY DEVELOPMENT
RT   INTERNATIONAL ORGANIZATIONS
RT   INTERNATIONAL POLICY
RT   REPORT LITERATURE
RT   SORTING CENTRES
RT   TECHNOLOGY TRANSFER
RT   TRAINING
RT   TRAINING CENTRES

INTERNATIONAL EXCHANGE
USE **INTERNATIONAL COOPERATION**

ASFIS Thesaurus

INTERNATIONAL EXPEDITIONS
USE **MULTISHIP EXPEDITIONS**

INTERNATIONAL JOINT VENTURES
USE **JOINT VENTURES**

INTERNATIONAL LAW
SN Added in 1980
UF international case law
BT1 LEGISLATION
NT1 LAW OF THE SEA
RT DISPUTES
RT INTERNATIONAL AGREEMENTS
RT INTERNATIONAL ORGANIZATIONS
RT INTERNATIONAL WATERS
RT LEGAL ASPECTS
RT MULTIPLE USE OF RESOURCES
RT SEABED CONVENTIONS
RT TRADE

INTERNATIONAL LAW OF THE SEA
USE **LAW OF THE SEA**

INTERNATIONAL ORGANISATIONS
USE **INTERNATIONAL ORGANIZATIONS**

INTERNATIONAL ORGANIZATIONS
UF international agencies
UF international organisations
BT1 ORGANIZATIONS
RT ACRONYMS
RT ANNUAL REPORTS
RT CONFERENCES
RT COUNTRIES
RT DEVELOPING COUNTRIES
RT INTERNATIONAL AGREEMENTS
RT INTERNATIONAL COOPERATION
RT INTERNATIONAL LAW
RT INTERNATIONAL POLICY
RT OCEAN POLICY
RT REPORT LITERATURE
RT RESOURCE CONSERVATION
RT SEABED CONVENTIONS

INTERNATIONAL POLICY
SN Added in 1980
UF policy (international)
BT1 POLICIES
RT INTERNATIONAL AGREEMENTS
RT INTERNATIONAL COOPERATION
RT INTERNATIONAL ORGANIZATIONS
RT INTERNATIONAL WATERS
RT NATURAL RESOURCES
RT OCEAN SPACE
RT RESEARCH PROGRAMMES

INTERNATIONAL RELATION
USE **INTERNATIONAL COOPERATION**

INTERNATIONAL SEA AREA
USE **INTERNATIONAL WATERS**

INTERNATIONAL TRADE
USE **TRADE**

INTERNATIONAL WATERS
UF international sea area
BT1 OCEAN SPACE
RT EXPLOITATION
RT HIGH SEAS
RT HIGH SEAS FISHERIES
RT INTERNATIONAL AGREEMENTS
RT INTERNATIONAL LAW
RT INTERNATIONAL POLICY
RT LAW OF THE SEA
RT RESOURCE DEVELOPMENT
RT RESOURCE MANAGEMENT

INTEROCEAN CANALS
BT1 CANALS
BT2 INLAND WATERS
RT MEAN SEA LEVEL
RT SHIP CANALS

INTEROCEPTORS
USE **RECEPTORS**

INTERSPECIFIC INTERACTIONS
USE **INTERSPECIFIC RELATIONSHIPS**

INTERSPECIFIC RELATIONSHIPS
UF interspecific interactions
NT1 COMMENSALISM
NT1 COMPETITION
NT1 EPIBIOSIS
NT1 PARASITISM
NT2 ECTOPARASITISM
NT2 ENDOPARASITISM
NT1 PREDATION
NT2 PREY SELECTION
NT1 SYMBIOSIS
RT BEHAVIOUR
RT BIOLOGICAL PHENOMENA
RT BIOTIC FACTORS
RT DISEASES
RT FOOD CHAINS
RT FOOD WEBS
RT INTRASPECIFIC RELATIONSHIPS
RT TROPHIC RELATIONSHIPS

INTERSTITIAL ENVIRONMENT
BT1 AQUATIC ENVIRONMENT
BT2 ENVIRONMENTS
RT BENTHIC ENVIRONMENT
RT BENTHOS
RT PORE WATER

INTERSTITIAL WATER
USE **PORE WATER**

INTERTIDAL ENVIRONMENT
UF tidal environment
BT1 MARINE ENVIRONMENT
BT2 AQUATIC ENVIRONMENT
BT3 ENVIRONMENTS
RT AIR EXPOSURE
RT BEACHES
RT BENTHIC ENVIRONMENT
RT ECOLOGICAL ZONATION
RT EULITTORAL ZONE
RT EXPOSED HABITATS
RT INTERTIDAL SEDIMENTATION
RT TIDAL CYCLES
RT TIDAL FLATS
RT TIDAL WAVES

INTERTIDAL FLATS
USE **TIDAL FLATS**

INTERTIDAL SEDIMENTATION
BT1 SEDIMENTATION
RT ESTUARINE SEDIMENTATION
RT EULITTORAL ZONE
RT INTERTIDAL ENVIRONMENT
RT NEARSHORE SEDIMENTATION
RT TIDAL DEPOSITS
RT TIDAL FLATS
RT WAVE-CUT PLATFORMS

INTERTIDAL ZONATION
USE **ECOLOGICAL ZONATION**

INTERTROPICAL CONVERGENCE ZONE
BT1 ATMOSPHERIC CONVERGENCES
BT2 CONVERGENCE ZONES
RT EQUATORIAL TROUGH
RT FRONTS

INTESTINES
BT1 ALIMENTARY ORGANS
BT2 ANIMAL ORGANS
BT3 BODY ORGANS
RT AMBERGRIS
RT DIGESTION
RT DIGESTIVE SYSTEM
RT FOOD ABSORPTION
RT PYLORIC CAECA

INTRASPECIFIC RELATIONSHIPS
SN Added in 1980
UF intraspecific selection
RT BEHAVIOUR
RT BIOLOGICAL PHENOMENA
RT COMPETITION
RT INTERSPECIFIC RELATIONSHIPS
RT PREDATION
RT TROPHIC RELATIONSHIPS

INTRASPECIFIC SELECTION
USE **INTRASPECIFIC RELATIONSHIPS**

INTRODUCED SPECIES
SN Establishment in a new geographical
area of a species by migration or
artificial transportation
UF alien species
BT1 SPECIES
BT2 TAXA
RT ARTIFICIAL LAKES
RT COLONIES
RT COLONIZATION
RT DOMESTIC SPECIES
RT ENDEMIC SPECIES
RT POPULATION CONTROL
RT TRANSPLANTATION

INTRUSIONS (IGNEOUS)
USE **IGNEOUS INTRUSIONS**

INUNDATION
USE **FLOODING**

INUNDATION (INTENTIONAL)
USE **IRRIGATION**

INVENTORIES
UF data catalogues
BT1 CATALOGUES
BT2 DOCUMENTS
RT DATA
RT DATA CENTRES
RT DATA COLLECTIONS

INVERSION LAYERS
USE **INVERSIONS**

INVERSIONS
UF inversion layers
NT1 TEMPERATURE INVERSIONS
NT2 DICOTHERMAL LAYER
NT2 TRADE WIND INVERSION
RT DISCONTINUITY LAYERS
RT LAYERS

INVERTEBRATE LARVAE
SN Use of a more specific term is
recommended
BT1 LARVAE
BT2 DEVELOPMENTAL STAGES
NT1 CRUSTACEAN LARVAE
NT2 MEGALOPS
NT2 NAUPLII
NT2 PHYLLOSOMAE
NT2 ZOEAE
NT1 INSECT LARVAE
NT2 INSTARS
NT2 NYMPHS
NT2 PUPAE

INVERTEBRATE LARVAE (cont'd)
NT1	MOLLUSCAN LARVAE
NT2	SPAT
NT2	VELIGERS
RT	BIOLOGICAL DRIFT
RT	LARVAL DEVELOPMENT
RT	LARVAL SETTLEMENT
RT	MEROPLANKTON
RT	METAMORPHOSIS
RT	MOULTING

INVERTEBRATE ROE
USE	**ROES**

INVERTEBRATE ZOOLOGY
BT1	ZOOLOGY
BT2	BIOLOGY
NT1	CARCINOLOGY
NT1	ENTOMOLOGY
NT1	MALACOLOGY
RT	BIOGEOGRAPHY
RT	TAXONOMY

INVESTMENT MANAGEMENT
USE	**FINANCIAL MANAGEMENT**

INVESTMENTS
SN	Added in 1980
UF	capital investments
RT	DEVELOPMENT PROJECTS
RT	FINANCING
RT	INSURANCE
RT	MARKET RESEARCH

IODATES
BT1	IODINE COMPOUNDS
BT2	HALOGEN COMPOUNDS

IODIDES
BT1	IODINE COMPOUNDS
BT2	HALOGEN COMPOUNDS
RT	HALIDES

IODINATED HYDROCARBONS
BT1	IODINE COMPOUNDS
BT2	HALOGEN COMPOUNDS
NT1	IODOMETHANE

IODINE
BT1	CHEMICAL ELEMENTS
RT	BROMINE
RT	CHLORINE
RT	FLUORINE
RT	HALOGENS
RT	IODINE COMPOUNDS
RT	IODINE ISOTOPES
RT	TRACE ELEMENTS

IODINE COMPOUNDS
BT1	HALOGEN COMPOUNDS
NT1	IODATES
NT1	IODIDES
NT1	IODINATED HYDROCARBONS
NT2	IODOMETHANE
RT	CHEMICAL COMPOUNDS
RT	IODINE

IODINE ISOTOPES
BT1	ISOTOPES
RT	IODINE

IODOMETHANE
BT1	IODINATED HYDROCARBONS
BT2	IODINE COMPOUNDS
BT3	HALOGEN COMPOUNDS

ION ACCUMULATION
UF	accumulation of ions
RT	ION EXCHANGE
RT	ION TRANSPORT
RT	IONS
RT	OSMOREGULATION

ION ASSOCIATION
RT	CHEMICAL REACTIONS
RT	IONS

ION EXCHANGE
UF	anion exchange
UF	cation exchange
BT1	SEPARATION PROCESSES
RT	ANIONS
RT	BIOLOGICAL MEMBRANES
RT	CATIONS
RT	CHEMICAL REACTIONS
RT	DEMINERALIZATION
RT	DESALINATION
RT	DIFFUSION
RT	ION ACCUMULATION
RT	ION TRANSPORT
RT	WATER PURIFICATION
RT	WATER TREATMENT

ION PAIRS
RT	IONS

ION SELECTIVE ELECTRODE ANALYSIS
BT1	ANALYTICAL TECHNIQUES

ION TRANSPORT
RT	BIOLOGICAL MEMBRANES
RT	DESALINATION
RT	DIFFUSION
RT	ELECTROLYSIS
RT	ION ACCUMULATION
RT	ION EXCHANGE
RT	IONS
RT	OSMOREGULATION

IONIUM
BT1	THORIUM ISOTOPES
BT2	ISOTOPES

IONIZING RADIATION
BT1	RADIATIONS
NT1	COSMIC RADIATION
NT1	NUCLEAR RADIATIONS
RT	IRRADIATION
RT	RADIOACTIVITY
RT	STERILIZATION

IONOSPHERE
BT1	UPPER ATMOSPHERE
BT2	EARTH ATMOSPHERE
BT3	PLANETARY ATMOSPHERES
RT	ATMOSPHERIC ELECTRICITY
RT	AURORA
RT	STRATOSPHERE

IONS
NT1	ANIONS
NT1	CATIONS
NT1	HYDROGEN IONS
NT1	METAL IONS
RT	CHEMORECEPTION
RT	DESALINATION
RT	EXCHANGE CAPACITY
RT	HYDRATES
RT	ION ACCUMULATION
RT	ION ASSOCIATION
RT	ION PAIRS
RT	ION TRANSPORT
RT	LIGANDS
RT	OSMOREGULATION

IR IMAGERY
USE	**INFRARED IMAGERY**

IRIDIUM
BT1	CHEMICAL ELEMENTS
RT	IRIDIUM COMPOUNDS
RT	IRIDIUM ISOTOPES
RT	METALS
RT	TRACE METALS

IRIDIUM COMPOUNDS
RT	CHEMICAL COMPOUNDS
RT	IRIDIUM

IRIDIUM ISOTOPES
BT1	ISOTOPES
RT	IRIDIUM

IRON
BT1	CHEMICAL ELEMENTS
RT	FERROMANGANESE NODULES
RT	FERROMANGANESE OXIDES
RT	HEAVY METALS
RT	IRON COMPOUNDS
RT	IRON ISOTOPES
RT	IRONSTONE
RT	METALLIFEROUS SEDIMENTS
RT	METALS
RT	TRACE ELEMENTS
RT	TRACE METALS
RT	TRANSITION ELEMENTS

IRON COMPOUNDS
UF	ferric compounds
UF	ferrous compounds
NT1	IRON OXIDES
NT1	IRON PHOSPHATES
NT1	IRON SILICATES
NT1	IRON SULPHIDES
RT	CHEMICAL COMPOUNDS
RT	IRON

IRON ISOTOPES
BT1	ISOTOPES
RT	IRON

IRON OXIDES
BT1	IRON COMPOUNDS
RT	HAEMATITE
RT	MAGNETITE
RT	OXIDES

IRON PHOSPHATES
UF	ferric phosphate
BT1	IRON COMPOUNDS
RT	PHOSPHATES

IRON SILICATES
BT1	IRON COMPOUNDS
RT	SILICATES

IRON SULPHIDES
BT1	IRON COMPOUNDS
RT	SULPHIDES

IRONSTONE
BT1	AUTHIGENIC MINERALS
BT2	SEDIMENTS
RT	FERRUGINOUS DEPOSITS
RT	IRON
RT	SEDIMENTARY ROCKS

IRRADIANCE
SN	Flux density of radiant energy in water
NT1	DOWNWARD IRRADIANCE
NT1	UPWARD IRRADIANCE
RT	COSINE COLLECTORS
RT	IRRADIANCE METERS
RT	LIGHT

IRRADIANCE (cont'd)
RT   LIGHT FIELDS
RT   OPTICAL CLASSIFICATION
RT   OPTICAL PROPERTIES
RT   OPTICAL WATER TYPES
RT   RADIANCE
RT   RADIATIVE TRANSFER
RT   SOLAR RADIATION
RT   VOLUME SCATTERING FUNCTION

IRRADIANCE METERS
BT1   LIGHT MEASURING INSTRUMENTS
BT2   MEASURING DEVICES
RT   IRRADIANCE
RT   QUANTA METERS

IRRADIATION
UF   irradiation (fishery products)
RT   IONIZING RADIATION
RT   POPULATION CONTROL
RT   PRESERVATION (FISHERY PRODUCTS)
RT   RADIOCHEMISTRY
RT   RADIOGRAPHY
RT   STERILITY

IRRADIATION (ACOUSTIC WAVES)
USE   **INSONIFICATION**

IRRADIATION (FISHERY PRODUCTS)
USE   **IRRADIATION**

IRRIGATION
UF   flooding (irrigation)
UF   inundation (intentional)
RT   AGRICULTURAL POLLUTION
RT   AGRICULTURAL RUNOFF
RT   AGRICULTURE
RT   CANALS
RT   EMBANKMENTS
RT   FISH PONDS
RT   IRRIGATION WATER
RT   LAKES
RT   LAND RECLAMATION
RT   PONDS
RT   RECLAMATION
RT   RESERVOIRS (WATER)
RT   WASTE WATER
RT   WATER POLICY
RT   WATER RIGHTS

IRRIGATION CANALS
USE   **CANALS**

IRRIGATION WATER
BT1   WATER
RT   DAMS
RT   IRRIGATION
RT   RESERVOIRS (WATER)
RT   RIPARIAN RIGHTS
RT   WATER MANAGEMENT
RT   WATER POLICY
RT   WATER RIGHTS

IRROTATIONAL FLOW
USE   **POTENTIAL FLOW**

ISENTROPIC ANALYSIS
BT1   ANALYTICAL TECHNIQUES
RT   ANALYSIS
RT   ENTROPY
RT   ISENTROPIC PROCESSES
RT   ISENTROPIC SURFACES

ISENTROPIC PROCESSES
RT   ENTROPY
RT   ISENTROPIC ANALYSIS
RT   ISENTROPIC SURFACES
RT   THERMODYNAMICS

ISENTROPIC SURFACES
RT   ENTROPY
RT   ISENTROPIC ANALYSIS
RT   ISENTROPIC PROCESSES
RT   POTENTIAL TEMPERATURE
RT   SURFACES

ISLAND ARCS
UF   arcs (island)
RT   ACTIVE MARGINS
RT   CONTINENTAL MARGINS
RT   CONTINENTS
RT   CONVERGING PLATE BOUNDARIES
RT   FOREARC BASINS
RT   ISLANDS
RT   MARGINAL BASINS
RT   OCEANIC ISLANDS
RT   PLATE CONVERGENCE
RT   SUBDUCTION
RT   TRENCHES (OCEANIC)
RT   VOLCANIC ISLANDS
RT   VOLCANISM

ISLAND SLOPE
UF   insular slope
BT1   SUBMARINE FEATURES
BT2   TOPOGRAPHIC FEATURES
RT   ARCHIPELAGIC APRONS
RT   CONTINENTAL SLOPE
RT   OCEANIC ISLANDS
RT   SLOPES (TOPOGRAPHY)

ISLANDS
BT1   LANDFORMS
BT2   TOPOGRAPHIC FEATURES
NT1   ATOLLS
NT1   CAYS
NT1   OCEANIC ISLANDS
NT2   VOLCANIC ISLANDS
RT   ARCHIPELAGOES
RT   ARTIFICIAL ISLANDS
RT   BARRIER ISLANDS
RT   BEACHES
RT   ICE ISLANDS
RT   ISLAND ARCS

ISOBARIC SURFACES
RT   BAROCLINIC MODE
RT   BAROTROPIC MODE
RT   DYNAMIC HEIGHT ANOMALY
RT   DYNAMIC TOPOGRAPHY
RT   HYDROSTATIC PRESSURE
RT   ISOBARS
RT   ISOPYCNIC SURFACES
RT   LEVEL OF NO MOTION
RT   PRESSURE FIELD
RT   SURFACES

ISOBARS
BT1   ISOPLETHS
BT2   MAP GRAPHICS
BT3   GRAPHICS
BT4   AUDIOVISUAL MATERIAL
RT   ANTICYCLONES
RT   ATMOSPHERIC PRESSURE
RT   HYDROSTATIC PRESSURE
RT   ISOBARIC SURFACES
RT   METEOROLOGICAL DATA
RT   PRESSURE
RT   PRESSURE FIELD
RT   SEA LEVEL PRESSURE
RT   WEATHER MAPS

ISOBATHS
SN   Added in 1982
UF   depth contours
BT1   CONTOURS
BT2   ISOPLETHS
BT3   MAP GRAPHICS
BT4   GRAPHICS

ISOBATHS (cont'd)
RT   BATHYMETRIC CHARTS
RT   BATHYMETRY
RT   BOTTOM TOPOGRAPHY
RT   DEPTH RECORDERS
RT   WATER DEPTH

ISOCHRONES
BT1   ISOPLETHS
BT2   MAP GRAPHICS
BT3   GRAPHICS
BT4   AUDIOVISUAL MATERIAL
RT   ABSOLUTE AGE
RT   COTIDAL LINES

ISOCLINIC LINES
USE   **ISOMAGNETIC LINES**

ISODYNAMIC ENZYMES
USE   **ENZYMES**

ISOENZYMES
SN   Added in 1980
UF   isozymes
RT   ELECTROPHORESIS
RT   ENZYMES

ISOGONIC LINES
USE   **ISOMAGNETIC LINES**

ISOGRAMS
USE   **ISOMAGNETIC LINES**

ISOHALINES
BT1   ISOPLETHS
BT2   MAP GRAPHICS
BT3   GRAPHICS
BT4   AUDIOVISUAL MATERIAL
RT   ENVIRONMENTAL CHARTS
RT   HALOCLINE
RT   MIXED LAYER
RT   SALINITY
RT   SALINITY CHARTS
RT   SALINITY SECTIONS

ISOHYETS
BT1   ISOPLETHS
BT2   MAP GRAPHICS
BT3   GRAPHICS
BT4   AUDIOVISUAL MATERIAL
RT   ATMOSPHERIC PRECIPITATIONS
RT   CLIMATOLOGICAL CHARTS
RT   RAINFALL

ISOLATING MECHANISMS
SN   Methods that prevent breeding between populations, so that the genes of each do not mix. Added in 1980
NT1   GENETIC ISOLATION
NT1   GEOGRAPHICAL ISOLATION
NT1   SEXUAL ISOLATION
RT   BIOLOGICAL SPECIATION
RT   POPULATION GENETICS

ISOLATION (GENETICS)
USE   **GENETIC ISOLATION**

ISOLATION (GEOGRAPHICAL)
USE   **GEOGRAPHICAL ISOLATION**

ISOLATION (SEXUAL)
USE   **SEXUAL ISOLATION**

ISOLINES
USE   **ISOPLETHS**

ISOMAGNETIC LINES
UF	isoclinic lines
UF	isogonic lines
UF	isograms
BT1	ISOPLETHS
BT2	MAP GRAPHICS
BT3	GRAPHICS
BT4	AUDIOVISUAL MATERIAL
RT	MAGNETIC CHARTS
RT	MAGNETIC INCLINATION
RT	MAGNETIC INTENSITY
RT	MAGNETIC VARIATIONS

ISOMERASES
SN	Added in 1980
BT1	ENZYMES

ISOMERIZATION
BT1	CHEMICAL REACTIONS

ISOPACH MAPS
BT1	GEOLOGICAL MAPS
BT2	MAPS
BT3	GRAPHICS
BT4	AUDIOVISUAL MATERIAL
RT	ISOPACHS
RT	SEDIMENT DISTRIBUTION
RT	STRATIGRAPHY

ISOPACHS
SN	Isopleths drawn through points of equal thickness of a layer of sediment
BT1	ISOPLETHS
BT2	MAP GRAPHICS
BT3	GRAPHICS
BT4	AUDIOVISUAL MATERIAL
RT	ISOPACH MAPS

ISOPLETHS
SN	Descriptor to be used only as a qualifier
UF	isolines
BT1	MAP GRAPHICS
BT2	GRAPHICS
BT3	AUDIOVISUAL MATERIAL
BT4	DOCUMENTS
NT1	CONTOURS
NT2	ISOBATHS
NT1	CORANGE LINES
NT1	COTIDAL LINES
NT1	ISOBARS
NT1	ISOCHRONES
NT1	ISOHALINES
NT1	ISOHYETS
NT1	ISOMAGNETIC LINES
NT1	ISOPACHS
NT1	ISOPYCNICS
NT1	ISOSTERES
NT1	ISOTHERMS
RT	GRAPHS

ISOPYCNIC SURFACES
RT	BAROCLINIC MODE
RT	BAROTROPIC MODE
RT	ISOBARIC SURFACES
RT	ISOPYCNICS
RT	ISOSTERIC SURFACES
RT	SURFACES
RT	WATER DENSITY

ISOPYCNICS
BT1	ISOPLETHS
BT2	MAP GRAPHICS
BT3	GRAPHICS
BT4	AUDIOVISUAL MATERIAL
RT	DENSITY CHARTS
RT	DENSITY FRONTS
RT	ISOPYCNIC SURFACES
RT	ISOSTERES

ISOPYCNICS (cont'd)
RT	PYCNOCLINE
RT	SPECIFIC VOLUME
RT	WATER DENSITY

ISOSTASY
UF	compensation depth (isostasy)
UF	isostatic adjustment
UF	isostatic compensation
UF	isostatic equilibrium
BT1	CRUSTAL ADJUSTMENT
BT2	TECTONICS
BT3	GEOLOGY
BT4	EARTH SCIENCES
RT	ASTHENOSPHERE
RT	CONTINENTS
RT	DEGLACIATION
RT	EARTH CRUST
RT	EMERGENT SHORELINES
RT	EPEIROGENY
RT	EQUILIBRIUM
RT	EUSTATIC CHANGES
RT	GEODESY
RT	GLACIATION
RT	ICE VOLUME
RT	PLUMBLINE DEFLECTION
RT	PROGRADATION
RT	RAISED BEACHES
RT	REGRESSIONS
RT	RETROGRADATION
RT	SEA LEVEL CHANGES
RT	SUBMERGED SHORELINES
RT	SUBMERGENCE
RT	TRANSGRESSIONS
RT	VERTICAL TECTONICS

ISOSTATIC ADJUSTMENT
USE	**ISOSTASY**

ISOSTATIC COMPENSATION
USE	**ISOSTASY**

ISOSTATIC EQUILIBRIUM
USE	**ISOSTASY**

ISOSTATIC SEA LEVEL
BT1	SEA LEVEL
RT	PRESSURE
RT	SEA LEVEL PRESSURE
RT	STERIC SEA LEVEL

ISOSTERES
BT1	ISOPLETHS
BT2	MAP GRAPHICS
BT3	GRAPHICS
BT4	AUDIOVISUAL MATERIAL
RT	ISOPYCNICS
RT	ISOSTERIC SURFACES
RT	SPECIFIC VOLUME

ISOSTERIC SURFACES
RT	BAROCLINIC MODE
RT	BAROTROPIC MODE
RT	ISOPYCNIC SURFACES
RT	ISOSTERES
RT	SPECIFIC VOLUME
RT	SURFACES

ISOTHERMAL PROCESSES
NT1	ADIABATIC PROCESSES
RT	THERMODYNAMICS
RT	THERMOSTERIC ANOMALIES

ISOTHERMS
UF	temperature contours
BT1	ISOPLETHS
BT2	MAP GRAPHICS
BT3	GRAPHICS
BT4	AUDIOVISUAL MATERIAL
RT	AIR TEMPERATURE

ISOTHERMS (cont'd)
RT	ENVIRONMENTAL CHARTS
RT	TEMPERATURE CHARTS
RT	TEMPERATURE SECTIONS
RT	THERMOCLINE
RT	WATER TEMPERATURE

ISOTOPE DATING
USE	**RADIOMETRIC DATING**

ISOTOPE DILUTION
BT1	TRACER TECHNIQUES
RT	ISOTOPES

ISOTOPE FRACTIONATION
RT	ISOTOPES

ISOTOPES
UF	nuclides
NT1	ACTINIUM ISOTOPES
NT1	ALUMINIUM ISOTOPES
NT1	AMERICIUM ISOTOPES
NT1	ANTIMONY ISOTOPES
NT1	ARGON ISOTOPES
NT1	ARSENIC ISOTOPES
NT1	ASTATINE ISOTOPES
NT1	BARIUM ISOTOPES
NT1	BERKELIUM ISOTOPES
NT1	BERYLLIUM ISOTOPES
NT1	BISMUTH ISOTOPES
NT1	BORON ISOTOPES
NT1	BROMINE ISOTOPES
NT1	CADMIUM ISOTOPES
NT1	CAESIUM ISOTOPES
NT2	CAESIUM 137
NT1	CALCIUM ISOTOPES
NT1	CALIFORNIUM ISOTOPES
NT1	CARBON ISOTOPES
NT2	CARBON 13
NT2	CARBON 14
NT1	CERIUM ISOTOPES
NT1	CHLORINE ISOTOPES
NT1	CHROMIUM ISOTOPES
NT1	COBALT ISOTOPES
NT1	COPPER ISOTOPES
NT1	CURIUM ISOTOPES
NT1	DYSPROSIUM ISOTOPES
NT1	EINSTEINIUM ISOTOPES
NT1	ERBIUM ISOTOPES
NT1	EUROPIUM ISOTOPES
NT1	FERMIUM ISOTOPES
NT1	FLUORINE ISOTOPES
NT1	FRANCIUM ISOTOPES
NT1	GADOLINIUM ISOTOPES
NT1	GALLIUM ISOTOPES
NT1	GERMANIUM ISOTOPES
NT1	GOLD ISOTOPES
NT1	HAFNIUM ISOTOPES
NT1	HELIUM ISOTOPES
NT1	HOLMIUM ISOTOPES
NT1	HYDROGEN ISOTOPES
NT2	DEUTERIUM
NT2	TRITIUM
NT1	INDIUM ISOTOPES
NT1	IODINE ISOTOPES
NT1	IRIDIUM ISOTOPES
NT1	IRON ISOTOPES
NT1	KRYPTON ISOTOPES
NT1	LANTHANIUM ISOTOPES
NT1	LAWRENCIUM ISOTOPES
NT1	LEAD ISOTOPES
NT2	LEAD 210
NT1	LITHIUM ISOTOPES
NT1	LUTETIUM ISOTOPES
NT1	MAGNESIUM ISOTOPES
NT1	MANGANESE ISOTOPES
NT1	MENDELEVIUM ISOTOPES
NT1	MERCURY ISOTOPES

ASFIS Thesaurus

ISOTOPES (cont'd)

NT1	MOLYBDENUM ISOTOPES
NT1	NEODYMIUM ISOTOPES
NT1	NEON ISOTOPES
NT1	NEPTUNIUM ISOTOPES
NT1	NICKEL ISOTOPES
NT1	NIOBIUM ISOTOPES
NT1	NITROGEN ISOTOPES
NT1	NOBELIUM ISOTOPES
NT1	OSMIUM ISOTOPES
NT1	OXYGEN ISOTOPES
NT1	PALLADIUM ISOTOPES
NT1	PHOSPHORUS ISOTOPES
NT1	PLATINUM ISOTOPES
NT1	PLUTONIUM ISOTOPES
NT1	POLONIUM ISOTOPES
NT1	POTASSIUM ISOTOPES
NT1	PRASEODYMIUM ISOTOPES
NT1	PROMETHIUM ISOTOPES
NT1	PROTACTINIUM ISOTOPES
NT1	RADIOISOTOPES
NT1	RADIUM ISOTOPES
NT1	RADON ISOTOPES
NT1	RHENIUM ISOTOPES
NT1	RHODIUM ISOTOPES
NT1	RUBIDIUM ISOTOPES
NT1	RUTHENIUM ISOTOPES
NT1	SAMARIUM ISOTOPES
NT1	SCANDIUM ISOTOPES
NT1	SELENIUM ISOTOPES
NT1	SILICON ISOTOPES
NT1	SILVER ISOTOPES
NT1	SODIUM ISOTOPES
NT1	STRONTIUM ISOTOPES
NT1	SULPHUR ISOTOPES
NT1	TANTALUM ISOTOPES
NT1	TECHNETIUM ISOTOPES
NT1	TELLURIUM ISOTOPES
NT1	TERBIUM ISOTOPES
NT1	THALLIUM ISOTOPES
NT1	THORIUM ISOTOPES
NT2	IONIUM
NT1	THULIUM ISOTOPES
NT1	TIN ISOTOPES
NT1	TITANIUM ISOTOPES
NT1	TUNGSTEN ISOTOPES
NT1	URANIUM ISOTOPES
NT1	VANADIUM ISOTOPES
NT1	XENON ISOTOPES
NT1	YTTERBIUM ISOTOPES
NT1	YTTRIUM ISOTOPES
NT1	ZINC ISOTOPES
NT1	ZIRCONIUM ISOTOPES
RT	CHEMICAL ELEMENTS
RT	FISSION PRODUCTS
RT	ISOTOPE DILUTION
RT	ISOTOPE FRACTIONATION
RT	RADIOACTIVE TRACERS
RT	RADIOMETRIC DATING
RT	TRACERS

ISOTOPIC LABELLING
USE **RADIOACTIVE LABELLING**

ISOTROPIC MATERIALS

BT1	MATERIALS
RT	ANISOTROPY
RT	ISOTROPY

ISOTROPIC TURBULENCE
USE **TURBULENCE**

ISOTROPY

RT	ANISOTROPY
RT	ISOTROPIC MATERIALS
RT	ORIENTATION

ISOZYMES
USE **ISOENZYMES**

JACK FISHERIES
USE **CARANGID FISHERIES**

JACKETS
USE **PILED PLATFORMS**

JACKUP PLATFORMS

SN	Towed or self-propelled platforms supportable on extending legs
BT1	MOBILE PLATFORMS
BT2	FLOATING STRUCTURES
BT3	OFFSHORE STRUCTURES
BT4	HYDRAULIC STRUCTURES
RT	SUBMERSIBLE PLATFORMS

JAROSITE

BT1	SULPHATE MINERALS
BT2	MINERALS

JASPILITE

BT1	AUTHIGENIC MINERALS
BT2	SEDIMENTS
RT	FERRUGINOUS DEPOSITS

JELLY BOTTLES

BT1	CURRENT MEASURING EQUIPMENT
BT2	FLOW MEASURING EQUIPMENT

JET STREAM

UF	polar front jet stream
UF	subtropical jet stream
RT	CLEAR AIR TURBULENCE
RT	JETS
RT	PLANETARY WAVES
RT	TROPOSPHERE

JETS

UF	turbulent jets
BT1	FLUID FLOW
BT2	FLUID MOTION
NT1	BUOYANT JETS
NT1	COASTAL JETS
RT	JET STREAM

JETSAM
USE **FLOTSAM**

JETTIES
USE **PORT INSTALLATIONS**

JIGGING

BT1	LINE FISHING
BT2	CATCHING METHODS
RT	CEPHALOPOD FISHERIES
RT	HANDLINING
RT	LINES
RT	PELAGIC FISHERIES

JOINT VENTURES

SN	Enterprises owned jointly by interests of different nationalities. Added in 1980
UF	international joint ventures
RT	BILATERAL AGREEMENTS
RT	DEVELOPING COUNTRIES
RT	ECONOMICS
RT	FISHING RIGHTS
RT	FOREIGN FISHING

JOINTS

UF	nodes
RT	NODE CONSTRUCTION
RT	OFFSHORE STRUCTURES

JURASSIC

SN	Before 1982 search JURASSIC PERIOD
BT1	MESOZOIC
BT2	GEOLOGICAL TIME

JURISDICTION

SN	Added in 1980
UF	federal jurisdiction
UF	state jurisdiction
NT1	EXTENDED JURISDICTION
RT	COASTAL STATES
RT	CONTIGUOUS ZONES
RT	CONTINENTAL SHELVES
RT	CONTINENTAL SLOPE
RT	FISHING RIGHTS
RT	LAKES
RT	LEGAL ASPECTS
RT	LEGISLATION
RT	MARINE RESOURCES
RT	OCEAN FLOOR
RT	OCEAN SPACE
RT	OUTER CONTINENTAL SHELF
RT	POLITICAL ASPECTS
RT	RIVERS

JUVENILE WATER

BT1	WATER
RT	HYDROTHERMAL SOLUTIONS

JUVENILES

UF	elvers
UF	parrs
UF	post larvae
BT1	DEVELOPMENTAL STAGES
BT1	PUPS
RT	FRY
RT	GROWING PONDS
RT	GROWTH
RT	MEGALOPS
RT	METAMORPHOSIS
RT	NURSERY GROUNDS
RT	NURSERY PONDS
RT	PUPAE
RT	SMOLTS

KAINITE

BT1	SULPHATE MINERALS
BT2	MINERALS

KALMAN FILTERS

BT1	FILTERS

KAMABOKO
USE **MINCED PRODUCTS**

KANSITE

BT1	SULPHIDE MINERALS
BT2	MINERALS

KAOLIN

BT1	CLAY MINERALS
BT2	SILICATE MINERALS
BT3	MINERALS
RT	CLAYS
RT	KAOLINITE

KAOLINITE

BT1	CLAY MINERALS
BT2	SILICATE MINERALS
BT3	MINERALS
RT	KAOLIN

KARYOKINESIS
USE **MITOSIS**

KARYOLOGICAL STUDIES
USE **KARYOLOGY**

KARYOLOGY
SN	Added in 1980
UF	karyological studies
BT1	CYTOLOGY
BT2	BIOLOGY
RT	CHROMOSOMES
RT	MEIOSIS
RT	MITOSIS
RT	NUCLEI

KARYOMITES
USE	CHROMOSOMES

KARYOTYPES
RT	CHROMOSOMES
RT	GENOMES
RT	GENOTYPES

KATADROMOUS SPECIES
USE	CATADROMOUS SPECIES

KEEL CLEARANCE
UF	under keel clearance
UF	underkeel clearance
RT	GROUNDINGS
RT	NAVIGATIONAL CHANNELS
RT	NEGATIVE STORM SURGES
RT	SAND WAVES

KELPS
SN	Brown algae harvested and dried as a source of alginic acid or for animal feeding. Added in 1980
UF	tangle
RT	ALGINATES
RT	HOLDFASTS
RT	SEAWEED PRODUCTS
RT	SEAWEEDS

KELT
SN	Added in 1980
UF	spawned salmon
UF	spawned trout
RT	SPAWNING MIGRATIONS

KELVIN-HELMHOLTZ BILLOWS
USE	BILLOWS

KELVIN-HELMHOLTZ INSTABILITY
UF	helmholtz instability
UF	shear flow instability
UF	shear instability
BT1	INSTABILITY
RT	BILLOWS
RT	CLEAR AIR TURBULENCE
RT	TRANS-ISOPYCNAL MIXING

KELVIN WAVES
UF	double kelvin waves
BT1	TRAPPED WAVES
BT2	WATER WAVES
NT1	EQUATORIAL TRAPPED WAVES
RT	EQUATORIAL DYNAMICS
RT	NONLINEAR WAVES

KEROGEN
BT1	PETROLEUM HYDROCARBONS
BT2	HYDROCARBONS
BT3	ORGANIC COMPOUNDS
RT	OIL SHALE
RT	ORGANIC MATTER
RT	SAPROPELITE

KETONES
BT1	ORGANIC COMPOUNDS
NT1	ACETONE

KETTLE LAKES
USE	GLACIAL LAKES

KEYS
USE	IDENTIFICATION KEYS

KEYS (ISLANDS)
USE	CAYS

KIDNEYS
SN	Before 1982 search KIDNEY
UF	nephrons
BT1	EXCRETORY ORGANS
BT2	ANIMAL ORGANS
BT3	BODY ORGANS
RT	ADRENAL GLANDS
RT	URINARY SYSTEM
RT	URINE
RT	WATER BALANCE

KIMBERLITES
RT	BIOTITE
RT	CONGLOMERATES
RT	DIAMONDS
RT	PERIDOTITE

KINEMATIC EDDY VISCOSITY
RT	KINEMATIC VISCOSITY

KINEMATIC VISCOSITY
BT1	VISCOSITY
BT2	MECHANICAL PROPERTIES
BT3	PHYSICAL PROPERTIES
BT4	PROPERTIES
RT	DYNAMIC VISCOSITY
RT	EDDY VISCOSITY
RT	KINEMATIC EDDY VISCOSITY
RT	MOLECULAR VISCOSITY COEFFICIENTS
RT	REYNOLDS NUMBER

KINEMATICS
BT1	MECHANICS
BT2	PHYSICS
RT	ACCELERATION
RT	VELOCITY

KINESIS
BT1	ORIENTATION BEHAVIOUR
BT2	BEHAVIOUR
RT	SENSE FUNCTIONS
RT	SENSE ORGANS
RT	STIMULI
RT	TROPISM

KINETIC ENERGY
BT1	ENERGY
NT1	EDDY KINETIC ENERGY
RT	DRAG COEFFICIENT
RT	FROUDE NUMBER
RT	POTENTIAL ENERGY

KINETICS
BT1	MECHANICS
BT2	PHYSICS
NT1	RADIONUCLIDE KINETICS
RT	CHEMICAL KINETICS
RT	PHYSICAL PROPERTIES

KINETICS OF CHEMICAL REACTIONS
USE	CHEMICAL KINETICS

KING CRAB FISHERIES
USE	CRAB FISHERIES

KING MACKEREL FISHERIES
USE	TUNA FISHERIES

KNOLLS (SUBMARINE)
USE	SEAKNOLLS

KNUDSEN SAMPLERS
BT1	WATER SAMPLERS
BT2	SAMPLERS

KNUDSEN TABLES
BT1	CONVERSION TABLES
BT2	TABLES
BT3	DOCUMENTS
RT	CHLORINITY
RT	IN SITU DENSITY
RT	OCEANOGRAPHIC TABLES
RT	SALINITY
RT	SIGMA-T
RT	WATER DENSITY

KORTWEG DEVRIES EQUATION
BT1	EQUATIONS

KRILL FISHERIES
SN	Added in 1982
BT1	CRUSTACEAN FISHERIES
BT2	FISHERIES
RT	EXPERIMENTAL FISHING
RT	KRILL PRODUCTS
RT	MARINE FISHERIES
RT	PELAGIC FISHERIES
RT	POTENTIAL RESOURCES

KRILL MEAL
USE	KRILL PRODUCTS

KRILL PASTE
USE	KRILL PRODUCTS

KRILL POWDERS
USE	KRILL PRODUCTS

KRILL PRODUCTS
SN	Added in 1982
UF	krill meal
UF	krill paste
UF	krill powders
UF	krill protein concentrates
BT1	PROCESSED FISHERY PRODUCTS
BT2	FISHERY PRODUCTS
BT3	PRODUCTS
RT	KRILL FISHERIES
RT	PRODUCT DEVELOPMENT

KRILL PROTEIN CONCENTRATES
USE	KRILL PRODUCTS

KRYOGENIC MARKING
USE	COLD BRANDING

KRYPTON
BT1	CHEMICAL ELEMENTS
RT	KRYPTON ISOTOPES
RT	RARE GASES

KRYPTON ISOTOPES
BT1	ISOTOPES
RT	KRYPTON

KURTOSIS
RT	COEFFICIENTS
RT	PARTICLE DISTRIBUTION
RT	PARTICLE SIZE
RT	SKEWNESS
RT	STATISTICAL ANALYSIS

KYANITE
BT1	SILICATE MINERALS
BT2	MINERALS

ASFIS Thesaurus

LABELLING (RADIOACTIVE)
USE   **RADIOACTIVE LABELLING**

LABOR
USE   **LABOUR**

LABORATORIES
RT   EXPERIMENTAL RESEARCH
RT   LABORATORY EQUIPMENT
RT   RESEARCH INSTITUTIONS
RT   SCIENTIFIC PERSONNEL

LABORATORY CONDITIONS
USE   **CONTROLLED CONDITIONS**

LABORATORY CULTURE
UF   biological culture
NT1   CELL CULTURE
NT1   MICROBIOLOGICAL CULTURE
NT1   TISSUE CULTURE
RT   ALGAL CULTURE
RT   AQUACULTURE
RT   AQUACULTURE SYSTEMS
RT   AQUACULTURE TECHNIQUES
RT   ARTIFICIAL AERATION
RT   ARTIFICIAL FEEDING
RT   BATCH CULTURE
RT   BRINE SHRIMP CULTURE
RT   CONTINUOUS CULTURE
RT   CONTROLLED CONDITIONS
RT   CULTURE MEDIA
RT   CULTURE TANKS
RT   CULTURES
RT   EXPERIMENTAL CULTURE
RT   PHYTOPLANKTON CULTURE
RT   REARING
RT   ULTRAVIOLET STERILIZATION
RT   ZOOPLANKTON CULTURE

LABORATORY EQUIPMENT
BT1   EQUIPMENT
NT1   CENTRIFUGES
NT1   FLUMES
NT1   MICROSCOPES
RT   ANALYTICAL TECHNIQUES
RT   AQUARIOLOGY
RT   ELECTRON MICROSCOPY
RT   LABORATORIES
RT   LIMNOLOGICAL EQUIPMENT
RT   MEASURING DEVICES
RT   OCEANOGRAPHIC EQUIPMENT
RT   RESEARCH INSTITUTIONS
RT   SALINOMETERS
RT   SCALE MODELS
RT   TEST EQUIPMENT
RT   TOWING TANKS
RT   WAVE GENERATORS
RT   WAVE TANKS

LABORATORY MODELS
USE   **SCALE MODELS**

LABORATORY REARING
USE   **REARING**

LABORATORY RESEARCH
USE   **EXPERIMENTAL RESEARCH**

LABORATORY TESTS
USE   **TESTS**

LABOUR
UF   labor
RT   ARTISANAL FISHING
RT   COOPERATIVES
RT   FISHERMEN
RT   FISHERMEN STATISTICS
RT   LABOUR COSTS
RT   LABOUR LEGISLATION
RT   LEGISLATION

LABOUR (cont'd)
RT   OIL AND GAS LEGISLATION
RT   PERSONNEL
RT   SOCIOLOGICAL ASPECTS

LABOUR COSTS
SN   Added in 1980
BT1   COSTS
RT   LABOUR
RT   LABOUR LEGISLATION

LABOUR LEGISLATION
SN   Before 1982 search LABOUR
BT1   LEGISLATION
RT   FISHERMEN
RT   LABOUR
RT   LABOUR COSTS
RT   PERSONNEL

LACCOLITHS
BT1   IGNEOUS INTRUSIONS
RT   BATHOLITHS
RT   IGNEOUS DIKES
RT   IGNEOUS ROCKS

LACTATION
SN   The process of milk production by
       the mammary glands. Added in 1980
RT   AQUATIC MAMMALS
RT   EXCRETORY ORGANS
RT   HORMONES

LACUSTRINE SEDIMENTATION
BT1   SEDIMENTATION
RT   ANOXIC SEDIMENTS
RT   LAKE DEPOSITS
RT   LAKES
RT   LENITIC ENVIRONMENT
RT   LIMNOLOGY
RT   SEDIMENTARY ENVIRONMENTS

LAGGING
USE   **INSULATING MATERIALS**

LAGOON FISHERIES
BT1   INLAND FISHERIES
BT2   FISHERIES
RT   ARTISANAL FISHING
RT   BARRIERS
RT   BRACKISHWATER FISH
RT   DEMERSAL FISHERIES
RT   FISHING BARRIERS
RT   LAGOONS
RT   SHRIMP FISHERIES
RT   TRAP NETS

LAGOONAL SEDIMENTATION
BT1   SEDIMENTATION
RT   BRACKISHWATER ENVIRONMENT
RT   LAGOONS
RT   SEDIMENTARY ENVIRONMENTS

LAGOONS
NT1   ATOLL LAGOONS
NT1   COASTAL LAGOONS
NT1   INLAND LAGOONS
RT   AQUACULTURE
RT   ATOLLS
RT   BACKWATERS
RT   BARRIER REEFS
RT   BRACKISH WATER
RT   BRACKISHWATER ENVIRONMENT
RT   CORAL REEFS
RT   LAGOON FISHERIES
RT   LAGOONAL SEDIMENTATION
RT   LENITIC ENVIRONMENT
RT   SHALLOW WATER
RT   VALLICULTURE
RT   WATER BODIES
RT   WATER RESOURCES

LAGRANGIAN CURRENT MEASUREMENT
SN   Before 1982 search also LAGRANGIAN
       METHODS (CURRENT MEASUREMENT)
UF   lagrangian methods (current
       measurement)
BT1   CURRENT MEASUREMENT
BT2   FLOW MEASUREMENT
BT3   MEASUREMENT
RT   DATA BUOYS
RT   DRIFTERS
RT   DROGUES
RT   RHODAMINE B-DYE
RT   SHIP DRIFT
RT   SUBSURFACE DRIFTERS

LAGRANGIAN DRIFTERS
USE   **DRIFTERS**

LAGRANGIAN DRIFTING BUOYS
USE   **DRIFTING DATA BUOYS**

LAGRANGIAN METHODS (CURRENT MEASUREMENT)
USE   **LAGRANGIAN CURRENT MEASUREMENT**

LAKE BASINS
RT   BASINS
RT   CATCHMENT AREA
RT   LAKE DEPOSITS
RT   LAKE MORPHOLOGY
RT   LAKES
RT   RIVER BASINS
RT   WATERSHEDS

LAKE BEACHES
USE   **LAKE SHORES**

LAKE BREEZES
USE   **SEA BREEZES**

LAKE CIRCULATION
USE   **LAKE DYNAMICS**

LAKE CURRENTS
SN   Before 1982 search also LENITIC
       CURRENTS
UF   lenitic currents
BT1   WATER CURRENTS
BT2   WATER MOTION
RT   BOTTOM CURRENTS
RT   COASTAL JETS
RT   LAKE DYNAMICS
RT   LAKES
RT   LIMNOLOGICAL SURVEYS
RT   LONGSHORE CURRENTS
RT   PHYSICAL LIMNOLOGY
RT   SUBSURFACE CURRENTS
RT   SURFACE CURRENTS

LAKE DEPOSITS
RT   ANOXIC SEDIMENTS
RT   GLACIAL DEPOSITS
RT   GLACIAL SEDIMENTATION
RT   LACUSTRINE SEDIMENTATION
RT   LAKE BASINS
RT   LAKE MORPHOLOGY
RT   LAKES
RT   PEAT
RT   PLAYAS
RT   SEDIMENTS
RT   VARVES

LAKE DYNAMICS
UF   lake circulation
UF   reservoir dynamics
BT1   WATER CIRCULATION
BT2   WATER MOTION
RT   COASTAL BOUNDARY LAYER
RT   COASTAL JETS
RT   FLUSHING TIME

LAKE DYNAMICS (cont'd)
RT	LAKE CURRENTS
RT	NEARSHORE DYNAMICS
RT	OVERTURN
RT	PHYSICAL LIMNOLOGY
RT	RESERVOIRS (WATER)
RT	SEICHES
RT	SURFACE CIRCULATION
RT	WATER LEVELS
RT	WIND SETUP

LAKE FISHERIES
BT1	INLAND FISHERIES
BT2	FISHERIES
RT	ARTISANAL FISHING
RT	COASTAL FISHERIES
RT	DEMERSAL FISHERIES
RT	FEE FISHING
RT	FISHERY LIMNOLOGY
RT	FRESHWATER FISH
RT	ICE FISHING
RT	LAKE RECLAMATION
RT	PELAGIC FISHERIES
RT	RESERVOIR FISHERIES
RT	SALMON FISHERIES

LAKE ICE
BT1	ICE
RT	FAST ICE
RT	FLOATING ICE
RT	FRESHWATER ICE
RT	FRESHWATER LAKES
RT	ICE-WATER INTERFACE
RT	LAKES
RT	PHYSICAL LIMNOLOGY
RT	WINTERKILL

LAKE MORPHOLOGY
BT1	GEOMORPHOLOGY
BT2	GEOLOGY
BT3	EARTH SCIENCES
RT	BEACHES
RT	LAKE BASINS
RT	LAKE DEPOSITS
RT	LAKES

LAKE RECLAMATION
SN	Added in 1980
UF	reclamation (lakes)
BT1	RECLAMATION
RT	COASTAL ZONE MANAGEMENT
RT	FRESHWATER AQUACULTURE
RT	LAKE FISHERIES
RT	LAKES
RT	PROPERTY RIGHTS
RT	SHORE PROTECTION
RT	WATER RIGHTS

LAKE SHORES
UF	lake beaches
RT	COASTAL MORPHOLOGY
RT	INLAND SEAS
RT	LAKES

LAKES
BT1	INLAND WATERS
NT1	ARTIFICIAL LAKES
NT1	DYSTROPHIC LAKES
NT1	EUTROPHIC LAKES
NT1	FRESHWATER LAKES
NT1	GLACIAL LAKES
NT1	MEROMICTIC LAKES
NT1	OLIGOTROPHIC LAKES
NT1	OXBOW LAKES
NT1	RELICT LAKES
NT1	SALT LAKES
NT1	STRIP MINE LAKES
NT1	TROPICAL LAKES
RT	BOTTOM WATER
RT	EUTROPHICATION

LAKES (cont'd)
RT	FOSSIL SEA WATER
RT	FRESH WATER
RT	HABITAT IMPROVEMENT
RT	HYDROLOGY
RT	IMPOUNDMENTS
RT	INLAND SEAS
RT	IRRIGATION
RT	JURISDICTION
RT	LACUSTRINE SEDIMENTATION
RT	LAKE BASINS
RT	LAKE CURRENTS
RT	LAKE DEPOSITS
RT	LAKE ICE
RT	LAKE MORPHOLOGY
RT	LAKE RECLAMATION
RT	LAKE SHORES
RT	LENITIC ENVIRONMENT
RT	LIMNOLOGICAL SURVEYS
RT	LIMNOLOGY
RT	MORPHOMETRY
RT	OVERTURN
RT	PITS
RT	PROPERTY RIGHTS
RT	RIVER OUTFLOW
RT	STOCKING (ORGANISMS)
RT	SWAMPS
RT	THERMAL STRATIFICATION
RT	VOLUME
RT	WATER BODIES
RT	WATER LEVELS
RT	WATER RESOURCES

LAMELLAR TEARING
BT1	DEFECTS
RT	CRACKS
RT	WELDING

LAMINAR BOUNDARY LAYER
BT1	BOUNDARY LAYERS
BT2	LAYERS
RT	LAMINAR FLOW
RT	TURBULENT BOUNDARY LAYER

LAMINAR FLOW
UF	poiseuille flow
BT1	FLUID FLOW
BT2	FLUID MOTION
NT1	COUETTE FLOW
RT	ATMOSPHERIC TURBULENCE
RT	CHANNEL FLOW
RT	FORCED CONVECTION
RT	LAMINAR BOUNDARY LAYER
RT	MOLECULAR VISCOSITY
RT	MULTIPHASE FLOW
RT	REYNOLDS NUMBER
RT	STRATIFIED FLOW
RT	TURBULENT FLOW
RT	UNSTEADY FLOW

LAMPARA NETS
BT1	SURROUNDING NETS
BT2	FISHING NETS
BT3	FISHING GEAR
RT	CEPHALOPOD FISHERIES
RT	PELAGIC FISHERIES
RT	SEINERS
RT	SEINING

LAMPREY ATTACHMENT
UF	attachment (lampreys)
RT	ECTOPARASITES
RT	LESIONS
RT	NOXIOUS ORGANISMS

LAND AND SEA BREEZES
BT1	BREEZES
BT2	LOCAL WINDS
BT3	WINDS
BT4	ATMOSPHERIC MOTION

LAND AND SEA BREEZES (cont'd)
RT	COASTAL METEOROLOGY
RT	LAND BREEZES
RT	SEA BREEZES

LAND BREEZES
SN	Blowing from land to sea
BT1	BREEZES
BT2	LOCAL WINDS
BT3	WINDS
BT4	ATMOSPHERIC MOTION
RT	LAND AND SEA BREEZES
RT	SEA BREEZES

LAND BRIDGES
RT	EUSTATIC CHANGES
RT	MIGRATIONS
RT	PALAEOECOLOGY

LAND FORMS
USE	**LANDFORMS**

LAND ICE
SN	Use of a more specific term is recommended
BT1	ICE
NT1	ICE CAPS
RT	FRESHWATER ICE
RT	ICE VOLUME
RT	PERMAFROST

LAND RECLAMATION
SN	Restoring degraded land or recovering land from the sea. Added in 1980
UF	coastal reclamation
UF	reclamation (land)
BT1	RECLAMATION
RT	COASTAL EROSION
RT	COASTAL ZONE MANAGEMENT
RT	IRRIGATION
RT	LAND USE
RT	POLDERS
RT	WETLANDS

LAND USE
SN	Added in 1980
UF	commercial land use
UF	industrial land use
UF	land utilization
RT	LAND RECLAMATION
RT	NATURAL RESOURCES
RT	RECREATION
RT	TOPOGRAPHY
RT	WATER USE

LAND UTILIZATION
USE	**LAND USE**

LANDFORMS
UF	land forms
BT1	TOPOGRAPHIC FEATURES
NT1	ALLUVIAL FANS
NT1	ALLUVIAL TERRACES
NT1	COASTAL LANDFORMS
NT2	BARRIER ISLANDS
NT2	BEACHES
NT3	BARRIER BEACHES
NT3	RAISED BEACHES
NT2	CAVES
NT2	CHENIER PLAINS
NT2	CLIFFS
NT2	DELTAS
NT2	HEADLANDS
NT3	CUSPATE FORELANDS
NT2	PALAEOSHORELINES
NT2	ROCKY SHORES
NT2	STACKS
NT2	TIDAL FLATS
NT1	COASTS

LANDFORMS (cont'd)	
NT2	EMERGENT SHORELINES
NT2	RELICT SHORELINES
NT2	STRANDLINES
NT2	SUBMERGED SHORELINES
NT3	RIA COASTS
NT1	CONTINENTS
NT1	FLOOD PLAINS
NT1	ISLANDS
NT2	ATOLLS
NT2	CAYS
NT2	OCEANIC ISLANDS
NT3	VOLCANIC ISLANDS
NT1	MOUNTAINS
NT1	PLAINS
NT1	PLATEAUX
NT1	RIFT VALLEYS
NT1	VALLEYS
NT2	RIVER VALLEYS
NT1	WETLANDS
NT2	MARSHES
NT3	SALT MARSHES
NT2	SWAMPS
NT3	MANGROVE SWAMPS
RT	ALLUVIAL DEPOSITS
RT	EROSION
RT	EROSION FEATURES
RT	GEOGRAPHY
RT	GEOMORPHOLOGY
RT	GLACIAL FEATURES
RT	PHYSIOGRAPHIC PROVINCES
RT	SUBAEREAL TOPOGRAPHY
RT	TOPOGRAPHIC MAPS
RT	TOPOGRAPHY

LANDING STATISTICS	
BT1	FISHERY STATISTICS
RT	CATCH STATISTICS
RT	COMMERCIAL FISHING
RT	FISHERY DATA
RT	FISHING TIME
RT	STOCK ASSESSMENT
RT	TRADE

LANDLOCKED COUNTRIES	
USE	**LANDLOCKED STATES**

LANDLOCKED STATES	
SN	Added in 1980
UF	continental nations
UF	landlocked countries
BT1	COUNTRIES
RT	COASTAL STATES
RT	INLAND FISHERIES
RT	INLAND WATERS

LANDSLIDES	
BT1	SLIDES
BT2	MASS MOVEMENT
BT3	SEDIMENT MOVEMENT
RT	CLIFFS
RT	COASTAL MORPHOLOGY
RT	CREEP
RT	GEOLOGICAL HAZARDS
RT	RETROGRADATION
RT	SLOPE STABILITY
RT	SLUMPING
RT	TSUNAMI GENERATION

LANGMUIR CIRCULATION	
BT1	FLUID MOTION
RT	CONVERGENCE
RT	DIVERGENCE
RT	SURFACE CIRCULATION
RT	SURFACE LAYERS
RT	VORTICES
RT	WINDROWS
RT	WINDS

LANTHANIDES	
USE	**RARE EARTHS**

LANTHANIUM	
UF	lanthanum
BT1	CHEMICAL ELEMENTS
RT	LANTHANIUM COMPOUNDS
RT	LANTHANIUM ISOTOPES
RT	RARE EARTHS
RT	TRANSITION ELEMENTS

LANTHANIUM COMPOUNDS	
RT	CHEMICAL COMPOUNDS
RT	LANTHANIUM

LANTHANIUM ISOTOPES	
BT1	ISOTOPES
RT	LANTHANIUM

LANTHANUM	
USE	**LANTHANIUM**

LAPLACE EQUATION	
BT1	EQUATIONS
RT	HARMONIC FUNCTIONS
RT	POISSON'S EQUATION
RT	TIDAL EQUATIONS

LAPLACE TRANSFORMATION	
BT1	FUNCTIONAL ANALYSIS
BT2	NUMERICAL ANALYSIS
BT3	MATHEMATICAL ANALYSIS
RT	DIFFERENTIAL EQUATIONS

LARGE SPAR BUOYS	
UF	flip spar buoys
BT1	SPAR BUOYS
BT2	BUOY HULLS
BT3	HULLS
RT	INSTRUMENT PLATFORMS
RT	RESEARCH VESSELS

LARVAE	
UF	larval stages
BT1	DEVELOPMENTAL STAGES
NT1	FISH LARVAE
NT2	FINGERLINGS
NT2	FRY
NT1	INVERTEBRATE LARVAE
NT2	CRUSTACEAN LARVAE
NT3	MEGALOPS
NT3	NAUPLII
NT3	PHYLLOSOMAE
NT3	ZOEAE
NT2	INSECT LARVAE
NT3	INSTARS
NT3	NYMPHS
NT3	PUPAE
NT2	MOLLUSCAN LARVAE
NT3	SPAT
NT3	VELIGERS
RT	EMBRYOS
RT	FECUNDITY
RT	LARVAL DEVELOPMENT
RT	MEROPLANKTON
RT	METAMORPHOSIS
RT	MOULTING
RT	NEOTENY
RT	REARING
RT	SEED (AQUACULTURE)
RT	ZOOPLANKTON CULTURE

LARVAE DEVELOPMENT	
USE	**LARVAL DEVELOPMENT**

LARVAL DEVELOPMENT	
UF	larvae development
BT1	BIOLOGICAL DEVELOPMENT
RT	CONTROLLED CONDITIONS
RT	DEVELOPMENTAL STAGES

LARVAL DEVELOPMENT (cont'd)	
RT	INVERTEBRATE LARVAE
RT	LARVAE
RT	METAMORPHOSIS
RT	MOLLUSCAN LARVAE
RT	REARING
RT	ZOOPLANKTON CULTURE

LARVAL SETTLEMENT	
UF	larval settling
UF	settlement (larvae)
BT1	BIOLOGICAL SETTLEMENT
RT	ARTIFICIAL SUBSTRATA
RT	COLONIZATION
RT	CULTCH
RT	INVERTEBRATE LARVAE
RT	METAMORPHOSIS
RT	MOLLUSCAN LARVAE
RT	SETTLING BEHAVIOUR
RT	SPAT
RT	SUBSTRATE PREFERENCES

LARVAL SETTLING	
USE	**LARVAL SETTLEMENT**

LARVAL STAGES	
USE	**LARVAE**

LARYNX	
SN	Before 1982 search RESPIRATORY ORGANS
BT1	RESPIRATORY ORGANS
BT2	ANIMAL ORGANS
BT3	BODY ORGANS
RT	SOUND PRODUCTION
RT	VOCAL ORGANS

LASER ALTIMETERS	
RT	ALTIMETERS
RT	LASER ALTIMETRY
RT	LASER BATHYMETERS

LASER ALTIMETRY	
BT1	ALTIMETRY
RT	LASER ALTIMETERS
RT	LASERS
RT	WAVE MEASUREMENT

LASER BATHYMETERS	
UF	airborne laser bathymeters
BT1	BATHYMETERS
BT2	MEASURING DEVICES
RT	AIRBORNE EQUIPMENT
RT	AIRBORNE SENSING
RT	BATHYMETRY
RT	DEPTH MEASUREMENT
RT	LASER ALTIMETERS
RT	LASER BATHYMETRY
RT	LASERS
RT	REMOTE SENSING EQUIPMENT

LASER BATHYMETRY	
BT1	BATHYMETRY
BT2	DEPTH MEASUREMENT
BT3	MEASUREMENT
RT	LASER BATHYMETERS
RT	LASERS

LASERS	
UF	optical masers
UF	pulsed lasers
RT	ELECTROMAGNETIC RADIATION
RT	HOLOGRAPHY
RT	INFRARED DETECTORS
RT	LASER ALTIMETRY
RT	LASER BATHYMETERS
RT	LASER BATHYMETRY
RT	LIDAR
RT	LIGHT SOURCES
RT	LUMINESCENCE
RT	OPTICS

LATENT HEAT OF FUSION
USE **FUSION HEAT**

LATENT HEAT OF SUBLIMATION
USE **SUBLIMATION HEAT**

LATENT HEAT OF VAPORIZATION
USE **VAPORIZATION HEAT**

LATENT HEAT TRANSFER
BT1 HEAT EXCHANGE
BT2 HEAT TRANSFER
RT BOWEN RATIO
RT EVAPORATION

LATERAL LINE
UF lateral line system
BT1 SENSE ORGANS
BT2 ANIMAL ORGANS
BT3 BODY ORGANS
RT FISH
RT MECHANICAL STIMULI
RT MECHANORECEPTORS

LATERAL LINE SYSTEM
USE **LATERAL LINE**

LATITUDE
BT1 GEOGRAPHICAL COORDINATES
BT2 COORDINATE SYSTEMS
NT1 PALAEOLATITUDE
RT EQUATOR
RT LATITUDINAL VARIATIONS
RT POSITION FIXING

LATITUDE CORRECTION
USE **GRAVITY CORRECTIONS**

LATITUDINAL VARIATIONS
SN Variation in the value of some
physical property along a meridian
BT1 SPATIAL VARIATIONS
RT LATITUDE
RT MERIDIONAL DISTRIBUTION

LATTICE CHARTS
SN Navigational charts overprinted
with intersecting patterns of
hyperbolic lines of position
BT1 NAVIGATIONAL CHARTS
BT2 MAPS
BT3 GRAPHICS
BT4 AUDIOVISUAL MATERIAL
RT RADIO NAVIGATION

LAUNCHING
RT CONSTRUCTION
RT DEPLOYMENT
RT INSTALLATION
RT LIFTING TACKLE
RT RECOVERY

LAVA
BT1 VOLCANIC ROCKS
BT2 IGNEOUS ROCKS
BT3 ROCKS
NT1 PILLOW LAVA
RT BASALTS
RT LAVA FLOWS

LAVA FLOWS
RT LAVA
RT VOLCANOES

LAW ENFORCEMENT
USE **SURVEILLANCE AND ENFORCEMENT**

LAW OF THE SEA
SN National and international laws
concerning marine water and its
resources. Before 1982 search also
SEA LAW
UF international law of the sea
UF ocean law
UF sea law
BT1 INTERNATIONAL LAW
BT2 LEGISLATION
RT BOUNDARIES
RT COUNTRIES
RT DEEP-SEA MINING
RT ENVIRONMENTAL LEGISLATION
RT FISHING RIGHTS
RT INTERNATIONAL BOUNDARIES
RT INTERNATIONAL WATERS
RT LEGAL ASPECTS
RT MULTIPLE USE OF RESOURCES
RT NAVIGATION
RT OCEAN POLICY
RT OCEAN SPACE
RT SEABED CONVENTIONS
RT TERRITORIAL WATERS

LAWRENCIUM
BT1 CHEMICAL ELEMENTS
RT LAWRENCIUM COMPOUNDS
RT LAWRENCIUM ISOTOPES
RT TRANSURANIC ELEMENTS

LAWRENCIUM COMPOUNDS
RT CHEMICAL COMPOUNDS
RT LAWRENCIUM

LAWRENCIUM ISOTOPES
BT1 ISOTOPES
RT LAWRENCIUM

LAYER OF NO MOTION
USE **LEVEL OF NO MOTION**

LAYERS
NT1 BOUNDARY LAYERS
NT2 ATMOSPHERIC BOUNDARY LAYER
NT2 BENTHIC BOUNDARY LAYER
NT2 COASTAL BOUNDARY LAYER
NT2 EKMAN LAYERS
NT3 BOTTOM EKMAN LAYER
NT3 SURFACE EKMAN LAYER
NT2 LAMINAR BOUNDARY LAYER
NT2 OCEANIC BOUNDARY LAYER
NT2 TURBULENT BOUNDARY LAYER
NT1 CORE LAYERS (WATER)
NT2 OXYGEN MAXIMUM LAYER
NT2 OXYGEN MINIMUM LAYER
NT2 SALINITY MAXIMUM LAYER
NT2 SALINITY MINIMUM LAYER
NT2 TEMPERATURE MAXIMUM LAYER
NT2 TEMPERATURE MINIMUM LAYER
NT1 DISCONTINUITY LAYERS
NT2 HALOCLINE
NT2 LYSOCLINE
NT2 NEPHELOID LAYER
NT2 PYCNOCLINE
NT2 SCATTERING LAYERS
NT2 THERMOCLINE
NT3 DIURNAL THERMOCLINE
NT3 PERMANENT THERMOCLINE
NT3 SEASONAL THERMOCLINE
NT1 WATER COLUMN
NT2 DEEP LAYER
NT2 MIXED LAYER
NT3 BOTTOM MIXED LAYER
NT3 SURFACE MIXED LAYER
NT2 SURFACE LAYERS
NT3 NEAR-SURFACE LAYER
NT3 SURFACE MICROLAYER
RT DEEP LAYER
RT DICOTHERMAL LAYER

LAYERS (cont'd)
RT EKMAN LAYERS
RT INVERSIONS
RT LEVELS
RT SEISMIC LAYERS
RT STRATIFICATION
RT SURFACE FILMS
RT SURFACES
RT TEMPERATURE INVERSIONS

LEACHING
BT1 SEPARATION PROCESSES
RT DEGRADATION
RT DIFFUSION
RT DISSOLUTION
RT FERTILIZERS
RT GEOCHEMISTRY
RT PERCOLATION
RT PERMEABILITY
RT SEDIMENT CHEMISTRY
RT SOLUBILITY
RT SOLUTIONS
RT SOLVENT EXTRACTION
RT WEATHERING

LEAD
BT1 CHEMICAL ELEMENTS
RT FERROMANGANESE NODULES
RT HEAVY METALS
RT HOT BRINES
RT LEAD COMPOUNDS
RT LEAD ISOTOPES
RT METALLIFEROUS SEDIMENTS
RT METALS
RT TRACE METALS

LEAD COMPOUNDS
RT CHEMICAL COMPOUNDS
RT LEAD

LEAD ISOTOPES
BT1 ISOTOPES
NT1 LEAD 210
RT LEAD

LEAD 210
BT1 LEAD ISOTOPES
BT2 ISOTOPES
RT ABSOLUTE AGE

LEADS
UF ice leads
NT1 FLAW LEADS
RT FLOATING ICE
RT NAVIGATION IN ICE
RT POLYNYAS

LEAF
USE **LEAVES**

LEAKS
RT DEFECTS
RT MARINE POLLUTION
RT REPAIR
RT SEALS (STOPPERS)

LEAKS (OIL)
USE **OIL SPILLS**

LEARNING BEHAVIOUR
SN Conditioned response or reflex of
aquatic organisms
BT1 BEHAVIOUR
NT1 IMPRINTING
RT CETOLOGY
RT STIMULI

ASFIS Thesaurus

LEASES
RT OIL AND GAS EXPLORATION

LEAST SQUARES METHOD
BT1 APPROXIMATION
BT2 NUMERICAL ANALYSIS
BT3 MATHEMATICAL ANALYSIS
RT REGRESSION ANALYSIS

LEAVES
SN Added in 1980
UF leaf
BT1 PLANT ORGANS
BT2 BODY ORGANS
RT HUMUS
RT PHOTOSYNTHESIS
RT STOMATA

LECTURES
UF talks
RT CONFERENCES
RT PUBLICITY MATERIAL

LEE EDDIES
SN Eddies formed on the lee of obstacles. Before 1982 search EDDIES (LEE)
UF eddies (lee)
BT1 WATER MOTION
RT CURRENT SCOURING
RT FLOW AROUND OBJECTS
RT OFFSHORE STRUCTURES
RT PILES
RT VORTICES

LEE WAVES
UF mountain waves
BT1 INTERNAL WAVES
BT2 WATER WAVES
RT ATMOSPHERIC MOTION
RT INTERFACIAL WAVES
RT INTERNAL WAVE GENERATION
RT STRATIFIED SHEAR FLOW
RT TOPOGRAPHIC EFFECTS

LEGAL ASPECTS
SN Before 1982 search LEGISLATION
RT COMMERCIAL LEGISLATION
RT DISPUTES
RT EXPLORATION RIGHTS
RT FISHERY DISPUTES
RT FISHERY REGULATIONS
RT FISHING RIGHTS
RT INTERNATIONAL AGREEMENTS
RT INTERNATIONAL LAW
RT JURISDICTION
RT LAW OF THE SEA
RT LEGISLATION
RT MORATORIA
RT NAVIGATION REGULATIONS
RT PERMITS
RT PLANNING
RT PROPERTY RIGHTS
RT PUBLIC HEALTH
RT RIGHTS
RT SAFETY REGULATIONS
RT TAXES
RT WATER USE REGULATIONS

LEGISLATION
UF regulations
NT1 AQUACULTURE REGULATIONS
NT1 BILATERAL AGREEMENTS
NT1 COMMERCIAL LEGISLATION
NT2 FISH INSPECTION REGULATIONS
NT1 ENVIRONMENTAL LEGISLATION
NT2 POLLUTION LEGISLATION
NT1 FISHERY INDUSTRY LEGISLATION
NT1 FISHERY REGULATIONS
NT2 MESH REGULATIONS

LEGISLATION (cont'd)
NT2 QUOTA REGULATIONS
NT2 SEASON REGULATIONS
NT2 SIZE-LIMIT REGULATIONS
NT2 WHALING REGULATIONS
NT1 INTERNATIONAL AGREEMENTS
NT2 POLLUTION CONVENTION
NT2 SEABED CONVENTIONS
NT1 INTERNATIONAL LAW
NT2 LAW OF THE SEA
NT1 LABOUR LEGISLATION
NT1 MARITIME LEGISLATION
NT1 NAVIGATION REGULATIONS
NT2 HARBOUR REGULATIONS
NT2 QUARANTINE REGULATIONS
NT1 OIL AND GAS LEGISLATION
NT1 SAFETY REGULATIONS
NT2 DIVING REGULATIONS
NT1 WATER USE REGULATIONS
RT EXTENDED JURISDICTION
RT GOVERNMENTS
RT HYGIENE
RT JURISDICTION
RT LABOUR
RT LEGAL ASPECTS
RT OCEAN SPACE
RT PATENTS
RT PLANNING
RT POLICIES
RT POLITICAL ASPECTS
RT RIGHTS
RT RIPARIAN RIGHTS
RT SURVEILLANCE AND ENFORCEMENT
RT WATER RIGHTS

LEGS (STRUCTURAL)
RT FIXED PLATFORMS

LEISURE ACTIVITIES
USE **RECREATION**

LENGTH
SN Used only as a qualifier
BT1 DIMENSIONS
NT1 MIXING LENGTH

LENGTH-WEIGHT RELATIONSHIPS
UF size-weight relationships
UF weight-length relationships
BT1 POPULATION FACTORS
RT BODY SHAPE
RT BODY SIZE
RT BODY WEIGHT
RT CONDITION FACTOR
RT GROWTH CURVES
RT POPULATION STRUCTURE
RT SIZE DISTRIBUTION
RT WEIGHT

LENITIC CURRENTS
USE **LAKE CURRENTS**

LENITIC ENVIRONMENT
UF lentic environments
BT1 INLAND WATER ENVIRONMENT
BT2 AQUATIC ENVIRONMENT
BT3 ENVIRONMENTS
RT APHOTIC ZONE
RT BENTHIC ENVIRONMENT
RT DISPHOTIC ZONE
RT EUPHOTIC ZONE
RT INLAND LAGOONS
RT LACUSTRINE SEDIMENTATION
RT LAGOONS
RT LAKES
RT LOTIC ENVIRONMENT
RT MARSHES
RT PELAGIC ENVIRONMENT
RT PONDS
RT RESERVOIRS (WATER)

LENTIC ENVIRONMENTS
USE **LENITIC ENVIRONMENT**

LEPTOCEPHALUS
USE **FISH LARVAE**

LESIONS
SN For either aquatic animals or man
UF scars
RT AUTOTOMY
RT ECTOPARASITES
RT INJURIES
RT LAMPREY ATTACHMENT
RT NOXIOUS ORGANISMS
RT REGENERATION
RT STINGING ORGANS

LETHAL EFFECTS
SN Added in 1980
RT BIOACCUMULATION
RT BIOLOGICAL POISONS
RT BIOTESTING
RT DISEASES
RT MORTALITY CAUSES
RT POLLUTANTS
RT POLLUTION EFFECTS
RT POLLUTION TOLERANCE
RT SUBLETHAL EFFECTS
RT TOXICANTS
RT TOXICITY
RT TOXICITY TESTS
RT TOXICOLOGY

LETHAL LIMITS
RT BIOASSAYS
RT BIOLOGICAL POISONS
RT HAZARD ASSESSMENT
RT LIMITING FACTORS
RT MORTALITY
RT PESTICIDES
RT POLLUTANTS
RT STARVATION
RT SURVIVAL
RT TEST ORGANISMS
RT TOLERANCE
RT TOXICITY
RT TOXICITY TESTS
RT TOXICITY TOLERANCE

LETHAL MUTATIONS
USE **MUTATIONS**

LEUCINE
BT1 AMINO ACIDS
BT2 ORGANIC ACIDS
BT3 ORGANIC COMPOUNDS

LEUKOCYTES
BT1 BLOOD CELLS
BT2 CELLS
RT HAEMOLYMPH

LEVEES
BT1 EMBANKMENTS
RT ALLUVIAL DEPOSITS
RT BANKS (TOPOGRAPHY)
RT DEEP-SEA CHANNELS
RT FLOOD PLAINS
RT FLUVIAL FEATURES
RT FLUVIAL TRANSPORT
RT RIVER BANKS
RT SEACHANNELS

LEVEL OF NO MOTION
UF layer of no motion
UF surface of no motion
BT1 REFERENCE LEVELS
RT GEOSTROPHIC FLOW
RT GEOSTROPHIC METHOD

LEVEL OF NO MOTION (cont'd)
RT	ISOBARIC SURFACES
RT	LEVELS

LEVELLING
RT	BENCH MARKS
RT	DATUM LEVELS
RT	GEODESY
RT	GEOID
RT	MEAN SEA LEVEL

LEVELS
RT	LAYERS
RT	LEVEL OF NO MOTION
RT	SEA LEVEL
RT	SURFACES
RT	WATER LEVELS

LEXICONS
USE	**GLOSSARIES**

LIABILITY
RT	ACCIDENTS
RT	INSURANCE

LIBRARIANS
SN	Added in 1980
UF	archivists
BT1	PERSONNEL
RT	DIRECTORIES
RT	DOCUMENTATION
RT	INFORMATION SCIENTISTS
RT	LIBRARIES

LIBRARIES
BT1	INFORMATION CENTRES
BT2	ORGANIZATIONS
RT	DATA CENTRES
RT	DATA COLLECTIONS
RT	DOCUMENTATION
RT	DOCUMENTS
RT	INFORMATION HANDLING
RT	INFORMATION RETRIEVAL
RT	LIBRARIANS

LICENCES
NT1	CONCESSIONS
NT1	PERMITS
RT	LICENSING

LICENSING
RT	LICENCES

LIDAR
SN	Coherent Light Detection And Rangefinding
RT	HYGROMETRY
RT	LASERS
RT	METEOROLOGICAL INSTRUMENTS
RT	RADAR
RT	REMOTE SENSING EQUIPMENT
RT	SODAR

LIFE CYCLE
SN	Morphological changes and growth from egg to adult stages
BT1	CYCLES
RT	ADULTS
RT	BIOLOGICAL AGE
RT	BIOLOGICAL AGING
RT	BIOLOGICAL DEVELOPMENT
RT	DEVELOPMENTAL STAGES
RT	DIFFERENTIAL DISTRIBUTION
RT	EMBRYOLOGY
RT	FINGERLINGS
RT	LIFE HISTORY
RT	LONGEVITY
RT	METAMORPHOSIS
RT	ONTOGENY
RT	OTOLITH READING

LIFE CYCLE (cont'd)
RT	REPRODUCTION
RT	REPRODUCTIVE CYCLE
RT	SCALE READING
RT	SEXUAL MATURITY
RT	SYNOPSIS

LIFE HISTORY
SN	Taxonomic, biological and ecological studies of a species
RT	AUTECOLOGY
RT	BIOLOGY
RT	LIFE CYCLE
RT	SYNOPSIS

LIFE JACKETS
RT	LIFE SAVING EQUIPMENT
RT	LIFEBOATS
RT	SURVIVAL AT SEA

LIFE SAVING EQUIPMENT
RT	LIFE JACKETS
RT	LIFE SUPPORT SYSTEMS

LIFE SCIENCES (AGRICULTURE)
USE	**AGRICULTURE**

LIFE SCIENCES (BIOLOGY)
USE	**BIOLOGY**

LIFE SCIENCES (MEDICINE)
USE	**MEDICINE**

LIFE SPAN
USE	**LONGEVITY**

LIFE SUPPORT SYSTEMS
UF	atmosphere (life support)
NT1	BREATHING APPARATUS
RT	AIR
RT	AIR CONDITIONING
RT	BREATHING MIXTURES
RT	COMPRESSORS
RT	DECOMPRESSION CHAMBERS
RT	DIVING
RT	DIVING EQUIPMENT
RT	DIVING SUITS
RT	HEATING
RT	LIFE SAVING EQUIPMENT
RT	MANNED VEHICLES
RT	MIXED GAS
RT	ONE-ATMOSPHERE SYSTEMS
RT	SUBMERSIBLES
RT	UMBILICALS
RT	UNDERWATER HABITATS
RT	UNDERWATER MEDICINE
RT	VENTILATION

LIFEBOATS
UF	liferafts
UF	rafts (life)
UF	survival capsules
BT1	SURFACE CRAFT
BT2	VEHICLES
RT	ACCIDENTS
RT	INFLATABLE CRAFT
RT	LIFE JACKETS
RT	MARINE TRANSPORTATION
RT	RIGHTING
RT	SAFETY DEVICES
RT	SHIP STABILITY
RT	SURVIVAL AT SEA

LIFERAFTS
USE	**LIFEBOATS**

LIFT-NETS
UF	scooping gear
BT1	FISHING NETS
BT2	FISHING GEAR
RT	BOATS
RT	COASTAL FISHERIES
RT	INLAND FISHERIES

LIFTING
UF	hoisting
UF	loading (operation)
RT	INSTALLATION
RT	LIFTING TACKLE
RT	REMOVAL
RT	SALVAGING

LIFTING GEAR
USE	**LIFTING TACKLE**

LIFTING TACKLE
UF	lifting gear
BT1	DECK EQUIPMENT
BT2	EQUIPMENT
NT1	CRANES
NT1	DAVITS
NT1	WINCHES
RT	LAUNCHING
RT	LIFTING
RT	SALVAGE EQUIPMENT
RT	SALVAGING

LIGANDS
RT	IONS
RT	MOLECULES
RT	ORGANOMETALLIC COMPLEXES

LIGASES
SN	Before 1982 search ENZYMES
BT1	ENZYMES
RT	ATP

LIGHT
UF	light rays
UF	visible radiation
BT1	ELECTROMAGNETIC RADIATION
BT2	RADIATIONS
RT	ABIOTIC FACTORS
RT	ATMOSPHERIC OPTICAL PHENOMENA
RT	BIOLUMINESCENCE
RT	CHEMILUMINESCENCE
RT	COLOUR
RT	FLUORESCENCE
RT	IRRADIANCE
RT	LIGHT ABSORPTION
RT	LIGHT ATTENUATION
RT	LIGHT FIELDS
RT	LIGHT INTENSITY
RT	LIGHT MEASUREMENT
RT	LIGHT MEASURING INSTRUMENTS
RT	LIGHT PENETRATION
RT	LIGHT REFLECTION
RT	LIGHT REFRACTION
RT	LIGHT SCATTERING
RT	LIGHT SOURCES
RT	LIGHT TRANSMISSION
RT	LUMINESCENCE
RT	OPTICAL PROPERTIES
RT	OPTICS
RT	PHOSPHORESCENCE
RT	PHOTOMETERS
RT	PHOTOMETRY
RT	PHOTOPERIODICITY
RT	PHOTORECEPTORS
RT	PHOTOSYNTHESIS
RT	PHOTOTAXIS
RT	PHOTOTROPISM
RT	PHYSICS
RT	POLARIZATION
RT	RADIANCE
RT	SOLAR ECLIPSE

LIGHT (cont'd)
RT	SOLAR RADIATION
RT	SPECTRAL COMPOSITION
RT	ULTRAVIOLET RADIATION

LIGHT ABSORPTION
SN	Before 1982 search also ABSORPTIVITY
UF	absorption (light)
BT1	ABSORPTION (PHYSICS)
RT	ABSORPTANCE
RT	ABSORPTION COEFFICIENT
RT	ABSORPTION SPECTRA
RT	CHROMATOGRAPHIC TECHNIQUES
RT	EXTINCTION COEFFICIENT
RT	LIGHT
RT	LIGHT ATTENUATION
RT	LIGHT PENETRATION
RT	LIGHT PROPAGATION
RT	LIGHT TRANSMISSION
RT	OPTICAL FILTERS
RT	PARTICLE CONCENTRATION
RT	PHOTOMETERS
RT	SUSPENDED PARTICULATE MATTER
RT	TRANSMISSOMETERS
RT	TRANSPARENCY
RT	TURBIDITY
RT	WATER COLOUR
RT	WATER TRANSPARENCY

LIGHT ATTENUATION
UF	attenuation (light)
BT1	ATTENUATION
RT	ATTENUANCE
RT	BEAM TRANSMITTANCE
RT	EXTINCTION COEFFICIENT
RT	LIGHT
RT	LIGHT ABSORPTION
RT	LIGHT PENETRATION
RT	LIGHT SCATTERING
RT	TRANSMITTANCE
RT	TURBIDITY
RT	WATER TRANSPARENCY

LIGHT DIFFRACTION
UF	diffraction (light)
BT1	DIFFRACTION
RT	ELECTROMAGNETIC RADIATION
RT	HOLOGRAPHY

LIGHT DISPERSION
BT1	DISPERSION
RT	COLOUR
RT	LIGHT REFRACTION
RT	REFRACTIVE INDEX

LIGHT DURATION
USE	**PHOTOPERIODS**

LIGHT EFFECTS
UF	photoperiod effects
BT1	ENVIRONMENTAL EFFECTS
RT	CHROMATIC BEHAVIOUR
RT	LIGHT PENETRATION
RT	NYCTIMERAL RHYTHMS
RT	OPTICAL PROPERTIES
RT	PHOTOPERIODICITY
RT	PHOTOPERIODS
RT	PHOTOTAXIS
RT	PHOTOTROPISM
RT	VERTICAL MIGRATIONS

LIGHT FIELDS
UF	radiance distribution
RT	FIELDS
RT	IRRADIANCE
RT	LIGHT
RT	LIGHT MEASUREMENT
RT	RADIANCE
RT	RADIATIVE TRANSFER

LIGHT FISHING
SN	Use of light to attract fish for capture with different types of gears
BT1	CATCHING METHODS
RT	ATTRACTING TECHNIQUES
RT	AUTOMATED FISHING PLATFORMS
RT	CEPHALOPOD FISHERIES
RT	FISHING
RT	PELAGIC FISHERIES
RT	PUMP FISHING
RT	SEINE NETS
RT	SURROUNDING NETS

LIGHT INTENSITY
UF	light quantity
RT	LIGHT
RT	LIGHT PENETRATION
RT	OPTICAL PROPERTIES
RT	PHOTOMETERS
RT	PHOTOMETRY

LIGHT MEASUREMENT
BT1	MEASUREMENT
NT1	PHOTOMETRY
RT	IMMERSION EFFECTS
RT	LIGHT
RT	LIGHT FIELDS
RT	LIGHT MEASURING INSTRUMENTS
RT	SPECTROPHOTOMETERS

LIGHT MEASURING INSTRUMENTS
BT1	MEASURING DEVICES
NT1	BEAM TRANSMITTANCE METERS
NT1	COSINE COLLECTORS
NT1	IRRADIANCE METERS
NT1	PHOTOMETERS
NT2	SPECTROPHOTOMETERS
NT1	QUANTA METERS
NT1	RADIANCE METERS
NT1	SCATTERANCE METERS
NT1	SECCHI DISCS
NT1	TRANSMISSOMETERS
RT	COLORIMETRIC TECHNIQUES
RT	COSINE RESPONSE
RT	FLUORIMETERS
RT	IMMERSION EFFECTS
RT	LIGHT
RT	LIGHT MEASUREMENT
RT	NEPHELOMETERS
RT	OPTICAL INSTRUMENTS
RT	PYRANOMETERS
RT	RADIOMETERS
RT	SENSORS
RT	TURBIDIMETERS

LIGHT MICROSCOPES
USE	**MICROSCOPES**

LIGHT MICROSCOPY
UF	optical microscopy
BT1	MICROSCOPY
BT2	ANALYTICAL TECHNIQUES
RT	CYTOLOGY
RT	HISTOLOGY
RT	MICROSCOPES
RT	OPTICAL PROPERTIES

LIGHT ORGANS
USE	**PHOTOPHORES**

LIGHT PENETRATION
RT	ABSORPTION COEFFICIENT
RT	ABSORPTION SPECTRA
RT	APHOTIC ZONE
RT	AQUATIC ENVIRONMENT
RT	CARBONATE COMPENSATION DEPTH
RT	COMPENSATION DEPTH
RT	DISPHOTIC ZONE
RT	EUPHOTIC ZONE
RT	LIGHT

LIGHT PENETRATION (cont'd)
RT	LIGHT ABSORPTION
RT	LIGHT ATTENUATION
RT	LIGHT EFFECTS
RT	LIGHT INTENSITY
RT	LIGHT REFLECTION
RT	LIGHT REFRACTION
RT	LIGHT SCATTERING
RT	OPTICAL PROPERTIES
RT	PHOTOMETERS
RT	PHOTOMETRY
RT	PHOTOSYNTHESIS
RT	PHOTOTAXIS
RT	PHOTOTROPISM
RT	PRIMARY PRODUCTION
RT	SECCHI DISCS
RT	SOLAR RADIATION
RT	SPECTRAL COMPOSITION
RT	TRANSMITTANCE
RT	TURBIDITY
RT	WATER TRANSPARENCY

LIGHT PROPAGATION
RT	LIGHT ABSORPTION
RT	LIGHT TRANSMISSION

LIGHT QUANTITY
USE	**LIGHT INTENSITY**

LIGHT RAYS
USE	**LIGHT**

LIGHT REFLECTION
UF	reflection (light)
BT1	REFLECTION
RT	AIR-WATER INTERFACE
RT	GLITTER
RT	LIGHT
RT	LIGHT PENETRATION
RT	LIGHT REFRACTION
RT	OPTICAL PROPERTIES
RT	REFLECTANCE

LIGHT REFRACTION
SN	Before 1982 search also REFRACTION
UF	refraction (light)
BT1	REFRACTION
RT	AIR-WATER INTERFACE
RT	COLORIMETRIC TECHNIQUES
RT	LIGHT
RT	LIGHT DISPERSION
RT	LIGHT PENETRATION
RT	LIGHT REFLECTION
RT	OPTICAL PROPERTIES
RT	REFRACTIVE INDEX
RT	TRANSPARENCY
RT	WATER TRANSPARENCY

LIGHT SCATTERING
UF	scattering (light)
NT1	PARTICLE SCATTERING
RT	FLUORESCENCE
RT	LIGHT
RT	LIGHT ATTENUATION
RT	LIGHT PENETRATION
RT	NEPHELOID LAYER
RT	NEPHELOMETERS
RT	PARTICLE CONCENTRATION
RT	POLARIZATION
RT	REFRACTIVE INDEX
RT	SCATTERANCE METERS
RT	SCATTERING COEFFICIENT
RT	SUSPENDED PARTICULATE MATTER
RT	TRANSMISSOMETERS
RT	TURBIDITY
RT	VOLUME SCATTERING FUNCTION
RT	WATER TRANSPARENCY

ASFIS Thesaurus

LIGHT SENSITIVE PIGMENTS
    USE   **VISUAL PIGMENTS**

LIGHT SOURCES
UF	underwater light sources
RT	LASERS
RT	LIGHT
RT	LIGHTING SYSTEMS
RT	UNDERWATER CAMERAS
RT	UNDERWATER PHOTOGRAPHY
RT	UNDERWATER TELEVISION
RT	VISIBILITY UNDERWATER
RT	WORKING UNDERWATER

LIGHT STIMULI
SN	Added in 1982
BT1	STIMULI
RT	PHOTOPERIODICITY
RT	PHOTORECEPTION
RT	PHOTOSYNTHESIS
RT	PHOTOTAXIS
RT	PHOTOTROPISM
RT	VISION

LIGHT TRANSMISSION
BT1	TRANSMISSION
RT	LIGHT
RT	LIGHT ABSORPTION
RT	LIGHT PROPAGATION
RT	OPTICAL FILTERS
RT	TRANSPARENCY

LIGHT VESSELS
    USE   **LIGHTSHIPS**

LIGHTERING
    USE   **LIGHTERS**

LIGHTERS
SN	A type of barge used to transport cargo from ships anchored offshore to the dockside
UF	lightering
BT1	SHIPS
BT2	SURFACE CRAFT
BT3	VEHICLES
RT	NAVIGATION

LIGHTHOUSES
BT1	NAVIGATIONAL AIDS

LIGHTING SYSTEMS
UF	illumination
RT	LIGHT SOURCES

LIGHTNING
BT1	ATMOSPHERIC ELECTRICITY
BT2	ELECTRICITY
RT	STORMS
RT	THUNDERSTORMS
RT	WEATHER

LIGHTSHIPS
UF	light vessels
BT1	SHIPS
BT2	SURFACE CRAFT
BT3	VEHICLES
RT	INSHORE STATIONS
RT	NAVIGATIONAL AIDS

LIMESTONE
BT1	CARBONATE ROCKS
RT	BIOHERMS
RT	CALCARENITE
RT	CALCITE
RT	DOLOMITIZATION
RT	MARLSTONE
RT	OOLITES
RT	SEDIMENTARY ROCKS

LIMITING FACTORS
UF	limiting nutrients
RT	ANTHROPOGENIC FACTORS
RT	ECOLOGICAL DISTRIBUTION
RT	ENVIRONMENTAL CONDITIONS
RT	ENVIRONMENTAL EFFECTS
RT	ENVIRONMENTAL FACTORS
RT	LETHAL LIMITS
RT	NUTRIENTS (MINERAL)
RT	TOLERANCE

LIMITING NUTRIENTS
    USE   **LIMITING FACTORS**

LIMNOLOGICAL DATA
UF	data (limnological)
BT1	DATA
RT	ACOUSTIC DATA
RT	BATHYMETRIC DATA
RT	CRUISES
RT	ENVIRONMENTAL CONDITIONS
RT	ENVIRONMENTAL FACTORS
RT	ENVIRONMENTAL SURVEYS
RT	LIMNOLOGICAL SURVEYS
RT	LIMNOLOGY
RT	MULTISHIP EXPEDITIONS
RT	TEMPERATURE DATA
RT	WATER SAMPLING
RT	WATER TEMPERATURE

LIMNOLOGICAL EQUIPMENT
BT1	EQUIPMENT
RT	BATHYMETERS
RT	BATHYTHERMOGRAPHS
RT	COLLECTING DEVICES
RT	HYDROGRAPHIC WIRE
RT	LABORATORY EQUIPMENT
RT	LIMNOLOGICAL SURVEYS
RT	LIMNOLOGY
RT	MEASURING DEVICES
RT	PLANKTON COLLECTING DEVICES
RT	RECORDING EQUIPMENT
RT	THERMOMETERS
RT	WATER SAMPLERS
RT	WATER SAMPLING
RT	WINCHES

LIMNOLOGICAL INSTITUTIONS
BT1	RESEARCH INSTITUTIONS
BT2	ORGANIZATIONS
RT	BIOLOGICAL INSTITUTIONS
RT	FISHERY INSTITUTIONS
RT	LIMNOLOGY
RT	RESEARCH VESSELS

LIMNOLOGICAL SURVEYS
BT1	ENVIRONMENTAL SURVEYS
BT2	SURVEYS
RT	ENVIRONMENTAL CONDITIONS
RT	HYDROLOGY
RT	LAKE CURRENTS
RT	LAKES
RT	LIMNOLOGICAL DATA
RT	LIMNOLOGICAL EQUIPMENT
RT	LIMNOLOGY
RT	RIVERS

LIMNOLOGISTS
    USE   **FRESHWATER SCIENTISTS**

LIMNOLOGY
NT1	CHEMICAL LIMNOLOGY
NT1	FISHERY LIMNOLOGY
NT1	PALAEOLIMNOLOGY
NT1	PHYSICAL LIMNOLOGY
RT	AQUATIC SCIENCES
RT	ENVIRONMENTAL SURVEYS
RT	EUTROPHICATION
RT	FRESH WATER
RT	FRESHWATER ECOLOGY

LIMNOLOGY (cont'd)
RT	FRESHWATER SCIENCES
RT	FRESHWATER SCIENTISTS
RT	HYDROGRAPHY
RT	HYDROLOGY
RT	INLAND WATER ENVIRONMENT
RT	LACUSTRINE SEDIMENTATION
RT	LAKES
RT	LIMNOLOGICAL DATA
RT	LIMNOLOGICAL EQUIPMENT
RT	LIMNOLOGICAL INSTITUTIONS
RT	LIMNOLOGICAL SURVEYS
RT	METEOROLOGY
RT	PONDS
RT	RESERVOIRS (WATER)
RT	WATER
RT	WATER ANALYSIS
RT	WATER SAMPLING

LIMNOLOGY (BIOLOGICAL)
    USE   **FRESHWATER ECOLOGY**

LIMNOLOGY (CHEMICAL)
    USE   **CHEMICAL LIMNOLOGY**

LIMNOLOGY (PHYSICAL)
    USE   **PHYSICAL LIMNOLOGY**

LIMONITE
BT1	OXIDE MINERALS
BT2	MINERALS

LINE FISHING
SN	Any type of fishing using lines, movable or fixed, with or without attached hooks, gorges, or other catching means
BT1	CATCHING METHODS
NT1	HANDLINING
NT1	JIGGING
NT1	LONGLINING
NT1	POLE-LINE FISHING
NT1	TROLLING
RT	BAIT
RT	BAIT FISH
RT	LINES
RT	REEF FISHERIES

LINE FISHING GEAR
    USE   **LINES**

LINE PIPE
    USE   **PIPES**

LINEAR PROGRAMMING
SN	Used only as a qualifier
BT1	MATHEMATICAL PROGRAMMING
BT2	OPERATIONS RESEARCH
RT	COMPUTER PROGRAMS
RT	ECONOMETRICS
RT	ECONOMIC MODELS
RT	GAME THEORY
RT	MATHEMATICAL MODELS

LINEAR WAVES
UF	airy waves
UF	infinitesimal waves
UF	sinusoidal waves
BT1	WATER WAVES
RT	NONLINEAR WAVES

LINERS
UF	trollers
BT1	FISHING VESSELS
BT2	SURFACE CRAFT
BT3	VEHICLES
RT	COASTAL FISHERIES
RT	DEMERSAL FISHERIES
RT	LINES
RT	PELAGIC FISHERIES

LINERS (cont'd)
RT   TROLLING

LINERS (PASSENGERS)
  USE   **PASSENGER SHIPS**

LINES
UF   drift-lines
UF   hand-lines
UF   line fishing gear
UF   set-lines
UF   troll-lines
BT1   FISHING GEAR
NT1   HOOKS
RT   COASTAL FISHERIES
RT   DEMERSAL FISHERIES
RT   INLAND FISHERIES
RT   JIGGING
RT   LINE FISHING
RT   LINERS
RT   LONGLINING
RT   PELAGIC FISHERIES
RT   SPORT FISHING
RT   TROLLING
RT   YARNS

LIPIDS
SN   Before 1982 search FATS
BT1   ORGANIC COMPOUNDS
NT1   COMPLEX LIPIDS
NT1   DERIVED LIPIDS
NT1   FATS
NT1   STEROIDS
NT2   STEROLS
NT3   ACANSTEROL
NT3   CHOLESTEROL
NT3   FUCOSTEROL
NT3   SITOSTEROLS
NT1   WAXES
RT   CHEMICAL EXTRACTION
RT   CHOLINE
RT   ESTERS
RT   LIPOPROTEINS
RT   NUTRITION

LIPOPROTEINS
SN   Before 1982 search PROTEINS
BT1   PROTEINS
BT2   ORGANIC COMPOUNDS
RT   BLOOD
RT   LIPIDS
RT   LYMPH

LIQUEFACTION
BT1   PHASE CHANGES
RT   FLUIDIZATION
RT   LIQUEFIED SEDIMENT FLOW
RT   LIQUIDS
RT   SLUMPING

LIQUEFIED NATURAL GAS
UF   lng
BT1   NATURAL GAS
BT2   PETROLEUM
BT3   FOSSIL FUELS
BT4   SUBSURFACE DEPOSITS
RT   GAS PROCESSING
RT   GAS TERMINALS

LIQUEFIED PETROLEUM GAS
UF   lpg
BT1   FUELS
RT   GAS TERMINALS
RT   PETROLEUM

LIQUEFIED SEDIMENT FLOW
  USE   **FLUIDIZED SEDIMENT FLOW**

LIQUEFIED SEDIMENT FLOW
BT1   SEDIMENT GRAVITY FLOWS
BT2   SEDIMENT MOVEMENT
RT   FLUIDIZATION
RT   GRAIN FLOW
RT   LIQUEFACTION

LIQUID FISH PRODUCTS
  USE   **FISH SILAGE**

LIQUIDS
BT1   FLUIDS
RT   DILUTION
RT   GASES
RT   LIQUEFACTION

LITERATURE REVIEWS
UF   literature surveys
UF   review (literature)
UF   review articles
UF   state-of-the-art reviews
RT   BIBLIOGRAPHIES
RT   DOCUMENTATION
RT   DOCUMENTS

LITERATURE SURVEYS
  USE   **LITERATURE REVIEWS**

LITHIFICATION
BT1   DIAGENESIS
BT2   SEDIMENTATION
RT   CEMENTATION
RT   COMPACTION
RT   COMPRESSION
RT   CONSOLIDATION

LITHIUM
BT1   CHEMICAL ELEMENTS
RT   ALKALI METALS
RT   LITHIUM COMPOUNDS
RT   LITHIUM ISOTOPES

LITHIUM COMPOUNDS
RT   CHEMICAL COMPOUNDS
RT   LITHIUM

LITHIUM ISOTOPES
BT1   ISOTOPES
RT   LITHIUM

LITHOFACIES
BT1   FACIES
RT   LITHOLOGY
RT   SEDIMENTS

LITHOGENESIS
RT   LITHOLOGY
RT   ROCKS

LITHOLOGY
BT1   GEOLOGY
BT2   EARTH SCIENCES
RT   LITHOFACIES
RT   LITHOGENESIS
RT   PETROLOGY

LITHOSPHERE
SN   Use as tectonic term. Do not use as
       part of classification: atmosphere,
       hydrosphere, lithosphere
BT1   EARTH STRUCTURE
RT   ASTHENOSPHERE
RT   BENIOFF ZONE
RT   EARTH
RT   EARTH CRUST
RT   MOHO
RT   PLATE TECTONICS
RT   PLATES
RT   UPPER MANTLE

LITHOSPHERIC PLATES
  USE   **PLATES**

LITTORAL CURRENTS
  USE   **NEARSHORE CURRENTS**

LITTORAL DEPOSITS
BT1   SEDIMENTS
RT   LONGSHORE SEDIMENT TRANSPORT
RT   NEARSHORE SEDIMENTATION

LITTORAL DRIFT
  USE   **LONGSHORE SEDIMENT TRANSPORT**

LITTORAL SEDIMENTATION
  USE   **NEARSHORE SEDIMENTATION**

LITTORAL STATES
  USE   **COASTAL STATES**

LITTORAL TRANSPORT
  USE   **LONGSHORE SEDIMENT TRANSPORT**

LITTORAL ZONATION
  USE   **ECOLOGICAL ZONATION**

LITTORAL ZONE
BT1   BENTHIC ENVIRONMENT
BT2   AQUATIC ENVIRONMENT
BT3   ENVIRONMENTS
NT1   EULITTORAL ZONE
NT1   SUBLITTORAL ZONE
NT1   SUPRALITTORAL ZONE
RT   BEACHES
RT   COASTAL WATERS
RT   COASTAL ZONE
RT   CONTINENTAL SHELVES
RT   ECOLOGICAL ZONATION
RT   EPIPELAGIC ZONE
RT   NERITIC PROVINCE
RT   SHALLOW WATER

LIVE FEED
  USE   **FOOD ORGANISMS**

LIVE FOOD
  USE   **FOOD ORGANISMS**

LIVE STORAGE
SN   Storage of live fish. Added in 1980
RT   FISH CULTURE
RT   FISH STORAGE
RT   STORAGE

LIVE WEIGHT
  USE   **BIOMASS**

LIVER
BT1   DIGESTIVE GLANDS
BT2   GLANDS
BT3   SECRETORY ORGANS
RT   BILE
RT   GLYCOGEN
RT   METABOLISM

LIVESTOCK FOOD
SN   Added in 1982
RT   AQUATIC PLANTS
RT   FISH WASTES
RT   FOOD
RT   FRESHWATER WEEDS
RT   PLANT UTILIZATION

LIVING FOSSILS
SN   Any organism alive today whose
       closest relatives are known only as
       fossils. Added in 1980
RT   FOSSILS
RT   RELICT SPECIES

ASFIS Thesaurus

LIVING QUARTERS
USE **ACCOMMODATION**

LIVING RESOURCES
SN   Applies to both plant and animal
        resources of the aquatic
        environment. Added in 1980
UF   aquatic living resources
UF   biological resources
UF   biotic natural resources
BT1   NATURAL RESOURCES
BT2   RESOURCES
NT1   BOTANICAL RESOURCES
NT1   FISHERY RESOURCES
RT   ANIMAL PRODUCTS
RT   AQUACULTURE PRODUCTS
RT   AQUATIC ORGANISMS
RT   COMMERCIAL SPECIES
RT   FISHERY DEVELOPMENT
RT   FISHERY MANAGEMENT
RT   FISHERY ORGANIZATIONS
RT   FOOD RESOURCES
RT   MARINE MAMMALS
RT   MARINE RESOURCES
RT   POTENTIAL RESOURCES
RT   PROCESSED FISHERY PRODUCTS
RT   PROTECTED RESOURCES
RT   RARE RESOURCES
RT   RENEWABLE RESOURCES
RT   RESOURCE CONSERVATION
RT   SEAWEED PRODUCTS
RT   SEDENTARY SPECIES
RT   UNCONVENTIONAL RESOURCES
RT   UNDERUTILIZED SPECIES

LNG
USE   **LIQUEFIED NATURAL GAS**

LOAD PRESSURE
USE   **LOADS (FORCES)**

LOADING (OPERATION)
USE   **LIFTING**

LOADING BUOYS
BT1   MOORING BUOYS
BT2   BUOYS
RT   ARTICULATED COLUMNS
RT   FLOATING HOSES
RT   OFFSHORE TERMINALS
RT   SINGLE POINT MOORINGS
RT   TANKER LOADING
RT   TANKER SHIPS

LOADS (FORCES)
UF   load pressure
BT1   FORCES (MECHANICS)
NT1   CURRENT FORCES
NT1   CYCLIC LOADING
NT1   DYNAMIC LOADS
NT1   EARTHQUAKE LOADING
NT1   ICE LOADS
NT1   OCEAN LOADING
NT1   WAVE FORCES
NT1   WAVE-INDUCED LOADING
NT1   WIND PRESSURE
RT   BALLAST
RT   BEARING CAPACITY
RT   PRESSURE
RT   WEIGHT

LOBSTER CULTURE
SN   Before 1982 search CRUSTACEAN CULTURE
BT1   CRUSTACEAN CULTURE
BT2   SHELLFISH CULTURE
BT3   AQUACULTURE
RT   CAGE CULTURE
RT   CULTURE TANKS
RT   MARINE AQUACULTURE

LOBSTER FISHERIES
SN   Added in 1982
UF   cape rock lobster fisheries
UF   crayfish fisheries
UF   deep sea lobster fisheries
UF   northern lobster fisheries
UF   rocklobster fisheries
UF   spiny lobster fisheries
BT1   CRUSTACEAN FISHERIES
BT2   FISHERIES
RT   COASTAL FISHERIES
RT   DEMERSAL FISHERIES
RT   MARINE FISHERIES
RT   TRAP FISHING

LOBSTER POTS
USE   **POTS**

LOCAL MOVEMENTS
SN   Movements of organisms other than
        migrational movements, within home
        range. Added in 1980
UF   movements (local)
RT   ACTIVITY PATTERNS
RT   HOME RANGE
RT   HOMING BEHAVIOUR
RT   LOCOMOTION
RT   MIGRATIONS

LOCAL NAMES
USE   **VERNACULAR NAMES**

LOCAL WINDS
UF   bora
BT1   WINDS
BT2   ATMOSPHERIC MOTION
NT1   BREEZES
NT2   LAND AND SEA BREEZES
NT2   LAND BREEZES
NT2   SEA BREEZES
NT1   MISTRAL

LOCATING
NT1   UNDERWATER OBJECT LOCATION
RT   ACOUSTIC BEACONS
RT   DETECTION
RT   DYNAMIC POSITIONING
RT   HOLE RE-ENTRY
RT   POSITION FIXING
RT   SALVAGING
RT   SEARCH AND RESCUE
RT   SONAR
RT   SURVEYING
RT   TRACKING
RT   WRECK LOCATION

LOCATIONS (WORKING)
RT   OFFSHORE OPERATIONS
RT   WORKING UNDERWATER

LOCKOUT SUBMERSIBLES
SN   Manned submersibles from which
        divers may exit and re-enter
BT1   SUBMERSIBLES
BT2   MANNED VEHICLES
BT3   UNDERWATER VEHICLES
BT4   VEHICLES
RT   DECOMPRESSION CHAMBERS
RT   SATURATION DIVING

LOCOMOTION
SN   Including theory of locomotion in
        aquatic organisms
NT1   FLYING
NT1   SWIMMING
RT   ACTIVITY PATTERNS
RT   ANIMAL APPENDAGES
RT   ANIMAL NAVIGATION
RT   CILIA
RT   FINS

LOCOMOTION (cont'd)
RT   LOCAL MOVEMENTS
RT   LOCOMOTORY APPENDAGES

LOCOMOTORY APPENDAGES
UF   locomotory organs
BT1   ANIMAL APPENDAGES
NT1   FINS
NT2   BONY FINS
NT1   WINGS
RT   ANIMAL NAVIGATION
RT   FLAGELLA
RT   LOCOMOTION

LOCOMOTORY ORGANS
USE   **LOCOMOTORY APPENDAGES**

LOGBOOKS
UF   scientific logbooks
UF   ships logbooks
BT1   DOCUMENTS
RT   ARCHIVES
RT   CRUISES
RT   RECORDS
RT   SHIP SPEED
RT   SHIPS
RT   STATION LISTS

LOGGING
NT1   WELL LOGGING

LONG-CRESTED WAVES
BT1   SURFACE WATER WAVES
BT2   WATER WAVES
RT   DIRECTIONAL SPECTRA
RT   SHORT-CRESTED WAVES
RT   WAVE CRESTS
RT   WAVE DIRECTION

LONG GRAVITY WAVES
USE   **SHALLOW-WATER WAVES**

LONG-LINE CULTURE
USE   **OFF-BOTTOM CULTURE**

LONG-PERIOD SEISMIC WAVES
USE   **SEISMIC WAVES**

LONG-PERIOD TIDES
BT1   TIDES
BT2   TIDAL MOTION
RT   NODAL TIDES
RT   POLE TIDES

LONG-PERIOD WATER WAVES
USE   **SHALLOW-WATER WAVES**

LONG-PERIOD WAVES
USE   **SHALLOW-WATER WAVES**

LONG-TERM CHANGES
UF   long-term variations
UF   secular fluctuations
BT1   TEMPORAL VARIATIONS
NT1   SEA LEVEL CHANGES
RT   BASELINE STUDIES
RT   CLIMATIC CHANGES
RT   CLIMATOLOGY
RT   DATA COLLECTIONS
RT   LONG-TERM RECORDS
RT   MONITORING
RT   OCEANOGRAPHY
RT   PERIODIC VARIATIONS
RT   PREDICTION
RT   SHORT-TERM CHANGES
RT   SOLAR ACTIVITY
RT   SOLAR-TERRESTRIAL ACTIVITY
RT   TEMPORAL DISTRIBUTION

LONG-TERM PLANNING
SN   Added in 1980
BT1   PLANNING
RT   SHORT-TERM PLANNING

LONG-TERM RECORDS
RT   CURRENT DATA
RT   LONG-TERM CHANGES
RT   SALINITY DATA
RT   TEMPERATURE DATA
RT   TEMPORAL DISTRIBUTION

LONG-TERM VARIATIONS
USE   **LONG-TERM CHANGES**

LONG WAVE RADIATION
USE   **TERRESTRIAL RADIATION**

LONG WAVE-SHORT WAVE INTERACTIONS
USE   **SHORT WAVE-LONG WAVE INTERACTIONS**

LONG WAVES
USE   **SHALLOW-WATER WAVES**

LONGEVITY
SN   Added in 1980
UF   life span
BT1   BIOLOGICAL PROPERTIES
BT2   PROPERTIES
RT   BIOLOGICAL AGE
RT   BIOLOGICAL AGING
RT   LIFE CYCLE
RT   MORTALITY

LONGITUDE
BT1   GEOGRAPHICAL COORDINATES
BT2   COORDINATE SYSTEMS
RT   POSITION FIXING

LONGITUDINAL DISPERSION
BT1   DISPERSION
RT   ESTUARINE DYNAMICS

LONGLINING
BT1   LINE FISHING
BT2   CATCHING METHODS
RT   BAIT FISH
RT   DEMERSAL FISHERIES
RT   FLATFISH FISHERIES
RT   LINES
RT   PELAGIC FISHERIES
RT   TUNA FISHERIES

LONGSHORE BARS
BT1   NEARSHORE BARS
BT2   BEACH FEATURES
RT   BREAK-POINT BARS

LONGSHORE CURRENTS
SN   Currents bordering coastlines.
       Before 1982 search ONSHORE CURRENTS
BT1   NEARSHORE CURRENTS
BT2   WATER CURRENTS
BT3   WATER MOTION
RT   BEACH CUSPS
RT   COASTAL JETS
RT   ESTUARINE DYNAMICS
RT   GROYNES
RT   LAKE CURRENTS
RT   LONGSHORE SEDIMENT TRANSPORT
RT   MOMENTUM TRANSFER
RT   RIP CURRENTS
RT   SURF ZONE
RT   TIDAL CURRENTS
RT   UPWELLING
RT   WAVE PROCESSES ON BEACHES
RT   WAVE SETUP
RT   WAVE-CURRENT INTERACTION
RT   WIND-DRIVEN CURRENTS

LONGSHORE DRIFT
USE   **LONGSHORE SEDIMENT TRANSPORT**

LONGSHORE SAND TRANSPORT
USE   **LONGSHORE SEDIMENT TRANSPORT**

LONGSHORE SEDIMENT TRANSPORT
SN   Before 1982 search also LONGSHORE
       SAND TRANSPORT
UF   littoral drift
UF   littoral transport
UF   longshore drift
UF   longshore sand transport
BT1   SEDIMENT TRANSPORT
RT   BARRIER SPITS
RT   BEACH NOURISHMENT
RT   GROYNES
RT   LITTORAL DEPOSITS
RT   LONGSHORE CURRENTS

LOPHOPHORES
SN   Filter feeding organs. Added in 1980
BT1   ALIMENTARY ORGANS
BT2   ANIMAL ORGANS
BT3   BODY ORGANS
RT   FILTER FEEDERS

LORAN
BT1   RADIO NAVIGATION
BT2   POSITION FIXING
RT   NAVIGATIONAL TABLES

LOTIC ENVIRONMENT
BT1   INLAND WATER ENVIRONMENT
BT2   AQUATIC ENVIRONMENT
BT3   ENVIRONMENTS
RT   BENTHIC ENVIRONMENT
RT   LENITIC ENVIRONMENT
RT   RIVERS
RT   SPRING STREAMS
RT   WATER SPRINGS

LOVE WAVES
BT1   SURFACE SEISMIC WAVES
BT2   SEISMIC WAVES
BT3   ELASTIC WAVES

LOW FREQUENCY
SN   Used only as a qualifier
BT1   FREQUENCY

LOW PRESSURE SYSTEMS
NT1   CYCLONES
NT1   LOW PRESSURE TROUGHS
NT2   EQUATORIAL TROUGH
RT   ATMOSPHERIC DISTURBANCES
RT   ATMOSPHERIC PRESSURE
RT   TORNADOES

LOW PRESSURE TROUGHS
BT1   LOW PRESSURE SYSTEMS
NT1   EQUATORIAL TROUGH
RT   ATMOSPHERIC DISTURBANCES

LOW TEMPERATURE
BT1   TEMPERATURE
BT2   THERMODYNAMIC PROPERTIES
BT3   PHYSICAL PROPERTIES
BT4   PROPERTIES
RT   METAMORPHISM
RT   PHASE CHANGES

LOW TEMPERATURE WEATHERING
USE   **HALMYROLYSIS**

LOW TIDE
UF   low water
RT   EBB CURRENTS
RT   HIGH WATER
RT   TIDAL CYCLES

LOW TIDE (cont'd)
RT   TIDES

LOW-VELOCITY LAYER
BT1   SEISMIC LAYERS
BT2   EARTH STRUCTURE
RT   ASTHENOSPHERE
RT   SEISMIC VELOCITIES

LOW WATER
USE   **LOW TIDE**

LOWER MANTLE
BT1   EARTH MANTLE
BT2   EARTH STRUCTURE
RT   UPPER MANTLE

LOWER TERTIARY
USE   **PALAEOGENE**

LOWEST ASTRONOMICAL TIDES
BT1   ASTRONOMICAL TIDES
BT2   TIDES
BT3   TIDAL MOTION
RT   EXTREME VALUES
RT   HIGHEST ASTRONOMICAL TIDES
RT   TIDAL DATUM

LPG
USE   **LIQUEFIED PETROLEUM GAS**

LUBRICANTS
RT   FUELS
RT   MOTORS

LUCIFERIN
UF   photophelein
BT1   PROTEINS
BT2   ORGANIC COMPOUNDS
RT   LUMINOUS ORGANISMS

LUMINESCENCE
NT1   BIOLUMINESCENCE
NT1   CHEMILUMINESCENCE
NT1   FLUORESCENCE
NT1   PHOSPHORESCENCE
RT   AIRGLOW
RT   CHEMICAL PROPERTIES
RT   ELECTRICAL PROPERTIES
RT   ELECTROMAGNETIC RADIATION
RT   LASERS
RT   LIGHT
RT   LUMINOUS ORGANISMS
RT   OPTICAL PROPERTIES
RT   PHYSICAL PROPERTIES
RT   SPECTRAL COMPOSITION

LUMINESCENT ORGANS
USE   **PHOTOPHORES**

LUMINOUS ORGANISMS
SN   Added in 1982
BT1   AQUATIC ORGANISMS
RT   LUCIFERIN
RT   LUMINESCENCE
RT   PHOTOPHORES
RT   PLANKTON

LUMINOUS ORGANS
USE   **PHOTOPHORES**

LUNAR CYCLES
USE   **MOON PHASES**

LUNAR DIURNAL TIDES
BT1   LUNAR TIDES
BT2   TIDES
BT3   TIDAL MOTION
RT   TIDAL CONSTITUENTS

LUNAR EFFECTS
USE   **MOON PHASES**

LUNAR SEMIDIURNAL TIDES
BT1   LUNAR TIDES
BT2   TIDES
BT3   TIDAL MOTION
RT   TIDAL CONSTITUENTS

LUNAR TIDES
SN   Before 1982 search TIDES
BT1   TIDES
BT2   TIDAL MOTION
NT1   LUNAR DIURNAL TIDES
NT1   LUNAR SEMIDIURNAL TIDES
RT   TIDAL CONSTITUENTS

LUNGS
SN   Before 1982 search RESPIRATORY ORGANS
BT1   RESPIRATORY ORGANS
BT2   ANIMAL ORGANS
BT3   BODY ORGANS
RT   AEROBIC RESPIRATION

LURES
USE   **BAIT**

LURING
USE   **ATTRACTING TECHNIQUES**

LUTETIUM
BT1   CHEMICAL ELEMENTS
RT   LUTETIUM COMPOUNDS
RT   LUTETIUM ISOTOPES
RT   RARE EARTHS
RT   TRANSITION ELEMENTS

LUTETIUM COMPOUNDS
RT   CHEMICAL COMPOUNDS
RT   LUTETIUM

LUTETIUM ISOTOPES
BT1   ISOTOPES
RT   LUTETIUM

LUTITES
RT   ARGILLACEOUS DEPOSITS
RT   BENTONITE
RT   MARLSTONE
RT   MUDSTONE
RT   SHALE
RT   SILT
RT   SILTSTONE

LYASES
SN   Before 1982 search ENZYMES
BT1   ENZYMES

LYMPH
SN   Before 1982 search BODY FLUIDS
BT1   BODY FLUIDS
RT   LIPOPROTEINS
RT   LYMPHATIC SYSTEM
RT   LYMPHOCYTES

LYMPH SYSTEM
USE   **LYMPHATIC SYSTEM**

LYMPH VESSELS
USE   **LYMPHATIC SYSTEM**

LYMPHATIC SYSTEM
SN   Added in 1980
UF   lymph system
UF   lymph vessels
BT1   ANATOMICAL STRUCTURES
RT   LYMPH

LYMPHOCYTES
BT1   BLOOD CELLS
BT2   CELLS
RT   EXCRETORY PRODUCTS
RT   LYMPH
RT   SPLEEN

LYSINE
BT1   AMINO ACIDS
BT2   ORGANIC ACIDS
BT3   ORGANIC COMPOUNDS

LYSOCLINE
BT1   DISCONTINUITY LAYERS
BT2   LAYERS
RT   CARBONATE COMPENSATION DEPTH

MACHINERY
BT1   EQUIPMENT

MACKEREL FISHERIES
SN   Added in 1982
BT1   FINFISH FISHERIES
BT2   FISHERIES
RT   DEMERSAL FISHERIES
RT   MARINE FISHERIES
RT   PELAGIC FISHERIES
RT   TUNA FISHERIES

MACROBENTHOS
USE   **BENTHOS**

MACROPHAGES
SN   A large phagocytic cell. Added in 1982
BT1   BLOOD CELLS
BT2   CELLS
RT   DISEASE CONTROL
RT   PHAGOCYTOSIS

MACROPLANKTON
USE   **ZOOPLANKTON**

MAFIC MAGMA
UF   mafics
BT1   MAGMA

MAFICS
USE   **MAFIC MAGMA**

MAGHEMITE
BT1   OXIDE MINERALS
BT2   MINERALS

MAGMA
UF   magmatism
NT1   MAFIC MAGMA
RT   ASTHENOSPHERE
RT   HOT SPOTS
RT   IGNEOUS ROCKS
RT   MAGMA CHAMBERS
RT   VOLCANISM

MAGMA CHAMBERS
UF   magma reservoirs
RT   IGNEOUS INTRUSIONS
RT   MAGMA

MAGMA RESERVOIRS
USE   **MAGMA CHAMBERS**

MAGMATISM
USE   **MAGMA**

MAGNESITE
BT1   CARBONATE MINERALS
BT2   MINERALS

MAGNESIUM
BT1   CHEMICAL ELEMENTS
RT   ALKALINE EARTH METALS
RT   BARIUM
RT   DISSOLVED CHEMICALS
RT   FERROMANGANESE NODULES
RT   MAGNESIUM COMPOUNDS
RT   MAGNESIUM ISOTOPES
RT   TRACE ELEMENTS

MAGNESIUM COMPOUNDS
BT1   ALKALINE EARTH METAL COMPOUNDS
NT1   MAGNESIUM FLUORIDES
NT1   MAGNESIUM PHOSPHATES
NT1   MAGNESIUM SILICATES
NT1   MAGNESIUM SULPHATES
RT   CHEMICAL COMPOUNDS
RT   MAGNESIUM

MAGNESIUM FLUORIDES
BT1   MAGNESIUM COMPOUNDS
BT2   ALKALINE EARTH METAL COMPOUNDS
RT   FLUORIDES

MAGNESIUM ISOTOPES
BT1   ISOTOPES
RT   MAGNESIUM

MAGNESIUM PHOSPHATES
BT1   MAGNESIUM COMPOUNDS
BT2   ALKALINE EARTH METAL COMPOUNDS
RT   PHOSPHATES

MAGNESIUM SILICATES
BT1   MAGNESIUM COMPOUNDS
BT2   ALKALINE EARTH METAL COMPOUNDS
RT   SILICATES

MAGNESIUM SULPHATES
BT1   MAGNESIUM COMPOUNDS
BT2   ALKALINE EARTH METAL COMPOUNDS
RT   SULPHATES

MAGNETIC ANOMALIES
BT1   ANOMALIES
RT   GEOMAGNETIC FIELD
RT   GRAVITY ANOMALIES
RT   MAGNETIC ANOMALY CHARTS
RT   MAGNETIC DATA
RT   MAGNETIC EXPLORATION
RT   PALAEOMAGNETISM
RT   SEAFLOOR SPREADING

MAGNETIC ANOMALY CHARTS
BT1   MAGNETIC CHARTS
BT2   GEOLOGICAL MAPS
BT3   MAPS
BT4   GRAPHICS
RT   MAGNETIC ANOMALIES

MAGNETIC CHARTS
BT1   GEOLOGICAL MAPS
BT2   MAPS
BT3   GRAPHICS
BT4   AUDIOVISUAL MATERIAL
NT1   MAGNETIC ANOMALY CHARTS
RT   ISOMAGNETIC LINES
RT   MAGNETIC DATA
RT   MAGNETIC EXPLORATION
RT   MAGNETIC INTENSITY
RT   MAGNETIC VARIATIONS

MAGNETIC COMPASSES
USE   **COMPASSES**

MAGNETIC CORE ORIENTATION
USE   **CORE ORIENTATION**

MAGNETIC DATA
BT1	GEOPHYSICAL DATA
BT2	DATA
RT	MAGNETIC ANOMALIES
RT	MAGNETIC CHARTS
RT	MAGNETIC EXPLORATION

MAGNETIC DECLINATION
USE	**MAGNETIC VARIATIONS**

MAGNETIC DIP
USE	**MAGNETIC INCLINATION**

MAGNETIC EXPLORATION
UF	geomagnetic surveys
UF	magnetic surveys
BT1	GEOPHYSICAL EXPLORATION
BT2	EXPLORATION
RT	AEROMAGNETIC SURVEYS
RT	COAST EFFECT
RT	GEOPHYSICAL SURVEYS
RT	MAGNETIC ANOMALIES
RT	MAGNETIC CHARTS
RT	MAGNETIC DATA
RT	MAGNETOMETERS

MAGNETIC FIELD (EARTH)
USE	**GEOMAGNETIC FIELD**

MAGNETIC FIELD ELEMENTS
BT1	MAGNETIC PROPERTIES
BT2	PHYSICAL PROPERTIES
BT3	PROPERTIES
NT1	MAGNETIC INCLINATION
NT1	MAGNETIC INTENSITY
NT1	MAGNETIC VARIATIONS
RT	GEOMAGNETIC FIELD

MAGNETIC FIELDS
NT1	GEOMAGNETIC FIELD
RT	ELECTROMAGNETIC RADIATION
RT	ELECTROMAGNETISM
RT	MAGNETISM
RT	MAGNETS

MAGNETIC INCLINATION
UF	magnetic dip
BT1	MAGNETIC FIELD ELEMENTS
BT2	MAGNETIC PROPERTIES
BT3	PHYSICAL PROPERTIES
BT4	PROPERTIES
RT	GEOMAGNETIC FIELD
RT	ISOMAGNETIC LINES

MAGNETIC INTENSITY
BT1	MAGNETIC FIELD ELEMENTS
BT2	MAGNETIC PROPERTIES
BT3	PHYSICAL PROPERTIES
BT4	PROPERTIES
RT	GEOMAGNETIC FIELD
RT	ISOMAGNETIC LINES
RT	MAGNETIC CHARTS

MAGNETIC PARTICLE TESTING
USE	**NONDESTRUCTIVE TESTING**

MAGNETIC PERMEABILITY
BT1	MAGNETIC PROPERTIES
BT2	PHYSICAL PROPERTIES
BT3	PROPERTIES

MAGNETIC PROPERTIES
BT1	PHYSICAL PROPERTIES
BT2	PROPERTIES
NT1	MAGNETIC FIELD ELEMENTS
NT2	MAGNETIC INCLINATION
NT2	MAGNETIC INTENSITY
NT2	MAGNETIC VARIATIONS
NT1	MAGNETIC PERMEABILITY
NT1	MAGNETIC SUSCEPTIBILITY

MAGNETIC PROPERTIES (cont'd)
NT1	REMANENT MAGNETIZATION
RT	GEOMAGNETISM
RT	MAGNETISM
RT	MAGNETS

MAGNETIC REMANENCE
USE	**REMANENT MAGNETIZATION**

MAGNETIC REVERSALS
UF	geomagnetic reversals
RT	GEOMAGNETIC FIELD
RT	MAGNETOSTRATIGRAPHY
RT	PALAEOMAGNETISM
RT	POLE POSITIONS

MAGNETIC SPHERULES
USE	**COSMIC SPHERULES**

MAGNETIC STRATIGRAPHY
USE	**MAGNETOSTRATIGRAPHY**

MAGNETIC SURVEYS
USE	**MAGNETIC EXPLORATION**

MAGNETIC SUSCEPTIBILITY
BT1	MAGNETIC PROPERTIES
BT2	PHYSICAL PROPERTIES
BT3	PROPERTIES
RT	ANISOTROPY
RT	GEOMAGNETIC FIELD
RT	PALAEOMAGNETISM

MAGNETIC TAPE RECORDINGS
RT	AUDIO RECORDINGS
RT	RECORDS
RT	VIDEOTAPE RECORDINGS

MAGNETIC TAPES
RT	AUDIO RECORDINGS
RT	AUDIOVISUAL MATERIAL
RT	VIDEOTAPE RECORDINGS

MAGNETIC VARIATIONS
UF	magnetic declination
UF	variations (magnetic)
BT1	MAGNETIC FIELD ELEMENTS
BT2	MAGNETIC PROPERTIES
BT3	PHYSICAL PROPERTIES
BT4	PROPERTIES
RT	GEOMAGNETIC FIELD
RT	ISOMAGNETIC LINES
RT	MAGNETIC CHARTS

MAGNETISM
NT1	ELECTROMAGNETISM
RT	GEOMAGNETISM
RT	MAGNETIC FIELDS
RT	MAGNETIC PROPERTIES
RT	MAGNETS
RT	PALAEOMAGNETISM
RT	PHYSICS

MAGNETITE
BT1	OXIDE MINERALS
BT2	MINERALS
RT	COSMIC SPHERULES
RT	IRON OXIDES
RT	PLACERS

MAGNETOMETERS
BT1	MEASURING DEVICES
RT	GEOMAGNETISM
RT	GEOPHYSICAL EQUIPMENT
RT	MAGNETIC EXPLORATION

MAGNETOSTRATIGRAPHY
UF	magnetic stratigraphy
BT1	STRATIGRAPHY
BT2	GEOLOGY
BT3	EARTH SCIENCES
RT	MAGNETIC REVERSALS
RT	STRATIGRAPHIC CORRELATION

MAGNETOTELLURIC METHODS
UF	magnetotelluric surveys
RT	COAST EFFECT
RT	ELECTRICAL RESISTIVITY
RT	ELECTROMAGNETIC EXPLORATION
RT	GEOMAGNETIC FIELD
RT	GEOMAGNETISM
RT	TELLURIC CURRENTS

MAGNETOTELLURIC SURVEYS
USE	**MAGNETOTELLURIC METHODS**

MAGNETS
RT	MAGNETIC FIELDS
RT	MAGNETIC PROPERTIES
RT	MAGNETISM

MAINTENANCE
NT1	REPAIR
RT	CORROSION CONTROL
RT	DETERIORATION
RT	EQUIPMENT
RT	FOULING CONTROL
RT	INSPECTION
RT	SCALING
RT	UNDERWATER INSPECTION

MAJOR CONSTITUENTS
SN	Used only as a qualifier
RT	COMPOSITION

MALACOLOGISTS
SN	Added in 1980
BT1	ZOOLOGISTS
BT2	BIOLOGISTS
BT3	SCIENTIFIC PERSONNEL
BT4	PERSONNEL
RT	DIRECTORIES
RT	FISHERY BIOLOGISTS
RT	MALACOLOGY
RT	TAXONOMISTS

MALACOLOGY
BT1	INVERTEBRATE ZOOLOGY
BT2	ZOOLOGY
BT3	BIOLOGY
RT	CONCHOLOGY
RT	FRESHWATER MOLLUSCS
RT	HYDROBIOLOGY
RT	MALACOLOGISTS
RT	MARINE MOLLUSCS
RT	SHELLS

MALARIA
SN	Added in 1980
UF	paludism
BT1	HUMAN DISEASES
BT2	DISEASES
RT	AQUATIC INSECTS
RT	INFECTIOUS DISEASES
RT	INSECT LARVAE
RT	PARASITIC DISEASES
RT	PROTOZOAN DISEASES

MALES
SN	Added in 1980
BT1	SEX
RT	SEX CHARACTERS
RT	SEX RATIO
RT	SEXUAL MATURITY
RT	SPERM

MALFORMATIONS
USE **ABNORMALITIES**

MAMMALIAN PHYSIOLOGY
SN   Added in 1980
UF   physiology (aquatic mammals)
BT1   ANIMAL PHYSIOLOGY
BT2   PHYSIOLOGY
BT3   BIOLOGY
RT   AQUATIC MAMMALS
RT   CETOLOGY
RT   DIVING PHYSIOLOGY

MAMMALOGISTS
BT1   ZOOLOGISTS
BT2   BIOLOGISTS
BT3   SCIENTIFIC PERSONNEL
BT4   PERSONNEL
NT1   CETOLOGISTS
RT   AQUATIC MAMMALS
RT   DIRECTORIES
RT   MAMMALOGY
RT   MARINE MAMMALS

MAMMALOGY
BT1   VERTEBRATE ZOOLOGY
BT2   ZOOLOGY
BT3   BIOLOGY
NT1   CETOLOGY
RT   AQUATIC MAMMALS
RT   MAMMALOGISTS
RT   MARINE MAMMALS

MAMMALS (AQUATIC)
USE   **AQUATIC MAMMALS**

MAMMALS (MARINE)
USE   **MARINE MAMMALS**

MAN-INDUCED EFFECTS
SN   Effects of human activities on
      aquatic ecosystems. Added in 1982
UF   anthropogenic effects
UF   human impact
RT   ENVIRONMENTAL IMPACT
RT   MARINE PARKS
RT   POLLUTION EFFECTS

MAN-MADE DISASTERS
USE   **ACCIDENTS**

MAN-MADE LAKES
USE   **ARTIFICIAL LAKES**

MANAGEMENT
SN   Use of a more specific term is
      recommended. Added in 1980
UF   administration
NT1   COASTAL ZONE MANAGEMENT
NT2   SHORE PROTECTION
NT1   ECOSYSTEM MANAGEMENT
NT2   ENVIRONMENT MANAGEMENT
NT1   FINANCIAL MANAGEMENT
NT1   PRODUCTION MANAGEMENT
NT1   RESOURCE MANAGEMENT
NT2   FISHERY MANAGEMENT
NT2   WATER MANAGEMENT
NT1   RIVER BASIN MANAGEMENT
RT   ACCESS
RT   ECONOMICS
RT   ECONOMISTS
RT   FINANCING
RT   INDUSTRIAL PRODUCTION
RT   MARKETING
RT   OPERATIONS RESEARCH
RT   PERSONNEL
RT   PERT
RT   PLANNING
RT   POLICIES
RT   REGIONAL PLANNING

MANAGEMENT (cont'd)
RT   SOCIOLOGICAL ASPECTS
RT   TECHNOLOGY

MANAGEMENT (RESOURCES)
USE   **RESOURCE MANAGEMENT**

MANEUVERABILITY
USE   **MANOEUVRABILITY**

MANGANESE
BT1   CHEMICAL ELEMENTS
RT   FERROMANGANESE NODULES
RT   FERROMANGANESE OXIDES
RT   HEAVY METALS
RT   MANGANESE COMPOUNDS
RT   MANGANESE ISOTOPES
RT   METALLIFEROUS SEDIMENTS
RT   METALS
RT   TRACE ELEMENTS
RT   TRANSITION ELEMENTS

MANGANESE COMPOUNDS
SN   Use of a specific compound is
      recommended
NT1   MANGANESE DIOXIDE
NT1   MANGANESE OXIDES
RT   CHEMICAL COMPOUNDS
RT   MANGANESE
RT   TRANSITION ELEMENT COMPOUNDS

MANGANESE DEPOSITS
BT1   CHEMICAL SEDIMENTS
BT2   SEDIMENTS
RT   FERROMANGANESE NODULES
RT   MANGANESE OXIDES

MANGANESE DIOXIDE
BT1   MANGANESE COMPOUNDS
RT   OXIDES

MANGANESE ISOTOPES
BT1   ISOTOPES
RT   MANGANESE

MANGANESE MINERALS
BT1   MINERALS
RT   PYROLUSITE

MANGANESE NODULES
USE   **FERROMANGANESE NODULES**

MANGANESE OXIDES
BT1   MANGANESE COMPOUNDS
RT   MANGANESE DEPOSITS
RT   OXIDES

MANGANITE
BT1   OXIDE MINERALS
BT2   MINERALS

MANGROVE SWAMPS
SN   Mangrove aquatic environment and
      its communities
BT1   SWAMPS
BT2   WETLANDS
BT3   LANDFORMS
BT4   TOPOGRAPHIC FEATURES
RT   BRACKISHWATER AQUACULTURE
RT   BRACKISHWATER ECOLOGY
RT   BRACKISHWATER ENVIRONMENT

MANIFOLDS
SN   Seabed multiple flowline connectors
RT   CONNECTORS
RT   FLOWLINES
RT   WELLHEADS

MANIPULATORS
RT   DIVING SUITS
RT   ROBOTS
RT   UNDERWATER VEHICLES

MANNED SUBMERSIBLES
USE   **SUBMERSIBLES**

MANNED VEHICLES
UF   diving chambers
UF   diving vehicles
BT1   UNDERWATER VEHICLES
BT2   VEHICLES
NT1   DIVING BELLS
NT1   OBSERVATION CHAMBERS
NT2   BATHYSPHERES
NT1   SUBMARINES
NT2   SUBMARINE TANKERS
NT1   SUBMERSIBLES
NT2   LOCKOUT SUBMERSIBLES
NT2   WET SUBMERSIBLES
RT   DIVING
RT   HYPERTHERMIA
RT   LIFE SUPPORT SYSTEMS
RT   NAVIGATION UNDERWATER
RT   ONE-ATMOSPHERE SYSTEMS
RT   UNDERWATER MEDICINE
RT   UNMANNED VEHICLES

MANNOSE
BT1   MONOSACCHARIDES
BT2   SACCHARIDES
BT3   CARBOHYDRATES
BT4   ORGANIC COMPOUNDS
RT   ALDEHYDES

MANOEUVRABILITY
UF   maneuverability
RT   PROPULSION SYSTEMS
RT   SHIP HANDLING
RT   STEERING SYSTEMS
RT   VEHICLES

MANOMETERS
BT1   MEASURING DEVICES
RT   BAROMETERS
RT   PRESSURE
RT   PRESSURE GAUGES

MANPOWER RESOURCES
USE   **HUMAN RESOURCES**

MANTLE
SN   Fold of epidermal tissue covering
      dorsal/lateral surfaces of the body
      of the Mollusca and Brachiopoda;
      body wall of the Urochordata. For
      earth mantle use EARTH MANTLE.
      Added in 1980
BT1   BODY WALLS
RT   GILLS
RT   MANTLE CAVITY
RT   SHELLS

MANTLE (EARTH)
USE   **EARTH MANTLE**

MANTLE CAVITY
SN   Added in 1980
BT1   BODY CAVITIES
RT   GILLS
RT   MANTLE

MANTLE CONVECTION
BT1   CONVECTION
BT2   ADVECTION
BT3   TRANSPORT PROCESSES
RT   CELLULAR CONVECTION
RT   EARTH MANTLE
RT   HEAT FLOW

MANTLE CONVECTION (cont'd)		
RT	MANTLE PLUMES	
RT	PLATE TECTONICS	
RT	SEAFLOOR SPREADING	

MANTLE PLUMES
BT1	PLUMES
BT2	FLUID FLOW
BT3	FLUID MOTION
RT	DIVERGING PLATE BOUNDARIES
RT	HOT SPOTS
RT	MANTLE CONVECTION
RT	PLATE DIVERGENCE
RT	PLATE TECTONICS

MANUALS
SN	Documents containing instructions and/or procedures for performing operations or handling equipment
BT1	DOCUMENTS
NT1	INSTRUMENT HANDBOOKS
RT	METHODOLOGY
RT	TRAINING AIDS
RT	TRAINING CENTRES

MANUFACTURING COSTS
USE	**OPERATIONAL COSTS**

MANURE
SN	Any substance, usually of natural origin, used as fertilizer. Added in 1980
UF	animal manure
UF	artificial manure
UF	dung
UF	manurial salts
RT	AQUACULTURE
RT	FERTILIZERS
RT	HABITAT IMPROVEMENT (FERTILIZATION)
RT	WASTES

MANURIAL SALTS
USE	**MANURE**

MANUSCRIPTS (HISTORICAL)
USE	**ARCHIVES**

MAP GRAPHICS
SN	Cartographic representation of data on maps. Use of a more specific term is recommended
BT1	GRAPHICS
BT2	AUDIOVISUAL MATERIAL
BT3	DOCUMENTS
NT1	CURRENT ROSES
NT1	ISOPLETHS
NT2	CONTOURS
NT3	ISOBATHS
NT2	CORANGE LINES
NT2	COTIDAL LINES
NT2	ISOBARS
NT2	ISOCHRONES
NT2	ISOHALINES
NT2	ISOHYETS
NT2	ISOMAGNETIC LINES
NT2	ISOPACHS
NT2	ISOPYCNICS
NT2	ISOSTERES
NT2	ISOTHERMS
NT1	STREAMLINES
NT1	VERTICAL SECTIONS
NT2	GEOLOGICAL SECTIONS
NT2	HYDROGRAPHIC SECTIONS
NT3	BATHYMETRIC PROFILES
NT3	DENSITY SECTIONS
NT3	OXYGEN SECTIONS
NT3	SALINITY SECTIONS
NT3	TEMPERATURE SECTIONS
NT3	VELOCITY SECTIONS
NT1	WIND ROSES

MAP GRAPHICS (cont'd)
NT1	WIND VECTORS
RT	CARTOGRAPHY
RT	HODOGRAPHS
RT	MAPPING

MAP PROJECTIONS
RT	CARTOGRAPHY
RT	GEOGRAPHICAL COORDINATES
RT	MAPPING
RT	MAPS

MAPPING
SN	Mapping of aquatic and terrestrial environments. Before 1982 search CHARTING for aquatic environments
UF	cartographic methods
UF	charting (distributions)
UF	charting (environmental conditions)
BT1	GRAPHIC METHODS
NT1	AUTOMATED CARTOGRAPHY
NT1	SEAFLOOR MAPPING
RT	AERIAL PHOTOGRAPHS
RT	AERIAL PHOTOGRAPHY
RT	BIOGEOGRAPHY
RT	CARTOGRAPHY
RT	DATA
RT	GEOGRAPHY
RT	MAP GRAPHICS
RT	MAP PROJECTIONS
RT	MAPS
RT	MEASURING DEVICES
RT	PLOTTING
RT	SATELLITE MOSAICS
RT	SURVEYING
RT	SURVEYS
RT	TOPOGRAPHY

MAPS
SN	Before 1982 search also CHARTS (MAPS)
UF	charts (maps)
BT1	GRAPHICS
BT2	AUDIOVISUAL MATERIAL
BT3	DOCUMENTS
NT1	BIOLOGICAL CHARTS
NT1	CLIMATOLOGICAL CHARTS
NT1	CONTROL CHARTS
NT1	ENVIRONMENTAL CHARTS
NT1	FISHERY CHARTS
NT1	GEOLOGICAL MAPS
NT2	GRAVITY CHARTS
NT3	BOUGUER GRAVITY CHARTS
NT3	FREE AIR GRAVITY CHARTS
NT2	ISOPACH MAPS
NT2	MAGNETIC CHARTS
NT3	MAGNETIC ANOMALY CHARTS
NT1	HYDROGRAPHIC CHARTS
NT2	BATHYMETRIC CHARTS
NT2	CURRENT CHARTS
NT2	DENSITY CHARTS
NT2	ICE CHARTS
NT2	SALINITY CHARTS
NT2	TEMPERATURE CHARTS
NT2	TIDAL CHARTS
NT3	CORANGE CHARTS
NT3	COTIDAL CHARTS
NT1	METEOROLOGICAL CHARTS
NT2	WEATHER MAPS
NT1	NAVIGATIONAL CHARTS
NT2	LATTICE CHARTS
NT2	PILOT CHARTS
NT1	POLLUTION MAPS
NT1	TOPOGRAPHIC MAPS
NT1	TRACK CHARTS
RT	ATLASES
RT	BIOGEOGRAPHY
RT	CARTOGRAPHY
RT	CATALOGUES
RT	CHART CATALOGUES
RT	CHART DATUM

MAPS (cont'd)
RT	DATA
RT	GRAPHIC METHODS
RT	MAP PROJECTIONS
RT	MAPPING
RT	SEASONAL DISTRIBUTION

MARCASITE
BT1	SULPHIDE MINERALS
BT2	MINERALS

MARGINAL BASINS
UF	back-arc basins
UF	inter-arc basins
BT1	STRUCTURAL BASINS
RT	ACTIVE MARGINS
RT	BASINS
RT	CONTINENTAL SLOPE
RT	FOREARC BASINS
RT	ISLAND ARCS
RT	MARGINAL SEAS
RT	SUBDUCTION

MARGINAL FIELDS
BT1	OIL AND GAS FIELDS
RT	ECONOMIC FEASIBILITY
RT	OIL AND GAS PRODUCTION

MARGINAL SEAS
UF	adjacent seas
UF	deep adjacent seas
NT1	SEMI-ENCLOSED SEAS
NT1	SHELF SEAS
RT	ANOXIC BASINS
RT	COASTAL WATERS
RT	CONTINENTS
RT	HYDROSPHERE
RT	MARGINAL BASINS
RT	OCEANS
RT	WATER BODIES

MARGINS (CONTINENTAL)
USE	**CONTINENTAL MARGINS**

MARGINS (PLATE)
USE	**PLATE MARGINS**

MARICULTURE
USE	**MARINE AQUACULTURE**

MARIGRAM
USE	**TIDAL CURVES**

MARINAS
UF	yacht harbours
BT1	ARTIFICIAL HARBOURS
BT2	COASTAL STRUCTURES
BT3	HYDRAULIC STRUCTURES
RT	RECREATIONAL WATERS
RT	YACHTS

MARINATED PRODUCTS
USE	**CURED PRODUCTS**

MARINE ADVECTION
USE	**ADVECTION**

MARINE AEROSOLS
USE	**AEROSOLS**

MARINE AQUACULTURE
UF	coastal aquaculture
UF	mariculture
UF	ocean farming
UF	open sea aquaculture
UF	sea farming
BT1	AQUACULTURE
RT	ALGAL CULTURE
RT	AQUACULTURE TECHNIQUES
RT	ARTIFICIAL REEFS

ASFIS Thesaurus

MARINE AQUACULTURE (cont'd)
RT	CAGE CULTURE
RT	CLAM CULTURE
RT	CORAL FARMING
RT	CRUSTACEAN CULTURE
RT	ENCLOSURES
RT	FISH CULTURE
RT	FISH PONDS
RT	HATCHERIES
RT	LOBSTER CULTURE
RT	MARINE FISH
RT	MONOSEX CULTURE
RT	OYSTER CULTURE
RT	PEARL CULTURE
RT	SCALLOP CULTURE
RT	SEA WATER
RT	SEAFOOD
RT	SEAWEED CULTURE
RT	SHELLFISH CULTURE
RT	SHRIMP CULTURE
RT	SPONGE CULTURE
RT	SUBMERGED CAGES

MARINE ARCHAEOLOGY
USE	**ARCHAEOLOGY**

MARINE BIOLOGICAL NOISE
USE	**BIOLOGICAL NOISE**

MARINE BIOLOGISTS
USE	**MARINE ECOLOGISTS**

MARINE BIOLOGY
USE	**MARINE ECOLOGY**

MARINE BIOTELEMETRY
USE	**BIOTELEMETRY**

MARINE BIRDS
SN	Added in 1980
UF	birds (marine)
BT1	AQUATIC BIRDS
BT2	AQUATIC ANIMALS
NT1	GUANO BIRDS
RT	MARINE ORGANISMS
RT	ORNITHOLOGY

MARINE CHEMISTRY
USE	**CHEMICAL OCEANOGRAPHY**

MARINE CRAB CULTURE
USE	**CRAB CULTURE**

MARINE CRUSTACEANS
UF	crustaceans (marine)
BT1	AQUATIC ANIMALS
RT	CARCINOLOGY
RT	COMMERCIAL SPECIES
RT	CRUSTACEAN CULTURE
RT	ECDYSONS
RT	EYESTALK EXTIRPATION
RT	MARINE ORGANISMS
RT	MEGALOPS
RT	MOULTING
RT	NAUPLII
RT	PARASITIC CASTRATION
RT	PHOTOPHORES
RT	PHYLLOSOMAE
RT	SEAFOOD
RT	SHELLFISH
RT	SHELLFISH CATCH STATISTICS
RT	SHELLFISH FISHERIES
RT	VERNACULAR NAMES
RT	ZOEAE

MARINE ECOLOGISTS
SN	Added in 1980
UF	marine biologists
BT1	ECOLOGISTS
BT2	SCIENTIFIC PERSONNEL

MARINE ECOLOGISTS (cont'd)
BT3	PERSONNEL
RT	DIRECTORIES
RT	MARINE ECOLOGY

MARINE ECOLOGY
UF	biological oceanography
UF	marine biology
UF	oceanology (biological)
BT1	ECOLOGY
RT	AQUATIC ANIMALS
RT	AQUATIC COMMUNITIES
RT	AQUATIC PLANTS
RT	ENVIRONMENTAL FACTORS
RT	HYDROBIOLOGY
RT	MARINE ECOLOGISTS
RT	MARINE SCIENCES
RT	OCEANOGRAPHY
RT	WATER ANALYSIS

MARINE ENGINEERING
USE	**SHIP TECHNOLOGY**

MARINE ENVIRONMENT
SN	Related to oceans and seas
UF	ocean environment
BT1	AQUATIC ENVIRONMENT
BT2	ENVIRONMENTS
NT1	INTERTIDAL ENVIRONMENT
RT	APHOTIC ZONE
RT	BENTHIC ENVIRONMENT
RT	BRACKISHWATER ENVIRONMENT
RT	COASTAL ZONE
RT	CONTINENTAL SHELVES
RT	CONTINENTAL SLOPE
RT	CORAL REEFS
RT	DISPHOTIC ZONE
RT	EUPHOTIC ZONE
RT	EUTROPHIC WATERS
RT	FJORDS
RT	ICEBERGS
RT	MARINE FISH
RT	OCEANOGRAPHY
RT	OUTER CONTINENTAL SHELF
RT	PACK ICE
RT	PELAGIC ENVIRONMENT
RT	SEA WATER

MARINE FISH
BT1	FISH
BT2	AQUATIC ANIMALS
NT1	REEF FISH
RT	COASTAL FISHERIES
RT	COMMERCIAL SPECIES
RT	DEMERSAL FISHERIES
RT	FISHERY RESOURCES
RT	MARINE AQUACULTURE
RT	MARINE ENVIRONMENT
RT	MARINE FISHERIES
RT	MARINE ORGANISMS
RT	PELAGIC FISHERIES
RT	SEAFOOD
RT	TROPICAL FISH

MARINE FISHERIES
UF	sea fisheries
BT1	FISHERIES
NT1	DEEP-SEA FISHERIES
NT1	HIGH SEAS FISHERIES
NT1	REEF FISHERIES
NT1	SEAWEED HARVESTING
RT	CARANGID FISHERIES
RT	CEPHALOPOD FISHERIES
RT	CLAM FISHERIES
RT	CLUPEOID FISHERIES
RT	COASTAL FISHERIES
RT	CRAB FISHERIES
RT	CRUSTACEAN FISHERIES
RT	DEMERSAL FISHERIES
RT	ECHINODERM FISHERIES

MARINE FISHERIES (cont'd)
RT	ESTUARINE FISHERIES
RT	FINFISH FISHERIES
RT	FLATFISH FISHERIES
RT	GADOID FISHERIES
RT	GASTROPOD FISHERIES
RT	KRILL FISHERIES
RT	LOBSTER FISHERIES
RT	MACKEREL FISHERIES
RT	MARINE FISH
RT	MOLLUSC FISHERIES
RT	MUSSEL FISHERIES
RT	PEARL FISHERIES
RT	PELAGIC FISHERIES
RT	REDFISH FISHERIES
RT	SALMON FISHERIES
RT	SCALLOP FISHERIES
RT	SHARK FISHERIES
RT	SHELLFISH FISHERIES
RT	SHRIMP FISHERIES
RT	SPONGE FISHERIES
RT	SQUAT LOBSTER FISHERIES
RT	TUNA FISHERIES

MARINE FITTINGS
USE	**SHIPBOARD EQUIPMENT**

MARINE FOUNDATIONS
USE	**FOUNDATIONS**

MARINE GEODESY
BT1	GEODESY
BT2	GEOPHYSICS
BT3	EARTH SCIENCES
RT	COASTAL GEODESY
RT	DYNAMICAL OCEANOGRAPHY
RT	GEOID
RT	MARINE SCIENCES
RT	POSITION FIXING
RT	SURFACE TOPOGRAPHY

MARINE GEOLOGY
UF	geological oceanography
UF	submarine geology
BT1	GEOLOGY
BT2	EARTH SCIENCES
NT1	SHELF GEOLOGY
RT	CONTINENTAL DRIFT
RT	CONTINENTAL SHELVES
RT	CONTINENTAL SLOPE
RT	DRILLING
RT	GEOCHEMISTRY
RT	GEOLOGICAL DISTRIBUTION
RT	GEOPHYSICS
RT	MARINE SCIENCES
RT	MINERAL RESOURCES
RT	MINERALOGY
RT	OCEANIC CRUST
RT	OCEANOGRAPHY
RT	OUTER CONTINENTAL SHELF
RT	SEDIMENTOLOGY
RT	SEISMIC ACTIVITY
RT	STRATIGRAPHY
RT	SUBMARINE FEATURES
RT	SUBMARINE VOLCANOES
RT	TECTONICS

MARINE INSURANCE
USE	**INSURANCE**

MARINE INVERTEBRATES
SN	Added in 1982
BT1	AQUATIC ANIMALS
RT	MARINE ORGANISMS

MARINE MAMMALS
SN	Before 1982 search AQUATIC MAMMALS
UF	mammals (marine)
BT1	AQUATIC MAMMALS
BT2	AQUATIC ANIMALS

MARINE MAMMALS (cont'd)			**MARINE POLLUTION** (cont'd)			**MARINE TECHNOLOGY** (cont'd)	
RT	COMMERCIAL SPECIES		RT	POLLUTANTS		RT	OFFSHORE DOCKING
RT	HUNTING		RT	POLLUTION EFFECTS		RT	OFFSHORE ENGINEERING
RT	LIVING RESOURCES		RT	POLLUTION MONITORING		RT	OIL AND GAS INDUSTRY
RT	MAMMALOGISTS		RT	RADIOACTIVE CONTAMINATION		RT	RESOURCE DEVELOPMENT
RT	MAMMALOGY		RT	SEA WATER			
RT	MARINE ORGANISMS		RT	THERMAL POLLUTION		**MARINE TRANSGRESSIONS**	
RT	MARINE RESOURCES		RT	WASTES		USE	**TRANSGRESSIONS**
RT	MILK		RT	WATER POLLUTION TREATMENT			
RT	PUPS					**MARINE TRANSPORTATION**	
RT	WHALING		**MARINE PROPULSION**			SN	All forms of waterborne
			USE	**PROPULSION SYSTEMS**			transportation
MARINE METEOROLOGY						BT1	TRANSPORTATION
USE	**METEOROLOGY**		**MARINE REGRESSIONS**			RT	BARGES
			USE	**REGRESSIONS**		RT	CARGOES
MARINE MOLLUSCS						RT	HARBOURS
UF	molluscs (marine)		**MARINE RESERVES**			RT	HYDROFOILS
UF	mollusks (marine)		USE	**MARINE PARKS**		RT	LIFEBOATS
BT1	AQUATIC ANIMALS					RT	MERCHANT SHIPS
RT	COMMERCIAL SPECIES		**MARINE RESOURCES**			RT	MOTHER SHIPS
RT	MALACOLOGY		SN	Added in 1980		RT	NAVIGATION
RT	MARINE ORGANISMS		BT1	NATURAL RESOURCES		RT	PORT INSTALLATIONS
RT	MOLLUSC CULTURE		BT2	RESOURCES		RT	SHIP TECHNOLOGY
RT	OYSTER CULTURE		RT	COASTAL STATES		RT	SHIPPING LANES
RT	PARASITIC CASTRATION		RT	ENERGY RESOURCES		RT	SHIPS
RT	PEARLS		RT	FOOD RESOURCES		RT	SUPPLY BOATS
RT	RADULAE		RT	INTERNATIONAL AGREEMENTS		RT	SUPPORT SHIPS
RT	SEAFOOD		RT	JURISDICTION		RT	SURFACE CRAFT
RT	SHELLFISH		RT	LIVING RESOURCES		RT	UNDERWATER VEHICLES
RT	SHELLFISH CATCH STATISTICS		RT	MARINE MAMMALS			
RT	SHELLFISH FISHERIES		RT	MARITIME LEGISLATION		**MARINE WATER**	
RT	SHELLS		RT	MINERAL RESOURCES		USE	**SEA WATER**
RT	SPAT		RT	OCEAN POLICY			
RT	VERNACULAR NAMES		RT	RENEWABLE RESOURCES		**MARITIME LEGISLATION**	
			RT	SEAFOOD		SN	Added in 1980
MARINE ORGANISMS						BT1	LEGISLATION
BT1	AQUATIC ORGANISMS		**MARINE RISERS**			RT	FISHERY REGULATIONS
RT	MARINE BIRDS		USE	**RISER PIPES**		RT	MARINE RESOURCES
RT	MARINE CRUSTACEANS					RT	NAVIGATION
RT	MARINE FISH		**MARINE SCIENCES**			RT	OCEAN SPACE
RT	MARINE INVERTEBRATES		BT1	AQUATIC SCIENCES		RT	SHIPPING
RT	MARINE MAMMALS		RT	ALGOLOGY			
RT	MARINE MOLLUSCS		RT	CHEMICAL OCEANOGRAPHY		**MARITIME SPACE**	
RT	SEAFOOD		RT	FISHERY OCEANOGRAPHY		USE	**OCEAN SPACE**
RT	VERNACULAR NAMES		RT	HYDROBIOLOGY			
			RT	MARINE ECOLOGY		**MARITIME STRUCTURES**	
MARINE PARKS			RT	MARINE GEODESY		USE	**HYDRAULIC STRUCTURES**
SN	Marine areas protected against		RT	MARINE GEOLOGY			
	human impact		RT	MARINE SCIENTISTS		**MARKER BUOYS**	
UF	marine reserves		RT	MARINE TECHNOLOGY		BT1	BUOYS
UF	nature reserves		RT	OCEANOGRAPHY		RT	NAVIGATIONAL AIDS
RT	ENVIRONMENTAL LEGISLATION		RT	PHYSICAL OCEANOGRAPHY			
RT	MAN-INDUCED EFFECTS		RT	PLANKTONOLOGY		**MARKET CRAB FISHERIES**	
RT	NATURE CONSERVATION					USE	**CRAB FISHERIES**
RT	PROTECTED RESOURCES		**MARINE SCIENTISTS**				
RT	RARE SPECIES		UF	oceanographers		**MARKET MANAGEMENT**	
RT	RECREATION		BT1	SCIENTIFIC PERSONNEL		USE	**PRODUCTION MANAGEMENT**
RT	RECREATIONAL WATERS		BT2	PERSONNEL			
RT	REFUGES		RT	DIRECTORIES		**MARKET PRICES**	
RT	SANCTUARIES		RT	MARINE SCIENCES		USE	**PRICING**
RT	SOCIOLOGICAL ASPECTS		RT	OCEANOGRAPHY			
RT	WATER CONSERVATION					**MARKET RESEARCH**	
			MARINE SEDIMENTATION			UF	marketing research
MARINE PHYSICS			USE	**SEDIMENTATION**		RT	COMMERCIAL AVAILABILITY
USE	**PHYSICAL OCEANOGRAPHY**					RT	CONSUMERS
			MARINE SHRIMP CULTURE			RT	COST ANALYSIS
MARINE POLICY			USE	**SHRIMP CULTURE**		RT	ECONOMIC ANALYSIS
USE	**OCEAN POLICY**					RT	ECONOMICS
			MARINE SNOW			RT	FISHERY ECONOMICS
MARINE POLLUTION			USE	**SUSPENDED PARTICULATE MATTER**		RT	INVESTMENTS
UF	pollution (marine)					RT	MARKETING
BT1	WATER POLLUTION		**MARINE STRUCTURES**			RT	PRICING
BT2	POLLUTION		USE	**OFFSHORE STRUCTURES**		RT	PROCESSED FISHERY PRODUCTS
RT	CHEMICAL POLLUTION					RT	TRADE
RT	GROUNDWATER POLLUTION		**MARINE TECHNOLOGY**				
RT	INDUSTRIAL WASTES		BT1	TECHNOLOGY		**MARKETING**	
RT	LEAKS		RT	COASTAL ENGINEERING		SN	All aspects related to the
RT	MICROBIAL CONTAMINATION		RT	EXPLOITATION			structure, process and logistics as
RT	OCEAN DUMPING		RT	EXPLORATION			well as performance of marketing
RT	OIL POLLUTION		RT	MARINE SCIENCES			system

MARKETING (cont'd)
UF	commercialization
UF	marketing and distribution
UF	markets
RT	AQUACULTURE ECONOMICS
RT	CAPTURE FISHERY ECONOMICS
RT	COMMERCIAL LEGISLATION
RT	CONSUMERS
RT	COSTS
RT	ECONOMIC ANALYSIS
RT	ECONOMICS
RT	FINANCING
RT	FISH HANDLING
RT	FISHERY ECONOMICS
RT	INDUSTRIAL PRODUCTION
RT	MANAGEMENT
RT	MARKET RESEARCH
RT	PLANNING
RT	PRICING
RT	PROCESSED FISHERY PRODUCTS
RT	PRODUCT DEVELOPMENT
RT	PRODUCTS
RT	RESOURCE MANAGEMENT
RT	TRADE
RT	UTILIZATION

MARKETING AND DISTRIBUTION
USE	**MARKETING**

MARKETING LEGISLATION
USE	**COMMERCIAL LEGISLATION**

MARKETING RESEARCH
USE	**MARKET RESEARCH**

MARKETS
USE	**MARKETING**

MARKING
SN	Any procedure which makes fish subsequently identifiable which does not employ the use of tags.
UF	electrophoretic marking
NT1	COLD BRANDING
RT	MIGRATIONS
RT	STAINING
RT	TAGGING
RT	TAGGING MORTALITY

MARKING MORTALITY
USE	**TAGGING MORTALITY**

MARL
RT	ARGILLACEOUS DEPOSITS
RT	CLAYS
RT	MARLSTONE
RT	MUD
RT	SEDIMENTARY ROCKS

MARLSTONE
BT1	CLASTICS
BT2	SEDIMENTS
RT	ARGILLACEOUS DEPOSITS
RT	LIMESTONE
RT	LUTITES
RT	MARL
RT	SEDIMENTARY ROCKS

MARSDEN CHART
USE	**MARSDEN SQUARES**

MARSDEN SQUARES
UF	marsden chart
BT1	GEOGRAPHICAL REFERENCE SYSTEMS
RT	DATA
RT	GEOGRAPHICAL COORDINATES
RT	METEOROLOGICAL DATA
RT	OCEANOGRAPHIC DATA

MARSHES
UF	bogs
BT1	WETLANDS
BT2	LANDFORMS
BT3	TOPOGRAPHIC FEATURES
NT1	SALT MARSHES
RT	LENITIC ENVIRONMENT
RT	SHALLOW WATER
RT	STAGNANT WATER
RT	SWAMPS
RT	TIDAL FLATS

MASCARET
USE	**TIDAL BORES**

MASS
BT1	PHYSICAL PROPERTIES
BT2	PROPERTIES
RT	CONSERVATION OF MASS
RT	WEIGHT

MASS CULTURE
SN	Culture of organisms in large number. Before 1982 search PHYTOPLANKTON CULTURE
BT1	AQUACULTURE SYSTEMS
RT	ALGAL CULTURE
RT	BRINE SHRIMP CULTURE
RT	CRUSTACEAN CULTURE
RT	CULTURE TANKS
RT	HATCHERIES
RT	PHYTOPLANKTON CULTURE
RT	SEED PRODUCTION
RT	SHRIMP CULTURE

MASS EXTINCTIONS
RT	CLIMATIC CHANGES
RT	CRETACEOUS

MASS GRAVITY TRANSPORT (SEDIMENTS)
SN	Use of a more specific term is recommended
BT1	SEDIMENT TRANSPORT
NT1	DEBRIS FLOW
NT1	SLUMPING

MASS MORTALITY
USE	**FISH KILL**

MASS MOVEMENT
BT1	SEDIMENT MOVEMENT
NT1	SLIDES
NT2	LANDSLIDES
RT	CREEP
RT	SEDIMENT TRANSPORT
RT	SLOPE STABILITY

MASS SPECTROSCOPY
BT1	SPECTROSCOPIC TECHNIQUES
BT2	ANALYTICAL TECHNIQUES

MASS TRANSFER
RT	CONVECTION
RT	DIFFUSION
RT	ENERGY TRANSFER
RT	HEAT TRANSFER
RT	OSMOSIS

MASS TRANSFER (AIR-WATER EXCHANGES)
USE	**MOISTURE TRANSFER**

MASS TRANSPORT
UF	mass transport (water waves)
RT	NEARSHORE DYNAMICS
RT	SVERDRUP TRANSPORT
RT	TRANSPORT
RT	WAVE DRIFT VELOCITY
RT	WAVE SETUP

MASS TRANSPORT (WATER CURRENTS)
USE	**VOLUME TRANSPORT**

MASS TRANSPORT (WATER WAVES)
USE	**MASS TRANSPORT**

MASS TRANSPORT VELOCITY
USE	**WAVE DRIFT VELOCITY**

MASTICATORY STOMACH
BT1	STOMACH
BT2	ALIMENTARY ORGANS
BT3	ANIMAL ORGANS
BT4	BODY ORGANS

MASTS
SN	Use only for masts on buoys to carry an array of meteorological instruments
RT	DATA BUOYS
RT	INSTRUMENT PLATFORMS
RT	METEOROLOGICAL INSTRUMENTS
RT	METEOROLOGICAL OBSERVATIONS

MATERIALS
SN	Use of a more specific term is recommended
NT1	ALLOYS
NT2	FERROUS ALLOYS
NT3	STEEL
NT4	STAINLESS STEEL
NT2	NONFERROUS ALLOYS
NT1	BIOGENIC MATERIAL
NT1	BUOYANCY MATERIALS
NT1	CERAMICS
NT1	COATING MATERIALS
NT2	PAINTS
NT2	PLASTIC COATINGS
NT2	PRIMERS
NT1	COMPOSITE MATERIALS
NT1	CONSTRUCTION MATERIALS
NT2	CONCRETE
NT3	PRESTRESSED CONCRETE
NT3	REINFORCED CONCRETE
NT1	FIBRE GLASS
NT1	GEAR MATERIALS
NT2	NETTING MATERIALS
NT2	YARNS
NT1	HAZARDOUS MATERIALS
NT1	INSULATING MATERIALS
NT2	ACOUSTIC INSULATION
NT2	ELECTRICAL INSULATION
NT2	THERMAL INSULATION
NT1	ISOTROPIC MATERIALS
NT1	PACKING MATERIALS
NT1	PLASTICS
NT2	ACRYLICS
NT2	GLASS-REINFORCED PLASTICS
NT1	RADIOACTIVE MATERIALS
NT2	FISSION PRODUCTS
NT1	RAW MATERIALS
NT1	RUBBER
NT1	WOOD
RT	COMPONENTS
RT	MATERIALS TECHNOLOGY
RT	MATERIALS TESTING

MATERIALS SCIENCE
USE	**MATERIALS TECHNOLOGY**

MATERIALS TECHNOLOGY
UF	materials science
BT1	TECHNOLOGY
RT	MATERIALS
RT	MATERIALS TESTING

ASFIS Thesaurus

MATERIALS TESTING
BT1	TESTING
NT1	NONDESTRUCTIVE TESTING
RT	CORROSION
RT	INSPECTION
RT	MATERIALS
RT	MATERIALS TECHNOLOGY
RT	QUALITY CONTROL

MATHEMATICAL ANALYSIS
SN	Used only as a qualifier
NT1	CONVOLUTION
NT1	DECONVOLUTION
NT1	FOURIER ANALYSIS
NT1	NUMERICAL ANALYSIS
NT2	APPROXIMATION
NT3	BOUSSINESQ APPROXIMATION
NT3	CLOSURE APPROXIMATION
NT3	LEAST SQUARES METHOD
NT2	FINITE DIFFERENCE METHOD
NT2	FINITE ELEMENT METHOD
NT2	FUNCTIONAL ANALYSIS
NT3	FOURIER TRANSFORMS
NT3	HARMONIC ANALYSIS
NT3	LAPLACE TRANSFORMATION
NT2	PERTURBATION METHOD
NT1	SPECTRAL ANALYSIS
NT2	MAXIMUM ENTROPY SPECTRAL ANALYSIS
NT1	STATISTICAL ANALYSIS
NT2	CORRELATION ANALYSIS
NT3	AUTOCORRELATION
NT3	CROSS CORRELATION
NT2	FREQUENCY ANALYSIS
NT2	REGRESSION ANALYSIS
NT2	TIME SERIES ANALYSIS
NT2	VARIANCE ANALYSIS
NT3	MULTIVARIATE ANALYSIS
RT	GREEN'S FUNCTION
RT	MATHEMATICS
RT	STRUCTURAL ANALYSIS

MATHEMATICAL MODELS
SN	Used only as a qualifier
UF	compartmental models
UF	computer models
UF	numerical models
UF	stochastic models
BT1	MODELS
NT1	ECONOMIC MODELS
NT1	STATISTICAL MODELS
NT1	TIDAL MODELS
RT	ALGORITHMS
RT	ANALOGS
RT	BOUNDARY CONDITIONS
RT	ECONOMIC ANALYSIS
RT	FORMULAE
RT	GAME THEORY
RT	LINEAR PROGRAMMING
RT	MATHEMATICS
RT	MODELLING
RT	OPERATIONS RESEARCH
RT	PROBABILITY THEORY
RT	SCALE MODELS
RT	STOCHASTIC PROCESSES
RT	STORM SURGE PREDICTION
RT	SYSTEM ANALYSIS

MATHEMATICAL PROGRAMMING
SN	Used only as a qualifier
BT1	OPERATIONS RESEARCH
NT1	LINEAR PROGRAMMING
RT	GAME THEORY
RT	MODELLING

MATHEMATICAL TABLES
USE	**TABLES**

MATHEMATICS
SN	Used only as a qualifier
RT	BIOMETRICS
RT	DIFFERENTIAL EQUATIONS
RT	EIGENFUNCTIONS
RT	EQUATIONS
RT	MATHEMATICAL ANALYSIS
RT	MATHEMATICAL MODELS
RT	NUMERICAL ANALYSIS
RT	STATISTICS

MATURATION
USE	**SEXUAL MATURITY**

MAXIMUM ENTROPY SPECTRAL ANALYSIS
BT1	SPECTRAL ANALYSIS
BT2	MATHEMATICAL ANALYSIS

MAXIMUM SUSTAINABLE YIELD
USE	**POTENTIAL YIELD**

MEAN SEA LEVEL
SN	Before 1982 search SEA LEVEL
BT1	SEA LEVEL
RT	EQUILIBRIUM TIDES
RT	GEODESY
RT	GEOID
RT	INTEROCEAN CANALS
RT	LEVELLING
RT	SEA LEVEL CHANGES
RT	TIDAL DATUM
RT	WATER LEVELS

MEANDERING
BT1	WATER MOTION
NT1	CURRENT MEANDERING
NT1	RIVER MEANDERS
RT	FLUID MOTION

MEANDERING (CURRENTS)
USE	**CURRENT MEANDERING**

MEANDERS (CURRENT)
USE	**CURRENT RINGS**

MEANDERS (RIVERS)
USE	**RIVER MEANDERS**

MEANS
USE	**RESOURCES**

MEASUREMENT
SN	Used only as a qualifier
UF	measuring
UF	measuring techniques
NT1	DENSITY MEASUREMENT
NT1	DEPTH MEASUREMENT
NT2	BATHYMETRY
NT3	LASER BATHYMETRY
NT2	INSTRUMENT DEPTH MEASUREMENT
NT1	FLOW MEASUREMENT
NT2	CURRENT MEASUREMENT
NT3	EULERIAN CURRENT MEASUREMENT
NT3	LAGRANGIAN CURRENT MEASUREMENT
NT2	TURBULENCE MEASUREMENT
NT2	WIND MEASUREMENT
NT1	GRANULOMETRY
NT1	GRAVIMETRY
NT1	LIGHT MEASUREMENT
NT2	PHOTOMETRY
NT1	PHOTOGRAMMETRY
NT1	PRESSURE MEASUREMENT
NT1	SALINITY MEASUREMENT
NT1	SOUND MEASUREMENT
NT1	TEMPERATURE MEASUREMENT
NT2	GEOTHERMAL MEASUREMENT
NT1	WATER LEVEL MEASUREMENT
NT2	SEA LEVEL MEASUREMENT
RT	ACCURACY
RT	HYGROMETRY

MEASUREMENT (cont'd)
RT	METHODOLOGY

MEASURING
USE	**MEASUREMENT**

MEASURING DEVICES
SN	Apparatus for measuring distance, volume, weight, etc.
UF	measuring equipment
UF	measuring instruments
NT1	ANEMOMETERS
NT1	BAROMETERS
NT1	BATHYMETERS
NT2	LASER BATHYMETERS
NT1	COMPASSES
NT2	GYROCOMPASSES
NT1	CURRENT METERS
NT2	ACOUSTIC CURRENT METERS
NT1	FLOWMETERS
NT1	GAUGES
NT1	GRAVITY METERS
NT1	HYDROMETERS
NT1	HYGROMETERS
NT2	PSYCHROMETERS
NT1	LIGHT MEASURING INSTRUMENTS
NT2	BEAM TRANSMITTANCE METERS
NT2	COSINE COLLECTORS
NT2	IRRADIANCE METERS
NT2	PHOTOMETERS
NT3	SPECTROPHOTOMETERS
NT2	QUANTA METERS
NT2	RADIANCE METERS
NT2	SCATTERANCE METERS
NT2	SECCHI DISCS
NT2	TRANSMISSOMETERS
NT1	MAGNETOMETERS
NT1	MANOMETERS
NT1	MESH GAUGES
NT1	MICROMETER CALIPERS
NT1	PRESSURE GAUGES
NT1	RESPIROMETERS
NT1	SALINOMETERS
NT1	SEISMOMETERS
NT2	OCEAN BOTTOM SEISMOMETERS
NT2	STRAIN SEISMOMETERS
NT1	SLOPE INDICATORS
NT2	INCLINOMETERS
NT2	TILTMETERS
NT2	WIRE ANGLE INDICATORS
NT1	SPEEDOMETERS
NT1	TENSOMETERS
NT1	THERMOMETERS
NT2	QUARTZ TEMPERATURE SENSORS
NT2	REVERSING THERMOMETERS
NT1	TIDE GAUGES
NT2	DEEP-SEA TIDE GAUGES
NT1	TURBIDIMETERS
NT1	WAVE MEASURING EQUIPMENT
NT2	WAVE DIRECTION SENSORS
NT2	WAVE GAUGES
RT	ACCELEROMETERS
RT	ACTINOMETERS
RT	ALTIMETERS
RT	AXBTs
RT	BATHYTHERMOGRAPHS
RT	CALIBRATION
RT	CONDUCTIVITY SENSORS
RT	DENSITY MEASURING EQUIPMENT
RT	DIRECTION INDICATORS
RT	EQUIPMENT
RT	FLOW MEASURING EQUIPMENT
RT	INSTRUMENT RESPONSES
RT	LABORATORY EQUIPMENT
RT	LIMNOLOGICAL EQUIPMENT
RT	MAPPING
RT	MONITORING SYSTEMS
RT	NEPHELOMETERS

MEASURING DEVICES (cont'd)
RT	OCEANOGRAPHIC EQUIPMENT
RT	PATENTS
RT	PENETROMETERS
RT	PYRANOMETERS
RT	RADIOMETERS
RT	RECORDING EQUIPMENT
RT	SALINITY MEASURING EQUIPMENT
RT	SCATTEROMETERS
RT	SENSORS
RT	STRAIN GAUGES
RT	TELEMETRY
RT	TELLUROMETERS
RT	TEST EQUIPMENT
RT	TILTMETERS
RT	VANE DEVICES

MEASURING EQUIPMENT
USE	**MEASURING DEVICES**

MEASURING INSTRUMENTS
USE	**MEASURING DEVICES**

MEASURING TECHNIQUES
USE	**MEASUREMENT**

MECHANICAL BATHYTHERMOGRAPHS
USE	**BATHYTHERMOGRAPHS**

MECHANICAL PROPERTIES
BT1	PHYSICAL PROPERTIES
BT2	PROPERTIES
NT1	ANELASTICITY
NT1	BRITTLENESS
NT1	COMPRESSIBILITY
NT1	DEFORMATION
NT2	ROCK DEFORMATION
NT3	DIAPIRISM
NT2	STRAIN
NT1	ELASTICITY
NT1	FLEXIBILITY
NT1	STRENGTH
NT2	BEARING CAPACITY
NT2	COLLAPSE STRENGTH
NT2	COMPRESSIVE STRENGTH
NT2	SHEAR STRENGTH
NT2	TENSILE STRENGTH
NT1	TOUGHNESS
NT1	VISCOSITY
NT2	DYNAMIC VISCOSITY
NT2	EDDY VISCOSITY
NT2	KINEMATIC VISCOSITY
NT2	MOLECULAR VISCOSITY
NT1	YIELD POINT
RT	ANISOTROPY
RT	BULK MODULUS
RT	ELASTIC CONSTANTS
RT	PLASTICITY
RT	SHEAR MODULUS
RT	STRESS
RT	STRESS-STRAIN RELATIONS

MECHANICAL STIMULI
BT1	STIMULI
RT	AUDITORY ORGANS
RT	LATERAL LINE

MECHANICS
BT1	PHYSICS
NT1	DYNAMICS
NT2	CABLE DYNAMICS
NT2	SEDIMENT DYNAMICS
NT2	STRUCTURAL DYNAMICS
NT1	FLUID MECHANICS
NT2	FLUID DYNAMICS
NT3	AERODYNAMICS
NT2	HYDRODYNAMICS
NT2	HYDROSTATICS
NT1	HYDRAULICS
NT1	KINEMATICS

MECHANICS (cont'd)
NT1	KINETICS
NT2	RADIONUCLIDE KINETICS
NT1	RHEOLOGY
NT1	ROCK MECHANICS
NT1	SOIL MECHANICS
RT	MOMENTUM

MECHANIZATION
SN	Added in 1980
RT	AQUACULTURE EQUIPMENT
RT	DECK EQUIPMENT
RT	FISHING GEAR
RT	HARVESTING MACHINES
RT	HATCHERIES

MECHANORECEPTORS
SN	Sense organs specialized to respond to mechanical stimuli such as pressure or deformation. Added in 1982
BT1	SENSE ORGANS
BT2	ANIMAL ORGANS
BT3	BODY ORGANS
RT	LATERAL LINE
RT	PRESSURE EFFECTS

MEDIAN LINES
RT	INTERNATIONAL BOUNDARIES

MEDIAN VALLEYS
SN	Before 1982 search RIFT VALLEYS
BT1	RIFT ZONES
RT	ESCARPMENTS
RT	FAULT ZONES
RT	FAULTS
RT	MID-OCEAN RIDGES
RT	PLATE DIVERGENCE
RT	RELIEF FORMS
RT	RIFT VALLEYS
RT	RIFTING
RT	SEAFLOOR SPREADING
RT	SUBMARINE FEATURES
RT	SUBMARINE SCARPS
RT	VALLEYS

MEDICAL PRACTICE
USE	**MEDICINE**

MEDICINE
SN	Restricted to marine and underwater medical practice
UF	life sciences (medicine)
UF	medical practice
BT1	HEALTH AND SAFETY
NT1	AETIOLOGY
NT1	UNDERWATER MEDICINE
RT	ACCIDENTS
RT	AQUATIC DRUGS
RT	BIOTECHNOLOGY
RT	DIVING PHYSIOLOGY
RT	DRUGS
RT	HUMAN PHYSIOLOGY
RT	HYPOTHERMIA
RT	IMMUNOLOGY
RT	INJURIES
RT	PHARMACOLOGY
RT	PUBLIC HEALTH
RT	RADIATION HAZARDS
RT	SEA SICKNESS
RT	SEARCH AND RESCUE
RT	SURVIVAL AT SEA
RT	SYMPTOMS
RT	THERAPY

MEETINGS
USE	**CONFERENCES**

MEGALOPAE
USE	**MEGALOPS**

MEGALOPS
SN	Added in 1980
UF	megalopae
BT1	CRUSTACEAN LARVAE
BT2	INVERTEBRATE LARVAE
BT3	LARVAE
BT4	DEVELOPMENTAL STAGES
RT	JUVENILES
RT	MARINE CRUSTACEANS

MEGARIPPLES
USE	**SAND WAVES**

MEIOBENTHIC ORGANISMS
USE	**MEIOBENTHOS**

MEIOBENTHOS
SN	Benthic micrometazoans and foraminiferans between 63 microns and 500 microns in size. Added in 1980
UF	meiobenthic organisms
UF	meiofauna
BT1	BENTHOS
BT2	AQUATIC COMMUNITIES
RT	SAND

MEIOFAUNA
USE	**MEIOBENTHOS**

MEIOSIS
UF	reduction division
BT1	CELL DIVISION
BT2	REPRODUCTION
RT	CHROMOSOMES
RT	KARYOLOGY
RT	MITOSIS
RT	NUCLEI

MELANGES
RT	BOUDINAGE
RT	DEBRIS FLOW
RT	DEFORMATION
RT	OLISTOSTROMES
RT	SEDIMENTS

MELANOPHORES
USE	**CHROMATOPHORES**

MELT WATER
BT1	WATER
RT	FRESH WATER
RT	ICE MELTING
RT	ICEBERGS
RT	MELTING

MELTING
BT1	PHASE CHANGES
NT1	ICE MELTING
RT	ABLATION
RT	FREEZING
RT	FUSION HEAT
RT	ICE BREAKUP
RT	MELT WATER
RT	MELTING POINT
RT	SOLIDIFICATION
RT	SUBLIMATION
RT	THAWING

MELTING POINT
BT1	TRANSITION TEMPERATURES
BT2	TEMPERATURE
BT3	THERMODYNAMIC PROPERTIES
BT4	PHYSICAL PROPERTIES
RT	ICE
RT	ICE MELTING
RT	MELTING

ASFIS Thesaurus

MEMBRANES
RT   DESALINATION

MEMBRANES (BIOLOGICAL)
USE   **BIOLOGICAL MEMBRANES**

MEMBRANES (CELLS)
USE   **CELL MEMBRANES**

MENDELEVIUM
BT1   CHEMICAL ELEMENTS
RT   MENDELEVIUM COMPOUNDS
RT   MENDELEVIUM ISOTOPES
RT   TRANSURANIC ELEMENTS

MENDELEVIUM COMPOUNDS
RT   CHEMICAL COMPOUNDS
RT   MENDELEVIUM

MENDELEVIUM ISOTOPES
BT1   ISOTOPES
RT   MENDELEVIUM

MERCHANT SHIPS
UF   cargo ships
BT1   SHIPS
BT2   SURFACE CRAFT
BT3   VEHICLES
NT1   BULK CARRIERS
NT1   CONTAINER SHIPS
NT1   PASSENGER SHIPS
NT1   SELECTED SHIPS
NT1   TANKER SHIPS
RT   CARGOES
RT   MARINE TRANSPORTATION
RT   SHIPPING LANES

MERCURY
SN   Before 1982 search also MERCURY (METAL)
UF   mercury (metal)
BT1   CHEMICAL ELEMENTS
RT   HEAVY METALS
RT   MERCURY COMPOUNDS
RT   MERCURY ISOTOPES
RT   METALS

MERCURY (METAL)
USE   **MERCURY**

MERCURY COMPOUNDS
RT   CHEMICAL COMPOUNDS
RT   MERCURY
RT   ORGANOMETALLIC COMPOUNDS

MERCURY ISOTOPES
BT1   ISOTOPES
RT   MERCURY

MERIDIONAL ATMOSPHERIC CIRCULATION
BT1   ATMOSPHERIC CIRCULATION
BT2   ATMOSPHERIC MOTION
RT   MERIDIONAL OCEANIC CIRCULATION

MERIDIONAL DISTRIBUTION
SN   Distribution North-South along lines of longitude. Used only as a qualifier
BT1   GEOGRAPHICAL DISTRIBUTION
BT2   DISTRIBUTION
RT   HYDROGRAPHIC SECTIONS
RT   LATITUDINAL VARIATIONS
RT   MERIDIONAL OCEANIC CIRCULATION
RT   ZONAL DISTRIBUTION

MERIDIONAL OCEANIC CIRCULATION
SN   North-South component of ocean circulation as seen in vertical section
BT1   OCEAN CIRCULATION

MERIDIONAL OCEANIC CIRCULATION (cont'd)
BT2   WATER CIRCULATION
BT3   WATER MOTION
RT   MERIDIONAL ATMOSPHERIC CIRCULATION
RT   MERIDIONAL DISTRIBUTION
RT   VERTICAL WATER MOVEMENT

MERISTIC CHARACTERS
USE   **MERISTIC COUNTS**

MERISTIC COUNTS
UF   meristic characters
NT1   FIN RAY COUNTS
NT1   GILLRAKER COUNTS
NT1   VERTEBRAE COUNTS
RT   BONY FINS
RT   NUMERICAL TAXONOMY
RT   STOCK IDENTIFICATION
RT   TAXONOMY

MEROMICTIC LAKES
BT1   LAKES
BT2   INLAND WATERS
RT   MEROMIXIS

MEROMIXIS
RT   MEROMICTIC LAKES

MEROPLANKTON
UF   temporary plankton
BT1   ZOOPLANKTON
BT2   PLANKTON
BT3   AQUATIC COMMUNITIES
RT   CRUSTACEAN LARVAE
RT   ICHTHYOPLANKTON
RT   INVERTEBRATE LARVAE
RT   LARVAE
RT   MOLLUSCAN LARVAE
RT   NAUPLII
RT   VELIGERS

MESH GAUGES
BT1   MEASURING DEVICES
RT   MESH REGULATIONS
RT   MESH SELECTIVITY

MESH REGULATIONS
BT1   FISHERY REGULATIONS
BT2   LEGISLATION
RT   MESH GAUGES
RT   MESH SELECTIVITY
RT   SIZE-LIMIT REGULATIONS

MESH SELECTIVITY
RT   ESCAPEMENT
RT   GEAR SELECTIVITY
RT   MESH GAUGES
RT   MESH REGULATIONS

MESOPELAGIC ZONE
SN   Waters between about 200 and 500 m depth
BT1   OCEANIC PROVINCE
BT2   PELAGIC ENVIRONMENT
BT3   AQUATIC ENVIRONMENT
BT4   ENVIRONMENTS
RT   BATHYAL-BENTHIC ZONE
RT   DISPHOTIC ZONE
RT   EUPHOTIC ZONE

MESOSCALE EDDIES
SN   Oceanic eddies of the order 100 km diameter
UF   mid-ocean eddies
BT1   OCEANIC EDDIES
BT2   OCEAN CIRCULATION
BT3   WATER CIRCULATION
BT4   WATER MOTION
RT   BAROCLINIC INSTABILITY
RT   CONSERVATION OF VORTICITY

MESOSCALE EDDIES (cont'd)
RT   CURRENT MEANDERING
RT   EDDY KINETIC ENERGY
RT   MESOSCALE FEATURES

MESOSCALE FEATURES
UF   mesoscale motion
NT1   FRONTAL FEATURES
RT   CURRENT MEANDERING
RT   MESOSCALE EDDIES

MESOSCALE MOTION
USE   **MESOSCALE FEATURES**

MESOSPHERE (EARTH)
BT1   EARTH STRUCTURE
RT   ASTHENOSPHERE
RT   EARTH CORE

MESOZOIC
SN   Before 1982 search MESOZOIC ERA
BT1   GEOLOGICAL TIME
NT1   CRETACEOUS
NT1   JURASSIC
NT1   TRIASSIC
RT   PHANEROZOIC

MESSENGERS
BT1   RELEASE MECHANISMS
RT   HYDROGRAPHIC WIRE
RT   OCEANOGRAPHIC EQUIPMENT
RT   REVERSING THERMOMETERS
RT   WATER SAMPLERS

MESSENGERS (CHEMICALS)
USE   **HORMONES**

MESSINIAN
UF   messinian events
BT1   MIOCENE
BT2   NEOGENE
BT3   TERTIARY
BT4   CENOZOIC
RT   PALAEOSALINITY

MESSINIAN EVENTS
USE   **MESSINIAN**

METABOLIC DISEASES
USE   **METABOLIC DISORDERS**

METABOLIC DISORDERS
SN   Added in 1982
UF   metabolic diseases
BT1   DISEASES
RT   METABOLISM
RT   NUTRITION DISORDERS

METABOLIC PROCESSES
USE   **METABOLISM**

METABOLIC RATE
USE   **METABOLISM**

METABOLISM
UF   metabolic processes
UF   metabolic rate
NT1   ANABOLISM
NT1   ANIMAL METABOLISM
NT1   CATABOLISM
NT1   PLANT METABOLISM
RT   ADRENAL GLANDS
RT   AESTIVATION
RT   BILE
RT   BIOCHEMICAL OXYGEN DEMAND
RT   BIOCHEMICAL PHENOMENA
RT   BIOCHEMISTRY
RT   BIOENERGETICS
RT   BODY TEMPERATURE
RT   DIGESTION

METABOLISM (cont'd)
RT	DORMANCY
RT	ENDOCRINOLOGY
RT	ENERGY FLOW
RT	ENZYMATIC ACTIVITY
RT	ENZYME INHIBITORS
RT	GLANDS
RT	GROWTH
RT	HIBERNATION
RT	HORMONES
RT	LIVER
RT	METABOLIC DISORDERS
RT	METABOLITES
RT	NUTRITION
RT	OXYGEN CONSUMPTION
RT	OXYGEN DEMAND
RT	PHYSIOLOGY
RT	RADIONUCLIDE KINETICS
RT	RESPIRATION
RT	THYMUS
RT	THYROID
RT	WATER BALANCE

METABOLITES
RT	BIOLOGICAL POISONS
RT	ECTOCRINES
RT	METABOLISM

METAL FATIGUE
BT1	FATIGUE (MATERIALS)
RT	STRESS CORROSION

METAL IONS
BT1	IONS
RT	METALS

METALIMNION
UF	seasonal thermocline (lakes)
UF	thermocline (lakes)
RT	EPILIMNION
RT	HYPOLIMNION
RT	INTERMEDIATE WATER MASSES
RT	RESERVOIRS (WATER)
RT	SEASONAL THERMOCLINE
RT	THERMAL STRATIFICATION
RT	THERMOCLINE

METALLIFEROUS BRINES
USE	HOT BRINES

METALLIFEROUS SEDIMENTS
BT1	CHEMICAL SEDIMENTS
BT2	SEDIMENTS
RT	COPPER
RT	HOT BRINES
RT	HYDROTHERMAL DEPOSITS
RT	IRON
RT	LEAD
RT	MANGANESE
RT	METALLOGENESIS
RT	MINERAL RESOURCES
RT	SEABED DEPOSITS
RT	SILVER
RT	SULPHIDE DEPOSITS
RT	ZINC

METALLOGENESIS
UF	metallogeny
RT	METALLIFEROUS SEDIMENTS
RT	MINERAL DEPOSITS

METALLOGENY
USE	METALLOGENESIS

METALLURGY
BT1	TECHNOLOGY
RT	ALLOYS
RT	MINERAL RESOURCES

METALS
UF	metals (chemical elements)
NT1	ACTINIDES
NT1	ALKALI METALS
NT1	ALKALINE EARTH METALS
NT1	HEAVY METALS
NT1	RARE EARTHS
NT1	TRANSURANIC ELEMENTS
RT	ALLOYS
RT	ALUMINIUM
RT	BISMUTH
RT	CADMIUM
RT	CHELATES
RT	CHEMICAL ELEMENTS
RT	CHROMIUM
RT	COBALT
RT	COPPER
RT	EUROPIUM
RT	GALLIUM
RT	GERMANIUM
RT	GOLD
RT	HAFNIUM
RT	INDIUM
RT	IRIDIUM
RT	IRON
RT	LEAD
RT	MANGANESE
RT	MERCURY
RT	METAL IONS
RT	MOLYBDENUM
RT	NICKEL
RT	NIOBIUM
RT	ORGANOMETALLIC COMPLEXES
RT	OSMIUM
RT	PALLADIUM
RT	PLATINUM
RT	POLONIUM
RT	RHENIUM
RT	RHODIUM
RT	RUTHENIUM
RT	SCANDIUM
RT	SILVER
RT	STEEL
RT	STRESS
RT	STRONTIUM
RT	TANTALUM
RT	TECHNETIUM
RT	TELLURIUM
RT	THALLIUM
RT	THORIUM
RT	TIN
RT	TITANIUM
RT	TRACE METALS
RT	TUNGSTEN
RT	VANADIUM
RT	ZINC
RT	ZIRCONIUM

METALS (CHEMICAL ELEMENTS)
USE	METALS

METALS (MATERIALS)
USE	ALLOYS

METAMORPHIC FACIES
BT1	FACIES
NT1	AMPHIBOLITE FACIES
NT1	GREENSCHIST FACIES
NT1	ZEOLITE FACIES

METAMORPHIC ROCKS
UF	rocks (metamorphic)
BT1	ROCKS
NT1	AMPHIBOLITES
NT2	HORNBLENDE
NT1	SCHISTS
NT2	GREENSCHISTS
NT1	SERPENTINITE
RT	BASEMENT ROCK
RT	METAMORPHISM

METAMORPHIC ROCKS (cont'd)
RT	SLATES
RT	ZEOLITES

METAMORPHISM
NT1	HYDROTHERMAL ALTERATION
RT	LOW TEMPERATURE
RT	METAMORPHIC ROCKS
RT	METASOMATISM
RT	ROCKS

METAMORPHOSIS
SN	Any marked change in stage of life cycle
BT1	BIOLOGICAL PHENOMENA
NT1	MOULTING
RT	CRUSTACEAN CULTURE
RT	DEVELOPMENTAL STAGES
RT	INSECT LARVAE
RT	INVERTEBRATE LARVAE
RT	JUVENILES
RT	LARVAE
RT	LARVAL DEVELOPMENT
RT	LARVAL SETTLEMENT
RT	LIFE CYCLE
RT	MOLLUSCAN LARVAE
RT	NAUPLII
RT	NYMPHS
RT	THYROID
RT	VELIGERS
RT	SERPENTINITIZATION

METASOMATISM
RT	CHERTIFICATION
RT	DIAGENESIS
RT	HYDROTHERMAL ALTERATION
RT	METAMORPHISM
RT	SERPENTINITIZATION
RT	SILICIFICATION

METEOROLOGICAL BALLOONS
USE	BALLOONS

METEOROLOGICAL BUOYS
USE	DATA BUOYS

METEOROLOGICAL CHARTS
SN	Use of a more specific term is recommended
BT1	MAPS
BT2	GRAPHICS
BT3	AUDIOVISUAL MATERIAL
BT4	DOCUMENTS
NT1	WEATHER MAPS
RT	ATMOSPHERIC PRESSURE
RT	METEOROLOGICAL DATA
RT	METEOROLOGY
RT	SEA LEVEL PRESSURE
RT	STORMS

METEOROLOGICAL DATA
BT1	DATA
NT1	CLIMATIC DATA
NT1	METEOROLOGICAL OBSERVATIONS
NT1	WIND DATA
RT	CLIMATE
RT	CLIMATOLOGY
RT	CRUISES
RT	DATA BUOYS
RT	HUMIDITY
RT	ISOBARS
RT	MARSDEN SQUARES
RT	METEOROLOGICAL CHARTS
RT	METEOROLOGICAL INSTRUMENTS
RT	METEOROLOGY
RT	MULTISHIP EXPEDITIONS
RT	OCEAN STATIONS
RT	SELECTED SHIPS
RT	TROPOSPHERE
RT	WEATHER SHIPS

METEOROLOGICAL EQUIPMENT	**METEOROLOGY** (cont'd)	**MICROBIAL CONTAMINATION** (cont'd)
USE **METEOROLOGICAL INSTRUMENTS**	RT METEOROLOGICAL CHARTS	RT PUBLIC HEALTH
	RT METEOROLOGICAL DATA	RT QUALITY CONTROL
METEOROLOGICAL FORCING	RT METEOROLOGISTS	RT VIRUSES
USE **ATMOSPHERIC FORCING**	RT OCEANOGRAPHIC SURVEYS	
	RT OCEANOGRAPHY	**MICROBIAL DEGRADATION**
METEOROLOGICAL FRONTS	RT PHYSICAL OCEANOGRAPHY	USE **BIODEGRADATION**
USE **ATMOSPHERIC FRONTS**	RT SEA LEVEL PRESSURE	
	RT SOLAR RADIATION	**MICROBIAL POLLUTION**
METEOROLOGICAL INSTRUMENTS	RT STORMS	USE **MICROBIAL CONTAMINATION**
UF meteorological equipment	RT WEATHER	
NT1 RAIN GAUGES	RT WEATHER FORECASTING	**MICROBIOLOGICAL ANALYSIS**
RT ACTINOMETERS	RT WEATHER SHIPS	RT ANALYSIS
RT BALLOONS	RT WINDS	RT BACTERIA
RT LIDAR		RT BIOLOGICAL POLLUTANTS
RT MASTS	**METHANE**	RT CULTURE MEDIA
RT METEOROLOGICAL DATA	BT1 ACYCLIC HYDROCARBONS	RT FUNGI
RT PSYCHROMETERS	BT2 SATURATED HYDROCARBONS	RT MICROBIAL CONTAMINATION
RT PYRANOMETERS	BT3 HYDROCARBONS	RT MICROBIOLOGICAL CULTURE
RT PYRHELIOMETERS	BT4 ORGANIC COMPOUNDS	RT MICROBIOLOGY
RT RADIOSONDES	RT CHLOROFORM	RT POLLUTION DETECTION
RT SODAR	RT GAS HYDRATES	
RT WIND MEASURING EQUIPMENT	RT METHANOGENESIS	**MICROBIOLOGICAL CULTURE**
RT WIND TUNNELS		BT1 LABORATORY CULTURE
	METHANOGENESIS	RT BACTERIA
METEOROLOGICAL OBSERVATIONS	RT METHANE	RT BACTERIA COLLECTING DEVICES
BT1 METEOROLOGICAL DATA		RT BACTERIOLOGY
BT2 DATA	**METHIONINE**	RT CULTURE MEDIA
RT AIRCRAFT	BT1 AMINO ACIDS	RT CULTURED ORGANISMS
RT MASTS	BT2 ORGANIC ACIDS	RT FUNGI
RT SEA LEVEL PRESSURE	BT3 ORGANIC COMPOUNDS	RT MICROBIOLOGICAL ANALYSIS
RT SELECTED SHIPS		RT MICROBIOLOGY
RT WEATHER MAPS	**METHODOLOGY**	
	SN Term to be used only as a qualifier	**MICROBIOLOGISTS**
METEOROLOGICAL SATELLITES	UF methods	BT1 BIOLOGISTS
USE **SCIENTIFIC SATELLITES**	RT ANALYTICAL TECHNIQUES	BT2 SCIENTIFIC PERSONNEL
	RT EQUIPMENT	BT3 PERSONNEL
METEOROLOGICAL TABLES	RT GRAPHIC METHODS	NT1 BACTERIOLOGISTS
UF conversion tables (meteorology)	RT MANUALS	NT1 MYCOLOGISTS
BT1 TABLES	RT MEASUREMENT	NT1 VIROLOGISTS
BT2 DOCUMENTS	RT PLANNING	RT DIRECTORIES
RT NAUTICAL ALMANACS	RT STANDARDIZATION	RT MICROBIOLOGY
RT OCEANOGRAPHIC TABLES	RT SYSTEM ANALYSIS	RT MYCOLOGY
	RT TECHNOLOGY	
METEOROLOGICAL TIDES		**MICROBIOLOGY**
BT1 TIDES	**METHODS**	BT1 BIOLOGY
BT2 TIDAL MOTION	USE **METHODOLOGY**	NT1 BACTERIOLOGY
RT ATMOSPHERIC TIDES		NT1 MYCOLOGY
RT RADIATIONAL TIDES	**METHYL MERCURY**	NT1 VIROLOGY
RT SOLAR TIDES	BT1 ORGANOMETALLIC COMPOUNDS	RT BACTERIOLOGISTS
RT STORM SURGES	BT2 ORGANIC COMPOUNDS	RT FOOD TECHNOLOGY
		RT INFECTIOUS DISEASES
METEOROLOGISTS	**MICAS**	RT MICROBIAL CONTAMINATION
UF climatologists	BT1 SILICATE MINERALS	RT MICROBIOLOGICAL ANALYSIS
BT1 SCIENTIFIC PERSONNEL	BT2 MINERALS	RT MICROBIOLOGICAL CULTURE
BT2 PERSONNEL	NT1 BIOTITE	RT MICROBIOLOGISTS
RT DIRECTORIES	NT1 GLAUCONITE	RT MICROORGANISMS
RT METEOROLOGY	NT1 HYDROBIOTITE	RT MYCOLOGISTS
	NT1 MUSCOVITE	RT PARASITOLOGY
METEOROLOGY	RT SLATES	RT PHARMACOLOGY
UF marine meteorology		RT TAXONOMY
NT1 POLAR METEOROLOGY	**MICROBENTHOS**	RT VIROLOGISTS
NT1 TROPICAL METEOROLOGY	USE **BENTHOS**	RT WATER ANALYSIS
RT AIR TEMPERATURE		
RT AIR-SEA COUPLING	**MICROBIAL CONTAMINATION**	**MICROCARDS**
RT AIR-SEA INTERACTION	UF microbial pollution	USE **MICROFORMS**
RT ATMOSPHERIC DISTURBANCES	UF pollution (microbial)	
RT ATMOSPHERIC FRONTS	RT BACTERIA	**MICROCOMPUTERS**
RT ATMOSPHERIC MOTION	RT BIOLOGICAL POLLUTANTS	USE **COMPUTERS**
RT ATMOSPHERIC PHYSICS	RT BOTULISM	
RT ATMOSPHERIC PRECIPITATIONS	RT DISEASES	**MICROCONTINENTS**
RT ATMOSPHERIC PRESSURE	RT DISINFECTION	BT1 SUBMARINE FEATURES
RT ATMOSPHERIC SCIENCES	RT EPIDEMICS	BT2 TOPOGRAPHIC FEATURES
RT ATMOSPHERIC TURBULENCE	RT FOOD POISONING	RT ASEISMIC RIDGES
RT CLIMATOLOGY	RT FUNGI	RT CONTINENTAL CRUST
RT EARTH ATMOSPHERE	RT MARINE POLLUTION	RT SUBMARINE PLATEAUX
RT EVAPORATION	RT MICROBIOLOGICAL ANALYSIS	
RT FISHERY OCEANOGRAPHY	RT MICROBIOLOGY	
RT HYDROLOGIC CYCLE	RT PATHOGENS	
RT LIMNOLOGY	RT POLLUTION EFFECTS	

MICROEARTHQUAKES
BT1	EARTHQUAKES
RT	MICROSEISMS
RT	SEISMOLOGY

MICROFAUNA
USE	**MICROORGANISMS**

MICROFICHES
USE	**MICROFORMS**

MICROFILMS
USE	**MICROFORMS**

MICROFLORA
USE	**MICROORGANISMS**

MICROFORMS
UF	microcards
UF	microfiches
UF	microfilms
BT1	AUDIOVISUAL MATERIAL
BT2	DOCUMENTS
RT	MICROPHOTOGRAPHY

MICROHABITATS
SN	Added in 1980
BT1	HABITAT
RT	BIOTOPES
RT	NICHES

MICROMETER CALIPERS
BT1	MEASURING DEVICES

MICRONEKTON
USE	**NEKTON**

MICROORGANISMS
SN	Before 1982 search MICRO-ORGANISMS
UF	microfauna
UF	microflora
NT1	BACTERIA
NT2	AEROBIC BACTERIA
NT2	ANAEROBIC BACTERIA
NT2	PATHOGENIC BACTERIA
NT1	VIRUSES
NT1	YEASTS
RT	AQUATIC ORGANISMS
RT	EPIPSAMMON
RT	FUNGI
RT	MICROBIOLOGY
RT	NANNOPLANKTON
RT	WATER ANALYSIS

MICROPALAEONTOLOGY
BT1	PALAEONTOLOGY
RT	FORAMINIFERA
RT	FOSSILS
RT	GEOID
RT	PALYNOLOGY
RT	STRATIGRAPHY

MICROPHONES
BT1	ACOUSTIC TRANSDUCERS
BT2	TRANSDUCERS
RT	ACOUSTIC EQUIPMENT
RT	HYDROPHONES

MICROPHOTOGRAPHY
BT1	PHOTOGRAPHY
BT2	IMAGERY
BT3	REMOTE SENSING
RT	MICROFORMS
RT	PHOTOGRAPHIC EQUIPMENT
RT	PHOTOGRAPHS

MICROPROCESSORS
RT	COMPUTERS
RT	ELECTRONIC EQUIPMENT

MICROSCOPES
UF	light microscopes
UF	optical microscopes
BT1	LABORATORY EQUIPMENT
BT2	EQUIPMENT
RT	ELECTRON MICROSCOPY
RT	LIGHT MICROSCOPY
RT	MICROSCOPY

MICROSCOPY
BT1	ANALYTICAL TECHNIQUES
NT1	ELECTRON MICROSCOPY
NT1	FLUORESCENCE MICROSCOPY
NT1	LIGHT MICROSCOPY
RT	CHEMICAL ANALYSIS
RT	CYTOLOGY
RT	HISTOLOGY
RT	MICROSCOPES

MICROSEISMS
BT1	SEISMIC WAVES
BT2	ELASTIC WAVES
RT	MICROEARTHQUAKES
RT	SEISMOLOGY
RT	WAVE FORECASTING

MICROSOMES
USE	**RIBOSOMES**

MICROSTRUCTURE
SN	Variations in the distribution of temperature, salinity and velocity on a scale of 10 cm or less
UF	oceanic microstructure
BT1	SPATIAL VARIATIONS
NT1	SALINITY MICROSTRUCTURE
NT1	THERMAL MICROSTRUCTURE
NT1	VELOCITY MICROSTRUCTURE
RT	DOUBLE DIFFUSION
RT	FINESTRUCTURE
RT	INTERNAL WAVES
RT	OCEANIC TURBULENCE
RT	SALT FINGERS

MICROTOPOGRAPHY
RT	BEACH FEATURES
RT	BOTTOM EROSION
RT	POCK MARKS
RT	SEACHANNELS

MICROWAVE IMAGERY
UF	radiometers (microwave)
BT1	IMAGERY
BT2	REMOTE SENSING
NT1	RADAR IMAGERY
RT	ELECTROMAGNETIC RADIATION
RT	GEOSENSING
RT	IMAGE ENHANCEMENT
RT	MICROWAVE RADIOMETERS
RT	MICROWAVES
RT	SATELLITE MOSAICS
RT	SATELLITE SENSING
RT	SEA ICE
RT	SEA STATE
RT	SURFACE TEMPERATURE
RT	WAVE MEASUREMENT

MICROWAVE RADAR
BT1	RADAR
BT2	REMOTE SENSING EQUIPMENT
BT3	EQUIPMENT
NT1	RADAR ALTIMETERS
NT1	SCATTEROMETERS
NT1	SYNTHETIC APERTURE RADAR
RT	MICROWAVES

MICROWAVE RADIATION
USE	**MICROWAVES**

MICROWAVE RADIOMETERS
BT1	RADIOMETERS
BT2	REMOTE SENSING EQUIPMENT
BT3	EQUIPMENT
RT	MICROWAVE IMAGERY
RT	MICROWAVES

MICROWAVES
UF	microwave radiation
BT1	ELECTROMAGNETIC RADIATION
BT2	RADIATIONS
RT	COMMUNICATION SYSTEMS
RT	MICROWAVE IMAGERY
RT	MICROWAVE RADAR
RT	MICROWAVE RADIOMETERS
RT	RADAR
RT	RADIO
RT	SCATTEROMETERS
RT	TELEMETRY
RT	TELEVISION SYSTEMS

MID-OCEAN EDDIES
USE	**MESOSCALE EDDIES**

MID-OCEAN RIDGES
UF	mid-ocean rises
UF	mid-oceanic ridges
UF	midocean ridges
UF	rise (oceanic)
BT1	SEISMIC RIDGES
BT2	SUBMARINE RIDGES
BT3	SUBMARINE FEATURES
BT4	TOPOGRAPHIC FEATURES
RT	DIVERGING PLATE BOUNDARIES
RT	FRACTURE ZONES
RT	HYDROTHERMAL ACTIVITY
RT	MEDIAN VALLEYS
RT	MOUNTAINS
RT	OCEAN FLOOR
RT	PLATE DIVERGENCE
RT	RELIEF FORMS
RT	RIDGES
RT	SEAFLOOR SPREADING
RT	SEISMIC ACTIVITY
RT	TRANSFORM FAULTS

MID-OCEAN RISES
USE	**MID-OCEAN RIDGES**

MID-OCEANIC RIDGES
USE	**MID-OCEAN RIDGES**

MIDLATITUDE ANTICYCLONES
USE	**ANTICYCLONES**

MIDLATITUDE CYCLONES
USE	**CYCLONES**

MIDOCEAN RIDGES
USE	**MID-OCEAN RIDGES**

MIDWATER CAGES
USE	**SUBMERGED CAGES**

MIDWATER TRAWLS
UF	beam trawls (midwater)
UF	floating trawls
UF	otter trawls (midwater)
UF	pair trawls (midwater)
BT1	TRAWL NETS
BT2	FISHING NETS
BT3	FISHING GEAR
RT	PELAGIC FISHERIES

MIGRANT SPECIES
USE   **MIGRATORY SPECIES**

MIGRATIONS
UF   animal migrations
NT1   FEEDING MIGRATIONS
NT1   OCEANODROMOUS MIGRATIONS
NT1   POTADROMOUS MIGRATIONS
NT1   SPAWNING MIGRATIONS
NT2   ANADROMOUS MIGRATIONS
NT2   CATADROMOUS MIGRATIONS
NT1   VERTICAL MIGRATIONS
RT   ACTIVITY PATTERNS
RT   ANIMAL NAVIGATION
RT   AQUATIC BIRDS
RT   AUTECOLOGY
RT   AVOIDANCE REACTIONS
RT   BEHAVIOUR
RT   BIOTELEMETRY
RT   DISPERSION
RT   ECOLOGICAL DISTRIBUTION
RT   GEOGRAPHICAL DISTRIBUTION
RT   HORIZONTAL DISTRIBUTION
RT   IMMIGRATIONS
RT   LAND BRIDGES
RT   LOCAL MOVEMENTS
RT   MARKING
RT   MIGRATORY SPECIES
RT   ORIENTATION
RT   ORIENTATION BEHAVIOUR
RT   OVERWINTERING
RT   PHENOLOGY
RT   PHOTOPERIODICITY
RT   REGIONAL VARIATIONS
RT   REPRODUCTIVE BEHAVIOUR
RT   SEASONAL DISTRIBUTION
RT   SEASONAL VARIATIONS
RT   SEASONALITY
RT   STAINING
RT   TAGGING
RT   TAGS
RT   TEMPERATURE EFFECTS
RT   TEMPORAL DISTRIBUTION
RT   TRACKING

MIGRATORY SPECIES
SN   Added in 1980
UF   highly migratory species
UF   migrant species
BT1   SPECIES
BT2   TAXA
RT   AQUATIC BIRDS
RT   ENDEMIC SPECIES
RT   FISHERY REGULATIONS
RT   FISHERY RESOURCES
RT   FISHING RIGHTS
RT   FOREIGN FISHING
RT   MIGRATIONS
RT   OVERWINTERING
RT   SALMON FISHERIES
RT   SEDENTARY SPECIES
RT   SHARED STOCKS
RT   SHRIMP FISHERIES
RT   TUNA FISHERIES

MILITARY ACTIVITIES
USE   **MILITARY OPERATIONS**

MILITARY OCEANOGRAPHY
BT1   OCEANOGRAPHY
BT2   EARTH SCIENCES
RT   DEFENCE CRAFT
RT   MILITARY OPERATIONS
RT   PREDICTION
RT   SONAR
RT   SUBMARINES
RT   UNDERSEA WARFARE

MILITARY OPERATIONS
UF   military activities
RT   DEFENCE CRAFT
RT   MILITARY OCEANOGRAPHY
RT   MILITARY PORTS
RT   SECURITY
RT   SURVEILLANCE AND ENFORCEMENT
RT   UNDERSEA WARFARE

MILITARY PORTS
BT1   ARTIFICIAL HARBOURS
BT2   COASTAL STRUCTURES
BT3   HYDRAULIC STRUCTURES
RT   MILITARY OPERATIONS
RT   NAVAL BASES

MILK
RT   MARINE MAMMALS

MILT
USE   **ROES**

MIMICRY
SN   Imitation of another organism or
      object in the environment (in form,
      color, and/or behaviour)
UF   adaptive colouration
BT1   ADAPTATIONS
BT2   BIOLOGICAL PHENOMENA
RT   CAMOUFLAGE
RT   DEFENCE MECHANISMS
RT   PROTECTIVE BEHAVIOUR

MINCED PRODUCTS
UF   comminuted products
UF   fish balls
UF   fish mince
UF   fish paste
UF   kamaboko
UF   surimi
BT1   PROCESSED FISHERY PRODUCTS
BT2   FISHERY PRODUCTS
BT3   PRODUCTS
RT   FERMENTED PRODUCTS
RT   FOOD TECHNOLOGY
RT   ORGANOLEPTIC PROPERTIES
RT   QUALITY CONTROL

MINE TAILINGS
BT1   WASTES
RT   MINING
RT   STRIP MINE LAKES

MINERAL ASSEMBLAGES
RT   MINERAL DEPOSITS

MINERAL COLLECTIONS
SN   Collections of materials obtained
      by geological surveys
BT1   COLLECTIONS
RT   GEOLOGICAL SURVEYS
RT   MINERAL RESOURCES
RT   MINERALOGY

MINERAL COMPOSITION
BT1   COMPOSITION
RT   HYDROTHERMAL ALTERATION
RT   MINERAL RESOURCES
RT   MINERALOGY

MINERAL DEPOSITS
BT1   MINERAL RESOURCES
BT2   NATURAL RESOURCES
BT3   RESOURCES
NT1   SEABED DEPOSITS
NT2   AGGREGATES
NT2   FERROMANGANESE NODULES
NT2   PHOSPHORITE NODULES
NT2   PLACERS
NT3   DIAMONDS

MINERAL DEPOSITS (cont'd)
NT1   SUBSURFACE DEPOSITS
NT2   FOSSIL FUELS
NT3   COAL
NT3   PETROLEUM
NT4   CRUDE OIL
NT4   GAS CONDENSATES
NT4   NATURAL GAS
NT4   PETROLEUM RESIDUES
NT2   PHOSPHATE DEPOSITS
RT   CHEMICAL SEDIMENTS
RT   DEEP-SEA MINING
RT   GEOLOGICAL MAPS
RT   METALLOGENESIS
RT   MINERAL ASSEMBLAGES
RT   MINERAL EXPLORATION
RT   MINERAL SAMPLES
RT   MINERALIZATION
RT   MINERALS
RT   MINING
RT   MINING EQUIPMENT
RT   NONRENEWABLE RESOURCES
RT   ORES
RT   OUTCROPS
RT   PLACER MINING
RT   OFFSHORE OPERATIONS

MINERAL EXPLORATION
UF   exploration (minerals)
UF   exploratory mining
BT1   RESOURCE EXPLORATION
BT2   EXPLORATION
RT   CONCESSIONS
RT   DEEP-SEA MINING
RT   GEOPHYSICAL EXPLORATION
RT   MINERAL DEPOSITS
RT   MINERAL INDUSTRY
RT   MINING
RT   OFFSHORE OPERATIONS
RT   PLACER MINING
RT   SEDIMENT SAMPLING

MINERAL INDUSTRY
SN   Industries of mineral resources or
      extraction of mineralized products
      of organic origin
BT1   INDUSTRIES
RT   BRINES
RT   DEEP-SEA MINING
RT   DESALINATION
RT   DESALINATION PLANTS
RT   FERROMANGANESE NODULES
RT   GUANO
RT   MINERAL EXPLORATION
RT   MINERAL PROCESSING
RT   MINERAL RESOURCES
RT   MINING
RT   NODULES
RT   SALTS

MINERAL OILS
USE   **PETROLEUM**

MINERAL PROCESSING
RT   MINERAL INDUSTRY
RT   MINERAL RESOURCES
RT   PROCESS PLANTS

MINERAL RESOURCES
BT1   NATURAL RESOURCES
BT2   RESOURCES
NT1   DISSOLVED CHEMICALS
NT1   MINERAL DEPOSITS
NT2   SEABED DEPOSITS
NT3   AGGREGATES
NT3   FERROMANGANESE NODULES
NT3   PHOSPHORITE NODULES
NT3   PLACERS
NT4   DIAMONDS
NT2   SUBSURFACE DEPOSITS

MINERAL RESOURCES (cont'd)
NT3	FOSSIL FUELS
NT4	COAL
NT4	PETROLEUM
NT3	PHOSPHATE DEPOSITS
NT1	ORES
RT	DEEP-SEA MINING
RT	EXPLOITATION
RT	GEOLOGICAL SURVEYS
RT	GUANO
RT	MARINE GEOLOGY
RT	MARINE RESOURCES
RT	METALLIFEROUS SEDIMENTS
RT	METALLURGY
RT	MINERAL COLLECTIONS
RT	MINERAL COMPOSITION
RT	MINERAL INDUSTRY
RT	MINERAL PROCESSING
RT	MINERALOGY
RT	NODULES
RT	NONRENEWABLE RESOURCES
RT	OUTER CONTINENTAL SHELF
RT	RESOURCE CONSERVATION
RT	RESOURCE DEVELOPMENT
RT	RESOURCE MANAGEMENT
RT	SALTS
RT	UNDERWATER EXPLOITATION
RT	UNDERWATER EXPLORATION

MINERAL SALTS
USE	**SALTS**

MINERAL SAMPLES
BT1	GEOLOGICAL SAMPLES
BT2	SAMPLES
RT	GEOLOGICAL COLLECTIONS
RT	GEOLOGICAL DATA
RT	MINERAL DEPOSITS
RT	MINERALOGY

MINERALIZATION
RT	MINERAL DEPOSITS

MINERALOGY
RT	GEOCHEMISTRY
RT	GEOLOGY
RT	MARINE GEOLOGY
RT	MINERAL COLLECTIONS
RT	MINERAL COMPOSITION
RT	MINERAL RESOURCES
RT	MINERAL SAMPLES
RT	SEDIMENT CHEMISTRY
RT	SEDIMENTOLOGY

MINERALS
NT1	BORATE MINERALS
NT2	BORAX
NT1	CARBONATE MINERALS
NT2	ARAGONITE
NT2	CALCITE
NT2	DOLOMITE
NT2	HYDROMAGNESITE
NT2	MAGNESITE
NT2	SIDERITE
NT1	GRAPHITE
NT1	HALIDE MINERALS
NT2	CARNALLITE
NT2	FLUORITE
NT2	HALITE
NT1	HEAVY MINERALS
NT1	MANGANESE MINERALS
NT1	OXIDE MINERALS
NT2	ANATASE
NT2	BAUXITE
NT2	BIRNESSITE
NT2	BOEHMITE
NT2	BRUCITE
NT2	CASSITERITE
NT2	CHROMITE
NT2	CRISTOBALITE

MINERALS (cont'd)
NT2	GIBBSITE
NT2	GOETHITE
NT2	HAEMATITE
NT2	ILMENITE
NT2	LIMONITE
NT2	MAGHEMITE
NT2	MAGNETITE
NT2	MANGANITE
NT2	PYROLUSITE
NT2	RUTILE
NT2	TODOROKITE
NT1	PHOSPHATE MINERALS
NT2	APATITE
NT2	FRANCOLITE
NT2	MONAZITE
NT1	SILICATE MINERALS
NT2	AMPHIBOLES
NT2	ANDALUSITE
NT2	CLAY MINERALS
NT3	CHLORITE
NT3	ILLITE
NT3	KAOLIN
NT3	KAOLINITE
NT3	MONTMORILLONITE
NT3	NONTRONITE
NT3	PALYGORSKITE
NT3	SAPONITE
NT3	SMECTITE
NT3	VERMICULITE
NT2	FELDSPARS
NT3	ANORTHITE
NT3	ANORTHOCLASE
NT3	ORTHOCLASE
NT3	PLAGIOCLASE
NT2	GARNET
NT2	KYANITE
NT2	MICAS
NT3	BIOTITE
NT3	GLAUCONITE
NT3	HYDROBIOTITE
NT3	MUSCOVITE
NT2	OLIVINE
NT2	OPAL
NT2	PYROPHYLLITE
NT2	PYROXENES
NT3	AUGITE
NT2	QUARTZ
NT2	QUARTZITE
NT2	SEPIOLITE
NT2	TITANITE
NT2	TOURMALINE
NT2	ZEOLITES
NT3	ANALCITE
NT3	CLINOPTILONITE
NT3	HEULANDITE
NT3	PHILLIPSITE
NT2	ZIRCON
NT1	SULPHATE MINERALS
NT2	ANHYDRITE
NT2	BARITE
NT2	CELESTITE
NT2	EPSOMITE
NT2	GYPSUM
NT2	JAROSITE
NT2	KAINITE
NT2	POLYHALITE
NT1	SULPHIDE MINERALS
NT2	GREIGITE
NT2	KANSITE
NT2	MARCASITE
NT2	PYRITE
NT2	PYRRHOTITE
RT	MINERAL DEPOSITS

MINICOMPUTERS
USE	**COMPUTERS**

MINING
UF	exploitation (minerals)
NT1	DEEP-SEA MINING
NT1	PLACER MINING
RT	COAL
RT	FOSSIL FUELS
RT	HARVESTING
RT	MINE TAILINGS
RT	MINERAL DEPOSITS
RT	MINERAL EXPLORATION
RT	MINERAL INDUSTRY
RT	MINING EQUIPMENT
RT	SEABED DEPOSITS
RT	SITE SELECTION

MINING EQUIPMENT
BT1	EQUIPMENT
RT	HYDRAULIC SYSTEMS
RT	MINERAL DEPOSITS
RT	MINING
RT	MINING VESSELS

MINING LEGISLATION
RT	CONCESSIONS

MINING VESSELS
BT1	SURFACE CRAFT
BT2	VEHICLES
RT	DEEP-SEA MINING
RT	MINING EQUIPMENT

MIOCENE
SN	Before 1982 search MIOCENE EPOCH
BT1	NEOGENE
BT2	TERTIARY
BT3	CENOZOIC
BT4	GEOLOGICAL TIME
NT1	MESSINIAN

MIRAGES
RT	ATMOSPHERIC OPTICAL PHENOMENA

MIST
USE	**FOG**

MISTRAL
BT1	LOCAL WINDS
BT2	WINDS
BT3	ATMOSPHERIC MOTION
RT	DEEP WATER FORMATION

MITOCHONDRIA
USE	**CELL ORGANELLES**

MITOSIS
UF	karyokinesis
BT1	CELL DIVISION
BT2	REPRODUCTION
RT	CHROMOSOMES
RT	KARYOLOGY
RT	MEIOSIS
RT	NUCLEI

MIXED GAS
UF	helium oxygen mixture
RT	DEEP-SEA DIVING
RT	DIVING PHYSIOLOGY
RT	LIFE SUPPORT SYSTEMS

MIXED LAYER
BT1	WATER COLUMN
BT2	LAYERS
NT1	BOTTOM MIXED LAYER
NT1	SURFACE MIXED LAYER
RT	ISOHALINES

ASFIS Thesaurus

MIXED LAYER DEPTH
UF	thermocline depth
BT1	DEPTH
BT2	DIMENSIONS
RT	ATMOSPHERIC FORCING
RT	HURRICANES
RT	PYCNOCLINE
RT	SURFACE MIXED LAYER
RT	THERMOCLINE

MIXED SPECIES CULTURE
USE	**POLYCULTURE**

MIXING (SEDIMENTS)
USE	**SEDIMENT MIXING**

MIXING (WATER)
USE	**WATER MIXING**

MIXING LENGTH
BT1	LENGTH
BT2	DIMENSIONS
RT	EDDY FLUX
RT	EDDY VISCOSITY
RT	EXCHANGE COEFFICIENTS
RT	SHEAR FLOW
RT	VORTICES

MIXING PROCESSES
RT	AERATION
RT	BIOTURBATION
RT	CABBELING
RT	DIFFUSION
RT	DISPERSION
RT	DOWNWELLING
RT	GAS TURBATION
RT	INTERFACES
RT	OVERTURN
RT	SEDIMENT MIXING
RT	TIDAL MIXING
RT	TRANS-ISOPYCNAL MIXING
RT	TURBULENT DIFFUSION
RT	TURBULENT ENTRAINMENT
RT	UPWELLING
RT	WATER MIXING

MIXING RATIO
BT1	DIMENSIONLESS NUMBERS
RT	DEW POINT
RT	HUMIDITY
RT	RELATIVE HUMIDITY
RT	SPECIFIC HUMIDITY
RT	VAPOUR PRESSURE
RT	WATER VAPOUR

MOBILE PLATFORMS
SN	Towed or self-propelled structures with the working level above water operated in a fixed position, excluding vessels in conventional ship form
BT1	FLOATING STRUCTURES
BT2	OFFSHORE STRUCTURES
BT3	HYDRAULIC STRUCTURES
NT1	JACKUP PLATFORMS
NT1	SEMISUBMERSIBLE PLATFORMS
NT1	SUBMERSIBLE PLATFORMS
NT1	WORKOVER BARGES
RT	DECKS
RT	FIXED PLATFORMS
RT	POSITIONING SYSTEMS

MODELLING
SN	Used only as a qualifier. Before 1982 search SIMULATION
RT	MATHEMATICAL MODELS
RT	MATHEMATICAL PROGRAMMING
RT	MODELS
RT	SIMULATION

MODELS
SN	Used only as a qualifier
NT1	ANALOG MODELS
NT2	ACOUSTIC MODELS
NT1	MATHEMATICAL MODELS
NT2	ECONOMIC MODELS
NT2	STATISTICAL MODELS
NT2	TIDAL MODELS
NT1	SCALE MODELS
NT2	HYDRAULIC MODELS
NT3	HARBOUR MODELS
NT2	SHIP MODELS
RT	COMPUTATION
RT	MODELLING
RT	SIMULATORS

MODES
SN	Used only as a qualifier
RT	BAROCLINIC MODE
RT	BAROTROPIC MODE

MODIFIERS
USE	**ADDITIVES**

MODULES
SN	Use for prefabricated units of equipment
UF	skid mounted units
RT	EQUIPMENT
RT	FIXED PLATFORMS
RT	INSTALLATION

MOHO
UF	mohorovicic discontinuity
BT1	SEISMIC DISCONTINUITIES
RT	ASTHENOSPHERE
RT	BASEMENT ROCK
RT	CONTINENTAL DRIFT
RT	EARTH MANTLE
RT	EARTH STRUCTURE
RT	LITHOSPHERE
RT	MOHOLE PROJECT
RT	PLATE TECTONICS
RT	SEAFLOOR SPREADING
RT	SEISMIC VELOCITIES
RT	TECTONOPHYSICS

MOHOLE PROJECT
RT	MOHO

MOHOROVICIC DISCONTINUITY
USE	**MOHO**

MOISTURE
RT	AIR-WATER EXCHANGES
RT	EVAPORATION
RT	MOISTURE TRANSFER

MOISTURE CONTENT
USE	**WATER CONTENT**

MOISTURE FLUX
USE	**MOISTURE TRANSFER**

MOISTURE TRANSFER
UF	mass transfer (air-water exchanges)
UF	moisture flux
UF	water vapour transfer
RT	AIR-WATER EXCHANGES
RT	AIR-WATER INTERFACE
RT	ATMOSPHERIC BOUNDARY LAYER
RT	ENERGY TRANSFER
RT	EVAPORATION
RT	MOISTURE
RT	WATER VAPOUR

MOLECULAR DIFFUSION
BT1	DIFFUSION
BT2	TRANSPORT PROCESSES
NT1	DOUBLE DIFFUSION
RT	HEAT
RT	MOMENTUM
RT	OSMOSIS
RT	SALTS

MOLECULAR HEAT CONDUCTION
USE	**HEAT CONDUCTION**

MOLECULAR MASS
USE	**MOLECULAR WEIGHT**

MOLECULAR STRUCTURE
SN	Added in 1980
RT	MOLECULAR WEIGHT
RT	MOLECULES

MOLECULAR TAXONOMY
USE	**CHEMOTAXONOMY**

MOLECULAR VISCOSITY
BT1	VISCOSITY
BT2	MECHANICAL PROPERTIES
BT3	PHYSICAL PROPERTIES
BT4	PROPERTIES
RT	LAMINAR FLOW
RT	MOLECULAR VISCOSITY COEFFICIENTS
RT	MOMENTUM TRANSFER
RT	WAVE DISSIPATION

MOLECULAR VISCOSITY COEFFICIENTS
BT1	VISCOSITY COEFFICIENTS
BT2	EXCHANGE COEFFICIENTS
RT	DYNAMIC VISCOSITY
RT	KINEMATIC VISCOSITY
RT	MOLECULAR VISCOSITY

MOLECULAR WEIGHT
UF	molecular mass
BT1	WEIGHT
BT2	PHYSICAL PROPERTIES
BT3	PROPERTIES
RT	CHEMICAL PROPERTIES
RT	MOLECULAR STRUCTURE

MOLECULES
RT	LIGANDS
RT	MOLECULAR STRUCTURE

MOLLUSC CULTURE
UF	mollusk culture
BT1	SHELLFISH CULTURE
BT2	AQUACULTURE
NT1	CLAM CULTURE
NT1	MUSSEL CULTURE
NT1	OYSTER CULTURE
NT1	SCALLOP CULTURE
NT1	SQUID CULTURE
RT	BOTTOM CULTURE
RT	BRACKISHWATER AQUACULTURE
RT	BRACKISHWATER MOLLUSCS
RT	CULTURES
RT	FRESHWATER MOLLUSCS
RT	GRADING
RT	HATCHERIES
RT	MARINE MOLLUSCS
RT	MOLLUSCAN LARVAE
RT	MUSSEL FISHERIES
RT	OFF-BOTTOM CULTURE
RT	RAFT CULTURE
RT	SEED COLLECTION

MOLLUSC FISHERIES
SN	Added in 1982
UF	mollusk fisheries
BT1	SHELLFISH FISHERIES
BT2	FISHERIES

MOLLUSC FISHERIES (cont'd)
NT1	CEPHALOPOD FISHERIES
NT1	CLAM FISHERIES
NT1	GASTROPOD FISHERIES
NT1	MUSSEL FISHERIES
NT1	OYSTER FISHERIES
NT1	SCALLOP FISHERIES
RT	INLAND FISHERIES
RT	MARINE FISHERIES

MOLLUSCAN LARVAE
SN	Added in 1980
UF	molluskan larvae
BT1	INVERTEBRATE LARVAE
BT2	LARVAE
BT3	DEVELOPMENTAL STAGES
NT1	SPAT
NT1	VELIGERS
RT	LARVAL DEVELOPMENT
RT	LARVAL SETTLEMENT
RT	MEROPLANKTON
RT	METAMORPHOSIS
RT	MOLLUSC CULTURE

MOLLUSCICIDES
UF	molluskicides
BT1	PESTICIDES
RT	HABITAT IMPROVEMENT (BIOLOGICAL)
RT	STOCKING (ORGANISMS)

MOLLUSCS (BRACKISHWATER)
    USE   **BRACKISHWATER MOLLUSCS**

MOLLUSCS (FRESHWATER)
    USE   **FRESHWATER MOLLUSCS**

MOLLUSCS (MARINE)
    USE   **MARINE MOLLUSCS**

MOLLUSK CULTURE
    USE   **MOLLUSC CULTURE**

MOLLUSK FISHERIES
    USE   **MOLLUSC FISHERIES**

MOLLUSKAN LARVAE
    USE   **MOLLUSCAN LARVAE**

MOLLUSKICIDES
    USE   **MOLLUSCICIDES**

MOLLUSKS (BRACKISHWATER)
    USE   **BRACKISHWATER MOLLUSCS**

MOLLUSKS (FRESHWATER)
    USE   **FRESHWATER MOLLUSCS**

MOLLUSKS (MARINE)
    USE   **MARINE MOLLUSCS**

MOLTING
    USE   **MOULTING**

MOLYBDENUM
BT1	CHEMICAL ELEMENTS
RT	FERROMANGANESE NODULES
RT	HEAVY METALS
RT	METALS
RT	MOLYBDENUM COMPOUNDS
RT	MOLYBDENUM ISOTOPES
RT	TRACE ELEMENTS

MOLYBDENUM COMPOUNDS
RT	CHEMICAL COMPOUNDS
RT	MOLYBDENUM

MOLYBDENUM ISOTOPES
BT1	ISOTOPES
RT	MOLYBDENUM

MOMENTUM
NT1	ANGULAR MOMENTUM
RT	AIR-WATER EXCHANGES
RT	CONSERVATION OF MOMENTUM
RT	DIFFUSION
RT	MECHANICS
RT	MOLECULAR DIFFUSION
RT	MOMENTUM TRANSFER

MOMENTUM CONSERVATION
    USE   **CONSERVATION OF MOMENTUM**

MOMENTUM FLUX
    USE   **MOMENTUM TRANSFER**

MOMENTUM TRANSFER
UF	momentum flux
RT	AIR-WATER EXCHANGES
RT	AIR-WATER INTERFACE
RT	ATMOSPHERIC BOUNDARY LAYER
RT	DYNAMIC VISCOSITY
RT	EDDY VISCOSITY
RT	ENERGY TRANSFER
RT	LONGSHORE CURRENTS
RT	MOLECULAR VISCOSITY
RT	MOMENTUM
RT	PRANDTL NUMBER
RT	REYNOLDS STRESSES
RT	WAVE INTERACTIONS
RT	WAVE SETUP
RT	WAVE-AIR INTERACTION
RT	WAVE-CURRENT INTERACTION
RT	WIND WAVE GENERATION

MONAZITE
BT1	PHOSPHATE MINERALS
BT2	MINERALS
RT	PLACERS
RT	THORIUM

MONIN-OBUKHOV LENGTH
RT	DENSITY STRATIFICATION
RT	STABILITY
RT	WATER DENSITY

MONITORING
SN	Used only as a qualifier
NT1	ENVIRONMENTAL MONITORING
NT1	POLLUTION MONITORING
RT	BASELINE STUDIES
RT	CONTROL
RT	DATA COLLECTIONS
RT	FISHERY REGULATIONS
RT	INSPECTION
RT	LONG-TERM CHANGES
RT	MONITORING SYSTEMS
RT	POPULATION CONTROL
RT	TELEMETRY

MONITORING STATIONS
    USE   **MONITORING SYSTEMS**

MONITORING SYSTEMS
SN	Before 1982 search MONITORING STATIONS
UF	monitoring stations
BT1	EQUIPMENT
RT	FIXED STATIONS
RT	MEASURING DEVICES
RT	MONITORING
RT	RECORDING EQUIPMENT
RT	TELEMETRY

MONOCULTURE
UF	monospecific culture
BT1	AQUACULTURE TECHNIQUES
RT	CAGE CULTURE
RT	CRUSTACEAN CULTURE
RT	FISH CULTURE
RT	FRESHWATER AQUACULTURE
RT	RACEWAY CULTURE

MONOCYCLIC HYDROCARBONS
    USE   **AROMATIC HYDROCARBONS**

MONOGRAPHS
    USE   **SYNOPSIS**

MONOLAYERS
    USE   **MONOMOLECULAR FILMS**

MONOMOLECULAR FILMS
UF	monolayers
BT1	SURFACE FILMS
RT	EVAPORATION REDUCTION
RT	SLICKS
RT	SURFACE MICROLAYER

MONOSACCHARIDES
BT1	SACCHARIDES
BT2	CARBOHYDRATES
BT3	ORGANIC COMPOUNDS
NT1	ARABINOSE
NT1	FUCOSE
NT1	GLUCOSE
NT1	MANNOSE
NT1	RIBOSE
NT1	XYLOSE

MONOSEX CULTURE
BT1	AQUACULTURE TECHNIQUES
RT	BRACKISHWATER AQUACULTURE
RT	CULTURES
RT	FISH CULTURE
RT	FISH PONDS
RT	FRESHWATER AQUACULTURE
RT	INTENSIVE CULTURE
RT	MARINE.AQUACULTURE

MONOSPECIFIC CULTURE
    USE   **MONOCULTURE**

MONOTERPENES
    USE   **TERPENES**

MONSOON REVERSAL
RT	CURRENT REVERSAL
RT	EQUATORIAL CIRCULATION
RT	EQUATORIAL DYNAMICS
RT	MONSOONS
RT	OCEAN CURRENTS
RT	TROPICAL OCEANOGRAPHY

MONSOONS
BT1	PLANETARY WINDS
BT2	WINDS
BT3	ATMOSPHERIC MOTION
RT	MONSOON REVERSAL
RT	RAINY SEASON
RT	SEA BREEZES
RT	SEASONALITY
RT	TROPICAL ENVIRONMENT
RT	TROPICAL METEOROLOGY
RT	TROPICAL OCEANOGRAPHY

MONTHLY
SN	Descriptor to be used only as a qualifier
BT1	PERIODICITY

ASFIS Thesaurus

MONTHLY DISTRIBUTION
SN	Descriptor to be used only as a qualifier	
BT1	TEMPORAL DISTRIBUTION	
BT2	DISTRIBUTION	

MONTMORILLONITE
BT1	CLAY MINERALS
BT2	SILICATE MINERALS
BT3	MINERALS
RT	BENTONITE

MOON
RT	ASTRONOMY

MOON EFFECTS
USE	**MOON PHASES**

MOON PHASES
SN	Moon phases and their influence on behaviour of aquatic organisms and on sea level
UF	lunar cycles
UF	lunar effects
UF	moon effects
RT	ASTRONOMY
RT	CIRCADIAN RHYTHMS
RT	CYCLES
RT	NYCTIMERAL RHYTHMS
RT	PHOTOTROPISM
RT	TIDES

MOORING BUOYS
BT1	BUOYS
NT1	LOADING BUOYS
RT	BERTHING
RT	BUOY MOORING SYSTEMS
RT	HARBOURS
RT	MOORING LINES
RT	MOORING SYSTEMS
RT	NAVIGATIONAL CHARTS
RT	SHIP MOORING SYSTEMS
RT	TANKER LOADING

MOORING LINES
BT1	CABLES
RT	BUOY MOORING SYSTEMS
RT	BUOYS
RT	CABLE DYNAMICS
RT	CATENARY
RT	CHAIN
RT	MOORING BUOYS
RT	MOORING MOTION EFFECTS
RT	MOORING SYSTEMS
RT	ROPES
RT	SHIP MOORING SYSTEMS
RT	TOWING LINES

MOORING MOTION EFFECTS
SN	Influence of motion on instrumental observations made from moored equipment
BT1	MOTION EFFECTS
RT	BUOY MOORING SYSTEMS
RT	BUOY MOTION
RT	BUOY MOTION EFFECTS
RT	MOORING LINES
RT	MOORING SYSTEMS
RT	NEAR-SURFACE LAYER
RT	SHIP MOORING SYSTEMS

MOORING RECOVERY
SN	Recovery of moorings for oceanographic equipment
BT1	RECOVERY
RT	BUOY MOORING SYSTEMS
RT	CURRENT METER ARRAYS
RT	OCEANOGRAPHIC EQUIPMENT

MOORING SHIPS
USE	**BERTHING**

MOORING SYSTEMS
SN	Use of a more specific term is recommended. Before 1982 search also MOORINGS
UF	moorings
NT1	BUOY MOORING SYSTEMS
NT1	CURRENT METER MOORINGS
NT1	SHIP MOORING SYSTEMS
NT2	SINGLE POINT MOORINGS
RT	ANCHORING
RT	FLOW AROUND OBJECTS
RT	MOORING BUOYS
RT	MOORING LINES
RT	MOORING MOTION EFFECTS
RT	OCEANOGRAPHIC EQUIPMENT

MOORINGS
USE	**MOORING SYSTEMS**

MORAINES
BT1	GLACIAL FEATURES
RT	GLACIAL DEPOSITS

MORATORIA
SN	Added in 1982
UF	moratorium
RT	LEGAL ASPECTS

MORATORIUM
USE	**MORATORIA**

MORBIDITY
USE	**DISEASES**

MORISON'S EQUATION
BT1	EQUATIONS
RT	WAVE FORCES

MORPHOGENESIS
SN	The development of form and structure of an organism or part of an organism
NT1	GAMETOGENESIS
NT2	OOGENESIS
NT2	SPERMATOGENESIS
RT	EMBRYOLOGY
RT	EMBRYONIC DEVELOPMENT
RT	EVOLUTION
RT	GENETICS
RT	ONTOGENY
RT	ORGANISM MORPHOLOGY
RT	ORGANOGENESIS
RT	VITELLOGENESIS

MORPHOLOGY (ANIMAL)
USE	**ANIMAL MORPHOLOGY**

MORPHOLOGY (BIOLOGY)
USE	**ORGANISM MORPHOLOGY**

MORPHOLOGY (COASTAL)
USE	**COASTAL MORPHOLOGY**

MORPHOLOGY (ORGANISMS)
USE	**ORGANISM MORPHOLOGY**

MORPHOLOGY (PLANT)
USE	**PLANT MORPHOLOGY**

MORPHOMETRIC ANALYSIS
USE	**MORPHOMETRY**

MORPHOMETRY
UF	morphometric analysis
RT	BATHYMETRY
RT	BOTTOM TOPOGRAPHY
RT	DIMENSIONS

MORPHOMETRY (cont'd)
RT	HYPSOMETRIC CURVES
RT	LAKES
RT	OCEANS
RT	SHAPE

MORTALITY
UF	death rate
UF	mortality rate
BT1	POPULATION FUNCTIONS
NT1	FISHING MORTALITY
NT1	NATURAL MORTALITY
NT1	TAGGING MORTALITY
NT1	TOTAL MORTALITY
RT	EPIDEMICS
RT	LETHAL LIMITS
RT	LONGEVITY
RT	MORTALITY CAUSES
RT	POPULATION DYNAMICS
RT	SURVIVAL
RT	TUMOURS

MORTALITY CAUSES
SN	Any known or hypothesized causes for mortality
RT	ALGAL BLOOMS
RT	ANOXIA
RT	ASPHYXIA
RT	BIOLOGICAL CONTROL
RT	BIOLOGICAL STRESS
RT	DISEASES
RT	DIVING ACCIDENTS
RT	DROWNING
RT	EPIDEMIOLOGY
RT	EUTROPHICATION
RT	FISH KILL
RT	HYPERCAPNIA
RT	HYPOTHERMIA
RT	LETHAL EFFECTS
RT	MORTALITY
RT	POLLUTANTS
RT	POLLUTION EFFECTS
RT	PREDATION
RT	STARVATION
RT	SURVIVAL
RT	TOXICANTS

MORTALITY RATE
USE	**MORTALITY**

MOTHER SHIPS
SN	Before 1982 search MOTHERSHIPS
BT1	SUPPORT SHIPS
BT2	SHIPS
BT3	SURFACE CRAFT
BT4	VEHICLES
RT	FISHING VESSELS
RT	MARINE TRANSPORTATION
RT	SUBMERSIBLES
RT	UNDERWATER VEHICLES

MOTION
SN	Used only as a qualifier
UF	movement
RT	ANTICYCLONIC MOTION
RT	ATMOSPHERIC MOTION
RT	BUOY MOTION
RT	CYCLONIC MOTION
RT	DISPLACEMENT
RT	DRIFT
RT	EARTH ROTATION
RT	FLUID MOTION
RT	GROUND MOTION
RT	INERTIA
RT	MOTION EFFECTS
RT	OSCILLATIONS
RT	PARTICLE MOTION
RT	ROTATION
RT	SEDIMENT MOVEMENT
RT	SHIP MOTION

MOTION (cont'd)
RT	TIDAL MOTION
RT	WATER MOTION

MOTION (GROUND)
USE	**GROUND MOTION**

MOTION (SHIPS)
USE	**SHIP MOTION**

MOTION EFFECTS
SN	Effects of motion on instrumental observations
NT1	BUOY MOTION EFFECTS
NT1	MOORING MOTION EFFECTS
RT	MOTION

MOTION SICKNESS
USE	**SEA SICKNESS**

MOTOR BOATS
SN	Before 1982 search BOATS
BT1	SHIPS
BT2	SURFACE CRAFT
BT3	VEHICLES
RT	FISHING
RT	MOTORS
RT	RECREATION

MOTOR FUELS
USE	**FUELS**

MOTORS
UF	engines
NT1	DIESEL ENGINES
NT1	TURBINES
RT	ELECTRIC GENERATORS
RT	ELECTRIC POWER SOURCES
RT	FUELS
RT	LUBRICANTS
RT	MOTOR BOATS
RT	PROPULSION SYSTEMS

MOULTING
UF	ecdysis
UF	molting
UF	moulting cycle
UF	moults
BT1	METAMORPHOSIS
BT2	BIOLOGICAL PHENOMENA
RT	AQUATIC INSECTS
RT	CUTICLES
RT	DEVELOPMENTAL STAGES
RT	ECDYSONS
RT	EYESTALK EXTIRPATION
RT	FRESHWATER CRUSTACEANS
RT	INSTARS
RT	INVERTEBRATE LARVAE
RT	LARVAE
RT	MARINE CRUSTACEANS

MOULTING CYCLE
USE	**MOULTING**

MOULTING HORMONES
USE	**ECDYSONS**

MOULTS
USE	**MOULTING**

MOUNTAIN BUILDING
USE	**OROGENY**

MOUNTAIN WAVES
USE	**LEE WAVES**

MOUNTAINS
BT1	LANDFORMS
BT2	TOPOGRAPHIC FEATURES
RT	MID-OCEAN RIDGES
RT	OROGENY
RT	RELIEF FORMS
RT	SEAMOUNTS
RT	SUBMARINE RIDGES

MOUTH PARTS
SN	Used for animals only
NT1	BALEENS
NT1	RADULAE
NT1	TEETH
RT	ALIMENTARY ORGANS
RT	FEEDING BEHAVIOUR
RT	INGESTION

MOVEMENT
USE	**MOTION**

MOVEMENTS (LOCAL)
USE	**LOCAL MOVEMENTS**

MUCINS
SN	Added in 1980
UF	mucoproteins
BT1	PROTEINS
BT2	ORGANIC COMPOUNDS
RT	EXOCRINE GLANDS
RT	MUCUS

MUCOPOLYSACCHARIDES
BT1	POLYSACCHARIDES
BT2	SACCHARIDES
BT3	CARBOHYDRATES
BT4	ORGANIC COMPOUNDS
NT1	CHITIN
NT1	HEPARIN

MUCOPROTEINS
USE	**MUCINS**

MUCUS
BT1	SECRETORY PRODUCTS
RT	BODY FLUIDS
RT	EXOCRINE GLANDS
RT	GLANDS
RT	MUCINS
RT	SECRETORY ORGANS

MUD
BT1	CLASTICS
BT2	SEDIMENTS
NT1	FLUID MUD
RT	CLAYS
RT	COHESIVE SEDIMENTS
RT	MARL
RT	MUD BANKS
RT	MUD FLATS
RT	OOZES
RT	SEDIMENT-WATER INTERFACE
RT	SILT
RT	SLUDGE
RT	SLURRIES
RT	SOILS
RT	TIDAL FLATS

MUD BANKS
BT1	BED FORMS
BT2	SEDIMENTARY STRUCTURES
RT	BANKS (TOPOGRAPHY)
RT	MUD
RT	SAND BANKS
RT	SUBMARINE BANKS
RT	TIDAL FLATS

MUD FLATS
BT1	SEDIMENTARY STRUCTURES
RT	ESTUARIES
RT	MUD

MUDFLOWS
USE	**DEBRIS FLOW**

MUDS (DRILLING)
USE	**DRILLING FLUIDS**

MUDSTONE
BT1	CLASTICS
BT2	SEDIMENTS
RT	LUTITES
RT	SEDIMENTARY ROCKS
RT	SILTSTONE
RT	SLATES

MULLET FISHERIES
SN	Added in 1982
BT1	FINFISH FISHERIES
BT2	FISHERIES
RT	ESTUARINE FISHERIES
RT	FISH CULTURE

MULTIBEAM SONAR
BT1	ACTIVE SONAR
BT2	SONAR
BT3	REMOTE SENSING EQUIPMENT
BT4	EQUIPMENT
RT	SEAFLOOR MAPPING

MULTINATIONAL EXPEDITIONS
USE	**MULTISHIP EXPEDITIONS**

MULTIPHASE FLOW
UF	three phase flow
UF	two phase flow
BT1	FLUID FLOW
BT2	FLUID MOTION
RT	LAMINAR FLOW
RT	TURBULENT FLOW
RT	UNSTEADY FLOW

MULTIPLE USE OF RESOURCES
SN	Added in 1980
RT	EXPLOITATION
RT	INTERNATIONAL LAW
RT	LAW OF THE SEA
RT	NATURAL RESOURCES
RT	NATURE CONSERVATION

MULTISHIP EXPEDITIONS
SN	Surveys involving the use of two or more research vessels
UF	expeditions (multiship)
UF	international expeditions
UF	multinational expeditions
BT1	EXPEDITIONS
RT	CRUISE PROGRAMMES
RT	CRUISE STATIONS
RT	CRUISES
RT	DATA REPORTS
RT	EXPEDITION REPORTS
RT	GEOLOGICAL DATA
RT	GEOPHYSICAL DATA
RT	LIMNOLOGICAL DATA
RT	METEOROLOGICAL DATA
RT	OCEANOGRAPHIC DATA
RT	OCEANOGRAPHIC INSTITUTIONS
RT	PLANNING
RT	PROGRAMMES
RT	RESEARCH VESSELS
RT	STATION LISTS
RT	SURVEYS
RT	TRACK CHARTS

ASFIS Thesaurus

MULTISPECIES FISHERIES
BT1	FISHERIES
RT	CATCH COMPOSITION
RT	DOMINANT SPECIES
RT	ECOLOGICAL SUCCESSION
RT	PREDATION
RT	STOCK ASSESSMENT

MULTISPECTRAL SCANNERS
RT	RADIOMETERS
RT	REMOTE SENSING EQUIPMENT
RT	SATELLITE PHOTOGRAPHY
RT	WATER COLOUR

MULTIVARIATE ANALYSIS
BT1	VARIANCE ANALYSIS
BT2	STATISTICAL ANALYSIS
BT3	MATHEMATICAL ANALYSIS

MUSCLE FIBERS
USE	**MUSCLES**

MUSCLES
SN	Added in 1980
UF	muscle fibers
UF	red muscles
UF	smooth muscles
UF	striated muscles
UF	tendous musculature
UF	white muscles
BT1	MUSCULOSKELETAL SYSTEM
RT	ACTIN
RT	BIOLOGICAL STRESS
RT	BOIL DISEASE
RT	CHOLINESTERASE INHIBITORS
RT	GLYCOGEN
RT	MYOGLOBINS
RT	MYOSIN
RT	TISSUES

MUSCOVITE
BT1	MICAS
BT2	SILICATE MINERALS
BT3	MINERALS

MUSCULAR SYSTEM
USE	**MUSCULOSKELETAL SYSTEM**

MUSCULOSKELETAL SYSTEM
SN	Before 1982 search MUSCULAR SYSTEM
	and/or SKELETON
UF	muscular system
NT1	MUSCLES
NT1	SKELETON
NT2	ENDOSKELETON
NT3	BONES
NT4	SKULL
NT4	VERTEBRAE
NT2	EXOSKELETON
NT3	CARAPACE
NT3	CUTICLES
NT3	SCALES
RT	BIOLOGICAL STRESS
RT	CARTILAGE
RT	CHOLINESTERASE INHIBITORS
RT	CONNECTIVE TISSUES

MUSEUM COLLECTIONS
SN	Added in 1980
BT1	COLLECTIONS
RT	HOLOTYPES
RT	MUSEUMS

MUSEUMS
BT1	INFORMATION CENTRES
BT2	ORGANIZATIONS
RT	ANNUAL REPORTS
RT	AQUARIA
RT	BROCHURES
RT	COLLECTIONS

MUSEUMS (cont'd)
RT	EXHIBITIONS
RT	MUSEUM COLLECTIONS
RT	OCEANOGRAPHIC INSTITUTIONS

MUSSEL CULTURE
SN	Before 1982 use MOLLUSC CULTURE
BT1	MOLLUSC CULTURE
BT2	SHELLFISH CULTURE
BT3	AQUACULTURE
RT	OFF-BOTTOM CULTURE
RT	PREDATOR CONTROL
RT	RAFT CULTURE
RT	SPAT

MUSSEL FISHERIES
SN	Added in 1982
BT1	MOLLUSC FISHERIES
BT2	SHELLFISH FISHERIES
BT3	FISHERIES
RT	MARINE FISHERIES
RT	MOLLUSC CULTURE

MUTAGENIC AGENTS
USE	**MUTAGENS**

MUTAGENS
SN	Substances producing mutations.
	Added in 1980
UF	mutagenic agents
RT	AGENTS
RT	GENETICS
RT	MUTATIONS

MUTATIONS
SN	Change in the characteristics of an
	organism by alteration of
	hereditary material
UF	chromosome mutations
UF	gene mutations
UF	lethal mutations
UF	somatic mutations
BT1	BIOLOGICAL PHENOMENA
RT	BIOLOGICAL SPECIATION
RT	BIOSELECTION
RT	CHROMOSOMES
RT	DEGENERATION
RT	EVOLUTION
RT	GENES
RT	GENETIC ABNORMALITIES
RT	GENETIC DRIFT
RT	GENETICS
RT	GENOTYPES
RT	MUTAGENS
RT	NEW SPECIES

MUTUALISM
USE	**SYMBIOSIS**

MYCOBACTERIAL INFECTIONS
USE	**TUBERCULOSIS**

MYCOLOGISTS
SN	Added in 1986
BT1	MICROBIOLOGISTS
BT2	BIOLOGISTS
BT3	SCIENTIFIC PERSONNEL
BT4	PERSONNEL
RT	DIRECTORIES
RT	MICROBIOLOGY
RT	MYCOLOGY

MYCOLOGY
SN	Added in 1986
BT1	MICROBIOLOGY
BT2	BIOLOGY
RT	FUNGAL DISEASES
RT	FUNGI
RT	FUNGICIDES
RT	MICROBIOLOGISTS

MYCOLOGY (cont'd)
RT	MYCOLOGISTS
RT	PARASITOLOGY

MYCOSES
USE	**FUNGAL DISEASES**

MYCOTIC DISEASES
USE	**FUNGAL DISEASES**

MYOGLOBINS
SN	Added in 1980
BT1	PROTEINS
BT2	ORGANIC COMPOUNDS
RT	BLOOD
RT	MUSCLES

MYONEME
USE	**CELL ORGANELLES**

MYOSIN
SN	Added in 1980
BT1	PROTEINS
BT2	ORGANIC COMPOUNDS
RT	ANIMAL PHYSIOLOGY
RT	MUSCLES

NANNOFOSSIL OOZE
RT	CALCAREOUS OOZE
RT	COCCOLITHS

NANNOPLANKTON
SN	Planktonic organisms smaller than
	60 microns
UF	bacterioplankton
UF	nanoplankton
BT1	PLANKTON
BT2	AQUATIC COMMUNITIES
RT	BACTERIA
RT	FILTER FEEDERS
RT	MICROORGANISMS
RT	PLANKTON FEEDERS

NANOPLANKTON
USE	**NANNOPLANKTON**

NANSEN BOTTLES
BT1	WATER SAMPLERS
BT2	SAMPLERS

NAPHTHALENE
BT1	AROMATIC HYDROCARBONS
BT2	UNSATURATED HYDROCARBONS
BT3	HYDROCARBONS
BT4	ORGANIC COMPOUNDS

NAPPES
SN	Large horizontal recumbent tectonic
	folds that have travelled along
	thrust planes
RT	TECTONICS

NARCOSIS
NT1	NITROGEN NARCOSIS
RT	DECOMPRESSION SICKNESS

NARCOTICS
BT1	DRUGS
RT	ANAESTHETICS
RT	INHIBITORS

NATALITY
USE	**FECUNDITY**

NATIONAL ALLOCATION
USE	**ALLOCATION SYSTEMS**

NATIONAL BOUNDARIES
USE **INTERNATIONAL BOUNDARIES**

NATIONAL PLANNING
SN   Added in 1980
UF   planning (national)
UF   planning at national level
BT1   PLANNING
RT   REGIONAL PLANNING

NATURAL BREEDING
USE   **BREEDING**

NATURAL DISASTERS
USE   **DISASTERS**

NATURAL FIBRE ROPE
USE   **FIBRE ROPE (NATURAL)**

NATURAL FOOD
USE   **FOOD ORGANISMS**

NATURAL FREQUENCY
USE   **RESONANT FREQUENCY**

NATURAL GAS
BT1   PETROLEUM
BT2   FOSSIL FUELS
BT3   SUBSURFACE DEPOSITS
BT4   MINERAL DEPOSITS
NT1   LIQUEFIED NATURAL GAS
RT   CRUDE OIL
RT   GAS CONDENSATES
RT   GAS FIELDS
RT   GAS PRODUCTION
RT   GAS SEEPAGES
RT   GAS TERMINALS
RT   GASES
RT   OIL
RT   OIL-GAS INTERFACE
RT   TANKER LOADING
RT   TANKER SHIPS
RT   TANKER TERMINALS

NATURAL HABITAT
USE   **HABITAT**

NATURAL IMMUNITY
USE   **IMMUNITY**

NATURAL INCREASE
USE   **BIOLOGICAL PRODUCTION**

NATURAL MORTALITY
UF   natural mortality coefficient
BT1   MORTALITY
BT2   POPULATION FUNCTIONS
RT   BIOTIC PRESSURE
RT   DISEASES
RT   EPIDEMIOLOGY
RT   FISH DISEASES
RT   PREDATION
RT   RECRUITMENT
RT   TOTAL MORTALITY

NATURAL MORTALITY COEFFICIENT
USE   **NATURAL MORTALITY**

NATURAL POPULATIONS
SN   All individual of a certain species
       inhabiting a specified region.
       Added in 1980
UF   populations (natural)
NT1   ANIMAL POPULATIONS
NT2   SPAWNING POPULATIONS
NT1   PLANT POPULATIONS
RT   ECOSYSTEM MANAGEMENT
RT   POPULATION CHARACTERISTICS
RT   POPULATION CONTROL
RT   POPULATION DYNAMICS

NATURAL POPULATIONS (cont'd)
RT   POPULATION FACTORS
RT   POPULATION FUNCTIONS
RT   POPULATION GENETICS
RT   POPULATION STRUCTURE
RT   STOCKS

NATURAL PRODUCTION
USE   **BIOLOGICAL PRODUCTION**

NATURAL RESOURCES
SN   Restricted to resources within or
       beneath the aquatic environment
UF   aquatic natural resources
BT1   RESOURCES
NT1   COMMON PROPERTY RESOURCES
NT1   ENERGY RESOURCES
NT2   GEOTHERMAL POWER
NT2   HYDROELECTRIC POWER
NT2   POWER FROM THE SEA
NT3   CURRENT POWER
NT3   ELECTROMAGNETIC POWER
NT3   SALINITY POWER
NT3   THERMAL POWER
NT4   OTEC
NT3   TIDAL POWER
NT3   WAVE POWER
NT2   SOLAR POWER
NT2   WIND POWER
NT1   FOOD RESOURCES
NT1   LIVING RESOURCES
NT2   BOTANICAL RESOURCES
NT2   FISHERY RESOURCES
NT1   MARINE RESOURCES
NT1   MINERAL RESOURCES
NT2   DISSOLVED CHEMICALS
NT2   MINERAL DEPOSITS
NT3   SEABED DEPOSITS
NT4   AGGREGATES
NT4   FERROMANGANESE NODULES
NT4   PHOSPHORITE NODULES
NT4   PLACERS
NT3   SUBSURFACE DEPOSITS
NT4   FOSSIL FUELS
NT4   PHOSPHATE DEPOSITS
NT2   ORES
NT1   NONRENEWABLE RESOURCES
NT1   RENEWABLE RESOURCES
NT1   UNCONVENTIONAL RESOURCES
NT1   WATER RESOURCES
RT   ABUNDANCE
RT   AQUATIC DRUGS
RT   DEPLETION
RT   DEVELOPMENT POTENTIAL
RT   ECONOMICS
RT   ECOSYSTEM MANAGEMENT
RT   ENVIRONMENT MANAGEMENT
RT   ENVIRONMENTAL LEGISLATION
RT   EXCLUSIVE RIGHTS
RT   EXPLOITATION
RT   INTERNATIONAL POLICY
RT   LAND USE
RT   MULTIPLE USE OF RESOURCES
RT   POLICIES
RT   PRODUCTS
RT   PROTECTED RESOURCES
RT   RARE RESOURCES
RT   RAW MATERIALS
RT   RESOURCE CONSERVATION
RT   RESOURCE DEVELOPMENT
RT   RESOURCE MANAGEMENT
RT   SOILS
RT   SURVEYS
RT   WATER SUPPLY

NATURAL SELECTION
SN   Survival of the fittest. Added in
       1980
BT1   BIOSELECTION
RT   COMPETITION

NATURAL SELECTION (cont'd)
RT   ENVIRONMENTAL EFFECTS
RT   EVOLUTION

NATURE CONSERVATION
UF   wildlife conservation
BT1   CONSERVATION
RT   ENVIRONMENT MANAGEMENT
RT   ENVIRONMENTAL LEGISLATION
RT   MARINE PARKS
RT   MULTIPLE USE OF RESOURCES
RT   RARE SPECIES
RT   REFUGES
RT   SANCTUARIES
RT   SITE SELECTION
RT   SPECIES EXTINCTION

NATURE RESERVES
USE   **MARINE PARKS**

NAUPLII
BT1   CRUSTACEAN LARVAE
BT2   INVERTEBRATE LARVAE
BT3   LARVAE
BT4   DEVELOPMENTAL STAGES
RT   MARINE CRUSTACEANS
RT   MEROPLANKTON
RT   METAMORPHOSIS

NAUTICAL ALMANACS
UF   ephemeris
BT1   ALMANACS
BT2   TABLES
BT3   DOCUMENTS
RT   ASTRONOMY
RT   CELESTIAL NAVIGATION
RT   METEOROLOGICAL TABLES
RT   NAVIGATIONAL TABLES

NAUTICAL ARCHAEOLOGY
USE   **ARCHAEOLOGY**

NAUTICAL BOTTOM
USE   **WATER DEPTH**

NAUTICAL CHARTS
USE   **NAVIGATIONAL CHARTS**

NAVAL ARCHITECTURE
USE   **SHIP TECHNOLOGY**

NAVAL BASES
BT1   HARBOURS
BT2   ANCHORAGES
RT   DEFENCE CRAFT
RT   MILITARY PORTS
RT   SECURITY
RT   SHIP TECHNOLOGY

NAVAL CRAFT
USE   **DEFENCE CRAFT**

NAVAL ENGINEERING
USE   **SHIP TECHNOLOGY**

NAVAL TECHNOLOGY
USE   **SHIP TECHNOLOGY**

NAVIER-STOKES EQUATIONS
RT   EQUATIONS
RT   HYDRODYNAMICS
RT   REYNOLDS STRESSES

NAVIFACE
USE   **AIR-WATER INTERFACE**

ASFIS Thesaurus

NAVIGABLE CHANNELS
USE   **NAVIGATIONAL CHANNELS**

NAVIGATION
SN   Use of a more specific term is
        recommended; used only for general
        aspects
UF   surface navigation
NT1   ACOUSTIC NAVIGATION
NT1   CELESTIAL NAVIGATION
NT1   DEAD RECKONING
NT1   DOPPLER NAVIGATION
NT1   NAVIGATION IN ICE
NT1   NAVIGATION UNDERWATER
NT2   NAVIGATION UNDER ICE
RT   BATHYMETRY
RT   CANALS
RT   COMMUNICATION SYSTEMS
RT   DIRECTION FINDING
RT   DYNAMIC POSITIONING
RT   FISHING OPERATIONS
RT   HYDROGRAPHIC SURVEYING
RT   HYDROGRAPHIC SURVEYS
RT   LAW OF THE SEA
RT   LIGHTERS
RT   MARINE TRANSPORTATION
RT   MARITIME LEGISLATION
RT   NAVIGATION POLICY
RT   NAVIGATION REGULATIONS
RT   NAVIGATIONAL AIDS
RT   NAVIGATIONAL BUOYS
RT   NAVIGATIONAL HAZARDS
RT   OCEAN POLICY
RT   POSITION FIXING
RT   RADAR
RT   RADIO AIDS
RT   RESEARCH VESSELS
RT   RIPARIAN RIGHTS
RT   SEAMANSHIP
RT   SHIP HANDLING
RT   SHIP ROUTEING
RT   SHIP SPEED
RT   SHIPS
RT   SPEEDOMETERS
RT   STANDARD SIGNALS
RT   STEERING SYSTEMS
RT   WATER POLICY

NAVIGATION (ANIMAL)
USE   **ANIMAL NAVIGATION**

NAVIGATION CANALS
USE   **SHIP CANALS**

NAVIGATION CHANNELS
USE   **NAVIGATIONAL CHANNELS**

NAVIGATION IN ICE
SN   Before 1982 search ICE NAVIGATION
UF   ice navigation
UF   polar navigation
BT1   NAVIGATION
RT   FLAW LEADS
RT   ICE
RT   ICE BREAKERS
RT   ICE BREAKING
RT   ICE BREAKUP
RT   ICE FORECASTING
RT   ICE FORMATION
RT   ICE JAMS
RT   ICE PREVENTION
RT   ICE ROUTEING
RT   ICE-FREE PERIODS
RT   LEADS
RT   NAVIGATION UNDER ICE
RT   PACK ICE
RT   POLAR EXPLORATION

NAVIGATION POLICY
SN   Added in 1980
BT1   POLICIES
RT   NAVIGATION
RT   NAVIGATION REGULATIONS

NAVIGATION REGULATIONS
UF   navigational regulations
UF   shipping rules
BT1   LEGISLATION
NT1   HARBOUR REGULATIONS
NT1   QUARANTINE REGULATIONS
RT   COLLISION AVOIDANCE
RT   HARBOUR REGULATIONS
RT   LEGAL ASPECTS
RT   NAVIGATION
RT   NAVIGATION POLICY
RT   OCEAN SPACE
RT   SHIPPING
RT   TRAFFIC MANAGEMENT

NAVIGATION SYSTEMS
RT   AUTOPILOTS
RT   NAVIGATIONAL AIDS

NAVIGATION UNDER ICE
BT1   NAVIGATION UNDERWATER
BT2   NAVIGATION
RT   ICE CANOPY
RT   ICE KEELS
RT   ICE PREVENTION
RT   INERTIAL NAVIGATION
RT   NAVIGATION IN ICE
RT   POLAR EXPLORATION
RT   POLYNYAS
RT   SUBMARINES

NAVIGATION UNDERWATER
UF   seabed acoustic position fixing
UF   underwater navigation
BT1   NAVIGATION
NT1   NAVIGATION UNDER ICE
RT   ACOUSTIC NAVIGATION
RT   ACOUSTIC TRACKING SYSTEMS
RT   INERTIAL NAVIGATION
RT   MANNED VEHICLES
RT   SUBMARINES
RT   SUBMERSIBLES

NAVIGATIONAL AIDS
NT1   LIGHTHOUSES
RT   ACOUSTIC BEACONS
RT   ACOUSTIC TRANSPONDERS
RT   AUTOPILOTS
RT   COLLISION AVOIDANCE
RT   COMPASSES
RT   EQUIPMENT
RT   GYROCOMPASSES
RT   LIGHTSHIPS
RT   MARKER BUOYS
RT   NAVIGATION
RT   NAVIGATION SYSTEMS
RT   NAVIGATIONAL BUOYS
RT   NAVIGATIONAL CHARTS
RT   NAVIGATIONAL TABLES
RT   POSITION FIXING
RT   RADAR
RT   SAILING DIRECTIONS

NAVIGATIONAL BUOYS
SN   Before 1982 search also NAVIGATION
        BUOYS
BT1   BUOYS
RT   NAVIGATION
RT   NAVIGATIONAL AIDS
RT   NAVIGATIONAL CHANNELS

NAVIGATIONAL CHANNELS
UF   navigable channels
UF   navigation channels
BT1   CHANNELS
RT   DREDGING
RT   KEEL CLEARANCE
RT   NAVIGATIONAL BUOYS
RT   NEGATIVE STORM SURGES
RT   SHIP CANALS
RT   SILTING

NAVIGATIONAL CHARTS
SN   Before 1982 search also NAVIGATION
        CHARTS
UF   nautical charts
BT1   MAPS
BT2   GRAPHICS
BT3   AUDIOVISUAL MATERIAL
BT4   DOCUMENTS
NT1   LATTICE CHARTS
NT1   PILOT CHARTS
RT   CHART CATALOGUES
RT   CHART DATUM
RT   HYDROGRAPHIC SURVEYING
RT   HYDROGRAPHIC SURVEYS
RT   MOORING BUOYS
RT   NAVIGATIONAL AIDS
RT   NAVIGATIONAL HAZARDS
RT   SOUNDINGS

NAVIGATIONAL HAZARDS
BT1   HAZARDS
RT   NAVIGATION
RT   NAVIGATIONAL CHARTS
RT   SHOALS
RT   WRECKS

NAVIGATIONAL REGULATIONS
USE   **NAVIGATION REGULATIONS**

NAVIGATIONAL SATELLITES
BT1   SATELLITES
BT2   VEHICLES
RT   SATELLITE NAVIGATION

NAVIGATIONAL TABLES
BT1   TABLES
BT2   DOCUMENTS
RT   DECCA
RT   LORAN
RT   NAUTICAL ALMANACS
RT   NAVIGATIONAL AIDS
RT   OCEANOGRAPHIC TABLES
RT   OMEGA
RT   TRAVERSE TABLES

NEAP TIDES
BT1   TIDES
BT2   TIDAL MOTION

NEAR-BOTTOM CURRENTS
USE   **BOTTOM CURRENTS**

NEAR-SURFACE CIRCULATION
USE   **SURFACE CIRCULATION**

NEAR-SURFACE LAYER
SN   Part of surface layer in which
        surface water wave motion is a
        major factor in buoy and mooring
        motions and instrument
        observations, e.g. current meter
        readings
BT1   SURFACE LAYERS
BT2   WATER COLUMN
BT3   LAYERS
RT   BUOY MOTION
RT   CURRENT OBSERVATIONS
RT   MOORING MOTION EFFECTS
RT   ORBITAL VELOCITY

NEAR-SURFACE LAYER (cont'd)
RT	PARTICLE MOTION
RT	SURFACE MICROLAYER
RT	SURFACE WATER WAVES

NEARSHORE BARS
UF	bars
UF	offshore bars
UF	submarine bars
BT1	BEACH FEATURES
NT1	BREAK-POINT BARS
NT1	LONGSHORE BARS
NT1	TRANSVERSE BARS
RT	BED FORMS
RT	DEPOSITION FEATURES
RT	DESTRUCTIVE WAVES
RT	NEARSHORE DYNAMICS
RT	SAND BARS

NEARSHORE CIRCULATION
USE	**NEARSHORE DYNAMICS**

NEARSHORE CURRENTS
SN	Before 1982 search LITTORAL
	CURRENTS and ONSHORE CURRENTS
UF	coastal currents (littoral)
UF	inshore currents
UF	littoral currents
UF	onshore currents
BT1	WATER CURRENTS
BT2	WATER MOTION
NT1	LONGSHORE CURRENTS
NT1	RIP CURRENTS
NT1	UNDERTOW
RT	COASTAL OCEANOGRAPHY
RT	ESTUARINE DYNAMICS
RT	NEARSHORE DYNAMICS
RT	SEDIMENT TRANSPORT
RT	UPWELLING
RT	WIND-DRIVEN CURRENTS

NEARSHORE DYNAMICS
UF	nearshore circulation
BT1	SHELF DYNAMICS
BT2	WATER CIRCULATION
BT3	WATER MOTION
RT	BAY DYNAMICS
RT	BEACH CUSPS
RT	BEACH FEATURES
RT	BEACH MORPHOLOGY
RT	BEACHES
RT	BED FORMS
RT	COASTAL BOUNDARY LAYER
RT	COASTAL CURRENTS
RT	COASTAL JETS
RT	COASTAL OCEANOGRAPHY
RT	COASTAL WATERS
RT	DYNAMICAL OCEANOGRAPHY
RT	ESTUARINE DYNAMICS
RT	LAKE DYNAMICS
RT	MASS TRANSPORT
RT	NEARSHORE BARS
RT	NEARSHORE CURRENTS
RT	NEARSHORE SEDIMENTATION
RT	ROCKY SHORES
RT	SURF ZONE
RT	WAVES ON BEACHES

NEARSHORE ENVIRONMENT
USE	**COASTAL ZONE**

NEARSHORE OCEANOGRAPHY
USE	**COASTAL OCEANOGRAPHY**

NEARSHORE SEDIMENTATION
UF	littoral sedimentation
BT1	SEDIMENTATION
RT	INTERTIDAL SEDIMENTATION
RT	LITTORAL DEPOSITS
RT	NEARSHORE DYNAMICS

NEARSHORE SEDIMENTATION (cont'd)
RT	SEDIMENTARY ENVIRONMENTS
RT	SUBLITTORAL ZONE

NECROSES
SN	Added in 1980
UF	gangrenes
UF	piscine erythrocyte necrosis
BT1	SYMPTOMS
RT	ANOXIA
RT	CELLS
RT	DISEASES
RT	ERYTHROCYTES
RT	FISH DISEASES
RT	INJURIES
RT	ULCERATIVE DERMAL NECROSIS

NECTON
USE	**NEKTON**

NECTON COLLECTING DEVICES
USE	**NEKTON COLLECTING DEVICES**

NEGATIVE IONS
USE	**ANIONS**

NEGATIVE STORM SURGES
BT1	STORM SURGES
BT2	SURFACE WATER WAVES
BT3	WATER WAVES
RT	KEEL CLEARANCE
RT	NAVIGATIONAL CHANNELS
RT	STORM SURGE PREDICTION
RT	STORM TIDE WARNING SERVICES

NEHRUNG
USE	**BARRIER SPITS**

NEKTON
UF	micronekton
UF	necton
BT1	AQUATIC COMMUNITIES
RT	FISH
RT	NEKTON COLLECTING DEVICES
RT	PELAGIC ENVIRONMENT

NEKTON COLLECTING DEVICES
UF	necton collecting devices
BT1	COLLECTING DEVICES
RT	AVOIDANCE REACTIONS
RT	ESCAPEMENT
RT	FISHING NETS
RT	ICHTHYOPLANKTON
RT	NEKTON
RT	ZOOPLANKTON

NEMATOCYSTS
USE	**STINGING ORGANS**

NEODYMIUM
BT1	CHEMICAL ELEMENTS
RT	NEODYMIUM COMPOUNDS
RT	NEODYMIUM ISOTOPES
RT	RARE EARTHS
RT	TRANSITION ELEMENTS

NEODYMIUM COMPOUNDS
RT	CHEMICAL COMPOUNDS
RT	NEODYMIUM

NEODYMIUM ISOTOPES
BT1	ISOTOPES
RT	NEODYMIUM

NEOGENE
UF	upper tertiary
BT1	TERTIARY
BT2	CENOZOIC
BT3	GEOLOGICAL TIME
NT1	MIOCENE

NEOGENE (cont'd)
NT2	MESSINIAN
NT1	PLIOCENE

NEON
BT1	CHEMICAL ELEMENTS
RT	NEON ISOTOPES
RT	RARE GASES

NEON ISOTOPES
BT1	ISOTOPES
RT	NEON

NEOPLASMS
USE	**TUMOURS**

NEOTENY
SN	Retention of larval characters
	beyond the usual period
UF	paedomorphism
BT1	BIOLOGICAL PROPERTIES
BT2	PROPERTIES
RT	LARVAE

NEPHELOID LAYER
UF	nepheloid zone
BT1	DISCONTINUITY LAYERS
BT2	LAYERS
RT	CONTINENTAL RISE
RT	CONTOUR CURRENTS
RT	LIGHT SCATTERING
RT	NEPHELOMETERS
RT	SUSPENDED PARTICULATE MATTER
RT	TURBIDITY
RT	TURBIDITY CURRENTS

NEPHELOID ZONE
USE	**NEPHELOID LAYER**

NEPHELOMETERS
RT	LIGHT MEASURING INSTRUMENTS
RT	LIGHT SCATTERING
RT	MEASURING DEVICES
RT	NEPHELOID LAYER
RT	OCEANOGRAPHIC EQUIPMENT
RT	PARTICLE CONCENTRATION
RT	PHOTOMETERS
RT	TRANSPARENCY
RT	TURBIDITY
RT	WATER TRANSPARENCY

NEPHRONS
USE	**KIDNEYS**

NEPTUNIUM
BT1	CHEMICAL ELEMENTS
RT	ACTINIDES
RT	NEPTUNIUM COMPOUNDS
RT	NEPTUNIUM ISOTOPES
RT	TRANSITION ELEMENTS
RT	TRANSURANIC ELEMENTS

NEPTUNIUM COMPOUNDS
BT1	ACTINIDE COMPOUNDS
RT	CHEMICAL COMPOUNDS
RT	NEPTUNIUM

NEPTUNIUM ISOTOPES
BT1	ISOTOPES
RT	NEPTUNIUM

NERITIC PROVINCE
UF	neritic region
UF	neritic zone
BT1	PELAGIC ENVIRONMENT
BT2	AQUATIC ENVIRONMENT
BT3	ENVIRONMENTS
RT	CONTINENTAL SHELVES
RT	EPIPELAGIC ZONE
RT	LITTORAL ZONE

NERITIC PROVINCE (cont'd)
RT	OCEANIC PROVINCE
RT	OUTER CONTINENTAL SHELF

NERITIC REGION
USE	**NERITIC PROVINCE**

NERITIC ZONE
USE	**NERITIC PROVINCE**

NERVE CELLS
USE	**NEURONES**

NERVE FIBERS
USE	**NERVES**

NERVE GANGLIA
USE	**GANGLIA**

NERVE TISSUES
USE	**NERVOUS TISSUES**

NERVES
UF	afferent nerves
UF	efferent nerves
UF	nerve fibers
UF	peripheral nerves
BT1	PERIPHERAL NERVOUS SYSTEM
BT2	NERVOUS SYSTEM
RT	BRAIN
RT	CONNECTIVE TISSUES
RT	GANGLIA
RT	NERVOUS TISSUES
RT	TISSUES

NERVOUS SYSTEM
NT1	AUTONOMIC NERVOUS SYSTEM
NT1	CENTRAL NERVOUS SYSTEM
NT2	BRAIN
NT3	HYPOTHALAMUS
NT3	PINEAL ORGAN
NT2	GANGLIA
NT2	SPINAL CORD
NT1	PERIPHERAL NERVOUS SYSTEM
NT2	NERVES
RT	ANATOMY
RT	NERVOUS TISSUES
RT	NEURONS
RT	NEUROPHYSIOLOGY
RT	NEUROSECRETION
RT	NEUROSECRETORY SYSTEM
RT	NEUROTRANSMITTERS
RT	SYNAPSES
RT	THYROID

NERVOUS TISSUES
SN	Added in 1980
UF	nerve tissues
BT1	TISSUES
RT	GANGLIA
RT	NERVES
RT	NERVOUS SYSTEM
RT	NEURONS
RT	NEUROSECRETION
RT	SENSE ORGANS

NESTING
SN	Added in 1980
UF	nesting activity
UF	nesting behaviour
RT	AQUATIC BIRDS
RT	BIRD EGGS
RT	BREEDING
RT	BREEDING SEASONS
RT	BREEDING SITES
RT	CLUTCH
RT	FISH
RT	HATCHING
RT	NESTS
RT	REPRODUCTIVE BEHAVIOUR

NESTING ACTIVITY
USE	**NESTING**

NESTING BEHAVIOUR
USE	**NESTING**

NESTS
SN	Added in 1980
RT	AQUATIC BIRDS
RT	BIRD EGGS
RT	BREEDING SITES
RT	CLUTCH
RT	FISH EGGS
RT	HATCHING
RT	NESTING
RT	REDDS

NET AVOIDANCE
USE	**AVOIDANCE REACTIONS**

NET CONSTRUCTION
USE	**GEAR CONSTRUCTION**

NET CULTURE
USE	**CAGE CULTURE**

NET FISHING
SN	Excluding seining and trawling
BT1	CATCHING METHODS
RT	FISHING
RT	FISHING NETS
RT	SEINING
RT	TRAWLING

NET RADIATION
USE	**RADIATION BALANCE**

NET SOLAR RADIATION
USE	**SOLAR RADIATION**

NET SOUNDERS
UF	netsondes
RT	ACOUSTIC EQUIPMENT
RT	INSTRUMENT DEPTH MEASUREMENT
RT	TRAWL NETS
RT	TRAWLING

NET TERRESTRIAL RADIATION
USE	**TERRESTRIAL RADIATION**

NETS
SN	For nets other than fishing nets
RT	FISHING NETS
RT	NETTING MATERIALS
RT	ROPES

NETSONDES
USE	**NET SOUNDERS**

NETTING MATERIALS
SN	Hand- or machine-made material for fishing nets
BT1	GEAR MATERIALS
BT2	MATERIALS
RT	FISHING NETS
RT	NETS
RT	SYNTHETIC FIBRES

NEUROHUMOR
USE	**NEUROTRANSMITTERS**

NEURONES
USE	**NEURONS**

NEURONS
SN	Added in 1980
UF	axons
UF	dendrites
UF	nerve cells
UF	neurones

NEURONS (cont'd)
BT1	CELLS
RT	NERVOUS SYSTEM
RT	NERVOUS TISSUES
RT	NEUROTRANSMITTERS
RT	RECEPTORS
RT	SYNAPSES

NEUROPHYSIOLOGY
SN	Added in 1980
BT1	PHYSIOLOGY
BT2	BIOLOGY
RT	NERVOUS SYSTEM
RT	NEUROSECRETORY SYSTEM
RT	NEUROTRANSMITTERS
RT	SENSE FUNCTIONS
RT	SENSE ORGANS

NEUROSECRETION
BT1	SECRETION
RT	HORMONES
RT	NERVOUS SYSTEM
RT	NERVOUS TISSUES
RT	NEUROSECRETORY SYSTEM
RT	PINEAL ORGAN

NEUROSECRETORY SYSTEM
SN	Added in 1980
BT1	ANATOMICAL STRUCTURES
RT	NERVOUS SYSTEM
RT	NEUROPHYSIOLOGY
RT	NEUROSECRETION
RT	PINEAL ORGAN

NEUROTOXINS
SN	Toxins which affect the nervous system. Before 1982 search POISONS (BIOLOGICAL)
BT1	BIOLOGICAL POISONS
RT	BOTULISM
RT	PUBLIC HEALTH
RT	TETRODOTOXIN

NEUROTRANSMITTERS
SN	Added in 1980
UF	acetylcholine
UF	neurohumor
BT1	HORMONES
BT2	SECRETORY PRODUCTS
RT	NERVOUS SYSTEM
RT	NEURONS
RT	NEUROPHYSIOLOGY
RT	SYNAPSES

NEUSTON
BT1	AQUATIC COMMUNITIES
RT	AIR-WATER INTERFACE
RT	PELAGIC ENVIRONMENT
RT	PLANKTON COLLECTING DEVICES
RT	SURFACE MICROLAYER

NEUTRALLY BUOYANT FLOATS
USE	**SWALLOW FLOATS**

NEUTRON ACTIVATION ANALYSIS
BT1	ACTIVATION ANALYSIS
BT2	ANALYTICAL TECHNIQUES

NEW CLASSES
SN	Added in 1980
BT1	NEW TAXA
RT	HOLOTYPES
RT	TAXONOMY

NEW DISTRIBUTION
USE	**NEW RECORDS**

ASFIS Thesaurus

NEW FAMILIES
SN	Added in 1980
BT1	NEW TAXA
RT	HOLOTYPES
RT	TAXONOMY

NEW GENERA
UF	new genus
BT1	NEW TAXA
RT	EVOLUTION
RT	HOLOTYPES
RT	IDENTIFICATION KEYS
RT	TAXONOMY

NEW GENUS
USE	**NEW GENERA**

NEW ORDERS
SN	Added in 1980
BT1	NEW TAXA
RT	HOLOTYPES
RT	TAXONOMY

NEW PRODUCT DEVELOPMENT
USE	**PRODUCT DEVELOPMENT**

NEW PRODUCTS
SN	Added in 1980
UF	improved products
BT1	PRODUCTS
RT	INDUSTRIAL PRODUCTS
RT	PRODUCT DEVELOPMENT

NEW RECORDS
UF	new distribution
BT1	DISTRIBUTION
RT	GEOGRAPHICAL DISTRIBUTION
RT	STRANDING

NEW SPECIES
BT1	NEW TAXA
RT	BIOLOGICAL SPECIATION
RT	CHECK LISTS
RT	EVOLUTION
RT	HOLOTYPES
RT	MUTATIONS
RT	SPECIES
RT	TAXONOMY

NEW TAXA
SN	Added in 1980
NT1	NEW CLASSES
NT1	NEW FAMILIES
NT1	NEW GENERA
NT1	NEW ORDERS
NT1	NEW SPECIES
NT1	NEW VARIETIES
RT	HOLOTYPES
RT	TAXA
RT	TAXONOMY
RT	TYPE LOCALITIES

NEW VARIETIES
SN	Added in 1980
BT1	NEW TAXA

NICHES
SN	Added in 1980
UF	ecological niches
RT	AQUATIC COMMUNITIES
RT	AQUATIC ORGANISMS
RT	BEHAVIOUR
RT	BIOTOPES
RT	ECOSYSTEMS
RT	HABITAT
RT	MICROHABITATS

NICKEL
BT1	CHEMICAL ELEMENTS
RT	FERROMANGANESE NODULES
RT	HEAVY METALS
RT	METALS
RT	NICKEL COMPOUNDS
RT	NICKEL ISOTOPES
RT	TRANSITION ELEMENTS

NICKEL COMPOUNDS
RT	CHEMICAL COMPOUNDS
RT	NICKEL

NICKEL ISOTOPES
BT1	ISOTOPES
RT	NICKEL

NICOTINIC ACID
BT1	ORGANIC ACIDS
BT2	ORGANIC COMPOUNDS

NIGHTTIME
RT	DAYTIME
RT	DIURNAL VARIATIONS

NIOBIUM
UF	columbian
BT1	CHEMICAL ELEMENTS
RT	METALS
RT	NIOBIUM COMPOUNDS
RT	NIOBIUM ISOTOPES
RT	TRACE METALS

NIOBIUM COMPOUNDS
RT	CHEMICAL COMPOUNDS
RT	NIOBIUM

NIOBIUM ISOTOPES
BT1	ISOTOPES
RT	NIOBIUM

NISKIN SAMPLERS
BT1	WATER SAMPLERS
BT2	SAMPLERS

NITRATE CYCLE
USE	**NITROGEN CYCLE**

NITRATES
BT1	NITROGEN COMPOUNDS
RT	CHEMICAL COMPOUNDS
RT	FERTILIZERS
RT	NITRITES
RT	NITROGEN CYCLE
RT	NUTRIENTS (MINERAL)
RT	SALTS

NITRIC ACID
USE	**NITRIC ACIDS**

NITRIC ACIDS
SN	Before 1978 search INORGANIC ACIDS
UF	nitric acid
UF	nitrous acid
BT1	INORGANIC ACIDS
BT2	HYDROGEN COMPOUNDS

NITRIFICATION
BT1	CHEMICAL REACTIONS
RT	BACTERIA
RT	DENITRIFICATION
RT	NITROGEN CYCLE

NITRITES
BT1	NITROGEN COMPOUNDS
RT	CHEMICAL COMPOUNDS
RT	NITRATES
RT	NITROGEN CYCLE
RT	SALTS

NITROGEN
BT1	CHEMICAL ELEMENTS
NT1	ORGANIC NITROGEN
NT2	DISSOLVED ORGANIC NITROGEN
NT2	PARTICULATE ORGANIC NITROGEN
RT	GASES
RT	NITROGEN COMPOUNDS
RT	NITROGEN CYCLE
RT	NITROGEN FIXATION
RT	NITROGEN ISOTOPES
RT	NON-CONSERVATIVE PROPERTIES

NITROGEN COMPOUNDS
UF	nitrogenous compounds
NT1	AMMONIA
NT1	NITRATES
NT1	NITRITES
NT1	NITROUS OXIDE
RT	AMINO ACIDS
RT	CHEMICAL COMPOUNDS
RT	CYANIDES
RT	FERTILIZERS
RT	NITROGEN
RT	NITROGEN CYCLE
RT	NITROGEN FIXATION
RT	NUTRIENTS (MINERAL)
RT	ORGANIC COMPOUNDS
RT	ORGANIC NITROGEN
RT	PROTEINS
RT	UREA

NITROGEN CYCLE
UF	nitrate cycle
BT1	NUTRIENT CYCLES
BT2	BIOGEOCHEMICAL CYCLE
BT3	CYCLES
RT	AMMONIA
RT	BACTERIA
RT	BIODEGRADATION
RT	CHEMICAL CYCLES
RT	DENITRIFICATION
RT	NITRATES
RT	NITRIFICATION
RT	NITRITES
RT	NITROGEN
RT	NITROGEN COMPOUNDS
RT	NITROGEN FIXATION

NITROGEN FIXATION
SN	The process by which certain bacteria are able to transform elemental nitrogen into ammonia
BT1	CHEMICAL REACTIONS
RT	AMMONIA
RT	BIOCHEMICAL PHENOMENA
RT	NITROGEN
RT	NITROGEN COMPOUNDS
RT	NITROGEN CYCLE

NITROGEN ISOTOPES
BT1	ISOTOPES
RT	NITROGEN

NITROGEN NARCOSIS
BT1	NARCOSIS
RT	DECOMPRESSION SICKNESS
RT	UNDERWATER MEDICINE

NITROGENOUS COMPOUNDS
USE	**NITROGEN COMPOUNDS**

NITROSAMINES
BT1	AMINES
BT2	ORGANIC COMPOUNDS

NITROUS ACID
USE	**NITRIC ACIDS**

ASFIS Thesaurus

NITROUS OXIDE
BT1   NITROGEN COMPOUNDS

NMR TECHNIQUES
USE   **NUCLEAR MAGNETIC RESONANCE**

NOBBING
USE   **GUTTING**

NOBELIUM
BT1   CHEMICAL ELEMENTS
RT   ACTINIDES
RT   NOBELIUM COMPOUNDS
RT   NOBELIUM ISOTOPES
RT   TRANSITION ELEMENTS
RT   TRANSURANIC ELEMENTS

NOBELIUM COMPOUNDS
RT   CHEMICAL COMPOUNDS
RT   NOBELIUM

NOBELIUM ISOTOPES
BT1   ISOTOPES
RT   NOBELIUM

NOBLE GASES
USE   **RARE GASES**

NODAL TIDES
BT1   TIDES
BT2   TIDAL MOTION
RT   LONG-PERIOD TIDES
RT   TIDAL PERTURBATION

NODE CONSTRUCTION
RT   JOINTS
RT   OFFSHORE STRUCTURES
RT   TUBING

NODES
USE   **JOINTS**

NODULES
SN   Use only for chemical sediments
        found on seafloor
BT1   CHEMICAL SEDIMENTS
BT2   SEDIMENTS
RT   CHERTS
RT   CONCRETIONS
RT   FERROMANGANESE NODULES
RT   MINERAL INDUSTRY
RT   MINERAL RESOURCES
RT   PHOSPHORITE NODULES
RT   SEABED DEPOSITS
RT   SEDIMENTARY STRUCTURES

NOISE (AMBIENT)
USE   **AMBIENT NOISE**

NOISE (ELECTRONICS)
USE   **ELECTRONIC NOISE**

NOISE (RADAR ECHOES)
USE   **RADAR CLUTTER**

NOISE (SOUND)
NT1   AMBIENT NOISE
NT2   BIOLOGICAL NOISE
NT2   SEDIMENT NOISE
NT2   SHIPPING NOISE
NT2   SURFACE NOISE
NT1   UNDERWATER NOISE
NT2   REVERBERATION
NT3   BOTTOM REVERBERATION
RT   VIBRATION

NOISE GENERATORS
USE   **SOUND GENERATORS**

NOISE REDUCTION
UF   noise suppression
BT1   DAMPING
RT   ACOUSTIC INSULATION

NOISE SUPPRESSION
USE   **NOISE REDUCTION**

NOMENCLATURE
USE   **TERMINOLOGY**

NOMOGRAMS
USE   **CONVERSION TABLES**

NON-COHESIVE SEDIMENTS
USE   **COHESIONLESS SEDIMENTS**

NON-CONSERVATIVE PROPERTIES
BT1   PROPERTIES
RT   CONSERVATIVE PROPERTIES
RT   DISSOLVED OXYGEN
RT   NITROGEN
RT   PHOSPHATES
RT   SEA WATER
RT   SILICATES
RT   WATER MASSES

NON-NEWTONIAN FLUIDS
BT1   FLUIDS
RT   RHEOLOGY

NON PENAEID SHRIMP FISHERIES
USE   **SHRIMP FISHERIES**

NONCONVENTIONAL RESOURCES
USE   **UNCONVENTIONAL RESOURCES**

NONDESTRUCTIVE TESTING
UF   acoustic emission testing
UF   flaw detection
UF   magnetic particle testing
UF   radiographic testing
UF   ultrasonic testing
BT1   MATERIALS TESTING
BT2   TESTING
RT   ACOUSTIC EMISSION
RT   DEFECTS
RT   DETECTION

NONFERROUS ALLOYS
BT1   ALLOYS
BT2   MATERIALS

NONLINEAR EQUATIONS
SN   Used only as a qulaifier
BT1   EQUATIONS
RT   DIFFERENTIAL EQUATIONS
RT   INTEGRAL EQUATIONS
RT   NUMERICAL ANALYSIS

NONLINEAR WAVE INTERACTIONS
BT1   WAVE INTERACTIONS

NONLINEAR WAVES
BT1   WATER WAVES
NT1   FINITE AMPLITUDE WAVES
NT1   STOKES WAVES
RT   CAPILLARY WAVES
RT   CNOIDAL WAVES
RT   EDGE WAVES
RT   INTERNAL WAVES
RT   KELVIN WAVES
RT   LINEAR WAVES
RT   SHALLOW-WATER WAVES
RT   SHELF WAVES
RT   SOLITARY WAVES
RT   SURFACE GRAVITY WAVES

NONLINEAR WAVES (cont'd)
RT   TIDAL BORES

NONLINEARITY
SN   Used only as a qualifier
RT   VARIABILITY

NONRENEWABLE RESOURCES
SN   Added in 1980
BT1   NATURAL RESOURCES
BT2   RESOURCES
RT   FOSSIL FUELS
RT   MINERAL DEPOSITS
RT   MINERAL RESOURCES
RT   OVEREXPLOITATION
RT   RENEWABLE RESOURCES
RT   RESOURCE AVAILABILITY
RT   RESOURCE CONSERVATION
RT   RESOURCE MANAGEMENT
RT   SEABED DEPOSITS

NONTRONITE
BT1   CLAY MINERALS
BT2   SILICATE MINERALS
BT3   MINERALS

NORTH ATLANTIC POLAR FRONT
BT1   POLAR CONVERGENCES
BT2   OCEANIC CONVERGENCES
BT3   CONVERGENCE ZONES

NORTHERN LOBSTER FISHERIES
USE   **LOBSTER FISHERIES**

NOXIOUS ORGANISMS
UF   injurious organisms
UF   stinging organisms
BT1   AQUATIC ORGANISMS
RT   LAMPREY ATTACHMENT
RT   LESIONS
RT   PARASITES
RT   POISONOUS ORGANISMS
RT   STINGING ORGANS
RT   VENOM APPARATUS

NUCLEAR DIVISION
USE   **CELL DIVISION**

NUCLEAR ENERGY
UF   atomic energy
BT1   ENERGY
RT   NUCLEAR POWER PLANTS
RT   POWER PLANTS
RT   RADIOACTIVE WASTES
RT   RADIOACTIVITY

NUCLEAR EXPLOSIONS
BT1   EXPLOSIONS
RT   FISSION PRODUCTS
RT   UNDERWATER EXPLOSIONS

NUCLEAR MAGNETIC RESONANCE
UF   nmr techniques
RT   SPECTROSCOPIC TECHNIQUES

NUCLEAR MEMBRANES
USE   **CELL MEMBRANES**

NUCLEAR PHYSICS
UF   atomic physics
BT1   PHYSICS
RT   RADIOACTIVITY
RT   RADIOISOTOPES

NUCLEAR POWER PLANTS
SN   Before 1982 search POWER PLANTS
UF   atomic power plants
BT1   POWER PLANTS
RT   COOLING PONDS
RT   COOLING WATER

NUCLEAR POWER PLANTS (cont'd)
- RT   ENERGY RESOURCES
- RT   NUCLEAR ENERGY
- RT   RADIOACTIVE CONTAMINATION
- RT   RADIOACTIVE WASTES
- RT   THERMAL AQUACULTURE
- RT   THERMAL PLUMES
- RT   THERMAL POLLUTION
- RT   WASTE HEAT

NUCLEAR PROPULSION
- BT1   PROPULSION SYSTEMS
- RT   RADIOACTIVE CONTAMINATION
- RT   SUBMARINES
- RT   UNDERWATER PROPULSION

NUCLEAR RADIATIONS
- BT1   IONIZING RADIATION
- BT2   RADIATIONS
- RT   ELECTROMAGNETIC RADIATION
- RT   FALLOUT
- RT   RADIOACTIVE WASTES
- RT   RADIOACTIVITY
- RT   RADIOCHEMISTRY
- RT   RADIOMETRIC DATING
- RT   STERILITY

NUCLEAR WASTES
- USE   **RADIOACTIVE WASTES**

NUCLEI
- UF   nucleus
- BT1   CELL CONSTITUENTS
- RT   GENOMES
- RT   ICE NUCLEI
- RT   KARYOLOGY
- RT   MEIOSIS
- RT   MITOSIS

NUCLEIC ACIDS
- BT1   ORGANIC ACIDS
- BT2   ORGANIC COMPOUNDS
- NT1   DNA
- NT1   RNA
- RT   CHEMICAL COMPOUNDS
- RT   GENETICS
- RT   NUCLEOTIDES
- RT   PROTEIN DENATURATION
- RT   PROTEINS

NUCLEOTIDES
- BT1   ORGANIC COMPOUNDS
- NT1   ADP
- NT1   AMP
- NT1   ATP
- RT   CHEMICAL COMPOUNDS
- RT   NUCLEIC ACIDS
- RT   ORGANIC ACIDS

NUCLEUS
- USE   **NUCLEI**

NUCLIDES
- USE   **ISOTOPES**

NUMERICAL ANALYSIS
- SN   Used only as a qualifier
- BT1   MATHEMATICAL ANALYSIS
- NT1   APPROXIMATION
- NT2   BOUSSINESQ APPROXIMATION
- NT2   CLOSURE APPROXIMATION
- NT2   LEAST SQUARES METHOD
- NT1   FINITE DIFFERENCE METHOD
- NT1   FINITE ELEMENT METHOD
- NT1   FUNCTIONAL ANALYSIS
- NT2   FOURIER TRANSFORMS
- NT2   HARMONIC ANALYSIS
- NT2   LAPLACE TRANSFORMATION
- NT1   PERTURBATION METHOD
- RT   ALGORITHMS

NUMERICAL ANALYSIS (cont'd)
- RT   ANALYSIS
- RT   BOUNDARY VALUE PROBLEMS
- RT   COMPUTER PROGRAMS
- RT   CONVERSION TABLES
- RT   CRITICAL PATH METHOD
- RT   DIFFERENTIAL EQUATIONS
- RT   GAME THEORY
- RT   INTEGRAL EQUATIONS
- RT   MATHEMATICS
- RT   NONLINEAR EQUATIONS
- RT   NUMERICAL TAXONOMY
- RT   PERT
- RT   SPLINES
- RT   STATISTICAL ANALYSIS
- RT   TIDAL EQUATIONS

NUMERICAL MODELS
- USE   **MATHEMATICAL MODELS**

NUMERICAL TAXONOMY
- BT1   TAXONOMY
- RT   BIOMETRICS
- RT   CLASSIFICATION SYSTEMS
- RT   CORRELATION ANALYSIS
- RT   MERISTIC COUNTS
- RT   NUMERICAL ANALYSIS
- RT   ORGANISM MORPHOLOGY
- RT   VARIANCE ANALYSIS

NURSERY GROUNDS
- SN   Regions particulary rich in food organisms where feeding of fish larvae and juveniles take place
- UF   feeding ground
- RT   FEEDING MIGRATIONS
- RT   FISH LARVAE
- RT   JUVENILES
- RT   SPAWNING
- RT   SPAWNING GROUNDS

NURSERY PONDS
- UF   fish rearing ponds
- BT1   FISH PONDS
- BT2   PONDS
- BT3   INLAND WATERS
- RT   AQUACULTURE FACILITIES
- RT   FINGERLINGS
- RT   FRY
- RT   JUVENILES
- RT   SHRIMP CULTURE

NUTRIENT CYCLES
- SN   Cycle of nutrients in aquatic environments
- BT1   BIOGEOCHEMICAL CYCLE
- BT2   CYCLES
- NT1   CARBON CYCLE
- NT1   NITROGEN CYCLE
- NT1   PHOSPHORUS CYCLE
- NT1   SILICON CYCLE
- RT   BIOCHEMICAL CYCLES
- RT   BIODEGRADATION
- RT   BIOGEOCHEMISTRY
- RT   BIOLOGICAL PRODUCTION
- RT   CHEMICAL CYCLES
- RT   NUTRIENT DEFICIENCY
- RT   NUTRIENTS (MINERAL)
- RT   SAPROPHYTES
- RT   SUSPENDED PARTICULATE MATTER

NUTRIENT DEFICIENCY
- UF   nutrient depletion
- BT1   DIETARY DEFICIENCIES
- RT   DEFICIENCY DISEASES
- RT   NUTRIENT CYCLES
- RT   NUTRIENTS (MINERAL)
- RT   NUTRITION
- RT   OLIGOTROPHIC LAKES
- RT   PLANT NUTRITION

NUTRIENT DEFICIENCY (cont'd)
- RT   VITAMIN DEFICIENCIES

NUTRIENT DEPLETION
- USE   **NUTRIENT DEFICIENCY**

NUTRIENT SALTS
- USE   **NUTRIENTS (MINERAL)**

NUTRIENTS (MINERAL)
- SN   Inorganic and organic nutrients in water
- UF   nutrient salts
- RT   ARTIFICIAL UPWELLING
- RT   BIOGEOCHEMICAL CYCLE
- RT   BIOLOGICAL PRODUCTION
- RT   CHEMOSYNTHESIS
- RT   ENERGY BUDGET
- RT   EUTROPHICATION
- RT   FERTILITY
- RT   FERTILIZERS
- RT   HYPERTROPHY
- RT   LIMITING FACTORS
- RT   NITRATES
- RT   NITROGEN COMPOUNDS
- RT   NUTRIENT CYCLES
- RT   NUTRIENT DEFICIENCY
- RT   NUTRITION
- RT   OCEANIC DESERTS
- RT   PHOSPHATES
- RT   PHOSPHORUS COMPOUNDS
- RT   PLANT NUTRITION
- RT   PRIMARY PRODUCTION
- RT   ROOTS
- RT   SILICATES
- RT   SILICON COMPOUNDS
- RT   TRACE ELEMENTS
- RT   UPWELLING
- RT   WATER ANALYSIS

NUTRITION
- SN   Use of a more specific term is recommended
- NT1   ANIMAL NUTRITION
- NT2   DEFAECATION
- NT2   DIGESTION
- NT2   FOOD ABSORPTION
- NT2   FOOD CONSUMPTION
- NT2   FOOD CONVERSION
- NT2   INGESTION
- NT1   PLANT NUTRITION
- RT   BODY CONDITIONS
- RT   FATS
- RT   FEEDING
- RT   FOOD
- RT   LIPIDS
- RT   METABOLISM
- RT   NUTRIENT DEFICIENCY
- RT   NUTRIENTS (MINERAL)
- RT   NUTRITIONAL REQUIREMENTS
- RT   NUTRITIONAL TYPES
- RT   NUTRITIVE VALUE
- RT   PHYSIOLOGY

NUTRITION (ANIMAL)
- USE   **ANIMAL NUTRITION**

NUTRITION (PLANTS)
- USE   **PLANT NUTRITION**

NUTRITION DISORDERS
- SN   Diseases caused by deficiencies and imbalances of major dietary components. Added in 1980
- UF   nutritional diseases
- BT1   DISEASES
- NT1   PROTEIN DEFICIENCY
- RT   ANAEMIA
- RT   ANIMAL DISEASES
- RT   ARTIFICIAL FEEDING

ASFIS Thesaurus

NUTRITION DISORDERS (cont'd)
RT	DIETS
RT	FISH DISEASES
RT	GILL DISEASE
RT	HUSBANDRY DISEASES
RT	METABOLIC DISORDERS
RT	NUTRITIONAL REQUIREMENTS
RT	STARVATION
RT	SUNBURN
RT	VITAMIN DEFICIENCIES

NUTRITIONAL DISEASES
USE	**NUTRITION DISORDERS**

NUTRITIONAL REQUIREMENTS
UF	food requirements
RT	ANIMAL NUTRITION
RT	ARTIFICIAL FEEDING
RT	BALANCED RATIONS
RT	BODY CONDITIONS
RT	DEFICIENCY DISEASES
RT	DIETARY DEFICIENCIES
RT	DIETS
RT	DISEASE RESISTANCE
RT	ECOLOGICAL EFFICIENCY
RT	FEEDING EXPERIMENTS
RT	FOOD
RT	FOOD CONSUMPTION
RT	NUTRITION
RT	NUTRITION DISORDERS
RT	NUTRITIVE VALUE
RT	TROPHODYNAMIC CYCLE
RT	VITAMIN A
RT	VITAMIN B
RT	VITAMIN C
RT	VITAMIN D
RT	VITAMIN DEFICIENCIES
RT	VITAMIN E
RT	VITAMINS

NUTRITIONAL TYPES
NT1	AUTOTROPHY
NT1	HETEROTROPHY
RT	HETEROTROPHIC ORGANISMS
RT	NUTRITION

NUTRITIVE VALUE
RT	BALANCED RATIONS
RT	BIOCHEMICAL ANALYSIS
RT	CALORIES
RT	CALORIMETRY
RT	CARBOHYDRATES
RT	DIETARY DEFICIENCIES
RT	DIETS
RT	DIGESTIBILITY
RT	FATS
RT	FEED
RT	FEED EFFICIENCY
RT	FOOD COMPOSITION
RT	FOOD FISH
RT	FOOD TECHNOLOGY
RT	HUMAN FOOD
RT	NUTRITION
RT	NUTRITIONAL REQUIREMENTS
RT	POWDERED PRODUCTS
RT	PROTEINS
RT	VITAMIN DEFICIENCIES
RT	VITAMINS

NYCTIMERAL RHYTHMS
BT1	BIOLOGICAL RHYTHMS
BT2	BIOLOGICAL PHENOMENA
RT	BIOLOGICAL CLOCKS
RT	DIURNAL VARIATIONS
RT	LIGHT EFFECTS
RT	MOON PHASES
RT	PHOTOTAXIS
RT	PHOTOTROPISM
RT	VERTICAL MIGRATIONS

NYMPHS
BT1	INSECT LARVAE
BT2	INVERTEBRATE LARVAE
BT3	LARVAE
BT4	DEVELOPMENTAL STAGES
RT	AQUATIC INSECTS
RT	EMERGENCE
RT	INSECT EGGS
RT	METAMORPHOSIS

OBDUCTION
RT	CONTINENTAL CRUST
RT	PLATE TECTONICS
RT	PLATES
RT	SUBDUCTION

OBITUARIES
RT	PERSONAL BIBLIOGRAPHIES
RT	SCIENTIFIC PERSONNEL

OBS
USE	**OCEAN BOTTOM SEISMOMETERS**

OBSERVATION CHAMBERS
BT1	MANNED VEHICLES
BT2	UNDERWATER VEHICLES
BT3	VEHICLES
NT1	BATHYSPHERES
RT	TETHERED VEHICLES

OBSERVATION PLATFORMS
USE	**INSTRUMENT PLATFORMS**

OBSIDIAN
BT1	GLASS
RT	VOLCANIC GLASS

OBSTACLE MARKS
UF	wreck marks
BT1	BED FORMS
BT2	SEDIMENTARY STRUCTURES
RT	SCOUR HOLLOWS

OCCLUDED FRONTS
USE	**ATMOSPHERIC FRONTS**

OCEAN-ATMOSPHERE SYSTEM
UF	atmosphere-ocean system
RT	AIR-SEA COUPLING
RT	AIR-SEA INTERACTION
RT	AIR-WATER EXCHANGES
RT	CLIMATE
RT	DYNAMICAL OCEANOGRAPHY
RT	EARTH ATMOSPHERE
RT	HYDROSPHERE
RT	OCEAN CIRCULATION
RT	OCEAN-ICE-ATMOSPHERE SYSTEM
RT	OCEANS
RT	TELECONNECTIONS

OCEAN BASIN FLOOR
USE	**OCEAN FLOOR**

OCEAN BASINS
SN	Use for studies on major ocean basins, their origin, evolution and present configuration. Use OCEAN FLOOR for basins with each ocean and for sedimentation studies
UF	submarine basins
BT1	SUBMARINE FEATURES
BT2	TOPOGRAPHIC FEATURES
RT	ABYSSAL PLAINS
RT	BASINS
RT	BOTTOM TOPOGRAPHY
RT	CONTINENTAL DRIFT
RT	EARTH STRUCTURE
RT	EPEIROGENY
RT	FOREARC BASINS
RT	OCEAN FLOOR

OCEAN BASINS (cont'd)
RT	OCEANIC CRUST
RT	PERMANENCE
RT	RELIEF FORMS
RT	STRUCTURAL BASINS

OCEAN BEACHES
USE	**BEACHES**

OCEAN BOTTOM SEISMOMETERS
UF	obs
UF	pubs
BT1	SEISMOMETERS
BT2	MEASURING DEVICES

OCEAN BOTTOM TOPOGRAPHY
USE	**BOTTOM TOPOGRAPHY**

OCEAN CIRCULATION
UF	general circulation (oceans)
UF	oceanic circulation
BT1	WATER CIRCULATION
BT2	WATER MOTION
NT1	ABYSSAL CIRCULATION
NT1	EQUATORIAL CIRCULATION
NT1	GYRES
NT1	MERIDIONAL OCEANIC CIRCULATION
NT1	OCEANIC EDDIES
NT2	CURRENT RINGS
NT2	MESOSCALE EDDIES
NT1	THERMOHALINE CIRCULATION
NT2	HALINE CIRCULATION
RT	ATMOSPHERIC CIRCULATION
RT	BOTTOM TOPOGRAPHY EFFECTS
RT	BOUNDARY CURRENTS
RT	CIRCULATION
RT	HEAT TRANSPORT
RT	OCEAN CURRENTS
RT	OCEAN-ATMOSPHERE SYSTEM
RT	SURFACE CIRCULATION
RT	SVERDRUP TRANSPORT
RT	WATER CURRENTS
RT	WIND-DRIVEN CIRCULATION

OCEAN CRUST
USE	**OCEANIC CRUST**

OCEAN CURRENT ENERGY CONVERSION
USE	**CURRENT POWER**

OCEAN CURRENTS
SN	Search also WATER CURRENTS
BT1	WATER CURRENTS
BT2	WATER MOTION
RT	ABYSSAL CURRENTS
RT	BENTHIC CURRENTS
RT	BOTTOM CURRENTS
RT	BOUNDARY CURRENTS
RT	COASTAL COUNTERCURRENTS
RT	CONTOUR CURRENTS
RT	CURRENT POWER
RT	CURRENT RINGS
RT	DEEP CURRENTS
RT	DYNAMICAL OCEANOGRAPHY
RT	EASTERN BOUNDARY CURRENTS
RT	EQUATORIAL COUNTERCURRENTS
RT	EQUATORIAL UNDERCURRENTS
RT	HEAT TRANSPORT
RT	MONSOON REVERSAL
RT	OCEAN CIRCULATION
RT	OCEANOGRAPHIC SURVEYS
RT	OCEANS
RT	PALAEOCURRENTS
RT	SHELF CURRENTS
RT	SUBSURFACE CURRENTS
RT	SURFACE CURRENTS
RT	UNDERCURRENTS
RT	WESTERN BOUNDARY CURRENTS
RT	WESTERN BOUNDARY UNDERCURRENTS
RT	WIND-DRIVEN CURRENTS

OCEAN DATA ROUTES
USE **STANDARD OCEAN SECTIONS**

OCEAN DUMPING
SN   The dumping of wastes at sea
UF   dumping
RT   INTERNATIONAL AGREEMENTS
RT   MARINE POLLUTION
RT   RADIOACTIVE WASTE DISPOSAL
RT   WASTE DISPOSAL
RT   WASTE DISPOSAL SITES
RT   WASTES

OCEAN ENGINEERING
USE   **OFFSHORE ENGINEERING**

OCEAN ENVIRONMENT
USE   **MARINE ENVIRONMENT**

OCEAN FARMING
USE   **MARINE AQUACULTURE**

OCEAN FLOOR
SN   Use for natural phenomena and
        processes taking place on seafloor.
        For tectonic studies use OCEAN
        BASINS. Before 1983 search also
        SEABED
UF   deep-sea bed
UF   floor (ocean)
UF   ocean basin floor
UF   sea bed
UF   sea floor
UF   seabed
RT   ABYSSAL PLAINS
RT   BOTTOM TOPOGRAPHY
RT   BOTTOM TOW
RT   BURYING
RT   CONTINENTAL RISE
RT   CONTINENTAL SLOPE
RT   DREDGING
RT   GEOTECHNOLOGY
RT   JURISDICTION
RT   MID-OCEAN RIDGES
RT   OCEAN BASINS
RT   OCEANIC CRUST
RT   POLITICAL ASPECTS
RT   SEABED VEHICLES
RT   SEAFLOOR SAMPLING
RT   SEDENTARY SPECIES
RT   SEDIMENT-WATER INTERFACE
RT   SUBMARINE CABLES
RT   SUBMARINE FEATURES
RT   SURVEYING UNDERWATER
RT   TRENCHES (PIPELINES)
RT   TRENCHING
RT   UNDERWATER HABITATS
RT   WELLHEADS

OCEAN FLOOR TOPOGRAPHY
USE   **BOTTOM TOPOGRAPHY**

OCEAN-ICE-ATMOSPHERE SYSTEM
RT   AIR-SEA COUPLING
RT   OCEAN-ATMOSPHERE SYSTEM
RT   SEA ICE

OCEAN LAW
USE   **LAW OF THE SEA**

OCEAN LOADING
UF   tidal loading
BT1   LOADS (FORCES)
BT2   FORCES (MECHANICS)
RT   CYCLIC LOADING
RT   EARTH TIDES
RT   TIDES

OCEAN OUTFALLS
USE   **OUTFALLS**

OCEAN PLATEAUX
USE   **SUBMARINE PLATEAUX**

OCEAN POLICY
SN   Added in 1980. Search also MARINE
        POLICY
UF   marine policy
BT1   POLICIES
RT   INTERNATIONAL AGREEMENTS
RT   INTERNATIONAL ORGANIZATIONS
RT   LAW OF THE SEA
RT   MARINE RESOURCES
RT   NAVIGATION
RT   OCEAN SPACE
RT   SEABED CONVENTIONS

OCEAN RANCHING
USE   **RANCHING**

OCEAN SPACE
SN   In the legal aspect only
UF   maritime space
NT1   CONTIGUOUS ZONES
NT1   EXCLUSIVE ECONOMIC ZONE
NT1   HIGH SEAS
NT1   INTERNATIONAL WATERS
NT1   TERRITORIAL WATERS
RT   ARCHIPELAGOES
RT   BOUNDARIES
RT   CONTINENTAL SHELVES
RT   DISPUTES
RT   ENVIRONMENTAL LEGISLATION
RT   EXPLOITATION
RT   EXTENDED JURISDICTION
RT   FISHERY DISPUTES
RT   FISHERY REGULATIONS
RT   INTERNATIONAL AGREEMENTS
RT   INTERNATIONAL POLICY
RT   JURISDICTION
RT   LAW OF THE SEA
RT   LEGISLATION
RT   MARITIME LEGISLATION
RT   NAVIGATION REGULATIONS
RT   OCEAN POLICY
RT   OUTER CONTINENTAL SHELF
RT   POLITICAL ASPECTS
RT   SURVEILLANCE AND ENFORCEMENT

OCEAN STATIONS
UF   ocean weather stations
BT1   FIXED STATIONS
BT2   OCEANOGRAPHIC STATIONS
RT   DATA BUOYS
RT   DATA REPORTS
RT   METEOROLOGICAL DATA
RT   OCEANOGRAPHIC DATA
RT   STANDARD OCEAN SECTIONS
RT   WEATHER SHIPS

OCEAN SURFACE TEMPERATURE
USE   **SURFACE TEMPERATURE**

OCEAN SURVEILLANCE
USE   **SURVEILLANCE AND ENFORCEMENT**

OCEAN THERMAL ENERGY CONVERSION
USE   **OTEC**

OCEAN TIDES
BT1   TIDES
BT2   TIDAL MOTION

OCEAN WATER
USE   **SEA WATER**

OCEAN WAVES
USE   **SURFACE WATER WAVES**

OCEAN WEATHER SHIPS
USE   **WEATHER SHIPS**

OCEAN WEATHER STATIONS
USE   **OCEAN STATIONS**

OCEANARIA
USE   **AQUARIA**

OCEANIC BOUNDARY LAYER
BT1   BOUNDARY LAYERS
BT2   LAYERS
RT   AIR-WATER INTERFACE
RT   SURFACE EKMAN LAYER
RT   SURFACE MIXED LAYER
RT   UPPER OCEAN

OCEANIC CIRCULATION
USE   **OCEAN CIRCULATION**

OCEANIC CONVECTION
BT1   CONVECTION
BT2   ADVECTION
BT3   TRANSPORT PROCESSES

OCEANIC CONVERGENCES
BT1   CONVERGENCE ZONES
NT1   POLAR CONVERGENCES
NT2   ANTARCTIC CONVERGENCE
NT2   NORTH ATLANTIC POLAR FRONT
NT1   SUBTROPICAL CONVERGENCES
RT   ADVECTION
RT   CONVERGENCE
RT   DOWNWELLING
RT   FRONTS
RT   OCEANIC DIVERGENCES
RT   WATER MASSES

OCEANIC CRUST
SN   Before 1983 search also SUBMARINE
        CRUST
UF   crust (ocean)
UF   crust (oceanic)
UF   ocean crust
UF   submarine crust
UF   suboceanic crust
BT1   EARTH CRUST
BT2   EARTH STRUCTURE
RT   CONTINENTAL BORDERLAND
RT   CONTINENTAL CRUST
RT   CRUSTAL ACCRETION
RT   CRUSTAL STRUCTURE
RT   CRUSTAL THICKNESS
RT   GEOLOGICAL SURVEYS
RT   MARINE GEOLOGY
RT   OCEAN BASINS
RT   OCEAN FLOOR
RT   OCEANIZATION
RT   OPHIOLITES
RT   SIMA
RT   SUBDUCTION

OCEANIC DESERTS
RT   FERTILITY
RT   GYRES
RT   NUTRIENTS (MINERAL)

OCEANIC DIVERGENCES
BT1   DIVERGENCE ZONES
RT   OCEANIC CONVERGENCES
RT   UPWELLING

OCEANIC EDDIES
SN   Before 1982 search EDDIES (OCEANIC)
UF   eddies (oceanic)
BT1   OCEAN CIRCULATION
BT2   WATER CIRCULATION

OCEANIC EDDIES (cont'd)			**OCEANIZATION** (cont'd)		**OCEANOGRAPHIC EQUIPMENT** (cont'd)

OCEANIC EDDIES (cont'd)
BT3   WATER MOTION
NT1   CURRENT RINGS
NT1   MESOSCALE EDDIES

OCEANIC FRONTS
UF   oceanographic fronts
BT1   FRONTS
NT1   BENTHIC FRONTS
NT1   DENSITY FRONTS
NT1   ESTUARINE FRONT
NT1   SHELF FRONTS
NT2   SHELF EDGE FRONTS
RT   FRONTAL FEATURES
RT   FRONTOGENESIS
RT   SUBTROPICAL CONVERGENCES

OCEANIC ISLANDS
BT1   ISLANDS
BT2   LANDFORMS
BT3   TOPOGRAPHIC FEATURES
NT1   VOLCANIC ISLANDS
RT   ARCHIPELAGIC APRONS
RT   ISLAND ARCS
RT   ISLAND SLOPE
RT   SEAMOATS
RT   SUBMARINE VOLCANOES
RT   VOLCANISM

OCEANIC MICROSTRUCTURE
USE   **MICROSTRUCTURE**

OCEANIC PROVINCE
UF   oceanic region
BT1   PELAGIC ENVIRONMENT
BT2   AQUATIC ENVIRONMENT
BT3   ENVIRONMENTS
NT1   ABYSSOPELAGIC ZONE
NT1   BATHYPELAGIC ZONE
NT1   EPIPELAGIC ZONE
NT1   MESOPELAGIC ZONE
RT   NERITIC PROVINCE

OCEANIC REGION
USE   **OCEANIC PROVINCE**

OCEANIC RESPONSE
UF   response (oceanic)
RT   ATMOSPHERIC FORCING
RT   HURRICANES
RT   RESPONSE TIME

OCEANIC RIDGES
USE   **SUBMARINE RIDGES**

OCEANIC TRENCHES
USE   **TRENCHES (OCEANIC)**

OCEANIC TURBULENCE
BT1   TURBULENCE
BT2   FLUID MOTION
RT   DYE DISPERSION
RT   MICROSTRUCTURE
RT   TURBULENCE MEASUREMENT
RT   TURBULENT DIFFUSION
RT   TURBULENT FLOW
RT   WATER MOTION
RT   WAVE DISSIPATION

OCEANITE
BT1   BASALTS
BT2   VOLCANIC ROCKS
BT3   IGNEOUS ROCKS
BT4   ROCKS

OCEANIZATION
SN   Conversion of continental crust into oceanic crust
RT   CONTINENTAL CRUST
RT   OCEANIC CRUST

OCEANIZATION (cont'd)
RT   PERMANENCE

OCEANODROMOUS MIGRATIONS
BT1   MIGRATIONS
RT   AQUATIC MAMMALS
RT   FEEDING MIGRATIONS
RT   SPAWNING MIGRATIONS

OCEANOGRAPHERS
USE   **MARINE SCIENTISTS**

OCEANOGRAPHIC ATLASES
BT1   ATLASES
BT2   DOCUMENTS
RT   CLIMATOLOGICAL CHARTS
RT   GEOLOGICAL MAPS
RT   HYDROGRAPHIC CHARTS
RT   HYDROGRAPHIC SECTIONS
RT   HYDROGRAPHY
RT   OCEANOGRAPHIC DATA
RT   OCEANOGRAPHY
RT   WAVE CLIMATE

OCEANOGRAPHIC BUOYS
USE   **DATA BUOYS**

OCEANOGRAPHIC CARTOGRAPHY
USE   **CARTOGRAPHY**

OCEANOGRAPHIC CHARTS
USE   **HYDROGRAPHIC CHARTS**

OCEANOGRAPHIC DATA
UF   data (oceanographic)
BT1   DATA
NT1   BATHYMETRIC DATA
NT2   SOUNDINGS
NT1   BATHYTHERMOGRAPHIC DATA
RT   ACOUSTIC DATA
RT   CRUISES
RT   CURRENT DATA
RT   DATA BUOYS
RT   ENVIRONMENTAL CONDITIONS
RT   ENVIRONMENTAL SURVEYS
RT   INSHORE STATIONS
RT   MARSDEN SQUARES
RT   MULTISHIP EXPEDITIONS
RT   OCEAN STATIONS
RT   OCEANOGRAPHIC ATLASES
RT   OCEANOGRAPHIC STATIONS
RT   OCEANOGRAPHIC SURVEYS
RT   OCEANOGRAPHY
RT   SALINITY
RT   SALINITY DATA
RT   SELECTED SHIPS
RT   STANDARD OCEAN SECTIONS
RT   TEMPERATURE DATA
RT   TIME SERIES
RT   WATER SAMPLING
RT   WATER TEMPERATURE
RT   WAVE DATA
RT   WEATHER SHIPS

OCEANOGRAPHIC EQUIPMENT
UF   oceanographic instruments
BT1   EQUIPMENT
RT   BATHYMETERS
RT   BATHYTHERMOGRAPHS
RT   CABLE DEPRESSORS
RT   CALIBRATION
RT   COLLECTING DEVICES
RT   CONDUCTIVITY SENSORS
RT   CTD PROFILERS
RT   CURRENT MEASURING EQUIPMENT
RT   CURRENT METERS
RT   DATA BUOYS
RT   DECK EQUIPMENT
RT   DEPLOYMENT
RT   DEPTH RECORDERS

OCEANOGRAPHIC EQUIPMENT (cont'd)
RT   ENVIRONMENTAL SURVEYS
RT   FLOWMETERS
RT   FREE-FALL INSTRUMENTS
RT   GEK
RT   GEOPHYSICAL EQUIPMENT
RT   HIGH PRESSURE EFFECTS
RT   HYDROGRAPHIC WIRE
RT   LABORATORY EQUIPMENT
RT   MEASURING DEVICES
RT   MESSENGERS
RT   MOORING RECOVERY
RT   MOORING SYSTEMS
RT   NEPHELOMETERS
RT   OCEANOGRAPHIC SURVEYS
RT   OCEANOGRAPHY
RT   PROFILERS
RT   RECORDING EQUIPMENT
RT   RECOVERY
RT   RELEASE MECHANISMS
RT   REMOTE SENSING EQUIPMENT
RT   REVERSING THERMOMETERS
RT   SALINITY MEASURING EQUIPMENT
RT   SALINOMETERS
RT   SAMPLERS
RT   SEDIMENT SAMPLERS
RT   SEDIMENT SAMPLES
RT   SEDIMENT SAMPLING
RT   SEDIMENT TRAPS
RT   SENSORS
RT   SONAR
RT   SONAR ARRAYS
RT   SOUND RECORDERS
RT   SOUNDING LINES
RT   STD PROFILERS
RT   STREAMERS
RT   THERMISTOR CHAINS
RT   THERMOMETERS
RT   TIDE GAUGES
RT   TURBIDIMETERS
RT   UNDULATORS
RT   WATER SAMPLERS
RT   WATER SAMPLING
RT   WAVE MEASURING EQUIPMENT
RT   WINCHES

OCEANOGRAPHIC FRONTS
USE   **OCEANIC FRONTS**

OCEANOGRAPHIC INSTITUTIONS
SN   Before 1982 use OCEANOLOGICAL INSTITUTIONS
UF   oceanological institutions
BT1   RESEARCH INSTITUTIONS
BT2   ORGANIZATIONS
RT   BIOLOGICAL INSTITUTIONS
RT   CRUISES
RT   FISHERY INSTITUTIONS
RT   GEOLOGICAL INSTITUTIONS
RT   MULTISHIP EXPEDITIONS
RT   MUSEUMS
RT   OCEANOGRAPHY
RT   RESEARCH VESSELS
RT   SURVEYS

OCEANOGRAPHIC INSTRUMENTS
USE   **OCEANOGRAPHIC EQUIPMENT**

OCEANOGRAPHIC SATELLITES
USE   **SCIENTIFIC SATELLITES**

OCEANOGRAPHIC STATIONS
SN   Use of a more specific term is recommended
UF   stations (oceanographic)
NT1   CRUISE STATIONS
NT1   DRIFTING STATIONS
NT1   FIXED STATIONS
NT2   INSHORE STATIONS
NT2   OCEAN STATIONS

ASFIS Thesaurus

OCEANOGRAPHIC STATIONS (cont'd)
NT1	STANDARD OCEAN SECTIONS
RT	OCEANOGRAPHIC DATA

OCEANOGRAPHIC SURVEYS
SN	Before 1983 search also ENVIRONMENTAL SURVEYS
BT1	ENVIRONMENTAL SURVEYS
BT2	SURVEYS
RT	CRUISES
RT	ENVIRONMENTAL CONDITIONS
RT	EXPEDITIONS
RT	GEOLOGICAL SURVEYS
RT	HYDROGRAPHY
RT	METEOROLOGY
RT	OCEAN CURRENTS
RT	OCEANOGRAPHIC DATA
RT	OCEANOGRAPHIC EQUIPMENT
RT	OCEANOGRAPHY
RT	RESEARCH VESSELS
RT	SITE SURVEYS
RT	STANDARD OCEAN SECTIONS
RT	WATER SAMPLING

OCEANOGRAPHIC TABLES
BT1	TABLES
BT2	DOCUMENTS
NT1	SALINITY TABLES
RT	CONVERSION TABLES
RT	KNUDSEN TABLES
RT	METEOROLOGICAL TABLES
RT	NAVIGATIONAL TABLES
RT	TIDE TABLES
RT	WATER PROPERTIES

OCEANOGRAPHY
SN	Before 1982 search also OCEANOLOGY
UF	oceanology
BT1	EARTH SCIENCES
NT1	CHEMICAL OCEANOGRAPHY
NT1	COASTAL OCEANOGRAPHY
NT1	DYNAMICAL OCEANOGRAPHY
NT1	FISHERY OCEANOGRAPHY
NT1	MILITARY OCEANOGRAPHY
NT1	PALAEOCEANOGRAPHY
NT1	PHYSICAL OCEANOGRAPHY
NT2	HYDROGRAPHY
NT1	POLAR OCEANOGRAPHY
NT1	RADIO OCEANOGRAPHY
NT1	TROPICAL OCEANOGRAPHY
RT	AQUATIC SCIENCES
RT	BRACKISHWATER ENVIRONMENT
RT	ENVIRONMENTAL SURVEYS
RT	LONG-TERM CHANGES
RT	MARINE ECOLOGY
RT	MARINE ENVIRONMENT
RT	MARINE GEOLOGY
RT	MARINE SCIENCES
RT	MARINE SCIENTISTS
RT	METEOROLOGY
RT	OCEANOGRAPHIC ATLASES
RT	OCEANOGRAPHIC DATA
RT	OCEANOGRAPHIC EQUIPMENT
RT	OCEANOGRAPHIC INSTITUTIONS
RT	OCEANOGRAPHIC SURVEYS
RT	SEA WATER
RT	WATER
RT	WATER ANALYSIS
RT	WATER MASSES
RT	WATER SAMPLING

OCEANOGRAPHY (CHEMICAL)
USE	**CHEMICAL OCEANOGRAPHY**

OCEANOGRAPHY (DYNAMIC)
USE	**DYNAMICAL OCEANOGRAPHY**

OCEANOGRAPHY (FISHERIES)
USE	**FISHERY OCEANOGRAPHY**

OCEANOGRAPHY (PHYSICAL)
USE	**PHYSICAL OCEANOGRAPHY**

OCEANOLOGICAL INSTITUTIONS
USE	**OCEANOGRAPHIC INSTITUTIONS**

OCEANOLOGY
USE	**OCEANOGRAPHY**

OCEANOLOGY (BIOLOGICAL)
USE	**MARINE ECOLOGY**

OCEANS
UF	seas
RT	MARGINAL SEAS
RT	MORPHOMETRY
RT	OCEAN CURRENTS
RT	OCEAN-ATMOSPHERE SYSTEM
RT	UPPER OCEAN
RT	WATER BODIES

OCS
USE	**OUTER CONTINENTAL SHELF**

OCTOPUS FISHERIES
USE	**CEPHALOPOD FISHERIES**

ODOR
USE	**ODOUR**

ODOUR
SN	Before 1982 search ORGANOLEPTIC PROPERTIES
UF	aroma
UF	odor
BT1	ORGANOLEPTIC PROPERTIES
BT2	PROPERTIES
RT	AIR POLLUTION
RT	BIOLOGICAL PROPERTIES
RT	CHEMICAL PROPERTIES
RT	CHLORINATION
RT	DECHLORINATION
RT	FISH WASTES
RT	FISHERY INDUSTRY PLANTS
RT	OLFACTION
RT	POLLUTION EFFECTS
RT	WATER QUALITY

ODOUR IMPRINTING
USE	**IMPRINTING**

OFF-BOTTOM CULTURE
UF	hanging culture
UF	long-line culture
UF	pole culture
UF	rack culture
BT1	AQUACULTURE TECHNIQUES
RT	CULTURES
RT	FOOD ORGANISMS
RT	MOLLUSC CULTURE
RT	MUSSEL CULTURE
RT	OYSTER CULTURE
RT	RAFT CULTURE
RT	SCALLOP CULTURE
RT	SEAWEED CULTURE
RT	SEED COLLECTION
RT	SHELLFISH CULTURE
RT	SPAT

OFFSHORE
SN	Use only as a qualifier
RT	CONTINENTAL SHELVES

OFFSHORE BARS
USE	**NEARSHORE BARS**

OFFSHORE COMPLETION
USE	**WELL COMPLETION**

OFFSHORE DOCKING
BT1	BERTHING
RT	ARTIFICIAL HARBOURS
RT	DEEP-WATER TERMINALS
RT	MARINE TECHNOLOGY
RT	TANKER SHIPS
RT	TANKER TERMINALS

OFFSHORE DRILLING
USE	**DRILLING**

OFFSHORE ENGINEERING
SN	Before 1982 search also MARINE ENGINEERING and OFFSHORE TECHNOLOGY
UF	ocean engineering
UF	offshore technology
UF	seabed engineering
UF	underwater engineering
BT1	ENGINEERING
RT	CORING
RT	DIVING INDUSTRY
RT	DRILLING EQUIPMENT
RT	EXPLOITATION
RT	GEOTECHNOLOGY
RT	MARINE TECHNOLOGY
RT	OFFSHORE STRUCTURES
RT	PETROLEUM ENGINEERING
RT	UNDERWATER EXPLOITATION
RT	UNDERWATER EXPLORATION
RT	UNDERWATER STRUCTURES

OFFSHORE EQUIPMENT
BT1	EQUIPMENT
RT	OFFSHORE OPERATIONS

OFFSHORE OPERATIONS
RT	DEEP-SEA MINING
RT	DRILLING
RT	EXPLOITATION
RT	LOCATIONS (WORKING)
RT	MINERAL EXPLOITATION
RT	MINERAL EXPLORATION
RT	OFFSHORE EQUIPMENT
RT	OIL AND GAS EXPLORATION
RT	TANKER LOADING

OFFSHORE PLATFORMS
USE	**OFFSHORE STRUCTURES**

OFFSHORE PROTECTION
USE	**SURVEILLANCE AND ENFORCEMENT**

OFFSHORE STRUCTURES
SN	Before 1982 search MARINE STRUCTURES
UF	marine structures
UF	offshore platforms
UF	platforms
BT1	HYDRAULIC STRUCTURES
NT1	ARTICULATED COLUMNS
NT1	ARTIFICIAL ISLANDS
NT2	ICE RAFTS
NT2	SAND STRUCTURES
NT1	ARTIFICIAL REEFS
NT1	CAISSONS
NT1	FIXED PLATFORMS
NT2	GRAVITY PLATFORMS
NT2	GUYED TOWERS
NT2	PILED PLATFORMS
NT2	TENSION LEG PLATFORMS
NT1	FLOATING STRUCTURES
NT2	MOBILE PLATFORMS
NT3	JACKUP PLATFORMS
NT3	SEMISUBMERSIBLE PLATFORMS
NT3	SUBMERSIBLE PLATFORMS

OFFSHORE STRUCTURES (cont'd)

NT3	WORKOVER BARGES
NT2	PONTOONS
NT1	UNDERWATER STRUCTURES
NT2	PIPELINES
NT3	FLOWLINES
NT3	GATHERING LINES
NT2	UNDERWATER HABITATS
NT2	WELLHEADS
RT	ACCOMMODATION
RT	ANCHORING
RT	CONCRETE STRUCTURES
RT	DESIGN WAVE
RT	DRILLING PLATFORMS
RT	EARTHQUAKE LOADING
RT	EVACUATION
RT	FLOW AROUND OBJECTS
RT	ICE BARRIERS
RT	ICING
RT	JOINTS
RT	LEE EDDIES
RT	NODE CONSTRUCTION
RT	OFFSHORE ENGINEERING
RT	OIL AND GAS INDUSTRY
RT	PERFORATED STRUCTURES
RT	PRODUCTION PLATFORMS
RT	SETTLEMENT (STRUCTURAL)
RT	SIGNIFICANT WAVE HEIGHT
RT	SPLASH ZONE
RT	STEEL STRUCTURES
RT	STRUCTURAL ENGINEERING
RT	STRUCTURES
RT	SURVEILLANCE AND ENFORCEMENT
RT	WAVE FORCES
RT	WIND PRESSURE
RT	WORK PLATFORMS

OFFSHORE TECHNOLOGY

USE	**OFFSHORE ENGINEERING**

OFFSHORE TERMINALS

BT1	TANKER TERMINALS
BT2	HARBOURS
BT3	ANCHORAGES
RT	BERTHING
RT	LOADING BUOYS
RT	PIPELINES
RT	TANKER LOADING
RT	TANKER SHIPS

OIL

RT	CRUDE OIL
RT	HYDROCARBONS
RT	NATURAL GAS
RT	OIL AND GAS
RT	OIL POLLUTION
RT	PETROLEUM

OIL AND GAS

RT	HYDROCARBONS
RT	OIL
RT	OIL AND GAS EXPLORATION
RT	OIL AND GAS FIELDS
RT	OIL AND GAS INDUSTRY
RT	OIL AND GAS LEGISLATION
RT	OIL AND GAS PRODUCTION
RT	PETROLEUM

OIL AND GAS EXPLORATION

UF	exploratory drilling
BT1	RESOURCE EXPLORATION
BT2	EXPLORATION
RT	CONCESSIONS
RT	DRILLING
RT	GEOPHYSICAL DATA
RT	GEOPHYSICAL EXPLORATION
RT	LEASES
RT	OFFSHORE OPERATIONS
RT	OIL AND GAS
RT	OIL AND GAS FIELDS

OIL AND GAS EXPLORATION (cont'd)

RT	OIL AND GAS INDUSTRY
RT	PETROLEUM GEOLOGY

OIL AND GAS FIELDS

NT1	GAS CONDENSATE FIELDS
NT1	GAS FIELDS
NT1	MARGINAL FIELDS
NT1	OIL FIELDS
RT	OIL AND GAS
RT	OIL AND GAS EXPLORATION
RT	OIL AND GAS INDUSTRY
RT	OIL AND GAS PRODUCTION
RT	PETROLEUM
RT	SURVEILLANCE AND ENFORCEMENT

OIL AND GAS INDUSTRY

SN	Before 1982 search OIL INDUSTRY
UF	gas industry
UF	oil industry
UF	petroleum industry
BT1	INDUSTRIES
RT	DIVING INDUSTRY
RT	EXPLOITATION
RT	FUELS
RT	GAS TERMINALS
RT	MARINE TECHNOLOGY
RT	OFFSHORE STRUCTURES
RT	OIL AND GAS
RT	OIL AND GAS EXPLORATION
RT	OIL AND GAS FIELDS
RT	OIL AND GAS LEGISLATION
RT	OIL AND GAS PRODUCTION
RT	OIL POLLUTION
RT	OIL REFINERIES
RT	OIL WASTES
RT	PETROLEUM
RT	PETROLEUM GEOLOGY
RT	PROCESS PLANTS
RT	TANKER LOADING

OIL AND GAS LEGISLATION

BT1	LEGISLATION
RT	CONCESSIONS
RT	LABOUR
RT	OIL AND GAS
RT	OIL AND GAS INDUSTRY

OIL AND GAS PRODUCTION

SN	Pertains to petroleum production
UF	exploitation (oil and gas)
UF	production (oil and gas)
NT1	GAS PRODUCTION
NT1	OIL PRODUCTION
RT	GAS OIL SEPARATION
RT	GAS PROCESSING
RT	MARGINAL FIELDS
RT	OIL AND GAS
RT	OIL AND GAS FIELDS
RT	OIL AND GAS INDUSTRY
RT	OIL RECOVERY
RT	OIL TREATING
RT	OIL WELLS
RT	PRODUCTION PLATFORMS
RT	SUBSEA PRODUCTION SYSTEMS
RT	WELL WORKOVER OPERATIONS

OIL BARRIERS

USE	**OIL REMOVAL**

OIL BOOMS

USE	**FLOATING BARRIERS**

OIL EXTRACTION (ANIMAL)

USE	**ANIMAL OIL EXTRACTION**

OIL FIELDS

BT1	OIL AND GAS FIELDS
RT	OIL PRODUCTION
RT	OIL RESERVOIRS

OIL FILMS

USE	**SURFACE FILMS**

OIL-GAS INTERFACE

UF	gas-oil interface
BT1	INTERFACES
RT	GASES
RT	NATURAL GAS
RT	OIL-WATER INTERFACE
RT	PETROLEUM

OIL GAS SEPARATION

USE	**GAS OIL SEPARATION**

OIL-GAS SEPARATION

USE	**GAS OIL SEPARATION**

OIL-ICE INTERFACE

USE	**ICE-OIL INTERFACE**

OIL IN WATER CONTENT

RT	EMULSIONS
RT	OIL PRODUCTION
RT	OIL-WATER INTERFACE

OIL INDUSTRY

USE	**OIL AND GAS INDUSTRY**

OIL LEAKS

USE	**OIL SPILLS**

OIL POLLUTION

UF	pollution (oil)
BT1	POLLUTION
RT	BRACKISHWATER POLLUTION
RT	DISPERSANTS
RT	FRESHWATER POLLUTION
RT	ICE-OIL INTERFACE
RT	MARINE POLLUTION
RT	OIL
RT	OIL AND GAS INDUSTRY
RT	OIL REFINERIES
RT	OIL REMOVAL
RT	OIL SEEPAGES
RT	OIL SLICKS
RT	OIL SPILLS
RT	OIL WASTES
RT	OIL WELLS
RT	PIPELINES
RT	POLLUTION CONTROL
RT	SEDIMENT POLLUTION
RT	TANKER LOADING
RT	TANKER SHIPS
RT	TAR BALLS
RT	WATER POLLUTION

OIL POTENTIAL

USE	**OIL RESERVES**

OIL PROCESSING

USE	**OIL TREATING**

OIL PRODUCTION

SN	Pertains to surface equipment and methods used to produce oil from underground reservoirs
UF	crude oil production
BT1	OIL AND GAS PRODUCTION
RT	CRUDE OIL
RT	OIL FIELDS
RT	OIL IN WATER CONTENT
RT	OIL RESERVES

OIL RECOVERY
RT	CRUDE OIL
RT	OIL AND GAS PRODUCTION

OIL REFINERIES
UF	refineries
RT	OIL AND GAS INDUSTRY
RT	OIL POLLUTION
RT	OIL TANKS
RT	PORT INSTALLATIONS
RT	PROCESS PLANTS
RT	TANKER TERMINALS

OIL REMOVAL
SN	Oil removal in aquatic environment by mechanical or chemical techniques. Before 1982 search also SKIMMERS and OIL SKIMMERS
UF	clean-up techniques
UF	oil barriers
UF	oil removers
UF	oil skimmers
UF	skimmers (oil removal)
RT	ADSORPTION
RT	DISPERSANTS
RT	FLOATING BARRIERS
RT	OIL POLLUTION
RT	OIL SLICKS
RT	OIL SPILLS
RT	SOLVENTS
RT	WATER POLLUTION TREATMENT

OIL REMOVERS
USE	**OIL REMOVAL**

OIL RESERVES
UF	oil potential
RT	ENERGY RESOURCES
RT	OIL PRODUCTION
RT	OIL RESERVOIRS

OIL RESERVOIRS
UF	reservoirs (oil)
RT	CAP ROCKS
RT	OIL FIELDS
RT	OIL RESERVES
RT	PETROLEUM GEOLOGY

OIL RIGS
USE	**DRILLING RIGS**

OIL SANDS
UF	tar sands
BT1	SANDSTONE
BT2	CLASTICS
BT3	SEDIMENTS
RT	ASPHALT
RT	BITUMENS
RT	HYDROCARBONS
RT	OIL SHALE
RT	PETROLEUM RESIDUES
RT	SUBSURFACE DEPOSITS
RT	TAR

OIL SEALS
USE	**SEALS (STOPPERS)**

OIL SEEPAGES
BT1	SEEPAGES
RT	OIL POLLUTION
RT	OIL WELLS
RT	UNDERWATER EXPLOITATION

OIL SHALE
BT1	SHALE
BT2	CLASTICS
BT3	SEDIMENTS
RT	HYDROCARBONS
RT	KEROGEN
RT	OIL SANDS

OIL SHALE (cont'd)
RT	PETROLEUM RESIDUES
RT	SAPROPELITE
RT	SUBSURFACE DEPOSITS

OIL SKIMMERS
USE	**OIL REMOVAL**

OIL SLICKS
SN	Layers of oily substances on water surface. Before 1982 search also SLICKS
UF	slicks (oil)
RT	CONTAINMENT
RT	OIL POLLUTION
RT	OIL REMOVAL
RT	OIL SPILLS
RT	OIL WASTES
RT	PETROLEUM
RT	SLICKS
RT	SURFACE FILMS
RT	SURFACE MICROLAYER

OIL SPILLS
SN	Spilling from tankers, pipelines and drilling operations
UF	leaks (oil)
UF	oil leaks
BT1	ACCIDENTS
RT	CONTAINMENT
RT	DISPERSANTS
RT	DRILLING
RT	FIRE
RT	FIRE HAZARDS
RT	ICE-OIL INTERFACE
RT	OIL POLLUTION
RT	OIL REMOVAL
RT	OIL SLICKS
RT	OIL WASTES
RT	PIPELINES
RT	SHIP LOSSES
RT	TANK CLEANING
RT	TANKER LOADING
RT	TANKER SHIPS

OIL TANKERS
USE	**TANKER SHIPS**

OIL TANKS
BT1	TANKS
BT2	CONTAINERS
RT	OIL REFINERIES
RT	TANKER TERMINALS
RT	UNDERWATER STRUCTURES

OIL TERMINALS
USE	**TANKER TERMINALS**

OIL TREATING
SN	Pertains to field operations
UF	crude oil treating
UF	oil processing
RT	GAS FLARING
RT	OIL AND GAS PRODUCTION
RT	SEPARATION
RT	SEPARATION PROCESSES

OIL WASTES
BT1	WASTES
RT	BIODEGRADATION
RT	FUELS
RT	INDUSTRIAL WASTES
RT	OIL AND GAS INDUSTRY
RT	OIL POLLUTION
RT	OIL SLICKS
RT	OIL SPILLS
RT	PETROLEUM

OIL-WATER INTERFACE
UF	water-oil interface
BT1	INTERFACES
RT	OIL IN WATER CONTENT
RT	OIL-GAS INTERFACE
RT	PETROLEUM
RT	WATER

OIL WATER SEPARATION
UF	water oil separation
BT1	SEPARATION
RT	ADSORPTION
RT	POLLUTION CONTROL
RT	WATER TREATMENT

OIL WELLS
UF	wells (oil and gas)
RT	DRILLING
RT	EXPLOITATION
RT	OIL AND GAS PRODUCTION
RT	OIL POLLUTION
RT	OIL SEEPAGES
RT	PETROLEUM
RT	PIPELINES
RT	UNDERWATER EXPLOITATION
RT	WELL COMPLETION

OILS (FISH)
USE	**FISH OILS**

OLEIC ACID
BT1	ORGANIC ACIDS
BT2	ORGANIC COMPOUNDS

OLFACTION
BT1	SENSE FUNCTIONS
RT	ALARM SUBSTANCES
RT	CHEMORECEPTORS
RT	ODOUR
RT	OLFACTORY ORGANS
RT	ORGANOLEPTIC PROPERTIES

OLFACTORY ORGANS
BT1	SENSE ORGANS
BT2	ANIMAL ORGANS
BT3	BODY ORGANS
RT	CHEMICAL STIMULI
RT	CHEMORECEPTION
RT	CHEMORECEPTORS
RT	CHEMOTAXIS
RT	OLFACTION

OLFACTORY STIMULI
USE	**CHEMICAL STIMULI**

OLIGOCENE
BT1	PALAEOGENE
BT2	TERTIARY
BT3	CENOZOIC
BT4	GEOLOGICAL TIME

OLIGOTROPHIC LAKES
BT1	LAKES
BT2	INLAND WATERS
RT	DYSTROPHIC LAKES
RT	EUTROPHIC LAKES
RT	NUTRIENT DEFICIENCY

OLISTOLITHS
BT1	SEDIMENTARY STRUCTURES
RT	ALLOCHTHONOUS DEPOSITS
RT	OLISTOSTROMES
RT	SEDIMENTS
RT	SLUMP STRUCTURES
RT	SLUMPING
RT	TURBIDITY CURRENT STRUCTURES

ASFIS Thesaurus

OLISTOSTROMES
RT	DEBRIS FLOW
RT	MELANGES
RT	OLISTOLITHS
RT	SEDIMENTARY STRUCTURES
RT	SLUMP STRUCTURES
RT	TURBIDITY CURRENT STRUCTURES

OLIVINE
BT1	SILICATE MINERALS
BT2	MINERALS

OMEGA
BT1	RADIO NAVIGATION
BT2	POSITION FIXING
RT	NAVIGATIONAL TABLES

OMNIVORES
BT1	HETEROTROPHIC ORGANISMS
BT2	AQUATIC ORGANISMS
RT	CARNIVORES
RT	DETRITUS FEEDERS
RT	FEEDING BEHAVIOUR
RT	HERBIVORES
RT	TROPHIC LEVELS

ONE-ATMOSPHERE SYSTEMS
RT	DEEP-SEA DIVING
RT	DIVING BELLS
RT	DIVING SUITS
RT	LIFE SUPPORT SYSTEMS
RT	MANNED VEHICLES

ONSHORE CURRENTS
USE	**NEARSHORE CURRENTS**

ONTOGENY
RT	BIOLOGICAL DEVELOPMENT
RT	DEVELOPMENTAL STAGES
RT	EMBRYOLOGY
RT	LIFE CYCLE
RT	MORPHOGENESIS
RT	ORGANOGENESIS
RT	PHYLOGENY

OOGENESIS
UF	ovogenesis
BT1	GAMETOGENESIS
BT2	MORPHOGENESIS
RT	EGGS
RT	OVARIES
RT	SEXUAL CELLS
RT	VITELLOGENESIS

OOIDS
RT	CONCRETIONS
RT	OOLITES

OOLITES
RT	CONCRETIONS
RT	LIMESTONE
RT	OOIDS

OOSPORES
USE	**SPORES**

OOZE (CALCAREOUS)
USE	**CALCAREOUS OOZE**

OOZE (SILICEOUS)
USE	**SILICEOUS OOZE**

OOZES
NT1	CALCAREOUS OOZE
NT2	FORAMINIFERAL OOZE
NT3	GLOBIGERINA OOZE
NT2	PTEROPOD OOZE
NT1	SILICEOUS OOZE
NT2	DIATOM OOZE
NT2	RADIOLARIAN OOZE

OOZES (cont'd)
RT	BIOGENIC DEPOSITS
RT	FOSSIL DIATOMS
RT	FOSSIL FORAMINIFERA
RT	MUD
RT	PELAGIC SEDIMENTS
RT	SAPROPELS
RT	SEDIMENTS
RT	SHELLS

OPAL
UF	opaline
BT1	SILICATE MINERALS
BT2	MINERALS

OPALINE
USE	**OPAL**

OPEN ACCESS RESOURCES
USE	**COMMON PROPERTY RESOURCES**

OPEN CHANNEL FLOW
USE	**CHANNEL FLOW**

OPEN MINES
USE	**PITS**

OPEN RUNNING WATER CULTURE
USE	**OPEN SYSTEMS**

OPEN SEA AQUACULTURE
USE	**MARINE AQUACULTURE**

OPEN SYSTEMS
SN	An aquaculture water system in which water continuously flows through the culture area and is discharged after a single pass. Added in 1980
UF	open running water culture
BT1	AQUACULTURE SYSTEMS
RT	COOLING SYSTEMS
RT	OTEC PLANTS
RT	THERMAL AQUACULTURE
RT	WASTEWATER AQUACULTURE

OPERATING COSTS
USE	**OPERATIONAL COSTS**

OPERATIONAL COSTS
SN	Added in 1980
UF	manufacturing costs
UF	operating costs
BT1	COSTS
RT	TAXES

OPERATIONS RESEARCH
NT1	CRITICAL PATH METHOD
NT1	GAME THEORY
NT1	MATHEMATICAL PROGRAMMING
NT2	LINEAR PROGRAMMING
NT1	PERT
RT	ECONOMIC MODELS
RT	FEASIBILITY
RT	FEASIBILITY STUDIES
RT	MANAGEMENT
RT	MATHEMATICAL MODELS
RT	PLANNING
RT	PROBABILITY THEORY
RT	RESOURCES
RT	SIMULATION
RT	STATISTICAL MODELS
RT	STOCHASTIC PROCESSES
RT	SYSTEM ANALYSIS

OPHIOLITE COMPLEXES
USE	**OPHIOLITES**

OPHIOLITES
UF	ophiolite complexes
BT1	ULTRAMAFIC ROCKS
BT2	IGNEOUS ROCKS
BT3	ROCKS
RT	GEOSYNCLINES
RT	OCEANIC CRUST
RT	PLATE TECTONICS

OPTICAL CLASSIFICATION
SN	Optical classification of water masses
RT	EXTINCTION COEFFICIENT
RT	IRRADIANCE
RT	OPTICAL PROPERTIES
RT	OPTICAL WATER TYPES
RT	SCATTERING COEFFICIENT
RT	WATER MASSES

OPTICAL FILTERS
BT1	FILTERS
RT	CAMERAS
RT	LIGHT ABSORPTION
RT	LIGHT TRANSMISSION
RT	OPTICAL INSTRUMENTS

OPTICAL INSTRUMENTS
RT	LIGHT MEASURING INSTRUMENTS
RT	OPTICAL FILTERS
RT	OPTICS

OPTICAL MASERS
USE	**LASERS**

OPTICAL MICROSCOPES
USE	**MICROSCOPES**

OPTICAL MICROSCOPY
USE	**LIGHT MICROSCOPY**

OPTICAL PROPERTIES
BT1	PHYSICAL PROPERTIES
BT2	PROPERTIES
NT1	ABSORPTANCE
NT1	ANGULAR DISTRIBUTION
NT1	ATTENUANCE
NT1	COLOUR
NT2	WATER COLOUR
NT1	EXTINCTION COEFFICIENT
NT1	REFLECTANCE
NT1	REFRACTIVE INDEX
NT1	SCATTERING COEFFICIENT
NT1	SPECTRAL COMPOSITION
NT1	TRANSMITTANCE
NT2	BEAM TRANSMITTANCE
NT1	TRANSPARENCY
NT2	WATER TRANSPARENCY
NT1	VOLUME SCATTERING FUNCTION
RT	ABSORPTION COEFFICIENT
RT	ALBEDO
RT	ANISOTROPY
RT	COLORIMETRIC TECHNIQUES
RT	EMISSIVITY
RT	IRRADIANCE
RT	LIGHT
RT	LIGHT EFFECTS
RT	LIGHT INTENSITY
RT	LIGHT MICROSCOPY
RT	LIGHT PENETRATION
RT	LIGHT REFLECTION
RT	LIGHT REFRACTION
RT	LUMINESCENCE
RT	OPTICAL CLASSIFICATION
RT	OPTICS
RT	ORIENTATION
RT	POLARIZATION
RT	RADIANCE
RT	SOLAR RADIATION
RT	SURFACE PROPERTIES
RT	TURBIDITY

ASFIS Thesaurus

OPTICAL WATER TYPES		**ORGANIC ACIDS** (cont'd)		**ORGANIC COMPOUNDS** (cont'd)	
BT1	WATER TYPES	NT2	THREONINE	NT4	DDT
BT2	WATER MASSES	NT2	TYROSINE	NT4	DIELDRIN
RT	IRRADIANCE	NT2	VALINE	NT4	TRICHLOROETHYLENE
RT	OPTICAL CLASSIFICATION	NT1	ARACHIDONIC ACID	NT3	FLUORINATED HYDROCARBONS
RT	TRANSMITTANCE	NT1	FATTY ACIDS	NT4	FREONS
		NT2	POLYUNSATURATED FATTY ACIDS	NT2	PETROLEUM HYDROCARBONS
OPTICS		NT1	FULVIC ACIDS	NT3	ASPHALT
BT1	PHYSICS	NT1	FUMARIC ACID	NT3	BITUMENS
RT	ATMOSPHERIC OPTICAL PHENOMENA	NT1	GLYCOLIC ACID	NT3	KEROGEN
RT	FIBRE OPTICS	NT1	HUMIC ACIDS	NT3	TAR
RT	LASERS	NT1	NICOTINIC ACID	NT3	VOLATILE HYDROCARBONS
RT	LIGHT	NT1	NUCLEIC ACIDS	NT2	SATURATED HYDROCARBONS
RT	OPTICAL INSTRUMENTS	NT2	DNA	NT3	ACYCLIC HYDROCARBONS
RT	OPTICAL PROPERTIES	NT2	RNA	NT4	BUTANE
RT	PHOTOGRAPHY	NT1	OLEIC ACID	NT4	DODECANE
RT	VISIBILITY	RT	ALGINATES	NT4	ETHANE
RT	VISION	RT	CHEMICAL COMPOUNDS	NT4	METHANE
		RT	INORGANIC ACIDS	NT4	PROPANE
ORBITAL VELOCITY		RT	NUCLEOTIDES	NT3	ALICYCLIC HYDROCARBONS
UF	particle velocity (waves)			NT2	UNSATURATED HYDROCARBONS
UF	wave particle velocity	**ORGANIC CARBON**		NT3	ALKENES
BT1	VELOCITY	BT1	CARBON	NT4	ETHENE
RT	NEAR-SURFACE LAYER	BT2	CHEMICAL ELEMENTS	NT3	ALKYNES
RT	PARTICLE MOTION	NT1	DISSOLVED ORGANIC CARBON	NT4	ETHYNE
RT	WATER WAVES	NT1	PARTICULATE ORGANIC CARBON	NT3	AROMATIC HYDROCARBONS
RT	WAVE DRIFT VELOCITY	NT1	TOTAL ORGANIC CARBON	NT3	BENZENE
RT	WAVE VELOCITY			NT4	NAPHTHALENE
		ORGANIC COMPOUNDS		NT4	PCB
ORDOVICIAN		UF	compounds (organic)	NT4	XYLENE
SN	Before 1982 search ORDOVICIAN SYSTEM	NT1	ALCOHOLS	NT3	POLYUNSATURATED HYDROCARBONS
BT1	PALAEOZOIC	NT2	CHOLINE	NT4	SQUALENE
BT2	GEOLOGICAL TIME	NT2	GLYCEROL	NT4	TERPENES
		NT1	ALDEHYDES	NT1	KETONES
ORE CARRIERS		NT1	ALKALOIDS	NT2	ACETONE
USE	**BULK CARRIERS**	NT1	AMINES	NT1	LIPIDS
		NT2	HEXOSAMINES	NT2	COMPLEX LIPIDS
ORES		NT3	GLUCOSAMINE	NT2	DERIVED LIPIDS
BT1	MINERAL RESOURCES	NT2	HYDROXYLAMINES	NT2	FATS
BT2	NATURAL RESOURCES	NT2	NITROSAMINES	NT2	STEROIDS
BT3	RESOURCES	NT2	PYRROLIDINE	NT3	STEROLS
RT	MINERAL DEPOSITS	NT1	AZINES	NT4	ACANSTEROL
RT	SHEAR ZONE	NT2	PYRIDINES	NT4	CHOLESTEROL
RT	SUBSURFACE DEPOSITS	NT2	PYRIMIDINES	NT4	FUCOSTEROL
		NT2	QUINOLINES	NT4	SITOSTEROLS
ORGAN REMOVAL		NT1	CARBOHYDRATES	NT2	WAXES
SN	Added in 1980	NT2	GLYCOGEN	NT1	NUCLEOTIDES
NT1	CASTRATION	NT2	GLYCOSIDES	NT2	ADP
NT1	EYESTALK EXTIRPATION	NT3	PIGMENTS	NT2	AMP
NT1	HYPOPHYSECTOMY	NT4	CHROMATIC PIGMENTS	NT2	ATP
RT	ANIMAL PHYSIOLOGY	NT4	PHOTOSYNTHETIC PIGMENTS	NT1	ORGANIC ACIDS
RT	BODY ORGANS	NT4	RESPIRATORY PIGMENTS	NT2	ACRYLIC ACID
RT	EXPERIMENTAL RESEARCH	NT4	VISUAL PIGMENTS	NT2	AMINO ACIDS
RT	REGENERATION	NT3	PORPHYRINS	NT3	ALANINE
RT	REMOVAL	NT3	SAPONINS	NT3	ARGININE
RT	TRANSPLANTS	NT2	SACCHARIDES	NT3	ASPARTIC ACID
		NT3	MONOSACCHARIDES	NT3	CYSTEINE
ORGANELLES		NT4	ARABINOSE	NT3	CYSTINE
USE	**CELL ORGANELLES**	NT4	FUCOSE	NT3	GLUTAMIC ACID
		NT4	GLUCOSE	NT3	GLYCINE
ORGANIC ACIDS		NT4	MANNOSE	NT3	LEUCINE
UF	acids (organic)	NT4	RIBOSE	NT3	LYSINE
UF	carboxylic acids	NT4	XYLOSE	NT3	METHIONINE
BT1	ORGANIC COMPOUNDS	NT3	POLYSACCHARIDES	NT3	ORNITHINE
NT1	ACRYLIC ACID	NT4	AGAROSE	NT3	PHENYLALANINE
NT1	AMINO ACIDS	NT4	ALGINIC ACID	NT3	PROLINE
NT2	ALANINE	NT4	CELLULOSE	NT3	SERINE
NT2	ARGININE	NT4	MUCOPOLYSACCHARIDES	NT3	THREONINE
NT2	ASPARTIC ACID	NT4	STARCH	NT3	TYROSINE
NT2	CYSTEINE	NT1	ESTERS	NT3	VALINE
NT2	CYSTINE	NT2	PHTHALATE ESTERS	NT2	ARACHIDONIC ACID
NT2	GLUTAMIC ACID	NT1	HISTAMINES	NT2	FATTY ACIDS
NT2	GLYCINE	NT1	HYDROCARBONS	NT3	POLYUNSATURATED FATTY ACIDS
NT2	LEUCINE	NT2	GAS HYDRATES	NT2	FULVIC ACIDS
NT2	LYSINE	NT2	HALOGENATED HYDROCARBONS	NT2	FUMARIC ACID
NT2	METHIONINE	NT3	BROMINATED HYDROCARBONS	NT2	GLYCOLIC ACID
NT2	ORNITHINE	NT3	CHLORINATED HYDROCARBONS	NT2	HUMIC ACIDS
NT2	PHENYLALANINE	NT4	ALDRIN	NT2	NICOTINIC ACID
NT2	PROLINE	NT4	CHLOROFORM	NT2	NUCLEIC ACIDS
NT2	SERINE	NT4	DDE	NT3	DNA

ORGANIC COMPOUNDS (cont'd)	
NT3	RNA
NT2	OLEIC ACID
NT1	ORGANOMETALLIC COMPOUNDS
NT2	METHYL MERCURY
NT1	PROTEINS
NT2	ACTIN
NT2	ALBUMINS
NT2	GLOBULINS
NT2	GLYCOPROTEINS
NT2	HISTONES
NT2	LIPOPROTEINS
NT2	LUCIFERIN
NT2	MUCINS
NT2	MYOGLOBINS
NT2	MYOSIN
NT2	PEPTIDES
NT3	POLYPEPTIDES
NT2	PEPTONES
NT2	SINGLE CELL PROTEINS
NT1	PURINES
NT1	UREA
RT	AROMATICS
RT	BORON COMPOUNDS
RT	CARBON COMPOUNDS
RT	CHELATES
RT	CHEMICAL COMPOUNDS
RT	CHLORINE COMPOUNDS
RT	DETRITUS
RT	FLUORINE COMPOUNDS
RT	HALOGEN COMPOUNDS
RT	NITROGEN COMPOUNDS
RT	ORGANIC CONSTITUENTS
RT	ORGANOMETALLIC COMPLEXES
RT	PHOSPHORUS COMPOUNDS
RT	SUSPENDED ORGANIC MATTER

ORGANIC CONSTITUENTS
SN	Any organic components of biological material
RT	AMINO ACIDS
RT	BIOCHEMICAL ANALYSIS
RT	BIOCHEMICAL COMPOSITION
RT	CARBOHYDRATES
RT	FATS
RT	ORGANIC COMPOUNDS
RT	PROTEINS

ORGANIC DETRITUS
USE	DETRITUS

ORGANIC MATTER
NT1	DISSOLVED ORGANIC MATTER
NT1	HUMUS
NT1	PARTICULATE ORGANIC MATTER
NT1	SUSPENDED ORGANIC MATTER
RT	ANOXIC SEDIMENTS
RT	HUMUS
RT	KEROGEN
RT	PEAT
RT	SAPROBIONTS
RT	SAPROPLANKTON
RT	SAPROZOITES

ORGANIC NITROGEN
BT1	NITROGEN
BT2	CHEMICAL ELEMENTS
NT1	DISSOLVED ORGANIC NITROGEN
NT1	PARTICULATE ORGANIC NITROGEN
RT	NITROGEN COMPOUNDS

ORGANIC PHOSPHORUS
BT1	PHOSPHORUS
BT2	CHEMICAL ELEMENTS
NT1	DISSOLVED ORGANIC PHOSPHORUS
NT1	PARTICULATE ORGANIC PHOSPHORUS
RT	PHOSPHORUS COMPOUNDS

ORGANIC PRODUCTION
USE	BIOLOGICAL PRODUCTION

ORGANIC SEDIMENTS
UF	carbonaceous deposits
BT1	BIOGENIC DEPOSITS
NT1	PEAT
NT1	SAPROPELS
RT	CHEMICAL SEDIMENTS
RT	PETROLEUM

ORGANIC SUSPENDED MATTER
USE	SUSPENDED ORGANIC MATTER

ORGANIC WASTES
SN	Added in 1980
UF	animal wastes
BT1	WASTES
RT	DOMESTIC WASTES
RT	FISH WASTES
RT	SEWAGE
RT	SLUDGE
RT	WATER POLLUTION
RT	WATER QUALITY

ORGANISATIONS
USE	ORGANIZATIONS

ORGANISM AGGREGATIONS
SN	A grouping or crowding of separate organisms. Added in 1980
UF	aggregations (organisms)
RT	AQUATIC COMMUNITIES
RT	AQUATIC ORGANISMS
RT	ECOLOGY

ORGANISM ASSOCIATIONS
USE	ECOLOGICAL ASSOCIATIONS

ORGANISM DATING
USE	AGE DETERMINATION

ORGANISM GUIDING
USE	GUIDING DEVICES

ORGANISM MORPHOLOGY
SN	Before 1982 search MORPHOLOGY (ORGANISMS)
UF	external anatomy
UF	morphology (biology)
UF	morphology (organisms)
BT1	BIOLOGY
NT1	ANIMAL MORPHOLOGY
NT1	CELL MORPHOLOGY
NT1	PLANT MORPHOLOGY
RT	ANATOMY
RT	BIOPOLYMORPHISM
RT	COMPARATIVE STUDIES
RT	FUNCTIONAL MORPHOLOGY
RT	ILLUSTRATIONS
RT	MORPHOGENESIS
RT	NUMERICAL TAXONOMY
RT	PHENOTYPES
RT	SEXUAL DIMORPHISM
RT	TAXONOMY

ORGANISMS (AQUATIC)
USE	AQUATIC ORGANISMS

ORGANIZATIONS
UF	associations
UF	organisations
UF	societies
NT1	COMPANIES
NT1	EDUCATION ESTABLISHMENTS
NT1	FINANCIAL INSTITUTIONS
NT1	FISHERY ORGANIZATIONS
NT2	COOPERATIVES
NT1	INFORMATION CENTRES
NT2	DATA CENTRES

ORGANIZATIONS (cont'd)	
NT2	LIBRARIES
NT2	MUSEUMS
NT2	WARNING SERVICES
NT3	STORM TIDE WARNING SERVICES
NT1	INTERNATIONAL ORGANIZATIONS
NT1	RESEARCH INSTITUTIONS
NT2	BIOLOGICAL INSTITUTIONS
NT2	FISHERY INSTITUTIONS
NT2	GEOLOGICAL INSTITUTIONS
NT2	LIMNOLOGICAL INSTITUTIONS
NT2	OCEANOGRAPHIC INSTITUTIONS
NT1	SORTING CENTRES
NT1	TRADE ORGANIZATIONS
NT1	WATER AUTHORITIES
RT	ACRONYMS
RT	ANNUAL REPORTS
RT	CONFERENCES
RT	DIRECTORIES
RT	GRANTS
RT	INSTITUTIONAL RESOURCES
RT	PERSONNEL

ORGANOGENESIS
SN	The formation and development of organs. Added in 1980
UF	organogeny
RT	BODY ORGANS
RT	EMBRYOLOGY
RT	MORPHOGENESIS
RT	ONTOGENY
RT	VITELLOGENESIS

ORGANOGENY
USE	ORGANOGENESIS

ORGANOLEPTIC PROPERTIES
BT1	PROPERTIES
NT1	DIGESTIBILITY
NT1	ODOUR
NT1	TASTE
RT	ACCEPTANCE TESTS
RT	BIOLOGICAL PROPERTIES
RT	CODEX STANDARDS
RT	COLOUR
RT	FISH FLOUR
RT	FISH SPOILAGE
RT	FOOD FISH
RT	HUMAN FOOD
RT	MINCED PRODUCTS
RT	OLFACTION
RT	PALATABILITY
RT	POWDERED PRODUCTS
RT	QUALITY CONTROL
RT	REPELLENTS
RT	TASTE FUNCTIONS
RT	TASTE TESTS
RT	WATER PROPERTIES
RT	WATER QUALITY

ORGANOMETALLIC COMPLEXES
RT	LIGANDS
RT	METALS
RT	ORGANIC COMPOUNDS

ORGANOMETALLIC COMPOUNDS
BT1	ORGANIC COMPOUNDS
NT1	METHYL MERCURY
RT	MERCURY COMPOUNDS

ORGANS (ANIMAL)
USE	ANIMAL ORGANS

ORGANS (BODY)
USE	BODY ORGANS

ORGANS (PLANT)
USE   **PLANT ORGANS**

ORIENTATION
SN   For biological purposes use
        ORIENTATION BEHAVIOUR
NT1   CORE ORIENTATION
NT1   GRAIN ORIENTATION
RT   ANIMAL NAVIGATION
RT   ANISOTROPY
RT   BIOTELEMETRY
RT   ISOTROPY
RT   MIGRATIONS
RT   OPTICAL PROPERTIES
RT   ORIENTATION BEHAVIOUR
RT   POLARIZATION
RT   SENSE ORGANS
RT   STIMULI
RT   VERTICAL MIGRATIONS

ORIENTATION (BIOLOGICAL)
USE   **ORIENTATION BEHAVIOUR**

ORIENTATION BEHAVIOUR
UF   animal orientation
UF   orientation (biological)
BT1   BEHAVIOUR
NT1   KINESIS
NT1   TAXIS
NT2   CHEMOTAXIS
NT2   PHOTOTAXIS
NT2   RHEOTAXIS
RT   ANTENNAE
RT   MIGRATIONS
RT   ORIENTATION
RT   SENSE FUNCTIONS
RT   SENSE ORGANS
RT   STIMULI
RT   TROPISM

ORMER FISHERIES
USE   **GASTROPOD FISHERIES**

ORNAMENTAL FISH
UF   aquarium fish
BT1   FISH
BT2   AQUATIC ANIMALS
RT   AQUARIA
RT   AQUARIOLOGY
RT   AQUARIUM CULTURE
RT   CAPTIVITY
RT   TROPICAL FISH
RT   WARM-WATER AQUACULTURE

ORNITHINE
BT1   AMINO ACIDS
BT2   ORGANIC ACIDS
BT3   ORGANIC COMPOUNDS

ORNITHOLOGISTS
BT1   ZOOLOGISTS
BT2   BIOLOGISTS
BT3   SCIENTIFIC PERSONNEL
BT4   PERSONNEL
RT   AQUATIC BIRDS
RT   DIRECTORIES
RT   ORNITHOLOGY

ORNITHOLOGY
SN   Added in 1980
BT1   VERTEBRATE ZOOLOGY
BT2   ZOOLOGY
BT3   BIOLOGY
RT   AQUATIC BIRDS
RT   MARINE BIRDS
RT   ORNITHOLOGISTS

OROGENESIS
USE   **OROGENY**

OROGENY
UF   mountain building
UF   orogenesis
BT1   TECTONICS
BT2   GEOLOGY
BT3   EARTH SCIENCES
RT   ACTIVE MARGINS
RT   EPEIROGENY
RT   GEOSYNCLINES
RT   MOUNTAINS
RT   PLATE TECTONICS
RT   RIFTING

ORTHOCLASE
BT1   FELDSPARS
BT2   SILICATE MINERALS
BT3   MINERALS

ORTHOGONALS
RT   CAUSTICS
RT   WAVE REFRACTION DIAGRAMS

ORTHOPHOSPHATE
BT1   PHOSPHATES
BT2   PHOSPHORUS COMPOUNDS

ORTHOTIDES
BT1   EQUILIBRIUM TIDES
BT2   TIDES
BT3   TIDAL MOTION
RT   RESPONSE ANALYSIS

OSCILLATIONS
NT1   FORCED OSCILLATIONS
RT   MOTION
RT   PERTURBATIONS
RT   RESONANCE
RT   SOUTHERN OSCILLATION
RT   TEMPORAL VARIATIONS
RT   TIDAL OSCILLATIONS
RT   VIBRATION

OSCILLATORY CURRENTS
USE   **OSCILLATORY FLOW**

OSCILLATORY FLOW
UF   oscillatory currents
RT   BED FORMS
RT   FLUID FLOW
RT   TIDAL CURRENTS
RT   UNIDIRECTIONAL FLOW

OSCILLATORY WAVES
BT1   WATER WAVES
NT1   PROGRESSIVE WAVES
NT1   STANDING WAVES

OSMIUM
BT1   CHEMICAL ELEMENTS
RT   METALS
RT   OSMIUM COMPOUNDS
RT   OSMIUM ISOTOPES
RT   TRACE METALS

OSMIUM COMPOUNDS
RT   CHEMICAL COMPOUNDS
RT   OSMIUM

OSMIUM ISOTOPES
BT1   ISOTOPES
RT   OSMIUM

OSMOREGULATION
RT   AMPHIHALINE SPECIES
RT   EURYHALINITY
RT   ION ACCUMULATION
RT   ION TRANSPORT

OSMOREGULATION (cont'd)
RT   IONS
RT   OSMOSIS
RT   OSMOTIC ADAPTATIONS
RT   OSMOTIC PRESSURE
RT   SALINITY TOLERANCE

OSMOSIS
BT1   SEPARATION PROCESSES
NT1   REVERSE OSMOSIS
RT   ADSORPTION
RT   DIALYSIS
RT   DIFFUSION
RT   MASS TRANSFER
RT   MOLECULAR DIFFUSION
RT   OSMOREGULATION
RT   OSMOTIC ADAPTATIONS
RT   OSMOTIC PRESSURE
RT   PERMEABILITY
RT   WATER BALANCE

OSMOTIC ADAPTATIONS
BT1   ADAPTATIONS
BT2   BIOLOGICAL PHENOMENA
RT   AMPHIHALINE SPECIES
RT   EURYHALINITY
RT   OSMOREGULATION
RT   OSMOSIS
RT   OSMOTIC PRESSURE

OSMOTIC PRESSURE
SN   Before 1982 search OSMOSIS
UF   pressure (osmotic)
BT1   PRESSURE
BT2   PHYSICAL PROPERTIES
BT3   PROPERTIES
RT   COLLIGATIVE PROPERTIES
RT   OSMOREGULATION
RT   OSMOSIS
RT   OSMOTIC ADAPTATIONS
RT   PLANT PHYSIOLOGY
RT   SALINITY POWER

OSTEOLOGY
SN   Added in 1980
BT1   VERTEBRATE ZOOLOGY
BT2   ZOOLOGY
BT3   BIOLOGY
RT   ANATOMY
RT   BONES
RT   SKELETON

OSTEONECROSIS
USE   **BONE NECROSIS**

OSTREACULTURE
USE   **OYSTER CULTURE**

OTEC
UF   ocean thermal energy conversion
UF   thalassothermal power
BT1   THERMAL POWER
BT2   POWER FROM THE SEA
BT3   ENERGY RESOURCES
BT4   NATURAL RESOURCES
RT   ARTIFICIAL UPWELLING
RT   OTEC PLANTS

OTEC PLANTS
RT   ELECTRIC POWER SOURCES
RT   HEAT EXCHANGERS
RT   IMPINGEMENT
RT   OPEN SYSTEMS
RT   OTEC
RT   PROCESS PLANTS

OTOLITH READING
BT1   AGE DETERMINATION
RT   GROWTH
RT   LIFE CYCLE
RT   OTOLITHS

OTOLITHS
RT   BONES
RT   ENDOSKELETON
RT   OTOLITH READING
RT   SKULL

OTTER BOARDS
RT   TRAWL NETS
RT   TRAWLING

OTTER TRAWLERS
USE   **TRAWLERS**

OTTER TRAWLS (BOTTOM)
USE   **BOTTOM TRAWLS**

OTTER TRAWLS (MIDWATER)
USE   **MIDWATER TRAWLS**

OUTCROPS
RT   MINERAL DEPOSITS
RT   ROCKS

OUTDOOR RECREATION
USE   **RECREATION**

OUTER CONTINENTAL SHELF
UF   ocs
BT1   CONTINENTAL SHELVES
BT2   SUBMARINE FEATURES
BT3   TOPOGRAPHIC FEATURES
RT   CONTINENTAL MARGINS
RT   CONTINENTAL SLOPE
RT   JURISDICTION
RT   MARINE ENVIRONMENT
RT   MARINE GEOLOGY
RT   MINERAL RESOURCES
RT   NERITIC PROVINCE
RT   OCEAN SPACE

OUTER MANTLE
USE   **UPPER MANTLE**

OUTFALLS
SN   Before 1986 search also SEWAGE
      OUTFALLS
UF   ocean outfalls
UF   sewage outfalls
BT1   HYDRAULIC STRUCTURES
RT   BUOYANT JETS
RT   SEWAGE
RT   SEWAGE DISPOSAL
RT   WATER POLLUTION

OUTFLOW
SN   Component of water budget
NT1   OVERFLOW
NT1   RIVER OUTFLOW
RT   INFLOW
RT   OUTFLOW WATERS
RT   WATER BUDGET
RT   WATER EXCHANGE

OUTFLOW WATERS
BT1   WATER MASSES
RT   CORE LAYER METHOD
RT   OUTFLOW
RT   OVERFLOW
RT   WATER MASS INTRUSIONS

OVA
USE   **EGGS**

OVALBUMIN
USE   **ALBUMINS**

OVARIES
BT1   ANIMAL REPRODUCTIVE ORGANS
RT   CASTRATION
RT   EGGS
RT   FECUNDITY
RT   OOGENESIS
RT   OVULATION
RT   PLACENTA
RT   SEXUAL REPRODUCTION
RT   STERILITY

OVERCROWDING
SN   Condition in which numerical
      densities of animals per unit area
      lead to disruptive and/or damaging
      physiological and behavioural
      effects. Added in 1980
RT   BIOCOENOSIS
RT   COMPETITION
RT   STOCKING DENSITY

OVEREXPLOITATION
RT   NONRENEWABLE RESOURCES
RT   RARE RESOURCES

OVERFISHING
SN   Fishing more intensely than a
      desirable level
UF   fishing overexploitation
RT   COMMERCIAL FISHING
RT   DEPLETED STOCKS
RT   FISHING
RT   FISHING MORTALITY
RT   SPECIES EXTINCTION
RT   STOCK ASSESSMENT
RT   YIELD

OVERFLOW
BT1   OUTFLOW
RT   BOLUSES
RT   CASCADING
RT   OUTFLOW WATERS

OVERTOPPING
UF   wave overtopping
RT   BREAKWATERS
RT   WATER WAVES

OVERTURN
UF   convective overturn
UF   overturning
UF   turnover
BT1   VERTICAL WATER MOVEMENT
BT2   WATER MOTION
RT   EPILIMNION
RT   FJORDS
RT   LAKE DYNAMICS
RT   LAKES
RT   MIXING PROCESSES
RT   RENEWAL
RT   RESERVOIRS (WATER)
RT   WATER MIXING

OVERTURNING
USE   **OVERTURN**

OVERWASH
SN   That portion of the uprush that
      carries over the crest of a berm or
      of a structure
RT   BERMS
RT   COASTAL STRUCTURES
RT   WATER WAVES

OVERWINTERING
SN   Added in 1982
UF   overwintering sites
RT   MIGRATIONS
RT   MIGRATORY SPECIES

OVERWINTERING SITES
USE   **OVERWINTERING**

OVERWINTERING TECHNIQUES
SN   Aquaculture technique to reduce
      winter effects on ponds. Added in
      1980
BT1   AQUACULTURE TECHNIQUES
RT   CAGE CULTURE
RT   FISH CULTURE
RT   FISH PONDS
RT   FRESHWATER AQUACULTURE
RT   POND CULTURE
RT   WINTER
RT   WINTERKILL

OVIPARITY
UF   oviparous
RT   EGGS
RT   OVOVIVIPARITY
RT   SEXUAL REPRODUCTION
RT   VIVIPARITY

OVIPAROUS
USE   **OVIPARITY**

OVOGENESIS
USE   **OOGENESIS**

OVOVIPAROUS
USE   **OVOVIVIPARITY**

OVOVIVIPARITY
UF   ovoviparous
RT   EGGS
RT   OVIPARITY
RT   SEXUAL REPRODUCTION

OVULATION
RT   EGGS
RT   OVARIES
RT   SEXUAL MATURITY
RT   SEXUAL REPRODUCTION

OWNERSHIP
USE   **PROPERTY RIGHTS**

OXBOW LAKES
SN   Added in 1980
BT1   LAKES
BT2   INLAND WATERS
RT   AQUACULTURE
RT   FLOOD PLAINS
RT   RIVER MEANDERS
RT   RIVERS

OXIC CONDITIONS
UF   aerobic conditions
RT   ANOXIC CONDITIONS
RT   OXIC SEDIMENTS

OXIC SEDIMENTS
UF   aerobic sediments
BT1   SEDIMENTS
RT   ANOXIC SEDIMENTS
RT   OXIC CONDITIONS

OXIDATION
BT1   CHEMICAL REACTIONS
RT   ANTIOXIDANTS
RT   BACTERIA
RT   BIODEGRADATION
RT   BIOGEOCHEMICAL CYCLE
RT   CORROSION

OXIDATION (cont'd)
RT	CYTOCHROMES
RT	DEGRADATION
RT	DETOXIFICATION
RT	ELECTROLYSIS
RT	OXYGEN DEMAND
RT	OXYGENATION
RT	REDOX POTENTIAL
RT	REDOX REACTIONS
RT	REDUCTION
RT	SEWAGE TREATMENT
RT	SLUDGE TREATMENT

OXIDATION LAGOONS
USE	**SEWAGE PONDS**

OXIDATION-REDUCTION POTENTIAL
USE	**REDOX POTENTIAL**

OXIDATION-REDUCTION REACTIONS
USE	**REDOX REACTIONS**

OXIDE MINERALS
BT1	MINERALS
NT1	ANATASE
NT1	BAUXITE
NT1	BIRNESSITE
NT1	BOEHMITE
NT1	BRUCITE
NT1	CASSITERITE
NT1	CHROMITE
NT1	CRISTOBALITE
NT1	GIBBSITE
NT1	GOETHITE
NT1	HAEMATITE
NT1	ILMENITE
NT1	LIMONITE
NT1	MAGHEMITE
NT1	MAGNETITE
NT1	MANGANITE
NT1	PYROLUSITE
NT1	RUTILE
NT1	TODOROKITE

OXIDES
BT1	OXYGEN COMPOUNDS
RT	FERROMANGANESE OXIDES
RT	IRON OXIDES
RT	MANGANESE DIOXIDE
RT	MANGANESE OXIDES

OXIDOREDUCTASES
SN	Before 1982 search ENZYMES
BT1	ENZYMES
RT	REDOX POTENTIAL
RT	REDOX REACTIONS

OXYGEN
BT1	CHEMICAL ELEMENTS
RT	AERATION
RT	AIR
RT	ANOXIA
RT	ANOXIC BASINS
RT	ANOXIC CONDITIONS
RT	ANOXIC SEDIMENTS
RT	BIOCHEMICAL OXYGEN DEMAND
RT	DISSOLVED OXYGEN
RT	GASES
RT	OXYGEN COMPOUNDS
RT	OXYGEN CONSUMPTION
RT	OXYGEN DEMAND
RT	OXYGEN DEPLETION
RT	OXYGEN ISOTOPES
RT	OXYGEN MINIMUM LAYER
RT	OXYGEN SECTIONS
RT	OZONE
RT	RESPIRATION

OXYGEN COMPOUNDS
NT1	OXIDES
RT	CHEMICAL COMPOUNDS
RT	OXYGEN

OXYGEN CONSUMPTION
SN	Consumption of oxygen by aquatic organisms, including consumption rate and measuring methods
RT	AEROBIC RESPIRATION
RT	ANOXIC CONDITIONS
RT	CARBON DIOXIDE
RT	CONVERSION FACTORS
RT	HYPOXIA
RT	METABOLISM
RT	OXYGEN
RT	OXYGEN DEPLETION
RT	RESPIROMETERS

OXYGEN CONTENT
USE	**DISSOLVED OXYGEN**

OXYGEN DEMAND
UF	total oxygen demand
NT1	BIOCHEMICAL OXYGEN DEMAND
NT1	CHEMICAL OXYGEN DEMAND
RT	AIR
RT	BIOLOGICAL PRODUCTION
RT	DEOXYGENATION
RT	DISSOLVED OXYGEN
RT	METABOLISM
RT	OXIDATION
RT	OXYGEN
RT	OXYGENATION
RT	PHOTOSYNTHESIS
RT	RESPIRATION
RT	WATER QUALITY

OXYGEN DEPLETION
SN	Depletion of dissolved oxygen by biological oxidation reduction process of organic matter or by mass development of phytoplankton
NT1	ANOXIA
RT	ALGAL BLOOMS
RT	ANOXIC BASINS
RT	ANOXIC CONDITIONS
RT	ANOXIC SEDIMENTS
RT	DEGRADATION
RT	DEOXYGENATION
RT	DEPLETION
RT	DISSOLVED OXYGEN
RT	FISH KILL
RT	HYPOXIA
RT	OXYGEN
RT	OXYGEN CONSUMPTION
RT	RED TIDES
RT	REDOX POTENTIAL
RT	WINTERKILL

OXYGEN ISOTOPE DATING
BT1	RADIOMETRIC DATING
BT2	GEOCHRONOMETRY
RT	OXYGEN ISOTOPES

OXYGEN ISOTOPE RATIO
RT	OXYGEN ISOTOPE STRATIGRAPHY
RT	OXYGEN ISOTOPES
RT	RADIOMETRIC DATING

OXYGEN ISOTOPE STRATIGRAPHY
BT1	STRATIGRAPHY
BT2	GEOLOGY
BT3	EARTH SCIENCES
RT	OXYGEN ISOTOPE RATIO
RT	OXYGEN ISOTOPES
RT	STRATIGRAPHIC CORRELATION

OXYGEN ISOTOPES
BT1	ISOTOPES
RT	OXYGEN
RT	OXYGEN ISOTOPE DATING
RT	OXYGEN ISOTOPE RATIO
RT	OXYGEN ISOTOPE STRATIGRAPHY

OXYGEN MAXIMUM LAYER
BT1	CORE LAYERS (WATER)
BT2	LAYERS
RT	OXYGEN PROFILES

OXYGEN MINIMUM LAYER
BT1	CORE LAYERS (WATER)
BT2	LAYERS
RT	DISSOLVED OXYGEN
RT	OXYGEN
RT	OXYGEN PROFILES
RT	OXYGEN SECTIONS

OXYGEN POISONING
USE	**HYPOXIA**

OXYGEN PROFILES
SN	Vertical distribution of dissolved oxygen in water bodies
BT1	VERTICAL PROFILES
BT2	PROFILES
RT	DISSOLVED OXYGEN
RT	OXYGEN MAXIMUM LAYER
RT	OXYGEN MINIMUM LAYER
RT	OXYGEN SECTIONS
RT	VERTICAL DISTRIBUTION

OXYGEN SECTIONS
BT1	HYDROGRAPHIC SECTIONS
BT2	VERTICAL SECTIONS
BT3	MAP GRAPHICS
BT4	GRAPHICS
RT	OXYGEN
RT	OXYGEN MINIMUM LAYER
RT	OXYGEN PROFILES
RT	VERTICAL DISTRIBUTION

OXYGENATION
RT	AERATION
RT	BIOCHEMICAL OXYGEN DEMAND
RT	DEOXYGENATION
RT	DISSOLVED OXYGEN
RT	OXIDATION
RT	OXYGEN DEMAND
RT	SOLUBILITY
RT	WATER PURIFICATION
RT	WATER TREATMENT

OYSTER BEDS
USE	**OYSTER REEFS**

OYSTER CULTURE
UF	ostreaculture
BT1	MOLLUSC CULTURE
BT2	SHELLFISH CULTURE
BT3	AQUACULTURE
RT	BOTTOM CULTURE
RT	BRACKISHWATER AQUACULTURE
RT	BRACKISHWATER MOLLUSCS
RT	CULTCH
RT	CULTURES
RT	GRADING
RT	MARINE AQUACULTURE
RT	MARINE MOLLUSCS
RT	OFF-BOTTOM CULTURE
RT	OYSTER FISHERIES
RT	OYSTER REEFS
RT	PEARL CULTURE
RT	RECIRCULATING SYSTEMS
RT	SEED COLLECTION
RT	SPAT
RT	TRAY CULTURE

ASFIS Thesaurus

OYSTER FISHERIES
SN	Added in 1982	
BT1	MOLLUSC FISHERIES	
BT2	SHELLFISH FISHERIES	
BT3	FISHERIES	
RT	ESTUARINE FISHERIES	
RT	OYSTER CULTURE	
RT	OYSTER REEFS	

OYSTER REEFS
SN	Added in 1980
UF	oyster beds
BT1	REEFS
RT	OYSTER CULTURE
RT	OYSTER FISHERIES
RT	SHELLFISH FISHERIES

OZONATION
SN	The sterilization of culture system water through the addition of ozone. Added in 1980
BT1	STERILIZATION
RT	AQUACULTURE SYSTEMS
RT	OZONE

OZONE
BT1	GASES
BT2	FLUIDS
RT	ATMOSPHERIC CHEMISTRY
RT	EARTH ATMOSPHERE
RT	OXYGEN
RT	OZONATION
RT	ULTRAVIOLET RADIATION

P-WAVES
UF	compressional waves (seismic)
UF	primary waves
BT1	BODY WAVES
BT2	SEISMIC WAVES
BT3	ELASTIC WAVES
RT	COMPRESSIONAL WAVE VELOCITIES
RT	S-WAVES

PACK ICE
UF	ice floes
BT1	FLOATING ICE
BT2	ICE
RT	ICE BARRIERS
RT	ICE CANOPY
RT	ICE DRIFT
RT	ICE FIELDS
RT	MARINE ENVIRONMENT
RT	NAVIGATION IN ICE

PACKAGES
USE	**CONTAINERS**

PACKAGING FISHERY PRODUCTS
USE	**PACKING FISHERY PRODUCTS**

PACKAGING MATERIALS
USE	**PACKING MATERIALS**

PACKING FISHERY PRODUCTS
SN	Referring to methods, techniques and material for packing industrial fishery products
UF	packaging fishery products
RT	FISHERY INDUSTRY
RT	FISHERY PRODUCTS
RT	PACKING MATERIALS
RT	PROCESSED FISHERY PRODUCTS

PACKING MATERIALS
SN	Added in 1980
UF	packaging materials
BT1	MATERIALS
RT	PACKING FISHERY PRODUCTS

PADDY FIELDS
USE	**RICE FIELDS**

PAEDOMORPHISM
USE	**NEOTENY**

PAINTS
BT1	COATING MATERIALS
BT2	MATERIALS
RT	ANTIOXIDANTS
RT	CHEMICAL POLLUTANTS
RT	CHEMICAL POLLUTION
RT	COATING PROCESSES
RT	PRIMERS

PAIR SEINES
USE	**BOAT SEINES**

PAIR TRAWLERS
USE	**TRAWLERS**

PAIR TRAWLING
USE	**TRAWLING**

PAIR TRAWLS (BOTTOM)
USE	**BOTTOM TRAWLS**

PAIR TRAWLS (MIDWATER)
USE	**MIDWATER TRAWLS**

PALAEMONID FISHERIES
USE	**SHRIMP FISHERIES**

PALAEO STUDIES
UF	paleo studies
RT	PALAEONTOLOGY

PALAEOBATHYMETRY
USE	**PALAEOTOPOGRAPHY**

PALAEOCEANOGRAPHY
SN	Before 1986 search also PALAEOOCEANOGRAPHY
UF	palaeooceanography
BT1	OCEANOGRAPHY
BT2	EARTH SCIENCES
RT	FOSSIL SEA WATER
RT	PALAEOCLIMATE
RT	PALAEOENVIRONMENTS
RT	PALAEOMAGNETISM
RT	PALAEONTOLOGY
RT	PALAEOSALINITY
RT	PALAEOTEMPERATURE
RT	PALAEOTOPOGRAPHY
RT	RAFTING

PALAEOCENE
SN	Before 1982 search PALEOCENE EPOCH
BT1	PALAEOGENE
BT2	TERTIARY
BT3	CENOZOIC
BT4	GEOLOGICAL TIME

PALAEOCLIMATE
BT1	CLIMATE
RT	CLIMATIC CHANGES
RT	CONTINENTAL DRIFT
RT	FOSSILS
RT	GEOLOGICAL TIME
RT	ICE AGES
RT	ICE COVER
RT	INTERGLACIAL PERIODS
RT	PALAEOCEANOGRAPHY
RT	PALAEOENVIRONMENTS
RT	PALAEOLIMNOLOGY
RT	PALAEONTOLOGY
RT	STRATIGRAPHY

PALAEOCLIMATOLOGY
BT1	CLIMATOLOGY
RT	CONTINENTAL DRIFT
RT	EOLIAN DUST
RT	GEOMORPHOLOGY
RT	PALAEONTOLOGY
RT	STRATIGRAPHY

PALAEOCURRENTS
RT	ICE RAFTING
RT	OCEAN CURRENTS
RT	PROVENANCE

PALAEOECOLOGY
BT1	ECOLOGY
RT	FOSSILS
RT	GEOLOGICAL TIME
RT	LAND BRIDGES
RT	PALAEONTOLOGY
RT	STRATIGRAPHY

PALAEOENVIRONMENTS
BT1	ENVIRONMENTS
RT	PALAEOCEANOGRAPHY
RT	PALAEOCLIMATE
RT	PALAEONTOLOGY
RT	PALAEOSALINITY
RT	PALAEOTEMPERATURE

PALAEOGENE
UF	lower tertiary
BT1	TERTIARY
BT2	CENOZOIC
BT3	GEOLOGICAL TIME
NT1	EOCENE
NT1	OLIGOCENE
NT1	PALAEOCENE

PALAEOLATITUDE
BT1	LATITUDE
BT2	GEOGRAPHICAL COORDINATES
BT3	COORDINATE SYSTEMS
RT	PALAEOMAGNETISM
RT	POLAR WANDERING

PALAEOLIMNOLOGY
BT1	LIMNOLOGY
RT	PALAEOCLIMATE
RT	PALAEONTOLOGY

PALAEOMAGNETISM
BT1	GEOPHYSICS
BT2	EARTH SCIENCES
RT	CONTINENTAL DRIFT
RT	GEOMAGNETISM
RT	MAGNETIC ANOMALIES
RT	MAGNETIC REVERSALS
RT	MAGNETIC SUSCEPTIBILITY
RT	MAGNETISM
RT	PALAEOCEANOGRAPHY
RT	PALAEOLATITUDE
RT	PLATE TECTONICS
RT	POLAR WANDERING
RT	POLE POSITIONS
RT	REMANENT MAGNETIZATION
RT	SEAFLOOR SPREADING

PALAEONTOLOGY
UF	paleontology
NT1	MICROPALAEONTOLOGY
RT	ARCHAEOLOGY
RT	BIOFACIES
RT	BIOSTRATIGRAPHY
RT	BOTANY
RT	CHRONOSTRATIGRAPHY
RT	CONTINENTAL DRIFT
RT	FOSSIL POLLEN
RT	FOSSILS
RT	GEOLOGY
RT	PALAEO STUDIES

PALAEONTOLOGY (cont'd)
RT	PALAEOCEANOGRAPHY
RT	PALAEOCLIMATE
RT	PALAEOCLIMATOLOGY
RT	PALAEOECOLOGY
RT	PALAEOENVIRONMENTS
RT	PALAEOLIMNOLOGY
RT	PALAEOSALINITY
RT	PALYNOLOGY
RT	SEDIMENTOLOGY
RT	STRATIGRAPHY
RT	TAXONOMY
RT	TRACE FOSSILS
RT	ZOOLOGY

PALAEOOCEANOGRAPHY
USE	**PALAEOCEANOGRAPHY**

PALAEOSALINITY
BT1	SALINITY
BT2	CHEMICAL PROPERTIES
BT3	PROPERTIES
RT	CLIMATIC CHANGES
RT	MESSINIAN
RT	PALAEOCEANOGRAPHY
RT	PALAEOENVIRONMENTS
RT	PALAEONTOLOGY

PALAEOSHORELINES
BT1	COASTAL LANDFORMS
BT2	LANDFORMS
BT3	TOPOGRAPHIC FEATURES
RT	COASTAL MORPHOLOGY
RT	PALAEOTOPOGRAPHY
RT	SEA LEVEL CHANGES

PALAEOTEMPERATURE
BT1	WATER TEMPERATURE
BT2	TEMPERATURE
BT3	THERMODYNAMIC PROPERTIES
BT4	PHYSICAL PROPERTIES
RT	CLIMATIC CHANGES
RT	PALAEOCEANOGRAPHY
RT	PALAEOENVIRONMENTS

PALAEOTOPOGRAPHY
UF	palaeobathymetry
BT1	BOTTOM TOPOGRAPHY
BT2	TOPOGRAPHY (GEOLOGY)
BT3	TOPOGRAPHY
RT	PALAEOCEANOGRAPHY
RT	PALAEOSHORELINES

PALAEOZOIC
SN	Before 1982 search PALEOZOIC ERA
BT1	GEOLOGICAL TIME
NT1	CAMBRIAN
NT1	CARBONIFEROUS
NT1	DEVONIAN
NT1	ORDOVICIAN
NT1	PERMIAN
NT1	SILURIAN
RT	PHANEROZOIC

PALAGONITE
BT1	VOLCANIC ROCKS
BT2	IGNEOUS ROCKS
BT3	ROCKS
RT	BASALT-SEAWATER INTERACTION
RT	GLASS
RT	PILLOW LAVA

PALATABILITY
RT	ARTIFICIAL FEEDING
RT	FOOD ADDITIVES
RT	FOOD FISH
RT	FOOD TECHNOLOGY
RT	HUMAN FOOD
RT	ORGANOLEPTIC PROPERTIES
RT	TASTE

PALATABILITY (cont'd)
RT	TASTE FUNCTIONS
RT	TASTE TESTS

PALATABILITY TESTS
USE	**TASTE TESTS**

PALEO STUDIES
USE	**PALAEO STUDIES**

PALEONTOLOGY
USE	**PALAEONTOLOGY**

PALLADIUM
BT1	CHEMICAL ELEMENTS
RT	METALS
RT	PALLADIUM COMPOUNDS
RT	PALLADIUM ISOTOPES
RT	TRACE METALS

PALLADIUM COMPOUNDS
RT	CHEMICAL COMPOUNDS
RT	PALLADIUM

PALLADIUM ISOTOPES
BT1	ISOTOPES
RT	PALLADIUM

PALUDISM
USE	**MALARIA**

PALYGORSKITE
BT1	CLAY MINERALS
BT2	SILICATE MINERALS
BT3	MINERALS

PALYNOLOGY
UF	pollen analysis
RT	BOTANY
RT	FOSSIL POLLEN
RT	FOSSIL SPORES
RT	GEOLOGY
RT	MICROPALAEONTOLOGY
RT	PALAEONTOLOGY
RT	POLLEN
RT	QUATERNARY
RT	TAXONOMY

PANCREAS
BT1	DIGESTIVE GLANDS
BT2	GLANDS
BT3	SECRETORY ORGANS
RT	INSULIN

PANDALID FISHERIES
USE	**SHRIMP FISHERIES**

PARAMETERIZATION
SN	Used only as a qualifier
RT	PARAMETERS

PARAMETERS
SN	Used only as a qualifier
RT	CORIOLIS PARAMETER
RT	PARAMETERIZATION
RT	PROPERTIES
RT	ROSSBY PARAMETER
RT	WIND WAVE PARAMETERS

PARASITE ATTACHMENT
SN	Added in 1980
UF	attachment (parasites)
UF	parasitic attachment
BT1	BIOLOGICAL ATTACHMENT
RT	ATTACHMENT ORGANS
RT	PARASITES
RT	PARASITISM

PARASITE CONTROL
BT1	CONTROL
RT	PARASITE RESISTANCE
RT	PARASITES
RT	PARASITIC DISEASES
RT	PARASITISM
RT	PARASITOLOGY
RT	PEST CONTROL
RT	PROTOZOAN DISEASES
RT	THERAPY

PARASITE RESISTANCE
SN	Added in 1980
UF	resistance to parasites
BT1	BIOLOGICAL RESISTANCE
BT2	BIOLOGICAL PROPERTIES
BT3	PROPERTIES
RT	PARASITE CONTROL
RT	PARASITES
RT	PARASITISM

PARASITES
UF	parasitofauna
NT1	ECTOPARASITES
NT1	ENDOPARASITES
RT	BIOLOGICAL VECTORS
RT	COMMENSALISM
RT	HOSTS
RT	INJURIES
RT	NOXIOUS ORGANISMS
RT	PARASITE ATTACHMENT
RT	PARASITE CONTROL
RT	PARASITE RESISTANCE
RT	PARASITIC DISEASES
RT	PARASITISM
RT	PARASITOLOGY
RT	PROTOZOAN DISEASES
RT	SYMBIOSIS

PARASITIC ATTACHMENT
USE	**PARASITE ATTACHMENT**

PARASITIC CASTRATION
SN	Failure of a host to reproduce due to partial or complete destruction of its gonads caused by parasitic activities. Added in 1982
UF	castration by parasites
RT	CASTRATION
RT	MARINE CRUSTACEANS
RT	MARINE MOLLUSCS
RT	PARASITIC DISEASES

PARASITIC DISEASES
UF	parasitic infestation
BT1	INFECTIOUS DISEASES
BT2	DISEASES
RT	ANTIHELMINTHIC AGENTS
RT	ANTIPARASITIC AGENTS
RT	ANTIPROTOZOAL AGENTS
RT	BIOLOGICAL VECTORS
RT	BOIL DISEASE
RT	FISH DISEASES
RT	FUNGAL DISEASES
RT	MALARIA
RT	PARASITE CONTROL
RT	PARASITES
RT	PARASITIC CASTRATION
RT	PARASITISM
RT	PARASITOLOGY
RT	PLANT DISEASES
RT	PROTOZOAN DISEASES
RT	WHIRLING DISEASE

PARASITIC INFESTATION
USE	**PARASITIC DISEASES**

PARASITISM
BT1	INTERSPECIFIC RELATIONSHIPS
NT1	ECTOPARASITISM
NT1	ENDOPARASITISM
RT	HOST PREFERENCES
RT	HOSTS
RT	PARASITE ATTACHMENT
RT	PARASITE CONTROL
RT	PARASITE RESISTANCE
RT	PARASITES
RT	PARASITIC DISEASES
RT	PARASITOLOGY
RT	PATHOLOGY
RT	PROPHYLAXIS
RT	PROTOZOAN DISEASES

PARASITOFAUNA
USE	**PARASITES**

PARASITOLOGY
BT1	ECOLOGY
RT	AUTECOLOGY
RT	BACTERIOLOGY
RT	BIOLOGICAL VECTORS
RT	BIOLOGY
RT	EPIDEMIOLOGY
RT	INFECTIOUS DISEASES
RT	MICROBIOLOGY
RT	MYCOLOGY
RT	PARASITE CONTROL
RT	PARASITES
RT	PARASITIC DISEASES
RT	PARASITISM
RT	PROTOZOAN DISEASES

PARASYMPATHETIC NERVOUS SYSTEM
USE	**AUTONOMIC NERVOUS SYSTEM**

PARATHYROID
USE	**THYROID**

PARENT STOCKS
USE	**BROOD STOCKS**

PARENTAL BEHAVIOUR
SN	Before 1982 search REPRODUCTIVE BEHAVIOUR
UF	parental care
BT1	BEHAVIOUR
RT	REPRODUCTIVE BEHAVIOUR

PARENTAL CARE
USE	**PARENTAL BEHAVIOUR**

PARRS
USE	**JUVENILES**

PARTHENOGENESIS
BT1	REPRODUCTION
RT	CLONES

PARTIAL TIDES
USE	**TIDAL CONSTITUENTS**

PARTIALLY-MIXED ESTUARIES
BT1	ESTUARIES
BT2	COASTAL INLETS
BT3	COASTAL WATERS
RT	ESTUARINE DYNAMICS

PARTICLE CONCENTRATION
SN	Use only for suspended particulate matter
RT	GRAVIMETRIC TECHNIQUES
RT	LIGHT ABSORPTION
RT	LIGHT SCATTERING
RT	NEPHELOMETERS
RT	PARTICLE COUNTERS
RT	PARTICLE SCATTERING
RT	SUSPENDED PARTICULATE MATTER

PARTICLE CONCENTRATION (cont'd)
RT	TRANSMISSOMETERS
RT	TURBIDITY

PARTICLE COUNTERS
BT1	COUNTERS
RT	PARTICLE CONCENTRATION
RT	SUSPENDED PARTICULATE MATTER

PARTICLE DISTRIBUTION
RT	KURTOSIS
RT	PARTICLE SCATTERING
RT	TURBIDITY

PARTICLE MOTION
UF	grain motion
UF	sediment particle motion
UF	suspended particle motion
UF	wave particle motion
NT1	PARTICLE SETTLING
RT	BOTTOM STRESS
RT	MOTION
RT	NEAR-SURFACE LAYER
RT	ORBITAL VELOCITY
RT	PARTICULATE FLUX
RT	RESUSPENDED SEDIMENTS
RT	SALTATION
RT	SEDIMENT DYNAMICS
RT	SEDIMENT MOVEMENT
RT	SEDIMENT TRANSPORT
RT	SETTLING RATE
RT	SUSPENSION
RT	TRACTION
RT	WATER DEPTH
RT	WATER WAVES
RT	WAVE ATTENUATION
RT	WAVE DRIFT VELOCITY

PARTICLE SCATTERING
SN	Use for scattering of light in water by suspended particles
BT1	LIGHT SCATTERING
RT	PARTICLE CONCENTRATION
RT	PARTICLE DISTRIBUTION
RT	PARTICLE SIZE
RT	SUSPENDED PARTICULATE MATTER

PARTICLE SETTLING
BT1	PARTICLE MOTION
RT	PARTICULATE FLUX
RT	SETTLING RATE
RT	STOKES LAW
RT	WINNOWING

PARTICLE SIZE
BT1	SIZE
BT2	DIMENSIONS
RT	KURTOSIS
RT	PARTICLE SCATTERING
RT	TURBIDITY

PARTICLE VELOCITY (WAVES)
USE	**ORBITAL VELOCITY**

PARTICULATE FLUX
SN	Vertical flux of particulates in water column
RT	PARTICLE MOTION
RT	PARTICLE SETTLING
RT	SEDIMENT TRAPS
RT	SETTLING RATE
RT	SUSPENDED PARTICULATE MATTER
RT	WATER COLUMN

PARTICULATE MATTER
USE	**SUSPENDED PARTICULATE MATTER**

PARTICULATE MATTER (AIR)
USE	**ATMOSPHERIC PARTICULATES**

PARTICULATE ORGANIC CARBON
BT1	ORGANIC CARBON
BT2	CARBON
BT3	CHEMICAL ELEMENTS
RT	PARTICULATE ORGANIC MATTER

PARTICULATE ORGANIC MATTER
BT1	ORGANIC MATTER
RT	PARTICULATE ORGANIC CARBON
RT	PARTICULATE ORGANIC NITROGEN
RT	PARTICULATE ORGANIC PHOSPHORUS

PARTICULATE ORGANIC NITROGEN
BT1	ORGANIC NITROGEN
BT2	NITROGEN
BT3	CHEMICAL ELEMENTS
RT	PARTICULATE ORGANIC MATTER

PARTICULATE ORGANIC PHOSPHORUS
BT1	ORGANIC PHOSPHORUS
BT2	PHOSPHORUS
BT3	CHEMICAL ELEMENTS
RT	PARTICULATE ORGANIC MATTER

PARTICULATES
NT1	ATMOSPHERIC PARTICULATES
NT2	SALT PARTICLES
NT1	SUSPENDED PARTICULATE MATTER
NT2	RESUSPENDED SEDIMENTS

PARTICULATES (AQUATIC)
USE	**SUSPENDED PARTICULATE MATTER**

PARTICULATES (ATMOSPHERIC)
USE	**ATMOSPHERIC PARTICULATES**

PARTURITION
SN	Added in 1980
UF	birth
BT1	SEXUAL REPRODUCTION
BT2	REPRODUCTION
RT	AQUATIC MAMMALS
RT	CETOLOGY
RT	FEMALES
RT	FOETUS
RT	PREGNANCY

PASSENGER SHIPS
UF	ferries
UF	liners (passengers)
BT1	MERCHANT SHIPS
BT2	SHIPS
BT3	SURFACE CRAFT
BT4	VEHICLES

PASSIVE MARGINS
UF	aseismic margins
UF	divergent margins
BT1	CONTINENTAL MARGINS
BT2	SUBMARINE FEATURES
BT3	TOPOGRAPHIC FEATURES
RT	PLATE DIVERGENCE

PASSIVE SONAR
BT1	SONAR
BT2	REMOTE SENSING EQUIPMENT
BT3	EQUIPMENT
RT	AMBIENT NOISE
RT	SONAR DETECTION
RT	SONOBUOYS

PATENTS
SN	Patent of new equipment and apparatus
BT1	DOCUMENTS
RT	ENGINEERING DRAWINGS
RT	EQUIPMENT
RT	LEGISLATION

PATENTS (cont'd)
- RT   MEASURING DEVICES
- RT   PROPULSION SYSTEMS
- RT   SHIP TECHNOLOGY
- RT   SPECIFICATIONS
- RT   TECHNOLOGY TRANSFER

PATHOGEN RESISTANCE
- USE   **DISEASE RESISTANCE**

PATHOGENIC BACTERIA
- SN   Added in 1980
- BT1   BACTERIA
- BT2   MICROORGANISMS
- RT   ANTIBIOTICS
- RT   BACTERIAL DISEASES

PATHOGENIC SPECIES
- USE   **PATHOGENS**

PATHOGENS
- UF   pathogenic species
- BT1   SPECIES
- BT2   TAXA
- RT   BACTERINS
- RT   DISEASE CONTROL
- RT   DISEASES
- RT   DISINFECTION
- RT   MICROBIAL CONTAMINATION
- RT   THERAPY

PATHOLOGY
- UF   animal pathology
- UF   fish pathology
- NT1   HISTOPATHOLOGY
- RT   BIOLOGICAL VECTORS
- RT   DISEASES
- RT   EPIDEMICS
- RT   HUMAN DISEASES
- RT   PARASITISM
- RT   PHYSIOLOGY
- RT   RESISTANCE MECHANISMS
- RT   THERAPY
- RT   TOXICITY

PATTERN RECOGNITION
- RT   IMAGE ENHANCEMENT

PCB
- SN   Before 1982 search also
  POLYCHLORINATED BIPHENYLS
- UF   polychlorinated biphenyls
- BT1   AROMATIC HYDROCARBONS
- BT2   UNSATURATED HYDROCARBONS
- BT3   HYDROCARBONS
- BT4   ORGANIC COMPOUNDS
- RT   CHEMICAL COMPOUNDS
- RT   CHEMICAL POLLUTANTS
- RT   CHEMICAL POLLUTION
- RT   INSECTICIDES
- RT   TOXICANTS

PEARL CULTURE
- BT1   AQUACULTURE
- RT   BRACKISHWATER AQUACULTURE
- RT   CULTURES
- RT   FRESHWATER AQUACULTURE
- RT   MARINE AQUACULTURE
- RT   OYSTER CULTURE
- RT   PEARL FISHERIES
- RT   PEARL OYSTERS
- RT   PEARLS
- RT   SEED COLLECTION
- RT   SHELLFISH CULTURE

PEARL FISHERIES
- SN   Added in 1982
- BT1   FISHERIES
- RT   FISHING BY DIVING
- RT   MARINE FISHERIES

PEARL FISHERIES (cont'd)
- RT   PEARL CULTURE
- RT   PEARL OYSTERS
- RT   PEARLS
- RT   SHELLS

PEARL OYSTERS
- RT   PEARL CULTURE
- RT   PEARL FISHERIES
- RT   PEARLS

PEARLS
- SN   Including their formation by
  natural or artificial biosynthetic
  processes
- BT1   ANIMAL PRODUCTS
- RT   BIOSYNTHESIS
- RT   BRACKISHWATER MOLLUSCS
- RT   FRESHWATER MOLLUSCS
- RT   MARINE MOLLUSCS
- RT   PEARL CULTURE
- RT   PEARL FISHERIES
- RT   PEARL OYSTERS

PEAT
- SN   Remains of bog and fen vegetation
- BT1   ORGANIC SEDIMENTS
- BT2   BIOGENIC DEPOSITS
- RT   HUMUS
- RT   LAKE DEPOSITS
- RT   ORGANIC MATTER
- RT   SAPROPELS

PEBBLES
- BT1   CLASTICS
- BT2   SEDIMENTS
- RT   RUDITES
- RT   SHINGLE

PECKING ORDER
- SN   Social hierarchy occurring in many
  animals that live together in
  groups. Added in 1980
- BT1   DOMINANCE HIERARCHIES
- BT2   SOCIAL BEHAVIOUR
- BT3   BEHAVIOUR
- RT   AGGRESSIVE BEHAVIOUR
- RT   AQUATIC BIRDS

PECTEN FISHERIES
- USE   **SCALLOP FISHERIES**

PEDUNCLE DISEASE
- SN   Added in 1980
- UF   cold water diseases
- BT1   FISH DISEASES
- BT2   ANIMAL DISEASES
- BT3   DISEASES
- RT   BACTERIAL DISEASES
- RT   ENVIRONMENTAL DISEASES
- RT   FISH CULTURE
- RT   HUSBANDRY DISEASES

PELAGIC CLAY
- UF   red clay
- BT1   CLAYS
- BT2   CLASTICS
- BT3   SEDIMENTS
- RT   CLAY MINERALS
- RT   PELAGIC SEDIMENTS

PELAGIC DEPOSITS
- USE   **PELAGIC SEDIMENTS**

PELAGIC ENVIRONMENT
- UF   pelagic regions
- BT1   AQUATIC ENVIRONMENT
- BT2   ENVIRONMENTS
- NT1   NERITIC PROVINCE
- NT1   OCEANIC PROVINCE

PELAGIC ENVIRONMENT (cont'd)
- NT2   ABYSSOPELAGIC ZONE
- NT2   BATHYPELAGIC ZONE
- NT2   EPIPELAGIC ZONE
- NT2   MESOPELAGIC ZONE
- RT   ABYSSAL ZONE
- RT   BATHYAL ZONE
- RT   LENITIC ENVIRONMENT
- RT   MARINE ENVIRONMENT
- RT   NEKTON
- RT   NEUSTON
- RT   PELAGIC SEDIMENTATION
- RT   PLANKTON

PELAGIC FISHERIES
- BT1   FISHERIES
- RT   CARANGID FISHERIES
- RT   CLUPEOID FISHERIES
- RT   FINFISH FISHERIES
- RT   GILLNETS
- RT   GILLNETTERS
- RT   JIGGING
- RT   KRILL FISHERIES
- RT   LAKE FISHERIES
- RT   LAMPARA NETS
- RT   LIGHT FISHING
- RT   LINERS
- RT   LINES
- RT   LONGLINING
- RT   MACKEREL FISHERIES
- RT   MARINE FISH
- RT   MARINE FISHERIES
- RT   MIDWATER TRAWLS
- RT   POLE-LINE FISHING
- RT   PURSE SEINES
- RT   SEINE NETS
- RT   SEINERS
- RT   SURROUNDING NETS
- RT   TRAWL NETS
- RT   TRAWLERS
- RT   TUNA FISHERIES
- RT   WOUNDING GEAR

PELAGIC REGIONS
- USE   **PELAGIC ENVIRONMENT**

PELAGIC SEDIMENTATION
- BT1   SEDIMENTATION
- RT   PELAGIC ENVIRONMENT
- RT   PELAGIC SEDIMENTS

PELAGIC SEDIMENTS
- UF   pelagic deposits
- BT1   SEDIMENTS
- RT   CARBONATE SEDIMENTS
- RT   CHEMICAL SEDIMENTS
- RT   EXTRATERRESTRIAL MATERIAL
- RT   OOZES
- RT   PELAGIC CLAY
- RT   PELAGIC SEDIMENTATION
- RT   RADIOLARITE
- RT   SILICEOUS SEDIMENTS

PELLET FEEDS
- SN   Added in 1982
- UF   pelleted foods
- BT1   FEED
- RT   AQUACULTURE
- RT   ARTIFICIAL FEEDING

PELLETED FOODS
- USE   **PELLET FEEDS**

PEN CULTURE
- USE   **CAGE CULTURE**

ASFIS Thesaurus

PENAEID SHRIMP FISHERIES
USE **SHRIMP FISHERIES**

PENETRATION DEPTH
RT GEOTECHNOLOGY
RT PENETROMETERS
RT SEDIMENT PROPERTIES
RT SOIL MECHANICS

PENETROMETERS
RT BEARING CAPACITY
RT CORERS
RT GEOLOGICAL EQUIPMENT
RT GEOTECHNICAL DATA
RT MEASURING DEVICES
RT PENETRATION DEPTH
RT SEAFLOOR SAMPLING
RT SEDIMENT SAMPLING

PEPTIDE SYNTHESIS
USE **PROTEIN SYNTHESIS**

PEPTIDES
BT1 PROTEINS
BT2 ORGANIC COMPOUNDS
NT1 POLYPEPTIDES
RT AMINO ACIDS

PEPTIZATION
USE **DEFLOCCULATION**

PEPTONES
SN Before 1982 search PROTEINS
BT1 PROTEINS
BT2 ORGANIC COMPOUNDS

PERCOID FISHERIES
SN Exclude carangid fisheries. Added in 1982
UF croaker fisheries
UF grouper fisheries
UF seabream fisheries
UF snapper fisheries
BT1 FINFISH FISHERIES
BT2 FISHERIES
RT CARANGID FISHERIES
RT COASTAL FISHERIES
RT DEMERSAL FISHERIES
RT REEF FISHERIES

PERCOLATION
BT1 FLUID FLOW
BT2 FLUID MOTION
RT GROUND WATER
RT LEACHING
RT POROSITY
RT SEEPAGES
RT VOIDS

PERFORATED STRUCTURES
RT OFFSHORE STRUCTURES
RT STRUCTURES

PERFORMANCE ASSESSMENT
SN Used only as a qualifier
BT1 EVALUATION
RT ACCEPTABILITY
RT CERTIFICATION
RT EFFICIENCY
RT EQUIPMENT
RT INTERCALIBRATION
RT INTERCOMPARISON
RT QUALITY CONTROL
RT RELIABILITY
RT SPECIFICATIONS
RT TESTING
RT TESTS

PERIDOTITE
BT1 ULTRAMAFIC ROCKS
BT2 IGNEOUS ROCKS
BT3 ROCKS
RT EARTH MANTLE
RT KIMBERLITES

PERIODIC VARIATIONS
BT1 TEMPORAL VARIATIONS
NT1 ANNUAL VARIATIONS
NT1 DIURNAL VARIATIONS
NT1 SEASONAL VARIATIONS
RT CYCLIC LOADING
RT LONG-TERM CHANGES
RT PERIODICITY

PERIODICITY
SN Used only as a qualifier
UF frequency (time)
NT1 ANNUAL
NT1 BIENNIAL
NT1 DAILY
NT1 HOURLY
NT1 MONTHLY
NT1 SEASONALITY
NT1 WEEKLY
RT FREQUENCY
RT PERIODIC VARIATIONS

PERIPHERAL NERVES
USE **NERVES**

PERIPHERAL NERVOUS SYSTEM
SN Added in 1980
UF pns
BT1 NERVOUS SYSTEM
NT1 NERVES
RT SENSE ORGANS

PERIPHYTON
SN Assemblage of organisms on submerged objects
BT1 AQUATIC COMMUNITIES
RT EPIPHYTES

PERITONEUM
USE **ABDOMEN**

PERMAFROST
UF submarine permafrost
RT ARCTIC ZONE
RT CRYOSPHERE
RT FREEZING
RT LAND ICE
RT SEDIMENTS
RT SOIL MECHANICS

PERMANENCE
RT CONTINENTAL DRIFT
RT CONTINENTS
RT OCEAN BASINS
RT OCEANIZATION

PERMANENT PLANKTON
USE **HOLOPLANKTON**

PERMANENT THERMOCLINE
BT1 THERMOCLINE
BT2 DISCONTINUITY LAYERS
BT3 LAYERS
RT SOFAR CHANNEL
RT UPPER OCEAN

PERMEABILITY
UF sediment permeability
BT1 PHYSICAL PROPERTIES
BT2 PROPERTIES
RT CAPILLARITY
RT DIFFUSION
RT ELECTRICAL RESISTIVITY

PERMEABILITY (cont'd)
RT GEOTECHNICAL DATA
RT GRAIN SIZE
RT LEACHING
RT OSMOSIS
RT POROSITY
RT SEDIMENT ANALYSIS
RT SEDIMENT PROPERTIES
RT SEDIMENT STRUCTURE
RT VOID RATIO
RT VOIDS

PERMEASES
SN Before 1982 search ENZYMES
UF transport agents
BT1 ENZYMES

PERMIAN
SN Before 1982 search PERMIAN SYSTEM
BT1 PALAEOZOIC
BT2 GEOLOGICAL TIME

PERMITS
SN Including statistics relating to fisheries licences and licence fees
BT1 LICENCES
RT DRILLING
RT LEGAL ASPECTS
RT QUOTA REGULATIONS
RT SPORT FISHING

PERSISTENCE
SN Used only as a qualifier
NT1 POLLUTANT PERSISTENCE
RT FATE
RT FLUSHING TIME

PERSONAL BIBLIOGRAPHIES
SN Bibliographies of individual workers
BT1 BIBLIOGRAPHIES
BT2 DOCUMENTS
RT FESTSCHRIFTEN
RT OBITUARIES
RT SCIENTIFIC PERSONNEL

PERSONNEL
SN Before 1982 search SCIENTIFIC PERSONNEL
UF employees
UF staff (personnel)
UF workers
NT1 COASTGUARDS
NT1 CONSULTANTS
NT1 CONTRACTORS
NT1 CREW
NT1 EXPERTS
NT2 DIVERS
NT2 ENGINEERS
NT2 TECHNICIANS
NT3 AQUACULTURISTS
NT1 FISHERMEN
NT1 LIBRARIANS
NT1 SCIENTIFIC PERSONNEL
NT2 BIOLOGISTS
NT3 ALGOLOGISTS
NT3 BOTANISTS
NT3 FISHERY BIOLOGISTS
NT3 GENETICISTS
NT3 MICROBIOLOGISTS
NT4 BACTERIOLOGISTS
NT4 MYCOLOGISTS
NT4 VIROLOGISTS
NT3 PHYSIOLOGISTS
NT4 ANIMAL PHYSIOLOGISTS
NT4 PLANT PHYSIOLOGISTS
NT3 TAXONOMISTS
NT3 ZOOLOGISTS
NT4 CARCINOLOGISTS
NT4 ENTOMOLOGISTS
NT4 ICHTHYOLOGISTS

PERSONNEL (cont'd)
NT4	MALACOLOGISTS
NT4	MAMMALOGISTS
NT4	ORNITHOLOGISTS
NT2	ECOLOGISTS
NT3	FRESHWATER ECOLOGISTS
NT3	MARINE ECOLOGISTS
NT2	ECONOMISTS
NT2	FRESHWATER SCIENTISTS
NT2	GEOLOGISTS
NT2	INFORMATION SCIENTISTS
NT2	MARINE SCIENTISTS
NT2	METEOROLOGISTS
NT2	STATISTICIANS
RT	CAREERS
RT	EDUCATION
RT	HUMAN RESOURCES
RT	LABOUR
RT	LABOUR LEGISLATION
RT	MANAGEMENT
RT	ORGANIZATIONS

PERT
UF	programme evaluation
UF	project evaluation
BT1	OPERATIONS RESEARCH
RT	CRITICAL PATH METHOD
RT	MANAGEMENT
RT	NUMERICAL ANALYSIS
RT	PLANNING

PERTURBATION METHOD
BT1	NUMERICAL ANALYSIS
BT2	MATHEMATICAL ANALYSIS
RT	PERTURBATIONS

PERTURBATIONS
RT	OSCILLATIONS
RT	PERTURBATION METHOD
RT	STEADY STATE
RT	TIDAL PERTURBATIONS

PEST CONTROL
BT1	CONTROL
RT	BIOLOGICAL CONTROL
RT	CHEMICAL CONTROL
RT	CONTROL RESISTANCE
RT	DISEASE CONTROL
RT	FISH DISEASES
RT	FLOODING
RT	INFESTATION
RT	PARASITE CONTROL
RT	PESTICIDES
RT	PLANT CONTROL
RT	PLANT DISEASES
RT	REPELLENTS

PESTICIDES
SN	Different chlorinated hydrocarbon products
UF	biocides
NT1	ALGICIDES
NT1	ANTIHELMINTHIC AGENTS
NT1	ANTIPARASITIC AGENTS
NT2	ANTIPROTOZOAL AGENTS
NT1	BACTERIOCIDES
NT1	FUNGICIDES
NT1	HERBICIDES
NT1	ICHTHYOCIDES
NT1	INSECTICIDES
NT1	MOLLUSCICIDES
RT	AGRICULTURAL POLLUTION
RT	AGRICULTURAL RUNOFF
RT	BIOACCUMULATION
RT	CHEMICAL CONTROL
RT	CHEMICAL POLLUTANTS
RT	CHEMICAL POLLUTION
RT	CHLORINATED HYDROCARBONS
RT	CONTROL RESISTANCE
RT	DDT

PESTICIDES (cont'd)
RT	DISINFECTANTS
RT	HAZARDOUS MATERIALS
RT	INFESTATION
RT	LETHAL LIMITS
RT	PEST CONTROL
RT	REPELLENTS
RT	TOXICANTS
RT	TOXICITY

PETROGENESIS
SN	Formation of rocks
BT1	GEOLOGY
BT2	EARTH SCIENCES
RT	ROCKS

PETROGRAPHY
USE	**PETROLOGY**

PETROLEUM
UF	mineral oils
BT1	FOSSIL FUELS
BT2	SUBSURFACE DEPOSITS
BT3	MINERAL DEPOSITS
BT4	MINERAL RESOURCES
NT1	CRUDE OIL
NT1	GAS CONDENSATES
NT1	NATURAL GAS
NT2	LIQUEFIED NATURAL GAS
NT1	PETROLEUM RESIDUES
RT	FUELS
RT	HYDROCARBON ANALYSIS
RT	INDUSTRIAL PRODUCTS
RT	LIQUEFIED PETROLEUM GAS
RT	OIL
RT	OIL AND GAS
RT	OIL AND GAS FIELDS
RT	OIL AND GAS INDUSTRY
RT	OIL SLICKS
RT	OIL WASTES
RT	OIL WELLS
RT	OIL-GAS INTERFACE
RT	OIL-WATER INTERFACE
RT	ORGANIC SEDIMENTS
RT	PETROLEUM ENGINEERING
RT	PETROLEUM HYDROCARBONS
RT	WAXES

PETROLEUM ENGINEERING
BT1	ENGINEERING
RT	CHEMICAL ENGINEERING
RT	OFFSHORE ENGINEERING
RT	PETROLEUM
RT	PETROLEUM RESIDUES

PETROLEUM GEOLOGY
BT1	GEOLOGY
BT2	EARTH SCIENCES
RT	OIL AND GAS EXPLORATION
RT	OIL AND GAS INDUSTRY
RT	OIL RESERVOIRS

PETROLEUM HYDROCARBON RESIDUES
USE	**PETROLEUM RESIDUES**

PETROLEUM HYDROCARBONS
BT1	HYDROCARBONS
BT2	ORGANIC COMPOUNDS
NT1	ASPHALT
NT1	BITUMENS
NT1	KEROGEN
NT1	TAR
NT1	VOLATILE HYDROCARBONS
RT	PETROLEUM
RT	PETROLEUM RESIDUES

PETROLEUM INDUSTRY
USE	**OIL AND GAS INDUSTRY**

PETROLEUM RESIDUES
UF	petroleum hydrocarbon residues
BT1	PETROLEUM
BT2	FOSSIL FUELS
BT3	SUBSURFACE DEPOSITS
BT4	MINERAL DEPOSITS
RT	ASPHALT
RT	BITUMENS
RT	OIL SANDS
RT	OIL SHALE
RT	PETROLEUM ENGINEERING
RT	PETROLEUM HYDROCARBONS
RT	TAR
RT	TAR BALLS

PETROLOGY
UF	petrography
UF	sedimentary petrography
BT1	GEOLOGY
BT2	EARTH SCIENCES
RT	GEOCHEMISTRY
RT	LITHOLOGY
RT	ROCKS
RT	SEDIMENTARY ROCKS
RT	SEDIMENTS

PH
UF	hydrogen ion concentration
BT1	CHEMICAL PROPERTIES
BT2	PROPERTIES
RT	ACIDIFICATION
RT	ACIDITY
RT	ALKALINITY
RT	BUFFERS
RT	HABITAT IMPROVEMENT (CHEMICAL)
RT	HYDROGEN
RT	INORGANIC ACIDS
RT	PH EFFECTS
RT	PH SENSORS
RT	WATER PROPERTIES

PH EFFECTS
SN	Added in 1980
BT1	ENVIRONMENTAL EFFECTS
RT	ACIDITY
RT	PH

PH SENSORS
RT	PH
RT	SENSORS

PHAGOCYTOSIS
BT1	DEFENCE MECHANISMS
RT	AMOEBOCYTES
RT	CELLS
RT	ENDOPARASITES
RT	ENDOPARASITISM
RT	MACROPHAGES

PHANEROZOIC
SN	Before 1982 search PHANEROZOIC EON
BT1	GEOLOGICAL TIME
RT	CENOZOIC
RT	MESOZOIC
RT	PALAEOZOIC

PHARMACEUTICAL PRODUCTS
USE	**DRUGS**

PHARMACODYNAMICS
USE	**PHARMACOLOGY**

PHARMACOLOGY
SN	Added in 1980
UF	pharmacodynamics
RT	BIOCHEMISTRY
RT	DRUGS

ASFIS Thesaurus

PHARMACOLOGY (cont'd)	
RT	MEDICINE
RT	MICROBIOLOGY
RT	THERAPY
RT	TOXICOLOGY
PHASE CHANGES	
UF	changes of state
UF	phase transformations
NT1	CONDENSATION
NT1	FLUIDIZATION
NT1	FREEZING
NT1	LIQUEFACTION
NT1	MELTING
NT2	ICE MELTING
NT1	SOLIDIFICATION
NT1	VAPORIZATION
NT2	EVAPORATION
NT3	EVAPOTRANSPIRATION
NT2	SUBLIMATION
RT	BOILING POINT
RT	FREEZING POINT
RT	LOW TEMPERATURE
RT	THERMODYNAMICS
RT	TRANSITION TEMPERATURES
PHASE TRANSFORMATIONS	
USE	**PHASE CHANGES**
PHASE VELOCITY	
BT1	VELOCITY
RT	GROUP VELOCITY
RT	WATER WAVES
RT	WAVE DISPERSION
RT	WAVE VELOCITY
PHENOLOGY	
RT	BEHAVIOUR
RT	BIOCLIMATOLOGY
RT	BIOLOGICAL RHYTHMS
RT	BREEDING
RT	CLIMATE
RT	CLIMATOLOGY
RT	ECOLOGY
RT	HYDROCLIMATE
RT	MIGRATIONS
RT	PHOTOPERIODICITY
RT	SEASONAL VARIATIONS
RT	TEMPORAL VARIATIONS
RT	VERTICAL MIGRATIONS
PHENOLS	
BT1	AROMATICS
RT	CHEMICAL COMPOUNDS
RT	CHEMICAL POLLUTANTS
RT	CHEMICAL POLLUTION
RT	INDUSTRIAL WASTES
RT	TOXICANTS
PHENOMENA (BIOLOGICAL)	
USE	**BIOLOGICAL PHENOMENA**
PHENOTYPES	
RT	ECOPHENE
RT	ENVIRONMENTAL EFFECTS
RT	GENOTYPES
RT	ORGANISM MORPHOLOGY
RT	PHENOTYPIC VARIATIONS
RT	TYPOLOGY
PHENOTYPIC VARIATIONS	
SN	Added in 1980
UF	variations (phenotypic)
RT	ENVIRONMENTAL EFFECTS
RT	PHENOTYPES

PHENYLALANINE	
BT1	AMINO ACIDS
BT2	ORGANIC ACIDS
BT3	ORGANIC COMPOUNDS
PHEROMONES	
BT1	HORMONES
BT2	SECRETORY PRODUCTS
RT	BEHAVIOUR
RT	ENDOCRINE GLANDS
RT	ENDOCRINOLOGY
PHILLIPSITE	
BT1	ZEOLITES
BT2	SILICATE MINERALS
BT3	MINERALS
PHONORECEPTORS	
USE	**AUDITORY ORGANS**
PHOSPHATE CYCLE	
USE	**PHOSPHORUS CYCLE**
PHOSPHATE DEPOSITS	
SN	Use only for deposits of economic value
BT1	SUBSURFACE DEPOSITS
BT2	MINERAL DEPOSITS
BT3	MINERAL RESOURCES
BT4	NATURAL RESOURCES
RT	AUTHIGENIC MINERALS
RT	GUANO
RT	PHOSPHATE ROCKS
RT	PHOSPHATES
RT	PHOSPHORITE NODULES
PHOSPHATE MINERALS	
BT1	MINERALS
NT1	APATITE
NT1	FRANCOLITE
NT1	MONAZITE
RT	PHOSPHATE ROCKS
RT	PHOSPHATES
RT	PHOSPHORITE NODULES
PHOSPHATE ROCKS	
BT1	CHEMICAL SEDIMENTS
BT2	SEDIMENTS
RT	PHOSPHATE DEPOSITS
RT	PHOSPHATE MINERALS
RT	PHOSPHATES
RT	PHOSPHORITE
RT	SEDIMENTARY ROCKS
PHOSPHATES	
BT1	PHOSPHORUS COMPOUNDS
NT1	ORTHOPHOSPHATE
RT	ADP
RT	AMP
RT	CALCIUM PHOSPHATES
RT	CHEMICAL COMPOUNDS
RT	FERTILIZERS
RT	IRON PHOSPHATES
RT	MAGNESIUM PHOSPHATES
RT	NON-CONSERVATIVE PROPERTIES
RT	NUTRIENTS (MINERAL)
RT	PHOSPHATE DEPOSITS
RT	PHOSPHATE MINERALS
RT	PHOSPHATE ROCKS
RT	PHOSPHATIZATION
RT	PHOSPHORIC ACID
RT	PHOSPHORUS CYCLE
RT	SALTS
PHOSPHATIC CONCRETIONS	
USE	**PHOSPHORITE NODULES**

PHOSPHATIZATION	
RT	PHOSPHATES
PHOSPHOLIPIDS	
USE	**COMPLEX LIPIDS**
PHOSPHORESCENCE	
UF	phosphorescent wheels
BT1	LUMINESCENCE
RT	BIOLOGICAL PROPERTIES
RT	BIOLUMINESCENCE
RT	CHEMICAL PROPERTIES
RT	CHEMILUMINESCENCE
RT	FLUORESCENCE
RT	LIGHT
PHOSPHORESCENT WHEELS	
USE	**PHOSPHORESCENCE**
PHOSPHORIC ACID	
SN	Before 1982 search also INORGANIC ACIDS
BT1	INORGANIC ACIDS
BT2	HYDROGEN COMPOUNDS
RT	PHOSPHATES
PHOSPHORITE	
RT	AUTHIGENIC MINERALS
RT	PHOSPHATE ROCKS
RT	PHOSPHORITE NODULES
PHOSPHORITE CONCRETIONS	
USE	**PHOSPHORITE NODULES**
PHOSPHORITE NODULES	
UF	phosphatic concretions
UF	phosphorite concretions
BT1	SEABED DEPOSITS
BT2	MINERAL DEPOSITS
BT3	MINERAL RESOURCES
BT4	NATURAL RESOURCES
RT	DEEP-SEA MINING
RT	NODULES
RT	PHOSPHATE DEPOSITS
RT	PHOSPHATE MINERALS
RT	PHOSPHORITE
PHOSPHORUS	
BT1	CHEMICAL ELEMENTS
NT1	ORGANIC PHOSPHORUS
NT2	DISSOLVED ORGANIC PHOSPHORUS
NT2	PARTICULATE ORGANIC PHOSPHORUS
RT	PHOSPHORUS COMPOUNDS
RT	PHOSPHORUS CYCLE
RT	PHOSPHORUS ISOTOPES
PHOSPHORUS COMPOUNDS	
NT1	PHOSPHATES
NT2	ORTHOPHOSPHATE
RT	CHEMICAL COMPOUNDS
RT	FERTILIZERS
RT	NUTRIENTS (MINERAL)
RT	ORGANIC COMPOUNDS
RT	ORGANIC PHOSPHORUS
RT	PHOSPHORUS
RT	PHOSPHORUS CYCLE
PHOSPHORUS CYCLE	
UF	phosphate cycle
BT1	NUTRIENT CYCLES
BT2	BIOGEOCHEMICAL CYCLE
BT3	CYCLES
RT	BACTERIA
RT	CHEMICAL CYCLES
RT	PHOSPHATES
RT	PHOSPHORUS
RT	PHOSPHORUS COMPOUNDS

PHOSPHORUS ISOTOPES
BT1	ISOTOPES
RT	PHOSPHORUS

PHOTIC ENVIRONMENT
USE	**EPIPELAGIC ZONE**

PHOTOCHEMICAL REACTIONS
SN	Added in 1980
UF	photoionization
UF	photoreduction
BT1	CHEMICAL REACTIONS
NT1	PHOTOLYSIS
NT1	PHOTOSYNTHESIS
NT2	CARBON FIXATION
RT	PHOTOCHEMISTRY

PHOTOCHEMISTRY
BT1	CHEMISTRY
RT	PHOTOCHEMICAL REACTIONS
RT	PHOTOLYSIS
RT	PHOTOSYNTHESIS

PHOTOGENIC ORGANS
USE	**PHOTOPHORES**

PHOTOGRAMMETRY
UF	photographic measurement
BT1	MEASUREMENT
RT	AERIAL PHOTOGRAPHY
RT	CARTOGRAPHY
RT	CURRENT MEASUREMENT
RT	PHOTOGRAPHS
RT	PHOTOGRAPHY
RT	STEREOPHOTOGRAPHY
RT	SURVEYING UNDERWATER
RT	WAVE MEASUREMENT

PHOTOGRAPHIC EQUIPMENT
BT1	EQUIPMENT
NT1	CAMERAS
NT2	UNDERWATER CAMERAS
RT	AERIAL PHOTOGRAPHY
RT	FILMS
RT	MICROPHOTOGRAPHY
RT	PHOTOGRAPHS
RT	PHOTOGRAPHY
RT	REMOTE SENSING EQUIPMENT
RT	SURVEYING EQUIPMENT
RT	UNDERWATER PHOTOGRAPHY

PHOTOGRAPHIC MEASUREMENT
USE	**PHOTOGRAMMETRY**

PHOTOGRAPHIC TECHNIQUES
USE	**PHOTOGRAPHY**

PHOTOGRAPHS
BT1	AUDIOVISUAL MATERIAL
BT2	DOCUMENTS
NT1	AERIAL PHOTOGRAPHS
NT1	UNDERWATER PHOTOGRAPHS
NT2	BOTTOM PHOTOGRAPHS
RT	MICROPHOTOGRAPHY
RT	PHOTOGRAMMETRY
RT	PHOTOGRAPHIC EQUIPMENT
RT	PHOTOGRAPHY

PHOTOGRAPHY
UF	photographic techniques
BT1	IMAGERY
BT2	REMOTE SENSING
NT1	AERIAL PHOTOGRAPHY
NT2	SATELLITE PHOTOGRAPHY
NT1	MICROPHOTOGRAPHY
NT1	STEREOPHOTOGRAPHY
NT1	UNDERWATER PHOTOGRAPHY
RT	CAMERAS
RT	FILMS
RT	HOLOGRAPHY

PHOTOGRAPHY (cont'd)
RT	OPTICS
RT	PHOTOGRAMMETRY
RT	PHOTOGRAPHIC EQUIPMENT
RT	PHOTOGRAPHS
RT	RADIOGRAPHY
RT	UNDERWATER EXPLORATION

PHOTOIONIZATION
USE	**PHOTOCHEMICAL REACTIONS**

PHOTOLYSIS
SN	Added in 1980
BT1	PHOTOCHEMICAL REACTIONS
BT2	CHEMICAL REACTIONS
RT	PHOTOCHEMISTRY

PHOTOMETERS
UF	hydrophotometers
BT1	LIGHT MEASURING INSTRUMENTS
BT2	MEASURING DEVICES
NT1	SPECTROPHOTOMETERS
RT	LIGHT
RT	LIGHT ABSORPTION
RT	LIGHT INTENSITY
RT	LIGHT PENETRATION
RT	NEPHELOMETERS
RT	PHOTOMETRY
RT	RADIOMETERS

PHOTOMETRY
BT1	LIGHT MEASUREMENT
BT2	MEASUREMENT
RT	CHEMICAL ANALYSIS
RT	COLORIMETRIC TECHNIQUES
RT	LIGHT
RT	LIGHT INTENSITY
RT	LIGHT PENETRATION
RT	PHOTOMETERS
RT	QUANTA METERS
RT	SPECTROSCOPIC TECHNIQUES

PHOTOPERIOD EFFECTS
USE	**LIGHT EFFECTS**

PHOTOPERIODICITY
UF	photoperiodism
RT	BIOLOGICAL RHYTHMS
RT	BREEDING
RT	DIAPAUSE
RT	DIURNAL VARIATIONS
RT	ECOLOGY
RT	LIGHT
RT	LIGHT EFFECTS
RT	LIGHT STIMULI
RT	MIGRATIONS
RT	PHENOLOGY
RT	PHOTOPERIODS
RT	REPRODUCTIVE BEHAVIOUR
RT	VERTICAL MIGRATIONS

PHOTOPERIODISM
USE	**PHOTOPERIODICITY**

PHOTOPERIODS
SN	Before 1982 search PHOTOPERIODICITY
UF	day length
UF	light duration
RT	CIRCADIAN RHYTHMS
RT	DIURNAL VARIATIONS
RT	ECOPHYSIOLOGY
RT	LIGHT EFFECTS
RT	PHOTOPERIODICITY

PHOTOPHELEIN
USE	**LUCIFERIN**

PHOTOPHORES
SN	Added in 1980
UF	light organs
UF	luminescent organs
UF	luminous organs
UF	photogenic organs
BT1	ANIMAL ORGANS
BT2	BODY ORGANS
RT	BIOLUMINESCENCE
RT	FISH
RT	LUMINOUS ORGANISMS
RT	MARINE CRUSTACEANS

PHOTOPOLYMERIZATION
USE	**POLYMERIZATION**

PHOTORECEPTION
SN	Added in 1982
BT1	SENSE FUNCTIONS
RT	LIGHT STIMULI
RT	VISION

PHOTORECEPTORS
BT1	SENSE ORGANS
BT2	ANIMAL ORGANS
BT3	BODY ORGANS
NT1	EYES
NT2	COMPOUND EYES
NT2	EYESTALKS
NT2	RETINAS
RT	LIGHT
RT	VISION

PHOTOREDUCTION
USE	**PHOTOCHEMICAL REACTIONS**

PHOTOSYNTHESIS
BT1	PHOTOCHEMICAL REACTIONS
BT2	CHEMICAL REACTIONS
NT1	CARBON FIXATION
RT	BIOGEOCHEMICAL CYCLE
RT	BIOSYNTHESIS
RT	CARBON DIOXIDE
RT	CAROTENOIDS
RT	CHEMICAL REACTIONS
RT	CHEMOSYNTHESIS
RT	CHLOROPHYLLS
RT	COMPENSATION DEPTH
RT	DISPHOTIC ZONE
RT	EUPHOTIC ZONE
RT	LEAVES
RT	LIGHT
RT	LIGHT PENETRATION
RT	LIGHT STIMULI
RT	OXYGEN DEMAND
RT	PHOTOCHEMISTRY
RT	PHOTOSYNTHETIC PIGMENTS
RT	PHYTOBENTHOS
RT	PHYTOPLANKTON
RT	PLANKTONOLOGY
RT	PLANT METABOLISM
RT	PLANT NUTRITION
RT	PLANT PHYSIOLOGY
RT	PRIMARY PRODUCTION
RT	QUANTA METERS
RT	SOLAR RADIATION
RT	TRANSPIRATION
RT	XANTHOPHYLLS

PHOTOSYNTHETIC PIGMENTS
BT1	PIGMENTS
BT2	GLYCOSIDES
BT3	CARBOHYDRATES
BT4	ORGANIC COMPOUNDS
NT1	CHLOROPHYLLS
NT1	XANTHOPHYLLS
RT	CAROTENOIDS
RT	CHLOROPLASTS
RT	PHOTOSYNTHESIS

PHOTOTAXIS		**PHYSICAL LIMNOLOGY** (cont'd)		**PHYSICAL PROPERTIES** (cont'd)	
BT1	TAXIS	RT	PHYSICAL PROPERTIES	NT3	TENSILE STRENGTH
BT2	ORIENTATION BEHAVIOUR	RT	PHYSICS	NT2	TOUGHNESS
BT3	BEHAVIOUR	RT	THERMAL STRATIFICATION	NT2	VISCOSITY
RT	LIGHT	RT	WATER ANALYSIS	NT3	DYNAMIC VISCOSITY
RT	LIGHT EFFECTS	RT	WATER CIRCULATION	NT3	EDDY VISCOSITY
RT	LIGHT PENETRATION	RT	WATER CURRENTS	NT3	KINEMATIC VISCOSITY
RT	LIGHT STIMULI	RT	WATER PROPERTIES	NT3	MOLECULAR VISCOSITY
RT	NYCTIMERAL RHYTHMS	RT	WATER TEMPERATURE	NT2	YIELD POINT
RT	PHOTOTROPISM	RT	WATER WAVES	NT1	OPTICAL PROPERTIES
RT	SOLAR RADIATION			NT2	ABSORPTANCE
RT	VERTICAL MIGRATIONS	**PHYSICAL MODELS**		NT2	ANGULAR DISTRIBUTION
		USE	**SCALE MODELS**	NT2	ATTENUANCE
PHOTOTROPISM				NT2	COLOUR
UF	thermophototropism	**PHYSICAL OCEANOGRAPHY**		NT3	WATER COLOUR
BT1	TROPISM	UF	marine physics	NT2	EXTINCTION COEFFICIENT
RT	CIRCADIAN RHYTHMS	UF	oceanography (physical)	NT2	REFLECTANCE
RT	LIGHT	BT1	OCEANOGRAPHY	NT2	REFRACTIVE INDEX
RT	LIGHT EFFECTS	BT2	EARTH SCIENCES	NT2	SCATTERING COEFFICIENT
RT	LIGHT PENETRATION	NT1	HYDROGRAPHY	NT2	SPECTRAL COMPOSITION
RT	LIGHT STIMULI	RT	HYDRODYNAMICS	NT2	TRANSMITTANCE
RT	MOON PHASES	RT	MARINE SCIENCES	NT3	BEAM TRANSMITTANCE
RT	NYCTIMERAL RHYTHMS	RT	METEOROLOGY	NT2	TRANSPARENCY
RT	PHOTOTAXIS	RT	PHYSICAL PROPERTIES	NT3	WATER TRANSPARENCY
RT	SOLAR RADIATION	RT	PHYSICS	NT2	VOLUME SCATTERING FUNCTION
RT	VERTICAL MIGRATIONS	RT	SEA ICE	NT1	PERMEABILITY
		RT	THERMAL STRATIFICATION	NT1	POROSITY
PHREATIC WATER		RT	WATER ANALYSIS	NT1	PRESSURE
USE	**GROUND WATER**	RT	WATER CIRCULATION	NT2	ATMOSPHERIC PRESSURE
		RT	WATER CURRENTS	NT3	SEA LEVEL PRESSURE
PHTHALATE ESTERS		RT	WATER PROPERTIES	NT2	BLOOD PRESSURE
UF	phthalic acid esters	RT	WATER TEMPERATURE	NT2	HYDROSTATIC PRESSURE
BT1	ESTERS	RT	WATER WAVES	NT3	BOTTOM PRESSURE
BT2	ORGANIC COMPOUNDS			NT2	OSMOTIC PRESSURE
RT	CHEMICAL POLLUTANTS	**PHYSICAL PROPERTIES**		NT2	PORE PRESSURE
RT	CHEMICAL POLLUTION	BT1	PROPERTIES	NT2	SOUND PRESSURE
		NT1	ACOUSTIC PROPERTIES	NT2	VAPOUR PRESSURE
PHTHALIC ACID ESTERS		NT1	ANISOTROPY	NT3	SATURATION VAPOUR PRESSURE
USE	**PHTHALATE ESTERS**	NT1	BUOYANCY	NT1	SPECIFIC GRAVITY
		NT1	COLLIGATIVE PROPERTIES	NT1	THERMODYNAMIC PROPERTIES
PHYCOLOGISTS		NT1	DENSITY	NT2	ENTHALPY
USE	**ALGOLOGISTS**	NT2	CURRENT DENSITY	NT3	FUSION HEAT
		NT2	SEDIMENT DENSITY	NT3	SUBLIMATION HEAT
PHYCOLOGY		NT3	WET BULK DENSITY	NT3	VAPORIZATION HEAT
USE	**ALGOLOGY**	NT2	WATER DENSITY	NT2	ENTROPY
		NT3	IN SITU DENSITY	NT2	FREE ENERGY
PHYLLOSOMAE		NT3	POTENTIAL DENSITY	NT2	SPECIFIC HEAT
SN	Added in 1980	NT3	RELATIVE DENSITY	NT2	TEMPERATURE
BT1	CRUSTACEAN LARVAE	NT3	SIGMA-T	NT3	AIR TEMPERATURE
BT2	INVERTEBRATE LARVAE	NT1	ELECTRICAL PROPERTIES	NT3	BODY TEMPERATURE
BT3	LARVAE	NT2	CAPACITANCE	NT3	LOW TEMPERATURE
BT4	DEVELOPMENTAL STAGES	NT2	DIELECTRIC CONSTANT	NT3	POTENTIAL TEMPERATURE
RT	MARINE CRUSTACEANS	NT2	ELECTRIC IMPEDANCE	NT3	SEDIMENT TEMPERATURE
		NT2	ELECTRICAL CONDUCTIVITY	NT3	TRANSITION TEMPERATURES
PHYLOGENETICS		NT2	ELECTRICAL RESISTIVITY	NT4	BOILING POINT
SN	The study of evolutionary	NT1	GEOTHERMAL PROPERTIES	NT4	DEW POINT
	relationships. Added in 1980	NT1	MAGNETIC PROPERTIES	NT4	FREEZING POINT
RT	BIOLOGICAL SPECIATION	NT2	MAGNETIC FIELD ELEMENTS	NT4	MELTING POINT
RT	EVOLUTION	NT3	MAGNETIC INCLINATION	NT3	WATER TEMPERATURE
RT	PHYLOGENY	NT3	MAGNETIC INTENSITY	NT4	BOTTOM TEMPERATURE
RT	TAXONOMY	NT3	MAGNETIC VARIATIONS	NT4	IN SITU TEMPERATURE
		NT2	MAGNETIC PERMEABILITY	NT4	PALAEOTEMPERATURE
PHYLOGENY		NT2	MAGNETIC SUSCEPTIBILITY	NT4	SURFACE TEMPERATURE
RT	BIOLOGICAL SPECIATION	NT2	REMANENT MAGNETIZATION	NT2	THERMAL CONDUCTIVITY
RT	BIOSELECTION	NT1	MASS	NT2	THERMAL DIFFUSIVITY
RT	EVOLUTION	NT1	MECHANICAL PROPERTIES	NT2	THERMAL EXPANSION
RT	ONTOGENY	NT2	ANELASTICITY	NT2	THERMODYNAMIC ACTIVITY
RT	PHYLOGENETICS	NT2	BRITTLENESS	NT2	THERMODYNAMIC EQUILIBRIUM
RT	TAXONOMY	NT2	COMPRESSIBILITY	NT1	TURBIDITY
		NT2	DEFORMATION	NT1	WATER HARDNESS
PHYSICAL LIMNOLOGY		NT3	ROCK DEFORMATION	NT1	WEIGHT
SN	Before 1982 search LIMNOLOGY	NT4	DIAPIRISM	NT2	DRY WEIGHT
	(PHYSICAL)	NT3	STRAIN	NT2	MOLECULAR WEIGHT
UF	limnology (physical)	NT2	ELASTICITY	NT2	WET WEIGHT
BT1	LIMNOLOGY	NT2	FLEXIBILITY	RT	CHEMICAL PROPERTIES
RT	HYDRODYNAMICS	NT2	STRENGTH	RT	DIFFUSION
RT	HYDROGRAPHY	NT3	BEARING CAPACITY	RT	ENVIRONMENTAL CHARTS
RT	LAKE CURRENTS	NT3	COLLAPSE STRENGTH	RT	ENVIRONMENTAL EFFECTS
RT	LAKE DYNAMICS	NT3	COMPRESSIVE STRENGTH	RT	ENVIRONMENTAL FACTORS
RT	LAKE ICE	NT3	SHEAR STRENGTH	RT	HABITAT IMPROVEMENT (PHYSICAL)

PHYSICAL PROPERTIES (cont'd)

RT	KINETICS
RT	LUMINESCENCE
RT	PHYSICAL LIMNOLOGY
RT	PHYSICAL OCEANOGRAPHY
RT	PHYSICOCHEMICAL PROPERTIES
RT	PHYSICS
RT	SEDIMENT PROPERTIES
RT	SOLUBILITY
RT	SURFACE PROPERTIES
RT	WATER ANALYSIS
RT	WATER PROPERTIES
RT	WAVE PROPERTIES

PHYSICOCHEMICAL PROPERTIES

BT1	PROPERTIES
RT	BIOLOGICAL PROPERTIES
RT	CHEMICAL PROPERTIES
RT	PHYSICAL PROPERTIES
RT	WATER PROPERTIES

PHYSICS

NT1	ACOUSTICS
NT2	BIOACOUSTICS
NT2	ULTRASONICS
NT1	ATMOSPHERIC PHYSICS
NT2	CLOUD PHYSICS
NT1	BIOPHYSICS
NT1	MECHANICS
NT2	DYNAMICS
NT3	CABLE DYNAMICS
NT3	SEDIMENT DYNAMICS
NT3	STRUCTURAL DYNAMICS
NT2	FLUID MECHANICS
NT3	FLUID DYNAMICS
NT4	AERODYNAMICS
NT3	HYDRODYNAMICS
NT3	HYDROSTATICS
NT2	HYDRAULICS
NT2	KINEMATICS
NT2	KINETICS
NT3	RADIONUCLIDE KINETICS
NT2	RHEOLOGY
NT2	ROCK MECHANICS
NT2	SOIL MECHANICS
NT1	NUCLEAR PHYSICS
NT1	OPTICS
NT1	THERMODYNAMICS
RT	ELECTROMAGNETISM
RT	ENERGY
RT	LIGHT
RT	MAGNETISM
RT	PHYSICAL LIMNOLOGY
RT	PHYSICAL OCEANOGRAPHY
RT	PHYSICAL PROPERTIES

PHYSIOCHEMISTRY

USE	**BIOCHEMISTRY**

PHYSIOGRAPHIC FEATURES

USE	**TOPOGRAPHIC FEATURES**

PHYSIOGRAPHIC PROVINCES

RT	BOTTOM TOPOGRAPHY
RT	LANDFORMS
RT	SUBMARINE FEATURES
RT	TOPOGRAPHIC FEATURES

PHYSIOGRAPHY

USE	**GEOMORPHOLOGY**

PHYSIOLOGICAL ADAPTATIONS

USE	**ACCLIMATIZATION**

PHYSIOLOGICAL CALCIFICATION

USE	**CALCIFICATION**

PHYSIOLOGICAL ECOLOGY

USE	**ECOPHYSIOLOGY**

PHYSIOLOGISTS

SN	Added in 1980
BT1	BIOLOGISTS
BT2	SCIENTIFIC PERSONNEL
BT3	PERSONNEL
NT1	ANIMAL PHYSIOLOGISTS
NT1	PLANT PHYSIOLOGISTS
RT	DIRECTORIES
RT	PHYSIOLOGY

PHYSIOLOGY

BT1	BIOLOGY
NT1	ANIMAL PHYSIOLOGY
NT2	AVIAN PHYSIOLOGY
NT2	FISH PHYSIOLOGY
NT2	MAMMALIAN PHYSIOLOGY
NT1	DIVING PHYSIOLOGY
NT1	ECOPHYSIOLOGY
NT1	ELECTROPHYSIOLOGY
NT1	ENDOCRINOLOGY
NT1	HUMAN PHYSIOLOGY
NT1	NEUROPHYSIOLOGY
NT1	PLANT PHYSIOLOGY
RT	ANATOMY
RT	BIOCHEMISTRY
RT	BIOPHYSICS
RT	BODY ORGANS
RT	CHOLINESTERASE INHIBITORS
RT	COMPARATIVE STUDIES
RT	CRYOBIOLOGY
RT	DIGESTION
RT	HORMONES
RT	METABOLISM
RT	NUTRITION
RT	PATHOLOGY
RT	PHYSIOLOGISTS
RT	REPRODUCTION
RT	RESPIRATION
RT	SYNERGISM

PHYSIOLOGY (ANIMAL)

USE	**ANIMAL PHYSIOLOGY**

PHYSIOLOGY (AQUATIC MAMMALS)

USE	**MAMMALIAN PHYSIOLOGY**

PHYSIOLOGY (FISH)

USE	**FISH PHYSIOLOGY**

PHYSIOLOGY (PLANTS)

USE	**PLANT PHYSIOLOGY**

PHYTOBENTHOS

UF	benthic algae
UF	benthic flora
BT1	BENTHOS
BT2	AQUATIC COMMUNITIES
RT	ALGOLOGY
RT	AQUATIC PLANTS
RT	ECOLOGICAL ZONATION
RT	PHOTOSYNTHESIS
RT	PRIMARY PRODUCTION

PHYTOGEOGRAPHY

USE	**BIOGEOGRAPHY**

PHYTOHORMONES

SN	Before 1982 search HORMONES
UF	cytokinins
UF	gibberellins
UF	plant hormones
BT1	HORMONES
BT2	SECRETORY PRODUCTS
RT	AQUATIC PLANTS
RT	AUXINS
RT	PLANT PHYSIOLOGY

PHYTOLOGY

USE	**BOTANY**

PHYTOPHAGOUS FISHES

USE	**HERBIVOROUS FISH**

PHYTOPLANKTON

UF	planktonic algae
BT1	PLANKTON
BT2	AQUATIC COMMUNITIES
RT	ALGAL BLOOMS
RT	ALGOLOGISTS
RT	ALGOLOGY
RT	AQUATIC PLANTS
RT	BOTANY
RT	CELL COUNTERS
RT	EUPHOTIC ZONE
RT	FOOD ORGANISMS
RT	PHOTOSYNTHESIS
RT	PHYTOPLANKTON CULTURE
RT	PLANKTONOLOGY
RT	PRIMARY PRODUCTION
RT	RED TIDES

PHYTOPLANKTON CULTURE

UF	diatom culture
UF	single cell culture
BT1	ALGAL CULTURE
BT2	AQUACULTURE
RT	CELL CULTURE
RT	CONTINUOUS CULTURE
RT	CONTROLLED CONDITIONS
RT	CULTURED ORGANISMS
RT	CULTURES
RT	LABORATORY CULTURE
RT	MASS CULTURE
RT	PHYTOPLANKTON
RT	PLANT CULTURE

PHYTOSOCIOLOGY

UF	plant sociology
BT1	ECOLOGY
RT	AQUATIC PLANTS
RT	BIOGEOGRAPHY
RT	BOTANY

PIERS

BT1	COASTAL STRUCTURES
BT2	HYDRAULIC STRUCTURES

PIEZOELECTRIC TRANSDUCERS

BT1	TRANSDUCERS
RT	ACOUSTIC TRANSDUCERS
RT	HYDROPHONES

PIGGING

RT	CLEANING
RT	PIPELINE PIGS

PIGMENTS

BT1	GLYCOSIDES
BT2	CARBOHYDRATES
BT3	ORGANIC COMPOUNDS
NT1	CHROMATIC PIGMENTS
NT2	CAROTENOIDS
NT1	PHOTOSYNTHETIC PIGMENTS
NT2	CHLOROPHYLLS
NT2	XANTHOPHYLLS
NT1	RESPIRATORY PIGMENTS
NT2	HAEMOCYANINS
NT2	HAEMOGLOBINS
NT1	VISUAL PIGMENTS
RT	CHROMATIC BEHAVIOUR
RT	CHROMATOPHORES
RT	DISCOLOURATION
RT	DYES
RT	PORPHYRINS

ASFIS Thesaurus

PIGS
USE **PIPELINE PIGS**

PILCHARD FISHERIES
USE **CLUPEOID FISHERIES**

PILE DRIVING
RT BEARING CAPACITY
RT GEOTECHNOLOGY
RT PILES

PILED PLATFORMS
UF jackets
BT1 FIXED PLATFORMS
BT2 OFFSHORE STRUCTURES
BT3 HYDRAULIC STRUCTURES
RT GUYED TOWERS

PILES
SN Before 1986 search also PILES
(FOUNDATIONS) and PILING
UF piles (foundations)
UF piling
BT1 FOUNDATIONS
RT GEOTECHNOLOGY
RT LEE EDDIES
RT PILE DRIVING
RT SCOUR PROTECTION

PILES (FOUNDATIONS)
USE **PILES**

PILING
USE **PILES**

PILLOW LAVA
BT1 LAVA
BT2 VOLCANIC ROCKS
BT3 IGNEOUS ROCKS
BT4 ROCKS
RT PALAGONITE
RT PILLOW STRUCTURES

PILLOW STRUCTURES
BT1 SEDIMENTARY STRUCTURES
RT PILLOW LAVA

PILOT CHARTS
UF routeing charts
BT1 NAVIGATIONAL CHARTS
BT2 MAPS
BT3 GRAPHICS
BT4 AUDIOVISUAL MATERIAL
RT SAILING DIRECTIONS

PILOT-SCALE CULTURE
USE **EXPERIMENTAL CULTURE**

PINEAL GLAND
USE **PINEAL ORGAN**

PINEAL ORGAN
UF pineal gland
BT1 BRAIN
BT2 CENTRAL NERVOUS SYSTEM
BT3 NERVOUS SYSTEM
RT NEUROSECRETION
RT NEUROSECRETORY SYSTEM

PINGERS
BT1 SOUND GENERATORS
BT2 ACOUSTIC EQUIPMENT
BT3 EQUIPMENT
RT ACOUSTIC TRACKING SYSTEMS
RT ELECTROACOUSTIC DEVICES
RT SWALLOW FLOATS
RT TRACKING

PIPE BUCKLING
UF buckling (pipe)
RT DEFORMATION

PIPE LAYING
SN Pipeline construction from barges
BT1 PIPELINE CONSTRUCTION
BT2 CONSTRUCTION

PIPE STRINGERS
UF stringers
RT PIPELAYING BARGES

PIPELAYING BARGES
BT1 BARGES
BT2 SURFACE CRAFT
BT3 VEHICLES
RT PIPE STRINGERS

PIPELINE CONSTRUCTION
BT1 CONSTRUCTION
NT1 BOTTOM TOW
NT1 PIPE LAYING
RT ANCHORING
RT BURYING
RT COATING PROCESSES
RT CONNECTING
RT PIPELINE CROSSING
RT PIPELINES
RT TRENCHING
RT WELDING

PIPELINE CROSSING
RT PIPELINE CONSTRUCTION
RT PIPELINES

PIPELINE PIGS
UF pigs
RT PIGGING

PIPELINE PROTECTION
BT1 EROSION CONTROL
BT2 CONTROL
RT ARTIFICIAL SEAWEED
RT BURYING
RT PIPELINES
RT SCOUR PROTECTION
RT SCOURING

PIPELINE PUMPING STATIONS
USE **PUMP STATIONS**

PIPELINES
UF submarine pipelines
BT1 UNDERWATER STRUCTURES
BT2 OFFSHORE STRUCTURES
BT3 HYDRAULIC STRUCTURES
NT1 FLOWLINES
NT1 GATHERING LINES
RT BURYING
RT EXPLOITATION
RT GAS TERMINALS
RT OFFSHORE TERMINALS
RT OIL POLLUTION
RT OIL SPILLS
RT OIL WELLS
RT PIPELINE CONSTRUCTION
RT PIPELINE CROSSING
RT PIPELINE PROTECTION
RT PUMP STATIONS
RT PUMPS
RT SCOUR PROTECTION
RT TRENCHES (PIPELINES)
RT UNDERWATER EXPLOITATION

PIPES
SN Before 1986 search also PIPE
UF line pipe
NT1 RISER PIPES
RT HOSES

PIPES (cont'd)
RT TUBING

PISCICIDES
USE **ICHTHYOCIDES**

PISCICULTURE
USE **FISH CULTURE**

PISCINE ERYTHROCYTE NECROSIS
USE **NECROSES**

PISTON CORERS
SN Before 1986 use also PISTON SAMPLERS
UF piston samplers
BT1 CORERS
BT2 SEDIMENT SAMPLERS
BT3 SAMPLERS

PISTON SAMPLERS
USE **PISTON CORERS**

PITCH (MINERAL)
USE **BITUMENS**

PITCH RESONANCE
BT1 RESONANCE
RT BUOY MOTION EFFECTS
RT PITCHING

PITCH RESPONSE
BT1 DYNAMIC RESPONSE
BT2 INSTRUMENT RESPONSES
RT BUOY MOTION EFFECTS
RT PITCHING

PITCHING
BT1 SHIP MOTION
RT BUOY MOTION
RT BUOY MOTION EFFECTS
RT DYNAMIC RESPONSE
RT PITCH RESONANCE
RT PITCH RESPONSE

PITS
SN Added in 1980
UF gravel pits
UF open mines
UF quarries
UF sand pits
RT AQUACULTURE FACILITIES
RT LAKES
RT SPORT FISHING
RT STRIP MINE LAKES

PITTING
USE **CORROSION**

PITUITARY GLAND
UF hypophysis
BT1 ENDOCRINE GLANDS
BT2 GLANDS
BT3 SECRETORY ORGANS
RT HORMONES
RT HYPOPHYSECTOMY

PLACENTA
SN Added in 1980
RT FOETUS
RT OVARIES
RT PREGNANCY
RT SPORANGIA
RT SPORES

PLACER DEPOSITS
USE **PLACERS**

PLACER MINING
BT1	MINING
RT	MINERAL DEPOSITS
RT	MINERAL EXPLORATION
RT	PLACERS

PLACERS
UF	placer deposits
BT1	SEABED DEPOSITS
BT2	MINERAL DEPOSITS
BT3	MINERAL RESOURCES
BT4	NATURAL RESOURCES
NT1	DIAMONDS
RT	ARENITES
RT	BARITE
RT	CASSITERITE
RT	CHROMITE
RT	GARNET
RT	GOLD
RT	ILMENITE
RT	MAGNETITE
RT	MONAZITE
RT	PLACER MINING
RT	PLATINUM
RT	RUTILE
RT	ZIRCON

PLAGIOCLASE
BT1	FELDSPARS
BT2	SILICATE MINERALS
BT3	MINERALS

PLAICE FISHERIES
USE	**FLATFISH FISHERIES**

PLAINS
BT1	LANDFORMS
BT2	TOPOGRAPHIC FEATURES
RT	ABYSSAL PLAINS
RT	FLOOD PLAINS

PLANATION SURFACES
USE	**EROSION SURFACES**

PLANETARY ATMOSPHERES
UF	atmosphere (planetary)
NT1	EARTH ATMOSPHERE
NT2	STRATOSPHERE
NT2	TROPOPAUSE
NT2	TROPOSPHERE
NT2	UPPER ATMOSPHERE
NT3	IONOSPHERE

PLANETARY BOUNDARY LAYER
USE	**ATMOSPHERIC BOUNDARY LAYER**

PLANETARY VORTICITY
BT1	VORTICITY
RT	CORIOLIS PARAMETERS
RT	WESTWARD INTENSIFICATION

PLANETARY WAVES
UF	quasi-geostrophic waves
UF	rossby waves
UF	topographic planetary waves
UF	waves (planetary)
RT	ATMOSPHERIC MOTION
RT	EQUATORIAL DYNAMICS
RT	FLUID MOTION
RT	JET STREAM
RT	ROSSBY PARAMETER
RT	WATER MOTION
RT	WATER WAVES

PLANETARY WINDS
UF	zonal wind systems
BT1	WINDS
BT2	ATMOSPHERIC MOTION
NT1	MONSOONS
NT1	TRADE WINDS

PLANETARY WINDS (cont'd)
NT2	EQUATORIAL EASTERLIES
NT1	WESTERLIES
NT2	EQUATORIAL WESTERLIES
RT	ATMOSPHERIC CIRCULATION

PLANKTIVORES
USE	**PLANKTON FEEDERS**

PLANKTON
BT1	AQUATIC COMMUNITIES
NT1	CRYOPLANKTON
NT1	NANNOPLANKTON
NT1	PHYTOPLANKTON
NT1	ZOOPLANKTON
NT2	HOLOPLANKTON
NT2	ICHTHYOPLANKTON
NT2	MEROPLANKTON
NT2	SAPROPLANKTON
RT	AIR-WATER EXCHANGES
RT	BIOLOGICAL PRODUCTION
RT	ENTRAINMENT
RT	FLOTATION
RT	INDICATOR SPECIES
RT	LUMINOUS ORGANISMS
RT	PELAGIC ENVIRONMENT
RT	PLANKTON COLLECTING DEVICES
RT	PLANKTON EQUIVALENTS
RT	PLANKTON FEEDERS
RT	PLANKTON SURVEYS
RT	PLANKTONOLOGY
RT	SESTON
RT	SINKING

PLANKTON BLOOMS
USE	**ALGAL BLOOMS**

PLANKTON COLLECTING DEVICES
UF	plankton nets
BT1	COLLECTING DEVICES
RT	AVOIDANCE REACTIONS
RT	ESCAPEMENT
RT	FISHING NETS
RT	ICHTHYOPLANKTON
RT	LIMNOLOGICAL EQUIPMENT
RT	NEUSTON
RT	PLANKTON
RT	PLANKTON SURVEYS
RT	PLANKTONOLOGY
RT	ZOOPLANKTON

PLANKTON ENTRAINMENT
USE	**ENTRAINMENT**

PLANKTON EQUIVALENTS
BT1	POPULATION FACTORS
RT	BIOCHEMICAL COMPOSITION
RT	BIOLOGICAL PRODUCTION
RT	BIOMASS
RT	PLANKTON

PLANKTON FEEDERS
UF	planktivores
BT1	HETEROTROPHIC ORGANISMS
BT2	AQUATIC ORGANISMS
RT	CARNIVORES
RT	FEEDING BEHAVIOUR
RT	FILTER FEEDERS
RT	HERBIVORES
RT	NANNOPLANKTON
RT	PLANKTON

PLANKTON NETS
USE	**PLANKTON COLLECTING DEVICES**

PLANKTON STUDIES
USE	**PLANKTONOLOGY**

PLANKTON SURVEYS
SN	Added in 1980
BT1	BIOLOGICAL SURVEYS
BT2	SURVEYS
NT1	ICHTHYOPLANKTON SURVEYS
RT	PLANKTON
RT	PLANKTON COLLECTING DEVICES
RT	SORTING CENTRES

PLANKTONIC ALGAE
USE	**PHYTOPLANKTON**

PLANKTONOLOGY
UF	plankton studies
BT1	ECOLOGY
RT	ECOLOGISTS
RT	FOOD CHAINS
RT	ICHTHYOPLANKTON
RT	ICHTHYOPLANKTON SURVEYS
RT	MARINE SCIENCES
RT	PHOTOSYNTHESIS
RT	PHYTOPLANKTON
RT	PLANKTON
RT	PLANKTON COLLECTING DEVICES
RT	PRIMARY PRODUCTION
RT	ZOOPLANKTON

PLANNING
SN	Added in 1980
UF	programming
NT1	LONG-TERM PLANNING
NT1	NATIONAL PLANNING
NT1	REGIONAL PLANNING
NT1	SHORT-TERM PLANNING
RT	CRUISE PROGRAMMES
RT	CRUISES
RT	ECONOMICS
RT	EXPLOITATION
RT	FINANCING
RT	LEGAL ASPECTS
RT	LEGISLATION
RT	MANAGEMENT
RT	MARKETING
RT	METHODOLOGY
RT	MULTISHIP EXPEDITIONS
RT	OPERATIONS RESEARCH
RT	PERT
RT	PROCEDURES
RT	PROGRAMMES
RT	RESEARCH PROGRAMMES
RT	SITE SELECTION

PLANNING (NATIONAL)
USE	**NATIONAL PLANNING**

PLANNING AT NATIONAL LEVEL
USE	**NATIONAL PLANNING**

PLANT (EQUIPMENT)
USE	**EQUIPMENT**

PLANT CONTROL
SN	Chemical, biological and mechanical control of aquatic weeds and injurious algae
UF	aquatic weed control
UF	vegetation control
UF	weed cutting
BT1	CONTROL
RT	ALGICIDES
RT	BIOLOGICAL CONTROL
RT	CHEMICAL CONTROL
RT	FRESHWATER WEEDS
RT	HABITAT IMPROVEMENT (BIOLOGICAL)
RT	HARVESTING
RT	HERBICIDES
RT	HERBIVOROUS FISH
RT	PEST CONTROL
RT	PLANT DISEASES
RT	PLANT UTILIZATION

PLANT CONTROL (cont'd)
RT	VEGETATION COVER
RT	WEEDS

PLANT CULTURE
SN	Applies only to culture of aquatic macrophytes. Added in 1980
UF	aquatic plant culture
BT1	AQUACULTURE
RT	AGROPISCICULTURE
RT	AQUACULTURE TECHNIQUES
RT	BOTANISTS
RT	CULTURES
RT	PHYTOPLANKTON CULTURE
RT	SEAWEED CULTURE

PLANT DISEASES
SN	Added in 1980
BT1	DISEASES
RT	AQUATIC PLANTS
RT	PARASITIC DISEASES
RT	PEST CONTROL
RT	PLANT CONTROL
RT	PLANT PHYSIOLOGY
RT	WEEDS

PLANT FOSSILS
USE	**VEGETAL FOSSILS**

PLANT GROWTH
USE	**GROWTH**

PLANT HORMONES
USE	**PHYTOHORMONES**

PLANT METABOLISM
SN	Before 1982 search METABOLISM
BT1	METABOLISM
RT	PHOTOSYNTHESIS
RT	PLANT PHYSIOLOGY

PLANT MORPHOLOGY
SN	Before 1982 search MORPHOLOGY (ORGANISMS)
UF	morphology (plant)
BT1	ORGANISM MORPHOLOGY
BT2	BIOLOGY
RT	AQUATIC PLANTS
RT	BUDS
RT	PLANT ORGANS
RT	PLANT PHYSIOLOGY

PLANT NUTRITION
UF	nutrition (plants)
BT1	NUTRITION
RT	AUTOTROPHY
RT	FERTILITY
RT	NUTRIENT DEFICIENCY
RT	NUTRIENTS (MINERAL)
RT	PHOTOSYNTHESIS
RT	PLANT PHYSIOLOGY

PLANT ORGANS
SN	Added in 1980
UF	organs (plant)
BT1	BODY ORGANS
NT1	HOLDFASTS
NT1	LEAVES
NT1	PLANT REPRODUCTIVE STRUCTURES
NT2	TURIONS
NT1	RHIZOMES
NT1	ROOTS
NT1	STEMS
NT1	THALLUS
RT	BUDS
RT	PLANT MORPHOLOGY
RT	PLANT PHYSIOLOGY
RT	TISSUES

PLANT PHYSIOLOGISTS
SN	Added in 1980
BT1	PHYSIOLOGISTS
BT2	BIOLOGISTS
BT3	SCIENTIFIC PERSONNEL
BT4	PERSONNEL
RT	ALGOLOGISTS
RT	BOTANISTS
RT	DIRECTORIES
RT	PLANT PHYSIOLOGY

PLANT PHYSIOLOGY
SN	Before 1982 search PHYSIOLOGY
UF	physiology (plants)
BT1	PHYSIOLOGY
BT2	BIOLOGY
RT	AESTIVATION
RT	ALGOLOGY
RT	AQUATIC PLANTS
RT	AUXINS
RT	BOTANY
RT	DROUGHT RESISTANCE
RT	OSMOTIC PRESSURE
RT	PHOTOSYNTHESIS
RT	PHYTOHORMONES
RT	PLANT DISEASES
RT	PLANT METABOLISM
RT	PLANT MORPHOLOGY
RT	PLANT NUTRITION
RT	PLANT ORGANS
RT	PLANT PHYSIOLOGISTS
RT	REPRODUCTION
RT	RESPIRATION
RT	STOMATA
RT	WEEDS

PLANT POPULATIONS
SN	Added in 1982
UF	population (plants)
BT1	NATURAL POPULATIONS
RT	AQUATIC PLANTS
RT	SEA GRASS
RT	WEEDS

PLANT REPRODUCTIVE STRUCTURES
SN	Added in 1982
UF	reproductive structures (plant)
BT1	PLANT ORGANS
BT2	BODY ORGANS
NT1	TURIONS
RT	ASEXUAL REPRODUCTION
RT	POLLEN
RT	POLLINATION
RT	RHIZOMES
RT	VEGETATIVE REPRODUCTION

PLANT SOCIOLOGY
USE	**PHYTOSOCIOLOGY**

PLANT UTILIZATION
SN	Added in 1982
UF	aquatic plant utilization
UF	aquatic weed utilization
UF	water weed utilization
BT1	UTILIZATION
RT	AQUATIC DRUGS
RT	AQUATIC PLANTS
RT	FERTILIZERS
RT	FRESHWATER WEEDS
RT	HARVESTING
RT	HUMAN FOOD
RT	LIVESTOCK FOOD
RT	PLANT CONTROL
RT	SEAWEEDS
RT	UNDERUTILIZED SPECIES
RT	WATER PURIFICATION

PLANTS (AQUATIC)
USE	**AQUATIC PLANTS**

PLASMA (BLOOD)
USE	**BLOOD**

PLASMA MEMBRANES
USE	**CELL MEMBRANES**

PLASMALEMMA
USE	**CELL MEMBRANES**

PLASTIC COATINGS
BT1	COATING MATERIALS
BT2	MATERIALS
RT	EPOXY RESINS
RT	PLASTICS

PLASTIC DEBRIS
BT1	SOLID IMPURITIES
BT2	POLLUTANTS
RT	PLASTICS

PLASTIC FLOW
RT	DEFORMATION
RT	PLASTICITY
RT	RHEOLOGY

PLASTIC MATERIALS
USE	**PLASTICS**

PLASTICITY
RT	COMPRESSIBILITY
RT	DEFORMATION
RT	ELASTICITY
RT	MECHANICAL PROPERTIES
RT	PLASTIC FLOW

PLASTICS
UF	plastic materials
BT1	MATERIALS
NT1	ACRYLICS
NT1	GLASS-REINFORCED PLASTICS
RT	PLASTIC COATINGS
RT	PLASTIC DEBRIS
RT	SOLID IMPURITIES
RT	SYNTHETIC FIBRES

PLATE BOUNDARIES
NT1	CONVERGING PLATE BOUNDARIES
NT1	DIVERGING PLATE BOUNDARIES
NT1	TRANSFORM PLATE BOUNDARIES
RT	ACTIVE MARGINS
RT	BOUNDARIES
RT	PLATE MARGINS
RT	PLATE TECTONICS
RT	PLATES
RT	SUBMARINE VOLCANOES
RT	TRIPLE JUNCTIONS
RT	VOLCANISM

PLATE CONVERGENCE
RT	ACTIVE MARGINS
RT	CONVERGENCE
RT	ISLAND ARCS
RT	PLATE MOTION
RT	PLATE TECTONICS
RT	SUBDUCTION ZONES
RT	TRENCHES (OCEANIC)

PLATE DIVERGENCE
RT	CRUSTAL ACCRETION
RT	DIVERGENCE
RT	DIVERGING PLATE BOUNDARIES
RT	MANTLE PLUMES
RT	MEDIAN VALLEYS
RT	MID-OCEAN RIDGES
RT	PASSIVE MARGINS
RT	PLATE MOTION
RT	RIFT ZONES

PLATE DIVERGENCE (cont'd)
RT   RIFTING
RT   SPREADING CENTRES

PLATE MARGINS
UF   margins (plate)
RT   ACTIVE MARGINS
RT   PLATE BOUNDARIES
RT   PLATES

PLATE MOTION
RT   PLATE CONVERGENCE
RT   PLATE DIVERGENCE
RT   PLATE MOTION
RT   PLATE TECTONICS
RT   PLATES
RT   ROTATION

PLATE TECTONICS
UF   global tectonics
BT1   TECTONICS
BT2   GEOLOGY
BT3   EARTH SCIENCES
RT   ASTHENOSPHERE
RT   BENIOFF ZONE
RT   CONTINENTAL DRIFT
RT   CRUSTAL ADJUSTMENT
RT   FRACTURE ZONES
RT   HEAT FLOW
RT   HOT SPOTS
RT   LITHOSPHERE
RT   MANTLE CONVECTION
RT   MANTLE PLUMES
RT   MOHO
RT   OBDUCTION
RT   OPHIOLITES
RT   OROGENY
RT   PALAEOMAGNETISM
RT   PLATE BOUNDARIES
RT   PLATE CONVERGENCE
RT   PLATE MOTION
RT   PLATES
RT   POLAR WANDERING
RT   RIFTING
RT   ROTATION
RT   SEAFLOOR SPREADING
RT   SPREADING CENTRES
RT   SUBDUCTION
RT   SUBDUCTION ZONES
RT   TRANSFORM FAULTS

PLATEAUX
BT1   LANDFORMS
BT2   TOPOGRAPHIC FEATURES
RT   RELIEF FORMS
RT   SUBMARINE PLATEAUX

PLATES
UF   lithospheric plates
UF   tectonic plates
BT1   EARTH STRUCTURE
RT   LITHOSPHERE
RT   OBDUCTION
RT   PLATE BOUNDARIES
RT   PLATE MARGINS
RT   PLATE MOTION
RT   PLATE TECTONICS
RT   ROTATION
RT   SUBDUCTION
RT   SUBDUCTION ZONES
RT   TRIPLE JUNCTIONS

PLATFORMS
USE   **OFFSHORE STRUCTURES**

PLATFORMS (GEOLOGY)
RT   CRATONS

PLATFORMS (INSTRUMENT)
USE   **INSTRUMENT PLATFORMS**

PLATFORMS (WORK)
USE   **WORK PLATFORMS**

PLATINUM
BT1   CHEMICAL ELEMENTS
RT   HEAVY METALS
RT   METALS
RT   PLACERS
RT   PLATINUM COMPOUNDS
RT   PLATINUM ISOTOPES
RT   TRACE METALS

PLATINUM COMPOUNDS
RT   CHEMICAL COMPOUNDS
RT   PLATINUM

PLATINUM ISOTOPES
BT1   ISOTOPES
RT   PLATINUM

PLAYAS
SN   Use for continental/inland sabkhas
BT1   SABKHAS
RT   ARID ENVIRONMENTS
RT   LAKE DEPOSITS
RT   SALT DEPOSITS
RT   SALT LAKES

PLEISTOCENE
SN   Before 1982 search PLEISTOCENE EPOCH
UF   glacial epoch
BT1   QUATERNARY
BT2   CENOZOIC
BT3   GEOLOGICAL TIME
RT   ICE AGES
RT   INTERGLACIAL PERIODS
RT   PLIO-PLEISTOCENE BOUNDARY

PLEUSTON
SN   Freefloating plants
BT1   AQUATIC COMMUNITIES
RT   AIR-WATER INTERFACE
RT   AQUATIC PLANTS
RT   WEEDS

PLIO-PLEISTOCENE BOUNDARY
RT   PLEISTOCENE
RT   PLIOCENE

PLIOCENE
SN   Before 1982 search PLIOCENE EPOCH
BT1   NEOGENE
BT2   TERTIARY
BT3   CENOZOIC
BT4   GEOLOGICAL TIME
RT   PLIO-PLEISTOCENE BOUNDARY

PLOTTING
RT   BATHYMETRIC DATA
RT   MAPPING
RT   SOUNDINGS

PLOUGHING TRENCHES
USE   **TRENCHING**

PLOUGHMARKS
UF   iceberg scour marks
BT1   BED FORMS
BT2   SEDIMENTARY STRUCTURES
RT   GLACIAL EROSION
RT   GLACIAL FEATURES
RT   ICEBERG SCOURING

PLOUGHS
UF   plows
RT   TRENCHING

PLOWS
USE   **PLOUGHS**

PLUMBLINE DEFLECTION
RT   DEFLECTION
RT   GEODESY
RT   GRAVITY
RT   ISOSTASY

PLUMES
SN   Before 1982 search PLUMES
        (AQUATIC). Use of a more specific
        term is recommended
BT1   FLUID FLOW
BT2   FLUID MOTION
NT1   CHEMICAL PLUMES
NT1   MANTLE PLUMES
NT1   RIVER PLUMES
NT1   THERMAL PLUMES
RT   BUOYANT JETS
RT   TURBULENT ENTRAINMENT
RT   WATER MIXING

PLUMULAE
USE   **FEATHERS**

PLUTONIUM
BT1   CHEMICAL ELEMENTS
RT   ACTINIDES
RT   PLUTONIUM COMPOUNDS
RT   PLUTONIUM ISOTOPES
RT   RADIOACTIVITY
RT   TRANSITION ELEMENTS
RT   TRANSURANIC ELEMENTS

PLUTONIUM COMPOUNDS
BT1   ACTINIDE COMPOUNDS
RT   CHEMICAL COMPOUNDS
RT   PLUTONIUM

PLUTONIUM ISOTOPES
BT1   ISOTOPES
RT   PLUTONIUM

PLUTONS
BT1   IGNEOUS ROCKS
BT2   ROCKS
RT   BATHOLITHS
RT   IGNEOUS INTRUSIONS

PNS
USE   **PERIPHERAL NERVOUS SYSTEM**

POCK MARKS
BT1   BED FORMS
BT2   SEDIMENTARY STRUCTURES
RT   GAS TURBATION
RT   MICROTOPOGRAPHY

POIKILOTHERMIC ANIMALS
USE   **POIKILOTHERMY**

POIKILOTHERMY
SN   Added in 1980
UF   cold blooded animals
UF   poikilothermic animals
BT1   BIOLOGICAL PROPERTIES
BT2   PROPERTIES
RT   BODY TEMPERATURE
RT   HOMOIOTHERMY
RT   THERMOREGULATION

ASFIS Thesaurus

POINCARE WAVES
USE **TIDAL WAVES**

POISEUILLE FLOW
USE **LAMINAR FLOW**

POISON FISHING
USE **FISH POISONING**

POISON TOLERANCE
USE **TOXICITY TOLERANCE**

POISONING
USE **FISH POISONING**

POISONOUS FISH
BT1 FISH
BT2 AQUATIC ANIMALS
RT CIGUATERA
RT CIGUATOXIN
RT FOOD CHAINS
RT HUMAN FOOD
RT POISONOUS ORGANISMS
RT VENOM APPARATUS

POISONOUS ORGANISMS
BT1 AQUATIC ORGANISMS
RT ALLERGIC REACTIONS
RT BIOLOGICAL POISONS
RT FOOD CHAINS
RT NOXIOUS ORGANISMS
RT POISONOUS FISH
RT RED TIDES

POISONS (BIOLOGICAL)
USE **BIOLOGICAL POISONS**

POISSON'S EQUATION
BT1 EQUATIONS
RT HARMONIC FUNCTIONS
RT LAPLACE EQUATION

POISSON'S RATIO
RT COMPRESSIVE STRENGTH
RT ELASTIC CONSTANTS
RT ELASTICITY
RT FLEXIBILITY
RT RATIOS
RT STRAIN
RT TENSILE STRENGTH

POLAR AIR MASSES
BT1 AIR MASSES
RT ANTARCTIC FRONT
RT POLAR METEOROLOGY

POLAR CONVERGENCES
BT1 OCEANIC CONVERGENCES
BT2 CONVERGENCE ZONES
NT1 ANTARCTIC CONVERGENCE
NT1 NORTH ATLANTIC POLAR FRONT

POLAR ENVIRONMENT
USE **POLAR ZONES**

POLAR EXPLORATION
BT1 EXPLORATION
RT GEOGRAPHICAL EXPLORATION
RT ICE
RT NAVIGATION IN ICE
RT NAVIGATION UNDER ICE
RT POLAR ZONES

POLAR FRONT JET STREAM
USE **JET STREAM**

POLAR FRONTS
SN Use only for semi-permanent front
separating air masses of tropical
and polar origin
UF atmospheric polar fronts
BT1 ATMOSPHERIC CONVERGENCES
BT2 CONVERGENCE ZONES
RT CYCLONES
RT FRONTS

POLAR METEOROLOGY
BT1 METEOROLOGY
RT ANTARCTIC FRONT
RT ARCTIC ZONE
RT POLAR AIR MASSES
RT POLAR OCEANOGRAPHY
RT POLAR ZONES

POLAR MIGRATION
USE **POLAR WANDERING**

POLAR MOTION
USE **POLAR WANDERING**

POLAR NAVIGATION
USE **NAVIGATION IN ICE**

POLAR OCEANOGRAPHY
BT1 OCEANOGRAPHY
BT2 EARTH SCIENCES
RT ARCTIC ZONE
RT ICE EDGE
RT ICE MELTING
RT POLAR METEOROLOGY
RT POLAR WATERS
RT POLAR ZONES

POLAR WANDERING
UF polar migration
UF polar motion
RT CONTINENTAL DRIFT
RT EARTH ROTATION
RT PALAEOLATITUDE
RT PALAEOMAGNETISM
RT PLATE TECTONICS
RT POLE POSITIONS
RT ROTATION

POLAR WATERS
UF antarctic waters
UF arctic waters
RT POLAR OCEANOGRAPHY
RT POLAR ZONES

POLAR ZONES
UF polar environment
BT1 CLIMATIC ZONES
NT1 ANTARCTIC ZONE
NT1 ARCTIC ZONE
RT COLD RESISTANCE
RT CRYOBIOLOGY
RT CRYOPLANKTON
RT ICE FISHING
RT POLAR EXPLORATION
RT POLAR METEOROLOGY
RT POLAR OCEANOGRAPHY
RT POLAR WATERS

POLARISATION
USE **POLARIZATION**

POLARIZATION
UF polarisation
UF polarizing
RT ELECTROLYSIS
RT ELECTROMAGNETIC RADIATION
RT LIGHT
RT LIGHT SCATTERING
RT OPTICAL PROPERTIES
RT ORIENTATION

POLARIZATION (cont'd)
RT RADIATIVE TRANSFER

POLARIZING
USE **POLARIZATION**

POLAROGRAPHY
BT1 ANALYTICAL TECHNIQUES
RT ELECTROANALYSIS
RT ELECTROLYSIS
RT REDOX REACTIONS
RT VOLTAMMETRY

POLDERS
RT EMBANKMENTS
RT LAND RECLAMATION
RT SEA LEVEL

POLE CULTURE
USE **OFF-BOTTOM CULTURE**

POLE-LINE FISHING
BT1 LINE FISHING
BT2 CATCHING METHODS
RT ANGLING
RT DEMERSAL FISHERIES
RT FISHING
RT PELAGIC FISHERIES
RT TUNA FISHERIES

POLE POSITIONS
RT GEOMAGNETIC FIELD
RT MAGNETIC REVERSALS
RT PALAEOMAGNETISM
RT POLAR WANDERING

POLE TIDES
BT1 TIDES
BT2 TIDAL MOTION
RT CHANDLER WOBBLE
RT LONG-PERIOD TIDES
RT TIDAL CONSTITUENTS

POLEWARD HEAT FLUX
USE **HEAT TRANSPORT**

POLICIES
SN Use of a more specific term is
recommended. Added in 1980
UF policy
NT1 FISHERY POLICY
NT1 INTERNATIONAL POLICY
NT1 NAVIGATION POLICY
NT1 OCEAN POLICY
NT1 WATER POLICY
RT GOVERNMENTS
RT LEGISLATION
RT MANAGEMENT
RT NATURAL RESOURCES
RT POLITICAL ASPECTS

POLICY
USE **POLICIES**

POLICY (INTERNATIONAL)
USE **INTERNATIONAL POLICY**

POLITICAL ASPECTS
SN Added in 1980
UF political constraints
RT COASTAL STATES
RT ECONOMICS
RT EXTENDED JURISDICTION
RT GOVERNMENTS
RT INTERNATIONAL AGREEMENTS
RT JURISDICTION
RT LEGISLATION
RT OCEAN FLOOR
RT OCEAN SPACE
RT POLICIES

POLITICAL ASPECTS (cont'd)
RT   RESOURCE DEVELOPMENT

POLITICAL CONSTRAINTS
USE   **POLITICAL ASPECTS**

POLLACK FISHERIES
USE   **GADOID FISHERIES**

POLLEN
SN   Added in 1980
RT   AQUATIC PLANTS
RT   ATMOSPHERIC PARTICULATES
RT   FOSSIL POLLEN
RT   PALYNOLOGY
RT   PLANT REPRODUCTIVE STRUCTURES
RT   POLLINATION

POLLEN ANALYSIS
USE   **PALYNOLOGY**

POLLINATION
SN   Added in 1980
UF   cross pollination
UF   self pollination
RT   AQUATIC PLANTS
RT   PLANT REPRODUCTIVE STRUCTURES
RT   POLLEN
RT   SEXUAL REPRODUCTION
RT   TRACE METALS

POLLUTANT DETECTION
USE   **POLLUTION DETECTION**

POLLUTANT IDENTIFICATION
BT1   IDENTIFICATION
RT   BIOACCUMULATION
RT   BIOASSAYS
RT   POLLUTANTS
RT   TOXICITY TESTS
RT   WATER ANALYSIS

POLLUTANT PERSISTENCE
SN   Added in 1982
BT1   PERSISTENCE
RT   FATE
RT   POLLUTANTS
RT   POLLUTION DATA
RT   POLLUTION EFFECTS

POLLUTANTS
SN   Harmful substances of chemical,
          physical or biological origin
UF   polluting substances
NT1   BIOLOGICAL POLLUTANTS
NT1   CHEMICAL POLLUTANTS
NT1   RADIOACTIVE POLLUTANTS
NT1   SOLID IMPURITIES
NT2   PLASTIC DEBRIS
NT2   TAR BALLS
RT   AIR POLLUTION
RT   BODY BURDEN
RT   BRACKISHWATER POLLUTION
RT   BYPRODUCTS
RT   FATE
RT   FLUSHING TIME
RT   FRESHWATER POLLUTION
RT   IDENTIFICATION
RT   LETHAL EFFECTS
RT   LETHAL LIMITS
RT   MARINE POLLUTION
RT   MORTALITY CAUSES
RT   POLLUTANT IDENTIFICATION
RT   POLLUTANT PERSISTENCE
RT   POLLUTION MAPS
RT   SUBLETHAL EFFECTS
RT   SURVIVAL
RT   TOXICOLOGY
RT   WASTES
RT   WATER POLLUTION

POLLUTING SUBSTANCES
USE   **POLLUTANTS**

POLLUTION
SN   Use of a more specific term is
          recommended. Added in 1980
UF   environmental contamination
UF   environmental pollution
NT1   AGRICULTURAL POLLUTION
NT1   AIR POLLUTION
NT1   CHEMICAL POLLUTION
NT1   OIL POLLUTION
NT1   RADIOACTIVE CONTAMINATION
NT1   SEDIMENT POLLUTION
NT1   THERMAL POLLUTION
NT1   WATER POLLUTION
NT2   BRACKISHWATER POLLUTION
NT2   FRESHWATER POLLUTION
NT2   GROUNDWATER POLLUTION
NT2   MARINE POLLUTION
RT   BASELINE STUDIES
RT   CONTIGUOUS ZONES
RT   ECOLOGICAL CRISIS
RT   ENVIRONMENT MANAGEMENT
RT   ENVIRONMENTAL LEGISLATION
RT   POLLUTION CONTROL
RT   POLLUTION CONVENTION
RT   POLLUTION DATA
RT   POLLUTION DETECTION
RT   POLLUTION EFFECTS
RT   POLLUTION LEGISLATION
RT   POLLUTION MAPS
RT   POLLUTION MONITORING
RT   POLLUTION SURVEYS
RT   POLLUTION TOLERANCE
RT   SEEPAGES
RT   URBANIZATION
RT   WASTES

POLLUTION (AGRICULTURE)
USE   **AGRICULTURAL POLLUTION**

POLLUTION (AIR)
USE   **AIR POLLUTION**

POLLUTION (BRACKISHWATER)
USE   **BRACKISHWATER POLLUTION**

POLLUTION (FRESHWATER)
USE   **FRESHWATER POLLUTION**

POLLUTION (GROUNDWATER)
USE   **GROUNDWATER POLLUTION**

POLLUTION (MARINE)
USE   **MARINE POLLUTION**

POLLUTION (MICROBIAL)
USE   **MICROBIAL CONTAMINATION**

POLLUTION (OIL)
USE   **OIL POLLUTION**

POLLUTION (SEDIMENT)
USE   **SEDIMENT POLLUTION**

POLLUTION (THERMAL)
USE   **THERMAL POLLUTION**

POLLUTION (WATER)
USE   **WATER POLLUTION**

POLLUTION ABATEMENT
USE   **POLLUTION CONTROL**

POLLUTION CHARTS
USE   **POLLUTION MAPS**

POLLUTION CONTROL
SN   Control of pollution in aquatic
          environment only
UF   pollution abatement
UF   pollution prevention
UF   water pollution control
BT1   CONTROL
NT1   CONTAINMENT
RT   AGRICULTURAL POLLUTION
RT   AIR POLLUTION
RT   AQUACULTURE EFFLUENTS
RT   CHEMICAL POLLUTION
RT   ENVIRONMENT MANAGEMENT
RT   ENVIRONMENTAL LEGISLATION
RT   ENVIRONMENTAL PROTECTION
RT   OIL POLLUTION
RT   OIL WATER SEPARATION
RT   POLLUTION
RT   POLLUTION CONVENTION
RT   POLLUTION LEGISLATION
RT   PROTECTION
RT   RIVER BASIN MANAGEMENT
RT   SANITARY ENGINEERING
RT   THERMAL POLLUTION
RT   WATER AUTHORITIES
RT   WATER MANAGEMENT
RT   WATER POLLUTION
RT   WATER POLLUTION TREATMENT
RT   WATER PURIFICATION
RT   WATER QUALITY CONTROL

POLLUTION CONTROL LEGISLATION
USE   **POLLUTION LEGISLATION**

POLLUTION CONVENTION
UF   pollution treaties
BT1   INTERNATIONAL AGREEMENTS
BT2   LEGISLATION
RT   ENVIRONMENTAL LEGISLATION
RT   POLLUTION
RT   POLLUTION CONTROL
RT   POLLUTION MONITORING

POLLUTION DATA
BT1   DATA
RT   POLLUTANT PERSISTENCE
RT   POLLUTION
RT   POLLUTION DISPERSION
RT   POLLUTION MONITORING
RT   POLLUTION SURVEYS

POLLUTION DETECTION
UF   detection (pollution)
UF   pollutant detection
BT1   DETECTION
RT   CHEMICAL ANALYSIS
RT   MICROBIOLOGICAL ANALYSIS
RT   POLLUTION
RT   POLLUTION LEGISLATION
RT   POLLUTION SURVEYS
RT   SEDIMENT ANALYSIS
RT   WATER ANALYSIS

POLLUTION DISPERSION
SN   Added in 1982
RT   POLLUTION DATA
RT   POLLUTION MONITORING
RT   POLLUTION SURVEYS

POLLUTION EFFECTS
SN   Pollution effects on aquatic
          environment, organisms, fisheries
          and human health
UF   water pollution effects
RT   ANOXIC CONDITIONS
RT   ANTHROPOGENIC FACTORS
RT   BASELINE STUDIES

POLLUTION EFFECTS (cont'd)
RT	BIOACCUMULATION
RT	BRACKISHWATER POLLUTION
RT	CARCINOGENESIS
RT	COMMUNITY COMPOSITION
RT	DISEASES
RT	ECOSYSTEMS
RT	ENVIRONMENTAL IMPACT
RT	EPIDEMICS
RT	EUTROPHICATION
RT	FATE
RT	FISH KILL
RT	FISHERY RESOURCES
RT	FRESHWATER POLLUTION
RT	HAZARD ASSESSMENT
RT	LETHAL EFFECTS
RT	MAN-INDUCED EFFECTS
RT	MARINE POLLUTION
RT	MICROBIAL CONTAMINATION
RT	MORTALITY CAUSES
RT	ODOUR
RT	POLLUTANT PERSISTENCE
RT	POLLUTION
RT	POLLUTION MONITORING
RT	POLLUTION SURVEYS
RT	POLLUTION TOLERANCE
RT	PUBLIC HEALTH
RT	RESOURCE CONSERVATION
RT	TASTE
RT	TOXICITY
RT	WATER POLLUTION

POLLUTION INDICATORS
RT	INDICATOR SPECIES
RT	INDICATORS
RT	POLLUTION MONITORING

POLLUTION LEGISLATION
SN	Added in 1980
UF	pollution control legislation
UF	pollution regulations
BT1	ENVIRONMENTAL LEGISLATION
BT2	LEGISLATION
RT	ENVIRONMENT MANAGEMENT
RT	ENVIRONMENTAL PROTECTION
RT	POLLUTION
RT	POLLUTION CONTROL
RT	POLLUTION DETECTION
RT	POLLUTION MONITORING

POLLUTION MAPS
SN	Before 1982 search POLLUTION CHARTS. Distributional charts of pollutants or polluted areas in aquatic environment
UF	pollution charts
BT1	MAPS
BT2	GRAPHICS
BT3	AUDIOVISUAL MATERIAL
BT4	DOCUMENTS
RT	POLLUTANTS
RT	POLLUTION
RT	POLLUTION MONITORING
RT	POLLUTION SURVEYS
RT	WATER POLLUTION
RT	WATER QUALITY

POLLUTION MEASUREMENTS
USE	**POLLUTION MONITORING**

POLLUTION MONITORING
UF	pollution measurements
UF	pollution surveillance
BT1	MONITORING
RT	BRACKISHWATER POLLUTION
RT	ENVIRONMENT MANAGEMENT
RT	ENVIRONMENTAL LEGISLATION
RT	FRESHWATER POLLUTION
RT	MARINE POLLUTION
RT	POLLUTION

POLLUTION MONITORING (cont'd)
RT	POLLUTION CONVENTION
RT	POLLUTION DATA
RT	POLLUTION DISPERSION
RT	POLLUTION EFFECTS
RT	POLLUTION INDICATORS
RT	POLLUTION LEGISLATION
RT	POLLUTION MAPS
RT	POLLUTION SURVEYS
RT	TAR BALLS
RT	WARNING SERVICES
RT	WATER POLLUTION
RT	WATER POLLUTION TREATMENT
RT	WATER QUALITY

POLLUTION PREVENTION
USE	**POLLUTION CONTROL**

POLLUTION REGULATIONS
USE	**POLLUTION LEGISLATION**

POLLUTION SELF-CONTROL
USE	**SELF PURIFICATION**

POLLUTION SURVEILLANCE
USE	**POLLUTION MONITORING**

POLLUTION SURVEYS
SN	Surveys of polluted areas of aquatic environment
BT1	SURVEYS
RT	ENVIRONMENT MANAGEMENT
RT	ENVIRONMENTAL SURVEYS
RT	POLLUTION
RT	POLLUTION DATA
RT	POLLUTION DETECTION
RT	POLLUTION DISPERSION
RT	POLLUTION EFFECTS
RT	POLLUTION MAPS
RT	POLLUTION MONITORING

POLLUTION TOLERANCE
SN	Added in 1980
BT1	TOLERANCE
BT2	BIOLOGICAL PROPERTIES
BT3	PROPERTIES
RT	BIOACCUMULATION
RT	LETHAL EFFECTS
RT	POLLUTION
RT	POLLUTION EFFECTS
RT	SUBLETHAL EFFECTS
RT	TOXICITY

POLLUTION TREATIES
USE	**POLLUTION CONVENTION**

POLONIUM
BT1	CHEMICAL ELEMENTS
RT	METALS
RT	POLONIUM COMPOUNDS
RT	POLONIUM ISOTOPES

POLONIUM COMPOUNDS
RT	CHEMICAL COMPOUNDS
RT	POLONIUM

POLONIUM ISOTOPES
BT1	ISOTOPES
RT	POLONIUM

POLYCHLORINATED BIPHENYLS
USE	**PCB**

POLYCHLOROPINENE
USE	**ICHTHYOCIDES**

POLYCULTURE
UF	composite cultures
UF	mixed species culture
BT1	AQUACULTURE TECHNIQUES
RT	BRACKISHWATER AQUACULTURE
RT	CRAB CULTURE
RT	CULTURES
RT	FEEDING BEHAVIOUR
RT	FISH CULTURE
RT	FISH PONDS
RT	FRESHWATER AQUACULTURE
RT	FROG CULTURE
RT	HERBIVOROUS FISH
RT	INTENSIVE CULTURE
RT	POND CULTURE
RT	PRAWN CULTURE
RT	SHRIMP CULTURE
RT	STOCKING DENSITY

POLYCYCLIC HYDROCARBONS
USE	**AROMATIC HYDROCARBONS**

POLYHALITE
BT1	SULPHATE MINERALS
BT2	MINERALS
RT	GYPSUM

POLYMERIZATION
SN	Added in 1982
UF	copolymerization
UF	photopolymerization
BT1	CHEMICAL REACTIONS
RT	DNA
RT	POLYMERS
RT	RNA

POLYMERS
RT	CHEMICAL COMPOUNDS
RT	POLYMERIZATION

POLYMETALLIC NODULES
USE	**FERROMANGANESE NODULES**

POLYMETALLIC SULPHIDE DEPOSITS
USE	**SULPHIDE DEPOSITS**

POLYMORPHISM (BIOLOGICAL)
USE	**BIOPOLYMORPHISM**

POLYNYAS
UF	ice clearings
RT	FLOATING ICE
RT	ICE CANOPY
RT	LEADS
RT	NAVIGATION UNDER ICE

POLYPEPTIDES
BT1	PEPTIDES
BT2	PROTEINS
BT3	ORGANIC COMPOUNDS

POLYPLOIDS
RT	CHROMOSOMES
RT	GENETICS

POLYPS
SN	Cylindrical sedentary body form in Hydrozoa and Anthozoa
RT	BUDDING
RT	BUDS
RT	CORAL REEFS
RT	DEVELOPMENTAL STAGES
RT	SEDENTARY SPECIES
RT	TENTACLES

POLYSACCHARIDES
BT1	SACCHARIDES
BT2	CARBOHYDRATES
BT3	ORGANIC COMPOUNDS
NT1	AGAROSE

POLYSACCHARIDES (cont'd)

NT1	ALGINIC ACID
NT1	CELLULOSE
NT1	MUCOPOLYSACCHARIDES
NT2	CHITIN
NT2	HEPARIN
NT1	STARCH
RT	AGAR

POLYSPERMY

RT	BIOLOGICAL FERTILIZATION
RT	SEXUAL CELLS
RT	SEXUAL REPRODUCTION
RT	SPERM

POLYUNSATURATED FATTY ACIDS

BT1	FATTY ACIDS
BT2	ORGANIC ACIDS
BT3	ORGANIC COMPOUNDS
RT	POLYUNSATURATED HYDROCARBONS

POLYUNSATURATED HYDROCARBONS

BT1	UNSATURATED HYDROCARBONS
BT2	HYDROCARBONS
BT3	ORGANIC COMPOUNDS
NT1	SQUALENE
NT1	TERPENES
RT	POLYUNSATURATED FATTY ACIDS

POND CONSTRUCTION

SN	Referring to design and hydrotechnical characteristics of pond construction mainly for aquaculture
RT	DAMS
RT	FISH PONDS
RT	HYDRAULIC ENGINEERING
RT	HYDRAULIC STRUCTURES
RT	POND CULTURE
RT	RACEWAY CULTURE
RT	SEWAGE PONDS

POND CULTURE

UF	fish pond culture
UF	static water culture
BT1	AQUACULTURE TECHNIQUES
RT	AGROPISCICULTURE
RT	AIR-BREATHING FISH
RT	AQUACULTURE EFFLUENTS
RT	CRAB CULTURE
RT	CRAYFISH CULTURE
RT	CRUSTACEAN CULTURE
RT	CULTURES
RT	EXTENSIVE CULTURE
RT	FISH CULTURE
RT	FISH PONDS
RT	FROG CULTURE
RT	HABITAT IMPROVEMENT
RT	INTERMEDIATE FISHING
RT	OVERWINTERING TECHNIQUES
RT	POLYCULTURE
RT	POND CONSTRUCTION
RT	PRAWN CULTURE
RT	SEED COLLECTION
RT	SEEDING (AQUACULTURE)
RT	SHRIMP CULTURE
RT	STOCKING DENSITY
RT	THERMAL AQUACULTURE
RT	VALLICULTURE
RT	WATER PUMPS

POND WEEDS

USE	**FRESHWATER WEEDS**

PONDERAL INDEX

USE	**CONDITION FACTOR**

PONDS

UF	pools
BT1	INLAND WATERS
NT1	COOLING PONDS
NT1	FISH PONDS
NT2	BREEDING PONDS
NT2	GROWING PONDS
NT2	NURSERY PONDS
NT2	STOCKING PONDS
NT1	SEWAGE PONDS
NT1	TEMPORARY PONDS
RT	DAMS
RT	FLOOD CONTROL
RT	FRESH WATER
RT	HYDROLOGY
RT	IRRIGATION
RT	LENITIC ENVIRONMENT
RT	LIMNOLOGY
RT	RESERVOIRS (WATER)
RT	WATER RESOURCES

PONTOONS

BT1	FLOATING STRUCTURES
BT2	OFFSHORE STRUCTURES
BT3	HYDRAULIC STRUCTURES
RT	BARGES
RT	SRIDGES
RT	CRANES

POOLS

USE	**PONDS**

POPEYE

USE	**EXOPHTHALMIA**

POPULATION (PLANTS)

USE	**PLANT POPULATIONS**

POPULATION ABUNDANCE (IN NUMBER)

USE	**POPULATION NUMBER**

POPULATION ABUNDANCE (WEIGHT)

USE	**BIOMASS**

POPULATION CHARACTERISTICS

UF	population estimates
UF	population parameters
NT1	BIOMASS
NT1	POPULATION DENSITY
NT1	POPULATION NUMBER
NT1	POPULATION STRUCTURE
NT2	AGE COMPOSITION
NT2	SEX RATIO
NT2	SIZE DISTRIBUTION
RT	ANIMAL POPULATIONS
RT	NATURAL POPULATIONS
RT	POPULATION DYNAMICS
RT	POPULATION FACTORS
RT	POPULATION FUNCTIONS
RT	STOCK ASSESSMENT

POPULATION CONTROL

SN	Inhibitive action on populations by biological (introduction, exclusion or removal of organisms), chemical or physical means
BT1	CONTROL
RT	BIOTIC PRESSURE
RT	DISEASES
RT	INTRODUCED SPECIES
RT	IRRADIATION
RT	MONITORING
RT	NATURAL POPULATIONS

POPULATION DENSITY

UF	density (population)
UF	density dependent factor
UF	stock density
BT1	POPULATION CHARACTERISTICS
RT	BIOMASS

POPULATION DENSITY (cont'd)

RT	BIOTIC PRESSURE
RT	CATCH/EFFORT
RT	DENSITY
RT	DENSITY DEPENDENCE
RT	POPULATION NUMBER
RT	QUANTITATIVE DISTRIBUTION
RT	RESOURCE AVAILABILITY

POPULATION DYNAMICS

SN	Studies of changes that take place during the life span of a population
UF	population studies
RT	CATCH STATISTICS
RT	FISHERY BIOLOGY
RT	GROWTH CURVES
RT	MORTALITY
RT	NATURAL POPULATIONS
RT	POPULATION CHARACTERISTICS
RT	POPULATION FACTORS
RT	POPULATION FUNCTIONS
RT	POPULATION STRUCTURE
RT	STOCK ASSESSMENT

POPULATION ESTIMATES

USE	**POPULATION CHARACTERISTICS**

POPULATION FACTORS

NT1	CONDITION FACTOR
NT1	FISH CONVERSION FACTORS
NT1	LENGTH-WEIGHT RELATIONSHIPS
NT1	PLANKTON EQUIVALENTS
RT	NATURAL POPULATIONS
RT	POPULATION CHARACTERISTICS
RT	POPULATION DYNAMICS
RT	POPULATION FUNCTIONS
RT	POPULATION STRUCTURE

POPULATION FUNCTIONS

SN	Including dynamic parameters (rates)
NT1	GROWTH
NT1	MORTALITY
NT2	FISHING MORTALITY
NT2	NATURAL MORTALITY
NT2	TAGGING MORTALITY
NT2	TOTAL MORTALITY
NT1	RECRUITMENT
RT	DENSITY DEPENDENCE
RT	NATURAL POPULATIONS
RT	POPULATION CHARACTERISTICS
RT	POPULATION DYNAMICS
RT	POPULATION FACTORS
RT	POPULATION STRUCTURE

POPULATION GENETICS

SN	Relative frequency of hereditary characters and alleles in samples of a population or populations of a given species
BT1	GENETICS
BT2	BIOLOGY
RT	BIOLOGICAL SPECIATION
RT	BIOPOLYMORPHISM
RT	EVOLUTION
RT	GENECOLOGY
RT	GENETIC DRIFT
RT	ISOLATING MECHANISMS
RT	NATURAL POPULATIONS
RT	STOCK IDENTIFICATION
RT	SUBPOPULATIONS
RT	SYMPATRIC POPULATIONS
RT	UNIT STOCKS

POPULATION NUMBER

UF	population abundance (in number)
UF	population size (in number)
UF	standing crop (in number)
UF	standing stock (in number)
BT1	POPULATION CHARACTERISTICS
RT	ABUNDANCE

POPULATION NUMBER (cont'd)
RT   BIOMASS
RT   CATCH/EFFORT
RT   POPULATION DENSITY
RT   QUANTITATIVE DISTRIBUTION
RT   RESOURCE AVAILABILITY
RT   STOCK ASSESSMENT
RT   YIELD

POPULATION PARAMETERS
USE   **POPULATION CHARACTERISTICS**

POPULATION PRESSURE
USE   **BIOTIC PRESSURE**

POPULATION SIZE (IN NUMBER)
USE   **POPULATION NUMBER**

POPULATION SIZE (IN WEIGHT)
USE   **BIOMASS**

POPULATION STRUCTURE
SN   Composition by size, sex and age
         groups of a breeding population
         (exploited or unexploited)
BT1   POPULATION CHARACTERISTICS
NT1   AGE COMPOSITION
NT1   SEX RATIO
NT1   SIZE DISTRIBUTION
RT   LENGTH-WEIGHT RELATIONSHIPS
RT   NATURAL POPULATIONS
RT   POPULATION DYNAMICS
RT   POPULATION FACTORS
RT   POPULATION FUNCTIONS
RT   RECRUITMENT
RT   STOCK ASSESSMENT
RT   SUBPOPULATIONS

POPULATION STUDIES
USE   **POPULATION DYNAMICS**

POPULATIONS (ANIMAL)
USE   **ANIMAL POPULATIONS**

POPULATIONS (NATURAL)
USE   **NATURAL POPULATIONS**

PORCELLANITE
BT1   SILICEOUS ROCKS
RT   SEDIMENTARY ROCKS

PORE PRESSURE
UF   pore water pressure
BT1   PRESSURE
BT2   PHYSICAL PROPERTIES
BT3   PROPERTIES
RT   FLUIDIZED SEDIMENT FLOW
RT   GEOTECHNICAL DATA
RT   HYDROSTATIC PRESSURE
RT   PORE WATER
RT   SEDIMENT PROPERTIES
RT   SHEAR STRENGTH
RT   WATER CONTENT
RT   WAVE-INDUCED LOADING

PORE WATER
SN   Before 1983 search also
         INTERSTITIAL WATER
UF   interstitial water
UF   pore water content
BT1   WATER
RT   DEWATERING
RT   FLUIDIZED SEDIMENT FLOW
RT   GEOCHEMISTRY
RT   HYDROTHERMAL SOLUTIONS
RT   INTERSTITIAL ENVIRONMENT
RT   PORE PRESSURE
RT   PORE WATER SAMPLERS
RT   SEDIMENT CHEMISTRY
RT   WATER CONTENT

PORE WATER CONTENT
USE   **PORE WATER**

PORE WATER PRESSURE
USE   **PORE PRESSURE**

PORE WATER SAMPLERS
BT1   SEDIMENT SAMPLERS
BT2   SAMPLERS
RT   GEOCHEMISTRY
RT   GEOLOGICAL EQUIPMENT
RT   PORE WATER
RT   SEDIMENT ANALYSIS
RT   WATER CONTENT
RT   WATER SAMPLERS

POROSITY
BT1   PHYSICAL PROPERTIES
BT2   PROPERTIES
RT   CAPILLARITY
RT   COMPACTION
RT   COMPRESSIBILITY
RT   ELECTRICAL RESISTIVITY
RT   GEOTECHNICAL DATA
RT   GRAIN SIZE
RT   PERCOLATION
RT   PERMEABILITY
RT   SEDIMENT ANALYSIS
RT   SEDIMENT PROPERTIES
RT   SEDIMENT STRUCTURE
RT   SEDIMENT TEXTURE
RT   TEXTURE
RT   VOID RATIO
RT   VOIDS
RT   WATER CONTENT
RT   WET BULK DENSITY

PORPHYRINS
BT1   GLYCOSIDES
BT2   CARBOHYDRATES
BT3   ORGANIC COMPOUNDS
RT   CHLOROPHYLLS
RT   PIGMENTS

PORT INSTALLATIONS
UF   docks
UF   harbour installations
UF   harbour structures
UF   jetties
UF   quays
BT1   COASTAL STRUCTURES
BT2   HYDRAULIC STRUCTURES
RT   ARTIFICIAL HARBOURS
RT   COASTAL ENGINEERING
RT   COASTAL INLETS
RT   FERRY TERMINALS
RT   GAS TERMINALS
RT   HARBOURS
RT   MARINE TRANSPORTATION
RT   OIL REFINERIES
RT   STRUCTURAL ENGINEERING
RT   TANKER TERMINALS

PORTS
USE   **HARBOURS**

POSITION FIXING
UF   fixing position
UF   position fixing systems
NT1   INERTIAL NAVIGATION
NT1   RADAR NAVIGATION
NT1   RADIO NAVIGATION
NT2   DECCA
NT2   LORAN
NT2   OMEGA
NT2   SHORAN
NT1   SATELLITE NAVIGATION
NT1   SOFAR
RT   GEOGRAPHICAL COORDINATES

POSITION FIXING (cont'd)
RT   LATITUDE
RT   LOCATING
RT   LONGITUDE
RT   MARINE GEODESY
RT   NAVIGATION
RT   NAVIGATIONAL AIDS
RT   POSITIONING SYSTEMS

POSITION FIXING SYSTEMS
USE   **POSITION FIXING**

POSITIONING
USE   **POSITIONING SYSTEMS**

POSITIONING SYSTEMS
SN   Systems for keeping ships, mobile
         platforms etc. on station relative
         to a point on the seabed
UF   positioning
NT1   DYNAMIC POSITIONING
RT   ACOUSTIC BEACONS
RT   BERTHING
RT   DRILLING VESSELS
RT   MOBILE PLATFORMS
RT   POSITION FIXING
RT   RESEARCH VESSELS
RT   SHIP MOORING SYSTEMS
RT   STEERING SYSTEMS

POST LARVAE
USE   **JUVENILES**

POT FISHING
BT1   CATCHING METHODS
RT   CEPHALOPOD FISHERIES
RT   POTS

POTADROMOUS MIGRATIONS
BT1   MIGRATIONS
RT   ANADROMOUS MIGRATIONS
RT   CATADROMOUS MIGRATIONS
RT   FRESHWATER FISH

POTASH DEPOSITS
RT   SUBSURFACE DEPOSITS

POTASSIUM
BT1   CHEMICAL ELEMENTS
RT   ALKALI METALS
RT   DISSOLVED CHEMICALS
RT   POTASSIUM COMPOUNDS
RT   POTASSIUM ISOTOPES

POTASSIUM-ARGON DATING
BT1   RADIOMETRIC DATING
BT2   GEOCHRONOMETRY
RT   ARGON ISOTOPES
RT   POTASSIUM ISOTOPES

POTASSIUM COMPOUNDS
RT   ALKALI METAL COMPOUNDS
RT   CHEMICAL COMPOUNDS
RT   POTASSIUM

POTASSIUM ISOTOPES
BT1   ISOTOPES
RT   POTASSIUM
RT   POTASSIUM-ARGON DATING

POTENTIAL DENSITY
SN   Use for potential density of
         seawater (sigma-Θ)
BT1   WATER DENSITY
BT2   DENSITY
BT3   PHYSICAL PROPERTIES
BT4   PROPERTIES
RT   ADIABATIC PROCESSES
RT   IN SITU DENSITY
RT   POTENTIAL TEMPERATURE

POTENTIAL DENSITY (cont'd)
RT   SALINITY
RT   SIGMA-T
RT   VERTICAL STABILITY

POTENTIAL ENERGY
UF   available potential energy
BT1   ENERGY
NT1   DYNAMIC HEIGHT
RT   FROUDE NUMBER
RT   KINETIC ENERGY

POTENTIAL FLOW
UF   irrotational flow
BT1   FLUID FLOW
BT2   FLUID MOTION
RT   VORTICITY

POTENTIAL RESOURCES
UF   reserves
BT1   RESOURCES
RT   EXPLORATORY FISHING
RT   FISHERY DEVELOPMENT
RT   FISHERY RESOURCES
RT   KRILL FISHERIES
RT   LIVING RESOURCES
RT   POTENTIAL YIELD
RT   UNCONVENTIONAL RESOURCES

POTENTIAL TEMPERATURE
BT1   TEMPERATURE
BT2   THERMODYNAMIC PROPERTIES
BT3   PHYSICAL PROPERTIES
BT4   PROPERTIES
RT   ADIABATIC LAPSE RATES
RT   ADIABATIC PROCESSES
RT   ADIABATIC TEMPERATURE GRADIENT
RT   AIR TEMPERATURE
RT   BOTTOM TEMPERATURE
RT   ISENTROPIC SURFACES
RT   POTENTIAL DENSITY
RT   TRENCHES (OCEANIC)
RT   VERTICAL STABILITY
RT   WATER TEMPERATURE

POTENTIAL VORTICITY
BT1   VORTICITY
RT   BAROCLINIC INSTABILITY
RT   BAROTROPIC INSTABILITY

POTENTIAL YIELD
UF   maximum sustainable yield
UF   sustainable yield
BT1   YIELD
RT   POTENTIAL RESOURCES
RT   UNCONVENTIONAL RESOURCES

POTENTIALITIES
USE   **RESOURCES**

POTENTIOMETRIC TITRATION
USE   **TITRATION**

POTS
UF   lobster pots
BT1   FISHING GEAR
RT   BARRIERS
RT   FISHING BARRIERS
RT   POT FISHING
RT   SPORT FISHING
RT   TRAP NETS

POUND NETS
USE   **TRAP NETS**

POWDERED PRODUCTS
BT1   PROCESSED FISHERY PRODUCTS
BT2   FISHERY PRODUCTS
BT3   PRODUCTS
NT1   FISH MEAL

POWDERED PRODUCTS (cont'd)
NT2   FISH FLOUR
RT   ANIMAL NUTRITION
RT   BYPRODUCTS
RT   FEED
RT   FISH MEAL PROCESSING
RT   FISH OILS
RT   FOOD COMPOSITION
RT   FOOD TECHNOLOGY
RT   HUMAN FOOD
RT   NUTRITIVE VALUE
RT   ORGANOLEPTIC PROPERTIES
RT   QUALITY CONTROL

POWER CABLES
BT1   ELECTRIC CABLES
BT2   CABLES
RT   ELECTRIC POWER SOURCES
RT   UMBILICALS

POWER CONSUMPTION
RT   ELECTRIC POWER SOURCES
RT   ELECTRICITY
RT   ELECTRONIC EQUIPMENT

POWER FROM THE SEA
BT1   ENERGY RESOURCES
BT2   NATURAL RESOURCES
BT3   RESOURCES
NT1   CURRENT POWER
NT1   ELECTROMAGNETIC POWER
NT1   SALINITY POWER
NT1   THERMAL POWER
NT2   OTEC
NT1   TIDAL POWER
NT1   WAVE POWER
RT   GEOTHERMAL POWER
RT   RENEWABLE RESOURCES
RT   SOLAR POWER
RT   WIND POWER

POWER PLANT ENTRAINMENT
USE   **ENTRAINMENT**

POWER PLANTS
UF   electric power plants
UF   power stations
NT1   FOSSIL FUELED POWER PLANTS
NT1   HYDROELECTRIC POWER PLANTS
NT2   TIDAL POWER PLANTS
NT1   NUCLEAR POWER PLANTS
RT   COOLING PONDS
RT   COOLING WATER
RT   DESALINATION
RT   ELECTRIC POWER SOURCES
RT   ENTRAINMENT
RT   HYDRAULIC STRUCTURES
RT   IMPINGEMENT
RT   NUCLEAR ENERGY
RT   SITE SELECTION
RT   THERMAL AQUACULTURE
RT   THERMAL POLLUTION
RT   TIDAL ENERGY
RT   TURBINES
RT   WASTE HEAT
RT   WATER USE

POWER SPECTRA
USE   **ENERGY SPECTRA**

POWER STATIONS
USE   **POWER PLANTS**

POWER SUPPLIES
USE   **ELECTRIC POWER SOURCES**

POWER SYSTEMS
USE   **ELECTRIC POWER SOURCES**

PRACTICAL SALINITY SCALE
SN   World standard for salinity data
BT1   SALINITY SCALES
RT   SALINITY
RT   STANDARDS

PRANDTL NUMBER
RT   DIMENSIONLESS NUMBERS
RT   FORCED CONVECTION
RT   HEAT TRANSFER
RT   MOMENTUM TRANSFER
RT   REYNOLDS NUMBER

PRASEODYMIUM
BT1   CHEMICAL ELEMENTS
RT   PRASEODYMIUM COMPOUNDS
RT   PRASEODYMIUM ISOTOPES
RT   RARE EARTHS
RT   TRANSITION ELEMENTS

PRASEODYMIUM COMPOUNDS
RT   CHEMICAL COMPOUNDS
RT   PRASEODYMIUM

PRASEODYMIUM ISOTOPES
BT1   ISOTOPES
RT   PRASEODYMIUM

PRAWN CULTURE
SN   Before 1982 search CRUSTACEAN CULTURE. Restricted to rearing of freshwater prawns
BT1   CRUSTACEAN CULTURE
BT2   SHELLFISH CULTURE
BT3   AQUACULTURE
RT   FRESHWATER AQUACULTURE
RT   HATCHERIES
RT   POLYCULTURE
RT   POND CULTURE

PRAWN FISHERIES
USE   **SHRIMP FISHERIES**

PRECAMBRIAN
SN   Before 1982 search PRECAMBRIAN ERA
UF   archean
UF   proterozoic
BT1   GEOLOGICAL TIME

PRECIPITATION (ATMOSPHERIC)
USE   **ATMOSPHERIC PRECIPITATIONS**

PRECIPITATION (CHEMISTRY)
USE   **CHEMICAL PRECIPITATION**

PRECIPITATION (METEOROLOGY)
USE   **ATMOSPHERIC PRECIPITATIONS**

PRECISION DEPTH RECORDERS
USE   **ECHOSOUNDERS**

PRECISION DEPTH RECORDERS
USE   **DEPTH RECORDERS**

PRECISION ECHOSOUNDERS
USE   **ECHOSOUNDERS**

PRECISION GYROSCOPES
USE   **GYROSCOPES**

PRECISION PRESSURE RECORDERS
USE   **PRESSURE SENSORS**

PREDATION
SN	Including predator/prey relationship
UF	prey
BT1	INTERSPECIFIC RELATIONSHIPS
NT1	PREY SELECTION
RT	ASSOCIATED SPECIES
RT	CAMOUFLAGE
RT	CYCLOMORPHOSIS
RT	DENSITY DEPENDENCE
RT	FEEDING BEHAVIOUR
RT	FISH KILL
RT	INTRASPECIFIC RELATIONSHIPS
RT	MORTALITY CAUSES
RT	MULTISPECIES FISHERIES
RT	NATURAL MORTALITY
RT	PREDATOR CONTROL
RT	PREDATORS

PREDATOR CONTROL
BT1	CONTROL
RT	AQUACULTURE
RT	BIOLOGICAL CONTROL
RT	BOTTOM CULTURE
RT	CLAM CULTURE
RT	MUSSEL CULTURE
RT	PREDATION
RT	PREDATORS
RT	PREY SELECTION
RT	STOCKING (ORGANISMS)

PREDATORS
BT1	HETEROTROPHIC ORGANISMS
BT2	AQUATIC ORGANISMS
RT	CANNIBALISM
RT	CARNIVORES
RT	COMPETITORS
RT	FEEDING BEHAVIOUR
RT	PREDATION
RT	PREDATOR CONTROL
RT	PREY SELECTION
RT	PROTECTIVE BEHAVIOUR
RT	SECONDARY PRODUCTION

PREDICTING
USE	**PREDICTION**

PREDICTION
SN	Used only as a qualifier
UF	forecasting
UF	forecasts
UF	predicting
UF	predictions
NT1	CLIMATE PREDICTION
NT1	CURRENT PREDICTION
NT1	EARTHQUAKE PREDICTION
NT1	FLOOD FORECASTING
NT1	ICE FORECASTING
NT1	STORM SURGE PREDICTION
NT1	TIDAL PREDICTION
NT1	TSUNAMI PREDICTION
NT1	WAVE PREDICTING
NT2	WAVE FORECASTING
NT2	WAVE HINDCASTING
NT1	WEATHER FORECASTING
NT1	YIELD PREDICTIONS
RT	ALMANACS
RT	APPROXIMATION
RT	CRITICAL PATH METHOD
RT	FEASIBILITY
RT	FISHERY OCEANOGRAPHY
RT	LONG-TERM CHANGES
RT	MILITARY OCEANOGRAPHY
RT	SHORT-TERM CHANGES
RT	SIMULATION
RT	STATISTICAL ANALYSIS
RT	TSUNAMIS
RT	WARNING SERVICES

PREDICTIONS
USE	**PREDICTION**

PREFERRED TEMPERATURE
USE	**TEMPERATURE PREFERENCES**

PREGNANCY
SN	Added in 1980
UF	gestation
RT	AQUATIC MAMMALS
RT	PARTURITION
RT	PLACENTA

PRESERVATION (FISHERY PRODUCTS)
SN	Methods for preserving fish and other fisheries products
UF	conservation (food)
RT	CODEX STANDARDS
RT	FISH HANDLING
RT	FISH SPOILAGE
RT	FISH STORAGE
RT	FISHERY INDUSTRY
RT	FIXATION
RT	FOOD ADDITIVES
RT	ICE
RT	IRRADIATION
RT	PRESERVATIVES
RT	PROCESSING FISHERY PRODUCTS
RT	STORAGE

PRESERVATION (ORGANISMS)
USE	**FIXATION**

PRESERVATIVES
SN	Added in 1980
RT	ADDITIVES
RT	AGENTS
RT	ANTICOAGULANTS
RT	FIXATION
RT	PRESERVATION (FISHERY PRODUCTS)

PRESSURE
BT1	PHYSICAL PROPERTIES
BT2	PROPERTIES
NT1	ATMOSPHERIC PRESSURE
NT2	SEA LEVEL PRESSURE
NT1	BLOOD PRESSURE
NT1	HYDROSTATIC PRESSURE
NT2	BOTTOM PRESSURE
NT1	OSMOTIC PRESSURE
NT1	PORE PRESSURE
NT1	SOUND PRESSURE
NT1	VAPOUR PRESSURE
NT2	SATURATION VAPOUR PRESSURE
RT	BAROMETERS
RT	BIOTIC PRESSURE
RT	COMPRESSION
RT	DECOMPRESSION CHAMBERS
RT	ISOBARS
RT	ISOSTATIC SEA LEVEL
RT	LOADS (FORCES)
RT	MANOMETERS
RT	PRESSURE EFFECTS
RT	PRESSURE MEASUREMENT
RT	WEIGHT

PRESSURE (ATMOSPHERIC)
USE	**ATMOSPHERIC PRESSURE**

PRESSURE (OSMOTIC)
USE	**OSMOTIC PRESSURE**

PRESSURE (POPULATIONS)
USE	**BIOTIC PRESSURE**

PRESSURE (WATER)
USE	**HYDROSTATIC PRESSURE**

PRESSURE CHAMBERS
USE	**DECOMPRESSION CHAMBERS**

PRESSURE EFFECTS
SN	Hydrostatic influence upon behaviour of aquatic organisms
UF	pressure tolerance
BT1	ENVIRONMENTAL EFFECTS
NT1	HIGH PRESSURE EFFECTS
RT	BEHAVIOUR
RT	DIVING
RT	DIVING PHYSIOLOGY
RT	HYDROSTATIC PRESSURE
RT	MECHANORECEPTORS
RT	PRESSURE

PRESSURE FIELD
RT	ATMOSPHERIC PRESSURE
RT	FIELDS
RT	HYDROSTATIC PRESSURE
RT	ISOBARIC SURFACES
RT	ISOBARS
RT	PRESSURE GRADIENTS

PRESSURE GAUGES
BT1	MEASURING DEVICES
RT	DECOMPRESSION CHAMBERS
RT	MANOMETERS
RT	PRESSURE MEASUREMENT
RT	PRESSURE SENSORS
RT	PRESSURE VESSELS

PRESSURE GRADIENTS
RT	HYDROSTATICS
RT	PRESSURE FIELD

PRESSURE MEASUREMENT
BT1	MEASUREMENT
RT	PRESSURE
RT	PRESSURE GAUGES

PRESSURE SENSORS
UF	precision pressure recorders
UF	pressure transducers
NT1	QUARTZ PRESSURE SENSORS
RT	DEEP-SEA TIDE GAUGES
RT	PRESSURE GAUGES
RT	SENSORS
RT	TIDE GAUGES
RT	TRANSDUCERS
RT	WAVE MEASURING EQUIPMENT

PRESSURE TEST FACILITIES
USE	**PRESSURE VESSELS**

PRESSURE TOLERANCE
USE	**PRESSURE EFFECTS**

PRESSURE TRANSDUCERS
USE	**PRESSURE SENSORS**

PRESSURE VESSELS
UF	pressure test facilities
RT	HIGH PRESSURE EFFECTS
RT	PRESSURE GAUGES

PRESSURE WAVES
USE	**ELASTIC WAVES**

PRESTRESSED CONCRETE
BT1	CONCRETE
BT2	CONSTRUCTION MATERIALS
BT3	MATERIALS

PREY
USE	**PREDATION**

ASFIS Thesaurus

PREY SELECTION
SN	Added in 1982
BT1	PREDATION
BT2	INTERSPECIFIC RELATIONSHIPS
RT	COMPETITION
RT	FEEDING BEHAVIOUR
RT	PREDATOR CONTROL
RT	PREDATORS

PRICES
USE	**COSTS**

PRICING
UF	market prices
RT	AQUACULTURE ECONOMICS
RT	CAPTURE FISHERY ECONOMICS
RT	CATALOGUES
RT	COMMERCIAL AVAILABILITY
RT	COMMERCIAL LEGISLATION
RT	COST ANALYSIS
RT	COSTS
RT	ECONOMIC ANALYSIS
RT	ECONOMICS
RT	FINANCING
RT	FISHERY ECONOMICS
RT	MARKET RESEARCH
RT	MARKETING
RT	PRODUCTION COST
RT	PRODUCTS
RT	TRADE

PRIMARY FISHERY PRODUCTS
USE	**FISHERY PRODUCTS**

PRIMARY PRODUCTION
BT1	BIOLOGICAL PRODUCTION
RT	ALGAL BLOOMS
RT	BIOGEOCHEMICAL CYCLE
RT	CARBON 14
RT	COMPENSATION DEPTH
RT	EUPHOTIC ZONE
RT	EUTROPHICATION
RT	FERTILITY
RT	FOOD CHAINS
RT	LIGHT PENETRATION
RT	NUTRIENTS (MINERAL)
RT	PHOTOSYNTHESIS
RT	PHYTOBENTHOS
RT	PHYTOPLANKTON
RT	PLANKTONOLOGY
RT	SECONDARY PRODUCTION

PRIMARY SEDIMENTARY STRUCTURES
USE	**SEDIMENTARY STRUCTURES**

PRIMARY WAVES
USE	**P-WAVES**

PRIMERS
BT1	COATING MATERIALS
BT2	MATERIALS
RT	PAINTS

PROBABILITY THEORY
SN	Used only as a qualifier
RT	GAME THEORY
RT	MATHEMATICAL MODELS
RT	OPERATIONS RESEARCH
RT	RANDOM PROCESSES
RT	STATISTICAL ANALYSIS
RT	STATISTICAL MODELS
RT	STATISTICAL SAMPLING
RT	STOCHASTIC PROCESSES
RT	TIME SERIES

PROBES (INSTRUMENTS)
USE	**SENSORS**

PROBES (SENSORS)
USE	**SENSORS**

PROCEDURES
SN	Used only as a qualifier
RT	PLANNING
RT	TESTS

PROCEEDINGS
USE	**CONFERENCES**

PROCESS PLANTS
RT	CHEMICAL ENGINEERING
RT	INDUSTRIAL PRODUCTION
RT	INDUSTRIAL PRODUCTS
RT	MINERAL PROCESSING
RT	OIL AND GAS INDUSTRY
RT	OIL REFINERIES
RT	OTEC PLANTS

PROCESSED FISHERY PRODUCTS
SN	Use of a more specific term is recommended. Before 1982 search FISHERY PRODUCTS
BT1	FISHERY PRODUCTS
BT2	PRODUCTS
NT1	CANNED PRODUCTS
NT1	CHILLED PRODUCTS
NT1	CURED PRODUCTS
NT1	DRIED PRODUCTS
NT1	FERMENTED PRODUCTS
NT1	FISH FILLETS
NT1	FISH GLUE
NT1	FISH OILS
NT1	FREEZE-DRIED PRODUCTS
NT1	FROZEN PRODUCTS
NT1	KRILL PRODUCTS
NT1	MINCED PRODUCTS
NT1	POWDERED PRODUCTS
NT2	FISH MEAL
NT3	FISH FLOUR
NT1	ROES
NT2	CAVIAR
NT1	SEAWEED PRODUCTS
NT2	AGAR
NT2	ALGINATES
NT2	CARRAGEENINS
NT1	STICKWATER
RT	ACCEPTANCE TESTS
RT	AQUACULTURE PRODUCTS
RT	ARTISANAL FISHING
RT	BYPRODUCTS
RT	DRESSING
RT	FISH CONSUMPTION
RT	FISH HANDLING
RT	FISH INSPECTION
RT	FISH INSPECTION REGULATIONS
RT	FISHERY ECONOMICS
RT	FISHERY INDUSTRY
RT	FISHERY TECHNOLOGY
RT	FOOD COMPOSITION
RT	FOOD TECHNOLOGY
RT	HUMAN FOOD
RT	INDUSTRIAL PRODUCTS
RT	INDUSTRIAL PRODUCTS STATISTICS
RT	LIVING RESOURCES
RT	MARKET RESEARCH
RT	MARKETING
RT	PACKING FISHERY PRODUCTS
RT	PROCESSING FISHERY PRODUCTS
RT	PRODUCTION COST
RT	QUALITY CONTROL
RT	SEAFOOD
RT	SHARK UTILIZATION
RT	STORAGE EFFECTS
RT	TASTE TESTS

PROCESSING FISHERY PRODUCTS
SN	Methods and techniques of processing commercial species, mainly fish and shellfish
BT1	FISHERY INDUSTRY
BT2	INDUSTRIES
NT1	ANIMAL OIL EXTRACTION
NT2	FISH OIL EXTRACTION
NT1	CANNING
NT1	CURING
NT1	DRYING
NT2	FREEZE-DRYING
NT1	FISH MEAL PROCESSING
NT1	REFRIGERATION
RT	CODEX STANDARDS
RT	COLD STORAGE
RT	FILLETTING
RT	FISH INSPECTION
RT	FISH INSPECTION REGULATIONS
RT	FISH UTILIZATION
RT	FISH WASTES
RT	FISHERY PRODUCTS
RT	FREEZING
RT	HEADING
RT	PRESERVATION (FISHERY PRODUCTS)
RT	PROCESSED FISHERY PRODUCTS
RT	QUALITY CONTROL
RT	REFRIGERATION
RT	SHARK UTILIZATION
RT	STORAGE EFFECTS
RT	UTILIZATION

PRODUCT DEVELOPMENT
SN	Added in 1980
UF	development (products)
UF	new product development
UF	product improvement
RT	KRILL PRODUCTS
RT	MARKETING
RT	NEW PRODUCTS
RT	PRODUCTION COST
RT	PRODUCTS
RT	QUALITY

PRODUCT IMPROVEMENT
USE	**PRODUCT DEVELOPMENT**

PRODUCTION (BIOLOGICAL)
USE	**BIOLOGICAL PRODUCTION**

PRODUCTION (INDUSTRIAL)
USE	**INDUSTRIAL PRODUCTION**

PRODUCTION (OIL AND GAS)
USE	**OIL AND GAS PRODUCTION**

PRODUCTION COST
UF	ger
UF	gross energy requirement
RT	COST ANALYSIS
RT	EXPLOITATION
RT	FEASIBILITY
RT	FEASIBILITY STUDIES
RT	INDUSTRIAL PRODUCTS
RT	PRICING
RT	PROCESSED FISHERY PRODUCTS
RT	PRODUCT DEVELOPMENT
RT	PRODUCTION MANAGEMENT
RT	RESOURCE DEVELOPMENT
RT	RESOURCE MANAGEMENT

PRODUCTION MANAGEMENT
SN	Added in 1980
UF	market management
BT1	MANAGEMENT
RT	INDUSTRIAL PRODUCTION
RT	INDUSTRIAL PRODUCTS
RT	PRODUCTION COST
RT	QUALITY CONTROL

ASFIS Thesaurus

PRODUCTION PLATFORMS
BT1	WORK PLATFORMS
BT2	VEHICLES
RT	DRILLING
RT	DRILLING EQUIPMENT
RT	DRILLING PLATFORMS
RT	DRILLING RIGS
RT	DRILLING VESSELS
RT	FIXED PLATFORMS
RT	OFFSHORE STRUCTURES
RT	OIL AND GAS PRODUCTION

PRODUCTION RATE
USE	**BIOLOGICAL PRODUCTION**

PRODUCTIVITY
USE	**BIOLOGICAL PRODUCTION**

PRODUCTS
SN	Added in 1980
UF	goods
NT1	AQUACULTURE PRODUCTS
NT1	BYPRODUCTS
NT1	FISHERY PRODUCTS
NT2	PROCESSED FISHERY PRODUCTS
NT3	CANNED PRODUCTS
NT3	CHILLED PRODUCTS
NT3	CURED PRODUCTS
NT3	DRIED PRODUCTS
NT3	FERMENTED PRODUCTS
NT3	FISH FILLETS
NT3	FISH GLUE
NT3	FISH OILS
NT3	FREEZE-DRIED PRODUCTS
NT3	FROZEN PRODUCTS
NT3	KRILL PRODUCTS
NT3	MINCED PRODUCTS
NT3	POWDERED PRODUCTS
NT4	FISH MEAL
NT3	ROES
NT4	CAVIAR
NT3	SEAWEED PRODUCTS
NT4	AGAR
NT4	ALGINATES
NT4	CARRAGEENINS
NT3	STICKWATER
NT1	NEW PRODUCTS
RT	INDUSTRIAL PRODUCTION
RT	INDUSTRIES
RT	MARKETING
RT	NATURAL RESOURCES
RT	PRICING
RT	PRODUCT DEVELOPMENT
RT	QUALITY CONTROL
RT	RAW MATERIALS
RT	TRADE
RT	WASTES

PROFESSIONALS
USE	**EXPERTS**

PROFILERS
UF	continuous profilers
NT1	BATHYTHERMOGRAPHS
NT2	AXBTs
NT2	XBTs
NT1	CTD PROFILERS
NT1	CYCLESONDE
NT1	DROPSONDE
NT1	FREE-FALL PROFILERS
NT1	SHEAR PROBES
NT1	STD PROFILERS
NT1	VELOCITY PROFILERS
RT	HORIZONTAL PROFILES
RT	OCEANOGRAPHIC EQUIPMENT
RT	PROFILES
RT	VERTICAL PROFILES

PROFILES
NT1	HORIZONTAL PROFILES
NT2	BEACH PROFILES
NT2	THALWEG
NT1	VERTICAL PROFILES
NT2	DENSITY PROFILES
NT2	OXYGEN PROFILES
NT2	SALINITY PROFILES
NT2	STD PROFILES
NT2	TEMPERATURE PROFILES
NT2	VELOCITY PROFILES
NT3	CURRENT PROFILES
NT3	WIND PROFILES
RT	CONTOURS
RT	GRADIENTS
RT	GRAPHS
RT	PROFILERS
RT	PROFILING

PROFILING
SN	Use of a more specific term is recommended
RT	PROFILES
RT	SEISMIC REFLECTION PROFILING
RT	SEISMIC REFRACTION PROFILING
RT	SUB-BOTTOM PROFILING
RT	VERTICAL PROFILES
RT	VERTICAL PROFILING

PROFILING CURRENT METERS
USE	**VELOCITY PROFILERS**

PROGRADATION
UF	coast accretion
RT	BEACH ACCRETION
RT	COASTAL MORPHOLOGY
RT	COASTS
RT	CONSTRUCTIVE WAVES
RT	DELTAS
RT	EMERGENT SHORELINES
RT	EUSTATIC CHANGES
RT	ISOSTASY
RT	REGRESSIONS
RT	RETROGRADATION
RT	SALT MARSHES
RT	UPLIFT

PROGRAMME EVALUATION
USE	**PERT**

PROGRAMMES
RT	COMPUTER PROGRAMS
RT	CRUISES
RT	MULTISHIP EXPEDITIONS
RT	PLANNING
RT	RESEARCH PROGRAMMES

PROGRAMMING
USE	**PLANNING**

PROGRESS REPORTS
SN	Used only as a qualifier
BT1	REPORT LITERATURE
BT2	DOCUMENTS
RT	ANNUAL REPORTS
RT	RESEARCH INSTITUTIONS
RT	RESEARCH PROGRAMMES

PROGRESSIVE WAVES
BT1	OSCILLATORY WAVES
BT2	WATER WAVES

PROJECT EVALUATION
USE	**PERT**

PROLINE
BT1	AMINO ACIDS
BT2	ORGANIC ACIDS
BT3	ORGANIC COMPOUNDS
RT	PYRROLIDINE

PROMETHIUM
BT1	CHEMICAL ELEMENTS
RT	PROMETHIUM COMPOUNDS
RT	PROMETHIUM ISOTOPES
RT	RARE EARTHS

PROMETHIUM COMPOUNDS
RT	CHEMICAL COMPOUNDS
RT	PROMETHIUM

PROMETHIUM ISOTOPES
BT1	ISOTOPES
RT	PROMETHIUM

PROMONTORIES
USE	**HEADLANDS**

PROPAGATION
USE	**REPRODUCTION**

PROPAGATION (WATER WAVES)
USE	**WAVE PROPAGATION**

PROPANE
BT1	ACYCLIC HYDROCARBONS
BT2	SATURATED HYDROCARBONS
BT3	HYDROCARBONS
BT4	ORGANIC COMPOUNDS

PROPELLERS
RT	CAVITATION
RT	PROPULSION SYSTEMS
RT	THRUSTERS

PROPERTIES
SN	Used only as a qualifier. Use of a more specific term is recommended
NT1	BIOLOGICAL PROPERTIES
NT2	BIOELECTRICITY
NT2	BIOLOGICAL RESISTANCE
NT3	COLD RESISTANCE
NT3	CONTROL RESISTANCE
NT3	DISEASE RESISTANCE
NT3	DROUGHT RESISTANCE
NT3	DRUG RESISTANCE
NT3	PARASITE RESISTANCE
NT2	EURYHALINITY
NT2	EURYTHERMY
NT2	FECUNDITY
NT2	HETEROSIS
NT2	HOMOIOTHERMY
NT2	IMMUNITY
NT2	LONGEVITY
NT2	NEOTENY
NT2	POIKILOTHERMY
NT2	SEXUAL MATURITY
NT2	STENOHALINITY
NT2	STENOTHERMY
NT2	TOLERANCE
NT3	EXPOSURE TOLERANCE
NT3	POLLUTION TOLERANCE
NT3	SALINITY TOLERANCE
NT3	TEMPERATURE TOLERANCE
NT3	TOXICITY TOLERANCE
NT2	TOXICITY
NT2	VULNERABILITY
NT1	CHEMICAL PROPERTIES
NT2	ACIDITY
NT2	ALKALINITY
NT2	PH
NT2	REDOX POTENTIAL
NT2	SALINITY
NT3	CHLORINITY
NT3	CHLOROSITY
NT3	PALAEOSALINITY
NT3	SURFACE SALINITY
NT2	SOLUBILITY
NT3	GAS SOLUBILITY
NT1	CONSERVATIVE PROPERTIES

PROPERTIES (cont'd)

NT1	ICE PROPERTIES
NT1	NON-CONSERVATIVE PROPERTIES
NT1	ORGANOLEPTIC PROPERTIES
NT2	DIGESTIBILITY
NT2	ODOUR
NT2	TASTE
NT1	PHYSICAL PROPERTIES
NT2	ACOUSTIC PROPERTIES
NT2	ANISOTROPY
NT2	BUOYANCY
NT2	COLLIGATIVE PROPERTIES
NT2	DENSITY
NT3	CURRENT DENSITY
NT3	SEDIMENT DENSITY
NT4	WET BULK DENSITY
NT3	WATER DENSITY
NT4	IN SITU DENSITY
NT4	POTENTIAL DENSITY
NT4	RELATIVE DENSITY
NT4	SIGMA-T
NT2	ELECTRICAL PROPERTIES
NT3	CAPACITANCE
NT3	DIELECTRIC CONSTANT
NT3	ELECTRIC IMPEDANCE
NT3	ELECTRICAL CONDUCTIVITY
NT3	ELECTRICAL RESISTIVITY
NT2	GEOTHERMAL PROPERTIES
NT2	MAGNETIC PROPERTIES
NT3	MAGNETIC FIELD ELEMENTS
NT4	MAGNETIC INCLINATION
NT4	MAGNETIC INTENSITY
NT4	MAGNETIC VARIATIONS
NT3	MAGNETIC PERMEABILITY
NT3	MAGNETIC SUSCEPTIBILITY
NT3	REMANENT MAGNETIZATION
NT2	MASS
NT2	MECHANICAL PROPERTIES
NT3	ANELASTICITY
NT3	BRITTLENESS
NT3	COMPRESSIBILITY
NT3	DEFORMATION
NT4	ROCK DEFORMATION
NT4	STRAIN
NT3	ELASTICITY
NT3	FLEXIBILITY
NT3	STRENGTH
NT4	BEARING CAPACITY
NT4	COLLAPSE STRENGTH
NT4	COMPRESSIVE STRENGTH
NT4	SHEAR STRENGTH
NT4	TENSILE STRENGTH
NT3	TOUGHNESS
NT3	VISCOSITY
NT4	DYNAMIC VISCOSITY
NT4	EDDY VISCOSITY
NT4	KINEMATIC VISCOSITY
NT4	MOLECULAR VISCOSITY
NT3	YIELD POINT
NT2	OPTICAL PROPERTIES
NT3	ABSORPTANCE
NT3	ANGULAR DISTRIBUTION
NT3	ATTENUANCE
NT3	COLOUR
NT4	WATER COLOUR
NT3	EXTINCTION COEFFICIENT
NT3	REFLECTANCE
NT3	REFRACTIVE INDEX
NT3	SCATTERING COEFFICIENT
NT3	SPECTRAL COMPOSITION
NT3	TRANSMITTANCE
NT4	BEAM TRANSMITTANCE
NT3	TRANSPARENCY
NT4	WATER TRANSPARENCY
NT3	VOLUME SCATTERING FUNCTION
NT2	PERMEABILITY
NT2	POROSITY
NT2	PRESSURE
NT3	ATMOSPHERIC PRESSURE
NT4	SEA LEVEL PRESSURE

PROPERTIES (cont'd)

NT3	BLOOD PRESSURE
NT3	HYDROSTATIC PRESSURE
NT4	BOTTOM PRESSURE
NT3	OSMOTIC PRESSURE
NT3	PORE PRESSURE
NT3	SOUND PRESSURE
NT3	VAPOUR PRESSURE
NT4	SATURATION VAPOUR PRESSURE
NT2	SPECIFIC GRAVITY
NT2	THERMODYNAMIC PROPERTIES
NT3	ENTHALPY
NT4	FUSION HEAT
NT4	SUBLIMATION HEAT
NT4	VAPORIZATION HEAT
NT3	ENTROPY
NT3	FREE ENERGY
NT3	SPECIFIC HEAT
NT3	TEMPERATURE
NT4	AIR TEMPERATURE
NT4	BODY TEMPERATURE
NT4	LOW TEMPERATURE
NT4	POTENTIAL TEMPERATURE
NT4	SEDIMENT TEMPERATURE
NT4	TRANSITION TEMPERATURES
NT4	WATER TEMPERATURE
NT3	THERMAL CONDUCTIVITY
NT3	THERMAL DIFFUSIVITY
NT3	THERMAL EXPANSION
NT3	THERMODYNAMIC ACTIVITY
NT3	THERMODYNAMIC EQUILIBRIUM
NT2	TURBIDITY
NT2	WATER HARDNESS
NT2	WEIGHT
NT3	DRY WEIGHT
NT3	MOLECULAR WEIGHT
NT3	WET WEIGHT
NT1	PHYSICOCHEMICAL PROPERTIES
NT1	SEDIMENT PROPERTIES
NT2	GRAIN PROPERTIES
NT2	SEDIMENT STABILITY
NT2	SEDIMENT STRUCTURE
NT2	SEDIMENT TEXTURE
NT1	SURFACE PROPERTIES
NT2	ROUGHNESS
NT3	BED ROUGHNESS
NT3	SURFACE ROUGHNESS
NT2	TEXTURE
NT1	WATER PROPERTIES
RT	PARAMETERS

PROPERTY RIGHTS

SN	Added in 1980
UF	ownership
BT1	RIGHTS
NT1	RENTAL
RT	AQUACULTURE
RT	INLAND WATER ENVIRONMENT
RT	LAKE RECLAMATION
RT	LAKES
RT	LEGAL ASPECTS
RT	RIPARIAN RIGHTS

PROPHYLAXIS

SN	Added in 1980
UF	disease preventive treatment
RT	DISEASE CONTROL
RT	DISEASES
RT	PARASITISM
RT	THERAPY

PROPOSED RESEARCH

USE	**RESEARCH PROPOSALS**

PROPULSION ENGINES

USE	**PROPULSION SYSTEMS**

PROPULSION SYSTEMS

SN	Before 1982 search also PROPULSION ENGINES. For propulsion of aquatic organisms use LOCOMOTION
UF	marine propulsion
UF	propulsion engines
NT1	NUCLEAR PROPULSION
NT1	SAILS
NT1	THRUSTERS
NT1	UNDERWATER PROPULSION
RT	BOATS
RT	DIESEL ENGINES
RT	FUEL ECONOMY
RT	MANOEUVRABILITY
RT	MOTORS
RT	PATENTS
RT	PROPELLERS
RT	SELF-PROPELLED VEHICLES
RT	SHIP TECHNOLOGY
RT	SHIPBOARD EQUIPMENT
RT	SHIPPING
RT	STEERING SYSTEMS
RT	SUBMERSIBLES
RT	TURBINES
RT	UNDERWATER VEHICLES
RT	VEHICLES

PROTACTINIUM

BT1	CHEMICAL ELEMENTS
RT	ACTINIDES
RT	PROTACTINIUM COMPOUNDS
RT	PROTACTINIUM ISOTOPES
RT	TRANSITION ELEMENTS

PROTACTINIUM COMPOUNDS

RT	CHEMICAL COMPOUNDS
RT	PROTACTINIUM

PROTACTINIUM ISOTOPES

BT1	ISOTOPES
RT	PROTACTINIUM

PROTANDRY

RT	HERMAPHRODITISM
RT	SELF FERTILIZATION

PROTECTED RESOURCES

SN	Added in 1980
BT1	RESOURCES
RT	LIVING RESOURCES
RT	MARINE PARKS
RT	NATURAL RESOURCES
RT	RARE RESOURCES
RT	RARE SPECIES
RT	RESOURCE CONSERVATION

PROTECTION

NT1	ENVIRONMENTAL PROTECTION
NT1	FISHERY PROTECTION
NT1	SCOUR PROTECTION
NT1	SEABED PROTECTION
RT	ACCIDENT PREVENTION
RT	ALARM SYSTEMS
RT	CORROSION CONTROL
RT	FOULING CONTROL
RT	HEALTH AND SAFETY
RT	POLLUTION CONTROL
RT	PROTECTION VESSELS
RT	RADIOACTIVE WASTE DISPOSAL
RT	SAFETY DEVICES
RT	SHORE PROTECTION

PROTECTION (COASTAL)

USE	**SHORE PROTECTION**

PROTECTION (HUMAN)

USE	**HEALTH AND SAFETY**

PROTECTION (SECURITY)
USE   **SURVEILLANCE AND ENFORCEMENT**

PROTECTION VESSELS
UF   fishery protection vessels
BT1   SHIPS
BT2   SURFACE CRAFT
BT3   VEHICLES
RT   DEFENCE CRAFT
RT   FISHERY PROTECTION
RT   FISHERY REGULATIONS
RT   PROTECTION
RT   SECURITY
RT   SURFACE CRAFT
RT   SURVEILLANCE AND ENFORCEMENT

PROTECTIVE BEHAVIOUR
SN   Avoiding or hiding from predators
BT1   BEHAVIOUR
RT   AUTOTOMY
RT   BURROWING ORGANISMS
RT   CAMOUFLAGE
RT   CHROMATIC BEHAVIOUR
RT   DEFENCE MECHANISMS
RT   MIMICRY
RT   PREDATORS
RT   SCHOOLING BEHAVIOUR

PROTECTIVE CLOTHING
RT   DIVING EQUIPMENT
RT   SAFETY DEVICES

PROTECTIVE COATINGS
USE   **COATING MATERIALS**

PROTEIN DEFICIENCY
SN   Added in 1980
BT1   NUTRITION DISORDERS
BT2   DISEASES
RT   PROTEIN SYNTHESIS
RT   PROTEINS

PROTEIN DENATURATION
SN   Added in 1980
UF   denaturation (proteins)
BT1   BIOCHEMICAL PHENOMENA
RT   NUCLEIC ACIDS
RT   PROTEIN SYNTHESIS
RT   PROTEINS

PROTEIN METABOLISM
USE   **PROTEIN SYNTHESIS**

PROTEIN SYNTHESIS
SN   Added in 1980
UF   peptide synthesis
UF   protein metabolism
BT1   BIOCHEMICAL PHENOMENA
RT   AMINO ACIDS
RT   PROTEIN DEFICIENCY
RT   PROTEIN DENATURATION
RT   PROTEINS
RT   RIBOSOMES

PROTEINASE
USE   **ENZYMES**

PROTEINS
BT1   ORGANIC COMPOUNDS
NT1   ACTIN
NT1   ALBUMINS
NT1   GLOBULINS
NT1   GLYCOPROTEINS
NT1   HISTONES
NT1   LIPOPROTEINS
NT1   LUCIFERIN
NT1   MUCINS
NT1   MYOGLOBINS
NT1   MYOSIN
NT1   PEPTIDES

PROTEINS (cont'd)
NT2   POLYPEPTIDES
NT1   PEPTONES
NT1   SINGLE CELL PROTEINS
RT   AMINO ACIDS
RT   BIOCHEMISTRY
RT   CHEMICAL COMPOUNDS
RT   CYTOCHROMES
RT   ELECTROPHORESIS
RT   ENZYMES
RT   HAEMOCYANINS
RT   INSULIN
RT   NITROGEN COMPOUNDS
RT   NUCLEIC ACIDS
RT   NUTRITIVE VALUE
RT   ORGANIC CONSTITUENTS
RT   PROTEIN DEFICIENCY
RT   PROTEIN DENATURATION
RT   PROTEIN SYNTHESIS
RT   RIBOSOMES
RT   SEROLOGICAL STUDIES
RT   SEROLOGICAL TAXONOMY
RT   YOLK

PROTEROZOIC
USE   **PRECAMBRIAN**

PROTISTS
SN   The primitive organisms from which
       animals and plants arose
UF   protobionta
RT   EVOLUTION

PROTOBIONTA
USE   **PROTISTS**

PROTOPLASM
USE   **CYTOPLASM**

PROTOTYPES
SN   Used only as a qualifier
RT   SPECIFICATIONS

PROTOZOAL DISEASES
USE   **PROTOZOAN DISEASES**

PROTOZOAL PESTICIDES
USE   **ANTIPROTOZOAL AGENTS**

PROTOZOAN DISEASES
UF   protozoal diseases
BT1   INFECTIOUS DISEASES
BT2   DISEASES
RT   ANTIBIOTICS
RT   ANTIPROTOZOAL AGENTS
RT   BIOLOGICAL CONTROL
RT   BIOLOGICAL VECTORS
RT   DISEASE CONTROL
RT   DRUGS
RT   FISH DISEASES
RT   IMMUNIZATION
RT   MALARIA
RT   PARASITE CONTROL
RT   PARASITES
RT   PARASITIC DISEASES
RT   PARASITISM
RT   PARASITOLOGY

PROVENANCE
UF   sediment source region
RT   PALAEOCURRENTS
RT   SEDIMENTATION
RT   SEDIMENTS

PSAMMON
SN   The biota existing immediately
       below the upper layer of sand on
       beaches, existing in films of water
       in the interstices. Added in 1982
BT1   AQUATIC COMMUNITIES

PSAMMON (cont'd)
RT   EPIPSAMMON
RT   SAND

PSYCHROMETERS
BT1   HYGROMETERS
BT2   MEASURING DEVICES
RT   HYGROMETRY
RT   METEOROLOGICAL INSTRUMENTS
RT   THERMOMETERS

PTEROPOD OOZE
BT1   CALCAREOUS OOZE
BT2   OOZES
RT   ARAGONITE
RT   FOSSIL PTEROPODS

PUBLIC ACCESS
BT1   ACCESS
RT   COASTAL ZONE MANAGEMENT
RT   RECREATION

PUBLIC HEALTH
UF   health
UF   human health
BT1   HEALTH AND SAFETY
RT   AIR POLLUTION
RT   EPIDEMICS
RT   HUMAN DISEASES
RT   HYGIENE
RT   LEGAL ASPECTS
RT   MEDICINE
RT   MICROBIAL CONTAMINATION
RT   NEUROTOXINS
RT   POLLUTION EFFECTS
RT   QUARANTINE REGULATIONS
RT   RADIATION PROTECTION
RT   RECREATIONAL WATERS
RT   SAFETY DEVICES
RT   SOCIOLOGICAL ASPECTS
RT   TOXICITY
RT   WATER POLLUTION TREATMENT
RT   WATER PURIFICATION

PUBLICATIONS
USE   **DOCUMENTS**

PUBLICITY MATERIAL
UF   advertisements
BT1   DOCUMENTS
RT   BROCHURES
RT   CONFERENCES
RT   LECTURES

PUBS
USE   **OCEAN BOTTOM SEISMOMETERS**

PULP WASTES
BT1   WASTES
RT   FOREST INDUSTRY

PULSED LASERS
USE   **LASERS**

PUMICE
BT1   VOLCANIC ROCKS
BT2   IGNEOUS ROCKS
BT3   ROCKS
RT   SURFACE DRIFTERS

PUMP FISHING
BT1   CATCHING METHODS
RT   ATTRACTING TECHNIQUES
RT   AUTOMATED FISHING PLATFORMS
RT   ELECTRIC FISHING
RT   LIGHT FISHING
RT   PUMPING
RT   PUMPS

PUMP STATIONS
	UF	booster stations
	UF	pipeline pumping stations
	RT	PIPELINES
	RT	PUMPS

PUMPING
	RT	PUMP FISHING
	RT	PUMPS
	RT	SLURRIES

PUMPS
	SN	Added in 1982
	UF	air pumps
	NT1	FISH PUMPS
	NT1	WATER PUMPS
	RT	PIPELINES
	RT	PUMP FISHING
	RT	PUMP STATIONS
	RT	PUMPING

PUMPS (WATER)
| | USE | **WATER PUMPS** |

PUPAE
	SN	Added in 1980
	BT1	INSECT LARVAE
	BT2	INVERTEBRATE LARVAE
	BT3	LARVAE
	BT4	DEVELOPMENTAL STAGES
	RT	JUVENILES

PUPS
| | NT1 | JUVENILES |
| | RT | MARINE MAMMALS |

PURCHASERS
| | USE | **CONSUMERS** |

PURCHASING
	RT	ACQUISITION
	RT	CONSUMERS
	RT	COSTS

PURIFICATION (WATER)
| | USE | **WATER PURIFICATION** |

PURINES
| | BT1 | ORGANIC COMPOUNDS |

PURSE SEINERS
| | USE | **SEINERS** |

PURSE SEINES
	BT1	SURROUNDING NETS
	BT2	FISHING NETS
	BT3	FISHING GEAR
	RT	PELAGIC FISHERIES
	RT	PURSE SEINING
	RT	SEINERS
	RT	SEINING

PURSE SEINING
	BT1	SEINING
	BT2	CATCHING METHODS
	RT	BAIT FISH
	RT	CLUPEOID FISHERIES
	RT	PURSE SEINES
	RT	SEINERS
	RT	SONAR
	RT	TUNA FISHERIES

PYCNOCLINE
	UF	density layer
	BT1	DISCONTINUITY LAYERS
	BT2	LAYERS
	RT	DENSITY FRONTS
	RT	DENSITY GRADIENTS
	RT	DENSITY PROFILES
	RT	DENSITY STRATIFICATION

PYCNOCLINE (cont'd)
	RT	ISOPYCNICS
	RT	MIXED LAYER DEPTH
	RT	THERMOCLINE
	RT	WATER DENSITY
	RT	WATER MASSES

PYLORIC CAECA
	BT1	ALIMENTARY ORGANS
	BT2	ANIMAL ORGANS
	BT3	BODY ORGANS
	RT	DIGESTION
	RT	DIGESTIVE GLANDS
	RT	FOOD ABSORPTION
	RT	INTESTINES
	RT	STOMACH

PYRANOMETERS
	UF	solarimeters
	BT1	ACTINOMETERS
	BT2	RADIOMETERS
	BT3	REMOTE SENSING EQUIPMENT
	BT4	EQUIPMENT
	RT	LIGHT MEASURING INSTRUMENTS
	RT	MEASURING DEVICES
	RT	METEOROLOGICAL INSTRUMENTS
	RT	SOLAR RADIATION
	RT	SUN

PYRGEOMETERS
	BT1	ACTINOMETERS
	BT2	RADIOMETERS
	BT3	REMOTE SENSING EQUIPMENT
	BT4	EQUIPMENT
	RT	TERRESTRIAL RADIATION

PYRHELIOMETERS
	BT1	ACTINOMETERS
	BT2	RADIOMETERS
	BT3	REMOTE SENSING EQUIPMENT
	BT4	EQUIPMENT
	RT	METEOROLOGICAL INSTRUMENTS
	RT	SOLAR RADIATION

PYRIDINES
| | BT1 | AZINES |
| | BT2 | ORGANIC COMPOUNDS |

PYRIMIDINES
| | BT1 | AZINES |
| | BT2 | ORGANIC COMPOUNDS |

PYRITE
| | BT1 | SULPHIDE MINERALS |
| | BT2 | MINERALS |

PYROCLASTICS
| | USE | **VOLCANIC ROCKS** |

PYROLUSITE
	BT1	OXIDE MINERALS
	BT2	MINERALS
	RT	MANGANESE MINERALS

PYROLYSIS
	BT1	DEGRADATION
	BT2	CHEMICAL REACTIONS
	RT	BIOGEOCHEMISTRY
	RT	DISSOCIATION
	RT	TEMPERATURE EFFECTS

PYROPHYLLITE
| | BT1 | SILICATE MINERALS |
| | BT2 | MINERALS |

PYROXENES
	BT1	SILICATE MINERALS
	BT2	MINERALS
	NT1	AUGITE
	RT	ALKALI BASALTS

PYROXENES (cont'd)
| | RT | THOLEIITE |

PYRRHOTITE
| | BT1 | SULPHIDE MINERALS |
| | BT2 | MINERALS |

PYRROLIDINE
	BT1	AMINES
	BT2	ORGANIC COMPOUNDS
	RT	PROLINE

QUAHOG FISHERIES
| | USE | **CLAM FISHERIES** |

QUALITY
	SN	Used only as a qualifier. Added in 1980
	UF	grades
	RT	PRODUCT DEVELOPMENT
	RT	QUALITY ASSURANCE
	RT	QUALITY CONTROL
	RT	TESTS

QUALITY ANALYSIS
| | USE | **QUALITY ASSURANCE** |

QUALITY ASSURANCE
	SN	Added in 1980
	UF	quality analysis
	UF	reliability assurance
	RT	QUALITY
	RT	QUALITY CONTROL
	RT	STORAGE LIFE
	RT	VISUAL INSPECTION

QUALITY CONTROL
	SN	Methods and procedures for testing and monitoring quality at acceptable levels
	BT1	CONTROL
	RT	ACCEPTABILITY
	RT	ACCEPTANCE TESTS
	RT	CERTIFICATION
	RT	CODEX STANDARDS
	RT	COMMERCIAL LEGISLATION
	RT	CONTROL CHARTS
	RT	DEFECTS
	RT	FISH HANDLING
	RT	FISH INSPECTION
	RT	FISH INSPECTION REGULATIONS
	RT	FISH SPOILAGE
	RT	FISHERY PRODUCTS
	RT	FOOD ADDITIVES
	RT	FOOD COMPOSITION
	RT	FOOD FISH
	RT	FOOD POISONING
	RT	FOOD TECHNOLOGY
	RT	HUMAN FOOD
	RT	INSPECTION
	RT	MATERIALS TESTING
	RT	MICROBIAL CONTAMINATION
	RT	MINCED PRODUCTS
	RT	ORGANOLEPTIC PROPERTIES
	RT	PERFORMANCE ASSESSMENT
	RT	POWDERED PRODUCTS
	RT	PROCESSED FISHERY PRODUCTS
	RT	PROCESSING FISHERY PRODUCTS
	RT	PRODUCTION MANAGEMENT
	RT	PRODUCTS
	RT	QUALITY
	RT	QUALITY ASSURANCE
	RT	RADIOGRAPHY
	RT	STANDARDIZATION
	RT	STANDARDS
	RT	STATISTICAL SAMPLING
	RT	STORAGE EFFECTS
	RT	TASTE TESTS
	RT	TESTS
	RT	VISUAL INSPECTION

QUALITY CONTROL (cont'd)
RT	WATER QUALITY CONTROL
RT	X-RAY INSPECTION

QUANTA METERS
BT1	LIGHT MEASURING INSTRUMENTS
BT2	MEASURING DEVICES
RT	IRRADIANCE METERS
RT	PHOTOMETRY
RT	PHOTOSYNTHESIS

QUANTITATIVE DISTRIBUTION
SN	Used only as a qualifier
BT1	DISTRIBUTION
RT	ABUNDANCE
RT	BIOLOGICAL CHARTS
RT	BIOMASS
RT	FISHERY CHARTS
RT	GEOGRAPHICAL DISTRIBUTION
RT	POPULATION DENSITY
RT	POPULATION NUMBER
RT	RESOURCE AVAILABILITY
RT	SPATIAL VARIATIONS
RT	TEMPORAL DISTRIBUTION

QUARANTINE REGULATIONS
SN	Regulations for protecting public health
BT1	NAVIGATION REGULATIONS
BT2	LEGISLATION
RT	PUBLIC HEALTH

QUARRIES
USE	**PITS**

QUARTER DIURNAL TIDES
BT1	TIDES
BT2	TIDAL MOTION
RT	SHALLOW-WATER TIDES

QUARTZ
BT1	SILICATE MINERALS
BT2	MINERALS
RT	THOLEIITE

QUARTZ CLOCKS
BT1	CHRONOMETERS
BT2	EQUIPMENT

QUARTZ PRESSURE SENSORS
BT1	PRESSURE SENSORS

QUARTZ TEMPERATURE SENSORS
BT1	THERMOMETERS
BT2	MEASURING DEVICES

QUARTZITE
BT1	SILICATE MINERALS
BT2	MINERALS

QUASI-GEOSTROPHIC MOTION
BT1	GEOSTROPHIC FLOW
BT2	FLUID FLOW
BT3	FLUID MOTION

QUASI-GEOSTROPHIC WAVES
USE	**PLANETARY WAVES**

QUATERNARY
SN	Before 1982 search also QUATERNARY PERIOD
UF	quaternary period
BT1	CENOZOIC
BT2	GEOLOGICAL TIME
NT1	HOLOCENE
NT1	PLEISTOCENE
RT	GEOMORPHOLOGY
RT	PALYNOLOGY
RT	SEA LEVEL

QUATERNARY PERIOD
USE	**QUATERNARY**

QUAYS
USE	**PORT INSTALLATIONS**

QUICKSANDS
BT1	SAND
BT2	CLASTICS
BT3	SEDIMENTS
RT	COHESIONLESS SEDIMENTS

QUINOLINES
BT1	AZINES
BT2	ORGANIC COMPOUNDS

QUOTA REGULATIONS
UF	catch limit
UF	catch quota
BT1	FISHERY REGULATIONS
BT2	LEGISLATION
RT	BLUE WHALE UNIT
RT	CATCH STATISTICS
RT	PERMITS
RT	WHALING

RACE
USE	**SUBPOPULATIONS**

RACEWAY CULTURE
UF	river culture
UF	running water culture
BT1	AQUACULTURE TECHNIQUES
RT	CRUSTACEAN CULTURE
RT	CULTURES
RT	FISH CULTURE
RT	FRESHWATER AQUACULTURE
RT	INTENSIVE CULTURE
RT	MONOCULTURE
RT	POND CONSTRUCTION

RACIAL STUDIES
RT	ELECTROPHORESIS
RT	GENETICS
RT	STOCK IDENTIFICATION
RT	SUBPOPULATIONS

RACK CULTURE
USE	**OFF-BOTTOM CULTURE**

RADAR
UF	radar equipment
UF	radar systems
BT1	REMOTE SENSING EQUIPMENT
BT2	EQUIPMENT
NT1	MICROWAVE RADAR
NT2	RADAR ALTIMETERS
NT2	SCATTEROMETERS
NT2	SYNTHETIC APERTURE RADAR
RT	DETECTION
RT	DOPPLER EFFECT
RT	ELECTRONIC EQUIPMENT
RT	ICEBERG DETECTION
RT	LIDAR
RT	MICROWAVES
RT	NAVIGATION
RT	NAVIGATIONAL AIDS
RT	RADAR ALTIMETRY
RT	RADAR CLUTTER
RT	RADAR IMAGERY
RT	RADAR NAVIGATION

RADAR ALTIMETERS
BT1	MICROWAVE RADAR
BT2	RADAR
BT3	REMOTE SENSING EQUIPMENT
BT4	EQUIPMENT
RT	ALTIMETERS
RT	WAVE MEASURING EQUIPMENT

RADAR ALTIMETRY
BT1	ALTIMETRY
RT	AIRCRAFT
RT	HELICOPTERS
RT	RADAR
RT	RADAR IMAGERY
RT	RADIO OCEANOGRAPHY
RT	SATELLITE ALTIMETRY
RT	STABILIZED PLATFORMS
RT	SURFACE ROUGHNESS
RT	SURFACE TOPOGRAPHY
RT	WAVE MEASUREMENT
RT	WAVE MEASURING PLATFORMS

RADAR CLUTTER
UF	noise (radar echoes)
NT1	SURFACE CLUTTER
RT	RADAR
RT	RADAR IMAGERY

RADAR EQUIPMENT
USE	**RADAR**

RADAR IMAGERY
UF	radar methods (sensing)
BT1	MICROWAVE IMAGERY
BT2	IMAGERY
BT3	REMOTE SENSING
RT	ELECTROMAGNETIC RADIATION
RT	GEOSENSING
RT	RADAR
RT	RADAR ALTIMETRY
RT	RADAR CLUTTER
RT	RADIO OCEANOGRAPHY
RT	SCATTEROMETERS
RT	SEA STATE
RT	WAVE MEASUREMENT

RADAR METHODS (SENSING)
USE	**RADAR IMAGERY**

RADAR NAVIGATION
BT1	POSITION FIXING
RT	COLLISION AVOIDANCE
RT	RADAR
RT	RADIO NAVIGATION

RADAR SYSTEMS
USE	**RADAR**

RADIANCE
SN	Flux of radiant energy in water
RT	EMISSIVITY
RT	IRRADIANCE
RT	LIGHT
RT	LIGHT FIELDS
RT	OPTICAL PROPERTIES
RT	RADIANCE METERS
RT	RADIATIVE TRANSFER
RT	SOLAR RADIATION

RADIANCE DISTRIBUTION
USE	**LIGHT FIELDS**

RADIANCE METERS
BT1	LIGHT MEASURING INSTRUMENTS
BT2	MEASURING DEVICES
RT	RADIANCE

RADIATION BALANCE
SN	Net flux of solar and terrestrial radiation at water surface
UF	net radiation
UF	radiation budget
RT	HEAT BUDGET
RT	HEAT EXCHANGE
RT	SOLAR RADIATION
RT	TERRESTRIAL RADIATION

RADIATION BUDGET
USE   **RADIATION BALANCE**

RADIATION FOG
USE   **FOG**

RADIATION HAZARDS
UF   radioactive exposure
BT1   HAZARDS
RT   MEDICINE
RT   RADIATION LEAKS
RT   RADIATION PROTECTION
RT   RADIOACTIVE CONTAMINATION
RT   RADIOACTIVE WASTES

RADIATION LEAKS
BT1   ACCIDENTS
RT   RADIATION HAZARDS
RT   RADIOACTIVE WASTE DISPOSAL

RADIATION MEASURING EQUIPMENT
USE   **RADIOMETERS**

RADIATION PROTECTION
UF   radiological protection
BT1   HEALTH AND SAFETY
RT   PUBLIC HEALTH
RT   RADIATION HAZARDS
RT   RADIOACTIVE CONTAMINATION
RT   RADIOACTIVE WASTE DISPOSAL
RT   SAFETY REGULATIONS

RADIATIONAL TIDES
BT1   TIDES
BT2   TIDAL MOTION
RT   METEOROLOGICAL TIDES
RT   SOLAR RADIATION
RT   TIDAL CONSTITUENTS

RADIATIONS
SN   Use of a more specific term is
        recommended
NT1   ELECTROMAGNETIC RADIATION
NT2   GAMMA RADIATION
NT2   INFRARED RADIATION
NT2   LIGHT
NT2   MICROWAVES
NT2   RADIO WAVES
NT2   SOLAR RADIATION
NT3   EXTRATERRESTRIAL RADIATION
NT3   REFLECTED GLOBAL RADIATION
NT2   TERRESTRIAL RADIATION
NT3   DOWNWARD LONG WAVE RADIATION
NT3   UPWARD LONG WAVE RADIATION
NT2   ULTRAVIOLET RADIATION
NT2   X-RAYS
NT1   IONIZING RADIATION
NT2   COSMIC RADIATION
NT2   NUCLEAR RADIATIONS
NT1   THERMAL RADIATION

RADIATIVE TRANSFER
UF   radiative transfer equation
BT1   ENERGY TRANSFER
RT   ELECTROMAGNETIC RADIATION
RT   HEAT TRANSFER
RT   IRRADIANCE
RT   LIGHT FIELDS
RT   POLARIZATION
RT   RADIANCE
RT   SOLAR RADIATION
RT   TERRESTRIAL RADIATION

RADIATIVE TRANSFER EQUATION
USE   **RADIATIVE TRANSFER**

RADIO
BT1   COMMUNICATION SYSTEMS
RT   MICROWAVES
RT   RADIO AIDS
RT   RADIO BUOYS
RT   TELEVISION SYSTEMS

RADIO AIDS
SN   Equipment used for position fixing
        in navigation
RT   EQUIPMENT
RT   FISHING OPERATIONS
RT   NAVIGATION
RT   RADIO

RADIO BUOYS
BT1   BUOYS
RT   COMMUNICATION SYSTEMS
RT   FISHING BUOYS
RT   RADIO

RADIO NAVIGATION
BT1   POSITION FIXING
NT1   DECCA
NT1   LORAN
NT1   OMEGA
NT1   SHORAN
RT   FISHING OPERATIONS
RT   LATTICE CHARTS
RT   RADAR NAVIGATION

RADIO OCEANOGRAPHY
BT1   OCEANOGRAPHY
BT2   EARTH SCIENCES
RT   RADAR ALTIMETRY
RT   RADAR IMAGERY
RT   REMOTE SENSING
RT   SATELLITE SENSING

RADIO TELEMETRY
BT1   TELEMETRY
BT2   COMMUNICATION SYSTEMS

RADIO TRACKING
USE   **TRACKING**

RADIO WAVES
BT1   ELECTROMAGNETIC RADIATION
BT2   RADIATIONS

RADIOACTIVE AEROSOLS
UF   radioactive particulates
BT1   AEROSOLS
BT2   COLLOIDS
RT   ATMOSPHERIC CHEMISTRY
RT   FALLOUT

RADIOACTIVE CONTAMINATION
UF   contamination (radioactive)
UF   radioactive pollution
BT1   POLLUTION
RT   BODY BURDEN
RT   BRACKISHWATER POLLUTION
RT   DUST
RT   FALLOUT
RT   MARINE POLLUTION
RT   NUCLEAR POWER PLANTS
RT   NUCLEAR PROPULSION
RT   RADIATION HAZARDS
RT   RADIATION PROTECTION
RT   RADIOACTIVE POLLUTANTS
RT   RADIOACTIVE WASTE DISPOSAL
RT   RADIOACTIVE WASTES
RT   RADIOACTIVITY
RT   RADIOCHEMISTRY
RT   RADIOECOLOGY
RT   RADIOISOTOPES
RT   RADIONUCLIDE KINETICS
RT   TOXICITY

RADIOACTIVE CONTAMINATION (cont'd)
RT   UNDERSEA WARFARE
RT   UNDERWATER EXPLOSIONS
RT   WATER POLLUTION

RADIOACTIVE DATING
USE   **RADIOMETRIC DATING**

RADIOACTIVE EXPOSURE
USE   **RADIATION HAZARDS**

RADIOACTIVE FALLOUT
USE   **FALLOUT**

RADIOACTIVE ISOTOPES
USE   **RADIOISOTOPES**

RADIOACTIVE LABELLING
SN   Added in 1982
UF   isotopic labelling
UF   labelling (radioactive)
UF   radioactive tagging
RT   RADIOACTIVE TRACERS
RT   RADIOACTIVITY

RADIOACTIVE MATERIALS
BT1   MATERIALS
NT1   FISSION PRODUCTS
RT   RADIOACTIVE WASTES
RT   RADIOISOTOPES

RADIOACTIVE PARTICULATES
USE   **RADIOACTIVE AEROSOLS**

RADIOACTIVE POLLUTANTS
BT1   POLLUTANTS
RT   CARCINOGENESIS
RT   CARCINOGENS
RT   FALLOUT
RT   RADIOACTIVE CONTAMINATION
RT   RADIOACTIVE WASTES
RT   RADIOACTIVITY
RT   RADIOISOTOPES
RT   SURFACE MICROLAYER

RADIOACTIVE POLLUTION
USE   **RADIOACTIVE CONTAMINATION**

RADIOACTIVE TAGGING
USE   **RADIOACTIVE LABELLING**

RADIOACTIVE TRACERS
BT1   TRACERS
RT   AUTORADIOGRAPHY
RT   CARBON 13
RT   CARBON 14
RT   ISOTOPES
RT   RADIOACTIVE LABELLING
RT   RADIOACTIVITY
RT   RADIOECOLOGY
RT   RADIOGRAPHY
RT   RADIOISOTOPES
RT   SEDIMENT TRANSPORT

RADIOACTIVE WASTE DISPOSAL
BT1   WASTE DISPOSAL
RT   OCEAN DUMPING
RT   PROTECTION
RT   RADIATION LEAKS
RT   RADIATION PROTECTION
RT   RADIOACTIVE CONTAMINATION
RT   RADIOACTIVE WASTES
RT   WASTE DISPOSAL SITES

RADIOACTIVE WASTES
SN   Radioactive wastes in aquatic
        environment
UF   nuclear wastes
BT1   WASTES
RT   BIOACCUMULATION

RADIOACTIVE WASTES (cont'd)
RT	FALLOUT
RT	FISSION PRODUCTS
RT	HAZARDOUS MATERIALS
RT	NUCLEAR ENERGY
RT	NUCLEAR POWER PLANTS
RT	NUCLEAR RADIATIONS
RT	RADIATION HAZARDS
RT	RADIOACTIVE CONTAMINATION
RT	RADIOACTIVE MATERIALS
RT	RADIOACTIVE POLLUTANTS
RT	RADIOACTIVE WASTE DISPOSAL
RT	RADIOACTIVITY
RT	RADIOECOLOGY
RT	SEWAGE DISPOSAL
RT	THERMAL POLLUTION
RT	WASTE DISPOSAL

RADIOACTIVITY
RT	ACTINIUM
RT	BODY BURDEN
RT	FALLOUT
RT	GAMMA SPECTROSCOPY
RT	GEIGER COUNTERS
RT	GEOPHYSICS
RT	IONIZING RADIATION
RT	NUCLEAR ENERGY
RT	NUCLEAR PHYSICS
RT	NUCLEAR RADIATIONS
RT	PLUTONIUM
RT	RADIOACTIVE CONTAMINATION
RT	RADIOACTIVE LABELLING
RT	RADIOACTIVE POLLUTANTS
RT	RADIOACTIVE TRACERS
RT	RADIOACTIVE WASTES
RT	RADIOCHEMISTRY
RT	RADIOECOLOGY
RT	RADIOGRAPHY
RT	RADIOISOTOPES
RT	RADIOMETRIC DATING
RT	RADIONUCLIDE KINETICS
RT	RADIUM
RT	URANIUM
RT	WATER QUALITY

RADIOCARBON DATING
BT1	RADIOMETRIC DATING
BT2	GEOCHRONOMETRY
RT	CARBON 13
RT	CARBON 14

RADIOCHEMISTRY
BT1	CHEMISTRY
RT	IRRADIATION
RT	NUCLEAR RADIATIONS
RT	RADIOACTIVE CONTAMINATION
RT	RADIOACTIVITY
RT	RADIOECOLOGY
RT	RADIOISOTOPES

RADIOECOLOGY
SN	Use of a more specific term is recommended
BT1	ECOLOGY
RT	RADIOACTIVE CONTAMINATION
RT	RADIOACTIVE TRACERS
RT	RADIOACTIVE WASTES
RT	RADIOACTIVITY
RT	RADIOCHEMISTRY
RT	RADIOISOTOPES

RADIOGRAPHIC TESTING
USE	**NONDESTRUCTIVE TESTING**

RADIOGRAPHY
NT1	AUTORADIOGRAPHY
RT	FLUORESCENCE MICROSCOPY
RT	IRRADIATION
RT	PHOTOGRAPHY
RT	QUALITY CONTROL

RADIOGRAPHY (cont'd)
RT	RADIOACTIVE TRACERS
RT	RADIOACTIVITY
RT	X-RAY SPECTROSCOPY

RADIOISOTOPE KINETICS
USE	**RADIONUCLIDE KINETICS**

RADIOISOTOPES
UF	radioactive isotopes
UF	radionuclides
BT1	ISOTOPES
RT	BIOACCUMULATION
RT	BIOLOGICAL HALF LIFE
RT	CARBON 13
RT	CARBON 14
RT	CHEMICAL ELEMENTS
RT	EUROPIUM
RT	FALLOUT
RT	NUCLEAR PHYSICS
RT	RADIOACTIVE CONTAMINATION
RT	RADIOACTIVE MATERIALS
RT	RADIOACTIVE POLLUTANTS
RT	RADIOACTIVE TRACERS
RT	RADIOACTIVITY
RT	RADIOCHEMISTRY
RT	RADIOECOLOGY
RT	RADIOMETRIC DATING
RT	RADIONUCLIDE KINETICS

RADIOLARIAN OOZE
BT1	SILICEOUS OOZE
BT2	OOZES
RT	FOSSIL RADIOLARIA
RT	RADIOLARITE

RADIOLARITE
BT1	SILICEOUS ROCKS
RT	CLASTICS
RT	PELAGIC SEDIMENTS
RT	RADIOLARIAN OOZE
RT	SEDIMENTARY ROCKS

RADIOLOGICAL PROTECTION
USE	**RADIATION PROTECTION**

RADIOMETERS
UF	radiation measuring equipment
BT1	REMOTE SENSING EQUIPMENT
BT2	EQUIPMENT
NT1	ACTINOMETERS
NT2	PYRANOMETERS
NT2	PYRGEOMETERS
NT2	PYRHELIOMETERS
NT1	INFRARED DETECTORS
NT1	MICROWAVE RADIOMETERS
RT	ELECTROMAGNETIC RADIATION
RT	LIGHT MEASURING INSTRUMENTS
RT	MEASURING DEVICES
RT	MULTISPECTRAL SCANNERS
RT	PHOTOMETERS
RT	SENSORS

RADIOMETERS (MICROWAVE)
USE	**MICROWAVE IMAGERY**

RADIOMETRIC DATING
SN	Before 1982 search RADIOACTIVE DATING
UF	isotope dating
UF	radioactive dating
BT1	GEOCHRONOMETRY
NT1	OXYGEN ISOTOPE DATING
NT1	POTASSIUM-ARGON DATING
NT1	RADIOCARBON DATING
NT1	RUBIDIUM-STRONTIUM DATING
NT1	THORIUM-230/THORIUM-232 DATING
NT1	URANIUM-HELIUM DATING
RT	ABSOLUTE AGE
RT	CARBON 13
RT	CARBON 14

RADIOMETRIC DATING (cont'd)
RT	GEOCHEMISTRY
RT	GEOLOGICAL TIME
RT	ISOTOPES
RT	NUCLEAR RADIATIONS
RT	OXYGEN ISOTOPE RATIO
RT	RADIOACTIVITY
RT	RADIOISOTOPES
RT	SEDIMENT CHEMISTRY
RT	URANIUM-234/URANIUM-238 RATIO

RADIONUCLIDE KINETICS
SN	For radionuclides in living organisms only. Added in 1980
UF	contamination (internal)
UF	radioisotope kinetics
UF	radionuclide metabolism
UF	radionuclide transfer (in organisms)
UF	radionuclide turnover (in organisms)
BT1	KINETICS
BT2	MECHANICS
BT3	PHYSICS
RT	BIOLOGICAL HALF LIFE
RT	BODY BURDEN
RT	EXCRETION
RT	METABOLISM
RT	RADIOACTIVE CONTAMINATION
RT	RADIOACTIVITY
RT	RADIOISOTOPES

RADIONUCLIDE METABOLISM
USE	**RADIONUCLIDE KINETICS**

RADIONUCLIDE TRANSFER (IN ORGANISMS)
USE	**RADIONUCLIDE KINETICS**

RADIONUCLIDE TURNOVER (IN ORGANISMS)
USE	**RADIONUCLIDE KINETICS**

RADIONUCLIDES
USE	**RADIOISOTOPES**

RADIOSONDES
UF	dropwindsondes
UF	rawinsondes
RT	AIR TEMPERATURE
RT	ATMOSPHERIC PRESSURE
RT	BALLOONS
RT	HUMIDITY
RT	INSTRUMENT PLATFORMS
RT	METEOROLOGICAL INSTRUMENTS
RT	WIND MEASURING EQUIPMENT

RADIUM
BT1	CHEMICAL ELEMENTS
RT	ALKALINE EARTH METALS
RT	RADIOACTIVITY
RT	RADIUM COMPOUNDS
RT	RADIUM ISOTOPES

RADIUM COMPOUNDS
RT	CHEMICAL COMPOUNDS
RT	RADIUM

RADIUM ISOTOPES
BT1	ISOTOPES
RT	RADIUM

RADON
BT1	CHEMICAL ELEMENTS
RT	RADON ISOTOPES
RT	RARE GASES

RADON ISOTOPES
BT1	ISOTOPES
RT	RADON

RADULAE
SN	Before 1982 search MOUTH PARTS
BT1	MOUTH PARTS
RT	ALIMENTARY ORGANS
RT	FRESHWATER MOLLUSCS
RT	MARINE MOLLUSCS
RT	TEETH

RAFT CULTURE
SN	Before 1982 search OFF-BOTTOM CULTURE
BT1	AQUACULTURE TECHNIQUES
RT	AQUACULTURE EQUIPMENT
RT	CAGE CULTURE
RT	CULTURES
RT	MOLLUSC CULTURE
RT	MUSSEL CULTURE
RT	OFF-BOTTOM CULTURE

RAFTING
BT1	SEDIMENT TRANSPORT
NT1	BIOLOGICAL RAFTING
NT1	ICE RAFTING
RT	GLACIAL DEPOSITS
RT	ICE DRIFT
RT	PALAEOCEANOGRAPHY

RAFTS
USE	**BOATS**

RAFTS (INSTRUMENT CARRIERS)
USE	**DATA BUOYS**

RAFTS (LIFE)
USE	**LIFEBOATS**

RAIL BRIDGES
USE	**BRIDGES**

RAIN
UF	rain water
BT1	WATER
RT	ACID RAIN
RT	ATMOSPHERIC PRECIPITATIONS
RT	DROUGHTS
RT	RAIN GAUGES
RT	RAINFALL
RT	RAINY SEASON
RT	SURFACE RADIATION TEMPERATURE

RAIN DROPS
USE	**DROPLETS**

RAIN GAUGES
BT1	METEOROLOGICAL INSTRUMENTS
RT	RAIN
RT	RAINFALL

RAIN WATER
USE	**RAIN**

RAINFALL
SN	Amount of both rain and water equivalent of frozen precipitation
RT	ACID RAIN
RT	ATMOSPHERIC PRECIPITATIONS
RT	CLIMATE
RT	DROUGHTS
RT	HAIL
RT	HYDROLOGIC CYCLE
RT	ISOHYETS
RT	RAIN
RT	RAIN GAUGES
RT	RIVER DISCHARGE
RT	RUNOFF
RT	SALINITY
RT	SNOW
RT	STORMWATER RUNOFF
RT	WEATHER

RAINY SEASON
UF	wet season
BT1	SEASONS
RT	DRY SEASON
RT	MONSOONS
RT	RAIN
RT	TROPICAL ENVIRONMENT
RT	TROPICAL LAKES

RAISED BEACHES
BT1	BEACHES
BT2	COASTAL LANDFORMS
BT3	LANDFORMS
BT4	TOPOGRAPHIC FEATURES
RT	COASTAL MORPHOLOGY
RT	EMERGENT SHORELINES
RT	EROSION FEATURES
RT	EUSTATIC CHANGES
RT	ISOSTASY
RT	SEA LEVEL CHANGES
RT	STRANDLINES
RT	TERRACES
RT	UPLIFT

RAKES
USE	**GRAPPLING GEAR**

RANCHING
SN	Use of the natural aquatic environment as free feeding grounds for culturing organisms. Added in 1980
UF	ocean ranching
RT	ANADROMOUS MIGRATIONS
RT	COASTAL ZONE
RT	FEEDING MIGRATIONS
RT	RENTAL
RT	SPORT FISHING
RT	STOCKING (ORGANISMS)
RT	WATER RIGHTS

RANDOM PROCESSES
RT	PROBABILITY THEORY
RT	STATISTICAL ANALYSIS
RT	STOCHASTIC PROCESSES

RANDOM SAMPLING
USE	**STATISTICAL SAMPLING**

RANGE ACTION
USE	**HARBOUR OSCILLATIONS**

RARE EARTH ELEMENTS
USE	**RARE EARTHS**

RARE EARTHS
UF	lanthanides
UF	rare earth elements
BT1	METALS
RT	CERIUM
RT	DYSPROSIUM
RT	ERBIUM
RT	EUROPIUM
RT	GADOLINIUM
RT	HOLMIUM
RT	LANTHANIUM
RT	LUTETIUM
RT	NEODYMIUM
RT	PRASEODYMIUM
RT	PROMETHIUM
RT	SAMARIUM
RT	TERBIUM
RT	THULIUM
RT	TRANSITION ELEMENTS
RT	YTTERBIUM

RARE GASES
UF	inert gases
UF	noble gases
BT1	GASES
BT2	FLUIDS
RT	ARGON
RT	HELIUM
RT	KRYPTON
RT	NEON
RT	RADON
RT	XENON

RARE RESOURCES
SN	Added in 1980
BT1	RESOURCES
RT	LIVING RESOURCES
RT	NATURAL RESOURCES
RT	OVEREXPLOITATION
RT	PROTECTED RESOURCES
RT	RARE SPECIES
RT	RESOURCE CONSERVATION

RARE SPECIES
SN	Added in 1980
UF	endangered organisms
UF	endangered species
UF	species rarity
BT1	SPECIES
BT2	TAXA
RT	AQUATIC ANIMALS
RT	AQUATIC PLANTS
RT	FISHERY RESOURCES
RT	MARINE PARKS
RT	NATURE CONSERVATION
RT	PROTECTED RESOURCES
RT	RARE RESOURCES
RT	SANCTUARIES
RT	SPECIES EXTINCTION

RATES AND TAXES
USE	**TAXES**

RATIOS
SN	Used only as a qualifier
RT	ALBEDO
RT	BOWEN RATIO
RT	CARBON/NITROGEN RATIO
RT	CARBON/PHOSPHORUS RATIO
RT	COEFFICIENTS
RT	CONSTANTS
RT	DIMENSIONLESS NUMBERS
RT	POISSON'S RATIO
RT	ROSSBY NUMBER
RT	SIGNAL-TO-NOISE RATIO
RT	VOID RATIO
RT	WAVE AGE

RAW MATERIALS
SN	Added in 1980
BT1	MATERIALS
RT	NATURAL RESOURCES
RT	PRODUCTS

RAWINSONDES
USE	**RADIOSONDES**

RAY PATHS
UF	seismic ray path
UF	sound ray paths
RT	SEISMIC PROPAGATION
RT	SEISMIC WAVES
RT	SOUND WAVES

RAYLEIGH WAVES
BT1	SURFACE SEISMIC WAVES
BT2	SEISMIC WAVES
BT3	ELASTIC WAVES
RT	STONELEY WAVES

ASFIS Thesaurus

RAYS FISHERIES
USE **SHARK FISHERIES**

RE-ENTRY (DEEP-SEA DRILLING)
USE **HOLE RE-ENTRY**

REACTION KINETICS
USE **CHEMICAL KINETICS**

REACTIONS (CHEMICAL)
USE **CHEMICAL REACTIONS**

READING LISTS
USE **BIBLIOGRAPHIES**

REARING
UF   artificial rearing
UF   experimental rearing
UF   laboratory rearing
RT   AQUACULTURE
RT   AQUACULTURE TECHNIQUES
RT   AQUARIA
RT   AQUARIOLOGY
RT   ARTIFICIAL FEEDING
RT   BRINE SHRIMP EGGS
RT   CONTROLLED CONDITIONS
RT   CULTURE TANKS
RT   CULTURED ORGANISMS
RT   EXPERIMENTAL CULTURE
RT   EXPERIMENTAL RESEARCH
RT   HATCHING
RT   INDUCED BREEDING
RT   LABORATORY CULTURE
RT   LARVAE
RT   LARVAL DEVELOPMENT
RT   ZOOPLANKTON CULTURE

RECENT EPOCH
USE **HOLOCENE**

RECEPTOR CELLS
USE **RECEPTORS**

RECEPTORS
SN   Added in 1980
UF   exteroceptors
UF   interoceptors
UF   receptor cells
UF   sensory receptors
BT1   CELLS
NT1   TARGET CELLS
RT   NEURONS
RT   SENSE ORGANS

RECIRCULATING SYSTEMS
UF   closed recirculating systems
UF   recirculating water systems
UF   recirculation systems
UF   water circulating systems
BT1   AQUACULTURE SYSTEMS
RT   AQUACULTURE EQUIPMENT
RT   BIOFILTERS
RT   CIRCULATION
RT   CRUSTACEAN CULTURE
RT   CULTURE TANKS
RT   EXPERIMENTAL CULTURE
RT   FISH CULTURE
RT   FRESHWATER AQUACULTURE
RT   OYSTER CULTURE
RT   SHELLFISH CULTURE
RT   WATER FILTRATION
RT   WATER PUMPS

RECIRCULATING WATER SYSTEMS
USE **RECIRCULATING SYSTEMS**

RECIRCULATION SYSTEMS
USE **RECIRCULATING SYSTEMS**

RECLAMATION
SN   Use of a more specific term is
        recommended. Added in 1980
NT1   LAKE RECLAMATION
NT1   LAND RECLAMATION
NT1   WATER RECLAMATION
RT   BASELINE STUDIES
RT   CONSERVATION
RT   DEPLETION
RT   ECONOMICS
RT   IRRIGATION
RT   SHORE PROTECTION
RT   WATER USE

RECLAMATION (LAKES)
USE **LAKE RECLAMATION**

RECLAMATION (LAND)
USE **LAND RECLAMATION**

RECLAMATION (WATER)
USE **WATER RECLAMATION**

RECORDERS
USE **RECORDING EQUIPMENT**

RECORDING EQUIPMENT
UF   recorders
UF   recording instrument
BT1   EQUIPMENT
NT1   DEPTH RECORDERS
NT1   SOUND RECORDERS
NT1   WAVE RECORDERS
RT   DATA BUOYS
RT   DATA LOGGERS
RT   ELECTRONIC EQUIPMENT
RT   LIMNOLOGICAL EQUIPMENT
RT   MEASURING DEVICES
RT   MONITORING SYSTEMS
RT   OCEANOGRAPHIC EQUIPMENT
RT   REMOTE CONTROL
RT   SENSORS
RT   TELEMETRY

RECORDING INSTRUMENT
USE **RECORDING EQUIPMENT**

RECORDS
SN   Used only as a qualifier
RT   ANALOG RECORDS
RT   ARCHIVES
RT   AUDIO RECORDINGS
RT   DIGITAL RECORDS
RT   DOCUMENTS
RT   LOGBOOKS
RT   MAGNETIC TAPE RECORDINGS
RT   TIDAL RECORDS
RT   VIDEOTAPE RECORDINGS

RECOVERY
SN   Recovery of materials and equipment
        including underwater vehicles
UF   recovery of equipment
NT1   CORE RECOVERY
NT1   MOORING RECOVERY
RT   CURRENT METER ARRAYS
RT   DEPLOYMENT
RT   DIVING
RT   GEAR HANDLING
RT   LAUNCHING
RT   OCEANOGRAPHIC EQUIPMENT
RT   SEAMANSHIP
RT   STATION KEEPING
RT   UNDERWATER VEHICLES

RECOVERY OF EQUIPMENT
USE **RECOVERY**

RECOVERY OF WRECKS
USE **SALVAGING**

RECREATION
SN   Added in 1980
UF   leisure activities
UF   outdoor recreation
NT1   BATHING
NT1   SPORT FISHING
NT1   SURFING
NT1   YACHTING
RT   BAIT FISHING
RT   BOATING
RT   DANGEROUS ORGANISMS
RT   DIVING INDUSTRY
RT   ICE FISHING
RT   LAND USE
RT   MARINE PARKS
RT   MOTOR BOATS
RT   PUBLIC ACCESS
RT   RECREATIONAL WATERS
RT   RIPARIAN RIGHTS
RT   ROW BOATS
RT   SCUBA DIVING
RT   SOCIOLOGICAL ASPECTS
RT   SPORT FISHING STATISTICS
RT   YACHTS

RECREATION (SWIMMING)
USE **BATHING**

RECREATIONAL FISHING
USE **SPORT FISHING**

RECREATIONAL SWIMMING
USE **BATHING**

RECREATIONAL WATERS
RT   BARRAGES
RT   BEACHES
RT   COASTAL ENGINEERING
RT   COASTAL ZONE MANAGEMENT
RT   DIVING
RT   MARINAS
RT   MARINE PARKS
RT   PUBLIC HEALTH
RT   RECREATION
RT   RIPARIAN RIGHTS
RT   SEDIMENTOLOGY
RT   SOCIOLOGICAL ASPECTS
RT   TAR BALLS
RT   TIDAL BARRAGES
RT   WATER
RT   WATER BODIES
RT   WATER POLICY
RT   WATER POLLUTION
RT   WATER QUALITY
RT   WATER RESOURCES
RT   WATER USE
RT   YACHTS

RECRUITMENT
SN   Including animal recruitment,
        length, weight and age at first
        capture, number of recruits
UF   recruitment rate
BT1   POPULATION FUNCTIONS
RT   AGE AT RECRUITMENT
RT   AGE COMPOSITION
RT   FECUNDITY
RT   NATURAL MORTALITY
RT   POPULATION STRUCTURE
RT   YIELD

RECRUITMENT RATE
USE **RECRUITMENT**

RED BLOOD CELLS
USE **ERYTHROCYTES**

RED BLOOD CORPUSCLES
USE **ERYTHROCYTES**

RED BOIL DISEASE
USE **BOIL DISEASE**

RED CLAY
USE **PELAGIC CLAY**

RED CRAB FISHERIES
USE **SQUAT LOBSTER FISHERIES**

RED MUSCLES
USE **MUSCLES**

RED PEST
USE **VIBRIOSIS**

RED TIDES
RT ALGAL BLOOMS
RT BIOLOGICAL POISONS
RT DISCOLOURED WATER
RT EUTROPHICATION
RT OXYGEN DEPLETION
RT PHYTOPLANKTON
RT POISONOUS ORGANISMS
RT TOXICITY

REDDS
SN Spawning area of trout or salmon on
the bottom of a lake or stream;
usually a clear circular depression
in gravel. Added in 1980
UF salmon nests
RT NESTS
RT SPAWNING GROUNDS

REDFISH FISHERIES
SN Added in 1982
UF rockfish fisheries
UF scorpionfish fisheries
BT1 FINFISH FISHERIES
BT2 FISHERIES
RT DEMERSAL FISHERIES
RT MARINE FISHERIES

REDMOUTH DISEASE
SN Added in 1980
UF enteric redmouth
UF hagermon redmouth
UF rm
BT1 FISH DISEASES
BT2 ANIMAL DISEASES
BT3 DISEASES
RT BACTERIAL DISEASES
RT HATCHERIES
RT HUSBANDRY DISEASES

REDOX POTENTIAL
UF eh
UF oxidation-reduction potential
BT1 CHEMICAL PROPERTIES
BT2 PROPERTIES
RT CHEMICAL REACTIONS
RT OXIDATION
RT OXIDOREDUCTASES
RT OXYGEN DEPLETION
RT REDOX REACTIONS
RT REDUCTION
RT WATER PROPERTIES

REDOX PROCESSES
USE **REDOX REACTIONS**

REDOX REACTIONS
UF oxidation-reduction reactions
UF redox processes
BT1 CHEMICAL REACTIONS
RT OXIDATION
RT OXIDOREDUCTASES
RT POLAROGRAPHY
RT REDOX POTENTIAL
RT REDUCTION

REDUCTION
BT1 CHEMICAL REACTIONS
NT1 SULPHATE REDUCTION
RT OXIDATION
RT REDOX POTENTIAL
RT REDOX REACTIONS

REDUCTION DIVISION
USE **MEIOSIS**

REEF FISH
SN Added in 1982
UF reef fishes
BT1 MARINE FISH
BT2 FISH
BT3 AQUATIC ANIMALS
RT ARTIFICIAL REEFS
RT CORAL REEFS

REEF FISHERIES
SN Added in 1982
BT1 MARINE FISHERIES
BT2 FISHERIES
RT ANGLING
RT ARTIFICIAL REEFS
RT CORAL REEFS
RT LINE FISHING
RT PERCOID FISHERIES

REEF FISHES
USE **REEF FISH**

REEF FORMATION
RT CORAL REEFS
RT REEFS
RT SEDIMENTATION

REEFS
NT1 BIOHERMS
NT1 OYSTER REEFS
RT ARTIFICIAL REEFS
RT ATOLLS
RT CORAL REEFS
RT GEOMORPHOLOGY
RT REEF FORMATION
RT SEDIMENTATION
RT SHALLOW WATER
RT SHOALS

REEFS (ARTIFICIAL)
USE **ARTIFICIAL REEFS**

REEFS (CORAL)
USE **CORAL REEFS**

REEFS (NAVIGATIONAL HAZARD)
USE **SHOALS**

REFERENCE LEVELS
NT1 DATUM LEVELS
NT2 CHART DATUM
NT2 TIDAL DATUM
NT1 LEVEL OF NO MOTION
RT DATA REDUCTION
RT SURFACES

REFINERIES
USE **OIL REFINERIES**

REFLECTANCE
UF reflectivity
BT1 OPTICAL PROPERTIES
BT2 PHYSICAL PROPERTIES
BT3 PROPERTIES
RT AIR-WATER INTERFACE
RT ALBEDO
RT GLITTER
RT LIGHT REFLECTION
RT REFLECTED GLOBAL RADIATION
RT SURFACE ROUGHNESS
RT WAVE EFFECTS

REFLECTED GLOBAL RADIATION
BT1 SOLAR RADIATION
BT2 ELECTROMAGNETIC RADIATION
BT3 RADIATIONS
RT AIR-WATER INTERFACE
RT REFLECTANCE

REFLECTION
NT1 LIGHT REFLECTION
NT1 SEISMIC REFLECTION
NT1 SOUND REFLECTION
NT1 WAVE REFLECTION
RT ABSORPTION (PHYSICS)
RT ALBEDO
RT REVERBERATION
RT TRANSMISSION
RT WAVE MOTION

REFLECTION (LIGHT)
USE **LIGHT REFLECTION**

REFLECTION (WATER WAVES)
USE **WAVE REFLECTION**

REFLECTION LOSS
USE **TRANSMISSION LOSS**

REFLECTIVITY
USE **REFLECTANCE**

REFRACTION
NT1 LIGHT REFRACTION
NT1 SEISMIC REFRACTION
NT1 SOUND REFRACTION
NT1 WAVE REFRACTION
RT TRANSPARENCY
RT WAVE MOTION

REFRACTION (LIGHT)
USE **LIGHT REFRACTION**

REFRACTION (WATER WAVES)
USE **WAVE REFRACTION**

REFRACTION LOSS
USE **TRANSMISSION LOSS**

REFRACTIVE INDEX
SN Before 1982 search REFRACTIVITY
UF refractivity
BT1 OPTICAL PROPERTIES
BT2 PHYSICAL PROPERTIES
BT3 PROPERTIES
RT ELECTRICAL CONDUCTIVITY
RT LIGHT DISPERSION
RT LIGHT REFRACTION
RT LIGHT SCATTERING
RT SALINITY
RT SALINITY MEASUREMENT
RT WATER TEMPERATURE

ASFIS Thesaurus

REFRACTIVITY
USE **REFRACTIVE INDEX**

REFRIGERATION
SN   Before 1982 search FREEZING
UF   freezing (fishery products)
BT1   PROCESSING FISHERY PRODUCTS
BT2   FISHERY INDUSTRY
BT3   INDUSTRIES
RT   ANTIFREEZES
RT   CHILLED PRODUCTS
RT   COLD STORAGE
RT   FREEZING
RT   FROZEN PRODUCTS
RT   PROCESSING FISHERY PRODUCTS
RT   REFRIGERATORS
RT   THAWING

REFRIGERATION STORAGE
USE **COLD STORAGE**

REFRIGERATORS
SN   Added in 1982
BT1   FISHERY INDUSTRY EQUIPMENT
BT2   EQUIPMENT
RT   COLD STORAGE
RT   FISHERY INDUSTRY PLANTS
RT   REFRIGERATION

REFUGES
SN   Isolated localities, where organisms are free from natural or man-induced pressures. Added in 1980
UF   refugia
RT   GEOGRAPHICAL DISTRIBUTION
RT   MARINE PARKS
RT   NATURE CONSERVATION
RT   RELICT SPECIES
RT   SANCTUARIES

REFUGIA
USE **REFUGES**

REFUSES
USE **WASTES**

REGENERATION
SN   Regeneration processes of tissue, organs and appendices lost by injuries in natural or experimental conditions
BT1   BIOLOGICAL PHENOMENA
RT   AUTOTOMY
RT   BODY ORGANS
RT   DEGENERATION
RT   GROWTH
RT   LESIONS
RT   ORGAN REMOVAL

REGIONAL PLANNING
SN   Added in 1980
BT1   PLANNING
RT   COASTAL ZONE MANAGEMENT
RT   MANAGEMENT
RT   NATIONAL PLANNING
RT   REGIONS

REGIONAL VARIATIONS
BT1   SPATIAL VARIATIONS
RT   ANNUAL VARIATIONS
RT   HORIZONTAL DISTRIBUTION
RT   MIGRATIONS
RT   SEASONAL VARIATIONS

REGIONS
RT   REGIONAL PLANNING

REGRESSION ANALYSIS
SN   Used only as a qualifier
BT1   STATISTICAL ANALYSIS
BT2   MATHEMATICAL ANALYSIS
RT   CORRELATION ANALYSIS
RT   LEAST SQUARES METHOD
RT   SCATTER DIAGRAMS
RT   VARIANCE ANALYSIS

REGRESSIONS
UF   marine regressions
RT   COASTS
RT   EMERGENT SHORELINES
RT   EUSTATIC CHANGES
RT   GLACIATION
RT   ISOSTASY
RT   PROGRADATION
RT   SEA LEVEL CHANGES
RT   TRANSGRESSIONS
RT   UPLIFT

REGULATE
USE **CONTROL**

REGULATIONS
USE **LEGISLATION**

REINFORCED CONCRETE
BT1   CONCRETE
BT2   CONSTRUCTION MATERIALS
BT3   MATERIALS
RT   STEEL

RELATIVE ABUNDANCE
USE **ABUNDANCE**

RELATIVE DENSITY
SN   Use for specific gravity of sea water. Before 1984 search also SPECIFIC GRAVITY
BT1   WATER DENSITY
BT2   DENSITY
BT3   PHYSICAL PROPERTIES
BT4   PROPERTIES
RT   SEA WATER
RT   SPECIFIC GRAVITY
RT   WATER PROPERTIES

RELATIVE HUMIDITY
BT1   HUMIDITY
RT   HYGROMETERS
RT   MIXING RATIO
RT   SATURATION VAPOUR PRESSURE
RT   SPECIFIC HUMIDITY
RT   VAPOUR PRESSURE

RELATIVE VORTICITY
BT1   VORTICITY
RT   ABSOLUTE VORTICITY
RT   VERTICAL SHEAR

RELEASE MECHANISMS
UF   acoustic release mechanisms
NT1   MESSENGERS
RT   OCEANOGRAPHIC EQUIPMENT

RELIABILITY
RT   ACCEPTABILITY
RT   ACCURACY
RT   CERTIFICATION
RT   EQUIPMENT
RT   EVALUATION
RT   FAILURES
RT   PERFORMANCE ASSESSMENT
RT   RISKS

RELIABILITY ASSURANCE
USE **QUALITY ASSURANCE**

RELICT LAKES
BT1   LAKES
BT2   INLAND WATERS
RT   FOSSIL SEA WATER

RELICT ORGANISMS
USE **RELICT SPECIES**

RELICT SEDIMENTS
BT1   SEDIMENTS

RELICT SHORELINES
BT1   COASTS
BT2   LANDFORMS
BT3   TOPOGRAPHIC FEATURES

RELICT SPECIES
SN   A species that is the remainder of a formerly more widely distributed species. Added in 1980
UF   relict organisms
BT1   SPECIES
BT2   TAXA
RT   ECOLOGICAL DISTRIBUTION
RT   GEOGRAPHICAL DISTRIBUTION
RT   LIVING FOSSILS
RT   REFUGES

RELIEF FORMS
RT   ABYSSAL HILLS
RT   BANKS (TOPOGRAPHY)
RT   CONTINENTAL RIDGES
RT   DROWNED VALLEYS
RT   ESCARPMENTS
RT   ESCARPMENTS
RT   FAULT SCARPS
RT   FRACTURE ZONES
RT   GUYOTS
RT   MEDIAN VALLEYS
RT   MID-OCEAN RIDGES
RT   MOUNTAINS
RT   OCEAN BASINS
RT   PLATEAUX
RT   RIDGES
RT   RIFT VALLEYS
RT   RIVER VALLEYS
RT   SEABIGHTS
RT   SEACHANNELS
RT   SEAKNOLLS
RT   SEAMOATS
RT   SEAMOUNT CHAINS
RT   SEAMOUNTS
RT   SHOALS
RT   SILLS
RT   SUBMARINE CANYONS
RT   SUBMARINE PLATEAUX
RT   SUBMARINE RIDGES
RT   SUBMARINE SCARPS
RT   SUBMARINE TROUGHS
RT   SUBMARINE VALLEYS
RT   TOPOGRAPHIC FEATURES
RT   TRENCHES (OCEANIC)
RT   VALLEYS

REMANENT MAGNETISM
USE **REMANENT MAGNETIZATION**

REMANENT MAGNETIZATION
UF   magnetic remanence
UF   remanent magnetism
UF   rock magnetism
BT1   MAGNETIC PROPERTIES
BT2   PHYSICAL PROPERTIES
BT3   PROPERTIES
RT   CORE ORIENTATION
RT   GEOMAGNETIC FIELD
RT   PALAEOMAGNETISM

REMOTE CONTROL
BT1	CONTROL
RT	ACOUSTIC COMMAND SYSTEMS
RT	AUTOMATION
RT	ELECTRONIC EQUIPMENT
RT	RECORDING EQUIPMENT
RT	ROBOTS
RT	TELEMETRY
RT	UNTETHERED VEHICLES

REMOTE SATELLITE SENSING
USE	**SATELLITE SENSING**

REMOTE SENSING
SN	Use only for publications concerned with the remote sensing of the environment from all locations, i.e. sea surface, space etc. For sensing from space use GEOSENSING
UF	remote sensing techniques
NT1	IMAGERY
NT2	ACOUSTIC IMAGERY
NT3	ACOUSTIC TOMOGRAPHY
NT3	SONAR IMAGERY
NT2	INFRARED IMAGERY
NT2	MICROWAVE IMAGERY
NT3	RADAR IMAGERY
NT2	PHOTOGRAPHY
NT3	AERIAL PHOTOGRAPHY
NT4	SATELLITE PHOTOGRAPHY
NT3	MICROPHOTOGRAPHY
NT3	STEREOPHOTOGRAPHY
NT3	UNDERWATER PHOTOGRAPHY
RT	AERIAL SURVEYS
RT	AIRBORNE SENSING
RT	AIRCRAFT
RT	DATA ACQUISITION
RT	DETECTION
RT	ECHOSOUNDING
RT	ELECTROMAGNETIC RADIATION
RT	ELECTRONIC EQUIPMENT
RT	GEOSENSING
RT	IMAGING TECHNIQUES
RT	INFRARED DETECTORS
RT	RADIO OCEANOGRAPHY
RT	REMOTE SENSING EQUIPMENT
RT	SENSORS
RT	SURVEYS

REMOTE SENSING (EARTH)
USE	**GEOSENSING**

REMOTE SENSING EQUIPMENT
UF	image sensors
UF	remote sensors
BT1	EQUIPMENT
NT1	RADAR
NT2	MICROWAVE RADAR
NT3	RADAR ALTIMETERS
NT3	SCATTEROMETERS
NT3	SYNTHETIC APERTURE RADAR
NT1	RADIOMETERS
NT2	ACTINOMETERS
NT3	PYRANOMETERS
NT3	PYRGEOMETERS
NT3	PYRHELIOMETERS
NT2	INFRARED DETECTORS
NT2	MICROWAVE RADIOMETERS
NT1	SONAR
NT2	ACTIVE SONAR
NT3	DOPPLER SONAR
NT3	ECHOSOUNDERS
NT3	MULTIBEAM SONAR
NT3	SIDE SCAN SONAR
NT2	PASSIVE SONAR
RT	CAMERAS
RT	ELECTRONIC EQUIPMENT
RT	LASER BATHYMETERS
RT	LIDAR
RT	MULTISPECTRAL SCANNERS

REMOTE SENSING EQUIPMENT (cont'd)
RT	OCEANOGRAPHIC EQUIPMENT
RT	PHOTOGRAPHIC EQUIPMENT
RT	REMOTE SENSING
RT	SCATTEROMETERS
RT	SODAR
RT	SURVEYING EQUIPMENT

REMOTE SENSING TECHNIQUES
USE	**REMOTE SENSING**

REMOTE SENSORS
USE	**REMOTE SENSING EQUIPMENT**

REMOTELY OPERATED VEHICLES
USE	**UNMANNED VEHICLES**

REMOVAL
SN	Used only as a qualifier
RT	LIFTING
RT	ORGAN REMOVAL
RT	REPLACING
RT	SALVAGING

RENEWABLE RESOURCES
SN	Added in 1980
BT1	NATURAL RESOURCES
BT2	RESOURCES
RT	DISSOLVED CHEMICALS
RT	FISHERY RESOURCES
RT	FOOD RESOURCES
RT	GEOTHERMAL POWER
RT	HYDROELECTRIC POWER
RT	LIVING RESOURCES
RT	MARINE RESOURCES
RT	NONRENEWABLE RESOURCES
RT	POWER FROM THE SEA
RT	SOLAR POWER
RT	WATER RESOURCES
RT	WIND POWER

RENEWAL
RT	FLUSHING TIME
RT	OVERTURN
RT	RESIDENCE TIME

RENT
USE	**RENTAL**

RENTAL
SN	Renting of land, water bodies or water resources for exploitation purposes. Added in 1980
UF	rent
UF	renting
BT1	PROPERTY RIGHTS
BT2	RIGHTS
RT	AQUACULTURE REGULATIONS
RT	CONCESSIONS
RT	COSTS
RT	EXPLOITATION
RT	FISHERY REGULATIONS
RT	FISHING RIGHTS
RT	RANCHING
RT	RESOURCE DEVELOPMENT
RT	SPORT FISHING
RT	WATER RIGHTS

RENTING
USE	**RENTAL**

REPAIR
BT1	MAINTENANCE
RT	DAMAGE
RT	DETERIORATION
RT	LEAKS
RT	REPLACING

REPELLENTS
SN	Added in 1980
NT1	FISH REPELLENTS
RT	INSECTICIDES
RT	ORGANOLEPTIC PROPERTIES
RT	PEST CONTROL
RT	PESTICIDES
RT	TOXICANTS

REPLACING
SN	Used only as qualifier
RT	FAILURES
RT	REMOVAL
RT	REPAIR

REPORT LITERATURE
SN	Unpublished scientific and technical documents, in most cases describing the results of research and development projects. Use of a more specific term is recommended. Before 1982 search REPORTS
UF	reports
BT1	DOCUMENTS
NT1	ANNUAL REPORTS
NT1	CLASSIFIED DOCUMENTS
NT1	CRUISE REPORTS
NT1	DATA REPORTS
NT2	STATION LISTS
NT1	PROGRESS REPORTS
RT	DATA COLLECTIONS
RT	INTERNATIONAL COOPERATION
RT	INTERNATIONAL ORGANIZATIONS
RT	RESEARCH INSTITUTIONS
RT	RESEARCH PROGRAMMES
RT	TRAINING CENTRES

REPORTS
USE	**REPORT LITERATURE**

REPRODUCTION
SN	Before 1982 search REPRODUCTION (BIOLOGY)
UF	propagation
UF	reproduction (biology)
UF	reproduction rate
NT1	ALTERNATE REPRODUCTION
NT1	ANDROGENESIS
NT1	ASEXUAL REPRODUCTION
NT2	BUDDING
NT1	CELL DIVISION
NT2	MEIOSIS
NT2	MITOSIS
NT1	PARTHENOGENESIS
NT1	SEXUAL REPRODUCTION
NT2	BIOLOGICAL FERTILIZATION
NT2	PARTURITION
NT1	VEGETATIVE REPRODUCTION
RT	ANIMAL PHYSIOLOGY
RT	ANIMAL REPRODUCTIVE ORGANS
RT	BIOGENESIS
RT	LIFE CYCLE
RT	PHYSIOLOGY
RT	PLANT PHYSIOLOGY
RT	REPRODUCTIVE CYCLE
RT	ZYGOTES

REPRODUCTION (BIOLOGY)
USE	**REPRODUCTION**

REPRODUCTION RATE
USE	**REPRODUCTION**

REPRODUCTIVE BEHAVIOUR
BT1	BEHAVIOUR
NT1	COURTSHIP
RT	BREEDING
RT	MIGRATIONS
RT	NESTING
RT	PARENTAL BEHAVIOUR

ASFIS Thesaurus

REPRODUCTIVE BEHAVIOUR (cont'd)
RT	PHOTOPERIODICITY
RT	SEX RATIO
RT	SEXUAL BEHAVIOUR
RT	SEXUAL REPRODUCTION
RT	SPAWNING
RT	SPAWNING GROUNDS
RT	SPAWNING MIGRATIONS
RT	SPAWNING SEASONS

REPRODUCTIVE CYCLE
SN	A period between hatching and the first spawning of a given generation. Added in 1982
UF	breeding cycle
RT	BREEDING
RT	LIFE CYCLE
RT	REPRODUCTION
RT	SPAWNING

REPRODUCTIVE FERTILIZATION
USE	**BIOLOGICAL FERTILIZATION**

REPRODUCTIVE ISOLATION
USE	**SEXUAL ISOLATION**

REPRODUCTIVE ORGANS (ANIMAL)
USE	**ANIMAL REPRODUCTIVE ORGANS**

REPRODUCTIVE STRUCTURES (PLANT)
USE	**PLANT REPRODUCTIVE STRUCTURES**

REPRODUCTIVE SYSTEM
USE	**ANIMAL REPRODUCTIVE ORGANS**

REPTILE CULTURE
SN	Added in 1982
UF	alligator culture
UF	crocodile farming
BT1	AQUACULTURE
RT	AQUATIC REPTILES
RT	SITE SELECTION

REPTILES (AQUATIC)
USE	**AQUATIC REPTILES**

RESCUE
USE	**SEARCH AND RESCUE**

RESEARCH
SN	Used only as a qualifier
UF	research and development
UF	scientific research
NT1	EXPERIMENTAL RESEARCH
RT	DESIGN
RT	RESEARCH INSTITUTIONS
RT	RESEARCH PROGRAMMES
RT	RESEARCH PROPOSALS
RT	SCIENTIFIC PERSONNEL

RESEARCH (EXPERIMENTAL)
USE	**EXPERIMENTAL RESEARCH**

RESEARCH AND DEVELOPMENT
USE	**RESEARCH**

RESEARCH INSTITUTIONS
UF	institutions (research)
BT1	ORGANIZATIONS
NT1	BIOLOGICAL INSTITUTIONS
NT1	FISHERY INSTITUTIONS
NT1	GEOLOGICAL INSTITUTIONS
NT1	LIMNOLOGICAL INSTITUTIONS
NT1	OCEANOGRAPHIC INSTITUTIONS
RT	ANNUAL REPORTS
RT	BROCHURES
RT	CRUISES
RT	DIRECTORIES
RT	EDUCATION
RT	HISTORICAL ACCOUNT

RESEARCH INSTITUTIONS (cont'd)
RT	INSTITUTIONAL RESOURCES
RT	LABORATORIES
RT	LABORATORY EQUIPMENT
RT	PROGRESS REPORTS
RT	REPORT LITERATURE
RT	RESEARCH
RT	RESEARCH PROGRAMMES
RT	RESEARCH VESSELS
RT	SCIENTIFIC PERSONNEL

RESEARCH PROGRAMMES
NT1	RESEARCH PROPOSALS
RT	ANNUAL REPORTS
RT	EDUCATION ESTABLISHMENTS
RT	FELLOWSHIPS
RT	FINANCING
RT	FISHERY INSTITUTIONS
RT	GRANTS
RT	INTERNATIONAL POLICY
RT	PLANNING
RT	PROGRAMMES
RT	PROGRESS REPORTS
RT	REPORT LITERATURE
RT	RESEARCH
RT	RESEARCH INSTITUTIONS
RT	SCIENTIFIC PERSONNEL

RESEARCH PROPOSALS
SN	Used only as a qualifier. Before 1982 search PROPOSED RESEARCH
UF	proposed research
BT1	RESEARCH PROGRAMMES
RT	CRUISE PROGRAMMES
RT	GRANTS
RT	RESEARCH

RESEARCH SHIPS
USE	**RESEARCH VESSELS**

RESEARCH VESSELS
SN	. Vessels used for oceanographic and limnological exploration
UF	research ships
BT1	SURFACE CRAFT
BT2	VEHICLES
RT	ACCOMMODATION
RT	BOATS
RT	CATAMARANS
RT	CRUISE PROGRAMMES
RT	CRUISES
RT	DECK EQUIPMENT
RT	HYDROGRAPHIC SURVEYING
RT	HYDROGRAPHIC SURVEYS
RT	INSTRUMENT PLATFORMS
RT	LARGE SPAR BUOYS
RT	LIMNOLOGICAL INSTITUTIONS
RT	MULTISHIP EXPEDITIONS
RT	NAVIGATION
RT	OCEANOGRAPHIC INSTITUTIONS
RT	OCEANOGRAPHIC SURVEYS
RT	POSITIONING SYSTEMS
RT	RESEARCH INSTITUTIONS
RT	SAMPLING
RT	SHIP TECHNOLOGY
RT	SURVEY VESSELS
RT	SURVEYS
RT	WEATHER SHIPS

RESEARCH WORKERS
USE	**SCIENTIFIC PERSONNEL**

RESEARCHERS
USE	**SCIENTIFIC PERSONNEL**

RESERVES
USE	**POTENTIAL RESOURCES**

RESERVOIR DYNAMICS
USE	**LAKE DYNAMICS**

RESERVOIR FISHERIES
SN	Added in 1980
BT1	INLAND FISHERIES
BT2	FISHERIES
RT	BAIT FISHING
RT	LAKE FISHERIES
RT	RESERVOIRS (WATER)
RT	STOCKING (ORGANISMS)

RESERVOIRS (OIL)
USE	**OIL RESERVOIRS**

RESERVOIRS (WATER)
UF	impounding lakes
UF	water reservoirs
BT1	INLAND WATERS
RT	AQUACULTURE FACILITIES
RT	ARTIFICIAL LAKES
RT	BACKWATERS
RT	BOTTOM WATER
RT	DAMS
RT	EPILIMNION
RT	FISHWAYS
RT	FLOOD CONTROL
RT	FLUSHING TIME
RT	HABITAT IMPROVEMENT
RT	HYDRAULIC ENGINEERING
RT	HYDRAULIC STRUCTURES
RT	HYDROLOGY
RT	HYPOLIMNION
RT	IRRIGATION
RT	IRRIGATION WATER
RT	LAKE DYNAMICS
RT	LENITIC ENVIRONMENT
RT	LIMNOLOGY
RT	METALIMNION
RT	OVERTURN
RT	PONDS
RT	RESERVOIR FISHERIES
RT	RIVER OUTFLOW
RT	STOCKING (ORGANISMS)
RT	THERMAL STRATIFICATION
RT	VOLUME
RT	WATER BODIES
RT	WATER LEVELS
RT	WATER RESOURCES
RT	WIND SETUP

RESIDENCE TIME
RT	AGE
RT	AGE OF SEAWATER
RT	CHEMICAL ELEMENTS
RT	FLUSHING TIME
RT	RENEWAL

RESIDUAL CIRCULATION
USE	**RESIDUAL FLOW**

RESIDUAL CURRENTS
USE	**RESIDUAL FLOW**

RESIDUAL FLOW
UF	residual circulation
UF	residual currents
RT	FLUID MOTION
RT	TIDAL CURRENTS
RT	UNIDIRECTIONAL FLOW
RT	WATER CURRENTS

RESILIENCE (ECOSYSTEM)
USE	**ECOSYSTEM RESILIENCE**

RESISTANCE (BIOLOGICAL)
USE	**BIOLOGICAL RESISTANCE**

RESISTANCE MECHANISMS
SN   Added in 1980
RT   BIOLOGICAL RESISTANCE
RT   DEFENCE MECHANISMS
RT   PATHOLOGY

RESISTANCE TO CHEMICALS
USE   **CONTROL RESISTANCE**

RESISTANCE TO DISEASE
USE   **DISEASE RESISTANCE**

RESISTANCE TO DRUGS
USE   **DRUG RESISTANCE**

RESISTANCE TO PARASITES
USE   **PARASITE RESISTANCE**

RESISTIVITY (ELECTRICAL)
USE   **ELECTRICAL RESISTIVITY**

RESISTIVITY PROBES
RT   ELECTRICAL RESISTIVITY
RT   GEOPHYSICAL EQUIPMENT
RT   SENSORS

RESOLUTION
SN   Use only as a qualifier
UF   instrument resolution
UF   resolving power
RT   ACCURACY
RT   ERRORS
RT   IMAGE ENHANCEMENT
RT   IMAGERY
RT   INSTRUMENTS

RESOLVING POWER
USE   **RESOLUTION**

RESONANCE
NT1   HEAVE RESONANCE
NT1   PITCH RESONANCE
NT1   ROLL RESONANCE
RT   OSCILLATIONS
RT   RESONANT FREQUENCY
RT   STANDING WAVES
RT   TIDAL RESONANCE
RT   VIBRATION

RESONANT FREQUENCY
UF   natural frequency
BT1   FREQUENCY
RT   DYNAMIC RESPONSE
RT   RESONANCE
RT   VIBRATION

RESONANT WAVE INTERACTION
BT1   WAVE INTERACTIONS
RT   INTERNAL WAVES
RT   WAVE-WAVE INTERACTION

RESOURCE AVAILABILITY
BT1   AVAILABILITY
RT   ABUNDANCE
RT   BASELINE STUDIES
RT   CATCH/EFFORT
RT   DEVELOPMENT POTENTIAL
RT   EXPLOITATION
RT   NONRENEWABLE RESOURCES
RT   POPULATION DENSITY
RT   POPULATION NUMBER
RT   QUANTITATIVE DISTRIBUTION
RT   RESOURCE SURVEYS
RT   RESOURCES
RT   VULNERABILITY

RESOURCE CONSERVATION
BT1   CONSERVATION
RT   ENVIRONMENT MANAGEMENT
RT   ENVIRONMENTAL LEGISLATION
RT   EXCLUSIVE ECONOMIC ZONE
RT   EXPLOITATION
RT   FISHERY ORGANIZATIONS
RT   FISHERY REGULATIONS
RT   FISHERY RESOURCES
RT   INTERNATIONAL ORGANIZATIONS
RT   LIVING RESOURCES
RT   MINERAL RESOURCES
RT   NATURAL RESOURCES
RT   NONRENEWABLE RESOURCES
RT   POLLUTION EFFECTS
RT   PROTECTED RESOURCES
RT   RARE RESOURCES
RT   RESOURCE MANAGEMENT
RT   RESOURCES
RT   SANCTUARIES
RT   WATER RESOURCES

RESOURCE DEPLETION
BT1   DEPLETION
RT   RESOURCE MANAGEMENT
RT   RESOURCES

RESOURCE DEVELOPMENT
SN   Economic development of living and
        non-living aquatic resources
UF   development (resources)
NT1   AQUACULTURE DEVELOPMENT
NT1   FISHERY DEVELOPMENT
RT   BIOLOGICAL DEVELOPMENT
RT   DEVELOPING COUNTRIES
RT   DEVELOPMENT POTENTIAL
RT   DEVELOPMENT PROJECTS
RT   ECONOMICS
RT   EXPLOITATION
RT   FINANCIAL INSTITUTIONS
RT   FINANCIAL RESOURCES
RT   FINANCING
RT   FISHERY ECONOMICS
RT   FISHERY ORGANIZATIONS
RT   INDUSTRIES
RT   INTERNATIONAL WATERS
RT   MARINE TECHNOLOGY
RT   MINERAL RESOURCES
RT   NATURAL RESOURCES
RT   POLITICAL ASPECTS
RT   PRODUCTION COST
RT   RENTAL
RT   RESOURCE MANAGEMENT
RT   RESOURCES
RT   SOCIOLOGICAL ASPECTS
RT   SURVEYS
RT   WATER RESOURCES

RESOURCE EXPLOITATION
USE   **EXPLOITATION**

RESOURCE EXPLORATION
BT1   EXPLORATION
NT1   MINERAL EXPLORATION
NT1   OIL AND GAS EXPLORATION
RT   RESOURCE SURVEYS
RT   RESOURCES

RESOURCE MANAGEMENT
UF   management (resources)
BT1   MANAGEMENT
NT1   FISHERY MANAGEMENT
NT1   WATER MANAGEMENT
RT   COST ANALYSIS
RT   DEVELOPMENT POTENTIAL
RT   ECONOMICS
RT   ENVIRONMENT MANAGEMENT
RT   ENVIRONMENTAL LEGISLATION
RT   EXCLUSIVE ECONOMIC ZONE
RT   EXPLOITATION

RESOURCE MANAGEMENT (cont'd)
RT   FEASIBILITY
RT   INTERNATIONAL WATERS
RT   MARKETING
RT   MINERAL RESOURCES
RT   NATURAL RESOURCES
RT   NONRENEWABLE RESOURCES
RT   PRODUCTION COST
RT   RESOURCE CONSERVATION
RT   RESOURCE DEPLETION
RT   RESOURCE DEVELOPMENT
RT   RESOURCES
RT   SOCIOLOGICAL ASPECTS
RT   TECHNOLOGY
RT   UNDERWATER EXPLOITATION

RESOURCE SURVEYS
BT1   SURVEYS
RT   RESOURCE AVAILABILITY
RT   RESOURCE EXPLORATION

RESOURCES
SN   Before 1982 search NATURAL RESOURCES
UF   economic resources
UF   facilities
UF   means
UF   potentialities
NT1   FINANCIAL RESOURCES
NT1   HUMAN RESOURCES
NT2   WOMEN
NT1   INSTITUTIONAL RESOURCES
NT1   NATURAL RESOURCES
NT2   COMMON PROPERTY RESOURCES
NT2   ENERGY RESOURCES
NT3   GEOTHERMAL POWER
NT3   HYDROELECTRIC POWER
NT3   POWER FROM THE SEA
NT4   CURRENT POWER
NT4   ELECTROMAGNETIC POWER
NT4   SALINITY POWER
NT4   THERMAL POWER
NT4   TIDAL POWER
NT4   WAVE POWER
NT3   SOLAR POWER
NT3   WIND POWER
NT2   FOOD RESOURCES
NT2   LIVING RESOURCES
NT3   BOTANICAL RESOURCES
NT3   FISHERY RESOURCES
NT2   MARINE RESOURCES
NT2   MINERAL RESOURCES
NT3   DISSOLVED CHEMICALS
NT3   MINERAL DEPOSITS
NT4   SEABED DEPOSITS
NT4   SUBSURFACE DEPOSITS
NT3   ORES
NT2   NONRENEWABLE RESOURCES
NT2   RENEWABLE RESOURCES
NT2   UNCONVENTIONAL RESOURCES
NT2   WATER RESOURCES
NT1   POTENTIAL RESOURCES
NT1   PROTECTED RESOURCES
NT1   RARE RESOURCES
RT   AQUATIC SCIENCES
RT   EXPLOITATION
RT   OPERATIONS RESEARCH
RT   RESOURCE AVAILABILITY
RT   RESOURCE CONSERVATION
RT   RESOURCE DEPLETION
RT   RESOURCE DEVELOPMENT
RT   RESOURCE EXPLORATION
RT   RESOURCE MANAGEMENT
RT   WORLD

RESPIRATION
UF   respiration rate
UF   respiratory quotients
NT1   AEROBIC RESPIRATION
NT1   ANAEROBIC RESPIRATION
RT   AIR

RESPIRATION (cont'd)
RT   ANIMAL PHYSIOLOGY
RT   BIOCHEMICAL OXYGEN DEMAND
RT   METABOLISM
RT   OXYGEN
RT   OXYGEN DEMAND
RT   PHYSIOLOGY
RT   PLANT PHYSIOLOGY
RT   RESPIRATORY ORGANS
RT   RESPIRATORY PIGMENTS
RT   RESPIRATORY SYSTEM
RT   STOMATA
RT   TRANSPIRATION

RESPIRATION RATE
USE   **RESPIRATION**

RESPIRATORY ORGANS
SN   Any respiratory organs of aquatic
        animals
UF   accessory respiratory organs
BT1   ANIMAL ORGANS
BT2   BODY ORGANS
NT1   GILLS
NT1   LARYNX
NT1   LUNGS
NT1   TRACHEA
RT   AEROBIC RESPIRATION
RT   ANATOMY
RT   RESPIRATION
RT   RESPIRATORY PIGMENTS
RT   RESPIRATORY SYSTEM

RESPIRATORY PIGMENTS
UF   respiratory proteins
BT1   PIGMENTS
BT2   GLYCOSIDES
BT3   CARBOHYDRATES
BT4   ORGANIC COMPOUNDS
NT1   HAEMOCYANINS
NT1   HAEMOGLOBINS
RT   RESPIRATION
RT   RESPIRATORY ORGANS

RESPIRATORY PROTEINS
USE   **RESPIRATORY PIGMENTS**

RESPIRATORY QUOTIENTS
USE   **RESPIRATION**

RESPIRATORY SYSTEM
RT   RESPIRATION
RT   RESPIRATORY ORGANS

RESPIROMETERS
BT1   MEASURING DEVICES
RT   AEROBIC RESPIRATION
RT   CARBON DIOXIDE
RT   OXYGEN CONSUMPTION

RESPONSE (OCEANIC)
USE   **OCEANIC RESPONSE**

RESPONSE ANALYSIS
RT   ORTHOTIDES
RT   TIDAL ANALYSIS

RESPONSE TIME
RT   ATMOSPHERIC FORCING
RT   OCEANIC RESPONSE
RT   SALINITY

RESTING EGGS
SN   Added in 1980
UF   winter eggs
BT1   EGGS
BT2   SEXUAL CELLS
BT3   CELLS
RT   DORMANCY
RT   ENVIRONMENTAL EFFECTS

RESTING EGGS (cont'd)
RT   RESTING STAGES

RESTING SPORES
BT1   SPORES
RT   ASEXUAL REPRODUCTION
RT   RESTING STAGES

RESTING STAGES
BT1   DEVELOPMENTAL STAGES
RT   ENVIRONMENTAL EFFECTS
RT   RESTING EGGS
RT   RESTING SPORES

RESTOCKING
USE   **STOCKING (ORGANISMS)**

RESUSPENDED SEDIMENTS
UF   sediments in suspension
UF   suspended sediments
BT1   SUSPENDED PARTICULATE MATTER
BT2   PARTICULATES
RT   PARTICLE MOTION
RT   RESUSPENSION
RT   SEDIMENT TRAPS
RT   SEDIMENTS
RT   SUSPENDED LOAD
RT   SUSPENSION

RESUSPENSION
RT   RESUSPENDED SEDIMENTS
RT   SUSPENDED LOAD

RETINAS
SN   Added in 1980
UF   blind spot
UF   fovea
BT1   EYES
BT2   PHOTORECEPTORS
BT3   SENSE ORGANS
BT4   ANIMAL ORGANS
RT   VISION
RT   VISUAL PIGMENTS
RT   VISUAL STIMULI

RETROGRADATION
RT   COASTAL EROSION
RT   COASTAL MORPHOLOGY
RT   COASTS
RT   EUSTATIC CHANGES
RT   ISOSTASY
RT   LANDSLIDES
RT   PROGRADATION
RT   RIA COASTS
RT   SUBMERGED SHORELINES
RT   SUBMERGENCE
RT   TRANSGRESSIONS

REVERBERATION
UF   sound reverberation
BT1   UNDERWATER NOISE
BT2   NOISE (SOUND)
NT1   BOTTOM REVERBERATION
RT   BACKSCATTER
RT   REFLECTION
RT   SOUND SCATTERING

REVERSE OSMOSIS
BT1   OSMOSIS
BT2   SEPARATION PROCESSES
RT   DESALINATION
RT   WASTEWATER TREATMENT

REVERSING THERMOMETERS
BT1   THERMOMETERS
BT2   MEASURING DEVICES
RT   CORRECTIONS
RT   IN SITU TEMPERATURE
RT   MESSENGERS
RT   OCEANOGRAPHIC EQUIPMENT

REVERSING THERMOMETERS (cont'd)
RT   WATER SAMPLERS
RT   WATER TEMPERATURE

REVIEW (LITERATURE)
USE   **LITERATURE REVIEWS**

REVIEW ARTICLES
USE   **LITERATURE REVIEWS**

REYNOLDS NUMBER
RT   DIMENSIONLESS NUMBERS
RT   DRAG COEFFICIENT
RT   FROUDE NUMBER
RT   KINEMATIC VISCOSITY
RT   LAMINAR FLOW
RT   PRANDTL NUMBER
RT   TURBULENT FLOW

REYNOLDS STRESSES
UF   eddy stresses
UF   turbulent shear stresses
BT1   STRESS
BT2   FORCES (MECHANICS)
RT   BOTTOM STRESS
RT   EDDY VISCOSITY
RT   MOMENTUM TRANSFER
RT   NAVIER-STOKES EQUATIONS
RT   SHEAR STRESS
RT   TURBULENCE
RT   TURBULENT BOUNDARY LAYER
RT   TURBULENT FLOW
RT   WIND STRESS

RHENIUM
BT1   CHEMICAL ELEMENTS
RT   METALS
RT   RHENIUM COMPOUNDS
RT   RHENIUM ISOTOPES
RT   TRACE METALS

RHENIUM COMPOUNDS
RT   CHEMICAL COMPOUNDS
RT   RHENIUM

RHENIUM ISOTOPES
BT1   ISOTOPES
RT   RHENIUM

RHEOLOGY
BT1   MECHANICS
BT2   PHYSICS
RT   DEFORMATION
RT   NON-NEWTONIAN FLUIDS
RT   PLASTIC FLOW
RT   ROCK DEFORMATION
RT   VISCOSITY

RHEOTAXIS
BT1   TAXIS
BT2   ORIENTATION BEHAVIOUR
BT3   BEHAVIOUR
RT   WATER CURRENTS

RHEOTROPISM
BT1   TROPISM
RT   WATER CURRENTS

RHIZOMES
SN   Added in 1980
BT1   PLANT ORGANS
BT2   BODY ORGANS
RT   PLANT REPRODUCTIVE STRUCTURES
RT   ROOTS
RT   STEMS
RT   STOMATA
RT   VEGETATIVE REPRODUCTION

RHODAMINE B-DYE

SN	Synthetic red or pink substance used as tracer in study of water currents, turbulence
BT1	DYES
BT2	TRACERS
RT	DYE DISPERSION
RT	LAGRANGIAN CURRENT MEASUREMENT
RT	TURBULENCE
RT	WATER CURRENTS

RHODIUM

BT1	CHEMICAL ELEMENTS
RT	METALS
RT	RHODIUM COMPOUNDS
RT	RHODIUM ISOTOPES
RT	TRACE METALS

RHODIUM COMPOUNDS

RT	CHEMICAL COMPOUNDS
RT	RHODIUM

RHODIUM ISOTOPES

BT1	ISOTOPES
RT	RHODIUM

RHODOPSIN

USE	VISUAL PIGMENTS

RHYOLITES

BT1	VOLCANIC ROCKS
BT2	IGNEOUS ROCKS
BT3	ROCKS

RHYTHMS

USE	CYCLES

RHYTHMS (BIOLOGICAL)

USE	BIOLOGICAL RHYTHMS

RIA COASTS

BT1	SUBMERGED SHORELINES
BT2	COASTS
BT3	LANDFORMS
BT4	TOPOGRAPHIC FEATURES
RT	DROWNED VALLEYS
RT	RETROGRADATION
RT	TRANSGRESSIONS

RIAS

USE	DROWNED VALLEYS

RIBOFLAVIN

USE	VITAMIN B

RIBONUCLEIC ACID

USE	RNA

RIBOSE

BT1	MONOSACCHARIDES
BT2	SACCHARIDES
BT3	CARBOHYDRATES
BT4	ORGANIC COMPOUNDS
RT	ALDEHYDES
RT	VITAMIN B

RIBOSOMES

SN	Added in 1980
UF	microsomes
RT	CYTOPLASM
RT	PROTEIN SYNTHESIS
RT	PROTEINS
RT	RNA

RICE-CUM-FISH CULTURE

USE	RICE FIELD AQUACULTURE

RICE FIELD AQUACULTURE

SN	Before 1982 search AGROPISCICULTURE
UF	rice-cum-fish culture
UF	rizipisciculture
BT1	AGROPISCICULTURE
RT	AGRICULTURE
RT	AQUACULTURE TECHNIQUES
RT	CRAYFISH CULTURE
RT	FISH CULTURE
RT	FRESHWATER AQUACULTURE
RT	RICE FIELDS

RICE FIELDS

SN	Added in 1982
UF	paddy fields
RT	FLOODING
RT	RICE FIELD AQUACULTURE

RICHARDSON NUMBER

RT	INSTABILITY
RT	SHEAR FLOW
RT	VERTICAL SHEAR

RICHTER SCALE

RT	EARTHQUAKES
RT	SEISMOLOGY

RIDGES

RT	CONTINENTAL RIDGES
RT	MID-OCEAN RIDGES
RT	RELIEF FORMS
RT	SILLS
RT	SUBMARINE RIDGES

RIFT SYSTEMS

USE	RIFT ZONES

RIFT VALLEYS

BT1	LANDFORMS
BT2	TOPOGRAPHIC FEATURES
RT	FAULT ZONES
RT	FAULTS
RT	GRABEN
RT	MEDIAN VALLEYS
RT	RELIEF FORMS
RT	RIFT ZONES
RT	RIFTING
RT	VALLEYS

RIFT ZONES

SN	Search also RIFTS
UF	rift systems
UF	rifts
NT1	MEDIAN VALLEYS
RT	DIVERGING PLATE BOUNDARIES
RT	FAULT ZONES
RT	FAULTS
RT	PLATE DIVERGENCE
RT	RIFT VALLEYS
RT	RIFTING
RT	VALLEYS

RIFTING

UF	taphrogeny
RT	FAULT ZONES
RT	MEDIAN VALLEYS
RT	OROGENY
RT	PLATE DIVERGENCE
RT	PLATE TECTONICS
RT	RIFT VALLEYS
RT	RIFT ZONES
RT	SEAFLOOR SPREADING
RT	TECTONICS

RIFTS

USE	RIFT ZONES

RIGGING

RT	DECK EQUIPMENT
RT	SURFACE CRAFT

RIGHTING

BT1	SHIP MOTION
RT	CAPSIZING
RT	LIFEBOATS
RT	SHIP STABILITY

RIGHTS

SN	Use of a more specific term is recommended. Added in 1980
NT1	EXCLUSIVE RIGHTS
NT1	EXPLORATION RIGHTS
NT1	FISHING RIGHTS
NT1	PROPERTY RIGHTS
NT2	RENTAL
NT1	WATER RIGHTS
NT2	RIPARIAN RIGHTS
RT	LEGAL ASPECTS
RT	LEGISLATION

RIGIDITY

USE	FLEXIBILITY

RIGIDITY MODULUS

USE	SHEAR MODULUS

RIGS

USE	DRILLING RIGS

RIP CHANNELS

BT1	BEACH FEATURES
RT	CHANNELS
RT	EROSION
RT	EROSION FEATURES
RT	RIP CURRENTS

RIP CURRENTS

BT1	NEARSHORE CURRENTS
BT2	WATER CURRENTS
BT3	WATER MOTION
RT	BEACH CUSPS
RT	COASTS
RT	EDGE WAVES
RT	LONGSHORE CURRENTS
RT	RIP CHANNELS
RT	SEDIMENT TRANSPORT
RT	SURF ZONE
RT	UNDERTOW
RT	WAVE-CURRENT INTERACTION
RT	WIND-DRIVEN CURRENTS

RIPARIAN RIGHTS

SN	Belonging to a person who owns land bordering a body of water. Added in 1980
BT1	WATER RIGHTS
BT2	RIGHTS
RT	FISHING RIGHTS
RT	IRRIGATION WATER
RT	LEGISLATION
RT	NAVIGATION
RT	PROPERTY RIGHTS
RT	RECREATION
RT	RECREATIONAL WATERS
RT	WASTE DISPOSAL
RT	WATER POLLUTION

RIPPLE MARKS

BT1	BEDDING STRUCTURES
BT2	SEDIMENTARY STRUCTURES
RT	SAND RIPPLES
RT	TRANSVERSE BED FORMS

ASFIS Thesaurus

RIPPLES (SAND)		
USE	**SAND RIPPLES**	

RIPPLES (WATER)	
USE	**WATER RIPPLES**

RIPRAP
BT1	BREAKWATERS
BT2	COAST DEFENCES
BT3	COASTAL STRUCTURES
BT4	HYDRAULIC STRUCTURES

RISE (CONTINENTAL)
USE	**CONTINENTAL RISE**

RISE (OCEANIC)
USE	**MID-OCEAN RIDGES**

RISER CABLES
BT1	CABLES
RT	CABLE DYNAMICS
RT	CATENARY
RT	ELECTRICAL CABLES

RISER PIPES
UF	marine risers
BT1	PIPES
RT	FLOWLINES

RISKS
SN	Includes risk analysis
RT	ECONOMICS
RT	FEASIBILITY
RT	HAZARDS
RT	INSURANCE
RT	RELIABILITY

RIVER BANKS
RT	BANKS (TOPOGRAPHY)
RT	EMBANKMENTS
RT	FLUVIAL MORPHOLOGY
RT	LEVEES
RT	RIVER BEDS
RT	RIVERS

RIVER BASIN MANAGEMENT
BT1	MANAGEMENT
RT	CONSERVATION
RT	ENVIRONMENTAL LEGISLATION
RT	FISHERY MANAGEMENT
RT	FLOOD CONTROL
RT	POLLUTION CONTROL
RT	RIVER BASINS
RT	WATER CONSERVATION
RT	WATER MANAGEMENT

RIVER BASINS
UF	drainage basins
RT	BASINS
RT	CATCHMENT AREA
RT	FLUVIAL FEATURES
RT	LAKE BASINS
RT	RIVER BASIN MANAGEMENT
RT	RIVER VALLEYS
RT	RIVERS
RT	RUNOFF
RT	VALLEYS
RT	WATERSHEDS

RIVER BEDS
RT	BED LOAD
RT	BED ROUGHNESS
RT	BOTTOM FRICTION
RT	FLUVIAL MORPHOLOGY
RT	RIVER BANKS
RT	RIVERS
RT	SEDIMENTS

RIVER CULTURE
USE	**RACEWAY CULTURE**

RIVER CURRENTS
USE	**STREAM FLOW**

RIVER DISCHARGE
SN	Flow from rivers into lakes and seas, contribution to water budget of seas and lakes, influence on environment and organisms
UF	river discharge effects
UF	river inflow
BT1	INFLOW
RT	ATMOSPHERIC PRECIPITATIONS
RT	BRACKISHWATER ENVIRONMENT
RT	DELTAS
RT	ESTUARIES
RT	ESTUARINE CHEMISTRY
RT	FLOOD CONTROL
RT	FLOOD PLAINS
RT	FLOODS
RT	FLUVIAL TRANSPORT
RT	FRESH WATER
RT	HYDROLOGIC CYCLE
RT	RAINFALL
RT	RIVER OUTFLOW
RT	RIVER PLUMES
RT	RIVERS
RT	SALINITY
RT	SALT BUDGET
RT	STREAM FLOW
RT	WATER BUDGET

RIVER DISCHARGE EFFECTS
USE	**RIVER DISCHARGE**

RIVER ENGINEERING
BT1	ENGINEERING
RT	COASTAL ENGINEERING
RT	EMBANKMENTS
RT	FLUVIAL MORPHOLOGY
RT	RIVERS
RT	STREAM FLOW
RT	STRUCTURAL ENGINEERING
RT	WEIRS

RIVER FISHERIES
UF	stream fisheries
BT1	INLAND FISHERIES
BT2	FISHERIES
RT	ARTISANAL FISHING
RT	CRUSTACEAN FISHERIES
RT	ESTUARINE FISHERIES
RT	RIVERS
RT	SALMON FISHERIES
RT	SHRIMP FISHERIES

RIVER FLOW
USE	**STREAM FLOW**

RIVER INFLOW
USE	**RIVER DISCHARGE**

RIVER MEANDERS
SN	Before 1986 use MEANDERS (RIVERS)
UF	meanders (rivers)
BT1	MEANDERING
BT2	WATER MOTION
RT	FLOOD PLAINS
RT	FLUVIAL FEATURES
RT	FLUVIAL MORPHOLOGY
RT	OXBOW LAKES
RT	RIVERS

RIVER MORPHOLOGY
USE	**FLUVIAL MORPHOLOGY**

RIVER OUTFLOW
SN	Outflow of water from lakes and other inland water bodies
BT1	OUTFLOW
RT	HYDROLOGIC CYCLE
RT	LAKES
RT	RESERVOIRS (WATER)
RT	RIVER DISCHARGE
RT	WATER BUDGET

RIVER PLUMES
SN	Plumes mainly caused by suspended material from river discharge into lakes, estuaries or marine coastal areas
BT1	PLUMES
BT2	FLUID FLOW
BT3	FLUID MOTION
RT	BUOYANT JETS
RT	ESTUARINE FRONT
RT	FLUVIAL FEATURES
RT	RIVER DISCHARGE
RT	SALT-WEDGE ESTUARIES
RT	SEDIMENT TRANSPORT
RT	SUSPENDED PARTICULATE MATTER
RT	THERMAL DECOMPOSITION
RT	TURBIDITY
RT	WATER MIXING

RIVER VALLEYS
UF	stream valleys
BT1	VALLEYS
BT2	LANDFORMS
BT3	TOPOGRAPHIC FEATURES
RT	ALLUVIAL FANS
RT	ALLUVIAL TERRACES
RT	EROSION
RT	FLOOD PLAINS
RT	FLUVIAL FEATURES
RT	FLUVIAL MORPHOLOGY
RT	GLACIAL EROSION
RT	GLACIERS
RT	RELIEF FORMS
RT	RIVER BASINS
RT	RIVERS
RT	STREAM FLOW
RT	THALWEG
RT	WATER TABLE

RIVER WATER
BT1	WATER
RT	RIVERS

RIVERS
UF	streams
BT1	INLAND WATERS
NT1	DISTRIBUTARIES
NT1	TRIBUTARIES
RT	ALLUVIAL DEPOSITS
RT	CHANNELS
RT	DELTAS
RT	ESTUARIES
RT	FLOOD PLAINS
RT	FLUVIAL FEATURES
RT	FLUVIAL MORPHOLOGY
RT	FLUVIAL SEDIMENTATION
RT	FLUVIAL TRANSPORT
RT	FRESH WATER
RT	HYDROLOGY
RT	ICE BREAKUP
RT	ICE JAMS
RT	JURISDICTION
RT	LIMNOLOGICAL SURVEYS
RT	LOTIC ENVIRONMENT
RT	OXBOW LAKES
RT	RIVER BANKS
RT	RIVER BASINS
RT	RIVER BEDS
RT	RIVER DISCHARGE
RT	RIVER ENGINEERING

RIVERS (cont'd)
RT	RIVER FISHERIES
RT	RIVER MEANDERS
RT	RIVER VALLEYS
RT	RIVER WATER
RT	RUNOFF
RT	STREAM FLOW
RT	STREAM FLOW RATE
RT	THALWEG
RT	VALLEYS
RT	WATER BODIES
RT	WATER RESOURCES
RT	WEIRS

RIZIPISCICULTURE
USE	**RICE FIELD AQUACULTURE**

RM
USE	**REDMOUTH DISEASE**

RNA
SN	Before 1982 search RIBONUCLEIC ACID
UF	ribonucleic acid
BT1	NUCLEIC ACIDS
BT2	ORGANIC ACIDS
BT3	ORGANIC COMPOUNDS
RT	CHEMICAL COMPOUNDS
RT	POLYMERIZATION
RT	RIBOSOMES

ROAD BRIDGES
USE	**BRIDGES**

ROADSTEADS
USE	**ANCHORAGES**

ROBOTS
BT1	ELECTRONIC EQUIPMENT
BT2	EQUIPMENT
RT	AUTOMATION
RT	COMPUTERS
RT	MANIPULATORS
RT	REMOTE CONTROL

ROCK DEFORMATION
BT1	DEFORMATION
BT2	MECHANICAL PROPERTIES
BT3	PHYSICAL PROPERTIES
BT4	PROPERTIES
NT1	DIAPIRISM
RT	FAULTS
RT	FOLDS
RT	RHEOLOGY
RT	ROCK MECHANICS
RT	ROCKS

ROCK DENSITY
USE	**SEDIMENT DENSITY**

ROCK FALLS
USE	**DEBRIS FLOW**

ROCK MAGNETISM
USE	**REMANENT MAGNETIZATION**

ROCK MECHANICS
UF	rock shear
UF	rock stress
BT1	MECHANICS
BT2	PHYSICS
RT	ELASTICITY
RT	ROCK DEFORMATION
RT	ROCKS
RT	SOIL MECHANICS

ROCK PROPERTIES
USE	**SEDIMENT PROPERTIES**

ROCK SAMPLES
USE	**SEDIMENT SAMPLES**

ROCK SAMPLING
USE	**SEDIMENT SAMPLING**

ROCK SHEAR
USE	**ROCK MECHANICS**

ROCK STRESS
USE	**ROCK MECHANICS**

ROCKFISH FISHERIES
USE	**REDFISH FISHERIES**

ROCKLOBSTER FISHERIES
USE	**LOBSTER FISHERIES**

ROCKS
NT1	IGNEOUS ROCKS
NT2	GABBROS
NT2	GRANITE
NT2	PLUTONS
NT2	ULTRAMAFIC ROCKS
NT3	OPHIOLITES
NT3	PERIDOTITE
NT2	VOLCANIC ROCKS
NT3	ANDESITE
NT3	BASALTS
NT4	ALKALI BASALTS
NT4	OCEANITE
NT4	THOLEIITE
NT4	THOLEIITIC BASALT
NT3	LAVA
NT4	PILLOW LAVA
NT3	PALAGONITE
NT3	PUMICE
NT3	RHYOLITES
NT3	TEPHRA
NT4	IGNIMBRITES
NT4	VOLCANIC BRECCIA
NT4	VOLCANIC LAPILLI
NT3	VOLCANIC ASH
NT3	VOLCANIC GLASS
NT1	METAMORPHIC ROCKS
NT2	AMPHIBOLITES
NT3	HORNBLENDE
NT2	SCHISTS
NT3	GREENSCHISTS
NT2	SERPENTINITE
NT1	SEDIMENTARY ROCKS
RT	BASEMENT ROCK
RT	LITHOGENESIS
RT	METAMORPHISM
RT	OUTCROPS
RT	PETROGENESIS
RT	PETROLOGY
RT	ROCK DEFORMATION
RT	ROCK MECHANICS
RT	ROCKY SHORES

ROCKS (IGNEOUS)
USE	**IGNEOUS ROCKS**

ROCKS (METAMORPHIC)
USE	**METAMORPHIC ROCKS**

ROCKS (SEDIMENTARY)
USE	**SEDIMENTARY ROCKS**

ROCKY SHORES
BT1	COASTAL LANDFORMS
BT2	LANDFORMS
BT3	TOPOGRAPHIC FEATURES
RT	COASTAL EROSION
RT	COASTAL MORPHOLOGY
RT	COASTS
RT	NEARSHORE DYNAMICS
RT	ROCKS
RT	WAVE PROCESSES ON BEACHES

ROE FISHERIES
SN	Added in 1982
BT1	FISHERIES
RT	ROES

ROES
SN	Gonads of fish or invertebrates marketed in various ways and usually referred to by individual species, e.g. cod roe, salmon roe, etc. Added in 1980
UF	fish roe
UF	hard roe
UF	invertebrate roe
UF	milt
UF	soft roe
BT1	PROCESSED FISHERY PRODUCTS
BT2	FISHERY PRODUCTS
BT3	PRODUCTS
NT1	CAVIAR
RT	HUMAN FOOD
RT	ROE FISHERIES

ROLL RESONANCE
BT1	RESONANCE
RT	BUOY MOTION EFFECTS
RT	ROLLING

ROLL RESPONSE
BT1	DYNAMIC RESPONSE
BT2	INSTRUMENT RESPONSES
RT	BUOY MOTION EFFECTS
RT	ROLLING

ROLLERS
BT1	SWELL
BT2	SURFACE WATER WAVES
BT3	WATER WAVES
RT	BREAKERS
RT	SHOALING WAVES

ROLLING
BT1	SHIP MOTION
RT	BUOY MOTION
RT	BUOY MOTION EFFECTS
RT	DYNAMIC RESPONSE
RT	ROLL RESONANCE
RT	ROLL RESPONSE
RT	YAWING

ROOT SYSTEMS
USE	**ROOTS**

ROOTS
SN	Added in 1980
UF	root systems
BT1	PLANT ORGANS
BT2	BODY ORGANS
RT	NUTRIENTS (MINERAL)
RT	RHIZOMES

ROPE
USE	**ROPES**

ROPES
UF	rope
NT1	FIBRE ROPE (NATURAL)
NT1	FIBRE ROPE (SYNTHETIC)
NT1	WIRE ROPE
NT2	HYDROGRAPHIC WIRE
RT	CABLES
RT	CHAIN
RT	MOORING LINES
RT	NETS
RT	SYNTHETIC FIBRES
RT	TOWING LINES
RT	WINCHES

ASFIS Thesaurus

ROSSBY NUMBER
RT	CORIOLIS FORCE
RT	DIMENSIONLESS NUMBERS
RT	INERTIA
RT	RATIOS

ROSSBY PARAMETER
RT	BAROCLINIC INSTABILITY
RT	BETA-PLANE
RT	CORIOLIS PARAMETERS
RT	PARAMETERS
RT	PLANETARY WAVES

ROSSBY WAVES
USE	**PLANETARY WAVES**

ROTARY CURRENTS
BT1	TIDAL CURRENTS
BT2	WATER CURRENTS
BT3	WATER MOTION
RT	CORIOLIS FORCE
RT	CURRENT ELLIPSES

ROTATING FLUIDS
BT1	FLUIDS
RT	FLUID MOTION
RT	SPINDOWN
RT	SPINUP
RT	VORTICES

ROTATION
NT1	EARTH ROTATION
RT	ANTICYCLONIC MOTION
RT	CYCLONIC MOTION
RT	MOTION
RT	PLATE MOTION
RT	PLATE TECTONICS
RT	PLATES
RT	POLAR WANDERING
RT	VORTICITY

ROTENONE
RT	FISH POISONING
RT	TOXICANTS

ROUGH FISH
USE	**TRASH FISH**

ROUGHNESS
SN	Use of a more specific term is recommended
BT1	SURFACE PROPERTIES
BT2	PROPERTIES
NT1	BED ROUGHNESS
NT1	SURFACE ROUGHNESS
RT	FRICTION

ROUTEING CHARTS
USE	**PILOT CHARTS**

ROVS
USE	**UNMANNED VEHICLES**

ROW BOATS
SN	Before 1982 search BOATS
BT1	SURFACE CRAFT
BT2	VEHICLES
RT	ARTISANAL FISHING
RT	RECREATION

RUBBER
SN	Rubber as a material used in the aquatic environment. For rubber cements or adhesives use ADHESIVES
BT1	MATERIALS

RUBBER (ADHESIVES)
USE	**ADHESIVES**

RUBBLEMOUND BREAKWATERS
BT1	BREAKWATERS
BT2	COAST DEFENCES
BT3	COASTAL STRUCTURES
BT4	HYDRAULIC STRUCTURES

RUBIDIUM
BT1	CHEMICAL ELEMENTS
RT	ALKALI METALS
RT	RUBIDIUM COMPOUNDS
RT	RUBIDIUM ISOTOPES
RT	TRACE ELEMENTS

RUBIDIUM COMPOUNDS
RT	CHEMICAL COMPOUNDS
RT	RUBIDIUM

RUBIDIUM ISOTOPES
BT1	ISOTOPES
RT	RUBIDIUM
RT	RUBIDIUM-STRONTIUM DATING

RUBIDIUM-STRONTIUM DATING
BT1	RADIOMETRIC DATING
BT2	GEOCHRONOMETRY
RT	RUBIDIUM ISOTOPES
RT	STRONTIUM ISOTOPES

RUDITES
RT	BOULDER CLAY
RT	BOULDERS
RT	BRECCIA
RT	COBBLESTONE
RT	PEBBLES

RUNNELS
BT1	BEACH FEATURES
RT	BEACHES
RT	CHANNELS

RUNNING WATER CULTURE
USE	**RACEWAY CULTURE**

RUNOFF
SN	Water derived from atmospheric precipitation which reaches streams and rivers. The term must not be confused in this thesaurus with RIVER DISCHARGE
BT1	DRAINAGE WATER
BT2	WATER
NT1	AGRICULTURAL RUNOFF
NT1	STORMWATER RUNOFF
NT1	URBAN RUNOFF
RT	CATCHMENT AREA
RT	FLOOD CONTROL
RT	FLOODS
RT	HYDROLOGY
RT	INLAND WATER ENVIRONMENT
RT	RAINFALL
RT	RIVER BASINS
RT	RIVERS
RT	STREAM FLOW
RT	WATERSHEDS

RUNOFF FROM AGRICULTURAL LAND
USE	**AGRICULTURAL RUNOFF**

RUST
USE	**CORROSION**

RUTHENIUM
BT1	CHEMICAL ELEMENTS
RT	METALS
RT	RUTHENIUM COMPOUNDS
RT	RUTHENIUM ISOTOPES
RT	TRACE METALS

RUTHENIUM COMPOUNDS
RT	CHEMICAL COMPOUNDS
RT	RUTHENIUM

RUTHENIUM ISOTOPES
BT1	ISOTOPES
RT	RUTHENIUM
BT1	CHEMICAL ELEMENTS
RT	CHEMICAL COMPOUNDS

RUTILE
BT1	OXIDE MINERALS
BT2	MINERALS
RT	HEAVY MINERALS
RT	PLACERS
RT	TITANIUM

S-WAVES
UF	secondary waves
UF	shear waves
BT1	BODY WAVES
BT2	SEISMIC WAVES
BT3	ELASTIC WAVES
RT	P-WAVES
RT	SHEAR WAVE VELOCITIES

SABKHAS
UF	salt flats
NT1	PLAYAS
RT	ARID ENVIRONMENTS
RT	COASTAL LAGOONS
RT	DESERTS
RT	EOLIAN DEPOSITS
RT	EVAPORITES
RT	SALT DEPOSITS
RT	SUPRALITTORAL ZONE

SACCHARIDES
UF	sugars
BT1	CARBOHYDRATES
BT2	ORGANIC COMPOUNDS
NT1	MONOSACCHARIDES
NT2	ARABINOSE
NT2	FUCOSE
NT2	GLUCOSE
NT2	MANNOSE
NT2	RIBOSE
NT2	XYLOSE
NT1	POLYSACCHARIDES
NT2	AGAROSE
NT2	ALGINIC ACID
NT2	CELLULOSE
NT2	MUCOPOLYSACCHARIDES
NT3	CHITIN
NT3	HEPARIN
NT2	STARCH

SACRIFICIAL ANODES
BT1	ANODES
BT2	ELECTRODES
BT3	ELECTRICAL EQUIPMENT
BT4	EQUIPMENT
RT	CATHODIC PROTECTION

SAFETY
USE	**HEALTH AND SAFETY**

SAFETY DEVICES
UF	deck safety equipment
UF	safety equipment
BT1	EQUIPMENT
RT	ACCIDENT PREVENTION
RT	ACCIDENTS
RT	ALARM SYSTEMS
RT	BREATHING APPARATUS
RT	DECK EQUIPMENT
RT	EMERGENCY VESSELS
RT	FIRE EXTINGUISHERS
RT	HAZARDS

SAFETY DEVICES (cont'd)
RT	HEALTH AND SAFETY
RT	LIFEBOATS
RT	PROTECTION
RT	PROTECTIVE CLOTHING
RT	PUBLIC HEALTH
RT	SAFETY REGULATIONS
RT	WARNING SERVICES
RT	WARNING SYSTEMS

SAFETY EQUIPMENT
USE	**SAFETY DEVICES**

SAFETY REGULATIONS
BT1	LEGISLATION
NT1	DIVING REGULATIONS
RT	ACCIDENT PREVENTION
RT	EXPLOSIVES
RT	FIRE PREVENTION
RT	HEALTH AND SAFETY
RT	LEGAL ASPECTS
RT	RADIATION PROTECTION
RT	SAFETY DEVICES

SAILING
USE	**BOATING**

SAILING DIRECTIONS
BT1	DOCUMENTS
RT	NAVIGATIONAL AIDS
RT	PILOT CHARTS

SAILING SHIPS
BT1	SHIPS
BT2	SURFACE CRAFT
BT3	VEHICLES
NT1	YACHTS
RT	FUEL ECONOMY
RT	SAILS

SAILS
BT1	PROPULSION SYSTEMS
RT	SAILING SHIPS
RT	YACHTING
RT	YACHTS

SALINE INTRUSION
RT	ESTUARIES
RT	GROUND WATER
RT	SALINE WATER
RT	SALT WEDGES
RT	SALT-WEDGE ESTUARIES

SALINE WATER
SN	Inland water bodies with high salt concentration
UF	salt water
BT1	WATER
RT	BRINES
RT	DESALINATION
RT	GROUNDWATER POLLUTION
RT	SALINE INTRUSION
RT	SALT LAKES
RT	SALT MARSHES
RT	SOLUTIONS
RT	WATER PROPERTIES

SALINITY
BT1	CHEMICAL PROPERTIES
BT2	PROPERTIES
NT1	CHLORINITY
NT1	CHLOROSITY
NT1	PALAEOSALINITY
NT1	SURFACE SALINITY
RT	ABIOTIC FACTORS
RT	ATMOSPHERIC PRECIPITATIONS
RT	CABBELING
RT	CONSERVATIVE PROPERTIES
RT	CTD PROFILERS
RT	DESALINATION

SALINITY (cont'd)
RT	DESALINATION PLANTS
RT	DILUTION
RT	DISSOLVED SALTS
RT	ELECTRICAL CONDUCTIVITY
RT	ENVIRONMENTAL CHARTS
RT	EVAPORATION
RT	HALOCLINE
RT	HYDROGRAPHY
RT	IN SITU DENSITY
RT	ISOHALINES
RT	KNUDSEN TABLES
RT	OCEANOGRAPHIC DATA
RT	POTENTIAL DENSITY
RT	PRACTICAL SALINITY SCALE
RT	RAINFALL
RT	REFRACTIVE INDEX
RT	RESPONSE TIME
RT	RIVER DISCHARGE
RT	SALINITY CHARTS
RT	SALINITY DATA
RT	SALINITY EFFECTS
RT	SALINITY GRADIENTS
RT	SALINITY MEASUREMENT
RT	SALINITY MEASURING EQUIPMENT
RT	SALINITY MICROSTRUCTURE
RT	SALINITY MINIMUM LAYER
RT	SALINITY POWER
RT	SALINITY PROFILES
RT	SALINITY SCALES
RT	SALINITY SECTIONS
RT	SALINITY TOLERANCE
RT	SALINOMETERS
RT	SALT FLUX
RT	SEA WATER
RT	SIGMA-T
RT	SOUND VELOCITY
RT	STD PROFILERS
RT	T/S DIAGRAMS
RT	WATER DENSITY
RT	WATER MASSES
RT	WATER PROPERTIES
RT	WATER TYPES

SALINITY CHARTS
BT1	HYDROGRAPHIC CHARTS
BT2	MAPS
BT3	GRAPHICS
BT4	AUDIOVISUAL MATERIAL
RT	ISOHALINES
RT	SALINITY
RT	SALINITY SECTIONS

SALINITY DATA
BT1	HYDROGRAPHIC DATA
BT2	DATA
RT	LONG-TERM RECORDS
RT	OCEANOGRAPHIC DATA
RT	SALINITY

SALINITY EFFECTS
BT1	ENVIRONMENTAL EFFECTS
RT	SALINITY
RT	SALINITY TOLERANCE

SALINITY GRADIENT ENERGY CONVERSION
USE	**SALINITY POWER**

SALINITY GRADIENTS
RT	DOUBLE DIFFUSION
RT	GRADIENTS
RT	SALINITY
RT	SALINITY POWER
RT	SALINITY PROFILES
RT	SALT FINGERS

SALINITY MAXIMUM LAYER
BT1	CORE LAYERS (WATER)
BT2	LAYERS
RT	CORE LAYER METHOD
RT	SALINITY MINIMUM LAYER
RT	SALINITY PROFILES
RT	SALINITY SECTIONS

SALINITY MEASUREMENT
BT1	MEASUREMENT
RT	CONDUCTIVITY SENSORS
RT	ELECTRICAL CONDUCTIVITY
RT	IN SITU MEASUREMENTS
RT	REFRACTIVE INDEX
RT	SALINITY
RT	SALINITY MEASURING EQUIPMENT
RT	SALINITY TABLES
RT	SALINOMETERS
RT	STANDARD SEA WATER
RT	TITRATION
RT	WATER ANALYSIS

SALINITY MEASURING DEVICES
USE	**SALINOMETERS**

SALINITY MEASURING EQUIPMENT
RT	CONDUCTIVITY SENSORS
RT	CTD PROFILERS
RT	MEASURING DEVICES
RT	OCEANOGRAPHIC EQUIPMENT
RT	SALINITY
RT	SALINITY MEASUREMENT
RT	SALINOMETERS
RT	STD PROFILERS

SALINITY MICROSTRUCTURE
SN	Variations in the distribution of salinity on a scale of 10 cm or less
BT1	MICROSTRUCTURE
BT2	SPATIAL VARIATIONS
RT	SALINITY

SALINITY MINIMUM LAYER
BT1	CORE LAYERS (WATER)
BT2	LAYERS
RT	CORE LAYER METHOD
RT	SALINITY
RT	SALINITY MAXIMUM LAYER
RT	SALINITY PROFILES
RT	SALINITY SECTIONS

SALINITY POWER
SN	Utilizing the osmotic pressure difference between two bodies of water of differing salinities as a source of energy
UF	salinity gradient energy conversion
BT1	POWER FROM THE SEA
BT2	ENERGY RESOURCES
BT3	NATURAL RESOURCES
BT4	RESOURCES
RT	OSMOTIC PRESSURE
RT	SALINITY
RT	SALINITY GRADIENTS

SALINITY PROFILES
BT1	VERTICAL PROFILES
BT2	PROFILES
RT	CTD PROFILERS
RT	SALINITY
RT	SALINITY GRADIENTS
RT	SALINITY MAXIMUM LAYER
RT	SALINITY MINIMUM LAYER
RT	SALINITY SECTIONS
RT	STD PROFILERS

ASFIS Thesaurus

SALINITY SCALES
NT1	PRACTICAL SALINITY SCALE
RT	SALINITY

SALINITY SECTIONS
BT1	HYDROGRAPHIC SECTIONS
BT2	VERTICAL SECTIONS
BT3	MAP GRAPHICS
BT4	GRAPHICS
RT	ISOHALINES
RT	SALINITY
RT	SALINITY CHARTS
RT	SALINITY MAXIMUM LAYER
RT	SALINITY MINIMUM LAYER
RT	SALINITY PROFILES
RT	STRATIFICATION
RT	VERTICAL DISTRIBUTION

SALINITY STRATIFICATION
BT1	STRATIFICATION
RT	DENSITY STRATIFICATION
RT	HALOCLINE
RT	SALT-WEDGE ESTUARIES

SALINITY TABLES
BT1	OCEANOGRAPHIC TABLES
BT2	TABLES
BT3	DOCUMENTS
RT	SALINITY MEASUREMENT

SALINITY TOLERANCE
BT1	TOLERANCE
BT2	BIOLOGICAL PROPERTIES
BT3	PROPERTIES
RT	AMPHIHALINE SPECIES
RT	ESTUARINE ORGANISMS
RT	EURYHALINITY
RT	INDICATOR SPECIES
RT	OSMOREGULATION
RT	SALINITY
RT	SALINITY EFFECTS
RT	STENOHALINITY

SALINOMETERS
UF	salinity measuring devices
BT1	MEASURING DEVICES
RT	LABORATORY EQUIPMENT
RT	OCEANOGRAPHIC EQUIPMENT
RT	SALINITY
RT	SALINITY MEASUREMENT
RT	SALINITY MEASURING EQUIPMENT

SALMON FISHERIES
SN	Added in 1982
UF	trout fisheries
BT1	FINFISH FISHERIES
BT2	FISHERIES
RT	ANGLING
RT	FISH CULTURE
RT	LAKE FISHERIES
RT	MARINE FISHERIES
RT	MIGRATORY SPECIES
RT	RIVER FISHERIES
RT	SPORT FISHING

SALMON NESTS
USE	**REDDS**

SALT ADVECTION
UF	salt transport
BT1	ADVECTION
BT2	TRANSPORT PROCESSES
RT	CONSERVATION OF SALT
RT	SALT BUDGET

SALT BUDGET
RT	CONSERVATION OF SALT
RT	DISSOLVED SALTS
RT	RIVER DISCHARGE
RT	SALT ADVECTION

SALT BUDGET (cont'd)
RT	SALT FLUX
RT	WATER BUDGET

SALT DEPOSITS
RT	DESALINATION
RT	EVAPORITES
RT	PLAYAS
RT	SABKHAS
RT	SALT LAKES
RT	SEDIMENTS
RT	SUBSURFACE DEPOSITS

SALT DOMES
BT1	STRUCTURAL DOMES
BT2	FOLDS
BT3	GEOLOGICAL STRUCTURES
RT	ANTICLINES
RT	CAP ROCKS
RT	DIAPIRISM
RT	DIAPIRS
RT	DOMES

SALT FINGER CONVECTION
USE	**DOUBLE DIFFUSION**

SALT FINGERING
USE	**DOUBLE DIFFUSION**

SALT FINGERS
RT	DISSOLVED SALTS
RT	DOUBLE DIFFUSION
RT	INTERFACE PHENOMENA
RT	MICROSTRUCTURE
RT	SALINITY GRADIENTS
RT	TRANSPORT PROCESSES

SALT FLATS
USE	**SABKHAS**

SALT FLUX
RT	DISSOLVED SALTS
RT	SALINITY
RT	SALT BUDGET

SALT LAKES
BT1	LAKES
BT2	INLAND WATERS
RT	DESALINATION
RT	DISSOLVED SALTS
RT	PLAYAS
RT	SALINE WATER
RT	SALT DEPOSITS
RT	WATER RESOURCES

SALT MARSHES
BT1	MARSHES
BT2	WETLANDS
BT3	LANDFORMS
BT4	TOPOGRAPHIC FEATURES
RT	ESTUARIES
RT	ESTUARINE SEDIMENTATION
RT	PROGRADATION
RT	SALINE WATER
RT	TIDAL FLATS

SALT NUCLEI
RT	AIR BUBBLES
RT	BUBBLE BURSTING
RT	CONDENSATION
RT	HYDROMETEORS
RT	SPRAY

SALT PARTICLES
UF	sea salt nuclei
BT1	ATMOSPHERIC PARTICULATES
BT2	PARTICULATES
RT	AEROSOLS
RT	AIR-WATER EXCHANGES
RT	BUBBLE BURSTING

SALT PARTICLES (cont'd)
RT	CONDENSATION
RT	HAZE
RT	HYDROMETEORS
RT	SPLASH ZONE
RT	SPRAY

SALT SPRAY
USE	**SPRAY**

SALT TRANSPORT
USE	**SALT ADVECTION**

SALT WATER
USE	**SALINE WATER**

SALT WATER WEDGES
USE	**SALT WEDGES**

SALT-WEDGE ESTUARIES
BT1	ESTUARIES
BT2	COASTAL INLETS
BT3	COASTAL WATERS
RT	ESTUARINE DYNAMICS
RT	FRESH WATER
RT	HALOCLINE
RT	RIVER PLUMES
RT	SALINE INTRUSION
RT	SALINITY STRATIFICATION
RT	SALT WEDGES
RT	SEA WATER
RT	TURBULENT ENTRAINMENT

SALT WEDGES
UF	salt water wedges
RT	ESTUARIES
RT	ESTUARINE CHEMISTRY
RT	ESTUARINE DYNAMICS
RT	SALINE INTRUSION
RT	SALT-WEDGE ESTUARIES

SALTATION
RT	BED LOAD
RT	PARTICLE MOTION
RT	SEDIMENT TRANSPORT
RT	SUSPENSION

SALTING
USE	**CURING**

SALTS
UF	mineral salts
NT1	DISSOLVED SALTS
NT2	BRINES
RT	CARBONATES
RT	CHEMICAL COMPOUNDS
RT	CHEMICAL EXTRACTION
RT	CYANIDES
RT	DESALINATION
RT	DESALINATION PLANTS
RT	DIFFUSION
RT	DILUTION
RT	DOUBLE DIFFUSION
RT	EVAPORATION
RT	HALOGEN COMPOUNDS
RT	INDUSTRIAL PRODUCTS
RT	MINERAL INDUSTRY
RT	MINERAL RESOURCES
RT	MOLECULAR DIFFUSION
RT	NITRATES
RT	NITRITES
RT	PHOSPHATES
RT	SEWAGE TREATMENT

SALTS EXTRACTION
USE	**DEMINERALIZATION**

SALTWATER SHRIMP CULTURE		**SAMPLES**		**SAND** (cont'd)	
USE	**SHRIMP CULTURE**	NT1	GEOLOGICAL SAMPLES	RT	SILICATES
		NT2	MINERAL SAMPLES	RT	SILT
SALVAGE		NT2	SEDIMENT SAMPLES	RT	SOILS
USE	**SALVAGING**	NT3	CORES		
		NT3	DREDGED SAMPLES	**SAND BANKS**	
SALVAGE EQUIPMENT		NT1	WATER SAMPLES	BT1	BED FORMS
BT1	. EQUIPMENT	RT	GEOLOGICAL COLLECTIONS	BT2	SEDIMENTARY STRUCTURES
RT	LIFTING TACKLE	RT	SAMPLE CONTAMINATION	RT	BANKS (TOPOGRAPHY)
RT	SALVAGING	RT	SAMPLE STORAGE	RT	MUD BANKS
RT	WATER PUMPS	RT	SAMPLING	RT	SHOALS
				RT	SUBMARINE BANKS
SALVAGING		**SAMPLING**			
SN	Before 1986 search also SALVAGE	SN	Use of a more specific term is	**SAND BARS**	
UF	recovery of wrecks		recommended	BT1	BED FORMS
UF	salvage	UF	sampling methods	BT2	SEDIMENTARY STRUCTURES
UF	wreck recovery	UF	sampling techniques	RT	NEARSHORE BARS
RT	LIFTING	NT1	AIR SAMPLING	RT	SAND
RT	LIFTING TACKLE	NT1	BIOLOGICAL SAMPLING		
RT	LOCATING	NT1	SEAFLOOR SAMPLING	**SAND DUNES (SUBAERIAL)**	
RT	REMOVAL	NT2	SEDIMENT SAMPLING	USE	**DUNES**
RT	SALVAGE EQUIPMENT	NT3	CORING		
RT	SEARCH AND RESCUE	NT1	STATISTICAL SAMPLING	**SAND PATCHES**	
RT	UNDERWATER OBJECT LOCATION	NT1	WATER SAMPLING	BT1	BED FORMS
RT	WRECKS	RT	CENSUS	BT2	SEDIMENTARY STRUCTURES
		RT	RESEARCH VESSELS	RT	SAND
SAMARIUM		RT	SAMPLE CONTAMINATION	RT	TRANSVERSE BED FORMS
BT1	CHEMICAL ELEMENTS	RT	SAMPLE STORAGE		
RT	RARE EARTHS	RT	SAMPLERS	**SAND PITS**	
RT	SAMARIUM COMPOUNDS	RT	SAMPLES	USE	**PITS**
RT	SAMARIUM ISOTOPES	RT	SURVEYS		
RT	TRANSITION ELEMENTS			**SAND RIBBONS**	
		SAMPLING (BIOLOGICAL)		BT1	BED FORMS
SAMARIUM COMPOUNDS		USE	**BIOLOGICAL SAMPLING**	BT2	SEDIMENTARY STRUCTURES
RT	CHEMICAL COMPOUNDS			RT	SAND
RT	SAMARIUM	**SAMPLING (STATISTICAL)**			
		USE	**STATISTICAL SAMPLING**	**SAND RIPPLES**	
SAMARIUM ISOTOPES				UF	ripples (sand)
BT1	ISOTOPES	**SAMPLING DEVICES**		UF	wave sand ripples
RT	SAMARIUM	USE	**SAMPLERS**	BT1	BED FORMS
				BT2	SEDIMENTARY STRUCTURES
SAMPLE CONTAMINATION		**SAMPLING METHODS**		RT	BEACH FEATURES
UF	contamination of samples	USE	**SAMPLING**	RT	RIPPLE MARKS
RT	SAMPLE STORAGE			RT	TRANSVERSE BED FORMS
RT	SAMPLES	**SAMPLING TECHNIQUES**			
RT	SAMPLING	USE	**SAMPLING**	**SAND STRUCTURES**	
RT	STORAGE EFFECTS			BT1	ARTIFICIAL ISLANDS
		SANCTUARIES		BT2	OFFSHORE STRUCTURES
SAMPLE STORAGE		SN	An area reserved for the protection	BT3	HYDRAULIC STRUCTURES
RT	CORE HANDLING		of particular species of animals	RT	GEOTECHNOLOGY
RT	SAMPLE CONTAMINATION		during part or all of the year.		
RT	SAMPLES		Added in 1982	**SAND TRANSPORT**	
RT	SAMPLING	RT	MARINE PARKS	USE	**SEDIMENT TRANSPORT**
RT	STORAGE EFFECTS	RT	NATURE CONSERVATION		
RT	WATER SAMPLES	RT	RARE SPECIES	**SAND TRAPS**	
		RT	REFUGES	USE	**SEDIMENT TRAPS**
SAMPLERS		RT	RESOURCE CONSERVATION		
UF	sampling devices			**SAND WAVES**	
NT1	SEDIMENT SAMPLERS	**SAND**		UF	megaripples
NT2	CORERS	BT1	CLASTICS	UF	waves (sand)
NT3	FREE-FALL CORERS	BT2	SEDIMENTS	BT1	BED FORMS
NT3	GRAVITY CORERS	NT1	QUICKSANDS	BT2	SEDIMENTARY STRUCTURES
NT3	PISTON CORERS	RT	AGGREGATES	RT	DUNES
NT3	VIBRATORY CORERS	RT	ALLUVIAL DEPOSITS	RT	KEEL CLEARANCE
NT2	DREDGES (GEOLOGY)	RT	ARENACEOUS DEPOSITS	RT	TIDAL CURRENTS
NT2	DRILLS	RT	ARENITES	RT	TRANSVERSE BED FORMS
NT2	GRABS	RT	BEACH ACCRETION	RT	WAVE SLOPE
NT2	PORE WATER SAMPLERS	RT	BEACHES		
NT1	WATER SAMPLERS	RT	BERMS	**SANDSTONE**	
NT2	KNUDSEN SAMPLERS	RT	DUNES	BT1	CLASTICS
NT2	NANSEN BOTTLES	RT	EPIPSAMMON	BT2	SEDIMENTS
NT2	NISKIN SAMPLERS	RT	GRAVEL	NT1	OIL SANDS
RT	COLLECTING DEVICES	RT	MEIOBENTHOS	RT	ARENITES
RT	OCEANOGRAPHIC EQUIPMENT	RT	PSAMMON	RT	EOLIAN DEPOSITS
RT	SAMPLING	RT	SAND BARS	RT	EOLIAN TRANSPORT
		RT	SAND PATCHES	RT	GRAYWACKE
		RT	SAND RIBBONS	RT	SAND
		RT	SANDSTONE	RT	SEDIMENTARY ROCKS
		RT	SEDIMENT LOAD	RT	SILICEOUS ROCKS
		RT	SEDIMENT TEXTURE		

SANDY BEACHES
USE **BEACHES**

SANITARY ENGINEERING
BT1 ENGINEERING
RT HYGIENE
RT POLLUTION CONTROL
RT SEWAGE DISPOSAL
RT SEWAGE PONDS
RT SEWAGE TREATMENT
RT SLUDGE TREATMENT
RT WASTE DISPOSAL
RT WASTE TREATMENT
RT WASTE WATER
RT WASTEWATER TREATMENT
RT WATER FILTRATION
RT WATER POLLUTION TREATMENT
RT WATER PURIFICATION
RT WATER SUPPLY

SAPONINS
BT1 GLYCOSIDES
BT2 CARBOHYDRATES
BT3 ORGANIC COMPOUNDS

SAPONITE
BT1 CLAY MINERALS
BT2 SILICATE MINERALS
BT3 MINERALS

SAPROBIONTS
SN Organisms feeding on decaying
organic matters. Added in 1982
UF saprophagic organisms
NT1 SAPROPHYTES
NT1 SAPROZOITES
RT ORGANIC MATTER

SAPROPELITE
RT COAL
RT KEROGEN
RT OIL SHALE
RT SAPROPELS

SAPROPELS
SN Before 1982 search SAPROPEL
BT1 ORGANIC SEDIMENTS
BT2 BIOGENIC DEPOSITS
RT ANOXIC CONDITIONS
RT ANOXIC SEDIMENTS
RT DETRITUS
RT HYDROCARBONS
RT OOZES
RT PEAT
RT SAPROPELITE
RT STAGNANT WATER
RT SUSPENDED ORGANIC MATTER

SAPROPHAGIC ORGANISMS
USE **SAPROBIONTS**

SAPROPHYTES
SN Plants that obtain nourishment from
dead or decaying organic matter.
Added in 1980
BT1 SAPROBIONTS
RT BACTERIA
RT FOOD CHAINS
RT FUNGI
RT NUTRIENT CYCLES

SAPROPLANKTON
SN Plankton found on the surface of
stagnant water, developing on
decaying organic matter. Added in
1982
BT1 ZOOPLANKTON
BT2 PLANKTON
BT3 AQUATIC COMMUNITIES
RT ORGANIC MATTER

SAPROPLANKTON (cont'd)
RT STAGNANT WATER

SAPROZOIC ORGANISMS
USE **SAPROZOITES**

SAPROZOITES
SN Animals living on dead or decaying
organic matter. Added in 1982
UF saprozoic organisms
BT1 SAPROBIONTS
RT ORGANIC MATTER

SARCOMA
USE **TUMOURS**

SARDINE FISHERIES
USE **CLUPEOID FISHERIES**

SARDINELLA FISHERIES
USE **CLUPEOID FISHERIES**

SATELLITE-AIDED NAVIGATION
USE **SATELLITE NAVIGATION**

SATELLITE-AIDED SENSING
USE **SATELLITE SENSING**

SATELLITE ALTIMETRY
UF satellite-borne radar altimetry
BT1 ALTIMETRY
RT GEOID
RT HEIGHT
RT RADAR ALTIMETRY
RT SEA LEVEL MEASUREMENT
RT SURFACE TOPOGRAPHY
RT WAVE MEASUREMENT

SATELLITE-BORNE RADAR ALTIMETRY
USE **SATELLITE ALTIMETRY**

SATELLITE COMMUNICATION
BT1 COMMUNICATION SYSTEMS
RT COMMUNICATION SATELLITES
RT TELEMETRY

SATELLITE IMAGERY
USE **SATELLITE SENSING**

SATELLITE MOSAICS
SN Satellite-sensed images assembled
to form a continuous picture of
portions of the Earth's surface
UF satellite photographs
BT1 AUDIOVISUAL MATERIAL
BT2 DOCUMENTS
RT AERIAL PHOTOGRAPHS
RT INFRARED IMAGERY
RT MAPPING
RT MICROWAVE IMAGERY
RT SATELLITE PHOTOGRAPHY
RT SATELLITE SENSING

SATELLITE NAVIGATION
UF satellite position fixing
UF satellite-aided navigation
BT1 POSITION FIXING
RT NAVIGATIONAL SATELLITES

SATELLITE PHOTOGRAPHS
USE **SATELLITE MOSAICS**

SATELLITE PHOTOGRAPHY
UF visible and near-infrared imagery
BT1 AERIAL PHOTOGRAPHY
BT2 PHOTOGRAPHY
BT3 IMAGERY
BT4 REMOTE SENSING
RT CAMERAS
RT MULTISPECTRAL SCANNERS

SATELLITE PHOTOGRAPHY (cont'd)
RT SATELLITE MOSAICS
RT SATELLITE SENSING

SATELLITE POSITION FIXING
USE **SATELLITE NAVIGATION**

SATELLITE SENSING
UF remote satellite sensing
UF satellite imagery
UF satellite-aided sensing
BT1 GEOSENSING
RT ICE OBSERVATIONS
RT INFRARED IMAGERY
RT MICROWAVE IMAGERY
RT RADIO OCEANOGRAPHY
RT SATELLITE MOSAICS
RT SATELLITE PHOTOGRAPHY
RT SATELLITES
RT SCIENTIFIC SATELLITES
RT SEA STATE
RT WEATHER FORECASTING

SATELLITE-TRACKED BUOYS
USE **DRIFTING DATA BUOYS**

SATELLITES
UF artificial satellites
UF satellites (artificial)
BT1 VEHICLES
NT1 COMMUNICATION SATELLITES
NT1 NAVIGATIONAL SATELLITES
NT1 SCIENTIFIC SATELLITES
RT AERIAL SURVEYS
RT ASTRONOMY
RT ELECTRONIC EQUIPMENT
RT SATELLITE SENSING
RT SURVEYS

SATELLITES (ARTIFICIAL)
USE **SATELLITES**

SATURATED HYDROCARBONS
UF aliphatic hydrocarbons
UF alkanes
BT1 HYDROCARBONS
BT2 ORGANIC COMPOUNDS
NT1 ACYCLIC HYDROCARBONS
NT2 BUTANE
NT2 DODECANE
NT2 ETHANE
NT2 METHANE
NT2 PROPANE
NT1 ALICYCLIC HYDROCARBONS

SATURATION
UF saturation index
NT1 SUPERSATURATION
RT CONDENSATION
RT EVAPORATION
RT SATURATION DEPTH
RT SATURATION VAPOUR PRESSURE
RT SOLUBILITY
RT SOLUTIONS

SATURATION DEPTH
RT SATURATION
RT WATER DEPTH

SATURATION DIVING
BT1 DIVING
RT BREATHING MIXTURES
RT DECOMPRESSION
RT DIVING BELLS
RT DIVING SUITS
RT LOCKOUT SUBMERSIBLES
RT WORKING UNDERWATER

SATURATION INDEX
USE   **SATURATION**

SATURATION VAPOUR PRESSURE
BT1   VAPOUR PRESSURE
BT2   PRESSURE
BT3   PHYSICAL PROPERTIES
BT4   PROPERTIES
RT   CONDENSATION
RT   DEW POINT
RT   HUMIDITY
RT   RELATIVE HUMIDITY
RT   SATURATION
RT   WATER VAPOUR

SCAD FISHERIES
USE   **CARANGID FISHERIES**

SCALE FORMATION
USE   **SCALING**

SCALE MODELS
UF   laboratory models
UF   physical models
BT1   MODELS
NT1   HYDRAULIC MODELS
NT2   HARBOUR MODELS
NT1   SHIP MODELS
RT   AUDIOVISUAL MATERIAL
RT   FLUMES
RT   LABORATORY EQUIPMENT
RT   MATHEMATICAL MODELS
RT   WAVE TANKS

SCALE READING
BT1   AGE DETERMINATION
RT   GROWTH
RT   LIFE CYCLE
RT   SCALES

SCALES
UF   dermal denticles
UF   fish scales
BT1   EXOSKELETON
BT2   SKELETON
BT3   MUSCULOSKELETAL SYSTEM
RT   INTEGUMENTARY SYSTEM
RT   SCALE READING

SCALING
SN   Lime or other scale formation on
       structures and equipment
UF   scale formation
RT   CLEANING
RT   COATING MATERIALS
RT   FOULING
RT   MAINTENANCE

SCALLOP CULTURE
SN   Before 1982 search MOLLUSC CULTURE
BT1   MOLLUSC CULTURE
BT2   SHELLFISH CULTURE
BT3   AQUACULTURE
RT   AQUACULTURE DEVELOPMENT
RT   MARINE AQUACULTURE
RT   OFF-BOTTOM CULTURE

SCALLOP FISHERIES
SN   Added in 1982
UF   pecten fisheries
BT1   MOLLUSC FISHERIES
BT2   SHELLFISH FISHERIES
BT3   FISHERIES
RT   COASTAL FISHERIES
RT   MARINE FISHERIES

SCANDIUM
BT1   CHEMICAL ELEMENTS
RT   METALS
RT   SCANDIUM COMPOUNDS
RT   SCANDIUM ISOTOPES
RT   TRACE METALS
RT   TRANSITION ELEMENTS

SCANDIUM COMPOUNDS
RT   CHEMICAL COMPOUNDS
RT   SCANDIUM

SCANDIUM ISOTOPES
BT1   ISOTOPES
RT   SCANDIUM

SCANNING ELECTRON MICROSCOPY
USE   **ELECTRON MICROSCOPY**

SCARPS
USE   **ESCARPMENTS**

SCARS
USE   **LESIONS**

SCATTER DIAGRAMS
BT1   STATISTICAL TABLES
BT2   TABLES
BT3   DOCUMENTS
RT   REGRESSION ANALYSIS

SCATTERANCE METERS
BT1   LIGHT MEASURING INSTRUMENTS
BT2   MEASURING DEVICES
RT   LIGHT SCATTERING
RT   SCATTERING COEFFICIENT
RT   VOLUME SCATTERING FUNCTION

SCATTERING (LIGHT)
USE   **LIGHT SCATTERING**

SCATTERING (SOUND)
USE   **SOUND SCATTERING**

SCATTERING (WATER WAVES)
USE   **WAVE SCATTERING**

SCATTERING COEFFICIENT
UF   total scattering coefficient
BT1   OPTICAL PROPERTIES
BT2   PHYSICAL PROPERTIES
BT3   PROPERTIES
RT   LIGHT SCATTERING
RT   OPTICAL CLASSIFICATION
RT   SCATTERANCE METERS

SCATTERING LAYERS
UF   deep scattering layers
UF   sound scattering layers
BT1   DISCONTINUITY LAYERS
BT2   LAYERS
RT   ECHOSOUNDING
RT   SWIM BLADDER
RT   ZOOPLANKTON

SCATTERING LOSS
USE   **TRANSMISSION LOSS**

SCATTEROMETERS
BT1   MICROWAVE RADAR
BT2   RADAR
BT3   REMOTE SENSING EQUIPMENT
BT4   EQUIPMENT
RT   BACKSCATTER
RT   MEASURING DEVICES
RT   MICROWAVES
RT   RADAR IMAGERY
RT   REMOTE SENSING EQUIPMENT
RT   SYNTHETIC APERTURE RADAR

SCAVENGERS
SN   Animals feeding on dead animal
       material. Added in 1980
BT1   HETEROTROPHIC ORGANISMS
BT2   AQUATIC ORGANISMS
RT   FEEDING BEHAVIOUR

SCHISTS
BT1   METAMORPHIC ROCKS
BT2   ROCKS
NT1   GREENSCHISTS

SCHOLARSHIPS
USE   **FELLOWSHIPS**

SCHOOLING BEHAVIOUR
SN   Swarming, herding and flocking of
       any aquatic population
BT1   SOCIAL BEHAVIOUR
BT2   BEHAVIOUR
RT   FEEDING BEHAVIOUR
RT   PROTECTIVE BEHAVIOUR

SCHOOLS
USE   **EDUCATION ESTABLISHMENTS**

SCIENTIFIC LOGBOOKS
USE   **LOGBOOKS**

SCIENTIFIC PERSONNEL
SN   Before 1986 search also SCIENTISTS.
       Added in 1980
UF   research workers
UF   researchers
UF   scientific research workers
UF   scientific researchers
UF   scientists
BT1   PERSONNEL
NT1   BIOLOGISTS
NT2   ALGOLOGISTS
NT2   BOTANISTS
NT2   FISHERY BIOLOGISTS
NT2   GENETICISTS
NT2   MICROBIOLOGISTS
NT3   BACTERIOLOGISTS
NT3   MYCOLOGISTS
NT3   VIROLOGISTS
NT2   PHYSIOLOGISTS
NT3   ANIMAL PHYSIOLOGISTS
NT3   PLANT PHYSIOLOGISTS
NT2   TAXONOMISTS
NT2   ZOOLOGISTS
NT3   CARCINOLOGISTS
NT3   ENTOMOLOGISTS
NT3   ICHTHYOLOGISTS
NT3   MALACOLOGISTS
NT3   MAMMALOGISTS
NT4   CETOLOGISTS
NT3   ORNITHOLOGISTS
NT1   ECOLOGISTS
NT2   FRESHWATER ECOLOGISTS
NT2   MARINE ECOLOGISTS
NT1   ECONOMISTS
NT1   FRESHWATER SCIENTISTS
NT1   GEOLOGISTS
NT1   INFORMATION SCIENTISTS
NT1   MARINE SCIENTISTS
NT1   METEOROLOGISTS
NT1   STATISTICIANS
RT   BIOGRAPHIES
RT   CONSULTANTS
RT   DIRECTORIES
RT   EXPERIMENTAL RESEARCH
RT   EXPERTS
RT   FELLOWSHIPS
RT   FESTSCHRIFTEN
RT   HUMAN RESOURCES
RT   LABORATORIES
RT   OBITUARIES
RT   PERSONAL BIBLIOGRAPHIES

ASFIS Thesaurus

SCIENTIFIC PERSONNEL (cont'd)
RT   RESEARCH
RT   RESEARCH INSTITUTIONS
RT   RESEARCH PROGRAMMES
RT   TECHNICIANS

SCIENTIFIC RESEARCH
USE   **RESEARCH**

SCIENTIFIC RESEARCH WORKERS
USE   **SCIENTIFIC PERSONNEL**

SCIENTIFIC RESEARCHERS
USE   **SCIENTIFIC PERSONNEL**

SCIENTIFIC SATELLITES
UF   meteorological satellites
UF   oceanographic satellites
BT1   SATELLITES
BT2   VEHICLES
RT   GEOSENSING
RT   INSTRUMENT PLATFORMS
RT   SATELLITE SENSING

SCIENTISTS
USE   **SCIENTIFIC PERSONNEL**

SCOOPING GEAR
USE   **LIFT-NETS**

SCORPIONFISH FISHERIES
USE   **REDFISH FISHERIES**

SCOTTISH SEINES
USE   **BOAT SEINES**

SCOUR AND FILL
BT1   SEDIMENTARY STRUCTURES
RT   CURRENT SCOURING
RT   SCOURING

SCOUR HOLLOWS
BT1   BED FORMS
BT2   SEDIMENTARY STRUCTURES
RT   CURRENT SCOURING
RT   OBSTACLE MARKS
RT   TIDAL CURRENTS

SCOUR MARKS
BT1   CURRENT MARKS
BT2   BEDDING STRUCTURES
BT3   SEDIMENTARY STRUCTURES
RT   CURRENT SCOURING

SCOUR PROTECTION
BT1   PROTECTION
RT   ARTIFICIAL SEAWEED
RT   CURRENT SCOURING
RT   PILES
RT   PIPELINE PROTECTION
RT   PIPELINES
RT   SCOURING

SCOURING
SN   Use of a more specific term is recommended
BT1   EROSION
NT1   CURRENT SCOURING
NT1   ICEBERG SCOURING
NT1   WAVE SCOURING
RT   ARTIFICIAL SEAWEED
RT   BOTTOM CURRENTS
RT   BRIDGES
RT   DETERIORATION
RT   FAILURES
RT   FOUNDATIONS
RT   GEOTECHNOLOGY
RT   PIPELINE PROTECTION
RT   SCOUR AND FILL
RT   SCOUR PROTECTION

SCOURING (cont'd)
RT   WIND ABRASION

SCP
USE   **SINGLE CELL PROTEINS**

SCREENS
UF   fish screens
RT   ANADROMOUS MIGRATIONS
RT   AQUACULTURE EQUIPMENT
RT   FISHWAYS
RT   HYDRAULIC STRUCTURES

SCUBA DIVING
SN   Before 1982 search DIVING
UF   skin diving
BT1   DIVING
RT   BREATHING APPARATUS
RT   BREATHING MIXTURES
RT   RECREATION

SEA-AIR EXCHANGES
USE   **AIR-WATER EXCHANGES**

SEA BED
USE   **OCEAN FLOOR**

SEA BLOOMS
USE   **ALGAL BLOOMS**

SEA BREEZES
SN   Blowing from sea to land
UF   lake breezes
BT1   BREEZES
BT2   LOCAL WINDS
BT3   WINDS
BT4   ATMOSPHERIC MOTION
RT   DAYTIME
RT   LAND AND SEA BREEZES
RT   LAND BREEZES
RT   MONSOONS

SEA CAVES
USE   **CAVES**

SEA CLUTTER
USE   **SURFACE CLUTTER**

SEA COAST
USE   **COASTS**

SEA CUCUMBER FISHERIES
USE   **ECHINODERM FISHERIES**

SEA FANS
USE   **DEEP-SEA FANS**

SEA FARMING
USE   **MARINE AQUACULTURE**

SEA FISHERIES
USE   **MARINE FISHERIES**

SEA FLOOR
USE   **OCEAN FLOOR**

SEA FLOOR TOPOGRAPHY
USE   **BOTTOM TOPOGRAPHY**

SEA FOG
USE   **FOG**

SEA GRASS
SN   Species of embryophytes living in marine coastal waters
UF   seagrass
RT   BOTANICAL RESOURCES
RT   HARVESTING
RT   PLANT POPULATIONS
RT   SEAWEEDS

SEA GRASS (cont'd)
RT   WEEDS

SEA ICE
BT1   ICE
RT   BRINES
RT   FAST ICE
RT   FLOATING ICE
RT   ICE BREAKING
RT   ICE FIELDS
RT   ICE PROPERTIES
RT   ICE RAFTING
RT   ICE-WATER INTERFACE
RT   MICROWAVE IMAGERY
RT   OCEAN-ICE-ATMOSPHERE SYSTEM
RT   PHYSICAL OCEANOGRAPHY
RT   SEA WATER

SEA LAW
USE   **LAW OF THE SEA**

SEA LEVEL
SN   Height or level of the sea surface
UF   half-tide level
UF   sea level data
UF   sea level records
UF   still water level
NT1   ISOSTATIC SEA LEVEL
NT1   MEAN SEA LEVEL
NT1   STERIC SEA LEVEL
RT   DATUM LEVELS
RT   EUSTATIC CHANGES
RT   HYPSOMETRY
RT   LEVELS
RT   POLDERS
RT   QUATERNARY
RT   SEA LEVEL CHANGES
RT   SEA LEVEL MEASUREMENT
RT   SEA LEVEL PRESSURE
RT   SEA LEVEL VARIATIONS
RT   SOUTHERN OSCILLATION
RT   SURFACE SLOPE
RT   SURFACE TOPOGRAPHY
RT   TIDES
RT   WATER LEVELS
RT   WAVE SETDOWN
RT   WAVE SETUP

SEA LEVEL CHANGES
BT1   LONG-TERM CHANGES
BT2   TEMPORAL VARIATIONS
RT   ATOLLS
RT   CLIMATIC CHANGES
RT   COAST DEFENCES
RT   ISOSTASY
RT   MEAN SEA LEVEL
RT   PALAEOSHORELINES
RT   RAISED BEACHES
RT   REGRESSIONS
RT   SEA LEVEL
RT   SEA LEVEL MEASUREMENT
RT   SEA LEVEL VARIATIONS
RT   SOLAR-TERRESTRIAL ACTIVITY
RT   STRANDLINES
RT   TRANSGRESSIONS

SEA LEVEL DATA
USE   **SEA LEVEL**

SEA LEVEL MEASUREMENT
SN   Before 1984 search also SEA LEVEL MEASURING
BT1   WATER LEVEL MEASUREMENT
BT2   MEASUREMENT
RT   BENCH MARKS
RT   SATELLITE ALTIMETRY
RT   SEA LEVEL
RT   SEA LEVEL CHANGES
RT   SEA LEVEL VARIATIONS
RT   SURFACE TOPOGRAPHY

SEA LEVEL MEASUREMENT (cont'd)
RT   TIDE GAUGES
RT   SEA LEVEL VARIATIONS

SEA LEVEL PRESSURE
BT1   ATMOSPHERIC PRESSURE
BT2   PRESSURE
BT3   PHYSICAL PROPERTIES
BT4   PROPERTIES
RT   ANTICYCLONES
RT   BAROMETERS
RT   CLIMATE
RT   CLIMATOLOGY
RT   HIGH PRESSURE SYSTEMS
RT   ISOBARS
RT   ISOSTATIC SEA LEVEL
RT   METEOROLOGICAL CHARTS
RT   METEOROLOGICAL OBSERVATIONS
RT   METEOROLOGY
RT   SEA LEVEL
RT   SEA LEVEL VARIATIONS
RT   SOUTHERN OSCILLATION
RT   STORM SURGES
RT   WEATHER
RT   WINDS

SEA LEVEL RECORDS
USE   **SEA LEVEL**

SEA LEVEL SLOPE
USE   **SURFACE SLOPE**

SEA LEVEL VARIATIONS
RT   BEACH MORPHOLOGY
RT   COAST DEFENCES
RT   SEA LEVEL
RT   SEA LEVEL CHANGES
RT   SEA LEVEL MEASUREMENT
RT   SEA LEVEL MEASURING
RT   SEA LEVEL PRESSURE
RT   SEICHES
RT   STERIC SEA LEVEL
RT   TSUNAMIS
RT   WAVE SETDOWN
RT   WAVE SETUP

SEA MIST
USE   **FOG**

SEA SALT NUCLEI
USE   **SALT PARTICLES**

SEA SICKNESS
UF   motion sickness
BT1   HUMAN DISEASES
BT2   DISEASES
RT   MEDICINE
RT   SHIP MOTION

SEA SMOKE
USE   **FOG**

SEA SNAIL FISHERIES
USE   **GASTROPOD FISHERIES**

SEA SPRAY
USE   **SPRAY**

SEA STATE
RT   ENVIRONMENTAL CONDITIONS
RT   MICROWAVE IMAGERY
RT   RADAR IMAGERY
RT   SATELLITE SENSING
RT   SEA STATE SCALES
RT   SURFACE WATER WAVES
RT   WAVE CLIMATE
RT   WAVE PREDICTING
RT   WEATHER

SEA STATE SCALES
UF   douglas scale
RT   BEAUFORT SCALE
RT   SEA STATE
RT   SURFACE WATER WAVES

SEA STATES
USE   **COASTAL STATES**

SEA SURFACE
RT   AIR-SEA INTERACTION
RT   AIR-WATER EXCHANGES
RT   AIR-WATER INTERFACE
RT   FOAMS
RT   SURFACE CHEMISTRY
RT   SURFACE FILMS
RT   SURFACE MICROLAYER
RT   SURFACE PROPERTIES
RT   SURFACE RADIATION TEMPERATURE
RT   SURFACE SALINITY
RT   SURFACE SLOPE
RT   SURFACE TEMPERATURE
RT   SURFACE TOPOGRAPHY
RT   SURFACE WATER WAVES
RT   SURFACES

SEA SURFACE CLUTTER
USE   **SURFACE CLUTTER**

SEA SURFACE FOLLOWERS
USE   **WAVE FOLLOWERS**

SEA SURFACE SALINITY
USE   **SURFACE SALINITY**

SEA SURFACE SLOPE
USE   **SURFACE SLOPE**

SEA SURFACE TEMPERATURE
USE   **SURFACE TEMPERATURE**

SEA SURFACE TOPOGRAPHY
USE   **SURFACE TOPOGRAPHY**

SEA URCHIN FISHERIES
USE   **ECHINODERM FISHERIES**

SEA WALLS
BT1   COAST DEFENCES
BT2   COASTAL STRUCTURES
BT3   HYDRAULIC STRUCTURES
RT   BREAKWATERS
RT   FLOODS
RT   ICE LOADS
RT   WAVE RUNUP

SEA WATER
UF   marine water
UF   ocean water
UF   seawater
BT1   WATER
NT1   ARTIFICIAL SEAWATER
NT1   DENSE WATER
NT1   FOSSIL SEA WATER
NT1   STANDARD SEA WATER
RT   AGE OF SEAWATER
RT   CONSERVATIVE PROPERTIES
RT   DESALINATION
RT   ESTUARIES
RT   FREEZING POINT
RT   GEOCHEMISTRY
RT   HYDROLOGIC CYCLE
RT   MARINE AQUACULTURE
RT   MARINE ENVIRONMENT
RT   MARINE POLLUTION
RT   NON-CONSERVATIVE PROPERTIES
RT   OCEANOGRAPHY
RT   RELATIVE DENSITY
RT   SALINITY
RT   SALT-WEDGE ESTUARIES

SEA WATER (cont'd)
RT   SEA ICE
RT   SEAWATER EVOLUTION
RT   T/S DIAGRAMS
RT   WATER MASSES
RT   WATER TYPES

SEA WATER CONVERSION
USE   **DESALINATION**

SEABED
USE   **OCEAN FLOOR**

SEABED ACOUSTIC POSITION FIXING
USE   **NAVIGATION UNDERWATER**

SEABED CONVENTIONS
UF   seabed treaties
BT1   INTERNATIONAL AGREEMENTS
BT2   LEGISLATION
RT   INTERNATIONAL LAW
RT   INTERNATIONAL ORGANIZATIONS
RT   LAW OF THE SEA
RT   OCEAN POLICY
RT   UNDERSEA WARFARE

SEABED DEPOSITS
BT1   MINERAL DEPOSITS
BT2   MINERAL RESOURCES
BT3   NATURAL RESOURCES
BT4   RESOURCES
NT1   AGGREGATES
NT1   FERROMANGANESE NODULES
NT1   PHOSPHORITE NODULES
NT1   PLACERS
NT2   DIAMONDS
RT   DEEP-SEA MINING
RT   METALLIFEROUS SEDIMENTS
RT   MINING
RT   NODULES
RT   NONRENEWABLE RESOURCES
RT   SULPHIDE DEPOSITS

SEABED DRIFTERS
BT1   SUBSURFACE DRIFTERS
BT2   DRIFTERS
BT3   CURRENT MEASURING EQUIPMENT
BT4   FLOW MEASURING EQUIPMENT
RT   BOTTOM CURRENTS
RT   CURRENT MEASUREMENT

SEABED ENGINEERING
USE   **OFFSHORE ENGINEERING**

SEABED FARMING
USE   **BOTTOM CULTURE**

SEABED FOUNDATIONS
USE   **FOUNDATIONS**

SEABED HABITATS
USE   **UNDERWATER HABITATS**

SEABED PROTECTION
BT1   PROTECTION
RT   ARTIFICIAL SEAWEED

SEABED SAMPLERS
USE   **SEDIMENT SAMPLERS**

SEABED SAMPLING
USE   **SEDIMENT SAMPLING**

SEABED SAMPLING
USE   **SEAFLOOR SAMPLING**

ASFIS Thesaurus

SEABED TREATIES
USE   **SEABED CONVENTIONS**

SEABED VEHICLES
UF	bottom crawlers
UF	crawlers
BT1	UNMANNED VEHICLES
BT2	UNDERWATER VEHICLES
BT3	VEHICLES
RT	OCEAN FLOOR
RT	SEAFLOOR SAMPLING
RT	SEDIMENT SAMPLING
RT	SELF-PROPELLED VEHICLES
RT	SITE SURVEYS
RT	TETHERED VEHICLES

SEABIGHTS
BT1	SUBMARINE FEATURES
BT2	TOPOGRAPHIC FEATURES
RT	RELIEF FORMS

SEABREAM FISHERIES
USE   **PERCOID FISHERIES**

SEACHANNELS
BT1	BED FORMS
BT2	SEDIMENTARY STRUCTURES
RT	ABYSSAL PLAINS
RT	BOTTOM EROSION
RT	CHANNELS
RT	DEEP-SEA FANS
RT	EROSION FEATURES
RT	LEVEES
RT	MICROTOPOGRAPHY
RT	RELIEF FORMS

SEACOAST
USE   **COASTS**

SEAFLOOR MAPPING
BT1	MAPPING
BT2	GRAPHIC METHODS
RT	BATHYMETRIC CHARTS
RT	BATHYMETRY
RT	ECHOSOUNDING
RT	GEOLOGICAL SURVEYS
RT	MULTIBEAM SONAR
RT	SEDIMENT SAMPLING
RT	SIDE SCAN SONAR
RT	SONOGRAPHS
RT	SOUNDINGS
RT	SURVEYING
RT	SWATHS
RT	UNDERWATER EXPLORATION

SEAFLOOR SAMPLING
UF	bottom sampling
UF	seabed sampling
BT1	SAMPLING
NT1	SEDIMENT SAMPLING
NT2	CORING
RT	BENTHOS
RT	BENTHOS COLLECTING DEVICES
RT	CORES
RT	CORING
RT	DREDGES (GEOLOGY)
RT	DRILLING
RT	GEOLOGICAL SURVEYS
RT	GEOTECHNICAL DATA
RT	OCEAN FLOOR
RT	PENETROMETERS
RT	SEABED VEHICLES
RT	SEDIMENT POLLUTION
RT	SEDIMENT SAMPLERS
RT	SEDIMENT SAMPLES
RT	SURVEYING UNDERWATER

SEAFLOOR SPREADING
UF	spreading rate
RT	CONTINENTAL DRIFT
RT	FRACTURE ZONES
RT	HEAT FLOW
RT	MAGNETIC ANOMALIES
RT	MANTLE CONVECTION
RT	MEDIAN VALLEYS
RT	MID-OCEAN RIDGES
RT	MOHO
RT	PALAEOMAGNETISM
RT	PLATE TECTONICS
RT	RIFTING
RT	SPREADING CENTRES

SEAFOOD
SN	Added in 1980
BT1	HUMAN FOOD
RT	COMMERCIAL SPECIES
RT	MARINE AQUACULTURE
RT	MARINE CRUSTACEANS
RT	MARINE FISH
RT	MARINE MOLLUSCS
RT	MARINE ORGANISMS
RT	MARINE RESOURCES
RT	PROCESSED FISHERY PRODUCTS
RT	SEAWEEDS
RT	SHELLFISH

SEAFOOD PRODUCTS
USE   **FISHERY PRODUCTS**

SEAGRASS
USE   **SEA GRASS**

SEAGRASS RESOURCES
USE   **BOTANICAL RESOURCES**

SEAKEEPING
USE   **SHIP MOTION**

SEAKNOLLS
UF	knolls (submarine)
BT1	SUBMARINE FEATURES
BT2	TOPOGRAPHIC FEATURES
RT	RELIEF FORMS

SEALING
USE   **SEALS (STOPPERS)**

SEALS (STOPPERS)
UF	oil seals
UF	sealing
RT	LEAKS

SEAMANSHIP
RT	DEPLOYMENT
RT	EDUCATION
RT	GEAR HANDLING
RT	NAVIGATION
RT	RECOVERY
RT	SHIP HANDLING
RT	SHIP MOTION
RT	SHIP STABILITY
RT	STATION KEEPING
RT	TRAINING AIDS

SEAMOATS
BT1	BED FORMS
BT2	SEDIMENTARY STRUCTURES
RT	BOTTOM CURRENTS
RT	BOTTOM EROSION
RT	EROSION FEATURES
RT	OCEANIC ISLANDS
RT	RELIEF FORMS
RT	SEAMOUNTS

SEAMOUNT CHAINS
BT1	SUBMARINE FEATURES
BT2	TOPOGRAPHIC FEATURES
RT	HOT SPOTS
RT	RELIEF FORMS
RT	SEAMOUNTS
RT	SUBMARINE VOLCANOES

SEAMOUNTS
BT1	SUBMARINE FEATURES
BT2	TOPOGRAPHIC FEATURES
NT1	GUYOTS
RT	ARCHIPELAGIC APRONS
RT	MOUNTAINS
RT	RELIEF FORMS
RT	SEAMOATS
RT	SEAMOUNT CHAINS

SEAQUAKES
RT	EARTHQUAKES

SEARCH AND RESCUE
UF	rescue
RT	ACCIDENTS
RT	DIVING
RT	EMERGENCY VESSELS
RT	LOCATING
RT	MEDICINE
RT	SALVAGING
RT	SUBMERSIBLES
RT	SURVIVAL AT SEA
RT	UNDERWATER OBJECT LOCATION

SEAS
USE   **OCEANS**

SEASHELLS
USE   **SHELLS**

SEASON REGULATIONS
UF	closed seasons
UF	fishing seasons
BT1	FISHERY REGULATIONS
BT2	LEGISLATION

SEASONAL CHANGES
USE   **SEASONAL VARIATIONS**

SEASONAL DISTRIBUTION
SN	Descriptor to be used only as a qualifier. Before 1982 search TEMPORAL DISTRIBUTION
BT1	TEMPORAL DISTRIBUTION
BT2	DISTRIBUTION
RT	MAPS
RT	MIGRATIONS
RT	SEASONAL VARIATIONS
RT	SEASONALITY

SEASONAL THERMOCLINE
BT1	THERMOCLINE
BT2	DISCONTINUITY LAYERS
BT3	LAYERS
RT	METALIMNION
RT	SEASONAL VARIATIONS

SEASONAL THERMOCLINE (LAKES)
USE   **METALIMNION**

SEASONAL VARIATIONS
SN	Changes between successive seasons. Used only as a qualifier
UF	seasonal changes
UF	within-year variations
BT1	PERIODIC VARIATIONS
BT2	TEMPORAL VARIATIONS
RT	ANNUAL
RT	ANNUAL VARIATIONS
RT	HORIZONTAL DISTRIBUTION
RT	MIGRATIONS

SEASONAL VARIATIONS (cont'd)
RT	PHENOLOGY
RT	REGIONAL VARIATIONS
RT	SEASONAL DISTRIBUTION
RT	SEASONAL THERMOCLINE
RT	SEASONALITY
RT	SEASONS
RT	SWAMP FISHERIES
RT	VERTICAL DISTRIBUTION

SEASONALITY
SN	Before 1982 search also SEASONAL VARIATIONS
BT1	PERIODICITY
RT	MIGRATIONS
RT	MONSOONS
RT	SEASONAL DISTRIBUTION
RT	SEASONAL VARIATIONS
RT	SEASONS

SEASONS
SN	Use of a more specific term is recommended. Added in 1980
NT1	AUTUMN
NT1	COLD SEASON
NT1	DRY SEASON
NT1	RAINY SEASON
NT1	SPRING
NT1	SUMMER
NT1	WINTER
RT	CLIMATE
RT	CLIMATIC ZONES
RT	CLIMATOLOGY
RT	HYDROCLIMATE
RT	SEASONAL VARIATIONS
RT	SEASONALITY
RT	SPAWNING SEASONS

SEAWALL WRIGHT EFFECT
USE	**GENETIC DRIFT**

SEAWATER
USE	**SEA WATER**

SEAWATER CONVERSION
USE	**DESALINATION**

SEAWATER EVOLUTION
UF	evolution (seawater)
UF	history of sea water
RT	ATMOSPHERE EVOLUTION
RT	EARTH
RT	GEOCHEMISTRY
RT	SEA WATER

SEAWEED (ARTIFICIAL)
USE	**ARTIFICIAL SEAWEED**

SEAWEED CULTURE
SN	Methods and techniques for culture and harvesting of seaweeds
UF	seaweed farming
BT1	AQUACULTURE
RT	BRACKISHWATER AQUACULTURE
RT	CULTURE TANKS
RT	CULTURES
RT	ENERGY RESOURCES
RT	FERTILIZERS
RT	MARINE AQUACULTURE
RT	OFF-BOTTOM CULTURE
RT	PLANT CULTURE
RT	SEAWEED STATISTICS
RT	SEAWEEDS
RT	SEED COLLECTION
RT	SPORES

SEAWEED FARMING
USE	**SEAWEED CULTURE**

SEAWEED HARVESTING
SN	Added in 1982
BT1	MARINE FISHERIES
BT2	FISHERIES
RT	HARVESTING MACHINES
RT	SEAWEED PROCESSING
RT	SEAWEED PRODUCTS
RT	SEAWEED STATISTICS
RT	SEAWEEDS

SEAWEED MEAL
USE	**ALGINATES**

SEAWEED PROCESSING
SN	Processing of marine plants and marine plant products
BT1	FISHERY INDUSTRY
BT2	INDUSTRIES
RT	SEAWEED HARVESTING
RT	SEAWEED PRODUCTS
RT	SEAWEEDS

SEAWEED PRODUCTS
BT1	PROCESSED FISHERY PRODUCTS
BT2	FISHERY PRODUCTS
BT3	PRODUCTS
NT1	AGAR
NT1	ALGINATES
NT1	CARRAGEENINS
RT	BOTANICAL RESOURCES
RT	FEED
RT	HUMAN FOOD
RT	KELPS
RT	LIVING RESOURCES
RT	SEAWEED HARVESTING
RT	SEAWEED PROCESSING
RT	SEAWEEDS

SEAWEED RESOURCES
USE	**BOTANICAL RESOURCES**

SEAWEED STATISTICS
SN	Tabulation of harvested macro algae from natural beds or artificial culture
BT1	CATCH STATISTICS
BT2	FISHERY STATISTICS
RT	AQUACULTURE STATISTICS
RT	BOTANICAL RESOURCES
RT	SEAWEED CULTURE
RT	SEAWEED HARVESTING
RT	SEAWEEDS

SEAWEEDS
SN	Any macro-algae of marine environment, mainly species of coastal region
BT1	WEEDS
RT	ALGOLOGISTS
RT	ALGOLOGY
RT	ARTIFICIAL SEAWEED
RT	BOTANICAL RESOURCES
RT	COMMERCIAL SPECIES
RT	FISHERY RESOURCES
RT	HARVESTING
RT	HOLDFASTS
RT	KELPS
RT	PLANT UTILIZATION
RT	SEA GRASS
RT	SEAFOOD
RT	SEAWEED CULTURE
RT	SEAWEED HARVESTING
RT	SEAWEED PROCESSING
RT	SEAWEED PRODUCTS
RT	SEAWEED STATISTICS
RT	TERPENES

SECCHI DISCS
BT1	LIGHT MEASURING INSTRUMENTS
BT2	MEASURING DEVICES
RT	EXTINCTION COEFFICIENT
RT	LIGHT PENETRATION
RT	VISIBILITY UNDERWATER

SECONDARY PRODUCTION
BT1	BIOLOGICAL PRODUCTION
RT	CARNIVORES
RT	FOOD CHAINS
RT	HERBIVORES
RT	PREDATORS
RT	PRIMARY PRODUCTION
RT	ZOOPLANKTON

SECONDARY SEDIMENTARY STRUCTURES
USE	**SEDIMENTARY STRUCTURES**

SECONDARY SEX CHARACTERISTICS
USE	**SECONDARY SEXUAL CHARACTERS**

SECONDARY SEXUAL CHARACTERS
SN	Added in 1980
UF	secondary sex characteristics
BT1	SEX CHARACTERS
RT	SEX HORMONES
RT	SEXUAL DIMORPHISM
RT	TAXONOMY

SECONDARY WAVES
USE	**S-WAVES**

SECRETION
NT1	NEUROSECRETION
RT	BYSSUS
RT	EXCRETION
RT	GLANDS
RT	HORMONES
RT	SECRETORY ORGANS
RT	SECRETORY PRODUCTS

SECRETORY ORGANS
NT1	GLANDS
NT2	DIGESTIVE GLANDS
NT3	HEPATOPANCREAS
NT3	LIVER
NT3	PANCREAS
NT2	ENDOCRINE GLANDS
NT3	ADRENAL GLANDS
NT3	PITUITARY GLAND
NT3	THYMUS
NT3	THYROID
NT2	EXOCRINE GLANDS
RT	ANATOMY
RT	MUCUS
RT	SECRETION
RT	SECRETORY PRODUCTS
RT	VENOM APPARATUS

SECRETORY PRODUCTS
NT1	HORMONES
NT2	ECDYSONS
NT2	INSULIN
NT2	NEUROTRANSMITTERS
NT2	PHEROMONES
NT2	PHYTOHORMONES
NT2	SEX HORMONES
NT1	MUCUS
RT	GLANDS
RT	SECRETION
RT	SECRETORY ORGANS
RT	SEMEN

SECULAR FLUCTUATIONS
USE	**LONG-TERM CHANGES**

SECURITY		
SN	Use for national defence, and for protective measures for drilling platforms, fishing fleets etc. against terrorism and sabotage	
UF	defence	
NT1	UNDERSEA WARFARE	
RT	ARTIFICIAL HARBOURS	
RT	DEFENCE CRAFT	
RT	FISHERY PROTECTION	
RT	MILITARY OPERATIONS	
RT	NAVAL BASES	
RT	PROTECTION VESSELS	

SEDENTARY ORGANISMS
USE **SESSILE SPECIES**

SEDENTARY RESOURCES
USE **SEDENTARY SPECIES**

SEDENTARY SPECIES
SN	Added in 1980
UF	sedentary resources
BT1	SPECIES
BT2	TAXA
RT	COASTAL STATES
RT	CONTINENTAL SHELVES
RT	FISHING RIGHTS
RT	LIVING RESOURCES
RT	MIGRATORY SPECIES
RT	OCEAN FLOOR
RT	POLYPS
RT	SESSILE SPECIES

SEDIMENT ANALYSIS
SN	Analysis of sediments for determination of organic and inorganic components including minerals
NT1	CORE ANALYSIS
RT	ANALYSIS
RT	ANALYTICAL TECHNIQUES
RT	CHEMICAL ANALYSIS
RT	COMPOSITION
RT	GEOCHEMISTRY
RT	GRAVIMETRIC TECHNIQUES
RT	HYDROCARBON ANALYSIS
RT	PERMEABILITY
RT	POLLUTION DETECTION
RT	PORE WATER SAMPLERS
RT	POROSITY
RT	SEDIMENT CHEMISTRY
RT	SEDIMENT COMPOSITION
RT	SEDIMENT DENSITY
RT	SEDIMENT POLLUTION
RT	SEDIMENT PROPERTIES
RT	SEDIMENT SAMPLERS
RT	SEDIMENT SAMPLES
RT	SEDIMENT STRUCTURE
RT	SEDIMENT TEXTURE
RT	SEDIMENTS
RT	WATER CONTENT

SEDIMENT CHEMISTRY
BT1	GEOCHEMISTRY
BT2	CHEMISTRY
RT	ATMOSPHERE EVOLUTION
RT	BIOGEOCHEMISTRY
RT	CHEMICAL PROPERTIES
RT	EARTH HISTORY
RT	GEOCHEMICAL CYCLE
RT	GEOLOGY
RT	GEOPHYSICS
RT	HYDROLOGY
RT	LEACHING
RT	MINERALOGY
RT	PORE WATER
RT	RADIOMETRIC DATING
RT	SEDIMENT ANALYSIS
RT	SEDIMENT COMPOSITION

SEDIMENT CHEMISTRY (cont'd)
RT	SULPHATE REDUCTION
RT	TRACE ELEMENTS
RT	WEATHERING

SEDIMENT COLLECTIONS
SN	Collections of sediment samples obtained mainly by coring
BT1	COLLECTIONS
RT	CORING
RT	SEDIMENT SAMPLING
RT	SEDIMENTS

SEDIMENT COMPOSITION
BT1	COMPOSITION
RT	SEDIMENT ANALYSIS
RT	SEDIMENT CHEMISTRY
RT	SEDIMENT TEXTURE

SEDIMENT DENSITY
UF	rock density
BT1	DENSITY
BT2	PHYSICAL PROPERTIES
BT3	PROPERTIES
NT1	WET BULK DENSITY
RT	DENSITY MEASUREMENT
RT	SEDIMENT ANALYSIS
RT	SEDIMENT PROPERTIES
RT	SEDIMENTS

SEDIMENT DEPOSITION
USE **SEDIMENTATION**

SEDIMENT DISTRIBUTION
SN	Geographic distribution of bottom sediments
BT1	DISTRIBUTION
RT	BOTTOM TOPOGRAPHY
RT	GEOGRAPHICAL DISTRIBUTION
RT	GEOLOGICAL MAPS
RT	ISOPACH MAPS
RT	SEDIMENTS

SEDIMENT DRIFTS
UF	sediment ridges
BT1	BED FORMS
BT2	SEDIMENTARY STRUCTURES
RT	BOTTOM CURRENTS
RT	DEPOSITION FEATURES
RT	SOIL MECHANICS

SEDIMENT DYNAMICS
BT1	DYNAMICS
BT2	MECHANICS
BT3	PHYSICS
RT	BOTTOM STRESS
RT	CHANNEL FLOW
RT	PARTICLE MOTION
RT	SEDIMENT MOVEMENT
RT	SEDIMENT STABILITY
RT	SEDIMENT TRANSPORT
RT	SOIL MECHANICS

SEDIMENT FLOW
USE **SEDIMENT GRAVITY FLOWS**

SEDIMENT GRAVITY FLOWS
UF	sediment flow
BT1	SEDIMENT MOVEMENT
NT1	FLUIDIZED SEDIMENT FLOW
NT1	GRAIN FLOW
NT1	LIQUEFIED SEDIMENT FLOW
NT1	TURBIDITY CURRENTS

SEDIMENT LOAD
NT1	BED LOAD
NT1	SUSPENDED LOAD
RT	CLAYS
RT	GRAVEL
RT	SAND

SEDIMENT LOAD (cont'd)
RT	SEDIMENT TRANSPORT

SEDIMENT MIXING
UF	mixing (sediments)
NT1	BIOTURBATION
NT1	GAS TURBATION
RT	MIXING PROCESSES
RT	SEDIMENT SORTING
RT	SEDIMENTS

SEDIMENT MOVEMENT
NT1	MASS MOVEMENT
NT2	SLIDES
NT3	LANDSLIDES
NT1	SEDIMENT GRAVITY FLOWS
NT2	FLUIDIZED SEDIMENT FLOW
NT2	GRAIN FLOW
NT2	LIQUEFIED SEDIMENT FLOW
NT2	TURBIDITY CURRENTS
RT	MOTION
RT	PARTICLE MOTION
RT	SEDIMENT DYNAMICS
RT	SEDIMENT NOISE
RT	SEDIMENT TRANSPORT
RT	SEDIMENTS

SEDIMENT NOISE
SN	Noise created by movement of sand and shingle due to currents and waves
BT1	AMBIENT NOISE
BT2	NOISE (SOUND)
RT	SEDIMENT MOVEMENT
RT	SEDIMENTS

SEDIMENT PARTICLE MOTION
USE **PARTICLE MOTION**

SEDIMENT PERMEABILITY
USE **PERMEABILITY**

SEDIMENT POLLUTION
SN	Pollution of sediments
UF	pollution (sediment)
BT1	POLLUTION
RT	CHEMICAL POLLUTION
RT	GROUNDWATER POLLUTION
RT	HEAVY METALS
RT	OIL POLLUTION
RT	SEAFLOOR SAMPLING
RT	SEDIMENT ANALYSIS
RT	SEDIMENT SAMPLING
RT	SEDIMENT-WATER INTERFACE

SEDIMENT PROPERTIES
UF	geotechnical properties
UF	rock properties
UF	soil properties
BT1	PROPERTIES
NT1	GRAIN PROPERTIES
NT1	SEDIMENT STABILITY
NT1	SEDIMENT STRUCTURE
NT1	SEDIMENT TEXTURE
RT	ACOUSTIC DATA
RT	ACOUSTIC IMPEDANCE
RT	BEARING CAPACITY
RT	COMPRESSIONAL WAVE VELOCITIES
RT	ELECTRICAL RESISTIVITY
RT	GAS HYDRATES
RT	GEOTECHNICAL DATA
RT	GRAIN SIZE
RT	PENETRATION DEPTH
RT	PERMEABILITY
RT	PHYSICAL PROPERTIES
RT	PORE PRESSURE
RT	POROSITY
RT	SEDIMENT ANALYSIS
RT	SEDIMENT DENSITY
RT	SEDIMENT TEMPERATURE
RT	SHEAR STRENGTH

SEDIMENT PROPERTIES (cont'd)
RT   SHEAR WAVE VELOCITIES
RT   SOIL MECHANICS
RT   SOUND VELOCITY
RT   THERMAL CONDUCTIVITY
RT   THERMAL DIFFUSIVITY
RT   WATER CONTENT

SEDIMENT RIDGES
USE   **SEDIMENT DRIFTS**

SEDIMENT SAMPLERS
UF   seabed samplers
BT1   SAMPLERS
NT1   CORERS
NT2   FREE-FALL CORERS
NT2   GRAVITY CORERS
NT2   PISTON CORERS
NT2   VIBRATORY CORERS
NT1   DREDGES (GEOLOGY)
NT1   DRILLS
NT1   GRABS
NT1   PORE WATER SAMPLERS
RT   GEOLOGICAL EQUIPMENT
RT   OCEANOGRAPHIC EQUIPMENT
RT   SEAFLOOR SAMPLING
RT   SEDIMENT ANALYSIS
RT   SEDIMENT SAMPLES
RT   SEDIMENT SAMPLING
RT   SEDIMENT TRAPS

SEDIMENT SAMPLES
UF   rock samples
BT1   GEOLOGICAL SAMPLES
BT2   SAMPLES
NT1   CORES
NT1   DREDGED SAMPLES
RT   GEOLOGICAL COLLECTIONS
RT   GEOLOGICAL DATA
RT   OCEANOGRAPHIC EQUIPMENT
RT   SEAFLOOR SAMPLING
RT   SEDIMENT ANALYSIS
RT   SEDIMENT SAMPLERS
RT   SEDIMENT SAMPLING
RT   STORAGE
RT   STORAGE CONDITIONS
RT   STORAGE EFFECTS

SEDIMENT SAMPLING
UF   rock sampling
UF   seabed sampling
UF   soil sampling
BT1   SEAFLOOR SAMPLING
BT2   SAMPLING
NT1   CORING
RT   CORE HANDLING
RT   CORERS
RT   CORES
RT   DRILLING
RT   GEOTECHNICAL DATA
RT   MINERAL EXPLORATION
RT   OCEANOGRAPHIC EQUIPMENT
RT   PENETROMETERS
RT   SEABED VEHICLES
RT   SEAFLOOR MAPPING
RT   SEDIMENT COLLECTIONS
RT   SEDIMENT POLLUTION
RT   SEDIMENT SAMPLERS
RT   SEDIMENT SAMPLES
RT   SURVEYING UNDERWATER

SEDIMENT SIZE
USE   **GRAIN SIZE**

SEDIMENT SORTING
NT1   WINNOWING
RT   GRAIN SIZE
RT   SEDIMENT MIXING
RT   SEDIMENT TRANSPORT
RT   SEDIMENTS

SEDIMENT SOURCE REGION
USE   **PROVENANCE**

SEDIMENT STABILITY
BT1   SEDIMENT PROPERTIES
BT2   PROPERTIES
RT   GEOLOGICAL HAZARDS
RT   SEDIMENT DYNAMICS
RT   SETTLEMENT (STRUCTURAL)
RT   SLOPE STABILITY
RT   SOIL MECHANICS
RT   STABILITY

SEDIMENT STRUCTURE
SN   Description of adhesive and cementive properties of sediment and sediment permeability and porosity
BT1   SEDIMENT PROPERTIES
BT2   PROPERTIES
RT   ADHESION
RT   PERMEABILITY
RT   POROSITY
RT   SEDIMENT ANALYSIS
RT   SEDIMENT TEXTURE
RT   STRATIGRAPHY

SEDIMENT TEMPERATURE
SN   Gradient or temperature fluxes in sediments
UF   beach temperature
BT1   TEMPERATURE
BT2   THERMODYNAMIC PROPERTIES
BT3   PHYSICAL PROPERTIES
BT4   PROPERTIES
RT   GEOTHERMAL MEASUREMENT
RT   HEAT FLOW
RT   HEAT PROBES
RT   SEDIMENT PROPERTIES
RT   SEDIMENT-WATER INTERFACE
RT   SEDIMENTS
RT   WATER TEMPERATURE

SEDIMENT TEMPERATURE MEASUREMENT
USE   **GEOTHERMAL MEASUREMENT**

SEDIMENT TEXTURE
SN   Description of particle size of sediments
BT1   SEDIMENT PROPERTIES
BT2   PROPERTIES
RT   GRAIN ORIENTATION
RT   GRAIN PACKING
RT   GRAIN SHAPE
RT   GRAIN SIZE
RT   GRAVEL
RT   POROSITY
RT   SAND
RT   SEDIMENT ANALYSIS
RT   SEDIMENT COMPOSITION
RT   SEDIMENT STRUCTURE
RT   SEDIMENTS

SEDIMENT TRANSPORT
UF   sand transport
UF   sediment transport rate
UF   subaqueous sediment transport
NT1   EOLIAN TRANSPORT
NT1   FLUVIAL TRANSPORT
NT1   GLACIAL TRANSPORT
NT1   LONGSHORE SEDIMENT TRANSPORT
NT1   MASS GRAVITY TRANSPORT (SEDIMENTS)
NT2   DEBRIS FLOW
NT2   SLUMPING
NT1   RAFTING
NT2   BIOLOGICAL RAFTING
NT2   ICE RAFTING
RT   ALLUVIAL DEPOSITS
RT   BED LOAD

SEDIMENT TRANSPORT (cont'd)
RT   BOTTOM CURRENTS
RT   BOTTOM STRESS
RT   CHANNEL FLOW
RT   COASTAL CURRENTS
RT   COASTAL EROSION
RT   CONTOUR CURRENTS
RT   CURRENT SCOURING
RT   DEEP CURRENTS
RT   EROSION
RT   GEOLOGICAL MAPS
RT   MASS MOVEMENT
RT   NEARSHORE CURRENTS
RT   PARTICLE MOTION
RT   RADIOACTIVE TRACERS
RT   RIP CURRENTS
RT   RIVER PLUMES
RT   SALTATION
RT   SEDIMENT DYNAMICS
RT   SEDIMENT LOAD
RT   SEDIMENT MOVEMENT
RT   SEDIMENT SORTING
RT   SEDIMENTATION
RT   SEDIMENTOLOGY
RT   SEDIMENTS
RT   SHELF GEOLOGY
RT   SHELF SEDIMENTATION
RT   SHOALING
RT   SHOALS
RT   SUSPENDED LOAD
RT   SUSPENDED PARTICULATE MATTER
RT   SUSPENSION
RT   TIDAL CURRENTS
RT   TRACERS
RT   TRACTION
RT   TRANSPORT
RT   TURBIDITY CURRENTS
RT   WAVE EFFECTS
RT   WINNOWING

SEDIMENT TRANSPORT RATE
USE   **SEDIMENT TRANSPORT**

SEDIMENT TRAPS
UF   sand traps
RT   COLLECTING DEVICES
RT   GEOLOGICAL EQUIPMENT
RT   OCEANOGRAPHIC EQUIPMENT
RT   PARTICULATE FLUX
RT   RESUSPENDED SEDIMENTS
RT   SEDIMENT SAMPLERS
RT   SILT METERS
RT   SUSPENDED PARTICULATE MATTER

SEDIMENT-WATER EXCHANGES
RT   GAS EXCHANGE
RT   HEAT FLOW
RT   SEDIMENT-WATER INTERFACE

SEDIMENT-WATER INTERFACE
SN   Including chemical or physical phenomena occurring in the sediment-water interface
BT1   INTERFACES
RT   BED FORMS
RT   BENTHIC ENVIRONMENT
RT   GAS EXCHANGE
RT   HALMYROLYSIS
RT   HEAT FLOW
RT   MUD
RT   OCEAN FLOOR
RT   SEDIMENT POLLUTION
RT   SEDIMENT TEMPERATURE
RT   SEDIMENT-WATER EXCHANGES
RT   SEDIMENTS
RT   WAVE-SEABED INTERACTION

ASFIS Thesaurus

SEDIMENTARY BASINS			**SEDIMENTARY STRUCTURES** (cont'd)			**SEDIMENTATION** (cont'd)	
RT	BASINS		NT2	SCOUR HOLLOWS		RT	SUSPENDED PARTICULATE MATTER
RT	SEDIMENTATION		NT2	SEACHANNELS			
RT	STRUCTURAL BASINS		NT2	SEAMOATS		**SEDIMENTOLOGY**	
			NT2	SEDIMENT DRIFTS		BT1	GEOLOGY
SEDIMENTARY DEPOSITS			NT2	TRANSVERSE BED FORMS		BT2	EARTH SCIENCES
USE	**SEDIMENTS**		NT1	BEDDING STRUCTURES		RT	DIAGENESIS
			NT2	CURRENT MARKS		RT	EROSION
SEDIMENTARY ENVIRONMENTS			NT3	FLUTE CASTS		RT	GEOLOGICAL MAPS
UF	depositional environments		NT3	SCOUR MARKS		RT	GEOMORPHOLOGY
BT1	ENVIRONMENTS		NT3	SOLE MARKS		RT	MARINE GEOLOGY
RT	DELTAIC SEDIMENTATION		NT2	RIPPLE MARKS		RT	MINERALOGY
RT	ESTUARINE SEDIMENTATION		NT2	VARVES		RT	PALAEONTOLOGY
RT	FLUVIAL SEDIMENTATION		NT1	BIOGENIC SEDIMENTARY STRUCTURES		RT	RECREATIONAL WATERS
RT	GLACIAL SEDIMENTATION		NT2	ALGAL MATS		RT	SEDIMENT TRANSPORT
RT	LACUSTRINE SEDIMENTATION		NT2	STROMATOLITES		RT	SEDIMENTATION
RT	LAGOONAL SEDIMENTATION		NT2	TRACE FOSSILS		RT	SEDIMENTS
RT	NEARSHORE SEDIMENTATION		NT3	FOSSILIZED TRACKS			
RT	SEDIMENTS		NT1	BOUDINAGE			
RT	SHELF SEDIMENTATION		NT1	FLOW STRUCTURES		**SEDIMENTS**	
			NT1	MUD FLATS		SN	Use of a more specific term is recommended; consult terms listed below
SEDIMENTARY PETROGRAPHY			NT1	OLISTOLITHS			
USE	**PETROLOGY**		NT1	PILLOW STRUCTURES			
			NT1	SCOUR AND FILL		UF	sedimentary deposits
SEDIMENTARY ROCKS			NT1	SLUMP STRUCTURES		NT1	ANOXIC SEDIMENTS
UF	rocks (sedimentary)		NT1	TURBIDITY CURRENT STRUCTURES		NT1	AUTHIGENIC MINERALS
UF	sediments (consolidated)		RT	CONCRETIONS		NT2	EVAPORITES
BT1	ROCKS		RT	GEOLOGICAL STRUCTURES		NT2	IRONSTONE
RT	BEACHROCK		RT	NODULES		NT2	JASPILITE
RT	BENTONITE		RT	OLISTOSTROMES		NT1	CHEMICAL SEDIMENTS
RT	BRECCIA		RT	SEDIMENTATION		NT2	CONCRETIONS
RT	CALCARENITE		RT	SEDIMENTS		NT2	FERRUGINOUS DEPOSITS
RT	CARBONATE ROCKS					NT2	FLINT
RT	CHALK		**SEDIMENTATION**			NT2	HYDROTHERMAL DEPOSITS
RT	CHERTS		SN	Before 1983 search also SEDIMENT DEPOSITION		NT2	MANGANESE DEPOSITS
RT	COBBLESTONE					NT2	METALLIFEROUS SEDIMENTS
RT	DIATOMITES		UF	accumulation of sediments		NT2	NODULES
RT	DOLOSTONE		UF	deposition (geology)		NT2	PHOSPHATE ROCKS
RT	EVAPORITES		UF	freshwater sedimentation		NT2	SUBMARINE CEMENTS
RT	FLINT		UF	geological deposition		NT2	SULPHIDE DEPOSITS
RT	GRAYWACKE		UF	marine sedimentation		NT1	CLASTICS
RT	GYPSUM		UF	sediment deposition		NT2	ARENITES
RT	IRONSTONE		NT1	DIAGENESIS		NT2	BENTONITE
RT	LIMESTONE		NT2	AUTHIGENESIS		NT2	BOULDERS
RT	MARL		NT2	CALCITIZATION		NT2	BRECCIA
RT	MARLSTONE		NT2	CEMENTATION		NT2	CLAYS
RT	MUDSTONE		NT2	COMPACTION		NT3	FULLERS EARTH
RT	PETROLOGY		NT2	CONSOLIDATION		NT3	PELAGIC CLAY
RT	PHOSPHATE ROCKS		NT2	DOLOMITIZATION		NT2	COBBLESTONE
RT	PORCELLANITE		NT2	LITHIFICATION		NT2	CONTOURITES
RT	RADIOLARITE		NT1	ESTUARINE SEDIMENTATION		NT2	FLYSCH
RT	SANDSTONE		NT1	FLUVIAL SEDIMENTATION		NT2	GRAVEL
RT	SEDIMENTS		NT1	GLACIAL SEDIMENTATION		NT2	MARLSTONE
RT	SHALE		NT1	INTERTIDAL SEDIMENTATION		NT2	MUD
RT	SILICEOUS ROCKS		NT1	LACUSTRINE SEDIMENTATION		NT3	FLUID MUD
RT	SILTSTONE		NT1	LAGOONAL SEDIMENTATION		NT2	MUDSTONE
RT	SLATES		NT1	NEARSHORE SEDIMENTATION		NT2	PEBBLES
RT	TEPHRA		NT1	PELAGIC SEDIMENTATION		NT2	SAND
RT	TURBIDITES		NT1	SHELF SEDIMENTATION		NT3	QUICKSANDS
			RT	ACCRETION		NT2	SANDSTONE
SEDIMENTARY STRUCTURES			RT	ALLUVIAL DEPOSITS		NT3	OIL SANDS
SN	Features that originate within layers of sediments or along the sediment-water interface prior to lithification		RT	BIOFACIES		NT2	SHALE
			RT	CHEMICAL PRECIPITATION		NT3	OIL SHALE
			RT	CONTINENTAL SLOPE		NT2	SHINGLE
			RT	DECANTATION		NT2	SILT
UF	primary sedimentary structures		RT	DELTAS		NT2	SILTSTONE
UF	secondary sedimentary structures		RT	EROSION		NT2	TURBIDITES
NT1	BED FORMS		RT	FLOOD PLAINS		NT1	COHESIVE SEDIMENTS
NT2	ANTIDUNES		RT	GEOLOGY		NT1	LITTORAL DEPOSITS
NT2	GRAVEL WAVES		RT	GEOMORPHOLOGY		NT1	OXIC SEDIMENTS
NT2	MUD BANKS		RT	PROVENANCE		NT1	PELAGIC SEDIMENTS
NT2	OBSTACLE MARKS		RT	REEF FORMATION		NT1	RELICT SEDIMENTS
NT2	PLOUGHMARKS		RT	REEFS		NT1	TERRIGENOUS SEDIMENTS
NT2	POCK MARKS		RT	SEDIMENT TRANSPORT		NT1	VOLCANOGENIC DEPOSITS
NT2	SAND BANKS		RT	SEDIMENTARY BASINS		RT	ACOUSTIC PROPERTIES
NT2	SAND BARS		RT	SEDIMENTARY STRUCTURES		RT	AGGREGATES
NT2	SAND PATCHES		RT	SEDIMENTOLOGY		RT	ALLOCHTHONOUS DEPOSITS
NT2	SAND RIBBONS		RT	SEDIMENTS		RT	ALLUVIAL DEPOSITS
NT2	SAND RIPPLES		RT	SILTING		RT	ARENACEOUS DEPOSITS
NT2	SAND WAVES		RT	STRATIGRAPHY			

SEDIMENTS (cont'd)

RT	ARGILLACEOUS DEPOSITS
RT	AUTOCHTHONOUS DEPOSITS
RT	BIOLOGICAL RAFTING
RT	BIOTURBATION
RT	CARBONATE SEDIMENTS
RT	CATAGENESIS
RT	COHESIONLESS SEDIMENTS
RT	COSMIC DUST
RT	DETRITAL DEPOSITS
RT	DETRITUS
RT	DEWATERING
RT	EOLIAN DEPOSITS
RT	EXTRATERRESTRIAL MATERIAL
RT	GEOTECHNOLOGY
RT	LAKE DEPOSITS
RT	LITHOFACIES
RT	MELANGES
RT	OLISTOLITHS
RT	OOZES
RT	PERMAFROST
RT	PETROLOGY
RT	PROVENANCE
RT	RESUSPENDED SEDIMENTS
RT	RIVER BEDS
RT	SALT DEPOSITS
RT	SEDIMENT ANALYSIS
RT	SEDIMENT COLLECTIONS
RT	SEDIMENT DENSITY
RT	SEDIMENT DISTRIBUTION
RT	SEDIMENT MIXING
RT	SEDIMENT MOVEMENT
RT	SEDIMENT NOISE
RT	SEDIMENT SORTING
RT	SEDIMENT TEMPERATURE
RT	SEDIMENT TEXTURE
RT	SEDIMENT TRANSPORT
RT	SEDIMENT-WATER INTERFACE
RT	SEDIMENTARY ENVIRONMENTS
RT	SEDIMENTARY ROCKS
RT	SEDIMENTARY STRUCTURES
RT	SEDIMENTATION
RT	SEDIMENTOLOGY
RT	SOILS
RT	STRATIGRAPHIC CORRELATION
RT	STRATIGRAPHY
RT	TIDAL DEPOSITS

SEDIMENTS (CONSOLIDATED)

USE	**SEDIMENTARY ROCKS**

SEDIMENTS IN SUSPENSION

USE	**RESUSPENDED SEDIMENTS**

SEED (AQUACULTURE)

UF	fish seed
UF	seedling
RT	AQUACULTURE PRODUCTS
RT	AQUACULTURE TECHNIQUES
RT	BATCH CULTURE
RT	FINGERLINGS
RT	FRY
RT	HYBRID CULTURE
RT	LARVAE
RT	SEED COLLECTION
RT	SEEDING (AQUACULTURE)
RT	SPAT
RT	STOCKING (ORGANISMS)
RT	STOCKING DENSITY
RT	TRANSPLANTATION

SEED COLLECTION

UF	fish fry collection
UF	spat collection
UF	spore collection
RT	AQUACULTURE
RT	AQUACULTURE TECHNIQUES
RT	BOTTOM CULTURE
RT	CLAM CULTURE
RT	CRUSTACEAN CULTURE

SEED COLLECTION (cont'd)

RT	EXTENSIVE CULTURE
RT	FISH CULTURE
RT	FRY
RT	HATCHERIES
RT	MOLLUSC CULTURE
RT	OFF-BOTTOM CULTURE
RT	OYSTER CULTURE
RT	PEARL CULTURE
RT	POND CULTURE
RT	SEAWEED CULTURE
RT	SEED (AQUACULTURE)
RT	SEED PRODUCTION
RT	SEEDING (AQUACULTURE)
RT	SHELLFISH CULTURE
RT	SPAT
RT	SPONGE CULTURE
RT	SPORES

SEED PRODUCTION

SN	Before 1982 search SEEDING (AQUACULTURE)
RT	BATCH CULTURE
RT	HATCHERIES
RT	MASS CULTURE
RT	SEED COLLECTION
RT	SEEDING (AQUACULTURE)

SEEDING (AQUACULTURE)

RT	AQUACULTURE
RT	COLONIZATION
RT	POND CULTURE
RT	SEED (AQUACULTURE)
RT	SEED COLLECTION
RT	SEED PRODUCTION
RT	STOCKING (ORGANISMS)
RT	TRANSPLANTATION

SEEDLING

USE	**SEED (AQUACULTURE)**

SEEPAGES

SN	Use of a more specific term is recommended
UF	seeps
NT1	GAS SEEPAGES
NT1	OIL SEEPAGES
RT	GEOTHERMAL SPRINGS
RT	HOT SPRINGS
RT	HYDROTHERMAL SPRINGS
RT	PERCOLATION
RT	POLLUTION
RT	SPRING STREAMS
RT	SUBMARINE SPRINGS
RT	WATER SPRINGS

SEEPS

USE	**SEEPAGES**

SEICHES

UF	surges (seiches)
BT1	SURFACE WATER WAVES
BT2	WATER WAVES
NT1	HARBOUR OSCILLATIONS
RT	DYNAMICAL OCEANOGRAPHY
RT	LAKE DYNAMICS
RT	SEA LEVEL VARIATIONS
RT	STANDING WAVES
RT	SURFACE GRAVITY WAVES
RT	SURGES

SEINE NETS

BT1	FISHING NETS
BT2	FISHING GEAR
NT1	BEACH SEINES
NT1	BOAT SEINES
RT	COASTAL FISHERIES
RT	DEMERSAL FISHERIES
RT	LIGHT FISHING
RT	PELAGIC FISHERIES

SEINE NETS (cont'd)

RT	SEINERS
RT	SEINING

SEINERS

SN	Any type of vessel used in seining or encircling operations
UF	purse seiners
BT1	FISHING VESSELS
BT2	SURFACE CRAFT
BT3	VEHICLES
RT	BOAT SEINES
RT	COASTAL FISHERIES
RT	DEMERSAL FISHERIES
RT	LAMPARA NETS
RT	PELAGIC FISHERIES
RT	PURSE SEINES
RT	PURSE SEINING
RT	SEINE NETS
RT	SEINING
RT	SURROUNDING NETS

SEINING

BT1	CATCHING METHODS
NT1	PURSE SEINING
RT	BOAT SEINES
RT	FISHING
RT	LAMPARA NETS
RT	NET FISHING
RT	PURSE SEINES
RT	SEINE NETS
RT	SEINERS
RT	SURROUNDING NETS

SEISMIC ACTIVITY

SN	General phenomena of earth movement and effects on aquatic environment and its exploitation. Before 1983 search also SEISMIC EFFECTS and SEISMICITY
UF	seismicity
RT	EARTHQUAKE LOADING
RT	EARTHQUAKES
RT	ENVIRONMENTAL FACTORS
RT	GROUND MOTION
RT	MARINE GEOLOGY
RT	MID-OCEAN RIDGES
RT	SEISMIC WAVES
RT	SEISMIC ZONES
RT	SEISMOLOGY

SEISMIC ARRAYS

BT1	ARRAYS
RT	ACOUSTIC ARRAYS
RT	GEOPHYSICAL EQUIPMENT
RT	SEISMIC ENERGY SOURCES
RT	SEISMIC EQUIPMENT

SEISMIC ATTENUATION

SN	seismic wave attenuation
BT1	ATTENUATION
RT	SEISMIC WAVES

SEISMIC DATA

BT1	GEOPHYSICAL DATA
BT2	DATA
RT	SEISMIC DATA PROCESSING

SEISMIC DATA PROCESSING

BT1	DATA PROCESSING
NT1	BRIGHT SPOT TECHNOLOGY
RT	ACOUSTIC HOLOGRAPHY
RT	CONVOLUTION
RT	DATA REDUCTION
RT	DECONVOLUTION
RT	GEOPHYSICAL DATA
RT	SEISMIC DATA

SEISMIC DECONVOLUTION
USE **DECONVOLUTION**

SEISMIC DIFFRACTION
UF   diffraction (seismic)
BT1   DIFFRACTION
RT   SEISMIC WAVES

SEISMIC DISCONTINUITIES
NT1   MOHO
RT   SEISMIC LAYERS
RT   SEISMIC VELOCITIES
RT   SURFACES

SEISMIC ENERGY SOURCES
NT1   AIR GUNS
NT1   BOOMERS
NT1   EXPLODING WIRE
NT1   GAS EXPLODERS
NT1   SPARKERS
RT   EXPLOSIVES
RT   GEOPHYSICAL EQUIPMENT
RT   SEISMIC ARRAYS
RT   SEISMIC EQUIPMENT
RT   SEISMIC EXPLORATION
RT   SOUND GENERATORS

SEISMIC EPICENTRES
USE **EPICENTRES**

SEISMIC EQUIPMENT
BT1   GEOPHYSICAL EQUIPMENT
BT2   EQUIPMENT
RT   SEISMIC ARRAYS
RT   SEISMIC ENERGY SOURCES
RT   SEISMIC EXPLORATION
RT   SEISMOMETERS
RT   SONOBUOYS
RT   STREAMERS

SEISMIC EVENTS
USE **EARTHQUAKES**

SEISMIC EXPLORATION
SN   Before 1983 search also SEISMIC
      PROFILING
UF   seismic methods
UF   seismic profiling
BT1   GEOPHYSICAL EXPLORATION
BT2   EXPLORATION
NT1   SEISMIC REFLECTION PROFILING
NT1   SEISMIC REFRACTION PROFILING
NT1   SUB-BOTTOM PROFILING
RT   GEOLOGICAL SURVEYS
RT   SEISMIC ENERGY SOURCES
RT   SEISMIC EQUIPMENT
RT   SEISMIC PROFILES
RT   SEISMOLOGY
RT   SURVEYS

SEISMIC LAYERS
BT1   EARTH STRUCTURE
NT1   LOW-VELOCITY LAYER
RT   LAYERS
RT   SEISMIC DISCONTINUITIES
RT   SEISMIC VELOCITIES

SEISMIC MARGINS
USE **ACTIVE MARGINS**

SEISMIC METHODS
USE **SEISMIC EXPLORATION**

SEISMIC PROFILES
UF   seismic sections
BT1   ANALOG RECORDS
BT2   GRAPHICS
BT3   AUDIOVISUAL MATERIAL
BT4   DOCUMENTS
NT1   SEISMIC REFLECTION PROFILES

SEISMIC PROFILES (cont'd)
NT1   SEISMIC REFRACTION PROFILES
RT   BRIGHT SPOT TECHNOLOGY
RT   GEOLOGICAL SECTIONS
RT   SEISMIC EXPLORATION
RT   SEISMIC STRATIGRAPHY
RT   VERTICAL SECTIONS

SEISMIC PROFILING
USE **SEISMIC EXPLORATION**

SEISMIC PROPAGATION
UF   seismic wave propagation
RT   RAY PATHS
RT   SEISMIC REFLECTION
RT   SEISMIC REFRACTION
RT   SEISMIC SCATTERING
RT   SEISMIC WAVES

SEISMIC RAY PATH
USE **RAY PATHS**

SEISMIC RECORDS
USE **SEISMOGRAMS**

SEISMIC REFLECTION
UF   seismic wave reflection
BT1   REFLECTION
RT   SEISMIC PROPAGATION
RT   SEISMIC REFLECTION PROFILES
RT   SEISMIC REFLECTION PROFILING
RT   SEISMIC SCATTERING
RT   SEISMIC WAVES

SEISMIC REFLECTION METHOD
USE **SEISMIC REFLECTION PROFILING**

SEISMIC REFLECTION PROFILES
BT1   SEISMIC PROFILES
BT2   ANALOG RECORDS
BT3   GRAPHICS
BT4   AUDIOVISUAL MATERIAL
RT   SEISMIC REFLECTION
RT   SEISMIC REFLECTION PROFILING

SEISMIC REFLECTION PROFILING
UF   seismic reflection method
BT1   SEISMIC EXPLORATION
BT2   GEOPHYSICAL EXPLORATION
BT3   EXPLORATION
RT   PROFILING
RT   SEISMIC REFLECTION
RT   SEISMIC REFLECTION PROFILES
RT   SUB-BOTTOM PROFILING

SEISMIC REFRACTION
UF   seismic wave refraction
BT1   REFRACTION
RT   SEISMIC PROPAGATION
RT   SEISMIC REFRACTION PROFILES
RT   SEISMIC REFRACTION PROFILING
RT   SEISMIC SCATTERING

SEISMIC REFRACTION METHOD
USE **SEISMIC REFRACTION PROFILING**

SEISMIC REFRACTION PROFILES
BT1   SEISMIC PROFILES
BT2   ANALOG RECORDS
BT3   GRAPHICS
BT4   AUDIOVISUAL MATERIAL
RT   SEISMIC REFRACTION
RT   SEISMIC REFRACTION PROFILING
RT   SEISMIC STRATIGRAPHY

SEISMIC REFRACTION PROFILING
UF   seismic refraction method
BT1   SEISMIC EXPLORATION
BT2   GEOPHYSICAL EXPLORATION
BT3   EXPLORATION

SEISMIC REFRACTION PROFILING (cont'd)
RT   PROFILING
RT   SEISMIC REFRACTION
RT   SEISMIC REFRACTION PROFILES
RT   SONOBUOYS

SEISMIC RIDGES
BT1   SUBMARINE RIDGES
BT2   SUBMARINE FEATURES
BT3   TOPOGRAPHIC FEATURES
NT1   MID-OCEAN RIDGES
RT   ASEISMIC RIDGES

SEISMIC SCATTERING
RT   SEISMIC PROPAGATION
RT   SEISMIC REFLECTION
RT   SEISMIC REFRACTION

SEISMIC SEA WAVES
USE **TSUNAMIS**

SEISMIC SECTIONS
USE **SEISMIC PROFILES**

SEISMIC STRATIGRAPHY
UF   acoustic stratigraphy
BT1   STRATIGRAPHY
BT2   GEOLOGY
BT3   EARTH SCIENCES
RT   SEISMIC PROFILES
RT   SEISMIC REFRACTION PROFILES
RT   STRATIGRAPHIC CORRELATION

SEISMIC VELOCITIES
UF   wave velocity (seismic)
BT1   VELOCITY
NT1   COMPRESSIONAL WAVE VELOCITIES
NT1   SHEAR WAVE VELOCITIES
RT   LOW-VELOCITY LAYER
RT   MOHO
RT   SEISMIC DISCONTINUITIES
RT   SEISMIC LAYERS
RT   SEISMIC WAVES

SEISMIC WAVE PROPAGATION
USE **SEISMIC PROPAGATION**

SEISMIC WAVE REFLECTION
USE **SEISMIC REFLECTION**

SEISMIC WAVE REFRACTION
USE **SEISMIC REFRACTION**

SEISMIC WAVES
UF   earth waves
UF   earthquake waves
UF   long-period seismic waves
UF   waves (seismic)
BT1   ELASTIC WAVES
NT1   BODY WAVES
NT2   P-WAVES
NT2   S-WAVES
NT1   MICROSEISMS
NT1   SURFACE SEISMIC WAVES
NT2   LOVE WAVES
NT2   RAYLEIGH WAVES
NT2   STONELEY WAVES
RT   ACOUSTIC PROPERTIES
RT   RAY PATHS
RT   SEISMIC ACTIVITY
RT   SEISMIC ATTENUATION
RT   SEISMIC DIFFRACTION
RT   SEISMIC PROPAGATION
RT   SEISMIC REFLECTION
RT   SEISMIC VELOCITIES
RT   SEISMOGRAMS
RT   SEISMOLOGY
RT   SEISMOMETERS
RT   WAVE PROPERTIES

SEISMIC ZONES
BT1	EARTH STRUCTURE
RT	ASEISMIC ZONES
RT	BENIOFF ZONE
RT	SEISMIC ACTIVITY

SEISMICITY
USE	**SEISMIC ACTIVITY**

SEISMOGRAMS
UF	seismic records
BT1	ANALOG RECORDS
BT2	GRAPHICS
BT3	AUDIOVISUAL MATERIAL
BT4	DOCUMENTS
RT	SEISMIC WAVES
RT	SEISMOMETERS

SEISMOGRAPHS
USE	**SEISMOMETERS**

SEISMOLOGY
BT1	GEOPHYSICS
BT2	EARTH SCIENCES
RT	ANISOTROPIC ROCKS
RT	EARTHQUAKES
RT	EPICENTRES
RT	GEOLOGY
RT	GEOMORPHOLOGY
RT	GROUND MOTION
RT	MICROEARTHQUAKES
RT	MICROSEISMS
RT	RICHTER SCALE
RT	SEISMIC ACTIVITY
RT	SEISMIC EXPLORATION
RT	SEISMIC WAVES
RT	SEISMOMETERS
RT	TILTMETERS

SEISMOMETERS
UF	geophones
UF	seismographs
BT1	MEASURING DEVICES
NT1	OCEAN BOTTOM SEISMOMETERS
NT1	STRAIN SEISMOMETERS
RT	ACCELEROMETERS
RT	GEOPHYSICAL EQUIPMENT
RT	SEISMIC EQUIPMENT
RT	SEISMIC WAVES
RT	SEISMOGRAMS
RT	SEISMOLOGY

SELECTED SHIPS
SN	Merchant vessels equipped to make basic meteorological and oceanographic observations
UF	ships of opportunity
BT1	MERCHANT SHIPS
BT2	SHIPS
BT3	SURFACE CRAFT
BT4	VEHICLES
RT	INSTRUMENT PLATFORMS
RT	METEOROLOGICAL DATA
RT	METEOROLOGICAL OBSERVATIONS
RT	OCEANOGRAPHIC DATA
RT	SHIPPING LANES

SELECTION (BIOLOGICAL)
USE	**BIOSELECTION**

SELECTIVE BREEDING
BT1	BREEDING
RT	AQUACULTURE TECHNIQUES
RT	BREEDING PONDS
RT	BROOD STOCKS
RT	DOMESTIC SPECIES
RT	FISH CULTURE
RT	GENETICS
RT	HATCHERIES
RT	HYBRID CULTURE

SELECTIVE BREEDING (cont'd)
RT	HYBRIDS
RT	INTENSIVE CULTURE

SELECTIVE FEEDING
SN	Added in 1980
BT1	ARTIFICIAL FEEDING
BT2	FEEDING
RT	DIETS
RT	FEED
RT	FOOD ORGANISMS

SELENIUM
BT1	CHEMICAL ELEMENTS
RT	SELENIUM COMPOUNDS
RT	SELENIUM ISOTOPES
RT	TRACE ELEMENTS

SELENIUM COMPOUNDS
RT	CHEMICAL COMPOUNDS
RT	SELENIUM

SELENIUM ISOTOPES
BT1	ISOTOPES
RT	SELENIUM

SELF FERTILIZATION
BT1	HERMAPHRODITISM
RT	ANIMAL REPRODUCTIVE ORGANS
RT	PROTANDRY
RT	SEXUAL REPRODUCTION

SELF POLLINATION
USE	**POLLINATION**

SELF-PROPELLED VEHICLES
BT1	UNDERWATER VEHICLES
BT2	VEHICLES
RT	FREE-SWIMMING VEHICLES
RT	PROPULSION SYSTEMS
RT	SEABED VEHICLES
RT	SUBMERSIBLES
RT	TETHERED FREE-SWIMMING VEHICLES
RT	UNTETHERED VEHICLES

SELF PURIFICATION
SN	Natural self purification of waters, sediments, organisms etc.
UF	depuration
UF	pollution self-control
RT	AERATION
RT	AEROBIC BACTERIA
RT	BIOCHEMICAL OXYGEN DEMAND
RT	WATER POLLUTION TREATMENT
RT	WATER PURIFICATION

SEMEN
SN	Added in 1980
RT	SECRETORY PRODUCTS
RT	SPERM
RT	TESTES

SEMI-ENCLOSED SEAS
BT1	MARGINAL SEAS
RT	EMBAYMENTS
RT	SHELF DYNAMICS
RT	SHELF SEAS

SEMIDIURNAL TIDES
BT1	TIDES
BT2	TIDAL MOTION

SEMINARS
USE	**CONFERENCES**

SEMISUBMERSIBLE PLATFORMS
SN	Towed or self-propelled structures partially submerged by flooding. Before 1982 search SEMISUBMERSIBLES
UF	semisubmersibles (drilling platforms)

SEMISUBMERSIBLE PLATFORMS (cont'd)
BT1	MOBILE PLATFORMS
BT2	FLOATING STRUCTURES
BT3	OFFSHORE STRUCTURES
BT4	HYDRAULIC STRUCTURES
RT	ANCHORING
RT	DYNAMIC POSITIONING
RT	SHIP MOORING SYSTEMS
RT	SUBMERSIBLE PLATFORMS

SEMISUBMERSIBLES (DRILLING PLATFORMS)
USE	**SEMISUBMERSIBLE PLATFORMS**

SENESCENCE
USE	**BIOLOGICAL AGING**

SENSE FUNCTIONS
NT1	AUDITION
NT1	OLFACTION
NT1	PHOTORECEPTION
NT1	TACTILE FUNCTIONS
NT1	TASTE FUNCTIONS
NT1	VISION
RT	ANIMAL APPENDAGES
RT	ANTENNAE
RT	CHEMORECEPTION
RT	KINESIS
RT	NEUROPHYSIOLOGY
RT	ORIENTATION BEHAVIOUR
RT	SENSE ORGANS
RT	STIMULI
RT	TAXIS

SENSE ORGANS
BT1	ANIMAL ORGANS
BT2	BODY ORGANS
NT1	AUDITORY ORGANS
NT1	BALANCE ORGANS
NT2	STATOCYSTS
NT1	CHEMORECEPTORS
NT1	LATERAL LINE
NT1	MECHANORECEPTORS
NT1	OLFACTORY ORGANS
NT1	PHOTORECEPTORS
NT2	EYES
NT3	COMPOUND EYES
NT3	EYESTALKS
NT3	RETINAS
NT1	TACTILE ORGANS
NT1	TASTE ORGANS
RT	ANATOMY
RT	CENTRAL NERVOUS SYSTEM
RT	KINESIS
RT	NERVOUS TISSUES
RT	NEUROPHYSIOLOGY
RT	ORIENTATION
RT	ORIENTATION BEHAVIOUR
RT	PERIPHERAL NERVOUS SYSTEM
RT	RECEPTORS
RT	SENSE FUNCTIONS
RT	SENSE TENTACLES
RT	STIMULI
RT	TAXIS
RT	THERMORECEPTORS

SENSE TENTACLES
BT1	TENTACLES
BT2	ANIMAL APPENDAGES
RT	SENSE ORGANS

SENSIBLE HEAT
BT1	HEAT
BT2	ENERGY
RT	AIR-WATER EXCHANGES
RT	HEAT CONDUCTION
RT	SENSIBLE HEAT TRANSFER

ASFIS Thesaurus

SENSIBLE HEAT FLUX
USE **SENSIBLE HEAT TRANSFER**

SENSIBLE HEAT TRANSFER
SN   Sensible heat flux across air-water
     interface and air-ice interface
UF   sensible heat flux
BT1   HEAT EXCHANGE
BT2   HEAT TRANSFER
RT   AIR-ICE INTERFACE
RT   AIR-WATER INTERFACE
RT   BOWEN RATIO
RT   CONVECTION
RT   SENSIBLE HEAT
RT   TEMPERATURE DIFFERENCES

SENSORS
UF   probes (instruments)
UF   probes (sensors)
BT1   ELECTRONIC EQUIPMENT
BT2   EQUIPMENT
NT1   TOWED SENSORS
RT   CONDUCTIVITY SENSORS
RT   FLOWMETERS
RT   LIGHT MEASURING INSTRUMENTS
RT   MEASURING DEVICES
RT   OCEANOGRAPHIC EQUIPMENT
RT   PH SENSORS
RT   PRESSURE SENSORS
RT   RADIOMETERS
RT   RECORDING EQUIPMENT
RT   REMOTE SENSING
RT   RESISTIVITY PROBES
RT   SOUND RECORDERS
RT   STREAMERS
RT   TEST EQUIPMENT
RT   TRANSDUCERS
RT   WAVE DIRECTION SENSORS

SENSORY RECEPTORS
USE **RECEPTORS**

SEPARATION
NT1   CENTRIFUGATION
NT1   CHEMICAL EXTRACTION
NT1   CHEMICAL PRECIPITATION
NT2   COPRECIPITATION
NT2   FLOCCULATION
NT1   DECANTATION
NT1   DESICCATION
NT1   FLOTATION
NT1   GAS OIL SEPARATION
NT1   GAS WATER SEPARATION
NT1   OIL WATER SEPARATION
RT   ADSORPTION
RT   AERATION
RT   ANIMAL OIL EXTRACTION
RT   DEHYDRATION
RT   DESALINATION
RT   DIFFUSION
RT   DISPERSION
RT   DRYING
RT   ELECTROPHORESIS
RT   GAS PROCESSING
RT   OIL TREATING
RT   TURBULENT ENTRAINMENT
RT   WATER PURIFICATION

SEPARATION PROCESSES
SN   Before 1982 search also SEPARATION
NT1   DEMINERALIZATION
NT1   DIALYSIS
NT2   ELECTRODIALYSIS
NT1   DISSOLUTION
NT2   CALCITE DISSOLUTION
NT1   DISTILLATION
NT1   ION EXCHANGE
NT1   LEACHING
NT1   OSMOSIS
NT2   REVERSE OSMOSIS

SEPARATION PROCESSES (cont'd)
NT1   SOLVENT EXTRACTION
RT   OIL TREATING

SEPIOLITE
BT1   SILICATE MINERALS
BT2   MINERALS

SEPTICAEMIA
SN   Added in 1980
UF   bacterial haemorrhagic septicaemia
UF   septicemia
UF   viral haemorrhagic septicaemia
BT1   INFECTIOUS DISEASES
BT2   DISEASES
RT   FISH DISEASES
RT   HAEMATOLOGICAL DISEASES
RT   VIRAL DISEASES

SEPTICEMIA
USE **SEPTICAEMIA**

SERINE
BT1   AMINO ACIDS
BT2   ORGANIC ACIDS
BT3   ORGANIC COMPOUNDS

SEROLOGICAL STUDIES
UF   serology
RT   ANTIBODIES
RT   ANTIGENS
RT   BIOPOLYMORPHISM
RT   BLOOD
RT   BODY FLUIDS
RT   ELECTROPHORESIS
RT   HAEMATOLOGY
RT   IMMUNOLOGY
RT   PROTEINS
RT   SEROLOGICAL TAXONOMY
RT   SERUM
RT   STOCK IDENTIFICATION

SEROLOGICAL TAXONOMY
BT1   TAXONOMY
RT   ANTIBODIES
RT   ELECTROPHORESIS
RT   PROTEINS
RT   SEROLOGICAL STUDIES
RT   SERUM

SEROLOGY
USE **SEROLOGICAL STUDIES**

SERPENTINITE
BT1   METAMORPHIC ROCKS
BT2   ROCKS
RT   SERPENTINITIZATION

SERPENTINITIZATION
RT   HYDROTHERMAL ALTERATION
RT   METASOMATISISM
RT   METASOMATISM
RT   SERPENTINITE

SERUM
BT1   BODY FLUIDS
NT1   ANTIBODIES
NT2   AGGLUTININS
RT   HAEMATOLOGY
RT   SEROLOGICAL STUDIES
RT   SEROLOGICAL TAXONOMY

SERUM ALBUMINS
USE **ALBUMINS**

SERUM GLOBULINS
USE **GLOBULINS**

SESSILE ORGANISMS
USE **SESSILE SPECIES**

SESSILE SPECIES
UF   sedentary organisms
UF   sessile organisms
BT1   SPECIES
BT2   TAXA
RT   BENTHOS
RT   SEDENTARY SPECIES
RT   SUBSTRATA

SESTON
BT1   AQUATIC COMMUNITIES
RT   PLANKTON
RT   SUSPENDED PARTICULATE MATTER

SET-LINES
USE **LINES**

SET NETS
USE **GILLNETS**

SETTLEMENT (BIOLOGICAL)
USE **BIOLOGICAL SETTLEMENT**

SETTLEMENT (LARVAE)
USE **LARVAL SETTLEMENT**

SETTLEMENT (STRUCTURAL)
UF   structural settlement
RT   COMPACTION
RT   FAILURES
RT   FOUNDATIONS
RT   GEOLOGICAL HAZARDS
RT   OFFSHORE STRUCTURES
RT   SEDIMENT STABILITY
RT   SOIL MECHANICS

SETTLING BEHAVIOUR
BT1   BEHAVIOUR
RT   ALGAL SETTLEMENTS
RT   ARTIFICIAL SUBSTRATA
RT   BIOLOGICAL SETTLEMENT
RT   COLONIZATION
RT   LARVAL SETTLEMENT
RT   SUBSTRATA

SETTLING RATE
UF   settling velocity
UF   sinking rate
BT1   VELOCITY
RT   PARTICLE MOTION
RT   PARTICLE SETTLING
RT   PARTICULATE FLUX
RT   STOKES LAW

SETTLING VELOCITY
USE **SETTLING RATE**

SETUP (WAVE)
USE **WAVE SETUP**

SETUP (WIND)
USE **WIND SETUP**

SEWAGE
SN   Before 1982 search also SEWAGE
     EFFLUENTS
UF   sewage effluents
BT1   WASTES
RT   BIOAERATION
RT   CHEMICAL POLLUTION
RT   DETERGENTS
RT   DOMESTIC WASTES
RT   DRAINAGE WATER
RT   FERTILIZERS
RT   INDUSTRIAL WASTES
RT   ORGANIC WASTES
RT   OUTFALLS

SEWAGE (cont'd)
RT	SEWAGE DISPOSAL
RT	SEWAGE PONDS
RT	SEWAGE TREATMENT
RT	SLUDGE
RT	URINE
RT	WASTE WATER

SEWAGE DISPOSAL
SN	Added in 1980
UF	sewage sludge disposal
BT1	WASTE DISPOSAL
RT	INDUSTRIAL WASTES
RT	OUTFALLS
RT	RADIOACTIVE WASTES
RT	SANITARY ENGINEERING
RT	SEWAGE
RT	SEWAGE PONDS
RT	SEWAGE TREATMENT
RT	WASTE WATER
RT	WATER POLLUTION

SEWAGE EFFLUENTS
USE	**SEWAGE**

SEWAGE OUTFALLS
USE	**OUTFALLS**

SEWAGE OXIDATION PONDS
USE	**SEWAGE PONDS**

SEWAGE PONDS
UF	oxidation lagoons
UF	sewage oxidation ponds
BT1	PONDS
BT2	INLAND WATERS
RT	BIODEGRADATION
RT	DECANTATION TANKS
RT	POND CONSTRUCTION
RT	SANITARY ENGINEERING
RT	SEWAGE
RT	SEWAGE DISPOSAL
RT	SEWAGE TREATMENT
RT	SLUDGE
RT	WASTE DISPOSAL

SEWAGE SLUDGE DISPOSAL
USE	SEWAGE DISPOSAL

SEWAGE TANKS
USE	**SEWAGE TREATMENT**

SEWAGE TREATMENT
UF	sewage tanks
BT1	WASTE TREATMENT
RT	AERATION
RT	BIODEGRADATION
RT	CHEMICAL DEGRADATION
RT	CHLORINATION
RT	DECHLORINATION
RT	DOMESTIC WASTES
RT	FLOCCULATION
RT	OXIDATION
RT	SALTS
RT	SANITARY ENGINEERING
RT	SEWAGE
RT	SEWAGE DISPOSAL
RT	SEWAGE PONDS
RT	SLUDGE TREATMENT
RT	WASTEWATER TREATMENT
RT	WATER FILTRATION

SEX
SN	Added in 1980
NT1	FEMALES
NT1	MALES
RT	SEX CHARACTERS
RT	SEX DETERMINATION
RT	SEX HORMONES
RT	SEX RATIO

SEX (cont'd)
RT	SEX REVERSAL
RT	SEXUAL BEHAVIOUR
RT	SEXUAL CELLS
RT	SEXUAL DIMORPHISM
RT	SEXUAL ISOLATION
RT	SEXUAL MATURITY
RT	SEXUAL REPRODUCTION
RT	SEXUAL SELECTION

SEX CHARACTERISTICS
USE	**SEX CHARACTERS**

SEX CHARACTERS
SN	Added in 1980
UF	sex characteristics
UF	sex differences
UF	sexual differences
NT1	SECONDARY SEXUAL CHARACTERS
RT	ANIMAL REPRODUCTIVE ORGANS
RT	FEMALES
RT	MALES
RT	SEX

SEX COMPOSITION
USE	**SEX RATIO**

SEX DETERMINATION
SN	Physiological mechanisms determining sex
RT	CHROMOSOMES
RT	HERMAPHRODITISM
RT	SEX
RT	SEX HORMONES
RT	SEX RATIO
RT	SEX REVERSAL
RT	SEXUAL DIMORPHISM

SEX DIFFERENCES
USE	**SEX CHARACTERS**

SEX DIMORPHISM
USE	**SEXUAL DIMORPHISM**

SEX HORMONES
SN	Any hormone having a morphological or physiological effect upon the reproductive organs, secondary sex characters or sexual behaviour. Added in 1980
UF	androgens
UF	estrogens
UF	gonad hormones
UF	gonadotropic hormones
BT1	HORMONES
BT2	SECRETORY PRODUCTS
RT	ANIMAL REPRODUCTIVE ORGANS
RT	SECONDARY SEXUAL CHARACTERS
RT	SEX
RT	SEX DETERMINATION
RT	SEX REVERSAL
RT	SEXUAL BEHAVIOUR

SEX RATIO
UF	sex composition
BT1	POPULATION STRUCTURE
BT2	POPULATION CHARACTERISTICS
RT	FEMALES
RT	MALES
RT	REPRODUCTIVE BEHAVIOUR
RT	SEX
RT	SEX DETERMINATION
RT	SEXUAL MATURITY
RT	SPAWNING MIGRATIONS

SEX REVERSAL
RT	ANIMAL REPRODUCTIVE ORGANS
RT	SEX
RT	SEX DETERMINATION
RT	SEX HORMONES

SEX REVERSAL (cont'd)
RT	SEXUAL REPRODUCTION

SEXUAL BEHAVIOUR
BT1	BEHAVIOUR
RT	REPRODUCTIVE BEHAVIOUR
RT	SEX
RT	SEX HORMONES
RT	SEXUAL REPRODUCTION

SEXUAL CELLS
UF	gametes
BT1	CELLS
NT1	EGGS
NT2	BIRD EGGS
NT2	BRINE SHRIMP EGGS
NT2	FISH EGGS
NT2	INSECT EGGS
NT2	RESTING EGGS
NT1	SPERM
RT	ANIMAL REPRODUCTIVE ORGANS
RT	BIOLOGICAL FERTILIZATION
RT	BREEDING
RT	GENOMES
RT	INDUCED BREEDING
RT	OOGENESIS
RT	POLYSPERMY
RT	SEX
RT	SEXUAL MATURITY
RT	SEXUAL REPRODUCTION
RT	ZYGOTES

SEXUAL DIFFERENCES
USE	**SEX CHARACTERS**

SEXUAL DIMORPHISM
UF	dimorphism (sexual)
UF	dwarfism
UF	sex dimorphism
RT	BIOPOLYMORPHISM
RT	ORGANISM MORPHOLOGY
RT	SECONDARY SEXUAL CHARACTERS
RT	SEX
RT	SEX DETERMINATION
RT	SEXUAL MATURITY
RT	SEXUAL SELECTION

SEXUAL GLANDS
USE	**ANIMAL REPRODUCTIVE ORGANS**

SEXUAL ISOLATION
SN	Added in 1980
UF	isolation (sexual)
UF	reproductive isolation
BT1	ISOLATING MECHANISMS
RT	BREEDING SEASONS
RT	SEX
RT	SEXUAL SELECTION

SEXUAL MATURITY
UF	maturation
BT1	BIOLOGICAL PROPERTIES
BT2	PROPERTIES
RT	ADULTS
RT	BREEDING
RT	EYESTALK EXTIRPATION
RT	FEMALES
RT	GAMETOGENESIS
RT	LIFE CYCLE
RT	MALES
RT	OVULATION
RT	SEX
RT	SEX RATIO
RT	SEXUAL CELLS
RT	SEXUAL DIMORPHISM
RT	SEXUAL REPRODUCTION
RT	SPERMATOPHORES

ASFIS Thesaurus

SEXUAL REPRODUCTION
SN	Natural or artificial sexual reproduction
BT1	REPRODUCTION
NT1	BIOLOGICAL FERTILIZATION
NT1	PARTURITION
RT	ANIMAL REPRODUCTIVE ORGANS
RT	BREEDING
RT	BREEDING SITES
RT	BROOD STOCKS
RT	CASTRATION
RT	COURTSHIP
RT	EMBRYOLOGY
RT	HERMAPHRODITISM
RT	OVARIES
RT	OVIPARITY
RT	OVOVIVIPARITY
RT	OVULATION
RT	POLLINATION
RT	POLYSPERMY
RT	REPRODUCTIVE BEHAVIOUR
RT	SELF FERTILIZATION
RT	SEX
RT	SEX REVERSAL
RT	SEXUAL BEHAVIOUR
RT	SEXUAL CELLS
RT	SEXUAL MATURITY
RT	SPAWNING
RT	SPERMATOPHORES
RT	TESTES
RT	VIVIPARITY

SEXUAL SELECTION
SN	Added in 1980
BT1	BIOSELECTION
RT	EVOLUTION
RT	SEX
RT	SEXUAL DIMORPHISM
RT	SEXUAL ISOLATION

SHALE
BT1	CLASTICS
BT2	SEDIMENTS
NT1	OIL SHALE
RT	LUTITES
RT	SEDIMENTARY ROCKS

SHALLOW WATER
RT	CONTINENTAL SHELVES
RT	DEEP WATER
RT	LAGOONS
RT	LITTORAL ZONE
RT	MARSHES
RT	REEFS
RT	SHALLOW-WATER TIDES
RT	SHALLOW-WATER WAVES
RT	SHELF DYNAMICS
RT	SHELF SEAS
RT	SHOALS
RT	SURFACE WATER
RT	SWAMPS
RT	WATER
RT	WATER DEPTH
RT	WAVE REFRACTION
RT	WAVE SCOURING

SHALLOW-WATER DYNAMICS
USE	**SHELF DYNAMICS**

SHALLOW-WATER TIDES
BT1	TIDES
BT2	TIDAL MOTION
RT	ESTUARINE TIDES
RT	QUARTER DIURNAL TIDES
RT	SHALLOW WATER
RT	TIDE-SURGE INTERACTION

SHALLOW-WATER WAVES
UF	long gravity waves
UF	long waves
UF	long-period water waves
UF	long-period waves
BT1	WATER WAVES
NT1	CNOIDAL WAVES
NT1	SOLITARY WAVES
NT1	TIDAL BORES
RT	NONLINEAR WAVES
RT	SHALLOW WATER
RT	STORM SURGES
RT	TIDAL WAVES
RT	TSUNAMIS
RT	WAVE SCOURING

SHAPE
SN	Used only as a qualifier
UF	configuration
NT1	GRAIN SHAPE
RT	CONTOURS
RT	DEFORMATION
RT	DIMENSIONS
RT	MORPHOMETRY
RT	SIZE

SHAPED CHARGES
BT1	EXPLOSIVES

SHARED FISHERY RESOURCES
USE	**SHARED STOCKS**

SHARED STOCKS
SN	Stocks of associated species occurring within the EEZ of two or more coastal states. Added in 1982
UF	shared fishery resources
UF	transboundary stocks
BT1	STOCKS
RT	ALLOCATION SYSTEMS
RT	EXCLUSIVE ECONOMIC ZONE
RT	FISHERY POLICY
RT	FISHERY RESOURCES
RT	INTERNATIONAL AGREEMENTS
RT	MIGRATORY SPECIES

SHARK ATTACKS
BT1	DIVING HAZARDS
BT2	HAZARDS
RT	BATHING
RT	DIVING
RT	FISH REPELLENTS
RT	HEALTH AND SAFETY

SHARK FISHERIES
SN	Added in 1982
UF	chimaeras fisheries
UF	rays fisheries
UF	skates fisheries
BT1	FINFISH FISHERIES
BT2	FISHERIES
RT	MARINE FISHERIES

SHARK REPELLENTS
USE	**FISH REPELLENTS**

SHARK UTILIZATION
SN	Added in 1982
BT1	UTILIZATION
RT	FISH MEAL
RT	FISH OILS
RT	HUMAN FOOD
RT	PROCESSED FISHERY PRODUCTS
RT	PROCESSING FISHERY PRODUCTS
RT	UNDERUTILIZED SPECIES

SHEAR
NT1	CURRENT SHEAR
NT1	VERTICAL SHEAR
NT1	WIND SHEAR
RT	DYNAMIC VISCOSITY
RT	SHEAR FLOW
RT	SHEAR MODULUS
RT	SHEAR PROBES
RT	SHEAR STRENGTH
RT	SHEAR STRESS

SHEAR FLOW
BT1	FLUID FLOW
BT2	FLUID MOTION
NT1	STRATIFIED SHEAR FLOW
NT1	TURBULENT SHEAR FLOW
RT	DYNAMIC VISCOSITY
RT	MIXING LENGTH
RT	RICHARDSON NUMBER
RT	SHEAR
RT	SHEAR PROBES
RT	VERTICAL SHEAR
RT	WAVE INTERACTIONS

SHEAR FLOW INSTABILITY
USE	**KELVIN-HELMHOLTZ INSTABILITY**

SHEAR INSTABILITY
USE	**KELVIN-HELMHOLTZ INSTABILITY**

SHEAR MODULUS
UF	rigidity modulus
BT1	ELASTIC CONSTANTS
RT	BULK MODULUS
RT	ELASTICITY
RT	MECHANICAL PROPERTIES
RT	SHEAR

SHEAR PROBES
BT1	PROFILERS
RT	CURRENT MEASURING EQUIPMENT
RT	CURRENT SHEAR
RT	FLOWMETERS
RT	SHEAR
RT	SHEAR FLOW
RT	VELOCITY PROFILERS
RT	VERTICAL SHEAR

SHEAR STRENGTH
BT1	STRENGTH
BT2	MECHANICAL PROPERTIES
BT3	PHYSICAL PROPERTIES
BT4	PROPERTIES
RT	BEARING CAPACITY
RT	COHESIVE SEDIMENTS
RT	FLUIDIZATION
RT	GAS HYDRATES
RT	GEOTECHNICAL DATA
RT	PORE PRESSURE
RT	SEDIMENT PROPERTIES
RT	SHEAR
RT	SLOPE STABILITY
RT	STRAIN
RT	STRESS
RT	TENSILE STRENGTH
RT	VANE DEVICES
RT	VANE SHEAR TESTING

SHEAR STRESS
UF	shearing stress
UF	tangential stresses
BT1	STRESS
BT2	FORCES (MECHANICS)
RT	BOTTOM STRESS
RT	COUETTE FLOW
RT	DYNAMIC VISCOSITY
RT	REYNOLDS STRESSES
RT	SHEAR
RT	TORQUE
RT	WIND STRESS

SHEAR WAVE VELOCITIES
BT1	SEISMIC VELOCITIES
BT2	VELOCITY
RT	S-WAVES
RT	SEDIMENT PROPERTIES

SHEAR WAVES
USE	**S-WAVES**

SHEAR ZONE
RT	FAULTS
RT	ORES

SHEARING STRESS
USE	**SHEAR STRESS**

SHELF CIRCULATION
USE	**SHELF DYNAMICS**

SHELF CURRENTS
BT1	WATER CURRENTS
BT2	WATER MOTION
RT	OCEAN CURRENTS
RT	SHELF DYNAMICS
RT	SHELF WAVES

SHELF DYNAMICS
UF	coastal circulation
UF	shallow-water dynamics
UF	shelf circulation
BT1	WATER CIRCULATION
BT2	WATER MOTION
NT1	BAY DYNAMICS
NT1	ESTUARINE DYNAMICS
NT1	FJORD DYNAMICS
NT1	NEARSHORE DYNAMICS
NT1	SHELF EDGE DYNAMICS
RT	COASTAL COUNTERCURRENTS
RT	COASTAL JETS
RT	COASTAL OCEANOGRAPHY
RT	COASTAL UPWELLING
RT	COASTAL WATERS
RT	CONTINENTAL SHELVES
RT	DYNAMICAL OCEANOGRAPHY
RT	SEMI-ENCLOSED SEAS
RT	SHALLOW WATER
RT	SHELF CURRENTS
RT	SHELF EDGE FRONTS
RT	SHELF FRONTS
RT	SHELF SEAS
RT	SHELF WAVES
RT	TIDAL MIXING

SHELF EDGE
UF	continental shelf break
UF	continental shelf edge
BT1	SUBMARINE FEATURES
BT2	TOPOGRAPHIC FEATURES
RT	CONTINENTAL SHELVES
RT	CONTINENTAL SLOPE
RT	SHELF EDGE DYNAMICS
RT	SHELF EDGE FRONTS
RT	SHELF SEAS

SHELF EDGE DYNAMICS
BT1	SHELF DYNAMICS
BT2	WATER CIRCULATION
BT3	WATER MOTION
RT	SHELF EDGE
RT	SHELF FRONTS
RT	SLOPE PROCESSES

SHELF EDGE FRONTS
BT1	SHELF FRONTS
BT2	OCEANIC FRONTS
BT3	FRONTS
RT	CONTINENTAL SHELVES
RT	SHELF DYNAMICS
RT	SHELF EDGE

SHELF FACIES
BT1	FACIES
RT	SHELF SEAS
RT	SHELF SEDIMENTATION

SHELF FRONTS
BT1	OCEANIC FRONTS
BT2	FRONTS
NT1	SHELF EDGE FRONTS
RT	SHELF DYNAMICS
RT	SHELF EDGE DYNAMICS
RT	SHELF SEAS

SHELF GEOLOGY
BT1	MARINE GEOLOGY
BT2	GEOLOGY
BT3	EARTH SCIENCES
RT	BED LOAD
RT	CONTINENTAL SHELVES
RT	SEDIMENT TRANSPORT
RT	SHELF SEAS
RT	SHELF SEDIMENTATION

SHELF LIFE
USE	**STORAGE LIFE**

SHELF SEAS
BT1	MARGINAL SEAS
RT	BOTTOM CURRENTS
RT	CONTINENTAL SHELVES
RT	SEMI-ENCLOSED SEAS
RT	SHALLOW WATER
RT	SHELF DYNAMICS
RT	SHELF EDGE
RT	SHELF FACIES
RT	SHELF FRONTS
RT	SHELF GEOLOGY
RT	SHELF SEDIMENTATION
RT	SUBSURFACE CURRENTS

SHELF SEDIMENTATION
BT1	SEDIMENTATION
RT	BED LOAD
RT	CONTINENTAL SHELVES
RT	SEDIMENT TRANSPORT
RT	SEDIMENTARY ENVIRONMENTS
RT	SHELF FACIES
RT	SHELF GEOLOGY
RT	SHELF SEAS
RT	TIDAL DEPOSITS

SHELF WAVES
BT1	TRAPPED WAVES
BT2	WATER WAVES
RT	NONLINEAR WAVES
RT	SHELF CURRENTS
RT	SHELF DYNAMICS

SHELLFISH
SN	Common category which includes shelled molluscs and crustaceans, especially those used as human food
RT	BOTULISM
RT	COMMERCIAL SPECIES
RT	FISHERY RESOURCES
RT	FRESHWATER CRUSTACEANS
RT	FRESHWATER MOLLUSCS
RT	HARVESTING
RT	MARINE CRUSTACEANS
RT	MARINE MOLLUSCS
RT	SEAFOOD
RT	SHELLFISH CATCH STATISTICS
RT	SHELLFISH CULTURE
RT	SHELLS

SHELLFISH CATCH STATISTICS
SN	Catch tabulation in number or weight of shellfish species
BT1	CATCH STATISTICS
BT2	FISHERY STATISTICS

SHELLFISH CATCH STATISTICS (cont'd)
RT	BY CATCH
RT	FRESHWATER CRUSTACEANS
RT	FRESHWATER MOLLUSCS
RT	MARINE CRUSTACEANS
RT	MARINE MOLLUSCS
RT	SHELLFISH
RT	SHELLFISH FISHERIES

SHELLFISH CULTURE
BT1	AQUACULTURE
NT1	CRUSTACEAN CULTURE
NT2	BRINE SHRIMP CULTURE
NT2	CRAB CULTURE
NT2	CRAYFISH CULTURE
NT2	LOBSTER CULTURE
NT2	PRAWN CULTURE
NT2	SHRIMP CULTURE
NT1	MOLLUSC CULTURE
NT2	CLAM CULTURE
NT2	MUSSEL CULTURE
NT2	OYSTER CULTURE
NT2	SCALLOP CULTURE
NT2	SQUID CULTURE
RT	BOTTOM CULTURE
RT	BRACKISHWATER AQUACULTURE
RT	CULTURE TANKS
RT	FRESHWATER AQUACULTURE
RT	FRESHWATER MOLLUSCS
RT	GRADING
RT	HATCHERIES
RT	HUSBANDRY DISEASES
RT	INTENSIVE CULTURE
RT	MARINE AQUACULTURE
RT	OFF-BOTTOM CULTURE
RT	PEARL CULTURE
RT	RECIRCULATING SYSTEMS
RT	SEED COLLECTION
RT	SHELLFISH
RT	SHELLFISH FISHERIES
RT	SHELLS
RT	SPAT
RT	THERMAL AQUACULTURE

SHELLFISH DISEASES
USE	**FISH DISEASES**

SHELLFISH FISHERIES
BT1	FISHERIES
NT1	ECHINODERM FISHERIES
NT1	MOLLUSC FISHERIES
NT2	CEPHALOPOD FISHERIES
NT2	CLAM FISHERIES
NT2	GASTROPOD FISHERIES
NT2	MUSSEL FISHERIES
NT2	OYSTER FISHERIES
NT2	SCALLOP FISHERIES
RT	FRESHWATER CRUSTACEANS
RT	FRESHWATER MOLLUSCS
RT	MARINE CRUSTACEANS
RT	MARINE FISHERIES
RT	MARINE MOLLUSCS
RT	OYSTER REEFS
RT	SHELLFISH CATCH STATISTICS
RT	SHELLFISH CULTURE

SHELLFISH POISONING
USE	**FISH POISONING**

SHELLS
SN	Description and composition of exoskeletons of different shellfish species and their use as commercial products
UF	seashells
BT1	ANIMAL PRODUCTS
RT	BRACKISHWATER MOLLUSCS
RT	CALCIFICATION
RT	CONCHOLOGY
RT	DECALCIFICATION

SHELLS (cont'd)
RT	EXOSKELETON
RT	FRESHWATER MOLLUSCS
RT	MALACOLOGY
RT	MANTLE
RT	MARINE MOLLUSCS
RT	OOZES
RT	PEARL FISHERIES
RT	SHELLFISH
RT	SHELLFISH CULTURE

SHELTERED ENVIRONMENTS
USE	**SHELTERED HABITATS**

SHELTERED HABITATS
SN	Added in 1980
UF	sheltered environments
BT1	HABITAT
RT	ECOLOGICAL ZONATION
RT	EXPOSURE TOLERANCE

SHELTERS
SN	Natural or artificial underwater shelters made for improvement of the habitat or for fishing purposes
UF	artificial shelters
RT	AQUACULTURE
RT	ARTIFICIAL REEFS
RT	ARTIFICIAL SPAWNING GROUNDS
RT	ATTRACTING TECHNIQUES
RT	HABITAT IMPROVEMENT (PHYSICAL)

SHINGLE
BT1	CLASTICS
BT2	SEDIMENTS
RT	BEACH ACCRETION
RT	BEACH RIDGES
RT	PEBBLES

SHINGLE BEACHES
USE	**BEACHES**

SHIP ANCHORS
USE	**ANCHORS**

SHIP BEHAVIOUR
USE	**SHIP MOTION**

SHIP CANALS
UF	navigation canals
BT1	CANALS
BT2	INLAND WATERS
RT	HARBOURS
RT	INTEROCEAN CANALS
RT	NAVIGATIONAL CHANNELS
RT	SHIPPING

SHIP DESIGN
BT1	DESIGN
BT2	ENGINEERING
RT	HULLS
RT	SHIP HULLS
RT	SHIP MODELS
RT	SHIP PERFORMANCE
RT	SHIP TECHNOLOGY

SHIP DRIFT
UF	drift (ships)
BT1	DRIFT
RT	DEAD RECKONING
RT	LAGRANGIAN CURRENT MEASUREMENT
RT	STATION KEEPING

SHIP FITTINGS
USE	**SHIPBOARD EQUIPMENT**

SHIP HANDLING
RT	HANDLING
RT	MANOEUVRABILITY
RT	NAVIGATION
RT	SEAMANSHIP

SHIP HULLS
BT1	HULLS
RT	CATAMARANS
RT	FOULING CONTROL
RT	SHIP DESIGN
RT	SHIP TECHNOLOGY

SHIP LOSSES
RT	CAPSIZING
RT	COLLISIONS
RT	FIRE
RT	GROUNDINGS
RT	OIL SPILLS
RT	SHIPPING
RT	WAVE EFFECTS
RT	WRECKS

SHIP MODELS
BT1	SCALE MODELS
BT2	MODELS
RT	SHIP DESIGN
RT	SHIP STABILITY
RT	SHIP TECHNOLOGY
RT	SHIPS
RT	TOWING TANKS
RT	UNDERWATER VEHICLES

SHIP MOORING SYSTEMS
SN	To include systems for fixed and mobile platforms
BT1	MOORING SYSTEMS
NT1	SINGLE POINT MOORINGS
RT	ANCHORING
RT	BERTHING
RT	FENDERS
RT	MOORING BUOYS
RT	MOORING LINES
RT	MOORING MOTION EFFECTS
RT	POSITIONING SYSTEMS
RT	SEMISUBMERSIBLE PLATFORMS
RT	SHIPS

SHIP MOTION
UF	motion (ships)
UF	seakeeping
UF	ship behaviour
NT1	CAPSIZING
NT1	HEAVING
NT1	PITCHING
NT1	RIGHTING
NT1	ROLLING
NT1	SURGING
NT1	SWAYING
NT1	YAWING
RT	HEAVE COMPENSATORS
RT	MOTION
RT	SEA SICKNESS
RT	SEAMANSHIP
RT	SHIP STABILITY
RT	SHIP TECHNOLOGY
RT	SHIPS
RT	STABILIZERS
RT	STATION KEEPING
RT	WAKES
RT	WAVE ACTION
RT	WAVE DAMPING
RT	WAVE EFFECTS
RT	WAVE FORCES

SHIP PERFORMANCE
RT	SHIP DESIGN
RT	SHIP SPEED
RT	SHIP STABILITY
RT	SHIP TECHNOLOGY

SHIP PERFORMANCE (cont'd)
RT	SHIPS

SHIP ROUTEING
UF	weather routeing
NT1	ICE ROUTEING
RT	HURRICANES
RT	NAVIGATION
RT	WAVE FORECASTING
RT	WEATHER FORECASTING

SHIP SPEED
BT1	VELOCITY
RT	LOGBOOKS
RT	NAVIGATION
RT	SHIP PERFORMANCE
RT	WAKES

SHIP STABILITY
BT1	STABILITY
RT	CAPSIZING
RT	ICING
RT	LIFEBOATS
RT	RIGHTING
RT	SEAMANSHIP
RT	SHIP MODELS
RT	SHIP MOTION
RT	SHIP PERFORMANCE
RT	SHIP TECHNOLOGY
RT	SHIPS
RT	STABILIZERS
RT	SURFACE CRAFT

SHIP TECHNOLOGY
SN	Restrict use to publications concerned with general aspects of the design and construction of vessels and propulsion systems. Before 1982 search SHIPBUILDING, MARINE ENGINEERING and NAVAL ARCHITECTURE
UF	marine engineering
UF	naval architecture
UF	naval engineering
UF	naval technology
UF	shipbuilding
BT1	TECHNOLOGY
RT	ARTIFICIAL HARBOURS
RT	DEFENCE CRAFT
RT	ENGINEERING
RT	ENGINEERING DRAWINGS
RT	FISHING VESSELS
RT	FUEL ECONOMY
RT	HYDROFOILS
RT	MARINE TRANSPORTATION
RT	NAVAL BASES
RT	PATENTS
RT	PROPULSION SYSTEMS
RT	RESEARCH VESSELS
RT	SHIP DESIGN
RT	SHIP HULLS
RT	SHIP MODELS
RT	SHIP MOTION
RT	SHIP PERFORMANCE
RT	SHIP STABILITY
RT	SHIPS
RT	STEERING SYSTEMS
RT	SURFACE CRAFT
RT	TOWED BODY DESIGN
RT	UNDERWATER VEHICLES

SHIPBOARD ANALYSIS
SN	Use for analysis aboard research vessels
BT1	WATER ANALYSIS
RT	ANALYSIS
RT	ANALYTICAL TECHNIQUES

SHIPBOARD COMPUTERS
USE **COMPUTERS**

SHIPBOARD EQUIPMENT
UF   marine fittings
UF   ship fittings
BT1   EQUIPMENT
RT   DIESEL ENGINES
RT   PROPULSION SYSTEMS
RT   THRUSTERS

SHIPBORNE WAVE RECORDERS
USE **WAVE RECORDERS**

SHIPBUILDING
USE **SHIP TECHNOLOGY**

SHIPPING
SN   Use only as a collective term in the context of transportation, navigation, traffic on high seas, trade, commerce, maritime law, etc.
RT   CERTIFICATION
RT   DEFENCE CRAFT
RT   MARITIME LEGISLATION
RT   NAVIGATION REGULATIONS
RT   PROPULSION SYSTEMS
RT   SHIP CANALS
RT   SHIP LOSSES
RT   SHIPPING LANES
RT   SHIPS
RT   SURFACE CRAFT
RT   TRAFFIC MANAGEMENT
RT   UNDERWATER VEHICLES
RT   VEHICLES
RT   WRECKS

SHIPPING LANES
SN   Routes used by merchant vessels
RT   MARINE TRANSPORTATION
RT   MERCHANT SHIPS
RT   SELECTED SHIPS
RT   SHIPPING
RT   TRAFFIC MANAGEMENT

SHIPPING NOISE
BT1   AMBIENT NOISE
BT2   NOISE (SOUND)
RT   SURFACE NOISE

SHIPPING RULES
USE **NAVIGATION REGULATIONS**

SHIPS
SN   Use of a more specific term is recommended. See also SURFACE CRAFT
BT1   SURFACE CRAFT
BT2   VEHICLES
NT1   CABLE SHIPS
NT1   LIGHTERS
NT1   LIGHTSHIPS
NT1   MERCHANT SHIPS
NT2   BULK CARRIERS
NT2   CONTAINER SHIPS
NT2   PASSENGER SHIPS
NT2   SELECTED SHIPS
NT2   TANKER SHIPS
NT1   MOTOR BOATS
NT1   PROTECTION VESSELS
NT1   SAILING SHIPS
NT2   YACHTS
NT1   SUPPLY BOATS
NT1   SUPPORT SHIPS
NT2   FACTORY SHIPS
NT2   MOTHER SHIPS
NT1   TUGS
NT1   WEATHER SHIPS
RT   COLLISION AVOIDANCE
RT   GROUNDINGS
RT   ICING

SHIPS (cont'd)
RT   LOGBOOKS
RT   MARINE TRANSPORTATION
RT   NAVIGATION
RT   SHIP MODELS
RT   SHIP MOORING SYSTEMS
RT   SHIP MOTION
RT   SHIP PERFORMANCE
RT   SHIP STABILITY
RT   SHIP TECHNOLOGY
RT   SHIPPING
RT   STEERING SYSTEMS
RT   TRANSPORTATION

SHIPS LOGBOOKS
USE **LOGBOOKS**

SHIPS OF OPPORTUNITY
USE **SELECTED SHIPS**

SHOALING
RT   BEACH CUSPS
RT   SEDIMENT TRANSPORT
RT   SHOALS
RT   WAVES ON BEACHES

SHOALING WAVES
RT   BEACH CUSPS
RT   BREAKING WAVES
RT   ROLLERS
RT   SHOALS
RT   WAVES ON BEACHES

SHOALS
SN   Submerged ridges, banks, bars and reefs constituting a danger for navigation
UF   reefs (navigational hazard)
BT1   SUBMARINE FEATURES
BT2   TOPOGRAPHIC FEATURES
RT   BANKS (TOPOGRAPHY)
RT   COASTAL WATERS
RT   COASTS
RT   CORAL REEFS
RT   GROUNDINGS
RT   NAVIGATIONAL HAZARDS
RT   REEFS
RT   RELIEF FORMS
RT   SAND BANKS
RT   SEDIMENT TRANSPORT
RT   SHALLOW WATER
RT   SHOALING
RT   SHOALING WAVES
RT   SUBMARINE BANKS

SHORAN
BT1   RADIO NAVIGATION
BT2   POSITION FIXING

SHORE PROTECTION
UF   coast protection
UF   protection (coastal)
BT1   COASTAL ZONE MANAGEMENT
BT2   MANAGEMENT
RT   ARTIFICIAL SEAWEED
RT   BEACH EROSION
RT   COAST DEFENCES
RT   COASTAL ENGINEERING
RT   COASTAL EROSION
RT   COASTAL STRUCTURES
RT   CONSERVATION
RT   ICE LOADS
RT   LAKE RECLAMATION
RT   PROTECTION
RT   RECLAMATION

SHORE STATIONS
USE **INSHORE STATIONS**

SHORE WHALING
USE **ARTISANAL WHALING**

SHORELINE EROSION
USE **COASTAL EROSION**

SHORELINE FEATURES
USE **COASTAL LANDFORMS**

SHORELINES
USE **COASTS**

SHORT-CRESTED WAVES
BT1   SURFACE WATER WAVES
BT2   WATER WAVES
RT   DIRECTIONAL SPECTRA
RT   LONG-CRESTED WAVES
RT   WAVE CRESTS
RT   WAVE DIRECTION

SHORT-TERM CHANGES
BT1   TEMPORAL VARIATIONS
RT   LONG-TERM CHANGES
RT   PREDICTION
RT   SHORT-TERM RECORDS

SHORT-TERM PLANNING
SN   Added in 1980
BT1   PLANNING
RT   LONG-TERM PLANNING

SHORT-TERM RECORDS
RT   SHORT-TERM CHANGES

SHORT WAVE-LONG WAVE INTERACTIONS
UF   long wave-short wave interactions
BT1   WAVE-WAVE INTERACTION
BT2   WAVE INTERACTIONS
RT   SURFACE WATER WAVES

SHORT WAVE RADIATION
USE **SOLAR RADIATION**

SHRIMP CULTURE
SN   Before 1982 search CRUSTACEAN CULTURE
UF   marine shrimp culture
UF   saltwater shrimp culture
UF   shrimp farming
BT1   CRUSTACEAN CULTURE
BT2   SHELLFISH CULTURE
BT3   AQUACULTURE
RT   BRACKISHWATER AQUACULTURE
RT   COASTAL LAGOONS
RT   CULTURE TANKS
RT   HATCHERIES
RT   MARINE AQUACULTURE
RT   MASS CULTURE
RT   NURSERY PONDS
RT   POLYCULTURE
RT   POND CULTURE

SHRIMP FARMING
USE **SHRIMP CULTURE**

SHRIMP FISHERIES
SN   Added in 1982
UF   cangronid fisheries
UF   caridean shrimp fisheries
UF   non penaeid shrimp fisheries
UF   palaemonid fisheries
UF   pandalid fisheries
UF   penaeid shrimp fisheries
UF   prawn fisheries
BT1   CRUSTACEAN FISHERIES
BT2   FISHERIES
RT   DEMERSAL FISHERIES
RT   LAGOON FISHERIES

SHRIMP FISHERIES (cont'd)
RT	MARINE FISHERIES
RT	MIGRATORY SPECIES
RT	RIVER FISHERIES

SIAL
UF	granitic layer
BT1	EARTH CRUST
BT2	EARTH STRUCTURE
RT	CONTINENTAL CRUST
RT	SIMA

SIBLING SPECIES
BT1	SPECIES
BT2	TAXA
RT	EVOLUTION
RT	GENETICS

SICKNESS
USE	**HUMAN DISEASES**

SIDE FILLETS
USE	**FISH FILLETS**

SIDE SCAN SONAR
BT1	ACTIVE SONAR
BT2	SONAR
BT3	REMOTE SENSING EQUIPMENT
BT4	EQUIPMENT
RT	GLORIA
RT	SEAFLOOR MAPPING
RT	SONOGRAPHS

SIDERITE
BT1	CARBONATE MINERALS
BT2	MINERALS

SIGMA-T
BT1	WATER DENSITY
BT2	DENSITY
BT3	PHYSICAL PROPERTIES
BT4	PROPERTIES
RT	ATMOSPHERIC PRESSURE
RT	DENSITY
RT	DENSITY SECTIONS
RT	IN SITU DENSITY
RT	IN SITU TEMPERATURE
RT	KNUDSEN TABLES
RT	POTENTIAL DENSITY
RT	SALINITY

SIGNAL PROCESSING
BT1	DATA PROCESSING
RT	FOURIER ANALYSIS
RT	SPECTRAL ANALYSIS
RT	TELEMETRY

SIGNAL-TO-NOISE RATIO
RT	ATTENUATION
RT	ELECTRONIC NOISE
RT	IMAGE ENHANCEMENT
RT	RATIOS

SIGNIFICANT WAVE HEIGHT
BT1	WAVE HEIGHT
RT	OFFSHORE STRUCTURES
RT	WAVE FORECASTING

SIGNIFICANT WAVES
BT1	SURFACE WATER WAVES
BT2	WATER WAVES
RT	WAVE HEIGHT
RT	WAVE PERIOD

SILAGE FROM FISH
USE	**FISH SILAGE**

SILICA
UF	silicon dioxide
BT1	SILICON COMPOUNDS
RT	CHERTS
RT	CRISTOBALITE
RT	SILICEOUS OOZE
RT	THOLEIITE

SILICATE MINERALS
BT1	MINERALS
NT1	AMPHIBOLES
NT1	ANDALUSITE
NT1	CLAY MINERALS
NT2	CHLORITE
NT2	ILLITE
NT2	KAOLIN
NT2	KAOLINITE
NT2	MONTMORILLONITE
NT2	NONTRONITE
NT2	PALYGORSKITE
NT2	SAPONITE
NT2	SMECTITE
NT2	VERMICULITE
NT1	FELDSPARS
NT2	ANORTHITE
NT2	ANORTHOCLASE
NT2	ORTHOCLASE
NT2	PLAGIOCLASE
NT1	GARNET
NT1	KYANITE
NT1	MICAS
NT2	BIOTITE
NT2	GLAUCONITE
NT2	HYDROBIOTITE
NT2	MUSCOVITE
NT1	OLIVINE
NT1	OPAL
NT1	PYROPHYLLITE
NT1	PYROXENES
NT2	AUGITE
NT1	QUARTZ
NT1	QUARTZITE
NT1	SEPIOLITE
NT1	TITANITE
NT1	TOURMALINE
NT1	ZEOLITES
NT2	ANALCITE
NT2	CLINOPTILONITE
NT2	HEULANDITE
NT2	PHILLIPSITE
NT1	ZIRCON
RT	SILICATES

SILICATES
BT1	SILICON COMPOUNDS
RT	CHEMICAL COMPOUNDS
RT	IRON SILICATES
RT	MAGNESIUM SILICATES
RT	NON-CONSERVATIVE PROPERTIES
RT	NUTRIENTS (MINERAL)
RT	SAND
RT	SILICATE MINERALS
RT	SILICIC ACID
RT	SILICON

SILICEOUS OOZE
UF	ooze (siliceous)
BT1	OOZES
NT1	DIATOM OOZE
NT1	RADIOLARIAN OOZE
RT	SILICA
RT	SILICEOUS SEDIMENTS

SILICEOUS ROCKS
NT1	CHERTS
NT1	DIATOMITES
NT1	PORCELLANITE
NT1	RADIOLARITE
RT	SANDSTONE
RT	SEDIMENTARY ROCKS

SILICEOUS ROCKS (cont'd)
RT	SILICEOUS SEDIMENTS

SILICEOUS SEDIMENTS
BT1	BIOGENIC DEPOSITS
RT	CHEMICAL SEDIMENTS
RT	FLINT
RT	PELAGIC SEDIMENTS
RT	SILICEOUS OOZE
RT	SILICEOUS ROCKS

SILICIC ACID
BT1	INORGANIC ACIDS
BT2	HYDROGEN COMPOUNDS
RT	SILICATES
RT	SILICON COMPOUNDS

SILICIFICATION
RT	CHERTIFICATION
RT	DIAGENESIS
RT	METASOMATISM

SILICON
BT1	CHEMICAL ELEMENTS
RT	SILICATES
RT	SILICON COMPOUNDS
RT	SILICON CYCLE
RT	SILICON ISOTOPES
RT	TRACE ELEMENTS

SILICON COMPOUNDS
NT1	SILICA
NT1	SILICATES
RT	ALUMINIUM COMPOUNDS
RT	CHEMICAL COMPOUNDS
RT	NUTRIENTS (MINERAL)
RT	SILICIC ACID
RT	SILICON
RT	SILICON CYCLE

SILICON CYCLE
BT1	NUTRIENT CYCLES
BT2	BIOGEOCHEMICAL CYCLE
BT3	CYCLES
RT	CHEMICAL CYCLES
RT	SILICON
RT	SILICON COMPOUNDS

SILICON DIOXIDE
USE	**SILICA**

SILICON ISOTOPES
BT1	ISOTOPES
RT	SILICON

SILL DEPTH
BT1	DEPTH
BT2	DIMENSIONS
RT	FJORDS
RT	SILLS

SILLS
BT1	SUBMARINE FEATURES
BT2	TOPOGRAPHIC FEATURES
RT	FJORDS
RT	RELIEF FORMS
RT	RIDGES
RT	SILL DEPTH
RT	SUBMARINE RIDGES

SILO CULTURE
SN	Added in 1982
BT1	AQUACULTURE TECHNIQUES
RT	FISH CULTURE
RT	INTENSIVE CULTURE

SILT
BT1	CLASTICS
BT2	SEDIMENTS
RT	COHESIONLESS SEDIMENTS
RT	FLUIDIZED SEDIMENT FLOW
RT	LUTITES
RT	MUD
RT	SAND
RT	SILT METERS
RT	SILTING
RT	SILTSTONE

SILT METERS
RT	SEDIMENT TRAPS
RT	SILT

SILTATION
USE	**SILTING**

SILTING
UF	siltation
BT1	DEPOSITION
RT	NAVIGATIONAL CHANNELS
RT	SEDIMENTATION
RT	SILT

SILTSTONE
BT1	CLASTICS
BT2	SEDIMENTS
RT	LUTITES
RT	MUDSTONE
RT	SEDIMENTARY ROCKS
RT	SILT
RT	SLATES

SILURIAN
SN	Before 1982 search SILURIAN PERIOD
BT1	PALAEOZOIC
BT2	GEOLOGICAL TIME

SILVER
BT1	CHEMICAL ELEMENTS
RT	FERROMANGANESE NODULES
RT	HEAVY METALS
RT	HOT BRINES
RT	METALLIFEROUS SEDIMENTS
RT	METALS
RT	SILVER COMPOUNDS
RT	SILVER ISOTOPES
RT	TRACE METALS

SILVER COMPOUNDS
RT	CHEMICAL COMPOUNDS
RT	SILVER

SILVER ISOTOPES
BT1	ISOTOPES
RT	SILVER

SIMA
UF	basaltic layer
BT1	EARTH CRUST
BT2	EARTH STRUCTURE
RT	OCEANIC CRUST
RT	SIAL

SIMILARITY INDEX
USE	**SPECIES DIVERSITY**

SIMULATION
SN	Used only as a qualifier
RT	GAME THEORY
RT	MODELLING
RT	OPERATIONS RESEARCH
RT	PREDICTION
RT	SIMULATORS
RT	SYSTEM ANALYSIS

SIMULATORS
RT	MODELS
RT	SIMULATION
RT	TRAINING AIDS

SINGLE ANCHOR LEG MOORING
USE	**SINGLE POINT MOORINGS**

SINGLE CELL CULTURE
USE	**PHYTOPLANKTON CULTURE**

SINGLE CELL PROTEINS
SN	Added in 1982
UF	ascp
UF	scp
BT1	PROTEINS
BT2	ORGANIC COMPOUNDS
RT	ARTIFICIAL FEEDING
RT	BACTERIA
RT	DIETS
RT	FEED
RT	FISH CULTURE
RT	SLUDGE
RT	YEASTS

SINGLE POINT MOORINGS
SN	Restricted to ships
UF	single anchor leg mooring
BT1	SHIP MOORING SYSTEMS
BT2	MOORING SYSTEMS
RT	ARTICULATED COLUMNS
RT	LOADING BUOYS
RT	TANKER LOADING

SINKING
SN	Added in 1982
UF	sinking rate
RT	COLLISIONS
RT	PLANKTON
RT	SUSPENDED PARTICULATE MATTER

SINKING RATE
USE	**SINKING**

SINKING RATE
USE	**SETTLING RATE**

SINUSOIDAL WAVES
USE	**LINEAR WAVES**

SITE EVALUATION
USE	**SITE SELECTION**

SITE EXPLORATION
USE	**SITE SURVEYS**

SITE INVESTIGATION
USE	**SITE SURVEYS**

SITE SELECTION
SN	Site selection and evaluation for aquaculture purposes, siting of power plants, fishing harbours etc. Added in 1980
UF	aquaculture sites
UF	site evaluation
BT1	EVALUATION
RT	AQUACULTURE FACILITIES
RT	AQUACULTURE TECHNIQUES
RT	ARTIFICIAL HARBOURS
RT	CAGE CULTURE
RT	DRILLING
RT	ECONOMIC FEASIBILITY
RT	ENCLOSURES
RT	ENVIRONMENTAL CONDITIONS
RT	ENVIRONMENTAL SURVEYS
RT	FEASIBILITY STUDIES
RT	FISHING HARBOURS
RT	MINING
RT	NATURE CONSERVATION

SITE SELECTION (cont'd)
RT	PLANNING
RT	POWER PLANTS
RT	REPTILE CULTURE
RT	SITE SURVEYS
RT	WASTE DISPOSAL SITES
RT	WATER QUALITY

SITE SURVEYS
SN	Before 1986 search also SITE INVESTIGATION
UF	site exploration
UF	site investigation
BT1	SURVEYS
RT	BOTTOM PHOTOGRAPHS
RT	DEEP-SEA MINING
RT	DRILLING
RT	GEOLOGICAL HAZARDS
RT	GEOLOGICAL SURVEYS
RT	GEOPHYSICAL SURVEYS
RT	HAZARDS
RT	HYDROGRAPHIC SURVEYS
RT	OCEANOGRAPHIC SURVEYS
RT	SEABED VEHICLES
RT	SITE SELECTION
RT	SLOPE STABILITY
RT	SURVEYING UNDERWATER
RT	WASTE DISPOSAL SITES

SITOSTEROLS
BT1	STEROLS
BT2	STEROIDS
BT3	LIPIDS
BT4	ORGANIC COMPOUNDS

SIZE
SN	Used only as a qualifier
BT1	DIMENSIONS
NT1	PARTICLE SIZE
RT	AREA
RT	SHAPE
RT	SIZE DISTRIBUTION
RT	VOLUME

SIZE COMPOSITION
USE	**SIZE DISTRIBUTION**

SIZE DISTRIBUTION
SN	Length and weight frequencies
UF	size composition
BT1	POPULATION STRUCTURE
BT2	POPULATION CHARACTERISTICS
RT	AGE COMPOSITION
RT	LENGTH-WEIGHT RELATIONSHIPS
RT	SIZE
RT	STATISTICAL ANALYSIS

SIZE GRADING
USE	**GRADING**

SIZE-LIMIT REGULATIONS
BT1	FISHERY REGULATIONS
BT2	LEGISLATION
RT	MESH REGULATIONS

SIZE-WEIGHT RELATIONSHIPS
USE	**LENGTH-WEIGHT RELATIONSHIPS**

SKATES FISHERIES
USE	**SHARK FISHERIES**

SKELETON
BT1	MUSCULOSKELETAL SYSTEM
NT1	ENDOSKELETON
NT2	BONES
NT3	SKULL
NT3	VERTEBRAE
NT1	EXOSKELETON
NT2	CARAPACE
NT2	CUTICLES

SKELETON (cont'd)
NT2	SCALES
RT	ANATOMY
RT	CARTILAGE
RT	OSTEOLOGY

SKEWNESS
SN	Used only as a qualifier
RT	COEFFICIENTS
RT	KURTOSIS
RT	STATISTICAL ANALYSIS

SKID MOUNTED UNITS
USE	**MODULES**

SKIMMERS (OIL REMOVAL)
USE	**OIL REMOVAL**

SKIN
UF	ectoderm
UF	epidermis
RT	BODY WALLS
RT	EPITHELIA

SKIN DIVING
USE	**SCUBA DIVING**

SKIN TEMPERATURE
USE	**SURFACE RADIATION TEMPERATURE**

SKIPJACK TUNA FISHERIES
USE	**TUNA FISHERIES**

SKULL
BT1	BONES
BT2	ENDOSKELETON
BT3	SKELETON
BT4	MUSCULOSKELETAL SYSTEM
RT	BRAIN
RT	HEAD
RT	OTOLITHS

SKY RADIATION
USE	**SOLAR RADIATION**

SLAMMING
USE	**WAVE FORCES**

SLATES
RT	ARGILLACEOUS SEDIMENTS
RT	CHLORITE
RT	METAMORPHIC ROCKS
RT	MICAS
RT	MUDSTONE
RT	SEDIMENTARY ROCKS
RT	SILTSTONE

SLICKS
NT1	WINDROWS
RT	MONOMOLECULAR FILMS
RT	OIL SLICKS
RT	SURFACE FILMS
RT	SURFACE LAYERS
RT	SURFACE MICROLAYER

SLICKS (OIL)
USE	**OIL SLICKS**

SLICKS (SURFACE)
USE	**SURFACE FILMS**

SLIDES
BT1	MASS MOVEMENT
BT2	SEDIMENT MOVEMENT
NT1	LANDSLIDES
RT	CREEP
RT	SLUMPING

SLIDES (PHOTOGRAPHIC)
BT1	AUDIOVISUAL MATERIAL
BT2	DOCUMENTS
RT	FILMSTRIPS
RT	GRAPHICS

SLIDING
USE	**SLUMPING**

SLIMICIDES
USE	**FUNGICIDES**

SLOPE CURRENTS
BT1	WATER CURRENTS
BT2	WATER MOTION

SLOPE ENVIRONMENT
RT	CONTINENTAL SLOPE

SLOPE FOLLOWERS
USE	**WAVE SLOPE FOLLOWERS**

SLOPE INDICATORS
BT1	MEASURING DEVICES
NT1	INCLINOMETERS
NT1	TILTMETERS
NT1	WIRE ANGLE INDICATORS
RT	GRADIENTS

SLOPE PROCESSES
RT	CASCADING
RT	SHELF EDGE DYNAMICS

SLOPE STABILITY
UF	soil stability
BT1	STABILITY
RT	COHESIONLESS SEDIMENTS
RT	COHESIVE SEDIMENTS
RT	CREEP
RT	FAILURES
RT	GEOLOGICAL HAZARDS
RT	LANDSLIDES
RT	MASS MOVEMENT
RT	SEDIMENT STABILITY
RT	SHEAR STRENGTH
RT	SITE SURVEYS
RT	SLOPES (TOPOGRAPHY)
RT	SLUMP STRUCTURES
RT	SLUMPING
RT	SOIL MECHANICS
RT	TRENCHES (PIPELINES)

SLOPE WATER
BT1	WATER MASSES

SLOPES (TOPOGRAPHY)
RT	CONTINENTAL SLOPE
RT	GRADIENTS
RT	ISLAND SLOPE
RT	SLOPE STABILITY
RT	TOPOGRAPHIC FEATURES

SLUDGE
UF	activated sludge
UF	sludge (wastes)
BT1	WASTES
RT	BIOAERATION
RT	MUD
RT	ORGANIC WASTES
RT	SEWAGE
RT	SEWAGE PONDS
RT	SINGLE CELL PROTEINS
RT	SLUDGE TREATMENT
RT	WASTEWATER AQUACULTURE

SLUDGE (DRILLING FLUIDS)
USE	**DRILLING FLUIDS**

SLUDGE (ICE)
USE	**ICE**

SLUDGE (WASTES)
USE	**SLUDGE**

SLUDGE TREATMENT
BT1	WASTE TREATMENT
RT	AERATION
RT	BIODEGRADATION
RT	CHEMICAL DEGRADATION
RT	DECANTATION
RT	OXIDATION
RT	SANITARY ENGINEERING
RT	SEWAGE TREATMENT
RT	SLUDGE
RT	WATER FILTRATION

SLUMP STRUCTURES
UF	slumps
BT1	SEDIMENTARY STRUCTURES
RT	OLISTOLITHS
RT	OLISTOSTROMES
RT	SLOPE STABILITY
RT	SLUMPING

SLUMPING
UF	sliding
BT1	MASS GRAVITY TRANSPORT (SEDIMENTS)
BT2	SEDIMENT TRANSPORT
RT	CONTINENTAL SLOPE
RT	CREEP
RT	EARTHQUAKES
RT	EROSION
RT	FLOW STRUCTURES
RT	FLUIDIZATION
RT	GEOLOGICAL HAZARDS
RT	LANDSLIDES
RT	LIQUEFACTION
RT	OLISTOLITHS
RT	SLIDES
RT	SLOPE STABILITY
RT	SLUMP STRUCTURES

SLUMPS
USE	**SLUMP STRUCTURES**

SLURRIES
RT	MUD
RT	PUMPING
RT	SUSPENSION

SMALL SCALE AQUACULTURE
SN	Added in 1982
UF	artisanal aquaculture
UF	subsistence aquaculture
BT1	AQUACULTURE SYSTEMS
RT	AQUACULTURE DEVELOPMENT
RT	FISH PONDS
RT	SOCIOLOGICAL ASPECTS

SMALL SCALE FISHING
USE	**ARTISANAL FISHING**

SMECTITE
BT1	CLAY MINERALS
BT2	SILICATE MINERALS
BT3	MINERALS

SMOKE
RT	AIR POLLUTION
RT	ATMOSPHERIC PARTICULATES
RT	FIRE

SMOKED PRODUCTS
USE	**CURED PRODUCTS**

SMOKING
USE **CURING**

SMOLTS
RT JUVENILES

SMOOTH MUSCLES
USE **MUSCLES**

SNAPPER FISHERIES
USE **PERCOID FISHERIES**

SNOW
BT1 ATMOSPHERIC PRECIPITATIONS
BT2 HYDROMETEORS
RT HAIL
RT ICE
RT RAINFALL

SNOW CRAB FISHERIES
USE **CRAB FISHERIES**

SOAPS
BT1 DETERGENTS
RT CHEMICAL POLLUTANTS
RT CHEMICAL POLLUTION
RT DOMESTIC WASTES
RT SURFACTANTS
RT WATER HARDNESS

SOCIAL ASPECTS
USE **SOCIOLOGICAL ASPECTS**

SOCIAL BEHAVIOUR
BT1 BEHAVIOUR
NT1 DOMINANCE HIERARCHIES
NT2 PECKING ORDER
NT1 SCHOOLING BEHAVIOUR
RT CETOLOGY
RT ECOLOGICAL AGGREGATIONS
RT GROUP EFFECTS

SOCIAL HIERARCHY
USE **DOMINANCE HIERARCHIES**

SOCIETIES
USE **ORGANIZATIONS**

SOCIOLOGICAL ASPECTS
UF social aspects
UF sociology
RT DEVELOPMENT PROJECTS
RT ECONOMICS
RT EDUCATION
RT FISHERY ORGANIZATIONS
RT LABOUR
RT MANAGEMENT
RT MARINE PARKS
RT PUBLIC HEALTH
RT RECREATION
RT RECREATIONAL WATERS
RT RESOURCE DEVELOPMENT
RT RESOURCE MANAGEMENT
RT SMALL SCALE AQUACULTURE
RT WOMEN
RT WORLD

SOCIOLOGY
USE **SOCIOLOGICAL ASPECTS**

SODAR
SN SOnic Detection And Rangefinding in the atmosphere
UF acoustic surveys (atmosphere)
RT ACOUSTIC IMAGERY
RT LIDAR
RT METEOROLOGICAL INSTRUMENTS
RT REMOTE SENSING EQUIPMENT

SODIUM
BT1 CHEMICAL ELEMENTS
RT ALKALI METALS
RT SODIUM COMPOUNDS
RT SODIUM ISOTOPES

SODIUM CHLORIDE
UF common salt
BT1 SODIUM COMPOUNDS
BT2 ALKALINE EARTH METAL COMPOUNDS
RT CHLORIDES
RT DISSOLVED CHEMICALS
RT EVAPORITES

SODIUM COMPOUNDS
BT1 ALKALINE EARTH METAL COMPOUNDS
NT1 SODIUM CHLORIDE
RT ALKALI METAL COMPOUNDS
RT CHEMICAL COMPOUNDS
RT DISSOLVED SALTS
RT SODIUM

SODIUM ISOTOPES
BT1 ISOTOPES
RT SODIUM

SOFAR
SN SOund Fixing And Rangefinding
BT1 POSITION FIXING
RT SOFAR CHANNEL
RT SOFAR FLOATS
RT SOUND CHANNELS

SOFAR AXIS
USE **SOFAR CHANNEL**

SOFAR CHANNEL
UF deep sound channel
UF sofar axis
BT1 SOUND CHANNELS
RT PERMANENT THERMOCLINE
RT SOFAR
RT SOFAR FLOATS
RT SOUND VELOCITY

SOFAR FLOATS
BT1 SWALLOW FLOATS
BT2 SUBSURFACE DRIFTERS
BT3 DRIFTERS
BT4 CURRENT MEASURING EQUIPMENT
RT SOFAR
RT SOFAR CHANNEL

SOFT ROE
USE **ROES**

SOIL CONSERVATION
BT1 CONSERVATION
RT COASTAL EROSION
RT EROSION
RT EROSION CONTROL
RT SOIL EROSION
RT SOILS
RT WIND EROSION

SOIL EROSION
BT1 EROSION
RT EROSION CONTROL
RT SOIL CONSERVATION
RT SOILS

SOIL MECHANICS
BT1 MECHANICS
BT2 PHYSICS
RT COHESIVE SEDIMENTS
RT COMPACTION
RT CONSOLIDATION
RT CREEP
RT ELASTIC CONSTANTS
RT ELASTICITY

SOIL MECHANICS (cont'd)
RT GEOTECHNOLOGY
RT PENETRATION DEPTH
RT PERMAFROST
RT ROCK MECHANICS
RT SEDIMENT DYMAMICS
RT SEDIMENT DYNAMICS
RT SEDIMENT PROPERTIES
RT SEDIMENT STABILITY
RT SETTLEMENT (STRUCTURAL)
RT SLOPE STABILITY
RT SOILS
RT STRESS-STRAIN RELATIONS
RT TRENCHING
RT VANE DEVICES
RT VOID RATIO
RT VOIDS

SOIL PROPERTIES
USE **SEDIMENT PROPERTIES**

SOIL SAMPLING
USE **SEDIMENT SAMPLING**

SOIL STABILITY
USE **SLOPE STABILITY**

SOILS
UF earth (soil)
RT AGRICULTURE
RT EROSION
RT GEOLOGY
RT GRAVEL
RT HUMUS
RT MUD
RT NATURAL RESOURCES
RT SAND
RT SEDIMENTS
RT SOIL CONSERVATION
RT SOIL EROSION
RT SOIL MECHANICS

SOLAR ACTIVITY
UF sunspots
RT ASTRONOMY
RT LONG-TERM CHANGES
RT SOLAR CONSTANT
RT SOLAR RADIATION
RT SOLAR-TERRESTRIAL ACTIVITY
RT SUN

SOLAR CELLS
BT1 ELECTRIC POWER SOURCES
RT SOLAR POWER
RT SOLAR RADIATION
RT SUN

SOLAR CONSTANT
RT CLIMATIC CHANGES
RT CONSTANTS
RT EXTRATERRESTRIAL RADIATION
RT SOLAR ACTIVITY
RT SOLAR RADIATION
RT SUN

SOLAR DIURNAL TIDES
BT1 SOLAR TIDES
BT2 TIDES
BT3 TIDAL MOTION
RT SUN
RT TIDAL CONSTITUENTS

SOLAR ECLIPSE
UF eclipse (solar)
RT ASTRONOMY
RT LIGHT
RT SOLAR RADIATION
RT SUN
RT VERTICAL MIGRATIONS

SOLAR POWER
BT1	ENERGY RESOURCES
BT2	NATURAL RESOURCES
BT3	RESOURCES
RT	POWER FROM THE SEA
RT	RENEWABLE RESOURCES
RT	SOLAR CELLS
RT	SOLAR RADIATION
RT	SUN

SOLAR RADIATION
UF	diffuse sky radiation
UF	global radiation
UF	net solar radiation
UF	short wave radiation
UF	sky radiation
BT1	ELECTROMAGNETIC RADIATION
BT2	RADIATIONS
NT1	EXTRATERRESTRIAL RADIATION
NT1	REFLECTED GLOBAL RADIATION
RT	ACTINOMETERS
RT	AIR-WATER INTERFACE
RT	ALBEDO
RT	ASTRONOMY
RT	CLIMATE
RT	CLOUD COVER
RT	ENERGY FLOW
RT	EVAPORATION
RT	INFRARED RADIATION
RT	INSOLATION
RT	IRRADIANCE
RT	LIGHT
RT	LIGHT PENETRATION
RT	METEOROLOGY
RT	OPTICAL PROPERTIES
RT	PHOTOSYNTHESIS
RT	PHOTOTAXIS
RT	PHOTOTROPISM
RT	PYRANOMETERS
RT	PYRHELIOMETERS
RT	RADIANCE
RT	RADIATION BALANCE
RT	RADIATIONAL TIDES
RT	RADIATIVE TRANSFER
RT	SOLAR ACTIVITY
RT	SOLAR CELLS
RT	SOLAR CONSTANT
RT	SOLAR ECLIPSE
RT	SOLAR POWER
RT	SOLAR-TERRESTRIAL ACTIVITY
RT	SUN
RT	THERMAL RADIATION
RT	ULTRAVIOLET RADIATION
RT	WATER VAPOUR

SOLAR SEMIDIURNAL TIDES
BT1	SOLAR TIDES
BT2	TIDES
BT3	TIDAL MOTION
RT	SUN
RT	TIDAL CONSTITUENTS

SOLAR-TERRESTRIAL ACTIVITY
UF	extraterrestrial interactions
RT	CLIMATIC CHANGES
RT	LONG-TERM CHANGES
RT	SEA LEVEL CHANGES
RT	SOLAR ACTIVITY
RT	SOLAR RADIATION
RT	SUN
RT	TELECONNECTIONS
RT	TEMPERATURE ANOMALIES

SOLAR TIDES
SN	Before 1982 search also TIDES
BT1	TIDES
BT2	TIDAL MOTION
NT1	SOLAR DIURNAL TIDES
NT1	SOLAR SEMIDIURNAL TIDES
RT	METEOROLOGICAL TIDES

SOLAR TIDES (cont'd)
RT	SUN
RT	TIDAL CONSTITUENTS

SOLARIMETERS
USE	PYRANOMETERS

SOLE FISHERIES
USE	FLATFISH FISHERIES

SOLE MARKS
BT1	CURRENT MARKS
BT2	BEDDING STRUCTURES
BT3	SEDIMENTARY STRUCTURES
RT	FLUTE CASTS

SOLID GAS HYDRATES
USE	GAS HYDRATES

SOLID HYDROCARBONS
USE	HYDROCARBONS

SOLID IMPURITIES
UF	solid wastes
BT1	POLLUTANTS
NT1	PLASTIC DEBRIS
NT1	TAR BALLS
RT	FLOTSAM
RT	PLASTICS

SOLID WASTES
USE	SOLID IMPURITIES

SOLIDIFICATION
BT1	PHASE CHANGES
RT	FREEZING
RT	MELTING

SOLIFLUCTION
USE	CREEP

SOLITARY WAVES
BT1	SHALLOW-WATER WAVES
BT2	WATER WAVES
RT	NONLINEAR WAVES
RT	SOLITONS
RT	SURFACE GRAVITY WAVES

SOLITONS
RT	SOLITARY WAVES

SOLUBILITY
BT1	CHEMICAL PROPERTIES
BT2	PROPERTIES
NT1	GAS SOLUBILITY
RT	CHEMICAL PRECIPITATION
RT	COMPENSATION DEPTH
RT	DISSOLUTION
RT	DISSOLVED GASES
RT	DISSOLVED OXYGEN
RT	LEACHING
RT	OXYGENATION
RT	PHYSICAL PROPERTIES
RT	SATURATION
RT	SOLUTES
RT	SOLUTIONS
RT	SOLVENTS
RT	SUPERSATURATION

SOLUTES
SN	Added in 1980
RT	SOLUBILITY
RT	SOLUTIONS
RT	SOLVENTS

SOLUTION
USE	DISSOLUTION

SOLUTIONS
SN	Used only as a qualifier
NT1	HYDROTHERMAL SOLUTIONS
NT2	HOT BRINES
RT	BRINES
RT	BUFFERS
RT	DISSOLUTION
RT	DISSOLVED OXYGEN
RT	DISSOLVED SALTS
RT	ELECTROANALYSIS
RT	EXCHANGE CAPACITY
RT	LEACHING
RT	SALINE WATER
RT	SATURATION
RT	SOLUBILITY
RT	SOLUTES
RT	SOLVENTS

SOLVATION
NT1	HYDRATION

SOLVENT EXTRACTION
BT1	SEPARATION PROCESSES
RT	DISSOLUTION
RT	LEACHING

SOLVENTS
RT	ADDITIVES
RT	AGENTS
RT	ANIMAL OIL EXTRACTION
RT	CHEMICAL EXTRACTION
RT	DISPERSANTS
RT	DISSOLUTION
RT	FISH OIL EXTRACTION
RT	OIL REMOVAL
RT	SOLUBILITY
RT	SOLUTES
RT	SOLUTIONS

SOMATIC MUTATIONS
USE	MUTATIONS

SONAR
UF	asdic
UF	sonar equipment
UF	sonar systems
BT1	REMOTE SENSING EQUIPMENT
BT2	EQUIPMENT
NT1	ACTIVE SONAR
NT2	DOPPLER SONAR
NT2	ECHOSOUNDERS
NT2	MULTIBEAM SONAR
NT2	SIDE SCAN SONAR
NT1	PASSIVE SONAR
RT	ACOUSTIC ARRAYS
RT	ACOUSTIC EQUIPMENT
RT	ACOUSTIC IMAGERY
RT	ACOUSTIC NAVIGATION
RT	DETECTION
RT	ECHO SURVEYS
RT	ELECTRONIC EQUIPMENT
RT	FISH DETECTION
RT	FISHING OPERATIONS
RT	LOCATING
RT	MILITARY OCEANOGRAPHY
RT	OCEANOGRAPHIC EQUIPMENT
RT	PURSE SEINING
RT	SONAR ARRAYS
RT	SONAR IMAGERY
RT	SONAR RECEIVERS
RT	SONAR TARGETS
RT	SOUND PROPAGATION
RT	SUBMARINES
RT	SURVEYING EQUIPMENT
RT	TRAWLING
RT	UNDERWATER EQUIPMENT
RT	UNDERWATER EXPLOITATION
RT	UNDERWATER OBJECT LOCATION

SONAR ARRAYS	
BT1	ACOUSTIC ARRAYS
BT2	ARRAYS
RT	ACOUSTIC EQUIPMENT
RT	OCEANOGRAPHIC EQUIPMENT
RT	SONAR

SONAR BUOYS	
USE	**SONOBUOYS**

SONAR COUNTERMEASURES	
RT	UNDERSEA WARFARE

SONAR DETECTION	
UF	acoustic detection
UF	sonar interception
RT	ACTIVE SONAR
RT	DETECTION
RT	ECHO LOCATION
RT	ECHO RANGING
RT	ECHOLOCATION
RT	FISH DETECTION
RT	PASSIVE SONAR
RT	SUBMARINES
RT	UNDERSEA WARFARE

SONAR EQUIPMENT	
USE	**SONAR**

SONAR IMAGERY	
BT1	ACOUSTIC IMAGERY
BT2	IMAGERY
BT3	REMOTE SENSING
RT	ACTIVE SONAR
RT	INSONIFICATION
RT	SONAR
RT	SONOGRAPHS

SONAR INTERCEPTION	
USE	**SONAR DETECTION**

SONAR NAVIGATION	
USE	**ACOUSTIC NAVIGATION**

SONAR RECEIVERS	
RT	ACOUSTIC EQUIPMENT
RT	SONAR

SONAR SYSTEMS	
USE	**SONAR**

SONAR TARGETS	
RT	ACOUSTIC EQUIPMENT
RT	SONAR

SONAR TRANSDUCERS	
BT1	ACOUSTIC TRANSDUCERS
BT2	TRANSDUCERS

SONAR TRANSPONDERS	
BT1	ACOUSTIC TRANSPONDERS
BT2	TRANSPONDERS

SONIC TAGS	
UF	acoustic tags
UF	tags (acoustic)
BT1	TAGS
RT	ACOUSTIC EQUIPMENT
RT	ACOUSTICS
RT	BIOTELEMETRY
RT	ELECTRONIC EQUIPMENT
RT	SOUND WAVES
RT	TAGGING
RT	TELEMETRY
RT	TRACKING

SONIC WAVES	
USE	**SOUND WAVES**

SONOBUOYS	
UF	sonar buoys
BT1	BUOYS
RT	HYDROPHONES
RT	PASSIVE SONAR
RT	SEISMIC EQUIPMENT
RT	SEISMIC REFRACTION PROFILING

SONOGRAMS	
USE	**SONOGRAPHS**

SONOGRAPHS	
UF	sonograms
RT	ACTIVE SONAR
RT	GLORIA
RT	INSONIFICATION
RT	SEAFLOOR MAPPING
RT	SIDE SCAN SONAR
RT	SONAR IMAGERY

SORPTION	
UF	absorption (chemistry)
UF	chemisorption
NT1	ADSORPTION
NT1	DESORPTION
RT	SURFACE PROPERTIES

SORTING CENTERS	
USE	**SORTING CENTRES**

SORTING CENTRES	
SN	Referring to national and international centres for sorting and preclassification of aquatic organisms
UF	sorting centers
BT1	ORGANIZATIONS
RT	BIOLOGICAL COLLECTIONS
RT	DATA CENTRES
RT	INFORMATION CENTRES
RT	INTERNATIONAL COOPERATION
RT	PLANKTON SURVEYS

SOUND	
UF	waves (sound)
RT	ACOUSTICS
RT	ELASTIC WAVES
RT	INSONIFICATION
RT	SOUND ABSORPTION
RT	SOUND DIFFRACTION
RT	SOUND GENERATORS
RT	SOUND PRESSURE
RT	SOUND PRODUCTION
RT	SOUND PROPAGATION
RT	SOUND REFLECTION
RT	SOUND REFRACTION
RT	SOUND SCATTERING
RT	SOUND SOURCES
RT	SOUND TRANSMISSION
RT	SOUND VELOCITY

SOUND ABSORPTION	
UF	absorption (sound)
UF	acoustic wave absorption
BT1	ABSORPTION (PHYSICS)
RT	ACOUSTIC INSULATION
RT	SOUND
RT	SOUND ATTENUATION
RT	SOUND PROPAGATION
RT	SOUND REFLECTION
RT	SOUND SCATTERING

SOUND ATTENUATION	
UF	acoustic wave attenuation
BT1	WAVE ATTENUATION
BT2	WAVE DISSIPATION
BT3	ENERGY DISSIPATION

SOUND ATTENUATION (cont'd)	
BT4	ENERGY TRANSFER
RT	ACOUSTIC PROPERTIES
RT	SOUND ABSORPTION
RT	SOUND PRESSURE
RT	SOUND SCATTERING
RT	SOUND TRANSMISSION

SOUND BACKSCATTER	
USE	**BACKSCATTER**

SOUND CHANNELS	
UF	acoustic channels
UF	channels (sound)
NT1	SOFAR CHANNEL
RT	ACOUSTICS
RT	DENSITY STRATIFICATION
RT	SOFAR
RT	SOUND VELOCITY
RT	THERMAL STRATIFICATION

SOUND DIFFRACTION	
UF	acoustic wave diffraction
UF	diffraction (sound)
BT1	DIFFRACTION
RT	SOUND
RT	SOUND DISPERSION
RT	SOUND PROPAGATION
RT	SOUND SCATTERING

SOUND DISPERSION	
UF	acoustic wave dispersion
BT1	DISPERSION
RT	SOUND DIFFRACTION
RT	SOUND PROPAGATION
RT	SOUND REFRACTION
RT	SOUND SCATTERING
RT	SOUND VELOCITY

SOUND EMISSION	
USE	**SOUND PRODUCTION**

SOUND GENERATION	
UF	generation (sound waves)
RT	SOUND GENERATORS
RT	SOUND PROPAGATION

SOUND GENERATORS	
UF	acoustic generators
UF	acoustic radiators
UF	noise generators
BT1	ACOUSTIC EQUIPMENT
BT2	EQUIPMENT
NT1	PINGERS
RT	SEISMIC ENERGY SOURCES
RT	SOUND
RT	SOUND GENERATION
RT	SOUND PRODUCTION
RT	SOUND SOURCES

SOUND INSULATION	
USE	**ACOUSTIC INSULATION**

SOUND INTENSITY	
UF	acoustic intensity
RT	ACOUSTIC PROPERTIES
RT	SOUND MEASUREMENT

SOUND MEASUREMENT	
UF	acoustic measurement
BT1	MEASUREMENT
RT	SOUND INTENSITY
RT	SOUND VELOCITY

SOUND PRESSURE	
BT1	PRESSURE
BT2	PHYSICAL PROPERTIES
BT3	PROPERTIES
RT	SOUND
RT	SOUND ATTENUATION

SOUND PRODUCTION
SN	Restricted to vocalization or other sources of sound production such as stridulation by animals. Before 1982 search SOUND PRODUCTION (BIOLOGICAL)
UF	sound emission
UF	sound production (biological)
RT	ANIMAL COMMUNICATION
RT	AUDIO RECORDINGS
RT	AUDITION
RT	AUDITORY ORGANS
RT	AUDITORY STIMULI
RT	BIOACOUSTICS
RT	BIOLOGICAL NOISE
RT	ECHOLOCATION
RT	LARYNX
RT	SOUND
RT	SOUND GENERATORS
RT	VOCAL ORGANS
RT	VOCALIZATION BEHAVIOUR

SOUND PRODUCTION (BIOLOGICAL)
USE	**SOUND PRODUCTION**

SOUND PROPAGATION
UF	acoustic wave propagation
RT	DEEP WATER
RT	DOPPLER EFFECT
RT	INTERNAL WAVE EFFECTS
RT	INTERNAL WAVES
RT	SONAR
RT	SOUND
RT	SOUND ABSORPTION
RT	SOUND DIFFRACTION
RT	SOUND DISPERSION
RT	SOUND GENERATION
RT	SOUND REFLECTION
RT	SOUND REFRACTION
RT	SOUND SCATTERING
RT	SOUND TRANSMISSION
RT	SOUND VELOCITY

SOUND PROPERTIES
USE	**ACOUSTIC PROPERTIES**

SOUND RANGING
USE	**ECHO RANGING**

SOUND RAY PATHS
USE	**RAY PATHS**

SOUND RECORDERS
BT1	RECORDING EQUIPMENT
BT2	EQUIPMENT
RT	ACOUSTIC EQUIPMENT
RT	ACOUSTICS
RT	AUDIO RECORDINGS
RT	ECHO SURVEYS
RT	ECHOSOUNDING
RT	HYDROPHONES
RT	OCEANOGRAPHIC EQUIPMENT
RT	SENSORS

SOUND RECORDINGS
USE	**AUDIO RECORDINGS**

SOUND REFLECTION
UF	acoustic wave reflection
BT1	REFLECTION
RT	SOUND
RT	SOUND ABSORPTION
RT	SOUND PROPAGATION
RT	SOUND SCATTERING
RT	TARGET STRENGTH

SOUND REFRACTION
UF	acoustic wave refraction
BT1	REFRACTION
RT	SOUND
RT	SOUND DISPERSION
RT	SOUND PROPAGATION
RT	SOUND SCATTERING

SOUND REVERBERATION
USE	**REVERBERATION**

SOUND SCATTERING
UF	acoustic wave scattering
UF	scattering (sound)
NT1	BACKSCATTER
NT1	BOTTOM SCATTERING
NT1	FORWARD SCATTERING
RT	REVERBERATION
RT	SOUND
RT	SOUND ABSORPTION
RT	SOUND ATTENUATION
RT	SOUND DIFFRACTION
RT	SOUND DISPERSION
RT	SOUND PROPAGATION
RT	SOUND REFLECTION
RT	SOUND REFRACTION

SOUND SCATTERING LAYERS
USE	**SCATTERING LAYERS**

SOUND SOURCES
UF	sound wave sources
RT	SOUND
RT	SOUND GENERATORS

SOUND SPECTRA
SN	Before 1986 search also ACOUSTIC SPECTRA
UF	acoustic spectra
BT1	SPECTRA

SOUND SPEED
USE	**SOUND VELOCITY**

SOUND TRANSMISSION
UF	acoustic wave transmission
BT1	TRANSMISSION
RT	SOUND
RT	SOUND ATTENUATION
RT	SOUND PROPAGATION
RT	THERMOCLINE
RT	TRANSMISSION LOSS

SOUND TRANSMISSION LOSS
USE	**TRANSMISSION LOSS**

SOUND VELOCITY
UF	sound speed
UF	wave velocity (sound)
BT1	VELOCITY
RT	ACOUSTIC DATA
RT	ACOUSTIC IMPEDANCE
RT	ACOUSTIC PROPERTIES
RT	COMPRESSIBILITY
RT	HYDROSTATIC PRESSURE
RT	SALINITY
RT	SEDIMENT PROPERTIES
RT	SOFAR CHANNEL
RT	SOUND
RT	SOUND CHANNELS
RT	SOUND DISPERSION
RT	SOUND MEASUREMENT
RT	SOUND PROPAGATION

SOUND WAVE SOURCES
USE	**SOUND SOURCES**

SOUND WAVES
SN	Sound waves and underwater transmission of sound waves
UF	acoustic waves
UF	sonic waves
UF	underwater sound transmission
UF	waves (acoustic)
BT1	ELASTIC WAVES
RT	ACOUSTIC EQUIPMENT
RT	ACOUSTICS
RT	BIOLOGICAL NOISE
RT	ECHOSOUNDING
RT	RAY PATHS
RT	SONIC TAGS
RT	WAVE PROPERTIES
RT	WAVE VELOCITY

SOUNDING (WATER DEPTH)
USE	**BATHYMETRY**

SOUNDING LINES
RT	BATHYMETRY
RT	DEPTH MEASUREMENT
RT	OCEANOGRAPHIC EQUIPMENT
RT	SOUNDINGS

SOUNDINGS
SN	Charted depth of water
UF	bathymetric observations
BT1	BATHYMETRIC DATA
BT2	OCEANOGRAPHIC DATA
BT3	DATA
RT	BATHYMETRIC CHARTS
RT	BATHYMETRY
RT	HYDROGRAPHIC SURVEYING
RT	NAVIGATIONAL CHARTS
RT	PLOTTING
RT	SEAFLOOR MAPPING
RT	SOUNDING LINES
RT	WATER DEPTH

SOUTHERN OSCILLATION
RT	AIR TEMPERATURE
RT	ATMOSPHERIC CIRCULATION
RT	EL NINO PHENOMENA
RT	OSCILLATIONS
RT	SEA LEVEL
RT	SEA LEVEL PRESSURE

SPALLING
BT1	DEFECTS
RT	DETERIORATION

SPAR BUOYS
BT1	BUOY HULLS
BT2	HULLS
NT1	LARGE SPAR BUOYS

SPARKERS
BT1	SEISMIC ENERGY SOURCES

SPAT
BT1	MOLLUSCAN LARVAE
BT2	INVERTEBRATE LARVAE
BT3	LARVAE
BT4	DEVELOPMENTAL STAGES
RT	CLAM CULTURE
RT	CULTCH
RT	GRADING
RT	LARVAL SETTLEMENT
RT	MARINE MOLLUSCS
RT	MUSSEL CULTURE
RT	OFF-BOTTOM CULTURE
RT	OYSTER CULTURE
RT	SEED (AQUACULTURE)
RT	SEED COLLECTION
RT	SHELLFISH CULTURE

SPAT COLLECTION
USE **SEED COLLECTION**

SPATIAL DISTRIBUTION
USE **GEOGRAPHICAL DISTRIBUTION**

SPATIAL ISOLATION
USE **GEOGRAPHICAL ISOLATION**

SPATIAL VARIATIONS
UF	variations (space)
NT1	FINESTRUCTURE
NT1	LATITUDINAL VARIATIONS
NT1	MICROSTRUCTURE
NT2	SALINITY MICROSTRUCTURE
NT2	THERMAL MICROSTRUCTURE
NT2	VELOCITY MICROSTRUCTURE
NT1	REGIONAL VARIATIONS
RT	DIMENSIONS
RT	HORIZONTAL DISTRIBUTION
RT	QUANTITATIVE DISTRIBUTION
RT	VERTICAL DISTRIBUTION

SPAWNED SALMON
USE **KELT**

SPAWNED TROUT
USE **KELT**

SPAWNERS
USE **SPAWNING POPULATIONS**

SPAWNING
NT1	WILD SPAWNING
RT	BREEDING
RT	NURSERY GROUNDS
RT	REPRODUCTIVE BEHAVIOUR
RT	REPRODUCTIVE CYCLE
RT	SEXUAL REPRODUCTION
RT	SPAWNING GROUNDS
RT	SPAWNING MIGRATIONS
RT	SPAWNING POPULATIONS
RT	SPAWNING SEASONS

SPAWNING GROUNDS
NT1	ARTIFICIAL SPAWNING GROUNDS
RT	ANADROMOUS SPECIES
RT	CATADROMOUS SPECIES
RT	FISHING GROUNDS
RT	ICHTHYOPLANKTON
RT	ICHTHYOPLANKTON SURVEYS
RT	NURSERY GROUNDS
RT	REDDS
RT	REPRODUCTIVE BEHAVIOUR
RT	SPAWNING
RT	SPAWNING MIGRATIONS
RT	SPAWNING POPULATIONS
RT	SPAWNING SEASONS

SPAWNING MIGRATIONS
BT1	MIGRATIONS
NT1	ANADROMOUS MIGRATIONS
NT1	CATADROMOUS MIGRATIONS
RT	AMPHIHALINE SPECIES
RT	ANADROMOUS SPECIES
RT	CATADROMOUS SPECIES
RT	KELT
RT	OCEANODROMOUS MIGRATIONS
RT	REPRODUCTIVE BEHAVIOUR
RT	SEX RATIO
RT	SPAWNING
RT	SPAWNING GROUNDS
RT	SPAWNING POPULATIONS
RT	SPAWNING SEASONS

SPAWNING POPULATIONS
SN	Added in 1982
UF	spawners
BT1	ANIMAL POPULATIONS
BT2	NATURAL POPULATIONS

SPAWNING POPULATIONS (cont'd)
RT	SPAWNING
RT	SPAWNING GROUNDS
RT	SPAWNING MIGRATIONS
RT	SPAWNING SEASONS

SPAWNING SEASONS
RT	ANADROMOUS SPECIES
RT	CATADROMOUS SPECIES
RT	ICHTHYOPLANKTON
RT	ICHTHYOPLANKTON SURVEYS
RT	REPRODUCTIVE BEHAVIOUR
RT	SEASONS
RT	SPAWNING
RT	SPAWNING GROUNDS
RT	SPAWNING MIGRATIONS
RT	SPAWNING POPULATIONS

SPEAR FISHING
SN	Impaling fish with a spear from either above or below the water surface. Added in 1980
BT1	CATCHING METHODS
RT	DIVING
RT	FISHING
RT	SPORT FISHING
RT	WOUNDING GEAR

SPECIALISTS
USE **EXPERTS**

SPECIATION (BIOLOGICAL)
USE **BIOLOGICAL SPECIATION**

SPECIES
SN	Used only as a qualifier. Use of a more specific term is recommended
BT1	TAXA
NT1	AMPHIBIOTIC SPECIES
NT1	AMPHIHALINE SPECIES
NT2	ANADROMOUS SPECIES
NT2	CATADROMOUS SPECIES
NT1	ASSOCIATED SPECIES
NT1	CAVERNICOLOUS SPECIES
NT1	COMMERCIAL SPECIES
NT2	UNDERUTILIZED SPECIES
NT1	COSMOPOLITE SPECIES
NT1	DOMESTIC SPECIES
NT1	DOMINANT SPECIES
NT1	ENDEMIC SPECIES
NT1	INDICATOR SPECIES
NT1	INTRODUCED SPECIES
NT1	MIGRATORY SPECIES
NT1	PATHOGENS
NT1	RARE SPECIES
NT1	RELICT SPECIES
NT1	SEDENTARY SPECIES
NT1	SESSILE SPECIES
NT1	SIBLING SPECIES
RT	AQUATIC ORGANISMS
RT	BEHAVIOUR
RT	BIOGEOGRAPHY
RT	BIOLOGICAL SPECIATION
RT	BOTANY
RT	CHECK LISTS
RT	ECOLOGY
RT	IDENTIFICATION KEYS
RT	NEW SPECIES
RT	ZOOLOGY

SPECIES COMPOSITION
USE **CHECK LISTS**

SPECIES DIVERSITY
SN	Added in 1980
UF	community diversity
UF	diversity index
UF	ecological diversity
UF	similarity index
RT	CLIMAX COMMUNITY

SPECIES DIVERSITY (cont'd)
RT	COMMUNITY COMPOSITION
RT	DOMINANT SPECIES
RT	ECOLOGICAL SUCCESSION

SPECIES EXTINCTION
SN	Added in 1980
UF	extinction of species
RT	NATURE CONSERVATION
RT	OVERFISHING
RT	RARE SPECIES

SPECIES RARITY
USE **RARE SPECIES**

SPECIFIC GRAVITY
BT1	PHYSICAL PROPERTIES
BT2	PROPERTIES
RT	DENSITY
RT	DRY WEIGHT
RT	RELATIVE DENSITY
RT	WEIGHT
RT	WET WEIGHT

SPECIFIC GRAVITY MEASUREMENT
USE **DENSITY MEASUREMENT**

SPECIFIC HEAT
UF	heat capacity
UF	thermal capacity
BT1	THERMODYNAMIC PROPERTIES
BT2	PHYSICAL PROPERTIES
BT3	PROPERTIES
RT	ENTHALPY
RT	HEAT
RT	SPECIFIC HUMIDITY
RT	THERMAL CONDUCTIVITY

SPECIFIC HUMIDITY
BT1	HUMIDITY
RT	MIXING RATIO
RT	RELATIVE HUMIDITY
RT	SPECIFIC HEAT
RT	WATER VAPOUR

SPECIFIC VOLUME
RT	ISOPYCNICS
RT	ISOSTERES
RT	ISOSTERIC SURFACES
RT	SPECIFIC VOLUME ANOMALIES
RT	THERMAL EXPANSION
RT	VOLUME
RT	WATER DENSITY

SPECIFIC VOLUME ANOMALIES
UF	steric anomalies
BT1	ANOMALIES
NT1	THERMOSTERIC ANOMALIES
RT	DYNAMIC HEIGHT ANOMALY
RT	SPECIFIC VOLUME
RT	WATER DENSITY

SPECIFICATIONS
SN	Used only as a qualifier
RT	DESIGN
RT	EQUIPMENT
RT	INSPECTION
RT	PATENTS
RT	PERFORMANCE ASSESSMENT
RT	PROTOTYPES
RT	STANDARDS

SPECIFICITY
SN	Used only as a qualifier
RT	BIOCHEMISTRY
RT	CHEMICAL REACTIONS
RT	HOST PREFERENCES
RT	SUBSTRATE PREFERENCES

ASFIS Thesaurus

SPECTRA
UF	spectrum
NT1	ABSORPTION SPECTRA
NT1	CURRENT SPECTRA
NT1	DIRECTIONAL SPECTRA
NT1	ENERGY SPECTRA
NT1	FREQUENCY SPECTRA
NT1	SOUND SPECTRA
NT1	WAVE SPECTRA

SPECTRAL ANALYSIS
BT1	MATHEMATICAL ANALYSIS
NT1	MAXIMUM ENTROPY SPECTRAL ANALYSIS
RT	DATA REDUCTION
RT	FREQUENCY ANALYSIS
RT	SIGNAL PROCESSING
RT	TEMPORAL VARIATIONS
RT	TIME SERIES ANALYSIS
RT	WAVEFORM ANALYSIS

SPECTRAL COMPOSITION
BT1	OPTICAL PROPERTIES
BT2	PHYSICAL PROPERTIES
BT3	PROPERTIES
RT	BIOLUMINESCENCE
RT	COLOUR
RT	LIGHT
RT	LIGHT PENETRATION
RT	LUMINESCENCE
RT	SPECTROPHOTOMETERS
RT	WATER COLOUR

SPECTROCHEMICAL ANALYSIS
RT	SPECTROPHOTOMETERS

SPECTROPHOTOMETERS
BT1	PHOTOMETERS
BT2	LIGHT MEASURING INSTRUMENTS
BT3	MEASURING DEVICES
RT	LIGHT MEASUREMENT
RT	SPECTRAL COMPOSITION
RT	SPECTROCHEMICAL ANALYSIS
RT	SPECTROSCOPIC TECHNIQUES

SPECTROSCOPIC TECHNIQUES
UF	spectroscopy
BT1	ANALYTICAL TECHNIQUES
NT1	ABSORPTION SPECTROSCOPY
NT1	ALPHA SPECTROSCOPY
NT1	EMISSION SPECTROSCOPY
NT1	FLUORESCENCE SPECTROSCOPY
NT1	GAMMA SPECTROSCOPY
NT1	INFRARED SPECTROSCOPY
NT1	MASS SPECTROSCOPY
NT1	X-RAY SPECTROSCOPY
NT2	X-RAY DIFFRACTION ANALYSIS
NT2	X-RAY EMISSION ANALYSIS
NT2	X-RAY FLUORESCENCE ANALYSIS
RT	CHROMATOGRAPHIC TECHNIQUES
RT	COLORIMETRIC TECHNIQUES
RT	FLUORESCENCE
RT	NUCLEAR MAGNETIC RESONANCE
RT	PHOTOMETRY
RT	SPECTROPHOTOMETERS

SPECTROSCOPY
USE	**SPECTROSCOPIC TECHNIQUES**

SPECTRUM
USE	**SPECTRA**

SPEECH DISTORTION
RT	BREATHING MIXTURES
RT	COMMUNICATION
RT	DIVERS
RT	DIVING PHYSIOLOGY

SPEED
USE	**VELOCITY**

SPEEDOMETERS
SN	Instruments for measuring vessel speed
BT1	MEASURING DEVICES
RT	BOATS
RT	FISHING OPERATIONS
RT	NAVIGATION

SPELAEOLOGY
SN	The study of caves, their flora and fauna. Added in 1980
UF	speleology
RT	CAVERNICOLOUS SPECIES
RT	CAVES
RT	GEOMORPHOLOGY

SPELEOLOGY
USE	**SPELAEOLOGY**

SPERM
SN	Before 1986 search also SPERMATOZOA
UF	spermatozoa
BT1	SEXUAL CELLS
BT2	CELLS
RT	FECUNDITY
RT	FREEZING STORAGE
RT	MALES
RT	POLYSPERMY
RT	SEMEN
RT	SPERMATOGENESIS
RT	SPERMATOPHORES
RT	TESTES

SPERM OILS
USE	**FISH OILS**

SPERMATOGENESIS
BT1	GAMETOGENESIS
BT2	MORPHOGENESIS
RT	SPERM
RT	TESTES

SPERMATOPHORES
RT	BIOLOGICAL FERTILIZATION
RT	SEXUAL MATURITY
RT	SEXUAL REPRODUCTION
RT	SPERM

SPERMATOZOA
USE	**SPERM**

SPHENE
USE	**TITANITE**

SPHERES
RT	HYDRODYNAMICS

SPHINGOLIPIDS
USE	**COMPLEX LIPIDS**

SPILLING WAVES
BT1	BREAKING WAVES
BT2	SURFACE WATER WAVES
BT3	WATER WAVES

SPIN FISHING
USE	**SPORT FISHING**

SPINAL CORD
SN	Added in 1980
BT1	CENTRAL NERVOUS SYSTEM
BT2	NERVOUS SYSTEM
RT	VERTEBRAE

SPINDOWN
RT	ROTATING FLUIDS
RT	SPINUP

SPINUP
RT	ROTATING FLUIDS
RT	SPINDOWN

SPINY LOBSTER FISHERIES
USE	**LOBSTER FISHERIES**

SPITS
BT1	BEACH FEATURES
NT1	BARRIER SPITS
RT	DEPOSITION FEATURES

SPLASH ZONE
UF	spray zone
RT	COAST DEFENCES
RT	COASTAL STRUCTURES
RT	CORROSION
RT	ICING
RT	OFFSHORE STRUCTURES
RT	SALT PARTICLES
RT	SPRAY

SPLEEN
BT1	EXCRETORY ORGANS
BT2	ANIMAL ORGANS
BT3	BODY ORGANS
RT	LYMPHOCYTES

SPLINES
RT	NUMERICAL ANALYSIS

SPOIL
RT	DREDGE SPOIL
RT	DREDGING
RT	WASTE DISPOSAL SITES

SPOILAGE (FISH)
USE	**FISH SPOILAGE**

SPONGE CULTURE
BT1	AQUACULTURE
RT	CULTURES
RT	MARINE AQUACULTURE
RT	SEED COLLECTION
RT	SPONGE FISHERIES
RT	SPONGES

SPONGE FISHERIES
SN	Added in 1983
UF	sponge harvesting
BT1	FISHERIES
RT	FISHING BY DIVING
RT	MARINE FISHERIES
RT	SPONGE CULTURE
RT	SPONGES

SPONGE HARVESTING
USE	**SPONGE FISHERIES**

SPONGES
BT1	ANIMAL PRODUCTS
RT	SPONGE CULTURE
RT	SPONGE FISHERIES

SPORANGIA
RT	ASEXUAL REPRODUCTION
RT	PLACENTA
RT	SPORES
RT	SPOROGENESIS

SPORE COLLECTION
USE	**SEED COLLECTION**

SPORE FORMATION
USE **SPOROGENESIS**

SPORES
UF aplanospores
UF ascospores
UF basidiospores
UF blastospores
UF oospores
UF zoospores
NT1 RESTING SPORES
RT ALGAL CULTURE
RT ASEXUAL REPRODUCTION
RT ATMOSPHERIC PARTICULATES
RT BACTERIA
RT BUDDING
RT CONIDIA
RT ENCYSTMENT
RT FOSSIL SPORES
RT FUNGI
RT GERMINATION
RT PLACENTA
RT SEAWEED CULTURE
RT SEED COLLECTION
RT SPORANGIA
RT SPOROGENESIS

SPOROGENESIS
SN Added in 1980
UF spore formation
UF sporogomy
UF sporulation
RT SPORANGIA
RT SPORES

SPOROGOMY
USE **SPOROGENESIS**

SPORT FISH
USE **GAME FISH**

SPORT FISHING
SN Any activities of fishing with
recreation or water sports purposes
UF flyfishing
UF recreational fishing
UF spin fishing
BT1 RECREATION
RT ANGLING
RT ARTIFICIAL REEFS
RT BAIT
RT BAIT CULTURE
RT BAIT FISH
RT BAIT FISHING
RT CATCHING METHODS
RT FEE FISHING
RT FISHERY MANAGEMENT
RT FISHING
RT FISHING GEAR
RT GAME FISH
RT GILLNETS
RT HOOKS
RT ICE FISHING
RT LINES
RT PERMITS
RT PITS
RT POTS
RT RANCHING
RT RENTAL
RT SALMON FISHERIES
RT SPEAR FISHING
RT SPORT FISHING STATISTICS
RT TRANSPLANTATION
RT TUNA FISHERIES

SPORT FISHING STATISTICS
SN Including number of sport fishermen
and catches
UF creel census
BT1 FISHERY STATISTICS

SPORT FISHING STATISTICS (cont'd)
RT GAME FISH
RT RECREATION
RT SPORT FISHING

SPORULATION
USE **SPOROGENESIS**

SPOTTED PEST
USE **VIBRIOSIS**

SPRAT FISHERIES
USE **CLUPEOID FISHERIES**

SPRAY
UF salt spray
UF sea spray
BT1 HYDROMETEORS
RT AEROSOLS
RT DROPLETS
RT ICING
RT SALT NUCLEI
RT SALT PARTICLES
RT SPLASH ZONE

SPRAY ZONE
USE **SPLASH ZONE**

SPREADING
USE **DISPERSION**

SPREADING AXIS
USE **SPREADING CENTRES**

SPREADING CENTRES
UF spreading axis
UF spreading ridges
RT DIVERGING PLATE BOUNDARIES
RT PLATE DIVERGENCE
RT PLATE TECTONICS
RT SEAFLOOR SPREADING

SPREADING RATE
USE **SEAFLOOR SPREADING**

SPREADING RIDGES
USE **SPREADING CENTRES**

SPRING
SN Used for the season. Added in 1980
UF spring (season)
BT1 SEASONS

SPRING (SEASON)
USE **SPRING**

SPRING STREAMS
BT1 WATER SPRINGS
RT FRESH WATER
RT GROUND WATER
RT INLAND WATER ENVIRONMENT
RT LOTIC ENVIRONMENT
RT SEEPAGES
RT WATER RESOURCES

SPRING TIDES
BT1 TIDES
BT2 TIDAL MOTION
RT AGE OF TIDE

SPRINGS (WATER)
USE **WATER SPRINGS**

SQUALENE
BT1 POLYUNSATURATED HYDROCARBONS
BT2 UNSATURATED HYDROCARBONS
BT3 HYDROCARBONS
BT4 ORGANIC COMPOUNDS

SQUAT LOBSTER FISHERIES
SN Added in 1982
UF galatheid fisheries
UF red crab fisheries
BT1 CRUSTACEAN FISHERIES
BT2 FISHERIES
RT COASTAL FISHERIES
RT MARINE FISHERIES

SQUID CULTURE
SN Before 1982 search MOLLUSC CULTURE
BT1 MOLLUSC CULTURE
BT2 SHELLFISH CULTURE
BT3 AQUACULTURE
RT AQUACULTURE DEVELOPMENT
RT CEPHALOPOD FISHERIES

SQUID FISHERIES
USE **CEPHALOPOD FISHERIES**

ST ELMO'S FIRE
USE **ATMOSPHERIC ELECTRICITY**

STABILITY
SN Use of a more specific term is
recommended
NT1 SHIP STABILITY
NT1 SLOPE STABILITY
NT1 VERTICAL STABILITY
RT BALLAST
RT BUOYANCY
RT EQUILIBRIUM
RT INSTABILITY
RT MONIN-OBUKHOV LENGTH
RT SEDIMENT STABILITY
RT STABILITY CONSTANTS
RT STABILIZING
RT STEADY STATE

STABILITY (ECOLOGICAL)
USE **ECOLOGICAL BALANCE**

STABILITY CONSTANTS
BT1 CONSTANTS
RT STABILITY

STABILITY FREQUENCY
USE **BRUNT-VAISALA FREQUENCY**

STABILIZATION
USE **STABILIZING**

STABILIZED PLATFORMS
BT1 INSTRUMENT PLATFORMS
BT2 VEHICLES
NT1 TOWERS
RT GYROSCOPES
RT INERTIAL GUIDANCE
RT RADAR ALTIMETRY

STABILIZERS
UF stabilizing fins
RT SHIP MOTION
RT SHIP STABILITY
RT STABILIZING

STABILIZING
UF stabilization
RT HEAVE COMPENSATORS
RT STABILITY
RT STABILIZERS

STABILIZING FINS
USE **STABILIZERS**

STACKS
BT1 COASTAL LANDFORMS
BT2 LANDFORMS
BT3 TOPOGRAPHIC FEATURES
RT EROSION FEATURES

STAFF (PERSONNEL)
    USE   **PERSONNEL**

STAGES (WATER)
    USE   **WATER LEVELS**

STAGNANT WATER
    BT1   WATER
    RT   ANOXIC CONDITIONS
    RT   DYSTROPHIC LAKES
    RT   EUTROPHICATION
    RT   HYPOLIMNION
    RT   MARSHES
    RT   SAPROPELS
    RT   SAPROPLANKTON
    RT   SWAMPS
    RT   WETLANDS

STAINING
    SN   Staining of tissues and organisms
    RT   DISCOLOURATION
    RT   DYES
    RT   HISTOCHEMISTRY
    RT   HISTOLOGY
    RT   MARKING
    RT   MIGRATIONS
    RT   TISSUES

STAINLESS STEEL
    BT1   STEEL
    BT2   FERROUS ALLOYS
    BT3   ALLOYS
    BT4   MATERIALS
    RT   CORROSION CONTROL

STANDARD DEPTHS
    SN   Recommended depths below sea
        surface at which water properties
        should be measured
    BT1   DEPTH
    BT2   DIMENSIONS
    RT   WATER PROPERTIES

STANDARD OCEAN SECTIONS
    SN   Routes along which oceanographic
        observations are made regularly
        over a period of time, e.g. Kola
        Section, Line P
    UF   ocean data routes
    BT1   OCEANOGRAPHIC STATIONS
    RT   FIXED STATIONS
    RT   HYDROGRAPHIC SECTIONS
    RT   OCEAN STATIONS
    RT   OCEANOGRAPHIC DATA
    RT   OCEANOGRAPHIC SURVEYS
    RT   TIME SERIES

STANDARD SEA WATER
    BT1   SEA WATER
    BT2   WATER
    RT   ARTIFICIAL SEAWATER
    RT   SALINITY MEASUREMENT
    RT   STANDARDS

STANDARD SIGNALS
    RT   COMMUNICATION SYSTEMS
    RT   FISHING OPERATIONS
    RT   NAVIGATION

STANDARDIZATION
    SN   Comparison of an instrument or
        device with a standard to determine
        its value in terms of an adopted
        unit. Used only as a qualifier
    NT1   CALIBRATION
    NT2   INTERCALIBRATION
    RT   COLLECTING DEVICES
    RT   EQUIPMENT
    RT   INTERCOMPARISON
    RT   METHODOLOGY

STANDARDIZATION (cont'd)
    RT   QUALITY CONTROL
    RT   STANDARDS
    RT   TERMINOLOGY

STANDARDS
    UF   codes of practice
    RT   ACCEPTABILITY
    RT   DOCUMENTS
    RT   PRACTICAL SALINITY SCALE
    RT   QUALITY CONTROL
    RT   SPECIFICATIONS
    RT   STANDARD SEA WATER
    RT   STANDARDIZATION
    RT   TERMINOLOGY

STANDBY VESSELS
    USE   **EMERGENCY VESSELS**

STANDING CROP (IN NUMBER)
    USE   **POPULATION NUMBER**

STANDING CROP (IN WEIGHT)
    USE   **BIOMASS**

STANDING STOCK (IN NUMBER)
    USE   **POPULATION NUMBER**

STANDING STOCK (IN WEIGHT)
    USE   **BIOMASS**

STANDING WAVES
    UF   clapotis
    UF   stationary waves
    BT1   OSCILLATORY WAVES
    BT2   WATER WAVES
    RT   HYDRAULIC JUMP
    RT   RESONANCE
    RT   SEICHES
    RT   WAVE REFLECTION

STARCH
    SN   Before 1982 search CARBOHYDRATES
    BT1   POLYSACCHARIDES
    BT2   SACCHARIDES
    BT3   CARBOHYDRATES
    BT4   ORGANIC COMPOUNDS
    RT   AQUATIC PLANTS

STARVATION
    UF   absolute food deficiency
    RT   FOOD AVAILABILITY
    RT   LETHAL LIMITS
    RT   MORTALITY CAUSES
    RT   NUTRITION DISORDERS
    RT   SURVIVAL
    RT   TOLERANCE

STATE GOVERNMENTS
    USE   **GOVERNMENTS**

STATE JURISDICTION
    USE   **JURISDICTION**

STATE-OF-THE-ART REVIEWS
    USE   **LITERATURE REVIEWS**

STATES (POLITICAL)
    USE   **COUNTRIES**

STATIC INSTABILITY
    BT1   INSTABILITY
    RT   VERTICAL STABILITY

STATIC STABILITY
    USE   **VERTICAL STABILITY**

STATIC WATER CULTURE
    USE   **POND CULTURE**

STATION KEEPING
    RT   CRUISE STATIONS
    RT   DEPLOYMENT
    RT   RECOVERY
    RT   SEAMANSHIP
    RT   SHIP DRIFT
    RT   SHIP MOTION

STATION LISTS
    BT1   DATA REPORTS
    BT2   REPORT LITERATURE
    BT3   DOCUMENTS
    RT   CRUISE STATIONS
    RT   CRUISES
    RT   DATA
    RT   LOGBOOKS
    RT   MULTISHIP EXPEDITIONS
    RT   TRACK CHARTS

STATIONARY WAVES
    USE   **STANDING WAVES**

STATIONS (OCEANOGRAPHIC)
    USE   **OCEANOGRAPHIC STATIONS**

STATISTICAL ANALYSIS
    SN   Used only as a qualifier
    UF   chi square test
    UF   statistical methods
    UF   statistical tests
    UF   statistics (mathematics)
    UF   tests for significant differences
    BT1   MATHEMATICAL ANALYSIS
    NT1   CORRELATION ANALYSIS
    NT2   AUTOCORRELATION
    NT2   CROSS CORRELATION
    NT1   FREQUENCY ANALYSIS
    NT1   REGRESSION ANALYSIS
    NT1   TIME SERIES ANALYSIS
    NT1   VARIANCE ANALYSIS
    NT2   MULTIVARIATE ANALYSIS
    RT   ANALYSIS
    RT   APPROXIMATION
    RT   BIOMETRICS
    RT   DATA PROCESSING
    RT   ECONOMIC ANALYSIS
    RT   GAUSSIAN DISTRIBUTION
    RT   GRAPHIC METHODS
    RT   GRAPHICAL ANALYSIS
    RT   KURTOSIS
    RT   NUMERICAL ANALYSIS
    RT   PREDICTION
    RT   PROBABILITY THEORY
    RT   RANDOM PROCESSES
    RT   SIZE DISTRIBUTION
    RT   SKEWNESS
    RT   STATISTICAL MODELS
    RT   STATISTICAL SAMPLING
    RT   STATISTICAL TABLES
    RT   STATISTICIANS
    RT   STATISTICS
    RT   STOCHASTIC PROCESSES

STATISTICAL CHARTS
    USE   **STATISTICAL TABLES**

STATISTICAL METHODS
    USE   **STATISTICAL ANALYSIS**

STATISTICAL MODELS
    SN   Used only as a qualifier
    BT1   MATHEMATICAL MODELS
    BT2   MODELS
    RT   GAME THEORY
    RT   OPERATIONS RESEARCH
    RT   PROBABILITY THEORY
    RT   STATISTICAL ANALYSIS

STATISTICAL MODELS (cont'd)
RT	STATISTICS
RT	SYSTEM ANALYSIS

STATISTICAL SAMPLING
SN	Used only as a qualifier. Before
	1982 search SAMPLING (STATISTICAL)
UF	random sampling
UF	sampling (statistical)
UF	stratified sampling
BT1	SAMPLING
RT	BIOLOGICAL SAMPLING
RT	DATA COLLECTIONS
RT	PROBABILITY THEORY
RT	QUALITY CONTROL
RT	STATISTICAL ANALYSIS
RT	STATISTICAL TABLES
RT	STATISTICS

STATISTICAL TABLES
SN	Used only as a qualifier
UF	statistical charts
UF	tables (statistical)
BT1	TABLES
BT2	DOCUMENTS
NT1	SCATTER DIAGRAMS
RT	CATCH STATISTICS
RT	DATA
RT	GRAPHIC METHODS
RT	GRAPHICAL ANALYSIS
RT	STATISTICAL ANALYSIS
RT	STATISTICAL SAMPLING
RT	STATISTICS

STATISTICAL TESTS
USE	**STATISTICAL ANALYSIS**

STATISTICIANS
SN	Added in 1980
BT1	SCIENTIFIC PERSONNEL
BT2	PERSONNEL
RT	DIRECTORIES
RT	FISHERY STATISTICS
RT	STATISTICAL ANALYSIS
RT	STATISTICS

STATISTICS
SN	Used only as a qualifier
NT1	WAVE STATISTICS
RT	BIOMETRICS
RT	DATA PROCESSING
RT	MATHEMATICS
RT	STATISTICAL ANALYSIS
RT	STATISTICAL MODELS
RT	STATISTICAL SAMPLING
RT	STATISTICAL TABLES
RT	STATISTICIANS

STATISTICS (MATHEMATICS)
USE	**STATISTICAL ANALYSIS**

STATOCYSTS
BT1	BALANCE ORGANS
BT2	SENSE ORGANS
BT3	ANIMAL ORGANS
BT4	BODY ORGANS

STD OBSERVATIONS
RT	CTD OBSERVATIONS
RT	HYDROGRAPHIC DATA
RT	STD PROFILES

STD PROBES
USE	**STD PROFILERS**

STD PROFILERS
SN	Salinity-temperature-depth profilers
UF	std probes
UF	std sensors
BT1	PROFILERS

STD PROFILERS (cont'd)
RT	CONDUCTIVITY SENSORS
RT	CTD PROFILERS
RT	OCEANOGRAPHIC EQUIPMENT
RT	SALINITY
RT	SALINITY MEASURING EQUIPMENT
RT	SALINITY PROFILES
RT	STD PROFILES
RT	THERMOMETERS
RT	VERTICAL PROFILES
RT	WATER TEMPERATURE

STD PROFILES
BT1	VERTICAL PROFILES
BT2	PROFILES
RT	HYDROGRAPHIC DATA
RT	STD OBSERVATIONS
RT	STD PROFILERS
RT	TEMPERATURE PROFILES

STD SENSORS
USE	**STD PROFILERS**

STEADY STATE
SN	Use only as a qualifier
RT	EQUILIBRIUM
RT	PERTURBATIONS
RT	STABILITY
RT	UNSTEADY STATE

STEAM FOG
USE	**FOG**

STEEL
BT1	FERROUS ALLOYS
BT2	ALLOYS
BT3	MATERIALS
NT1	STAINLESS STEEL
RT	METALS
RT	REINFORCED CONCRETE
RT	STEEL STRUCTURES
RT	TUBING

STEEL PLATFORMS
USE	**STEEL STRUCTURES**

STEEL STRUCTURES
UF	steel platforms
RT	COAST DEFENCES
RT	CONCRETE STRUCTURES
RT	OFFSHORE STRUCTURES
RT	STEEL
RT	STRUCTURES

STEEL WIRE
USE	**WIRE ROPE**

STEERING SYSTEMS
RT	MANOEUVRABILITY
RT	NAVIGATION
RT	POSITIONING SYSTEMS
RT	PROPULSION SYSTEMS
RT	SHIP TECHNOLOGY
RT	SHIPS
RT	VEHICLES

STEMS
SN	Added in 1980
BT1	PLANT ORGANS
BT2	BODY ORGANS
RT	RHIZOMES
RT	STOMATA

STENOHALINE ORGANISMS
USE	**STENOHALINITY**

STENOHALINITY
SN	Added in 1980
UF	stenohaline organisms
BT1	BIOLOGICAL PROPERTIES
BT2	PROPERTIES
RT	ECOLOGICAL DISTRIBUTION
RT	EURYHALINITY
RT	SALINITY TOLERANCE

STENOTHERMAL ORGANISMS
USE	**STENOTHERMY**

STENOTHERMY
SN	Added in 1980
UF	stenothermal organisms
BT1	BIOLOGICAL PROPERTIES
BT2	PROPERTIES
RT	ECOLOGICAL DISTRIBUTION
RT	EURYTHERMY
RT	TEMPERATURE TOLERANCE

STEREOPHOTOGRAPHY
BT1	PHOTOGRAPHY
BT2	IMAGERY
BT3	REMOTE SENSING
RT	AERIAL PHOTOGRAPHY
RT	DEPTH MEASUREMENT
RT	PHOTOGRAMMETRY
RT	SURVEYING UNDERWATER
RT	WAVE MEASUREMENT

STERIC ANOMALIES
USE	**SPECIFIC VOLUME ANOMALIES**

STERIC SEA LEVEL
BT1	SEA LEVEL
RT	ISOSTATIC SEA LEVEL
RT	SEA LEVEL VARIATIONS
RT	WATER LEVELS

STERILITY
SN	Natural or artificial sterility by
	irradiation or removal of
	reproductive organs
RT	ANIMAL REPRODUCTIVE ORGANS
RT	IRRADIATION
RT	NUCLEAR RADIATIONS
RT	OVARIES
RT	TESTES
RT	VITAMIN E

STERILIZATION
NT1	OZONATION
NT1	ULTRAVIOLET STERILIZATION
RT	BACTERIA
RT	CULTURE MEDIA
RT	IONIZING RADIATION
RT	ULTRAVIOLET RADIATION
RT	VIRUSES

STEROIDS
BT1	LIPIDS
BT2	ORGANIC COMPOUNDS
NT1	STEROLS
NT2	ACANSTEROL
NT2	CHOLESTEROL
NT2	FUCOSTEROL
NT2	SITOSTEROLS
RT	CHEMICAL COMPOUNDS
RT	DRUGS
RT	HORMONES
RT	VITAMIN D

STEROLS
BT1	STEROIDS
BT2	LIPIDS
BT3	ORGANIC COMPOUNDS
NT1	ACANSTEROL
NT1	CHOLESTEROL
NT1	FUCOSTEROL

ASFIS Thesaurus

STEROLS (cont'd)
NT1	SITOSTEROLS
RT	ALCOHOLS
RT	CHEMICAL COMPOUNDS

STICKWATER
UF	fish solubles
BT1	PROCESSED FISHERY PRODUCTS
BT2	FISHERY PRODUCTS
BT3	PRODUCTS
RT	BYPRODUCTS
RT	CHEMICAL EXTRACTION
RT	FISH OILS
RT	FISH WASTES

STILL WATER LEVEL
USE	**SEA LEVEL**

STIMULANTS (GROWTH)
USE	**GROWTH REGULATORS**

STIMULI
SN	Stimuli and their effects on aquatic organisms
NT1	AUDITORY STIMULI
NT1	CHEMICAL STIMULI
NT1	ELECTRIC STIMULI
NT1	LIGHT STIMULI
NT1	MECHANICAL STIMULI
NT1	TACTILE STIMULI
NT1	THERMAL STIMULI
NT1	VISUAL STIMULI
RT	ADAPTATIONS
RT	BEHAVIOUR
RT	BEHAVIOURAL RESPONSES
RT	BIOLOGICAL STRESS
RT	ECOLOGICAL AGGREGATIONS
RT	KINESIS
RT	LEARNING BEHAVIOUR
RT	ORIENTATION
RT	ORIENTATION BEHAVIOUR
RT	SENSE FUNCTIONS
RT	SENSE ORGANS
RT	TAXIS
RT	TROPISM

STINGING ORGANISMS
USE	**NOXIOUS ORGANISMS**

STINGING ORGANS
UF	nematocysts
RT	ELECTRIC ORGANS
RT	LESIONS
RT	NOXIOUS ORGANISMS
RT	VENOM APPARATUS

STOCHASTIC MODELS
USE	**MATHEMATICAL MODELS**

STOCHASTIC PROCESSES
RT	MATHEMATICAL MODELS
RT	OPERATIONS RESEARCH
RT	PROBABILITY THEORY
RT	RANDOM PROCESSES
RT	STATISTICAL ANALYSIS
RT	TIME SERIES ANALYSIS

STOCK ASSESSMENT
UF	stock evaluation
RT	AERIAL SURVEYS
RT	BIOMASS
RT	CATCH STATISTICS
RT	CATCH/EFFORT
RT	CENSUS
RT	ECHO SURVEYS
RT	EVALUATION
RT	EXPLORATORY FISHING
RT	FISH COUNTERS
RT	FISHERY DATA
RT	FISHERY SURVEYS

STOCK ASSESSMENT (cont'd)
RT	FISHING EFFORT
RT	LANDING STATISTICS
RT	MULTISPECIES FISHERIES
RT	OVERFISHING
RT	POPULATION CHARACTERISTICS
RT	POPULATION DYNAMICS
RT	POPULATION NUMBER
RT	POPULATION STRUCTURE
RT	STOCK IDENTIFICATION
RT	STOCKS
RT	TAGGING
RT	TAGS
RT	YIELD

STOCK DENSITY
USE	**POPULATION DENSITY**

STOCK DEPLETION
USE	**DEPLETED STOCKS**

STOCK EVALUATION
USE	**STOCK ASSESSMENT**

STOCK IDENTIFICATION
RT	ELECTROPHORESIS
RT	MERISTIC COUNTS
RT	POPULATION GENETICS
RT	RACIAL STUDIES
RT	SEROLOGICAL STUDIES
RT	STOCK ASSESSMENT
RT	SUBPOPULATIONS

STOCKING (ORGANISMS)
UF	restocking
UF	stocking operations
RT	AQUACULTURE
RT	AQUACULTURE TECHNIQUES
RT	CRAYFISH CULTURE
RT	DENSITY DEPENDENCE
RT	FEE FISHING
RT	HATCHERIES
RT	HERBIVOROUS FISH
RT	ICHTHYOCIDES
RT	LAKES
RT	MOLLUSCICIDES
RT	PREDATOR CONTROL
RT	RANCHING
RT	RESERVOIR FISHERIES
RT	RESERVOIRS (WATER)
RT	SEED (AQUACULTURE)
RT	SEEDING (AQUACULTURE)
RT	STOCKING DENSITY
RT	STOCKING PONDS
RT	TRANSPLANTATION

STOCKING DENSITY
UF	crowding
UF	density (stocking)
RT	BIOTIC FACTORS
RT	CAGE CULTURE
RT	DENSITY DEPENDENCE
RT	DOMINANCE HIERARCHIES
RT	GROWING PONDS
RT	OVERCROWDING
RT	POLYCULTURE
RT	POND CULTURE
RT	SEED (AQUACULTURE)
RT	STOCKING (ORGANISMS)
RT	STOCKING PONDS

STOCKING OPERATIONS
USE	**STOCKING (ORGANISMS)**

STOCKING PONDS
BT1	FISH PONDS
BT2	PONDS
BT3	INLAND WATERS
RT	AQUACULTURE FACILITIES
RT	FEE FISHING

STOCKING PONDS (cont'd)
RT	STOCKING (ORGANISMS)
RT	STOCKING DENSITY

STOCKS
SN	The exploitable group of individuals of the same species existing in a particular area at a particular time. Added in 1982
UF	fish stocks
UF	wild fish stocks
NT1	BROOD STOCKS
NT1	DEPLETED STOCKS
NT1	SHARED STOCKS
NT1	UNIT STOCKS
RT	ANIMAL POPULATIONS
RT	FISHERY RESOURCES
RT	NATURAL POPULATIONS
RT	STOCK ASSESSMENT

STOKES DRIFT
USE	**WAVE DRIFT VELOCITY**

STOKES LAW
RT	PARTICLE SETTLING
RT	SETTLING RATE
RT	VISCOSITY

STOKES WAVES
BT1	NONLINEAR WAVES
BT2	WATER WAVES

STOMA
USE	**STOMATA**

STOMACH
BT1	ALIMENTARY ORGANS
BT2	ANIMAL ORGANS
BT3	BODY ORGANS
NT1	MASTICATORY STOMACH
RT	DIGESTION
RT	DIGESTIVE SYSTEM
RT	PYLORIC CAECA
RT	STOMACH CONTENT

STOMACH CONTENT
RT	ECOLOGICAL EFFICIENCY
RT	FEEDING BEHAVIOUR
RT	FOOD CHAINS
RT	FOOD CONSUMPTION
RT	FOOD ORGANISMS
RT	STOMACH

STOMATA
SN	Added in 1980
UF	stoma
RT	AQUATIC PLANTS
RT	EVAPOTRANSPIRATION
RT	LEAVES
RT	PLANT PHYSIOLOGY
RT	RESPIRATION
RT	RHIZOMES
RT	STEMS
RT	TRANSPIRATION

STONELEY WAVES
BT1	SURFACE SEISMIC WAVES
BT2	SEISMIC WAVES
BT3	ELASTIC WAVES
RT	RAYLEIGH WAVES

STORAGE
SN	Use of a more specific term is recommended; consult terms listed below. Added in 1981
UF	capacity (storage)
RT	CHILLING STORAGE
RT	CODEX STANDARDS
RT	COLD STORAGE
RT	DATA STORAGE

STORAGE (cont'd)
RT	FISH STORAGE
RT	FREEZING STORAGE
RT	LIVE STORAGE
RT	PRESERVATION (FISHERY PRODUCTS)
RT	SEDIMENT SAMPLES
RT	STORAGE CONDITIONS
RT	STORAGE EFFECTS
RT	STORAGE LIFE
RT	STORAGE TANKS

STORAGE (FISH)
USE	**FISH STORAGE**

STORAGE CONDITIONS
SN	Added in 1980
UF	storage humidity
UF	storage temperature
RT	AIR TEMPERATURE
RT	ARCHIVES
RT	CARGOES
RT	COLD STORAGE
RT	FISH STORAGE
RT	FISHERY PRODUCTS
RT	HUMIDITY
RT	SEDIMENT SAMPLES
RT	STORAGE
RT	STORAGE EFFECTS
RT	STORAGE LIFE
RT	WATER SAMPLES

STORAGE EFFECTS
SN	Any action of storage on the quality of processed fishery products, sediment samples and water samples, etc.
RT	FISH INSPECTION
RT	FISH INSPECTION REGULATIONS
RT	FISH STORAGE
RT	FISHERY PRODUCTS
RT	PROCESSED FISHERY PRODUCTS
RT	PROCESSING FISHERY PRODUCTS
RT	QUALITY CONTROL
RT	SAMPLE CONTAMINATION
RT	SAMPLE STORAGE
RT	SEDIMENT SAMPLES
RT	STORAGE
RT	STORAGE CONDITIONS
RT	STORAGE LIFE
RT	WATER SAMPLES

STORAGE HUMIDITY
USE	**STORAGE CONDITIONS**

STORAGE LIFE
SN	Added in 1980
UF	shelf life
RT	CORROSION
RT	QUALITY ASSURANCE
RT	STORAGE
RT	STORAGE CONDITIONS
RT	STORAGE EFFECTS

STORAGE TANKS
SN	Added in 1980
BT1	TANKS
BT2	CONTAINERS
RT	FISH STORAGE
RT	GAS TERMINALS
RT	STORAGE

STORAGE TEMPERATURE
USE	**STORAGE CONDITIONS**

STORM SURGE BARRIERS
UF	tidal barriers
BT1	COAST DEFENCES
BT2	COASTAL STRUCTURES
BT3	HYDRAULIC STRUCTURES
RT	BARRAGES

STORM SURGE BARRIERS (cont'd)
RT	BARRIERS
RT	FLOODS
RT	STORM SURGES
RT	TIDE-SURGE INTERACTION

STORM SURGE FORECASTS
USE	**STORM SURGE PREDICTION**

STORM SURGE GENERATION
BT1	WAVE GENERATION
RT	STORM SURGES

STORM SURGE PREDICTING
USE	**STORM SURGE PREDICTION**

STORM SURGE PREDICTION
UF	storm surge forecasts
UF	storm surge predicting
BT1	PREDICTION
RT	MATHEMATICAL MODELS
RT	NEGATIVE STORM SURGES
RT	STORM SURGES
RT	STORM TIDE WARNING SERVICES
RT	WARNING SERVICES

STORM SURGES
UF	storm tides
UF	surges (storm)
BT1	SURFACE WATER WAVES
BT2	WATER WAVES
NT1	HURRICANE WAVES
NT1	NEGATIVE STORM SURGES
RT	ATMOSPHERIC PRESSURE
RT	BEACH MORPHOLOGY
RT	CATASTROPHIC WAVES
RT	COAST DEFENCES
RT	DISASTERS
RT	FLOODING
RT	HURRICANES
RT	METEOROLOGICAL TIDES
RT	SEA LEVEL PRESSURE
RT	SHALLOW-WATER WAVES
RT	STORM SURGE BARRIERS
RT	STORM SURGE GENERATION
RT	STORM SURGE PREDICTION
RT	STORM TIDE WARNING SERVICES
RT	SURFACE GRAVITY WAVES
RT	TIDE-SURGE INTERACTION
RT	WIND SETUP

STORM TIDE WARNING SERVICES
BT1	WARNING SERVICES
BT2	INFORMATION CENTRES
BT3	ORGANIZATIONS
RT	NEGATIVE STORM SURGES
RT	STORM SURGE PREDICTION
RT	STORM SURGES

STORM TIDES
USE	**STORM SURGES**

STORMS
UF	gales
BT1	WEATHER
BT2	CLIMATE
RT	FLOODS
RT	GALE FORCE WINDS
RT	HURRICANES
RT	LIGHTNING
RT	METEOROLOGICAL CHARTS
RT	METEOROLOGY
RT	THUNDERSTORMS
RT	TORNADOES
RT	WEATHER FORECASTING
RT	WEATHER HAZARDS
RT	WINDS

STORMWATER RUNOFF
BT1	RUNOFF
BT2	DRAINAGE WATER
BT3	WATER
RT	HYDROLOGY
RT	RAINFALL
RT	WASTE WATER

STRAIGHT CHAIN SATURATED HYDROCARBONS
USE	**ACYCLIC HYDROCARBONS**

STRAIN
BT1	DEFORMATION
BT2	MECHANICAL PROPERTIES
BT3	PHYSICAL PROPERTIES
BT4	PROPERTIES
RT	ELASTICITY
RT	POISSON'S RATIO
RT	SHEAR STRENGTH
RT	STRAIN GAUGES
RT	STRESS
RT	STRESS-STRAIN RELATIONS

STRAIN GAUGES
BT1	INSTRUMENTS
RT	GAUGES
RT	MEASURING DEVICES
RT	STRAIN
RT	STRAIN SEISMOMETERS
RT	TILTMETERS
RT	TRANSDUCERS

STRAIN SEISMOMETERS
BT1	SEISMOMETERS
BT2	MEASURING DEVICES
RT	STRAIN GAUGES

STRAITS
BT1	COASTAL WATERS
RT	CHANNELS
RT	TUNNELS
RT	WATER EXCHANGE

STRAND LINES
USE	**STRANDLINES**

STRANDED ORGANISMS
USE	**STRANDING**

STRANDFLATS
USE	**WAVE-CUT PLATFORMS**

STRANDING
SN	Whales or other organisms washed ashore. Added in 1980
UF	stranded organisms
UF	whale stranding
RT	AQUATIC MAMMALS
RT	CARCASSES
RT	GEOGRAPHICAL DISTRIBUTION
RT	NEW RECORDS

STRANDLINES
UF	ancient shorelines
UF	strand lines
BT1	COASTS
BT2	LANDFORMS
BT3	TOPOGRAPHIC FEATURES
RT	GLACIAL LAKES
RT	RAISED BEACHES
RT	SEA LEVEL CHANGES
RT	TERRACES
RT	WAVE-CUT PLATFORMS

STRATIFICATION
NT1	DENSITY STRATIFICATION
NT1	SALINITY STRATIFICATION
NT1	THERMAL STRATIFICATION
RT	BAROCLINIC MODE
RT	BAROTROPIC MODE

ASFIS Thesaurus

STRATIFICATION (cont'd)
RT	DESTRATIFICATION
RT	HYDROGRAPHY
RT	LAYERS
RT	SALINITY SECTIONS
RT	STRATIFIED FLOW
RT	TEMPERATURE GRADIENTS
RT	TEMPERATURE SECTIONS
RT	THERMAL STRUCTURE
RT	WATER COLUMN

STRATIFICATION (THERMAL)
USE	**THERMAL STRATIFICATION**

STRATIFIED FLOW
BT1	FLUID FLOW
BT2	FLUID MOTION
RT	BAROCLINIC MODE
RT	BAROCLINIC MOTION
RT	DENSITY FLOW
RT	LAMINAR FLOW
RT	STRATIFICATION
RT	STRATIFIED SHEAR FLOW

STRATIFIED SAMPLING
USE	**STATISTICAL SAMPLING**

STRATIFIED SHEAR FLOW
BT1	SHEAR FLOW
BT2	FLUID FLOW
BT3	FLUID MOTION
RT	LEE WAVES
RT	STRATIFIED FLOW

STRATIGRAPHIC CORRELATION
BT1	GEOLOGICAL CORRELATION
RT	BIOSTRATIGRAPHY
RT	CHRONOSTRATIGRAPHY
RT	CORRELATION
RT	GEOCHRONOMETRY
RT	MAGNETOSTRATIGRAPHY
RT	OXYGEN ISOTOPE STRATIGRAPHY
RT	SEDIMENTS
RT	SEISMIC STRATIGRAPHY
RT	STRATIGRAPHY

STRATIGRAPHIC SYSTEMS
USE	**GEOLOGICAL TIME**

STRATIGRAPHIC TRAPS
RT	GEOLOGICAL EQUIPMENT
RT	STRATIGRAPHY

STRATIGRAPHY
BT1	GEOLOGY
BT2	EARTH SCIENCES
NT1	BIOSTRATIGRAPHY
NT1	CHRONOSTRATIGRAPHY
NT1	MAGNETOSTRATIGRAPHY
NT1	OXYGEN ISOTOPE STRATIGRAPHY
NT1	SEISMIC STRATIGRAPHY
RT	FOSSILS
RT	GEOCHRONOMETRY
RT	GEOLOGICAL TIME
RT	ISOPACH MAPS
RT	MARINE GEOLOGY
RT	MICROPALAEONTOLOGY
RT	PALAEOCLIMATE
RT	PALAEOCLIMATOLOGY
RT	PALAEOECOLOGY
RT	PALAEONTOLOGY
RT	SEDIMENT STRUCTURE
RT	SEDIMENTATION
RT	SEDIMENTS
RT	STRATIGRAPHIC CORRELATION
RT	STRATIGRAPHIC TRAPS

STRATOSPHERE
BT1	EARTH ATMOSPHERE
BT2	PLANETARY ATMOSPHERES
RT	IONOSPHERE
RT	TROPOPAUSE
RT	TROPOSPHERE

STREAM FISHERIES
USE	**RIVER FISHERIES**

STREAM FLOW
UF	river currents
UF	river flow
BT1	WATER CURRENTS
BT2	WATER MOTION
RT	BACKWATERS
RT	FLOOD CONTROL
RT	FLUID MOTION
RT	HYDRODYNAMICS
RT	RIVER DISCHARGE
RT	RIVER ENGINEERING
RT	RIVER VALLEYS
RT	RIVERS
RT	RUNOFF
RT	STREAM FLOW RATE
RT	UNIDIRECTIONAL FLOW
RT	WATERSHEDS

STREAM FLOW RATE
BT1	CURRENT VELOCITY
BT2	VELOCITY
RT	FLOWMETERS
RT	RIVERS
RT	STREAM FLOW

STREAM FUNCTIONS
RT	CORIOLIS PARAMETERS
RT	DYNAMIC HEIGHT
RT	GEOSTROPHIC EQUILIBRIUM
RT	STREAMLINES

STREAM VALLEYS
USE	**RIVER VALLEYS**

STREAMERS
BT1	CABLES
RT	HYDROPHONES
RT	OCEANOGRAPHIC EQUIPMENT
RT	SEISMIC EQUIPMENT
RT	SENSORS
RT	TOWED SENSORS

STREAMLINES
BT1	MAP GRAPHICS
BT2	GRAPHICS
BT3	AUDIOVISUAL MATERIAL
BT4	DOCUMENTS
RT	CURRENT CHARTS
RT	CURRENT DIRECTION
RT	CURRENT VECTORS
RT	DYNAMIC TOPOGRAPHY
RT	STREAM FUNCTIONS
RT	WATER CURRENTS

STREAMS
USE	**RIVERS**

STRENGTH
SN	Use for mechanical strength
BT1	MECHANICAL PROPERTIES
BT2	PHYSICAL PROPERTIES
BT3	PROPERTIES
NT1	BEARING CAPACITY
NT1	COLLAPSE STRENGTH
NT1	COMPRESSIVE STRENGTH
NT1	SHEAR STRENGTH
NT1	TENSILE STRENGTH
RT	YIELD POINT

STRESS
SN	Restricted to mechanical stress. Before 1983 search also STRESS (MECHANICS)
UF	stress (mechanics)
BT1	FORCES (MECHANICS)
NT1	BOTTOM STRESS
NT1	COMPRESSION
NT1	REYNOLDS STRESSES
NT1	SHEAR STRESS
NT1	TENSION
NT2	SURFACE TENSION
NT1	TORQUE
NT1	WIND STRESS
RT	BIOLOGICAL STRESS
RT	ELASTICITY
RT	FATIGUE (MATERIALS)
RT	MECHANICAL PROPERTIES
RT	METALS
RT	SHEAR STRENGTH
RT	STRAIN
RT	STRESS-STRAIN RELATIONS
RT	TESTS

STRESS (BIOLOGICAL)
USE	**BIOLOGICAL STRESS**

STRESS (MECHANICS)
USE	**STRESS**

STRESS (PHYSIOLOGICAL)
USE	**BIOLOGICAL STRESS**

STRESS CORROSION
BT1	CORROSION
BT2	CHEMICAL REACTIONS
RT	EMBRITTLEMENT
RT	FATIGUE (MATERIALS)
RT	METAL FATIGUE

STRESS-STRAIN RELATIONS
RT	DEFORMATION
RT	MECHANICAL PROPERTIES
RT	SOIL MECHANICS
RT	STRAIN
RT	STRESS
RT	TENSILE STRENGTH

STRIATED MUSCLES
USE	**MUSCLES**

STRINGERS
USE	**PIPE STRINGERS**

STRIP MINE LAKES
BT1	LAKES
BT2	INLAND WATERS
RT	MINE TAILINGS
RT	PITS

STRIPPING ANALYSIS
UF	anodic stripping voltammetry
UF	cathodic stripping voltammetry
BT1	ANALYTICAL TECHNIQUES

STROMATOLITES
BT1	BIOGENIC SEDIMENTARY STRUCTURES
BT2	SEDIMENTARY STRUCTURES
RT	ALGAE
RT	ALGAL MATS

STRONTIUM
BT1	CHEMICAL ELEMENTS
RT	ALKALINE EARTH METALS
RT	DISSOLVED CHEMICALS
RT	METALS
RT	STRONTIUM COMPOUNDS
RT	STRONTIUM ISOTOPES
RT	TRACE ELEMENTS

STRONTIUM COMPOUNDS
RT	CHEMICAL COMPOUNDS
RT	STRONTIUM

STRONTIUM ISOTOPES
BT1	ISOTOPES
RT	RUBIDIUM-STRONTIUM DATING
RT	STRONTIUM

STRUCTURAL ANALYSIS
BT1	STRUCTURAL ENGINEERING
BT2	ENGINEERING
RT	DESIGN
RT	MATHEMATICAL ANALYSIS

STRUCTURAL BASINS
NT1	FOREARC BASINS
NT1	MARGINAL BASINS
RT	BASINS
RT	OCEAN BASINS
RT	SEDIMENTARY BASINS
RT	TECTONICS

STRUCTURAL DOMES
UF	geological domes
BT1	FOLDS
BT2	GEOLOGICAL STRUCTURES
NT1	SALT DOMES
RT	DIAPIRS
RT	DOMES

STRUCTURAL DYNAMICS
BT1	DYNAMICS
BT2	MECHANICS
BT3	PHYSICS
RT	DYNAMIC LOADS
RT	STRUCTURAL ENGINEERING

STRUCTURAL ENGINEERING
BT1	ENGINEERING
NT1	STRUCTURAL ANALYSIS
RT	BARRAGES
RT	COASTAL ENGINEERING
RT	DAMS
RT	GEOTECHNOLOGY
RT	HYDRAULIC STRUCTURES
RT	OFFSHORE STRUCTURES
RT	PORT INSTALLATIONS
RT	RIVER ENGINEERING
RT	STRUCTURAL DYNAMICS
RT	TIDAL BARRAGES

STRUCTURAL GEOLOGY
BT1	GEOLOGY
BT2	EARTH SCIENCES
RT	GEOLOGICAL STRUCTURES
RT	TECTONICS

STRUCTURAL SETTLEMENT
USE	**SETTLEMENT (STRUCTURAL)**

STRUCTURES
SN	Use only for man-made structures. Use of a more specific term is recommended
RT	COASTAL STRUCTURES
RT	CONCRETE STRUCTURES
RT	CYLINDRICAL STRUCTURES
RT	FLOATING STRUCTURES
RT	HYDRAULIC STRUCTURES
RT	OFFSHORE STRUCTURES
RT	PERFORATED STRUCTURES
RT	STEEL STRUCTURES
RT	UNDERWATER STRUCTURES

STRUMMING
USE	**VIBRATION**

STUPEFYING METHODS
RT	ELECTRIC FISHING
RT	ELECTRIFIED GEAR
RT	EXPLOSIVE FISHING
RT	FISH POISONING
RT	FISHING GEAR

SUB-BOTTOM PROFILING
SN	Profiling using systems employing discrete sound sources, e.g. echosounders
BT1	SEISMIC EXPLORATION
BT2	GEOPHYSICAL EXPLORATION
BT3	EXPLORATION
RT	ACOUSTIC EQUIPMENT
RT	ECHOSOUNDING
RT	PROFILING
RT	SEISMIC REFLECTION PROFILING

SUBAEREAL TOPOGRAPHY
BT1	TOPOGRAPHY (GEOLOGY)
BT2	TOPOGRAPHY
RT	LANDFORMS

SUBAQUEOUS SEDIMENT TRANSPORT
USE	**SEDIMENT TRANSPORT**

SUBDUCTION
RT	ACTIVE MARGINS
RT	FOREARC BASINS
RT	ISLAND ARCS
RT	MARGINAL BASINS
RT	OBDUCTION
RT	OCEANIC CRUST
RT	PLATE TECTONICS
RT	PLATES
RT	SUBDUCTION ZONES

SUBDUCTION ZONES
RT	BENIOFF ZONE
RT	CONVERGING PLATE BOUNDARIES
RT	PLATE CONVERGENCE
RT	PLATE TECTONICS
RT	PLATES
RT	SUBDUCTION
RT	TRENCHES (OCEANIC)

SUBGRAVEL FILTERS
USE	**BIOFILTERS**

SUBLETHAL EFFECTS
SN	Effects, not immediately identifiable, of harmful substances on organisms. Added in 1980
RT	BIOACCUMULATION
RT	BIOLOGICAL POISONS
RT	BIOTESTING
RT	DISEASES
RT	LETHAL EFFECTS
RT	POLLUTANTS
RT	POLLUTION TOLERANCE
RT	SURVIVAL
RT	TOXICITY
RT	TOXICITY TESTS
RT	TOXICITY TOLERANCE
RT	TOXICOLOGY

SUBLIMATION
BT1	VAPORIZATION
BT2	PHASE CHANGES
RT	ABLATION
RT	CONDENSATION
RT	EVAPORATION
RT	FREEZING
RT	HYDROMETEORS
RT	ICE FORMATION
RT	ICE MELTING
RT	MELTING
RT	SUBLIMATION HEAT
RT	WATER VAPOUR

SUBLIMATION HEAT
UF	latent heat of sublimation
BT1	ENTHALPY
BT2	THERMODYNAMIC PROPERTIES
BT3	PHYSICAL PROPERTIES
BT4	PROPERTIES
RT	ABLATION
RT	SUBLIMATION

SUBLITTORAL ZONE
BT1	LITTORAL ZONE
BT2	BENTHIC ENVIRONMENT
BT3	AQUATIC ENVIRONMENT
BT4	ENVIRONMENTS
RT	NEARSHORE SEDIMENTATION

SUBMARINE BANKS
BT1	SUBMARINE FEATURES
BT2	TOPOGRAPHIC FEATURES
RT	BANKS (TOPOGRAPHY)
RT	FISHING GROUNDS
RT	MUD BANKS
RT	SAND BANKS
RT	SHOALS

SUBMARINE BARS
USE	**NEARSHORE BARS**

SUBMARINE BASINS
USE	**OCEAN BASINS**

SUBMARINE CABLE BREAKS
UF	cable breaks
RT	SUBMARINE CABLES
RT	TURBIDITY CURRENTS

SUBMARINE CABLES
BT1	ELECTRIC CABLES
BT2	CABLES
RT	CABLE LAYING
RT	CABLE SHIPS
RT	COAXIAL CABLES
RT	COMMUNICATION SYSTEMS
RT	ELECTRIC POTENTIAL
RT	OCEAN FLOOR
RT	SUBMARINE CABLE BREAKS
RT	TELEPHONE SYSTEMS
RT	TRENCHES (PIPELINES)

SUBMARINE CANYONS
BT1	SUBMARINE FEATURES
BT2	TOPOGRAPHIC FEATURES
RT	BOTTOM CURRENTS
RT	CONTINENTAL SHELVES
RT	CONTINENTAL SLOPE
RT	DEEP-SEA FANS
RT	EROSION FEATURES
RT	RELIEF FORMS
RT	SUBMARINE VALLEYS
RT	THALWEG
RT	TURBIDITY CURRENTS
RT	VALLEYS

SUBMARINE CEMENTS
SN	Chemically precipitated mineral material
UF	cements (geology)
BT1	CHEMICAL SEDIMENTS
BT2	SEDIMENTS
RT	AUTHIGENIC MINERALS
RT	CEMENTATION

SUBMARINE CRUST
USE	**OCEANIC CRUST**

ASFIS Thesaurus

SUBMARINE EROSION		
USE	**BOTTOM EROSION**	
SUBMARINE ESCARPMENTS		
USE	**SUBMARINE SCARPS**	
SUBMARINE FANS		
USE	**DEEP-SEA FANS**	
SUBMARINE FEATURES		
UF	bottom features	
UF	submarine topographic features	
BT1	TOPOGRAPHIC FEATURES	
NT1	ABYSSAL HILLS	
NT1	ABYSSAL PLAINS	
NT1	ARCHIPELAGIC APRONS	
NT1	CONTINENTAL BORDERLAND	
NT1	CONTINENTAL MARGINS	
NT2	ACTIVE MARGINS	
NT2	PASSIVE MARGINS	
NT1	CONTINENTAL RIDGES	
NT1	CONTINENTAL RISE	
NT1	CONTINENTAL SHELVES	
NT2	OUTER CONTINENTAL SHELF	
NT1	CONTINENTAL SLOPE	
NT1	DEEP-SEA CHANNELS	
NT1	DEEP-SEA FANS	
NT1	FRACTURE ZONES	
NT1	ISLAND SLOPE	
NT1	MICROCONTINENTS	
NT1	OCEAN BASINS	
NT1	SEABIGHTS	
NT1	SEAKNOLLS	
NT1	SEAMOUNT CHAINS	
NT1	SEAMOUNTS	
NT2	GUYOTS	
NT1	SHELF EDGE	
NT1	SHOALS	
NT1	SILLS	
NT1	SUBMARINE BANKS	
NT1	SUBMARINE CANYONS	
NT1	SUBMARINE PLATEAUX	
NT1	SUBMARINE RIDGES	
NT2	ASEISMIC RIDGES	
NT2	SEISMIC RIDGES	
NT3	MID-OCEAN RIDGES	
NT1	SUBMARINE SCARPS	
NT1	SUBMARINE TROUGHS	
NT1	SUBMARINE VALLEYS	
NT1	TRENCHES (OCEANIC)	
RT	BATHYMETRIC CHARTS	
RT	BATHYMETRY	
RT	BOTTOM TOPOGRAPHY	
RT	EROSION FEATURES	
RT	GAZETEERS	
RT	MARINE GEOLOGY	
RT	MEDIAN VALLEYS	
RT	OCEAN FLOOR	
RT	PHYSIOGRAPHIC PROVINCES	
RT	SUBMARINE VOLCANOES	
SUBMARINE GEOLOGY		
USE	**MARINE GEOLOGY**	
SUBMARINE ICE PROFILES		
USE	**ICE CANOPY**	
SUBMARINE PERMAFROST		
USE	**PERMAFROST**	
SUBMARINE PIPELINES		
USE	**PIPELINES**	
SUBMARINE PLATEAUX		
UF	ocean plateaux	
BT1	SUBMARINE FEATURES	
BT2	TOPOGRAPHIC FEATURES	
RT	MICROCONTINENTS	
RT	PLATEAUX	
RT	RELIEF FORMS	

SUBMARINE RIDGES		
UF	oceanic ridges	
BT1	SUBMARINE FEATURES	
BT2	TOPOGRAPHIC FEATURES	
NT1	ASEISMIC RIDGES	
NT1	SEISMIC RIDGES	
NT2	MID-OCEAN RIDGES	
RT	MOUNTAINS	
RT	RELIEF FORMS	
RT	RIDGES	
RT	SILLS	
RT	SUBMARINE SCARPS	
SUBMARINE SCARPS		
SN	Before 1984 search also SCARPS and UNDERWATER ESCARPMENTS	
UF	submarine escarpments	
UF	underwater escarpments	
BT1	SUBMARINE FEATURES	
BT2	TOPOGRAPHIC FEATURES	
RT	ESCARPMENTS	
RT	FAULT SCARPS	
RT	FRACTURE ZONES	
RT	MEDIAN VALLEYS	
RT	RELIEF FORMS	
RT	SUBMARINE RIDGES	
SUBMARINE SPRINGS		
SN	Offshore emergence of fresh water	
UF	water seepages	
BT1	WATER SPRINGS	
RT	FRESH WATER	
RT	SEEPAGES	
SUBMARINE TANKERS		
BT1	SUBMARINES	
BT2	MANNED VEHICLES	
BT3	UNDERWATER VEHICLES	
BT4	VEHICLES	
RT	TANKER SHIPS	
SUBMARINE TERRACES		
USE	**TERRACES**	
SUBMARINE TOPOGRAPHIC FEATURES		
USE	**SUBMARINE FEATURES**	
SUBMARINE TRENCHES		
USE	**TRENCHES (OCEANIC)**	
SUBMARINE TROUGHS		
BT1	SUBMARINE FEATURES	
BT2	TOPOGRAPHIC FEATURES	
RT	RELIEF FORMS	
SUBMARINE VALLEYS		
BT1	SUBMARINE FEATURES	
BT2	TOPOGRAPHIC FEATURES	
RT	DROWNED VALLEYS	
RT	RELIEF FORMS	
RT	SUBMARINE CANYONS	
RT	VALLEYS	
SUBMARINE VOLCANOES		
BT1	VOLCANOES	
RT	MARINE GEOLOGY	
RT	OCEANIC ISLANDS	
RT	PLATE BOUNDARIES	
RT	SEAMOUNT CHAINS	
RT	SUBMARINE FEATURES	
RT	VOLCANIC ERUPTIONS	
RT	VOLCANIC ISLANDS	
SUBMARINE WEATHERING		
USE	**HALMYROLYSIS**	

SUBMARINES		
SN	Use only for manned underwater vehicles designed for military purposes	
BT1	MANNED VEHICLES	
BT2	UNDERWATER VEHICLES	
BT3	VEHICLES	
NT1	SUBMARINE TANKERS	
RT	DEFENCE CRAFT	
RT	MILITARY OCEANOGRAPHY	
RT	NAVIGATION UNDER ICE	
RT	NAVIGATION UNDERWATER	
RT	NUCLEAR PROPULSION	
RT	SONAR	
RT	SONAR DETECTION	
RT	SUBMERSIBLES	
RT	UNDERSEA WARFARE	
SUBMERGED CAGES		
SN	Added in 1980	
UF	bottom cages	
UF	midwater cages	
BT1	CAGES	
BT2	AQUACULTURE EQUIPMENT	
BT3	EQUIPMENT	
RT	CRUSTACEAN CULTURE	
RT	FISH CULTURE	
RT	MARINE AQUACULTURE	
SUBMERGED SHORELINES		
BT1	COASTS	
BT2	LANDFORMS	
BT3	TOPOGRAPHIC FEATURES	
NT1	RIA COASTS	
RT	DROWNED VALLEYS	
RT	EMERGENT SHORELINES	
RT	EPEIROGENY	
RT	EUSTATIC CHANGES	
RT	FJORDS	
RT	INTERGLACIAL PERIODS	
RT	ISOSTASY	
RT	RETROGRADATION	
RT	SUBMERGENCE	
RT	TRANSGRESSIONS	
SUBMERGENCE		
RT	EPEIROGENY	
RT	EUSTATIC CHANGES	
RT	FJORDS	
RT	INTERGLACIAL PERIODS	
RT	ISOSTASY	
RT	RETROGRADATION	
RT	SUBMERGED SHORELINES	
RT	TRANSGRESSIONS	
SUBMERSIBLE PLATFORMS		
SN	Towed or self-propelled platforms supportable on flooded hulls	
BT1	MOBILE PLATFORMS	
BT2	FLOATING STRUCTURES	
BT3	OFFSHORE STRUCTURES	
BT4	HYDRAULIC STRUCTURES	
RT	CAISSONS	
RT	JACKUP PLATFORMS	
RT	SEMISUBMERSIBLE PLATFORMS	
SUBMERSIBLES		
UF	manned submersibles	
UF	submersibles (manned)	
BT1	MANNED VEHICLES	
BT2	UNDERWATER VEHICLES	
BT3	VEHICLES	
NT1	LOCKOUT SUBMERSIBLES	
NT1	WET SUBMERSIBLES	
RT	DEEP-SEA DIVING	
RT	DIVING BELLS	
RT	DIVING EQUIPMENT	
RT	DIVING SUITS	
RT	FREE-SWIMMING VEHICLES	
RT	LIFE SUPPORT SYSTEMS	

SUBMERSIBLES (cont'd)
RT   MOTHER SHIPS
RT   NAVIGATION UNDERWATER
RT   PROPULSION SYSTEMS
RT   SEARCH AND RESCUE
RT   SELF-PROPELLED VEHICLES
RT   SUBMARINES
RT   UNDERWATER MEDICINE

SUBMERSIBLES (MANNED)
USE   **SUBMERSIBLES**

SUBMERSIBLES (UNMANNED)
USE   **UNMANNED VEHICLES**

SUBOCEANIC CRUST
USE   **OCEANIC CRUST**

SUBPOPULATIONS
SN   Subset of a population which comprises a self-sustained genetic unit
UF   race
RT   GENOTYPES
RT   POPULATION GENETICS
RT   POPULATION STRUCTURE
RT   RACIAL STUDIES
RT   STOCK IDENTIFICATION
RT   UNIT STOCKS

SUBSEA PRODUCTION SYSTEMS
RT   OIL AND GAS PRODUCTION
RT   WELLHEADS

SUBSIDENCE
SN   Use only in tectonic context
BT1   EPEIROGENY
BT2   TECTONICS
BT3   GEOLOGY
BT4   EARTH SCIENCES
RT   TECTONICS
RT   UPLIFT

SUBSISTENCE AQUACULTURE
USE   **SMALL SCALE AQUACULTURE**

SUBSTRATA
UF   substrates
RT   ARTIFICIAL SUBSTRATA
RT   BENTHIC ENVIRONMENT
RT   BENTHOS
RT   BOTTOM CULTURE
RT   BYSSUS
RT   ECOLOGICAL ZONATION
RT   ENVIRONMENTAL EFFECTS
RT   HABITAT
RT   SESSILE SPECIES
RT   SETTLING BEHAVIOUR
RT   SUBSTRATE PREFERENCES

SUBSTRATE AFFINITIES
USE   **SUBSTRATE PREFERENCES**

SUBSTRATE PREFERENCES
UF   substrate affinities
RT   ALGAL SETTLEMENTS
RT   ARTIFICIAL SUBSTRATA
RT   BIOLOGICAL SETTLEMENT
RT   COLONIZATION
RT   CULTCH
RT   LARVAL SETTLEMENT
RT   SPECIFICITY
RT   SUBSTRATA

SUBSTRATES
USE   **SUBSTRATA**

SUBSURFACE BUOYANCY FLOATS
USE   **BUOYANCY FLOATS**

SUBSURFACE CURRENTS
BT1   WATER CURRENTS
BT2   WATER MOTION
NT1   DEEP CURRENTS
RT   BOTTOM CURRENTS
RT   LAKE CURRENTS
RT   OCEAN CURRENTS
RT   SHELF SEAS

SUBSURFACE DEPOSITS
BT1   MINERAL DEPOSITS
BT2   MINERAL RESOURCES
BT3   NATURAL RESOURCES
BT4   RESOURCES
NT1   FOSSIL FUELS
NT2   COAL
NT2   PETROLEUM
NT3   CRUDE OIL
NT3   GAS CONDENSATES
NT3   NATURAL GAS
NT4   LIQUEFIED NATURAL GAS
NT3   PETROLEUM RESIDUES
NT1   PHOSPHATE DEPOSITS
RT   DEEP-SEA MINING
RT   OIL SANDS
RT   OIL SHALE
RT   ORES
RT   POTASH DEPOSITS
RT   SALT DEPOSITS

SUBSURFACE DRIFTERS
UF   floats (subsurface)
UF   subsurface floats
BT1   DRIFTERS
BT2   CURRENT MEASURING EQUIPMENT
BT3   FLOW MEASURING EQUIPMENT
NT1   SEABED DRIFTERS
NT1   SWALLOW FLOATS
NT2   SOFAR FLOATS
RT   CURRENT MEASUREMENT
RT   LAGRANGIAN CURRENT MEASUREMENT

SUBSURFACE FLOATS
USE   **SUBSURFACE DRIFTERS**

SUBSURFACE WATER
BT1   WATER MASSES
RT   AGE OF SEAWATER

SUBTROPICAL CONVERGENCES
BT1   OCEANIC CONVERGENCES
BT2   CONVERGENCE ZONES
RT   GYRES
RT   OCEANIC FRONTS

SUBTROPICAL GYRES
USE   **GYRES**

SUBTROPICAL JET STREAM
USE   **JET STREAM**

SUBTROPICAL ZONES
BT1   CLIMATIC ZONES

SUCCESSION (ECOLOGICAL)
USE   **ECOLOGICAL SUCCESSION**

SUFFOCATION
USE   **ASPHYXIA**

SUGARS
USE   **SACCHARIDES**

SULFIDE DEPOSITS
USE   **SULPHIDE DEPOSITS**

SULFUR
USE   **SULPHUR**

SULPHATE MINERALS
BT1   MINERALS
NT1   ANHYDRITE
NT1   BARITE
NT1   CELESTITE
NT1   EPSOMITE
NT1   GYPSUM
NT1   JAROSITE
NT1   KAINITE
NT1   POLYHALITE
RT   SULPHATES
RT   SULPHIDE DEPOSITS

SULPHATE REDUCTION
BT1   REDUCTION
BT2   CHEMICAL REACTIONS
RT   BIOGEOCHEMISTRY
RT   SEDIMENT CHEMISTRY
RT   SULPHATES

SULPHATES
SN   Before 1982 search SULPHUR COMPOUNDS
BT1   SULPHUR COMPOUNDS
RT   CALCIUM SULPHATES
RT   MAGNESIUM SULPHATES
RT   SULPHATE MINERALS
RT   SULPHATE REDUCTION
RT   SULPHIDE DEPOSITS

SULPHIDE DEPOSITS
UF   polymetallic sulphide deposits
UF   sulfide deposits
BT1   CHEMICAL SEDIMENTS
BT2   SEDIMENTS
RT   HYDROTHERMAL DEPOSITS
RT   METALLIFEROUS SEDIMENTS
RT   SEABED DEPOSITS
RT   SULPHATE MINERALS
RT   SULPHATES
RT   SULPHIDE MINERALS
RT   SULPHIDES

SULPHIDE MINERALS
BT1   MINERALS
NT1   GREIGITE
NT1   KANSITE
NT1   MARCASITE
NT1   PYRITE
NT1   PYRRHOTITE
RT   SULPHIDE DEPOSITS
RT   SULPHIDES

SULPHIDES
SN   Before 1982 search SULPHUR COMPOUNDS
BT1   SULPHUR COMPOUNDS
RT   HYDROGEN SULPHIDE
RT   IRON SULPHIDES
RT   SULPHIDE DEPOSITS
RT   SULPHIDE MINERALS

SULPHITES
SN   Before 1982 search SULPHUR COMPOUNDS
BT1   SULPHUR COMPOUNDS

SULPHONATES
BT1   SULPHUR COMPOUNDS

SULPHUR
UF   sulfur
BT1   CHEMICAL ELEMENTS
RT   DISSOLVED CHEMICALS
RT   SULPHUR COMPOUNDS
RT   SULPHUR ISOTOPES

SULPHUR COMPOUNDS
NT1	SULPHATES
NT1	SULPHIDES
NT1	SULPHITES
NT1	SULPHONATES
NT1	SULPHUR OXIDES
NT2	SULPHUR DIOXIDE
RT	ANOXIC BASINS
RT	CHEMICAL COMPOUNDS
RT	SULPHUR
RT	SULPHURIC ACID
RT	VOLATILE COMPOUNDS

SULPHUR DIOXIDE
BT1	SULPHUR OXIDES
BT2	SULPHUR COMPOUNDS

SULPHUR ISOTOPES
BT1	ISOTOPES
RT	SULPHUR

SULPHUR OXIDES
BT1	SULPHUR COMPOUNDS
NT1	SULPHUR DIOXIDE

SULPHURIC ACID
BT1	INORGANIC ACIDS
BT2	HYDROGEN COMPOUNDS
RT	SULPHUR COMPOUNDS

SUMMARIES
USE	**ABSTRACTS**

SUMMER
BT1	SEASONS

SUN
RT	ASTRONOMY
RT	PYRANOMETERS
RT	SOLAR ACTIVITY
RT	SOLAR CELLS
RT	SOLAR CONSTANT
RT	SOLAR ECLIPSE
RT	SOLAR POWER
RT	SOLAR RADIATION
RT	SOLAR SEMIDIURNAL TIDES
RT	SOLAR TIDES
RT	SOLAR-DIURNAL TIDES
RT	SOLAR-TERRESTRIAL ACTIVITY

SUN DRIED PRODUCTS
USE	**DRIED PRODUCTS**

SUNBURN
SN	Pathological condition ascribed to excessive level of ultraviolet irradiation. Added in 1980
BT1	FISH DISEASES
BT2	ANIMAL DISEASES
BT3	DISEASES
RT	CULTURED ORGANISMS
RT	ENVIRONMENTAL DISEASES
RT	FISH CULTURE
RT	HUSBANDRY DISEASES
RT	NUTRITION DISORDERS

SUNSPOTS
USE	**SOLAR ACTIVITY**

SUPERSATURATION
SN	Added in 1982
BT1	SATURATION
RT	CHEMICAL PRECIPITATION
RT	DISSOLUTION
RT	SOLUBILITY

SUPPLY BOATS
BT1	SHIPS
BT2	SURFACE CRAFT
BT3	VEHICLES
RT	MARINE TRANSPORTATION
RT	SUPPORT SHIPS

SUPPORT CRAFT
USE	**SUPPORT SHIPS**

SUPPORT SHIPS
SN	Applied to auxiliary ships of fishing fleets and from 1981 also to vessels serving oil rigs and other offshore installations
UF	support craft
UF	work boats
BT1	SHIPS
BT2	SURFACE CRAFT
BT3	VEHICLES
NT1	FACTORY SHIPS
NT1	MOTHER SHIPS
RT	CRANE BARGES
RT	DIVING BELLS
RT	DIVING EQUIPMENT
RT	EMERGENCY VESSELS
RT	FISHING OPERATIONS
RT	FISHING VESSELS
RT	MARINE TRANSPORTATION
RT	SUPPLY BOATS
RT	TUGS

SUPPRESSING
USE	**DAMPING**

SUPPRESSORS
RT	ACOUSTIC INSULATION

SUPRALITTORAL ZONE
UF	supratidal zone
BT1	LITTORAL ZONE
BT2	BENTHIC ENVIRONMENT
BT3	AQUATIC ENVIRONMENT
BT4	ENVIRONMENTS
RT	SABKHAS

SUPRARENAL GLANDS
USE	**ADRENAL GLANDS**

SUPRATIDAL ZONE
USE	**SUPRALITTORAL ZONE**

SURF
BT1	BREAKING WAVES
BT2	SURFACE WATER WAVES
BT3	WATER WAVES
RT	BEACHES
RT	EXPOSED HABITATS
RT	SURF ZONE
RT	SURFING
RT	WAVES ON BEACHES

SURF BEATS
BT1	TRAPPED WAVES
BT2	WATER WAVES
RT	WAVE SETDOWN
RT	WAVE SETUP

SURF ZONE
UF	breaker zone
BT1	BEACH FEATURES
RT	BREAKING WAVES
RT	LONGSHORE CURRENTS
RT	NEARSHORE DYNAMICS
RT	RIP CURRENTS
RT	SURF
RT	UNDERTOW
RT	WAVE DISSIPATION
RT	WAVES ON BEACHES

SURFACE ACTIVE AGENTS
USE	**SURFACTANTS**

SURFACE ACTIVITY
RT	SURFACE PROPERTIES

SURFACE AREA
USE	**AREA**

SURFACE BOUNDARY LAYER
USE	**ATMOSPHERIC BOUNDARY LAYER**

SURFACE CHEMISTRY
BT1	CHEMISTRY
RT	AIR-WATER EXCHANGES
RT	BUBBLE BURSTING
RT	FOAMS
RT	SEA SURFACE
RT	SURFACE FILMS
RT	SURFACE MICROLAYER
RT	SURFACE PROPERTIES
RT	SURFACTANTS

SURFACE CIRCULATION
UF	near-surface circulation
BT1	WATER CIRCULATION
BT2	WATER MOTION
RT	GYRES
RT	LAKE DYNAMICS
RT	LANGMUIR CIRCULATION
RT	OCEAN CIRCULATION
RT	SURFACE CURRENTS
RT	WIND-DRIVEN CIRCULATION

SURFACE CLUTTER
UF	sea clutter
UF	sea surface clutter
BT1	RADAR CLUTTER

SURFACE CRAFT
SN	Use of a narrower term is recommended
UF	surface vessels
UF	vessels
BT1	VEHICLES
NT1	BARGES
NT2	CRANE BARGES
NT2	PIPELAYING BARGES
NT1	BOATS
NT1	CANOES
NT1	CATAMARANS
NT1	DREDGERS
NT1	DRILLING VESSELS
NT1	EMERGENCY VESSELS
NT1	FISHING VESSELS
NT2	CATCHERS
NT2	GILLNETTERS
NT2	LINERS
NT2	SEINERS
NT2	TRAWLERS
NT1	HOVERCRAFT
NT1	HYDROFOILS
NT1	ICE BREAKERS
NT1	INFLATABLE CRAFT
NT1	LIFEBOATS
NT1	MINING VESSELS
NT1	RESEARCH VESSELS
NT1	ROW BOATS
NT1	SHIPS
NT2	CABLE SHIPS
NT2	LIGHTERS
NT2	LIGHTSHIPS
NT2	MERCHANT SHIPS
NT3	BULK CARRIERS
NT3	CONTAINER SHIPS
NT3	PASSENGER SHIPS
NT3	SELECTED SHIPS
NT3	TANKER SHIPS
NT2	MOTOR BOATS
NT2	PROTECTION VESSELS
NT2	SAILING SHIPS

SURFACE CRAFT (cont'd)

NT3	YACHTS
NT2	SUPPLY BOATS
NT2	SUPPORT SHIPS
NT3	FACTORY SHIPS
NT3	MOTHER SHIPS
NT2	TUGS
NT2	WEATHER SHIPS
NT1	SURVEY VESSELS
RT	CAPSIZING
RT	COLLISION AVOIDANCE
RT	DISPLACEMENT
RT	FLOATING STRUCTURES
RT	ICING
RT	INSTRUMENT PLATFORMS
RT	MARINE TRANSPORTATION
RT	PROTECTION VESSELS
RT	RIGGING
RT	SHIP STABILITY
RT	SHIP TECHNOLOGY
RT	SHIPPING
RT	TRANSPORTATION
RT	WAKES
RT	WORK PLATFORMS

SURFACE CURRENTS

BT1	WATER CURRENTS
BT2	WATER MOTION
NT1	CONTOUR CURRENTS
RT	LAKE CURRENTS
RT	OCEAN CURRENTS
RT	SURFACE CIRCULATION
RT	SURFACE LAYERS
RT	WIND-DRIVEN CURRENTS

SURFACE DRIFTERS

BT1	DRIFTERS
BT2	CURRENT MEASURING EQUIPMENT
BT3	FLOW MEASURING EQUIPMENT
NT1	DRIFT BOTTLES
NT1	DRIFT CARDS
NT1	DROGUES
RT	CURRENT MEASUREMENT
RT	DRIFTING DATA BUOYS
RT	FLOTSAM
RT	PUMICE

SURFACE EKMAN LAYER

BT1	EKMAN LAYERS
BT2	BOUNDARY LAYERS
BT3	LAYERS
RT	OCEANIC BOUNDARY LAYER
RT	WIND-DRIVEN CURRENTS

SURFACE ENERGY
USE **SURFACE TENSION**

SURFACE FILMS

UF	films (surface)
UF	oil films
UF	slicks (surface)
NT1	MONOMOLECULAR FILMS
RT	CAPILLARITY
RT	LAYERS
RT	OIL SLICKS
RT	SEA SURFACE
RT	SLICKS
RT	SURFACE CHEMISTRY
RT	SURFACE MICROLAYER
RT	WAVE DAMPING
RT	WINDROWS

SURFACE FOLLOWERS
USE **WAVE FOLLOWERS**

SURFACE GEOMETRY (WATER WAVES)
USE **WAVE GEOMETRY**

SURFACE GRAVITY WAVES

BT1	WATER WAVES
RT	CNOIDAL WAVES
RT	NONLINEAR WAVES
RT	SEICHES
RT	SOLITARY WAVES
RT	STORM SURGES
RT	SWELL
RT	TSUNAMIS
RT	WIND WAVES

SURFACE LAYER TEMPERATURE
USE **SURFACE TEMPERATURE**

SURFACE LAYERS

BT1	WATER COLUMN
BT2	LAYERS
NT1	NEAR-SURFACE LAYER
NT1	SURFACE MICROLAYER
RT	EPILIMNION
RT	LANGMUIR CIRCULATION
RT	SLICKS
RT	SURFACE CURRENTS
RT	SURFACE MIXED LAYER
RT	SURFACE WATER
RT	SURFACE WATER MASSES
RT	THERMOCLINE
RT	UPPER OCEAN
RT	WAVE INTERACTIONS

SURFACE MICROLAYER

BT1	SURFACE LAYERS
BT2	WATER COLUMN
BT3	LAYERS
RT	AEROSOLS
RT	AIR BUBBLES
RT	AIR POLLUTION
RT	AIR-WATER INTERFACE
RT	CHEMICAL POLLUTANTS
RT	CHEMICAL POLLUTION
RT	FOAMS
RT	MONOMOLECULAR FILMS
RT	NEAR-SURFACE LAYER
RT	NEUSTON
RT	OIL SLICKS
RT	RADIOACTIVE POLLUTANTS
RT	SEA SURFACE
RT	SLICKS
RT	SURFACE CHEMISTRY
RT	SURFACE FILMS
RT	SURFACE RADIATION TEMPERATURE
RT	SURFACE WATER
RT	SURFACTANTS

SURFACE MIXED LAYER

BT1	MIXED LAYER
BT2	WATER COLUMN
BT3	LAYERS
RT	ATMOSPHERIC FORCING
RT	EPILIMNION
RT	MIXED LAYER DEPTH
RT	OCEANIC BOUNDARY LAYER
RT	SURFACE LAYERS
RT	THERMOCLINE
RT	THERMOCLINE DECAY
RT	UPPER OCEAN

SURFACE NAVIGATION
USE **NAVIGATION**

SURFACE NOISE

SN	Wind-generated noise, wave breaking, etc.
UF	wind-generated noise
BT1	AMBIENT NOISE
BT2	NOISE (SOUND)
RT	SHIPPING NOISE

SURFACE OF NO MOTION
USE **LEVEL OF NO MOTION**

SURFACE PHENOMENA
USE **SURFACE PROPERTIES**

SURFACE POTENTIAL

RT	SURFACE PROPERTIES

SURFACE PROPERTIES

UF	surface phenomena
BT1	PROPERTIES
NT1	ROUGHNESS
NT2	BED ROUGHNESS
NT2	SURFACE ROUGHNESS
NT1	TEXTURE
RT	ADHESION
RT	ADSORPTION
RT	AIR-WATER INTERFACE
RT	ALBEDO
RT	CAPILLARITY
RT	DESORPTION
RT	EMISSIVITY
RT	FLOTATION
RT	INTERFACE PHENOMENA
RT	OPTICAL PROPERTIES
RT	PHYSICAL PROPERTIES
RT	SEA SURFACE
RT	SORPTION
RT	SURFACE ACTIVITY
RT	SURFACE CHEMISTRY
RT	SURFACE POTENTIAL
RT	SURFACE TENSION
RT	SURFACES
RT	SURFACTANTS
RT	WATER PROPERTIES
RT	WAVE GEOMETRY
RT	WINDROWS

SURFACE RADIATION TEMPERATURE

UF	brightness temperature
UF	brightness temperature (sea surface)
UF	skin temperature
BT1	SURFACE TEMPERATURE
BT2	WATER TEMPERATURE
BT3	TEMPERATURE
BT4	THERMODYNAMIC PROPERTIES
RT	AIR-WATER INTERFACE
RT	INFRARED IMAGERY
RT	RAIN
RT	SEA SURFACE
RT	SURFACE MICROLAYER
RT	TERRESTRIAL RADIATION

SURFACE ROUGHNESS

SN	Roughness of water surface
BT1	ROUGHNESS
BT2	SURFACE PROPERTIES
BT3	PROPERTIES
RT	DRAG COEFFICIENT
RT	RADAR ALTIMETRY
RT	REFLECTANCE
RT	WIND WAVE GENERATION

SURFACE SALINITY

UF	sea surface salinity
UF	water surface salinity
BT1	SALINITY
BT2	CHEMICAL PROPERTIES
BT3	PROPERTIES
RT	SEA SURFACE

SURFACE SEISMIC WAVES

SN	Use of a more specific term is recommended
UF	surface waves (seismic)
BT1	SEISMIC WAVES
BT2	ELASTIC WAVES
NT1	LOVE WAVES
NT1	RAYLEIGH WAVES

SURFACE SEISMIC WAVES (cont'd)		
NT1	STONELEY WAVES	
RT	GROUND MOTION	
SURFACE SLOPE		
UF	sea level slope	
UF	sea surface slope	
UF	water surface slope	
RT	DYNAMIC TOPOGRAPHY	
RT	GEOSTROPHIC FLOW	
RT	SEA LEVEL	
RT	SEA SURFACE	
RT	SURFACE TOPOGRAPHY	
RT	WAVE SLOPE	
SURFACE STRESS		
USE	**WIND STRESS**	
SURFACE TEMPERATURE		
SN	Before 1985 search also SEA SURFACE TEMPERATURE	
UF	ocean surface temperature	
UF	sea surface temperature	
UF	surface layer temperature	
UF	water surface temperature	
BT1	WATER TEMPERATURE	
BT2	TEMPERATURE	
BT3	THERMODYNAMIC PROPERTIES	
BT4	PHYSICAL PROPERTIES	
NT1	BUCKET TEMPERATURE	
NT1	INTAKE TEMPERATURE	
NT1	SURFACE RADIATION TEMPERATURE	
RT	INFRARED DETECTORS	
RT	MICROWAVE IMAGERY	
RT	SEA SURFACE	
SURFACE TENSION		
UF	interfacial tension	
UF	surface energy	
BT1	TENSION	
BT2	STRESS	
BT3	FORCES (MECHANICS)	
RT	CAPILLARITY	
RT	CAPILLARY WAVES	
RT	FLOTATION	
RT	INTERFACE PHENOMENA	
RT	SURFACE PROPERTIES	
RT	SURFACTANTS	
RT	WATER PROPERTIES	
SURFACE TENSION WAVES		
USE	**CAPILLARY WAVES**	
SURFACE TOPOGRAPHY		
SN	Before 1984 search also SEA SURFACE TOPOGRAPHY	
UF	sea surface topography	
UF	water surface topography	
BT1	TOPOGRAPHY	
RT	DYNAMIC TOPOGRAPHY	
RT	GEOID	
RT	GEOID ANOMALIES	
RT	MARINE GEODESY	
RT	RADAR ALTIMETRY	
RT	SATELLITE ALTIMETRY	
RT	SEA LEVEL	
RT	SEA LEVEL MEASUREMENT	
RT	SEA SURFACE	
RT	SURFACE SLOPE	
SURFACE VESSELS		
USE	**SURFACE CRAFT**	
SURFACE WATER		
BT1	WATER	
RT	BOTTOM WATER	
RT	EPILIMNION	
RT	EVAPORATION	
RT	SHALLOW WATER	
RT	SURFACE LAYERS	

SURFACE WATER (cont'd)		
RT	SURFACE MICROLAYER	
RT	SURFACE WATER MASSES	
RT	WATER SUPPLY	
SURFACE WATER BODIES		
USE	**WATER BODIES**	
SURFACE WATER MASSES		
BT1	WATER MASSES	
RT	SURFACE LAYERS	
RT	SURFACE WATER	
RT	UPPER OCEAN	
SURFACE WATER WAVES		
UF	ocean waves	
UF	surface waves (water)	
BT1	WATER WAVES	
NT1	BREAKING WAVES	
NT2	BREAKERS	
NT2	SPILLING WAVES	
NT2	SURF	
NT2	WHITECAPS	
NT1	CAPILLARY WAVES	
NT2	WATER RIPPLES	
NT1	CONSTRUCTIVE WAVES	
NT1	LONG-CRESTED WAVES	
NT1	SEICHES	
NT2	HARBOUR OSCILLATIONS	
NT1	SHORT-CRESTED WAVES	
NT1	SIGNIFICANT WAVES	
NT1	STORM SURGES	
NT2	HURRICANE WAVES	
NT2	NEGATIVE STORM SURGES	
NT1	SWELL	
NT2	ROLLERS	
NT1	TIDAL WAVES	
NT1	TSUNAMIS	
NT1	WIND WAVES	
RT	DESIGN WAVE	
RT	DIRECTIONAL SPECTRA	
RT	EXTREME WAVES	
RT	INTERFACIAL WAVES	
RT	NEAR-SURFACE LAYER	
RT	SEA STATE	
RT	SEA STATE SCALES	
RT	SEA SURFACE	
RT	SHORT WAVE-LONG WAVE INTERACTIONS	
RT	WAVE ANALYSIS	
RT	WAVE DAMPING	
RT	WAVE GEOMETRY	
RT	WAVE MEASURING EQUIPMENT	
RT	WAVE SCOURING	
SURFACE WAVE-INTERNAL WAVE INTERACTIONS		
BT1	WAVE-WAVE INTERACTION	
BT2	WAVE INTERACTIONS	
RT	DEAD WATER	
RT	INTERNAL WAVE GENERATION	
RT	INTERNAL WAVES	
SURFACE WAVE RECORDERS		
USE	**WAVE RECORDERS**	
SURFACE WAVES (SEISMIC)		
USE	**SURFACE SEISMIC WAVES**	
SURFACE WAVES (WATER)		
USE	**SURFACE WATER WAVES**	
SURFACES		
RT	AREA	
RT	BOUNDARIES	
RT	EROSION SURFACES	
RT	INTERFACES	
RT	ISENTROPIC SURFACES	
RT	ISOBARIC SURFACES	
RT	ISOPYCNIC SURFACES	
RT	ISOSTERIC SURFACES	
RT	LAYERS	

SURFACES (cont'd)		
RT	LEVELS	
RT	REFERENCE LEVELS	
RT	SEA SURFACE	
RT	SEISMIC DISCONTINUITIES	
RT	SURFACE PROPERTIES	
SURFACTANTS		
UF	surface active agents	
RT	AGENTS	
RT	DETERGENTS	
RT	DISPERSANTS	
RT	SOAPS	
RT	SURFACE CHEMISTRY	
RT	SURFACE MICROLAYER	
RT	SURFACE PROPERTIES	
RT	SURFACE TENSION	
SURFING		
BT1	RECREATION	
RT	BATHING	
RT	SURF	
SURGE RESPONSE		
BT1	DYNAMIC RESPONSE	
BT2	INSTRUMENT RESPONSES	
RT	BUOY MOTION EFFECTS	
RT	SURGING	
SURGE-TIDE INTERACTION		
USE	**TIDE-SURGE INTERACTION**	
SURGE WAVES		
USE	**SURGES**	
SURGES		
UF	surge waves	
RT	SEICHES	
RT	TIDES	
RT	WAVE PERIOD	
RT	WIND WAVES	
SURGES (BEACH)		
USE	**WAVE RUNUP**	
SURGES (SEICHES)		
USE	**SEICHES**	
SURGES (STORM)		
USE	**STORM SURGES**	
SURGING		
BT1	SHIP MOTION	
RT	BUOY MOTION	
RT	BUOY MOTION EFFECTS	
RT	DYNAMIC RESPONSE	
RT	SURGE RESPONSE	
SURIMI		
USE	**MINCED PRODUCTS**	
SURROUNDING NETS		
BT1	FISHING NETS	
BT2	FISHING GEAR	
NT1	LAMPARA NETS	
NT1	PURSE SEINES	
RT	LIGHT FISHING	
RT	PELAGIC FISHERIES	
RT	SEINERS	
RT	SEINING	
SURVEILLANCE AND ENFORCEMENT		
SN	Surveillance of marine space and enforcement of related laws. Added in 1980	
UF	law enforcement	
UF	ocean surveillance	
UF	offshore protection	
UF	protection (security)	
UF	vessel seizure	

ASFIS Thesaurus

SURVEILLANCE AND ENFORCEMENT (cont'd)
RT	ACOUSTIC TRACKING SYSTEMS
RT	COASTGUARDS
RT	DEFENCE CRAFT
RT	DETECTION
RT	EXCLUSIVE ECONOMIC ZONE
RT	EXPLOITATION
RT	FISHERY DISPUTES
RT	FISHERY PROTECTION
RT	ILLEGAL FISHING
RT	LEGISLATION
RT	MILITARY OPERATIONS
RT	OCEAN SPACE
RT	OFFSHORE STRUCTURES
RT	OIL AND GAS FIELDS
RT	PROTECTION VESSELS

SURVEY VESSELS
BT1	SURFACE CRAFT
BT2	VEHICLES
RT	HYDROGRAPHIC SURVEYING
RT	HYDROGRAPHIC SURVEYS
RT	INSTRUMENT PLATFORMS
RT	RESEARCH VESSELS

SURVEYING
SN	Use of a more specific term is recommended
NT1	HYDROGRAPHIC SURVEYING
NT2	SURVEYING UNDERWATER
NT1	TOPOGRAPHIC SURVEYING
RT	BENCH MARKS
RT	CARTOGRAPHY
RT	COMPASSES
RT	LOCATING
RT	MAPPING
RT	SEAFLOOR MAPPING
RT	SURVEYING EQUIPMENT
RT	SURVEYS

SURVEYING EQUIPMENT
BT1	EQUIPMENT
RT	ACOUSTIC EQUIPMENT
RT	AIRBORNE EQUIPMENT
RT	DIVING EQUIPMENT
RT	HYDROGRAPHIC EQUIPMENT
RT	PHOTOGRAPHIC EQUIPMENT
RT	REMOTE SENSING EQUIPMENT
RT	SONAR
RT	SURVEYING
RT	SURVEYS

SURVEYING UNDERWATER
UF	underwater surveying
BT1	HYDROGRAPHIC SURVEYING
BT2	SURVEYING
RT	ARCHAEOLOGY
RT	DIVING
RT	DIVING SURVEYS
RT	GEOLOGICAL SURVEYS
RT	OCEAN FLOOR
RT	PHOTOGRAMMETRY
RT	SEAFLOOR SAMPLING
RT	SEDIMENT SAMPLING
RT	SITE SURVEYS
RT	STEREOPHOTOGRAPHY
RT	UNDERWATER EXPLORATION
RT	UNDERWATER PHOTOGRAPHY
RT	WORKING UNDERWATER
RT	WRECK LOCATION

SURVEYS
SN	Use of a more specific term is recommended
NT1	AERIAL SURVEYS
NT1	AEROMAGNETIC SURVEYS
NT1	BIOLOGICAL SURVEYS
NT2	PLANKTON SURVEYS
NT3	ICHTHYOPLANKTON SURVEYS
NT1	DIVING SURVEYS

SURVEYS (cont'd)
NT1	ECHO SURVEYS
NT1	ENVIRONMENTAL SURVEYS
NT2	LIMNOLOGICAL SURVEYS
NT2	OCEANOGRAPHIC SURVEYS
NT1	FISHERY SURVEYS
NT1	GEOCHEMICAL SURVEYS
NT1	GEOLOGICAL SURVEYS
NT2	GEOPHYSICAL SURVEYS
NT3	GRAVITY SURVEYS
NT1	HYDROGRAPHIC SURVEYS
NT2	BATHYMETRIC SURVEYS
NT1	POLLUTION SURVEYS
NT1	RESOURCE SURVEYS
NT1	SITE SURVEYS
RT	AIRCRAFT
RT	BASELINE STUDIES
RT	CENSUS
RT	CRUISES
RT	DATA COLLECTIONS
RT	EXPEDITIONS
RT	EXPLORATION
RT	MAPPING
RT	MULTISHIP EXPEDITIONS
RT	NATURAL RESOURCES
RT	OCEANOGRAPHIC INSTITUTIONS
RT	REMOTE SENSING
RT	RESEARCH VESSELS
RT	RESOURCE DEVELOPMENT
RT	SAMPLING
RT	SATELLITES
RT	SEISMIC EXPLORATION
RT	SURVEYING
RT	SURVEYING EQUIPMENT

SURVIVAL
UF	survival aptitude
UF	survival rate
RT	BIOASSAYS
RT	ECOPHYSIOLOGY
RT	ESCAPEMENT
RT	LETHAL LIMITS
RT	MORTALITY
RT	MORTALITY CAUSES
RT	POLLUTANTS
RT	STARVATION
RT	SUBLETHAL EFFECTS
RT	TOLERANCE
RT	TOXICITY

SURVIVAL APTITUDE
USE	**SURVIVAL**

SURVIVAL AT SEA
RT	ACCIDENTS
RT	HYPOTHERMIA
RT	LIFE JACKETS
RT	LIFEBOATS
RT	MEDICINE
RT	SEARCH AND RESCUE

SURVIVAL CAPSULES
USE	**LIFEBOATS**

SURVIVAL RATE
USE	**SURVIVAL**

SUSPENDED INORGANIC MATTER
SN	Before 1983 search also INORGANIC SUSPENDED MATTER
UF	inorganic suspended matter
BT1	INORGANIC MATTER
NT1	COLLOIDAL CLAY
RT	SUSPENDED PARTICULATE MATTER
RT	TURBIDITY
RT	WATER COLOUR

SUSPENDED LOAD
SN	Sediment in transport
UF	suspended load transport
BT1	SEDIMENT LOAD
RT	BED LOAD
RT	RESUSPENDED SEDIMENTS
RT	RESUSPENSION
RT	SEDIMENT TRANSPORT
RT	SUSPENSION

SUSPENDED LOAD TRANSPORT
USE	**SUSPENDED LOAD**

SUSPENDED MATTER
USE	**SUSPENDED PARTICULATE MATTER**

SUSPENDED ORGANIC MATTER
SN	Before 1983 search also ORGANIC SUSPENDED MATTER
UF	organic suspended matter
BT1	ORGANIC MATTER
RT	ANOXIC BASINS
RT	BIOGENIC MATERIAL
RT	CHEMICAL COMPOSITION
RT	DETRITUS
RT	ORGANIC COMPOUNDS
RT	SAPROPELS
RT	SUSPENDED PARTICULATE MATTER
RT	TURBIDITY
RT	WASTEWATER AQUACULTURE
RT	WATER COLOUR

SUSPENDED PARTICLE MOTION
USE	**PARTICLE MOTION**

SUSPENDED PARTICLES
USE	**SUSPENDED PARTICULATE MATTER**

SUSPENDED PARTICULATE MATTER
SN	Before 1984 search also SUSPENDED MATTER
UF	marine snow
UF	particulate matter
UF	particulates (aquatic)
UF	suspended matter
UF	suspended particles
UF	suspended solids
UF	suspensoids
BT1	PARTICULATES
NT1	RESUSPENDED SEDIMENTS
RT	AIR-WATER EXCHANGES
RT	BIOGEOCHEMICAL CYCLE
RT	COLLOIDS
RT	DETRITAL DEPOSITS
RT	DETRITUS
RT	DISPERSION
RT	EOLIAN DUST
RT	FLOCCULATION
RT	LIGHT ABSORPTION
RT	LIGHT SCATTERING
RT	NEPHELOID LAYER
RT	NUTRIENT CYCLES
RT	PARTICLE CONCENTRATION
RT	PARTICLE COUNTERS
RT	PARTICLE SCATTERING
RT	PARTICULATE FLUX
RT	RIVER PLUMES
RT	SEDIMENT TRANSPORT
RT	SEDIMENT TRAPS
RT	SEDIMENTATION
RT	SESTON
RT	SINKING
RT	SUSPENDED INORGANIC MATTER
RT	SUSPENDED ORGANIC MATTER
RT	SUSPENSION
RT	TURBIDITY
RT	WATER COLOUR

ASFIS Thesaurus

SUSPENDED SEDIMENTS
    USE   **RESUSPENDED SEDIMENTS**

SUSPENDED SOLIDS
    USE   **SUSPENDED PARTICULATE MATTER**

SUSPENSION
    RT   FLOCCULATION
    RT   PARTICLE MOTION
    RT   RESUSPENDED SEDIMENTS
    RT   SALTATION
    RT   SEDIMENT TRANSPORT
    RT   SLURRIES
    RT   SUSPENDED LOAD
    RT   SUSPENDED PARTICULATE MATTER

SUSPENSION CURRENTS
    USE   **TURBIDITY CURRENTS**

SUSPENSION FEEDERS
    USE   **FILTER FEEDERS**

SUSPENSOIDS
    USE   **SUSPENDED PARTICULATE MATTER**

SUSTAINABLE YIELD
    USE   **POTENTIAL YIELD**

SVERDRUP TRANSPORT
    RT   MASS TRANSPORT
    RT   OCEAN CIRCULATION
    RT   TRANSPORT
    RT   WIND STRESS
    RT   WIND-DRIVEN CIRCULATION
    RT   WIND-DRIVEN CURRENTS

SWALLOW FLOATS
    UF   neutrally buoyant floats
    BT1   SUBSURFACE DRIFTERS
    BT2   DRIFTERS
    BT3   CURRENT MEASURING EQUIPMENT
    BT4   FLOW MEASURING EQUIPMENT
    NT1   SOFAR FLOATS
    RT   ACOUSTIC TRANSPONDERS
    RT   CURRENT MEASUREMENT
    RT   PINGERS

SWAMP FISHERIES
    SN   Added in 1982
    BT1   INLAND FISHERIES
    BT2   FISHERIES
    RT   SEASONAL VARIATIONS
    RT   SWAMPS

SWAMPS
    BT1   WETLANDS
    BT2   LANDFORMS
    BT3   TOPOGRAPHIC FEATURES
    NT1   MANGROVE SWAMPS
    RT   AQUATIC ENVIRONMENT
    RT   DELTAS
    RT   LAKES
    RT   MARSHES
    RT   SHALLOW WATER
    RT   STAGNANT WATER
    RT   SWAMP FISHERIES

SWASH
    USE   **WAVE RUNUP**

SWATHS
    RT   SEAFLOOR MAPPING

SWAYING
    BT1   SHIP MOTION
    RT   BUOY MOTION

SWELL
    UF   ground swell
    BT1   SURFACE WATER WAVES
    BT2   WATER WAVES
    NT1   ROLLERS
    RT   BEACH CUSPS
    RT   SURFACE GRAVITY WAVES
    RT   WIND WAVES

SWIM BLADDER
    SN   Considered as hydrostatic organ
    UF   air bladder
    UF   gas bladders
    BT1   BLADDERS
    BT2   ANIMAL ORGANS
    BT3   BODY ORGANS
    RT   BUOYANCY
    RT   FISH SIZING
    RT   FLOTATION
    RT   HYDROSTATIC BEHAVIOUR
    RT   SCATTERING LAYERS
    RT   SWIMMING
    RT   WHIRLING DISEASE

SWIMMING
    SN   Restricted to aquatic organisms.
            Before 1982 search LOCOMOTION
    BT1   LOCOMOTION
    RT   FINS
    RT   FISH PHYSIOLOGY
    RT   SWIM BLADDER

SWORDFISH FISHERIES
    USE   **TUNA FISHERIES**

SYLLABUSES
    USE   **CURRICULA**

SYMBIONTS
    UF   ectosymbionts
    UF   endosymbionts
    RT   COMMENSALS
    RT   EPIPHYTES
    RT   SYMBIOSIS
    RT   ZOOXANTHELLAE

SYMBIOSIS
    UF   mutualism
    BT1   INTERSPECIFIC RELATIONSHIPS
    RT   CLEANING BEHAVIOUR
    RT   COMMENSALISM
    RT   EPIBIOSIS
    RT   PARASITES
    RT   SYMBIONTS

SYMPATHETIC NERVOUS SYSTEM
    USE   **AUTONOMIC NERVOUS SYSTEM**

SYMPATRIC POPULATIONS
    SN   Populations of two or more closely
            related species living in the same
            geographical area or having
            overlapped geographical areas
    RT   ALLOPATRIC POPULATIONS
    RT   GEOGRAPHICAL DISTRIBUTION
    RT   POPULATION GENETICS

SYMPOSIA
    USE   **CONFERENCES**

SYMPTOMS
    SN   Added in 1980
    UF   syndromes
    NT1   EXOPHTHALMIA
    NT1   HAEMORRHAGE
    NT1   NECROSES
    RT   DIETARY DEFICIENCIES
    RT   DISEASE DETECTION
    RT   DISEASES
    RT   MEDICINE

SYNAPSES
    SN   Area of functional contact between
            two nerve cells. Added in 1980
    RT   NERVOUS SYSTEM
    RT   NEURONS
    RT   NEUROTRANSMITTERS

SYNCLINES
    BT1   FOLDS
    BT2   GEOLOGICAL STRUCTURES
    RT   ANTICLINES
    RT   GEOSYNCLINES

SYNCLINORIA
    BT1   FOLDS
    BT2   GEOLOGICAL STRUCTURES
    RT   ANTICLINORIA

SYNDROMES
    USE   **SYMPTOMS**

SYNECOLOGY
    UF   biosociology
    BT1   ECOLOGY
    RT   ADAPTATIONS
    RT   AQUATIC COMMUNITIES
    RT   BEHAVIOUR
    RT   ECOLOGICAL ASSOCIATIONS
    RT   ECOLOGISTS
    RT   ENVIRONMENTAL CONDITIONS
    RT   ENVIRONMENTAL EFFECTS

SYNERGETIC EFFECTS
    USE   **SYNERGISM**

SYNERGISM
    UF   synergetic effects
    UF   synergists
    RT   BEHAVIOUR
    RT   PHYSIOLOGY

SYNERGISTS
    USE   **SYNERGISM**

SYNGAMY
    USE   **BIOLOGICAL FERTILIZATION**

SYNONYMY
    SN   Added in 1980
    UF   alternative name
    UF   synonysm
    RT   TAXONOMY
    RT   TERMINOLOGY

SYNONYSM
    USE   **SYNONYMY**

SYNOPSIS
    SN   Comprehensive study on taxonomy and
            biology of a species
    UF   monographs
    BT1   DOCUMENTS
    RT   LIFE CYCLE
    RT   LIFE HISTORY
    RT   TAXONOMY

SYNTHETIC APERTURE RADAR
    BT1   MICROWAVE RADAR
    BT2   RADAR
    BT3   REMOTE SENSING EQUIPMENT
    BT4   EQUIPMENT
    RT   SCATTEROMETERS

SYNTHETIC FIBERS
    USE   **SYNTHETIC FIBRES**

SYNTHETIC FIBRE ROPE
USE **FIBRE ROPE (SYNTHETIC)**

SYNTHETIC FIBRES
SN   Any types of synthetic fibres used for construction of nets, ropes, etc.
UF   synthetic fibers
RT   GEAR MATERIALS
RT   NETTING MATERIALS
RT   PLASTICS
RT   ROPES
RT   YARNS

SYNTHETIC SEA WATER
USE **ARTIFICIAL SEAWATER**

SYSTEM ANALYSIS
SN   Including flow charting. Used only as a qualifier
UF   systems analysis
RT   COMPUTER PROGRAMS
RT   MATHEMATICAL MODELS
RT   METHODOLOGY
RT   OPERATIONS RESEARCH
RT   SIMULATION
RT   STATISTICAL MODELS

SYSTEMATICS
USE **TAXONOMY**

SYSTEMS ANALYSIS
USE **SYSTEM ANALYSIS**

T/S CURVES
USE **T/S DIAGRAMS**

T/S DIAGRAMS
UF   t/s curves
BT1   GRAPHS
BT2   GRAPHICS
BT3   AUDIOVISUAL MATERIAL
BT4   DOCUMENTS
RT   CORE LAYER METHOD
RT   CORE LAYERS (WATER)
RT   SALINITY
RT   SEA WATER
RT   VERTICAL PROFILES
RT   WATER
RT   WATER MASSES
RT   WATER TEMPERATURE
RT   WATER TYPES

TABLEMOUNTS
USE **GUYOTS**

TABLES
SN   Tabulations of predicted values or of conversions of units. Use of a more specific term is recommended. Used only as a qualifier. Added in 1984
UF   mathematical tables
UF   tables (data)
UF   tables (mathematics)
BT1   DOCUMENTS
NT1   ALMANACS
NT2   NAUTICAL ALMANACS
NT2   TIDE TABLES
NT1   CONVERSION TABLES
NT2   KNUDSEN TABLES
NT1   DECOMPRESSION TABLES
NT1   METEOROLOGICAL TABLES
NT1   NAVIGATIONAL TABLES
NT1   OCEANOGRAPHIC TABLES
NT2   SALINITY TABLES
NT1   STATISTICAL TABLES
NT2   SCATTER DIAGRAMS
NT1   TRAVERSE TABLES

TABLES (DATA)
USE **TABLES**

TABLES (MATHEMATICS)
USE **TABLES**

TABLES (STATISTICAL)
USE **STATISTICAL TABLES**

TABLES (TIDES)
USE **TIDE TABLES**

TABULAR BERGS
BT1   ICEBERGS
BT2   FLOATING ICE
BT3   ICE

TACTILE FUNCTIONS
BT1   SENSE FUNCTIONS
RT   TACTILE ORGANS

TACTILE ORGANS
BT1   SENSE ORGANS
BT2   ANIMAL ORGANS
BT3   BODY ORGANS
RT   BARBELS
RT   TACTILE FUNCTIONS
RT   TACTILE STIMULI

TACTILE STIMULI
BT1   STIMULI
RT   TACTILE ORGANS

TAG RETURNS
USE **TAGGING**

TAG SHEDDING
USE **TAGS**

TAGGING
UF   tag returns
RT   BIOTELEMETRY
RT   MARKING
RT   MIGRATIONS
RT   SONIC TAGS
RT   STOCK ASSESSMENT
RT   TAGGING MORTALITY
RT   TAGS

TAGGING MORTALITY
SN   Added in 1980
UF   marking mortality
BT1   MORTALITY
BT2   POPULATION FUNCTIONS
RT   MARKING
RT   TAGGING

TAGS
SN   Before 1982 search TAGGING. Restricted to tags for aquatic organisms
UF   tag shedding
NT1   SONIC TAGS
RT   MIGRATIONS
RT   STOCK ASSESSMENT
RT   TAGGING

TAGS (ACOUSTIC)
USE **SONIC TAGS**

TALKS
USE **LECTURES**

TALWEG
USE **THALWEG**

TANGENTIAL STRESSES
USE **SHEAR STRESS**

TANGLE
USE **KELPS**

TANGLE NETS
USE **GILLNETS**

TANK CLEANING
BT1   CLEANING
RT   OIL SPILLS
RT   TANKER SHIPS
RT   TANKS

TANKER LOADING
SN   Loading/unloading operations for oil tankers
RT   FLOATING HOSES
RT   LOADING BUOYS
RT   MOORING BUOYS
RT   NATURAL GAS
RT   OFFSHORE OPERATIONS
RT   OFFSHORE TERMINALS
RT   OIL AND GAS INDUSTRY
RT   OIL POLLUTION
RT   OIL SPILLS
RT   SINGLE POINT MOORINGS
RT   TANKER SHIPS
RT   TANKER TERMINALS

TANKER SHIPS
UF   oil tankers
UF   tankers
BT1   MERCHANT SHIPS
BT2   SHIPS
BT3   SURFACE CRAFT
BT4   VEHICLES
RT   LOADING BUOYS
RT   NATURAL GAS
RT   OFFSHORE DOCKING
RT   OFFSHORE TERMINALS
RT   OIL POLLUTION
RT   OIL SPILLS
RT   SUBMARINE TANKERS
RT   TANK CLEANING
RT   TANKER LOADING
RT   TANKER TERMINALS

TANKER TERMINALS
UF   oil terminals
UF   terminals (oil)
BT1   HARBOURS
BT2   ANCHORAGES
NT1   DEEP-WATER TERMINALS
NT1   OFFSHORE TERMINALS
RT   CRUDE OIL
RT   GAS TERMINALS
RT   NATURAL GAS
RT   OFFSHORE DOCKING
RT   OIL REFINERIES
RT   OIL TANKS
RT   PORT INSTALLATIONS
RT   TANKER LOADING
RT   TANKER SHIPS

TANKERS
USE **TANKER SHIPS**

TANKS
SN   Description of tanks, their construction and use
UF   water tanks
BT1   CONTAINERS
NT1   CULTURE TANKS
NT1   DECANTATION TANKS
NT1   EVAPORATION TANKS
NT1   OIL TANKS
NT1   STORAGE TANKS
NT1   TOWING TANKS

TANKS (cont'd)
NT1	WAVE TANKS
NT1	WIND TUNNELS
RT	TANK CLEANING

TANNER CRAB FISHERIES
USE	**CRAB FISHERIES**

TANTALUM
BT1	CHEMICAL ELEMENTS
RT	HEAVY METALS
RT	METALS
RT	TANTALUM COMPOUNDS
RT	TANTALUM ISOTOPES
RT	TRACE METALS

TANTALUM COMPOUNDS
RT	CHEMICAL COMPOUNDS
RT	TANTALUM

TANTALUM ISOTOPES
BT1	ISOTOPES
RT	TANTALUM

TAPE RECORDINGS (SOUND)
USE	**AUDIO RECORDINGS**

TAPHROGENY
USE	**RIFTING**

TAR
BT1	PETROLEUM HYDROCARBONS
BT2	HYDROCARBONS
BT3	ORGANIC COMPOUNDS
RT	OIL SANDS
RT	PETROLEUM RESIDUES
RT	TAR BALLS

TAR BALLS
BT1	SOLID IMPURITIES
BT2	POLLUTANTS
RT	OIL POLLUTION
RT	PETROLEUM RESIDUES
RT	POLLUTION MONITORING
RT	RECREATIONAL WATERS
RT	TAR

TAR SANDS
USE	**OIL SANDS**

TARGET CELLS
SN	Added in 1980
BT1	RECEPTORS
BT2	CELLS
RT	ANTIBODIES
RT	HORMONES

TARGET STRENGTH
RT	ACOUSTIC PROPERTIES
RT	FISH DETECTION
RT	FISH SIZING
RT	SOUND REFLECTION

TARNS
USE	**GLACIAL LAKES**

TASTE
SN	Before 1982 search ORGANOLEPTIC PROPERTIES
UF	flavor
UF	flavour
UF	gustation
BT1	ORGANOLEPTIC PROPERTIES
BT2	PROPERTIES
RT	BIOLOGICAL PROPERTIES
RT	FOOD FISH
RT	HUMAN FOOD
RT	PALATABILITY
RT	POLLUTION EFFECTS
RT	TASTE FUNCTIONS

TASTE (cont'd)
RT	TASTE TESTS
RT	WATER QUALITY

TASTE FUNCTIONS
BT1	SENSE FUNCTIONS
RT	CHEMORECEPTORS
RT	ORGANOLEPTIC PROPERTIES
RT	PALATABILITY
RT	TASTE
RT	TASTE ORGANS

TASTE ORGANS
BT1	SENSE ORGANS
BT2	ANIMAL ORGANS
BT3	BODY ORGANS
RT	CHEMORECEPTION
RT	CHEMORECEPTORS
RT	TASTE FUNCTIONS

TASTE TESTS
SN	Added in 1980
UF	flavour tests
UF	palatability tests
BT1	TESTS
RT	FOOD FISH
RT	HUMAN FOOD
RT	ORGANOLEPTIC PROPERTIES
RT	PALATABILITY
RT	PROCESSED FISHERY PRODUCTS
RT	QUALITY CONTROL
RT	TASTE

TAX RATES
USE	**TAXES**

TAXA
NT1	SPECIES
NT2	AMPHIBIOTIC SPECIES
NT2	AMPHIHALINE SPECIES
NT3	ANADROMOUS SPECIES
NT3	CATADROMOUS SPECIES
NT2	ASSOCIATED SPECIES
NT2	CAVERNICOLOUS SPECIES
NT2	COMMERCIAL SPECIES
NT3	UNDERUTILIZED SPECIES
NT2	COSMOPOLITE SPECIES
NT2	DOMESTIC SPECIES
NT2	DOMINANT SPECIES
NT2	ENDEMIC SPECIES
NT2	INDICATOR SPECIES
NT2	INTRODUCED SPECIES
NT2	MIGRATORY SPECIES
NT2	PATHOGENS
NT2	RARE SPECIES
NT2	RELICT SPECIES
NT2	SEDENTARY SPECIES
NT2	SESSILE SPECIES
NT2	SIBLING SPECIES
RT	NEW TAXA
RT	TAXONOMY

TAXATION
USE	**TAXES**

TAXES
SN	Added in 1980
UF	rates and taxes
UF	tax rates
UF	taxation
RT	COSTS
RT	LEGAL ASPECTS
RT	OPERATIONAL COSTS

TAXIS
BT1	ORIENTATION BEHAVIOUR
BT2	BEHAVIOUR
NT1	CHEMOTAXIS
NT1	PHOTOTAXIS
NT1	RHEOTAXIS

TAXIS (cont'd)
RT	SENSE FUNCTIONS
RT	SENSE ORGANS
RT	STIMULI
RT	TROPISM

TAXONOMIC KEYS
USE	**IDENTIFICATION KEYS**

TAXONOMISTS
SN	Added in 1980
BT1	BIOLOGISTS
BT2	SCIENTIFIC PERSONNEL
BT3	PERSONNEL
RT	ALGOLOGISTS
RT	BOTANISTS
RT	CARCINOLOGISTS
RT	DIRECTORIES
RT	ENTOMOLOGISTS
RT	ICHTHYOLOGISTS
RT	MALACOLOGISTS
RT	ZOOLOGISTS

TAXONOMY
UF	biological classification
UF	classification (biological)
UF	systematics
NT1	CHEMOTAXONOMY
NT1	NUMERICAL TAXONOMY
NT1	SEROLOGICAL TAXONOMY
RT	BIOLOGICAL SPECIATION
RT	BIOMETRICS
RT	BOTANY
RT	CLASSIFICATION SYSTEMS
RT	ELECTROPHORESIS
RT	EVOLUTION
RT	HOLOTYPES
RT	IDENTIFICATION KEYS
RT	INVERTEBRATE ZOOLOGY
RT	MERISTIC COUNTS
RT	MICROBIOLOGY
RT	NEW CLASSES
RT	NEW FAMILIES
RT	NEW GENERA
RT	NEW ORDERS
RT	NEW SPECIES
RT	NEW TAXA
RT	ORGANISM MORPHOLOGY
RT	PALAEONTOLOGY
RT	PALYNOLOGY
RT	PHYLOGENETICS
RT	PHYLOGENY
RT	SECONDARY SEXUAL CHARACTERS
RT	SYNONYMY
RT	SYNOPSIS
RT	TAXA
RT	TYPOLOGY
RT	VERTEBRATE ZOOLOGY
RT	ZOOLOGY

TEACHING
USE	**EDUCATION**

TEACHING AIDS
USE	**TRAINING AIDS**

TECHNETIUM
BT1	CHEMICAL ELEMENTS
RT	METALS
RT	TECHNETIUM COMPOUNDS
RT	TECHNETIUM ISOTOPES

TECHNETIUM COMPOUNDS
RT	CHEMICAL COMPOUNDS
RT	TECHNETIUM

ASFIS Thesaurus

TECHNETIUM ISOTOPES
BT1	ISOTOPES
RT	TECHNETIUM

TECHNICAL FEASIBILITY
SN	Term to be used only as a qualifier. Added in 1980
UF	feasibility (technical)
UF	technological feasibility
BT1	FEASIBILITY
RT	ENGINEERING
RT	FEASIBILITY STUDIES
RT	TECHNOLOGY

TECHNICIANS
SN	Added in 1980
BT1	EXPERTS
BT2	PERSONNEL
NT1	AQUACULTURISTS
RT	DIRECTORIES
RT	ENGINEERING
RT	SCIENTIFIC PERSONNEL
RT	TECHNOLOGY
RT	TECHNOLOGY TRANSFER

TECHNOLOGICAL FEASIBILITY
USE	**TECHNICAL FEASIBILITY**

TECHNOLOGICAL KNOWLEDGE
USE	**TECHNOLOGY**

TECHNOLOGY
UF	technological knowledge
NT1	FIBRE OPTICS
NT1	FISHERY TECHNOLOGY
NT1	FISHING TECHNOLOGY
NT1	FOOD TECHNOLOGY
NT1	MARINE TECHNOLOGY
NT1	MATERIALS TECHNOLOGY
NT1	METALLURGY
NT1	SHIP TECHNOLOGY
RT	ANALYTICAL TECHNIQUES
RT	CATCHING METHODS
RT	ENGINEERING
RT	EXPLOITATION
RT	GEOTECHNOLOGY
RT	MANAGEMENT
RT	METHODOLOGY
RT	RESOURCE MANAGEMENT
RT	TECHNICAL FEASIBILITY
RT	TECHNICIANS
RT	TECHNOLOGY TRANSFER
RT	UNDERWATER EXPLOITATION

TECHNOLOGY TRANSFER
SN	Added in 1980
UF	innovation processes
UF	transfer of technologies
RT	DEVELOPED COUNTRIES
RT	DEVELOPING COUNTRIES
RT	DEVELOPMENT PROJECTS
RT	INTERNATIONAL COOPERATION
RT	PATENTS
RT	TECHNICIANS
RT	TECHNOLOGY
RT	TRAINING

TECTONIC PLATES
USE	**PLATES**

TECTONICS
UF	geotectonics
BT1	GEOLOGY
BT2	EARTH SCIENCES
NT1	CRUSTAL ADJUSTMENT
NT2	ISOSTASY
NT1	EPEIROGENY
NT2	SUBSIDENCE
NT2	UPLIFT
NT1	OROGENY

TECTONICS (cont'd)
NT1	PLATE TECTONICS
NT1	VERTICAL TECTONICS
RT	GEOPHYSICS
RT	MARINE GEOLOGY
RT	NAPPES
RT	RIFTING
RT	STRUCTURAL BASINS
RT	STRUCTURAL GEOLOGY
RT	SUBSIDENCE
RT	TECTONOPHYSICS

TECTONOPHYSICS
UF	geodynamics
BT1	GEOPHYSICS
BT2	EARTH SCIENCES
RT	CONTINENTAL DRIFT
RT	EARTH CRUST
RT	GEOLOGY
RT	MOHO
RT	TECTONICS

TEETH
BT1	MOUTH PARTS
RT	ANATOMY
RT	RADULAE

TEKTITES
USE	**EXTRATERRESTRIAL MATERIAL**

TELECOMMUNICATIONS
USE	**COMMUNICATION SYSTEMS**

TELECONNECTIONS
SN	Correlations between oceanographic and climatic events thousands of miles apart
RT	AIR-SEA INTERACTION
RT	EL NINO PHENOMENA
RT	OCEAN-ATMOSPHERE SYSTEM
RT	SOLAR-TERRESTRIAL ACTIVITY
RT	TEMPERATURE ANOMALIES
RT	VARVES

TELEDETECTION
USE	**GEOSENSING**

TELEMETERING
USE	**TELEMETRY**

TELEMETRY
UF	telemetering
UF	telemetry systems
BT1	COMMUNICATION SYSTEMS
NT1	ACOUSTIC TELEMETRY
NT1	BIOTELEMETRY
NT1	RADIO TELEMETRY
RT	COMMUNICATION
RT	DATA TRANSMISSION
RT	ELECTRONIC EQUIPMENT
RT	GEAR RESEARCH
RT	MEASURING DEVICES
RT	MICROWAVES
RT	MONITORING
RT	MONITORING SYSTEMS
RT	RECORDING EQUIPMENT
RT	REMOTE CONTROL
RT	SATELLITE COMMUNICATION
RT	SIGNAL PROCESSING
RT	SONIC TAGS

TELEMETRY SYSTEMS
USE	**TELEMETRY**

TELEPHONE SYSTEMS
SN	Before 1983 search TELEPHONES
UF	telephones
BT1	COMMUNICATION SYSTEMS
RT	SUBMARINE CABLES

TELEPHONES
USE	**TELEPHONE SYSTEMS**

TELEVISION
USE	**TELEVISION SYSTEMS**

TELEVISION SYSTEMS
SN	Before 1982 search TELEVISION
UF	television
UF	video networks
BT1	COMMUNICATION SYSTEMS
NT1	UNDERWATER TELEVISION
RT	CAMERAS
RT	MICROWAVES
RT	RADIO

TELEX
BT1	COMMUNICATION SYSTEMS

TELLURIC CURRENTS
UF	earth currents
BT1	ELECTRIC CURRENTS
RT	COAST EFFECT
RT	GEOMAGNETIC FIELD
RT	MAGNETOTELLURIC METHODS
RT	TIDAL CURRENTS

TELLURIUM
BT1	CHEMICAL ELEMENTS
RT	HEAVY METALS
RT	METALS
RT	TELLURIUM COMPOUNDS
RT	TELLURIUM ISOTOPES

TELLURIUM COMPOUNDS
RT	CHEMICAL COMPOUNDS
RT	TELLURIUM

TELLURIUM ISOTOPES
BT1	ISOTOPES
RT	TELLURIUM

TELLUROMETERS
RT	MEASURING DEVICES

TELSON
SN	Added in 1980
BT1	ANIMAL APPENDAGES
RT	ABDOMEN

TEMPERATE ZONES
BT1	CLIMATIC ZONES

TEMPERATURE
BT1	THERMODYNAMIC PROPERTIES
BT2	PHYSICAL PROPERTIES
BT3	PROPERTIES
NT1	AIR TEMPERATURE
NT1	BODY TEMPERATURE
NT1	LOW TEMPERATURE
NT1	POTENTIAL TEMPERATURE
NT1	SEDIMENT TEMPERATURE
NT1	TRANSITION TEMPERATURES
NT2	BOILING POINT
NT2	DEW POINT
NT2	FREEZING POINT
NT2	MELTING POINT
NT1	WATER TEMPERATURE
NT2	BOTTOM TEMPERATURE
NT2	IN SITU TEMPERATURE
NT2	PALAEOTEMPERATURE
NT2	SURFACE TEMPERATURE
NT3	BUCKET TEMPERATURE
NT3	INTAKE TEMPERATURE
NT3	SURFACE RADIATION TEMPERATURE
RT	ENERGY BALANCE
RT	HEAT
RT	HEAT BUDGET
RT	HEAT TRANSFER
RT	TEMPERATURE DIFFERENCES

TEMPERATURE (cont'd)		
RT	TEMPERATURE MEASUREMENT	
RT	TEMPERATURE TOLERANCE	
RT	THERMAL RADIATION	
RT	THERMODYNAMICS	
RT	THERMOMETERS	
RT	THERMORECEPTORS	

TEMPERATURE (AIR-SEA)
RT   HURRICANES

TEMPERATURE ANOMALIES
BT1   ANOMALIES
RT   SOLAR-TERRESTRIAL ACTIVITY
RT   TELECONNECTIONS

TEMPERATURE CHARTS
SN   Charts showing distribution of
             water temperature
BT1   HYDROGRAPHIC CHARTS
BT2   MAPS
BT3   GRAPHICS
BT4   AUDIOVISUAL MATERIAL
RT   ISOTHERMS
RT   TEMPERATURE SECTIONS
RT   WATER TEMPERATURE

TEMPERATURE CONTOURS
USE   **ISOTHERMS**

TEMPERATURE DATA
BT1   HYDROGRAPHIC DATA
BT2   DATA
RT   LIMNOLOGICAL DATA
RT   LONG-TERM RECORDS
RT   OCEANOGRAPHIC DATA
RT   WATER TEMPERATURE

TEMPERATURE DIFFERENCES
NT1   AIR-WATER TEMPERATURE DIFFERENCE
RT   AIR-WATER EXCHANGES
RT   ARTIFICIAL UPWELLING
RT   HEAT TRANSFER
RT   SENSIBLE HEAT TRANSFER
RT   TEMPERATURE

TEMPERATURE EFFECTS
BT1   ENVIRONMENTAL EFFECTS
RT   BIOCLIMATOLOGY
RT   MIGRATIONS
RT   PYROLYSIS
RT   TEMPERATURE PREFERENCES
RT   TEMPERATURE TOLERANCE
RT   THERMAL AQUACULTURE
RT   THERMAL STIMULI
RT   WATER TEMPERATURE
RT   WINTERKILL
RT   FIELDS

TEMPERATURE GRADIENTS
NT1   ADIABATIC LAPSE RATES
NT1   ADIABATIC TEMPERATURE GRADIENT
NT1   GEOTHERMAL GRADIENT
RT   DOUBLE DIFFUSION
RT   STRATIFICATION
RT   TEMPERATURE INVERSIONS
RT   TEMPERATURE PROFILES
RT   THERMAL STRATIFICATION
RT   THERMAL STRUCTURE
RT   THERMOCLINE
RT   WATER TEMPERATURE

TEMPERATURE INVERSION LAYERS
USE   **TEMPERATURE INVERSIONS**

TEMPERATURE INVERSIONS
UF   temperature inversion layers
BT1   INVERSIONS
NT1   DICOTHERMAL LAYER
NT1   TRADE WIND INVERSION

TEMPERATURE INVERSIONS (cont'd)
RT   AIR POLLUTION
RT   LAYERS
RT   TEMPERATURE GRADIENTS
RT   THERMAL STRATIFICATION
RT   VERTICAL STABILITY

TEMPERATURE MAXIMUM LAYER
BT1   CORE LAYERS (WATER)
BT2   LAYERS
RT   TEMPERATURE PROFILES

TEMPERATURE MEASUREMENT
UF   temperature measuring
BT1   MEASUREMENT
NT1   GEOTHERMAL MEASUREMENT
RT   BUCKET TEMPERATURE
RT   INFRARED DETECTORS
RT   INTAKE TEMPERATURE
RT   TEMPERATURE

TEMPERATURE MEASURING
USE   **TEMPERATURE MEASUREMENT**

TEMPERATURE MINIMUM LAYER
BT1   CORE LAYERS (WATER)
BT2   LAYERS
RT   TEMPERATURE PROFILES

TEMPERATURE PREFERENCES
SN   Optimum temperature conditions for
             an organism. Added in 1980
UF   preferred temperature
RT   AQUACULTURE
RT   CULTURED ORGANISMS
RT   TEMPERATURE EFFECTS
RT   TEMPERATURE TOLERANCE
RT   THERMAL AQUACULTURE

TEMPERATURE PROFILES
BT1   VERTICAL PROFILES
BT2   PROFILES
RT   CTD PROFILES
RT   STD PROFILES
RT   TEMPERATURE GRADIENTS
RT   TEMPERATURE MAXIMUM LAYER
RT   TEMPERATURE MINIMUM LAYER
RT   TEMPERATURE SECTIONS
RT   WATER TEMPERATURE

TEMPERATURE SECTIONS
BT1   HYDROGRAPHIC SECTIONS
BT2   VERTICAL SECTIONS
BT3   MAP GRAPHICS
BT4   GRAPHICS
RT   BATHYTHERMOGRAPHIC DATA
RT   ISOTHERMS
RT   STRATIFICATION
RT   TEMPERATURE CHARTS
RT   TEMPERATURE PROFILES
RT   THERMAL STRUCTURE
RT   VERTICAL DISTRIBUTION
RT   WATER TEMPERATURE

TEMPERATURE TOLERANCE
SN   Used for hot or cold tolerance
UF   thermal tolerance
BT1   TOLERANCE
BT2   BIOLOGICAL PROPERTIES
BT3   PROPERTIES
RT   AESTIVATION
RT   COLD RESISTANCE
RT   CRYOBIOLOGY
RT   EURYTHERMY
RT   HOMOIOTHERMY
RT   INDICATOR SPECIES
RT   STENOTHERMY
RT   TEMPERATURE
RT   TEMPERATURE EFFECTS
RT   TEMPERATURE PREFERENCES

TEMPERATURE TOLERANCE (cont'd)
RT   THERMAL AQUACULTURE
RT   THERMAL STIMULI
RT   THERMOREGULATION

TEMPLATES
SN   Pertains to underwater drilling
RT   DRILLING
RT   WELLHEADS

TEMPORAL DISTRIBUTION
BT1   DISTRIBUTION
NT1   MONTHLY DISTRIBUTION
NT1   SEASONAL DISTRIBUTION
RT   ANNUAL VARIATIONS
RT   DIURNAL VARIATIONS
RT   GEOLOGICAL TIME
RT   LONG-TERM CHANGES
RT   LONG-TERM RECORDS
RT   MIGRATIONS
RT   QUANTITATIVE DISTRIBUTION

TEMPORAL VARIATIONS
UF   changes (time)
UF   variations (time)
NT1   LONG-TERM CHANGES
NT2   SEA LEVEL CHANGES
NT1   PERIODIC VARIATIONS
NT2   ANNUAL VARIATIONS
NT2   DIURNAL VARIATIONS
NT2   SEASONAL VARIATIONS
NT1   SHORT-TERM CHANGES
NT1   VARIABILITY
RT   OSCILLATIONS
RT   PHENOLOGY
RT   SPECTRAL ANALYSIS
RT   TIME SERIES
RT   TIME SERIES ANALYSIS

TEMPORARY PLANKTON
USE   **MEROPLANKTON**

TEMPORARY PONDS
SN   Natural water bodies which remain
             dry for part of the year. Added in
             1982
UF   ephemeral lakes
UF   temporary waters
BT1   PONDS
BT2   INLAND WATERS
RT   DROUGHT RESISTANCE
RT   DROUGHTS

TEMPORARY WATERS
USE   **TEMPORARY PONDS**

TENDOUS MUSCULATURE
USE   **MUSCLES**

TENSILE STRENGTH
BT1   STRENGTH
BT2   MECHANICAL PROPERTIES
BT3   PHYSICAL PROPERTIES
BT4   PROPERTIES
RT   DEFORMATION
RT   ELASTICITY
RT   POISSON'S RATIO
RT   SHEAR STRENGTH
RT   STRESS-STRAIN RELATIONS
RT   TENSION

TENSIOMETERS
USE   **TENSOMETERS**

TENSION
BT1   STRESS
BT2   FORCES (MECHANICS)
NT1   SURFACE TENSION
RT   TENSILE STRENGTH

TENSION LEG PLATFORMS
UF	tethered buoyant platforms
BT1	FIXED PLATFORMS
BT2	OFFSHORE STRUCTURES
BT3	HYDRAULIC STRUCTURES
RT	FLOATING STRUCTURES

TENSOMETERS
UF	tensiometers
BT1	MEASURING DEVICES
RT	TRAWLING
RT	WIRE ROPE

TENTACLES
BT1	ANIMAL APPENDAGES
NT1	SENSE TENTACLES
RT	POLYPS

TEPHRA
BT1	VOLCANIC ROCKS
BT2	IGNEOUS ROCKS
BT3	ROCKS
NT1	IGNIMBRITES
NT1	VOLCANIC BRECCIA
NT1	VOLCANIC LAPILLI
RT	ASH LAYERS
RT	CLASTICS
RT	SEDIMENTARY ROCKS
RT	VOLCANIC ERUPTIONS

TERATOGENS
SN	Agents that raise the incidence of congenital malformations. Added in 1980
RT	GENETIC ABNORMALITIES
RT	TERATOLOGY

TERATOLOGY
SN	Science treating malformations and monstrosities of plants and animals. Before 1982 search ABNORMALITIES
RT	ABNORMALITIES
RT	GENETIC ABNORMALITIES
RT	TERATOGENS

TERBIUM
BT1	CHEMICAL ELEMENTS
RT	RARE EARTHS
RT	TERBIUM COMPOUNDS
RT	TERBIUM ISOTOPES
RT	TRANSITION ELEMENTS

TERBIUM COMPOUNDS
RT	CHEMICAL COMPOUNDS
RT	TERBIUM

TERBIUM ISOTOPES
BT1	ISOTOPES
RT	TERBIUM

TERMINALS (OIL)
USE	**TANKER TERMINALS**

TERMINOLOGY
SN	Standardization of common or scientific names and definition of technical or biological terms
UF	definitions
UF	nomenclature
RT	ACRONYMS
RT	CLASSIFICATION SYSTEMS
RT	GLOSSARIES
RT	IDENTIFICATION
RT	STANDARDIZATION
RT	STANDARDS
RT	SYNONYMY
RT	THESAURUS
RT	VERNACULAR NAMES

TERPENES
UF	monoterpenes
BT1	POLYUNSATURATED HYDROCARBONS
BT2	UNSATURATED HYDROCARBONS
BT3	HYDROCARBONS
BT4	ORGANIC COMPOUNDS
RT	ANTIBIOTICS
RT	SEAWEEDS

TERRACES
UF	deep-sea terraces
UF	submarine terraces
RT	ALLUVIAL FANS
RT	ALLUVIAL TERRACES
RT	BEACH MORPHOLOGY
RT	EROSION FEATURES
RT	FLUVIAL MORPHOLOGY
RT	RAISED BEACHES
RT	STRANDLINES
RT	TOPOGRAPHIC FEATURES
RT	WAVE-CUT PLATFORMS

TERRESTRIAL ATMOSPHERE
USE	**EARTH ATMOSPHERE**

TERRESTRIAL MAGNETISM
USE	**GEOMAGNETISM**

TERRESTRIAL RADIATION
SN	Use for long wave radiation component of atmosphere
UF	long wave radiation
UF	net terrestrial radiation
BT1	ELECTROMAGNETIC RADIATION
BT2	RADIATIONS
NT1	DOWNWARD LONG WAVE RADIATION
NT1	UPWARD LONG WAVE RADIATION
RT	ACTINOMETERS
RT	CLOUD COVER
RT	GREENHOUSE EFFECT
RT	INFRARED RADIATION
RT	PYRGEOMETERS
RT	RADIATION BALANCE
RT	RADIATIVE TRANSFER
RT	SURFACE RADIATION TEMPERATURE

TERRIGENOUS DEPOSITS
USE	**TERRIGENOUS SEDIMENTS**

TERRIGENOUS SEDIMENTS
UF	terrigenous deposits
BT1	SEDIMENTS
RT	CLASTICS
RT	EOLIAN DEPOSITS
RT	EOLIAN DUST
RT	FLYSCH
RT	GLACIAL DEPOSITS
RT	TURBIDITES
RT	VOLCANIC ASH
RT	VOLCANOGENIC DEPOSITS

TERRITORIAL BEHAVIOUR
USE	**TERRITORIALITY**

TERRITORIAL BOUNDARIES
USE	**BOUNDARIES**

TERRITORIAL SEAS
USE	**TERRITORIAL WATERS**

TERRITORIAL WATERS
UF	territorial seas
BT1	OCEAN SPACE
RT	ANCHORAGES
RT	BILATERAL AGREEMENTS
RT	BOUNDARIES
RT	COASTAL STATES
RT	CONTIGUOUS ZONES
RT	CONTINENTAL SHELVES
RT	EXCLUSIVE ECONOMIC ZONE

TERRITORIAL WATERS (cont'd)
RT	EXPLOITATION
RT	FISHERY PROTECTION
RT	FISHING RIGHTS
RT	INTERNATIONAL AGREEMENTS
RT	INTERNATIONAL BOUNDARIES
RT	LAW OF THE SEA

TERRITORIALITY
SN	Animal behaviour related to defending a territory from intruders. Before 1984 search also TERRITORIAL BEHAVIOUR
UF	territorial behaviour
BT1	BEHAVIOUR
RT	AGGRESSIVE BEHAVIOUR
RT	COMPETITIVE BEHAVIOUR
RT	DOMINANCE HIERARCHIES
RT	FROG CULTURE
RT	HOME RANGE

TERRITORY
USE	**HOME RANGE**

TERTIARY
SN	Before 1982 search TERTIARY PERIOD
BT1	CENOZOIC
BT2	GEOLOGICAL TIME
NT1	NEOGENE
NT2	MIOCENE
NT3	MESSINIAN
NT2	PLIOCENE
NT1	PALAEOGENE
NT2	EOCENE
NT2	OLIGOCENE
NT2	PALAEOCENE

TEST EQUIPMENT
SN	Equipment used for testing apparatus and efficiency of gear
UF	test facilities
BT1	EQUIPMENT
RT	CALIBRATION
RT	COMPUTERS
RT	ELECTRONIC EQUIPMENT
RT	EXPERIMENTAL DATA
RT	GEAR SELECTIVITY
RT	HYDRAULIC MODELS
RT	LABORATORY EQUIPMENT
RT	MEASURING DEVICES
RT	SENSORS
RT	TESTING
RT	TESTS
RT	TOWING TANKS
RT	WAVE TANKS
RT	WIND TUNNELS

TEST FACILITIES
USE	**TEST EQUIPMENT**

TEST FISHING
USE	**EXPERIMENTAL FISHING**

TEST METHODS
USE	**TESTS**

TEST ORGANISMS
SN	Added in 1980
BT1	AQUATIC ORGANISMS
RT	BIOASSAYS
RT	INDICATOR SPECIES
RT	LETHAL LIMITS
RT	TESTS
RT	TOXICANTS
RT	TOXICITY TESTS

TESTES
BT1	ANIMAL REPRODUCTIVE ORGANS
RT	CASTRATION
RT	FECUNDITY
RT	SEMEN
RT	SEXUAL REPRODUCTION
RT	SPERM
RT	SPERMATOGENESIS
RT	STERILITY

TESTING
SN	Used only as a qualifier
NT1	MATERIALS TESTING
NT2	NONDESTRUCTIVE TESTING
RT	ACCEPTABILITY
RT	CALIBRATION
RT	INTERCOMPARISON
RT	PERFORMANCE ASSESSMENT
RT	TEST EQUIPMENT

TESTING (BIOLOGICAL)
USE	**BIOASSAYS**

TESTS
SN	Used only as a qualifier. More specific term is recommended. Added in 1980
UF	laboratory tests
UF	test methods
NT1	ACCEPTANCE TESTS
NT1	TASTE TESTS
NT1	TOXICITY TESTS
RT	ACCEPTABILITY
RT	ACCURACY
RT	ANALYTICAL TECHNIQUES
RT	BIOASSAYS
RT	CALIBRATION
RT	CERTIFICATION
RT	CHEMICAL ANALYSIS
RT	EXPERIMENTAL DATA
RT	INSPECTION
RT	PERFORMANCE ASSESSMENT
RT	PROCEDURES
RT	QUALITY
RT	QUALITY CONTROL
RT	STRESS
RT	TEST EQUIPMENT
RT	TEST ORGANISMS

TESTS FOR SIGNIFICANT DIFFERENCES
USE	**STATISTICAL ANALYSIS**

TETHERED BUOYANT PLATFORMS
USE	**TENSION LEG PLATFORMS**

TETHERED FREE-SWIMMING VEHICLES
BT1	UNMANNED VEHICLES
BT2	UNDERWATER VEHICLES
BT3	VEHICLES
RT	FREE-SWIMMING VEHICLES
RT	SELF-PROPELLED VEHICLES
RT	TETHERED VEHICLES

TETHERED VEHICLES
SN	Underwater vehicles cable controlled and/or powered through a surface connecting cable. Before 1982 search TOWED BODIES
BT1	UNDERWATER VEHICLES
BT2	VEHICLES
RT	CABLES
RT	DIVING BELLS
RT	OBSERVATION CHAMBERS
RT	SEABED VEHICLES
RT	TETHERED FREE-SWIMMING VEHICLES
RT	TOWED VEHICLES
RT	TOWING LINES
RT	UMBILICALS

TETRODOTOXIN
BT1	BIOLOGICAL POISONS
RT	NEUROTOXINS

TEXTURE
BT1	SURFACE PROPERTIES
BT2	PROPERTIES
RT	POROSITY

THALASSOTHERMAL POWER
USE	**OTEC**

THALLIUM
BT1	CHEMICAL ELEMENTS
RT	METALS
RT	THALLIUM COMPOUNDS
RT	THALLIUM ISOTOPES
RT	TRACE METALS

THALLIUM COMPOUNDS
RT	CHEMICAL COMPOUNDS
RT	THALLIUM

THALLIUM ISOTOPES
BT1	ISOTOPES
RT	THALLIUM

THALLUS
SN	Added in 1980
BT1	PLANT ORGANS
BT2	BODY ORGANS

THALWEG
UF	talweg
BT1	HORIZONTAL PROFILES
BT2	PROFILES
RT	BATHYMETRIC PROFILES
RT	RIVER VALLEYS
RT	RIVERS
RT	SUBMARINE CANYONS

THAW-DRIP
USE	**THAWING**

THAWING
SN	Thawing of frozen fishery products. For melting of ice/snow on land and in frozen soil, use ICE MELTING. For preventing and removing rime and glaze from decks, superstructures, equipment, etc., use DE-ICING
UF	defrosting
UF	thaw-drip
RT	FREEZING
RT	FROZEN PRODUCTS
RT	MELTING
RT	REFRIGERATION

THERAPY
UF	disease treatment
UF	treatment for diseases
RT	ANIMAL DISEASES
RT	ANTIBIOTICS
RT	DISEASE CONTROL
RT	DISEASE DETECTION
RT	DISEASES
RT	DRUGS
RT	IMMUNOLOGY
RT	MEDICINE
RT	PARASITE CONTROL
RT	PATHOGENS
RT	PATHOLOGY
RT	PHARMACOLOGY
RT	PROPHYLAXIS
RT	TUMOURS

THERMAL AQUACULTURE
UF	heated effluent systems
UF	thermal fish farming
BT1	AQUACULTURE TECHNIQUES
RT	CAGE CULTURE
RT	FISH CULTURE
RT	FOSSIL FUELED POWER PLANTS
RT	FRESHWATER AQUACULTURE
RT	NUCLEAR POWER PLANTS
RT	OPEN SYSTEMS
RT	POND CULTURE
RT	POWER PLANTS
RT	SHELLFISH CULTURE
RT	TEMPERATURE EFFECTS
RT	TEMPERATURE PREFERENCES
RT	TEMPERATURE TOLERANCE
RT	THERMAL PLUMES
RT	THERMAL POLLUTION
RT	THERMODYNAMIC PROPERTIES
RT	WARM-WATER AQUACULTURE
RT	WASTE HEAT

THERMAL CAPACITY
USE	**SPECIFIC HEAT**

THERMAL CONDUCTIVITY
UF	conductivity (thermal)
BT1	THERMODYNAMIC PROPERTIES
BT2	PHYSICAL PROPERTIES
BT3	PROPERTIES
RT	EDDY CONDUCTIVITY
RT	GEOTHERMAL GRADIENT
RT	HEAT CONDUCTION
RT	HEAT FLOW
RT	ICE PROPERTIES
RT	SEDIMENT PROPERTIES
RT	SPECIFIC HEAT
RT	THERMAL DIFFUSIVITY
RT	WATER PROPERTIES

THERMAL CONVECTION
USE	**CELLULAR CONVECTION**

THERMAL DECOMPOSITION
BT1	DEGRADATION
BT2	CHEMICAL REACTIONS
RT	RIVER PLUMES
RT	THERMAL PLUMES
RT	THERMAL POLLUTION
RT	THERMODYNAMIC PROPERTIES

THERMAL DIFFUSION
BT1	DIFFUSION
BT2	TRANSPORT PROCESSES
RT	THERMAL DIFFUSIVITY
RT	THERMAL PLUMES

THERMAL DIFFUSIVITY
UF	thermometric conductivity
BT1	THERMODYNAMIC PROPERTIES
BT2	PHYSICAL PROPERTIES
BT3	PROPERTIES
RT	EDDY DIFFUSIVITY
RT	SEDIMENT PROPERTIES
RT	THERMAL CONDUCTIVITY
RT	THERMAL DIFFUSION
RT	WATER PROPERTIES

THERMAL DOMES
RT	THERMAL STRUCTURE

THERMAL EFFLUENTS
USE	**THERMAL POLLUTION**

THERMAL EQUILIBRIUM
USE	**THERMODYNAMIC EQUILIBRIUM**

THERMAL EXPANSION
UF	thermal expansion coefficient
BT1	THERMODYNAMIC PROPERTIES
BT2	PHYSICAL PROPERTIES
BT3	PROPERTIES
RT	SPECIFIC VOLUME
RT	WATER PROPERTIES

THERMAL EXPANSION COEFFICIENT
USE	**THERMAL EXPANSION**

THERMAL FISH FARMING
USE	**THERMAL AQUACULTURE**

THERMAL FRONTS
BT1	FRONTS
RT	FRONTOGENESIS

THERMAL IMAGERY
USE	**INFRARED IMAGERY**

THERMAL INFRARED IMAGERY
USE	**INFRARED IMAGERY**

THERMAL INSULATION
BT1	INSULATING MATERIALS
BT2	MATERIALS
RT	ASBESTOS

THERMAL IR IMAGERY
USE	**INFRARED IMAGERY**

THERMAL MICROSTRUCTURE
SN	Variations in the distribution of temperature on a scale of 10 cm or less
BT1	MICROSTRUCTURE
BT2	SPATIAL VARIATIONS
RT	WATER TEMPERATURE

THERMAL PLUMES
SN	Plumes caused by discharge of heated effluents in lakes, estuaries or marine coastal zones
BT1	PLUMES
BT2	FLUID FLOW
BT3	FLUID MOTION
RT	FOSSIL FUELED POWER PLANTS
RT	NUCLEAR POWER PLANTS
RT	THERMAL AQUACULTURE
RT	THERMAL DECOMPOSITION
RT	THERMAL DIFFUSION
RT	THERMAL POLLUTION
RT	WATER MIXING

THERMAL POLLUTION
UF	pollution (thermal)
UF	thermal effluents
BT1	POLLUTION
RT	BRACKISHWATER POLLUTION
RT	COOLING PONDS
RT	COOLING WATER
RT	FOSSIL FUELED POWER PLANTS
RT	FRESHWATER POLLUTION
RT	HEAT
RT	MARINE POLLUTION
RT	NUCLEAR POWER PLANTS
RT	POLLUTION CONTROL
RT	POWER PLANTS
RT	RADIOACTIVE WASTES
RT	THERMAL AQUACULTURE
RT	THERMAL DECOMPOSITION
RT	THERMAL PLUMES
RT	THERMODYNAMIC PROPERTIES
RT	WASTE HEAT
RT	WATER POLLUTION
RT	WATER TEMPERATURE

THERMAL POWER
BT1	POWER FROM THE SEA
BT2	ENERGY RESOURCES
BT3	NATURAL RESOURCES
BT4	RESOURCES
NT1	OTEC
RT	ARTIFICIAL UPWELLING
RT	GEOTHERMAL POWER

THERMAL PROPERTIES
USE	**THERMODYNAMIC PROPERTIES**

THERMAL RADIATION
UF	heat radiation
BT1	RADIATIONS
RT	ELECTROMAGNETIC RADIATION
RT	HEAT
RT	HEAT TRANSFER
RT	SOLAR RADIATION
RT	TEMPERATURE
RT	THERMODYNAMIC PROPERTIES
RT	ULTRAVIOLET RADIATION

THERMAL SPRINGS (GEOTHERMAL)
USE	**GEOTHERMAL SPRINGS**

THERMAL SPRINGS (HOT)
USE	**HOT SPRINGS**

THERMAL SPRINGS (HYDROTHERMAL)
USE	**HYDROTHERMAL SPRINGS**

THERMAL STIMULI
SN	Added in 1980
BT1	STIMULI
RT	BODY TEMPERATURE
RT	TEMPERATURE EFFECTS
RT	TEMPERATURE TOLERANCE
RT	THERMODYNAMIC PROPERTIES
RT	THERMOREGULATION

THERMAL STRATIFICATION
UF	stratification (thermal)
BT1	STRATIFICATION
RT	DISCONTINUITY LAYERS
RT	EPILIMNION
RT	HEAT BUDGET
RT	HYDROGRAPHY
RT	HYPOLIMNION
RT	INTERMEDIATE WATER MASSES
RT	LAKES
RT	METALIMNION
RT	PHYSICAL LIMNOLOGY
RT	PHYSICAL OCEANOGRAPHY
RT	RESERVOIRS (WATER)
RT	SOUND CHANNELS
RT	TEMPERATURE GRADIENTS
RT	TEMPERATURE INVERSIONS
RT	THERMAL STRUCTURE
RT	THERMOCLINE
RT	THERMODYNAMIC PROPERTIES
RT	WATER CIRCULATION
RT	WATER TEMPERATURE

THERMAL STRUCTURE
RT	ATMOSPHERIC FORCING
RT	DICOTHERMAL LAYER
RT	HURRICANES
RT	HYDROGRAPHY
RT	STRATIFICATION
RT	TEMPERATURE GRADIENTS
RT	TEMPERATURE SECTIONS
RT	THERMAL DOMES
RT	THERMAL STRATIFICATION
RT	THERMOCLINE
RT	THERMOSTADS
RT	WATER TEMPERATURE

THERMAL TOLERANCE
USE	**TEMPERATURE TOLERANCE**

THERMISTOR ARRAYS
USE	**THERMISTOR CHAINS**

THERMISTOR CHAINS
UF	thermistor arrays
BT1	ARRAYS
RT	OCEANOGRAPHIC EQUIPMENT
RT	THERMISTORS

THERMISTORS
RT	ELECTRONIC EQUIPMENT
RT	FLOWMETERS
RT	THERMISTOR CHAINS
RT	XBTs

THERMOCLINE
BT1	DISCONTINUITY LAYERS
BT2	LAYERS
NT1	DIURNAL THERMOCLINE
NT1	PERMANENT THERMOCLINE
NT1	SEASONAL THERMOCLINE
RT	CLINES
RT	DICOTHERMAL LAYER
RT	ECOCLINES
RT	ENVIRONMENTAL FACTORS
RT	EPILIMNION
RT	HYPOLIMNION
RT	ISOTHERMS
RT	METALIMNION
RT	MIXED LAYER DEPTH
RT	PYCNOCLINE
RT	SOUND TRANSMISSION
RT	SURFACE LAYERS
RT	SURFACE MIXED LAYER
RT	TEMPERATURE GRADIENTS
RT	THERMAL STRATIFICATION
RT	THERMAL STRUCTURE
RT	THERMOCLINE DECAY
RT	VERTICAL DISTRIBUTION
RT	WATER COLUMN
RT	WATER MASSES
RT	WATER TEMPERATURE

THERMOCLINE (LAKES)
USE	**METALIMNION**

THERMOCLINE DECAY
UF	erosion (thermocline)
UF	thermocline erosion
RT	SURFACE MIXED LAYER
RT	THERMOCLINE

THERMOCLINE DEPTH
USE	**MIXED LAYER DEPTH**

THERMOCLINE EROSION
USE	**THERMOCLINE DECAY**

THERMOCOUPLE ARRAYS
BT1	ARRAYS
RT	ELECTRONIC EQUIPMENT
RT	THERMOCOUPLES

THERMOCOUPLES
RT	ELECTRONIC EQUIPMENT
RT	THERMOCOUPLE ARRAYS

THERMODYNAMIC ACTIVITY
UF	activity coefficient
UF	chemical activity
BT1	THERMODYNAMIC PROPERTIES
BT2	PHYSICAL PROPERTIES
BT3	PROPERTIES
RT	CHEMICAL EQUILIBRIUM
RT	CHEMICAL REACTIONS
RT	THERMODYNAMICS

ASFIS Thesaurus

THERMODYNAMIC EQUILIBRIUM
UF	thermal equilibrium
BT1	THERMODYNAMIC PROPERTIES
BT2	PHYSICAL PROPERTIES
BT3	PROPERTIES
RT	CHEMICAL EQUILIBRIUM
RT	EQUILIBRIUM
RT	THERMODYNAMICS

THERMODYNAMIC PROPERTIES
SN	Before 1982 search THERMAL PROPERTIES
UF	heat properties
UF	thermal properties
BT1	PHYSICAL PROPERTIES
BT2	PROPERTIES
NT1	ENTHALPY
NT2	FUSION HEAT
NT2	SUBLIMATION HEAT
NT2	VAPORIZATION HEAT
NT1	ENTROPY
NT1	FREE ENERGY
NT1	SPECIFIC HEAT
NT1	TEMPERATURE
NT2	AIR TEMPERATURE
NT2	BODY TEMPERATURE
NT2	LOW TEMPERATURE
NT2	POTENTIAL TEMPERATURE
NT2	SEDIMENT TEMPERATURE
NT2	TRANSITION TEMPERATURES
NT3	BOILING POINT
NT3	DEW POINT
NT3	FREEZING POINT
NT3	MELTING POINT
NT2	WATER TEMPERATURE
NT3	BOTTOM TEMPERATURE
NT3	IN SITU TEMPERATURE
NT3	PALAEOTEMPERATURE
NT3	SURFACE TEMPERATURE
NT4	BUCKET TEMPERATURE
NT4	INTAKE TEMPERATURE
NT4	SURFACE RADIATION TEMPERATURE
NT1	THERMAL CONDUCTIVITY
NT1	THERMAL DIFFUSIVITY
NT1	THERMAL EXPANSION
NT1	THERMODYNAMIC ACTIVITY
NT1	THERMODYNAMIC EQUILIBRIUM
RT	CHEMICAL PROPERTIES
RT	ELECTRICAL PROPERTIES
RT	HEAT
RT	THERMAL AQUACULTURE
RT	THERMAL DECOMPOSITION
RT	THERMAL POLLUTION
RT	THERMAL RADIATION
RT	THERMAL STIMULI
RT	THERMAL STRATIFICATION
RT	THERMODYNAMICS
RT	VAPOUR PRESSURE

THERMODYNAMICS
BT1	PHYSICS
RT	ADIABATIC PROCESSES
RT	ENERGY
RT	ENERGY BALANCE
RT	ENTHALPY
RT	ENTROPY
RT	EQUATIONS OF STATE
RT	HEAT
RT	HEAT SINKS
RT	HEAT TRANSFER
RT	ISENTROPIC PROCESSES
RT	ISOTHERMAL PROCESSES
RT	PHASE CHANGES
RT	TEMPERATURE
RT	THERMODYNAMIC ACTIVITY
RT	THERMODYNAMIC EQUILIBRIUM
RT	THERMODYNAMIC PROPERTIES

THERMOHALINE CIRCULATION
BT1	OCEAN CIRCULATION
BT2	WATER CIRCULATION
BT3	WATER MOTION
NT1	HALINE CIRCULATION
RT	WIND-DRIVEN CIRCULATION

THERMOMETERS
UF	deep-sea thermometers
BT1	MEASURING DEVICES
NT1	QUARTZ TEMPERATURE SENSORS
NT1	REVERSING THERMOMETERS
RT	AIR TEMPERATURE
RT	BATHYTHERMOGRAPHS
RT	CTD PROFILERS
RT	LIMNOLOGICAL EQUIPMENT
RT	OCEANOGRAPHIC EQUIPMENT
RT	PSYCHROMETERS
RT	STD PROFILERS
RT	TEMPERATURE
RT	WATER TEMPERATURE

THERMOMETRIC CONDUCTIVITY
USE	**THERMAL DIFFUSIVITY**

THERMOPHOTOTROPISM
USE	**PHOTOTROPISM**

THERMORECEPTORS
RT	SENSE ORGANS
RT	TEMPERATURE
RT	THERMOREGULATION
RT	WATER TEMPERATURE

THERMOREGULATION
UF	thermoregulators
UF	thermoregulatory behaviour
RT	AESTIVATION
RT	BODY TEMPERATURE
RT	DORMANCY
RT	HIBERNATION
RT	HOMOIOTHERMY
RT	POIKILOTHERMY
RT	TEMPERATURE TOLERANCE
RT	THERMAL STIMULI
RT	THERMORECEPTORS

THERMOREGULATORS
USE	**THERMOREGULATION**

THERMOREGULATORY BEHAVIOUR
USE	**THERMOREGULATION**

THERMOSTADS
RT	THERMAL STRUCTURE
RT	WATER MASSES
RT	WATER TEMPERATURE

THERMOSTERIC ANOMALIES
BT1	SPECIFIC VOLUME ANOMALIES
BT2	ANOMALIES
RT	IN SITU DENSITY
RT	ISOTHERMAL PROCESSES

THESAURUS
BT1	DOCUMENTS
RT	DOCUMENTATION
RT	INFORMATION HANDLING
RT	INFORMATION RETRIEVAL
RT	TERMINOLOGY

THIAMINE
USE	**VITAMIN B**

THICKNESS
SN	Used only as a qualifier
BT1	DIMENSIONS
NT1	CRUSTAL THICKNESS
NT1	ICE THICKNESS
RT	DEPTH

THIXOTROPY
RT	GELS

THOLEIITE
BT1	BASALTS
BT2	VOLCANIC ROCKS
BT3	IGNEOUS ROCKS
BT4	ROCKS
RT	PYROXENES
RT	QUARTZ
RT	SILICA
RT	THOLEIITIC BASALT

THOLEIITIC BASALT
BT1	BASALTS
BT2	VOLCANIC ROCKS
BT3	IGNEOUS ROCKS
BT4	ROCKS
RT	THOLEIITE

THORAX
SN	Added in 1980
BT1	BODY REGIONS
BT2	ANATOMICAL STRUCTURES
RT	ANIMAL APPENDAGES
RT	CEPHALOTHORAX

THORIUM
BT1	CHEMICAL ELEMENTS
RT	ACTINIDES
RT	HEAVY METALS
RT	METALS
RT	MONAZITE
RT	THORIUM COMPOUNDS
RT	THORIUM ISOTOPES
RT	TRANSITION ELEMENTS

THORIUM COMPOUNDS
BT1	ACTINIDE COMPOUNDS
RT	CHEMICAL COMPOUNDS
RT	THORIUM

THORIUM ISOTOPES
BT1	ISOTOPES
NT1	IONIUM
RT	THORIUM
RT	THORIUM-230/THORIUM-232 DATING

THORIUM-230/THORIUM-232 DATING
BT1	RADIOMETRIC DATING
BT2	GEOCHRONOMETRY
RT	THORIUM ISOTOPES

THREE PHASE FLOW
USE	**MULTIPHASE FLOW**

THREONINE
BT1	AMINO ACIDS
BT2	ORGANIC ACIDS
BT3	ORGANIC COMPOUNDS

THRUSTERS
BT1	PROPULSION SYSTEMS
RT	DYNAMIC POSITIONING
RT	PROPELLERS
RT	SHIPBOARD EQUIPMENT

THULIUM
BT1	CHEMICAL ELEMENTS
RT	RARE EARTHS
RT	THULIUM COMPOUNDS
RT	THULIUM ISOTOPES
RT	TRANSITION ELEMENTS

THULIUM COMPOUNDS
RT	CHEMICAL COMPOUNDS
RT	THULIUM

THULIUM ISOTOPES
BT1   ISOTOPES
RT   THULIUM

THUNDERSTORMS
RT   LIGHTNING
RT   STORMS

THYMUS
SN   Before 1982 search ENDOCRINE GLANDS
BT1   ENDOCRINE GLANDS
BT2   GLANDS
BT3   SECRETORY ORGANS
RT   HORMONES
RT   IMMUNITY
RT   METABOLISM

THYROID
SN   Before 1982 search ENDOCRINE GLANDS
UF   parathyroid
BT1   ENDOCRINE GLANDS
BT2   GLANDS
BT3   SECRETORY ORGANS
RT   HORMONES
RT   METABOLISM
RT   METAMORPHOSIS
RT   NERVOUS SYSTEM

TIDAL AMPLITUDE
BT1   WAVE AMPLITUDE
BT2   AMPLITUDE
BT3   DIMENSIONS
RT   ASTRONOMICAL TIDES
RT   CORANGE CHARTS
RT   CORANGE LINES
RT   TIDAL POWER
RT   TIDAL RANGE
RT   TIDAL WAVES

TIDAL ANALYSIS
BT1   WAVE ANALYSIS
RT   ANALYSIS
RT   EQUILIBRIUM TIDES
RT   FOURIER ANALYSIS
RT   HARMONIC ANALYSIS
RT   RESPONSE ANALYSIS
RT   TIDAL CONSTANTS
RT   TIDAL CONSTITUENTS
RT   TIDAL MOTION
RT   TIDAL PERTURBATION
RT   TIDAL PREDICTION
RT   TIDE GENERATING POTENTIAL
RT   TIDES
RT   TIME SERIES ANALYSIS

TIDAL BARRAGES
BT1   BARRAGES
BT2   HYDRAULIC STRUCTURES
RT   COASTAL ENGINEERING
RT   RECREATIONAL WATERS
RT   STRUCTURAL ENGINEERING
RT   TIDAL POWER
RT   TIDAL POWER PLANTS

TIDAL BARRIERS
USE   **STORM SURGE BARRIERS**

TIDAL BORES
UF   bores
UF   bores in estuaries
UF   eagre
UF   mascaret
BT1   SHALLOW-WATER WAVES
BT2   WATER WAVES
RT   HYDRAULIC JUMP
RT   NONLINEAR WAVES
RT   WAVE BREAKING

TIDAL CHANNELS
USE   **TIDAL INLETS**

TIDAL CHARTS
BT1   HYDROGRAPHIC CHARTS
BT2   MAPS
BT3   GRAPHICS
BT4   AUDIOVISUAL MATERIAL
NT1   CORANGE CHARTS
NT1   COTIDAL CHARTS
RT   CURRENT CHARTS
RT   TIDAL PREDICTION
RT   TIDE TABLES

TIDAL COMPONENTS
USE   **TIDAL CONSTITUENTS**

TIDAL CONSTANTS
UF   harmonic tidal constants
UF   tidal harmonic constants
RT   HARMONIC FUNCTIONS
RT   TIDAL ANALYSIS
RT   TIDAL CONSTITUENTS

TIDAL CONSTITUENTS
SN   Before 1983 search also TIDAL COMPONENTS
UF   harmonic tidal constituents
UF   partial tides
UF   tidal components
RT   HARMONIC FUNCTIONS
RT   LUNAR DIURNAL TIDES
RT   LUNAR SEMIDIURNAL TIDES
RT   LUNAR TIDES
RT   POLE TIDES
RT   RADIATIONAL TIDES
RT   SOLAR DIURNAL TIDES
RT   SOLAR SEMIDIURNAL TIDES
RT   SOLAR TIDES
RT   TIDAL ANALYSIS
RT   TIDAL CONSTANTS

TIDAL CURRENT CHARTS
USE   **CURRENT CHARTS**

TIDAL CURRENT TABLES
USE   **TIDE TABLES**

TIDAL CURRENTS
UF   tidal flow
UF   tidal stream
BT1   WATER CURRENTS
BT2   WATER MOTION
NT1   EBB CURRENTS
NT1   FLOOD CURRENTS
NT1   ROTARY CURRENTS
RT   BED FORMS
RT   CURRENT CHARTS
RT   ESTUARINE DYNAMICS
RT   LONGSHORE CURRENTS
RT   OSCILLATORY FLOW
RT   RESIDUAL FLOW
RT   SAND WAVES
RT   SCOUR HOLLOWS
RT   SEDIMENT TRANSPORT
RT   TELLURIC CURRENTS
RT   TIDAL INLETS
RT   TIDAL MIXING
RT   TIDAL WAVES
RT   TIDE TABLES
RT   TIDES

TIDAL CURVES
UF   marigram
BT1   ANALOG RECORDS
BT2   GRAPHICS
BT3   AUDIOVISUAL MATERIAL
BT4   DOCUMENTS
RT   TIDAL RECORDS

TIDAL CYCLES
BT1   CYCLES
RT   BEACH MORPHOLOGY
RT   EBB CURRENT
RT   EBB CURRENTS
RT   FLOOD CURRENTS
RT   HIGH WATER
RT   INTERTIDAL ENVIRONMENT
RT   LOW TIDE
RT   TIDAL FLATS
RT   TIDAL MODELS
RT   TIDAL RANGE
RT   TIDES

TIDAL DATUM
BT1   DATUM LEVELS
BT2   REFERENCE LEVELS
RT   LOWEST ASTRONOMICAL TIDES
RT   MEAN SEA LEVEL
RT   TIDE GAUGES

TIDAL DEPOSITS
RT   ESTUARINE SEDIMENTATION
RT   INTERTIDAL SEDIMENTATION
RT   SEDIMENTS
RT   SHELF SEDIMENTATION
RT   TRACE FOSSILS

TIDAL DISSIPATION
UF   tidal energy dissipation
BT1   WAVE DISSIPATION
BT2   ENERGY DISSIPATION
BT3   ENERGY TRANSFER
RT   TIDAL ENERGY
RT   TIDAL FRICTION
RT   TIDAL POWER

TIDAL DYNAMICS
BT1   WAVE DYNAMICS
RT   TIDAL MOTION
RT   TIDAL PROPAGATION
RT   TIDAL WAVES
RT   TIDES

TIDAL EFFECTS
SN   Added in 1982
BT1   ENVIRONMENTAL EFFECTS
RT   BEACH EROSION
RT   TIDES

TIDAL ELEVATION
USE   **TIDAL RANGE**

TIDAL ENERGY
SN   Used for the natural energy bound up in tidal motion of water bodies. For exploitation of that energy, e.g. for generating electricity, use TIDAL POWER
BT1   WAVE ENERGY
BT2   ENERGY
RT   POWER PLANTS
RT   TIDAL DISSIPATION
RT   TIDAL FRICTION
RT   TIDAL POWER

TIDAL ENERGY DISSIPATION
USE   **TIDAL DISSIPATION**

TIDAL ENVIRONMENT
USE   **INTERTIDAL ENVIRONMENT**

TIDAL EQUATIONS
RT   EQUATIONS
RT   LAPLACE EQUATION
RT   NUMERICAL ANALYSIS

TIDAL FLATS
UF	intertidal flats
BT1	COASTAL LANDFORMS
BT2	LANDFORMS
BT3	TOPOGRAPHIC FEATURES
RT	COASTAL ZONE
RT	ESTUARIES
RT	ESTUARINE SEDIMENTATION
RT	INTERTIDAL ENVIRONMENT
RT	INTERTIDAL SEDIMENTATION
RT	MARSHES
RT	MUD
RT	MUD BANKS
RT	SALT MARSHES
RT	TIDAL CYCLES
RT	TIDES

TIDAL FLOW
USE	**TIDAL CURRENTS**

TIDAL FRICTION
BT1	FRICTION
BT2	FORCES (MECHANICS)
RT	BOTTOM FRICTION
RT	EARTH ROTATION
RT	TIDAL DISSIPATION
RT	TIDAL ENERGY

TIDAL HARMONIC CONSTANTS
USE	**TIDAL CONSTANTS**

TIDAL INLETS
UF	tidal channels
BT1	COASTAL INLETS
BT2	COASTAL WATERS
RT	BARRIER ISLANDS
RT	CHANNELS
RT	COASTAL LAGOONS
RT	ESTUARIES
RT	FLUSHING
RT	FLUSHING TIME
RT	HARBOURS
RT	TIDAL CURRENTS

TIDAL LOADING
USE	**OCEAN LOADING**

TIDAL MIXING
UF	tidal stirring
BT1	WATER MIXING
RT	ESTUARINE DYNAMICS
RT	MIXING PROCESSES
RT	SHELF DYNAMICS
RT	TIDAL CURRENTS

TIDAL MODELS
BT1	MATHEMATICAL MODELS
BT2	MODELS
RT	TIDAL CYCLES

TIDAL MOTION
SN	Only to be used for general treatment of tidal motion in hydrosphere, atmosphere and solid earth
NT1	ATMOSPHERIC TIDES
NT1	EARTH TIDES
NT1	TIDES
NT2	ASTRONOMICAL TIDES
NT3	HIGHEST ASTRONOMICAL TIDES
NT3	LOWEST ASTRONOMICAL TIDES
NT2	BAROTROPIC TIDES
NT2	DIURNAL TIDES
NT2	EQUILIBRIUM TIDES
NT3	ORTHOTIDES
NT2	ESTUARINE TIDES
NT2	HIGH WATER
NT2	LONG-PERIOD TIDES
NT2	LUNAR TIDES
NT3	LUNAR DIURNAL TIDES

TIDAL MOTION (cont'd)
NT3	LUNAR SEMIDIURNAL TIDES
NT2	METEOROLOGICAL TIDES
NT2	NEAP TIDES
NT2	NODAL TIDES
NT2	OCEAN TIDES
NT2	POLE TIDES
NT2	QUARTER DIURNAL TIDES
NT2	RADIATIONAL TIDES
NT2	SEMIDIURNAL TIDES
NT2	SHALLOW-WATER TIDES
NT2	SOLAR TIDES
NT3	SOLAR DIURNAL TIDES
NT3	SOLAR SEMIDIURNAL TIDES
NT2	SPRING TIDES
RT	FLUID MOTION
RT	MOTION
RT	TIDAL ANALYSIS
RT	TIDAL DYNAMICS

TIDAL OSCILLATIONS
RT	OSCILLATIONS
RT	TIDAL RESONANCE

TIDAL PERTURBATION
RT	NODAL TIDES
RT	TIDAL ANALYSIS
RT	PERTURBATIONS

TIDAL POWER
BT1	POWER FROM THE SEA
BT2	ENERGY RESOURCES
BT3	NATURAL RESOURCES
BT4	RESOURCES
RT	HYDROELECTRIC POWER
RT	TIDAL AMPLITUDE
RT	TIDAL BARRAGES
RT	TIDAL DISSIPATION
RT	TIDAL ENERGY
RT	TIDAL POWER PLANTS
RT	TIDAL RANGE
RT	TIDES
RT	WAVE POWER

TIDAL POWER PLANTS
BT1	HYDROELECTRIC POWER PLANTS
BT2	POWER PLANTS
RT	TIDAL BARRAGES
RT	TIDAL POWER

TIDAL PREDICTION
UF	tide predicting machines
UF	tide prediction
BT1	PREDICTION
RT	COTIDAL CHARTS
RT	TIDAL ANALYSIS
RT	TIDAL CHARTS
RT	TIDE TABLES
RT	TIDES

TIDAL PROPAGATION
BT1	WAVE PROPAGATION
RT	COTIDAL CHARTS
RT	TIDAL DYNAMICS
RT	TIDAL WAVES

TIDAL RANGE
UF	tidal elevation
RT	AGE OF TIDE
RT	CORANGE CHARTS
RT	CORANGE LINES
RT	COTIDAL LINES
RT	TIDAL AMPLITUDE
RT	TIDAL CYCLES
RT	TIDAL POWER

TIDAL RECORDS
BT1	ANALOG RECORDS
BT2	GRAPHICS
BT3	AUDIOVISUAL MATERIAL
BT4	DOCUMENTS
RT	RECORDS
RT	TIDAL CURVES
RT	TIDE GAUGES

TIDAL RESONANCE
RT	AGE OF TIDE
RT	RESONANCE
RT	TIDAL OSCILLATIONS

TIDAL SCOUR
USE	**CURRENT SCOURING**

TIDAL STIRRING
USE	**TIDAL MIXING**

TIDAL STREAM
USE	**TIDAL CURRENTS**

TIDAL WAVES
SN	Not to be used for TSUNAMIS
UF	poincare waves
BT1	SURFACE WATER WAVES
BT2	WATER WAVES
RT	INTERTIDAL ENVIRONMENT
RT	SHALLOW-WATER WAVES
RT	TIDAL AMPLITUDE
RT	TIDAL CURRENTS
RT	TIDAL DYNAMICS
RT	TIDAL PROPAGATION
RT	TIDES
RT	TSUNAMIS

TIDE (AGE)
USE	**AGE OF TIDE**

TIDE GAUGE
USE	**TIDE GAUGES**

TIDE GAUGES
UF	tide gauge
UF	tide measuring equipment
UF	tide pole
UF	tide staff
BT1	MEASURING DEVICES
NT1	DEEP-SEA TIDE GAUGES
RT	GAUGES
RT	OCEANOGRAPHIC EQUIPMENT
RT	PRESSURE SENSORS
RT	SEA LEVEL MEASUREMENT
RT	TIDAL DATUM
RT	TIDAL RECORDS

TIDE GENERATING FORCES
USE	**TIDE GENERATING POTENTIAL**

TIDE GENERATING POTENTIAL
UF	tide generating forces
UF	tide potential
RT	EQUILIBRIUM TIDES
RT	TIDAL ANALYSIS

TIDE MEASURING EQUIPMENT
USE	**TIDE GAUGES**

TIDE POLE
USE	**TIDE GAUGES**

TIDE POTENTIAL
USE	**TIDE GENERATING POTENTIAL**

TIDE PREDICTING MACHINES
USE	**TIDAL PREDICTION**

TIDE PREDICTION	
USE	**TIDAL PREDICTION**

TIDE STAFF	
USE	**TIDE GAUGES**

TIDE-SURGE INTERACTION	
UF	surge-tide interaction
BT1	WAVE-WAVE INTERACTION
BT2	WAVE INTERACTIONS
RT	INTERACTIONS
RT	SHALLOW-WATER TIDES
RT	STORM SURGE BARRIERS
RT	STORM SURGES

TIDE TABLES	
UF	tables (tides)
UF	tidal current tables
BT1	ALMANACS
BT2	TABLES
BT3	DOCUMENTS
RT	COTIDAL CHARTS
RT	CURRENT CHARTS
RT	CURRENT VELOCITY
RT	OCEANOGRAPHIC TABLES
RT	TIDAL CHARTS
RT	TIDAL CURRENTS
RT	TIDAL PREDICTION

TIDES	
SN	Use for general papers on tidal motion in oceans, seas, lakes etc.
UF	tides (hydrosphere)
BT1	TIDAL MOTION
NT1	ASTRONOMICAL TIDES
NT2	HIGHEST ASTRONOMICAL TIDES
NT2	LOWEST ASTRONOMICAL TIDES
NT1	BAROTROPIC TIDES
NT1	DIURNAL TIDES
NT1	EQUILIBRIUM TIDES
NT2	ORTHOTIDES
NT1	ESTUARINE TIDES
NT1	HIGH WATER
NT1	LONG-PERIOD TIDES
NT1	LUNAR TIDES
NT2	LUNAR DIURNAL TIDES
NT2	LUNAR SEMIDIURNAL TIDES
NT1	METEOROLOGICAL TIDES
NT1	NEAP TIDES
NT1	NODAL TIDES
NT1	OCEAN TIDES
NT1	POLE TIDES
NT1	QUARTER DIURNAL TIDES
NT1	RADIATIONAL TIDES
NT1	SEMIDIURNAL TIDES
NT1	SHALLOW-WATER TIDES
NT1	SOLAR TIDES
NT2	SOLAR DIURNAL TIDES
NT2	SOLAR SEMIDIURNAL TIDES
NT1	SPRING TIDES
RT	ATMOSPHERIC TIDES
RT	BAROTROPIC MOTION
RT	COASTAL ZONE
RT	DYNAMICAL OCEANOGRAPHY
RT	EARTH TIDES
RT	ECOLOGICAL ZONATION
RT	INLETS (WATERWAYS)
RT	LOW TIDE
RT	MOON PHASES
RT	OCEAN LOADING
RT	SEA LEVEL
RT	SURGES
RT	TIDAL ANALYSIS
RT	TIDAL CURRENTS
RT	TIDAL CYCLES
RT	TIDAL DYNAMICS
RT	TIDAL EFFECTS
RT	TIDAL FLATS
RT	TIDAL POWER
RT	TIDAL PREDICTION

TIDES (cont'd)	
RT	TIDAL WAVES

TIDES (ATMOSPHERIC)	
USE	**ATMOSPHERIC TIDES**

TIDES (EARTH)	
USE	**EARTH TIDES**

TIDES (HYDROSPHERE)	
USE	**TIDES**

TIE-IN	
USE	**CONNECTING**

TILL	
USE	**BOULDER CLAY**

TILTMETERS	
BT1	SLOPE INDICATORS
BT2	MEASURING DEVICES
RT	EARTH TIDES
RT	GEOPHYSICAL EQUIPMENT
RT	INCLINOMETERS
RT	MEASURING DEVICES
RT	SEISMOLOGY
RT	STRAIN GAUGES

TIME MEASURING EQUIPMENT	
USE	**CHRONOMETERS**

TIME SERIES	
RT	DATA
RT	FIXED STATIONS
RT	OCEANOGRAPHIC DATA
RT	PROBABILITY THEORY
RT	STANDARD OCEAN SECTIONS
RT	TEMPORAL VARIATIONS
RT	TIME SERIES ANALYSIS

TIME SERIES ANALYSIS	
BT1	STATISTICAL ANALYSIS
BT2	MATHEMATICAL ANALYSIS
RT	ANALYSIS
RT	CORRELATION ANALYSIS
RT	FOURIER ANALYSIS
RT	HARMONIC ANALYSIS
RT	SPECTRAL ANALYSIS
RT	STOCHASTIC PROCESSES
RT	TEMPORAL VARIATIONS
RT	TIDAL ANALYSIS
RT	TIME SERIES

TIMING DEVICES	
USE	**CHRONOMETERS**

TIN	
BT1	CHEMICAL ELEMENTS
RT	CASSITERITE
RT	HEAVY METALS
RT	METALS
RT	TIN COMPOUNDS
RT	TIN ISOTOPES
RT	TRACE METALS

TIN COMPOUNDS	
RT	CHEMICAL COMPOUNDS
RT	TIN

TIN ISOTOPES	
BT1	ISOTOPES
RT	TIN

TISSUE CULTURE	
BT1	LABORATORY CULTURE
RT	CELL CULTURE
RT	CULTURE MEDIA
RT	TISSUES

TISSUE MORPHOLOGY	
USE	**HISTOLOGY**

TISSUES	
SN	Aggregation of similar cells having the same functions
UF	biological tissues
NT1	CONNECTIVE TISSUES
NT2	CARTILAGE
NT1	EPITHELIA
NT1	NERVOUS TISSUES
RT	ANATOMICAL STRUCTURES
RT	ANIMAL ORGANS
RT	CALCIFICATION
RT	CELLS
RT	FIXATIVES
RT	GRAFTING
RT	HISTOCHEMISTRY
RT	HISTOLOGY
RT	HISTOPATHOLOGY
RT	MUSCLES
RT	NERVES
RT	PLANT ORGANS
RT	STAINING
RT	TISSUE CULTURE
RT	TRANSPLANTS
RT	ULTRASTRUCTURE

TITANITE	
UF	sphene
BT1	SILICATE MINERALS
BT2	MINERALS

TITANIUM	
BT1	CHEMICAL ELEMENTS
RT	FERROMANGANESE NODULES
RT	ILMENITE
RT	METALS
RT	RUTILE
RT	TITANIUM COMPOUNDS
RT	TITANIUM ISOTOPES
RT	TRACE METALS
RT	TRANSITION ELEMENTS

TITANIUM COMPOUNDS	
RT	CHEMICAL COMPOUNDS
RT	TITANIUM

TITANIUM ISOTOPES	
BT1	ISOTOPES
RT	TITANIUM

TITRATION	
UF	amperometric titration
UF	chelatometric titration
UF	potentiometric titration
UF	titration techniques
BT1	ANALYTICAL TECHNIQUES
RT	CHEMICAL REACTIONS
RT	SALINITY MEASUREMENT
RT	VOLUMETRIC ANALYSIS

TITRATION TECHNIQUES	
USE	**TITRATION**

TOC	
USE	**TOTAL ORGANIC CARBON**

TOCOPHEROL	
USE	**VITAMIN E**

TODOROKITE	
BT1	OXIDE MINERALS
BT2	MINERALS

TOLERANCE	
BT1	BIOLOGICAL PROPERTIES
BT2	PROPERTIES
NT1	EXPOSURE TOLERANCE
NT1	POLLUTION TOLERANCE

TOLERANCE (cont'd)		**TOPOGRAPHIC FEATURES** (cont'd)		**TOPOGRAPHIC WAVES**	
NT1	SALINITY TOLERANCE	NT1	SUBMARINE FEATURES	BT1	WATER WAVES
NT1	TEMPERATURE TOLERANCE	NT2	ABYSSAL HILLS		
NT1	TOXICITY TOLERANCE	NT2	ABYSSAL PLAINS	**TOPOGRAPHY**	
RT	ACCLIMATION	NT2	ARCHIPELAGIC APRONS	NT1	DYNAMIC TOPOGRAPHY
RT	ACCLIMATIZATION	NT2	CONTINENTAL BORDERLAND	NT1	SURFACE TOPOGRAPHY
RT	ADAPTATIONS	NT2	CONTINENTAL MARGINS	NT1	TOPOGRAPHY (GEOLOGY)
RT	BIOLOGICAL RESISTANCE	NT3	ACTIVE MARGINS	NT2	BOTTOM TOPOGRAPHY
RT	ECOPHYSIOLOGY	NT3	PASSIVE MARGINS	NT3	PALAEOTOPOGRAPHY
RT	ENVIRONMENTAL EFFECTS	NT2	CONTINENTAL RIDGES	NT2	SUBAEREAL' TOPOGRAPHY
RT	LETHAL LIMITS	NT2	CONTINENTAL RISE	RT	CONTOURS
RT	LIMITING FACTORS	NT2	CONTINENTAL SHELVES	RT	LAND USE
RT	STARVATION	NT3	OUTER CONTINENTAL SHELF	RT	LANDFORMS
RT	SURVIVAL	NT2	CONTINENTAL SLOPE	RT	MAPPING
		NT2	DEEP-SEA CHANNELS	RT	TOPOGRAPHIC FEATURES
TOLERANCES (DIMENSIONAL)		NT2	DEEP-SEA FANS		
RT	DESIGN	NT2	FRACTURE ZONES	**TOPOGRAPHY (GEOLOGY)**	
		NT2	ISLAND SLOPE	BT1	TOPOGRAPHY
TOMBOLOS		NT2	MICROCONTINENTS	NT1	BOTTOM TOPOGRAPHY
BT1	BEACH FEATURES	NT2	OCEAN BASINS	NT2	PALAEOTOPOGRAPHY
		NT2	SEABIGHTS	NT1	SUBAEREAL TOPOGRAPHY
TOMOGRAPHY (ACOUSTIC)		NT2	SEAKNOLLS	RT	TOPOGRAPHIC FEATURES
USE	**ACOUSTIC TOMOGRAPHY**	NT2	SEAMOUNT CHAINS		
		NT2	SEAMOUNTS	**TOPSET BEDS**	
TOOLS (UNDERWATER)		NT3	GUYOTS	BT1	DELTAIC FEATURES
USE	**DIVING TOOLS**	NT2	SHELF EDGE	RT	BOTTOMSET BEDS
		NT2	SHOALS	RT	DELTAIC DEPOSITS
TOPOGRAPHIC EFFECTS		NT2	SILLS	RT	DELTAIC SEDIMENTATION
SN	Influence of topography on fluid flow	NT2	SUBMARINE BANKS		
NT1	BOTTOM TOPOGRAPHY EFFECTS	NT2	SUBMARINE CANYONS	**TORNADOES**	
RT	AIR FLOW OVER LAND	NT2	SUBMARINE PLATEAUX	RT	ATMOSPHERIC DISTURBANCES
RT	CONTOUR CURRENTS	NT2	SUBMARINE RIDGES	RT	LOW PRESSURE SYSTEMS
RT	FLOW OVER SURFACES	NT3	ASEISMIC RIDGES	RT	STORMS
RT	LEE WAVES	NT3	SEISMIC RIDGES	RT	VORTICES
RT	WAVE TRAPPING	NT4	MID-OCEAN RIDGES	RT	WATERSPOUTS
		NT2	SUBMARINE SCARPS	RT	WINDS
TOPOGRAPHIC FEATURES		NT2	SUBMARINE TROUGHS		
UF	physiographic features	NT2	SUBMARINE VALLEYS	**TORQUE**	
NT1	LANDFORMS	NT2	TRENCHES (OCEANIC)	BT1	STRESS
NT2	ALLUVIAL FANS	RT	BANKS (TOPOGRAPHY)	BT2	FORCES (MECHANICS)
NT2	ALLUVIAL TERRACES	RT	BASINS	RT	SHEAR STRESS
NT2	COASTAL LANDFORMS	RT	BEACH FEATURES		
NT3	BARRIER ISLANDS	RT	BED FORMS	**TOTAL MORTALITY**	
NT3	BEACHES	RT	BOTTOM TOPOGRAPHY	UF	total mortality coefficient
NT4	BARRIER BEACHES	RT	CHANNELS	BT1	MORTALITY
NT4	RAISED BEACHES	RT	COASTAL INLETS	BT2	POPULATION FUNCTIONS
NT3	CAVES	RT	EROSION	RT	FISHING MORTALITY
NT3	CHENIER PLAINS	RT	EROSION FEATURES	RT	NATURAL MORTALITY
NT3	CLIFFS	RT	ESCARPMENTS		
NT3	DELTAS	RT	GEOGRAPHY	**TOTAL MORTALITY COEFFICIENT**	
NT3	HEADLANDS	RT	GEOMORPHOLOGY	USE	**TOTAL MORTALITY**
NT4	CUSPATE FORELANDS	RT	GLACIAL FEATURES		
NT3	PALAEOSHORELINES	RT	INLETS (WATERWAYS)	**TOTAL ORGANIC CARBON**	
NT3	ROCKY SHORES	RT	PHYSIOGRAPHIC PROVINCES	UF	toc
NT3	STACKS	RT	RELIEF FORMS	BT1	ORGANIC CARBON
NT3	TIDAL FLATS	RT	SLOPES (TOPOGRAPHY)	BT2	CARBON
NT2	COASTS	RT	TERRACES	BT3	CHEMICAL ELEMENTS
NT3	EMERGENT SHORELINES	RT	TOPOGRAPHIC MAPS	RT	DISSOLVED ORGANIC CARBON
NT3	RELICT SHORELINES	RT	TOPOGRAPHY		
NT3	STRANDLINES	RT	TOPOGRAPHY (GEOLOGY)	**TOTAL OXYGEN DEMAND**	
NT3	SUBMERGED SHORELINES			USE	**OXYGEN DEMAND**
NT4	RIA COASTS	**TOPOGRAPHIC MAPS**			
NT2	CONTINENTS	BT1	MAPS	**TOTAL SCATTERING COEFFICIENT**	
NT2	FLOOD PLAINS	BT2	GRAPHICS	USE	**SCATTERING COEFFICIENT**
NT2	ISLANDS	BT3	AUDIOVISUAL MATERIAL		
NT3	ATOLLS	BT4	DOCUMENTS	**TOUGHNESS**	
NT3	CAYS	RT	BATHYMETRIC CHARTS	UF	durability
NT3	OCEANIC ISLANDS	RT	GEOLOGICAL MAPS	BT1	MECHANICAL PROPERTIES
NT4	VOLCANIC ISLANDS	RT	LANDFORMS	BT2	PHYSICAL PROPERTIES
NT2	MOUNTAINS	RT	TOPOGRAPHIC FEATURES	BT3	PROPERTIES
NT2	PLAINS	RT	TOPOGRAPHIC SURVEYING	RT	WEAR
NT2	PLATEAUX				
NT2	RIFT VALLEYS	**TOPOGRAPHIC PLANETARY WAVES**		**TOURMALINE**	
NT2	VALLEYS	USE	**PLANETARY WAVES**	BT1	SILICATE MINERALS
NT3	RIVER VALLEYS			BT2	MINERALS
NT2	WETLANDS	**TOPOGRAPHIC SURVEYING**			
NT3	MARSHES	BT1	SURVEYING		
NT4	SALT MARSHES	RT	BEACH PROFILES		
NT3	SWAMPS	RT	TOPOGRAPHIC MAPS		
NT4	MANGROVE SWAMPS				

TOWED BODIES
RT	TOWED BODY DESIGN
RT	TOWED SENSORS
RT	TOWING
RT	UNDERWATER VEHICLES

TOWED BODY DESIGN
BT1	DESIGN
BT2	ENGINEERING
RT	CABLES
RT	SHIP TECHNOLOGY
RT	TOWED BODIES
RT	TOWED SENSORS
RT	TOWED VEHICLES
RT	TOWING
RT	UNDERWATER VEHICLES

TOWED SENSORS
UF	fish (towed sensors)
BT1	SENSORS
BT2	ELECTRONIC EQUIPMENT
BT3	EQUIPMENT
RT	CABLE DEPRESSORS
RT	STREAMERS
RT	TOWED BODIES
RT	TOWED BODY DESIGN
RT	TOWED VEHICLES
RT	TOWING LINES
RT	UNDERWATER VEHICLES
RT	UNDULATORS

TOWED VEHICLES
SN	Unmanned underwater vehicles lacking self-propulsion and free-swimming capability
UF	deep tow
BT1	UNMANNED VEHICLES
BT2	UNDERWATER VEHICLES
BT3	VEHICLES
NT1	GLORIA
NT1	UNDULATORS
RT	TETHERED VEHICLES
RT	TOWED BODY DESIGN
RT	TOWED SENSORS
RT	TOWING
RT	TOWING LINES

TOWERS
SN	Fixed structures used as instrument platforms
BT1	STABILIZED PLATFORMS
BT2	INSTRUMENT PLATFORMS
BT3	VEHICLES
RT	FIXED PLATFORMS

TOWING
RT	BARGES
RT	BOTTOM TOW
RT	TOWED BODIES
RT	TOWED BODY DESIGN
RT	TOWED VEHICLES
RT	TOWING LINES
RT	TUGS
RT	WINCHES

TOWING LINES
BT1	CABLES
RT	CABLE DEPRESSORS
RT	CABLE DYNAMICS
RT	MOORING LINES
RT	ROPES
RT	TETHERED VEHICLES
RT	TOWED SENSORS
RT	TOWED VEHICLES
RT	TOWING

TOWING TANKS
BT1	TANKS
BT2	CONTAINERS
RT	LABORATORY EQUIPMENT
RT	SHIP MODELS
RT	TEST EQUIPMENT
RT	WAVE TANKS

TOXICANTS
SN	Artificial poisons and their effects
RT	ALGICIDES
RT	BIOASSAYS
RT	CHEMICAL CONTROL
RT	DDT
RT	DETOXIFICATION
RT	HAZARDOUS MATERIALS
RT	HEAVY METALS
RT	HERBICIDES
RT	IDENTIFICATION
RT	INSECTICIDES
RT	LETHAL EFFECTS
RT	MORTALITY CAUSES
RT	PCB
RT	PESTICIDES
RT	PHENOLS
RT	REPELLENTS
RT	ROTENONE
RT	TEST ORGANISMS
RT	TOXICITY
RT	TOXICITY TESTS
RT	TOXICOLOGY

TOXICITY
SN	Nature and virulence of toxic and poisonous substances
BT1	BIOLOGICAL PROPERTIES
BT2	PROPERTIES
RT	ALLERGIC REACTIONS
RT	ANTIBODIES
RT	BIOASSAYS
RT	BIOLOGICAL POISONS
RT	BIOTESTING
RT	DETOXIFICATION
RT	ENDOPARASITES
RT	FOOD POISONING
RT	HEAVY METALS
RT	IMMUNOLOGY
RT	LETHAL EFFECTS
RT	LETHAL LIMITS
RT	PATHOLOGY
RT	PESTICIDES
RT	POLLUTION EFFECTS
RT	POLLUTION TOLERANCE
RT	PUBLIC HEALTH
RT	RADIOACTIVE CONTAMINATION
RT	RED TIDES
RT	SUBLETHAL EFFECTS
RT	SURVIVAL
RT	TOXICANTS
RT	TOXICITY TESTS
RT	TOXICOLOGY

TOXICITY INDICES
USE	**TOXICITY TESTS**

TOXICITY TESTS
UF	toxicity indices
BT1	TESTS
RT	BIOASSAYS
RT	BIOTESTING
RT	CHEMICAL POLLUTANTS
RT	CHEMICAL POLLUTION
RT	HAZARD ASSESSMENT
RT	LETHAL EFFECTS
RT	LETHAL LIMITS
RT	POLLUTANT IDENTIFICATION
RT	SUBLETHAL EFFECTS
RT	TEST ORGANISMS
RT	TOXICANTS
RT	TOXICITY

TOXICITY TESTS (cont'd)
RT	TOXICITY TOLERANCE
RT	TOXICOLOGY

TOXICITY TOLERANCE
SN	Added in 1982
UF	poison tolerance
BT1	TOLERANCE
BT2	BIOLOGICAL PROPERTIES
BT3	PROPERTIES
RT	BIOACCUMULATION
RT	LETHAL LIMITS
RT	SUBLETHAL EFFECTS
RT	TOXICITY TESTS
RT	TOXICOLOGY

TOXICOLOGY
SN	Added in 1980
UF	drug toxicology
RT	BIOLOGICAL POISONS
RT	DETOXIFICATION
RT	DRUG RESISTANCE
RT	HAZARD ASSESSMENT
RT	LETHAL EFFECTS
RT	PHARMACOLOGY
RT	POLLUTANTS
RT	SUBLETHAL EFFECTS
RT	TOXICANTS
RT	TOXICITY
RT	TOXICITY TESTS
RT	TOXICITY TOLERANCE
RT	VACCINES

TOXINS
USE	**BIOLOGICAL POISONS**

TRACE ELEMENTS
NT1	TRACE METALS
RT	BORON
RT	BROMINE
RT	CHEMICAL ELEMENTS
RT	CHROMIUM
RT	COBALT
RT	COPPER
RT	FLUORINE
RT	GEOCHEMISTRY
RT	IODINE
RT	IRON
RT	MAGNESIUM
RT	MANGANESE
RT	MOLYBDENUM
RT	NUTRIENTS (MINERAL)
RT	RUBIDIUM
RT	SEDIMENT CHEMISTRY
RT	SELENIUM
RT	SILICON
RT	STRONTIUM
RT	TRACERS
RT	TUNGSTEN
RT	VANADIUM
RT	WATER ANALYSIS
RT	WATER PROPERTIES
RT	ZINC

TRACE FOSSILS
BT1	BIOGENIC SEDIMENTARY STRUCTURES
BT2	SEDIMENTARY STRUCTURES
NT1	FOSSILIZED TRACKS
RT	BIOTURBATION
RT	BURROWS
RT	FAECAL PELLETS
RT	FOSSILS
RT	PALAEONTOLOGY
RT	TIDAL DEPOSITS

TRACE METALS
BT1	TRACE ELEMENTS
RT	ALUMINIUM
RT	EUROPIUM
RT	GALLIUM

TRACE METALS (cont'd)
RT	GERMANIUM
RT	GOLD
RT	HAFNIUM
RT	INDIUM
RT	IRIDIUM
RT	IRON
RT	LEAD
RT	METALS
RT	NIOBIUM
RT	OSMIUM
RT	PALLADIUM
RT	PLATINUM
RT	POLLONIUM
RT	RHENIUM
RT	RHODIUM
RT	RUTHENIUM
RT	SCANDIUM
RT	SILVER
RT	TANTALUM
RT	THALLIUM
RT	TIN
RT	TITANIUM
RT	TUNGSTEN
RT	VANADIUM
RT	ZIRCONIUM

TRACER TECHNIQUES
NT1	ISOTOPE DILUTION
RT	TRACERS

TRACERS
NT1	DYES
NT2	RHODAMINE B-DYE
NT1	RADIOACTIVE TRACERS
RT	ISOTOPES
RT	SEDIMENT TRANSPORT
RT	TRACE ELEMENTS
RT	TRACER TECHNIQUES

TRACHEA
SN	Before 1982 search RESPIRATORY ORGANS
UF	tracheal system
BT1	RESPIRATORY ORGANS
BT2	ANIMAL ORGANS
BT3	BODY ORGANS
RT	AQUATIC INSECTS

TRACHEAL SYSTEM
USE	**TRACHEA**

TRACK CHARTS
BT1	MAPS
BT2	GRAPHICS
BT3	AUDIOVISUAL MATERIAL
BT4	DOCUMENTS
RT	CRUISE REPORTS
RT	CRUISE STATIONS
RT	CRUISES
RT	MULTISHIP EXPEDITIONS
RT	STATION LISTS

TRACKING
SN	Added in 1982
UF	acoustic tracking
UF	continuous tracking
UF	fish tracking
UF	radio tracking
UF	tracking systems
UF	ultrasonic tracking
NT1	HURRICANE TRACKING
RT	ACOUSTIC BEACONS
RT	BEHAVIOUR
RT	BIOTELEMETRY
RT	DETECTION
RT	ECHO SURVEYS
RT	IDENTIFICATION
RT	LOCATING
RT	MIGRATIONS
RT	PINGERS

TRACKING (cont'd)
RT	SONIC TAGS

TRACKING SYSTEMS
USE	**TRACKING**

TRACTION
RT	BED LOAD
RT	PARTICLE MOTION
RT	SEDIMENT TRANSPORT

TRACTION LOAD
USE	**BED LOAD**

TRADE
SN	Restricted to international trade of products of aquatic origin
UF	exports
UF	foreign trade
UF	imports
UF	international trade
RT	AQUACULTURE ECONOMICS
RT	AQUACULTURE STATISTICS
RT	CAPTURE FISHERY ECONOMICS
RT	CATCH STATISTICS
RT	COMMERCE
RT	COMMERCIAL AVAILABILITY
RT	CONSUMERS
RT	ECONOMICS
RT	FISHERY ECONOMICS
RT	FISHERY STATISTICS
RT	INDUSTRIAL PRODUCTS STATISTICS
RT	INTERNATIONAL LAW
RT	LANDING STATISTICS
RT	MARKET RESEARCH
RT	MARKETING
RT	PRICING
RT	PRODUCTS
RT	TRADE ORGANIZATIONS
RT	WORLD

TRADE ASSOCIATIONS
USE	**TRADE ORGANIZATIONS**

TRADE ORGANIZATIONS
UF	trade associations
BT1	ORGANIZATIONS
RT	TRADE

TRADE SHOWS
USE	**EXHIBITIONS**

TRADE WIND INVERSION
BT1	TEMPERATURE INVERSIONS
BT2	INVERSIONS
RT	TRADE WINDS

TRADE WINDS
UF	tropical easterlies
BT1	PLANETARY WINDS
BT2	WINDS
BT3	ATMOSPHERIC MOTION
NT1	EQUATORIAL EASTERLIES
RT	COASTAL UPWELLING
RT	TRADE WIND INVERSION
RT	TROPICAL METEOROLOGY

TRAFFIC MANAGEMENT
RT	COLLISION AVOIDANCE
RT	NAVIGATION REGULATIONS
RT	SHIPPING
RT	SHIPPING LANES

TRAINING
SN	Before 1982 search EDUCATION
RT	DEVELOPING COUNTRIES
RT	EDUCATION
RT	FISHERY SCIENCES
RT	INTERNATIONAL COOPERATION
RT	TECHNOLOGY TRANSFER

TRAINING (cont'd)
RT	TRAINING AIDS
RT	TRAINING CENTRES

TRAINING AIDS
UF	teaching aids
RT	AUDIOVISUAL MATERIAL
RT	EDUCATION
RT	GEAR HANDLING
RT	MANUALS
RT	SEAMANSHIP
RT	SIMULATORS
RT	TRAINING
RT	TRAINING CENTRES

TRAINING CENTERS
USE	**TRAINING CENTRES**

TRAINING CENTRES
UF	training centers
RT	CURRICULA
RT	DEVELOPING COUNTRIES
RT	EDUCATION
RT	EDUCATION ESTABLISHMENTS
RT	INTERNATIONAL COOPERATION
RT	MANUALS
RT	REPORT LITERATURE
RT	TRAINING
RT	TRAINING AIDS

TRAINING PROGRAMMES
USE	**CURRICULA**

TRAMMELS
USE	**ENTANGLING NETS**

TRANS-ISOPYCNAL MIXING
BT1	WATER MIXING
RT	DOUBLE DIFFUSIVE INSTABILITY
RT	INTERNAL WAVE BREAKING
RT	KELVIN-HELMHOLTZ INSTABILITY
RT	MIXING PROCESSES

TRANSBOUNDARY STOCKS
USE	**SHARED STOCKS**

TRANSDUCER ARRAYS
BT1	ACOUSTIC ARRAYS
BT2	ARRAYS
RT	HYDROPHONES
RT	TRANSDUCERS

TRANSDUCERS
NT1	ACOUSTIC TRANSDUCERS
NT2	HYDROPHONES
NT2	MICROPHONES
NT2	SONAR TRANSDUCERS
NT1	PIEZOELECTRIC TRANSDUCERS
NT1	ULTRASONIC TRANSDUCERS
RT	ACCELEROMETERS
RT	ACOUSTIC ARRAYS
RT	PRESSURE SENSORS
RT	SENSORS
RT	STRAIN GAUGES
RT	TRANSDUCER ARRAYS

TRANSFER CHAMBERS
BT1	DECOMPRESSION CHAMBERS
BT2	DIVING EQUIPMENT
BT3	EQUIPMENT
RT	DECK COMPRESSION CHAMBERS
RT	DIVING BELLS

TRANSFER OF PROPERTIES
USE	**ENERGY TRANSFER**

TRANSFER OF TECHNOLOGIES
USE   **TECHNOLOGY TRANSFER**

TRANSFERASES
SN   Before 1982 search ENZYMES
BT1   ENZYMES

TRANSFORM FAULTS
BT1   FAULTS
BT2   GEOLOGICAL STRUCTURES
RT   FRACTURE ZONES
RT   MID-OCEAN RIDGES
RT   PLATE TECTONICS
RT   TRANSFORM PLATE BOUNDARIES

TRANSFORM PLATE BOUNDARIES
BT1   PLATE BOUNDARIES
RT   TRANSFORM FAULTS

TRANSGRESSIONS
UF   marine transgressions
RT   COASTS
RT   DEGLACIATION
RT   EUSTATIC CHANGES
RT   ISOSTASY
RT   REGRESSIONS
RT   RETROGRADATION
RT   RIA COASTS
RT   SEA LEVEL CHANGES
RT   SUBMERGED SHORELINES
RT   SUBMERGENCE

TRANSIENT POLYMORPHISM
USE   **BIOPOLYMORPHISM**

TRANSITION ELEMENT COMPOUNDS
RT   CHEMICAL COMPOUNDS
RT   MANGANESE COMPOUNDS
RT   TRANSITION ELEMENTS

TRANSITION ELEMENTS
RT   ACTINIDES
RT   ACTINIUM
RT   AMERICIUM
RT   BERKELIUM
RT   CALIFORNIUM
RT   CERIUM
RT   CHROMIUM
RT   COBALT
RT   CURIUM
RT   DYSPROSIUM
RT   ERBIUM
RT   EUROPIUM
RT   FERMIUM
RT   GADOLINIUM
RT   HOLMIUM
RT   IRON
RT   LANTHANIUM
RT   LUTETIUM
RT   MANGANESE
RT   NEODYMIUM
RT   NEPTUNIUM
RT   NICKEL
RT   NOBELIUM
RT   PLUTONIUM
RT   PRASEODYMIUM
RT   PROTACTINIUM
RT   RARE EARTHS
RT   SAMARIUM
RT   SCANDIUM
RT   TERBIUM
RT   THORIUM
RT   THULIUM
RT   TITANIUM
RT   TRANSITION ELEMENT COMPOUNDS
RT   URANIUM
RT   VANADIUM
RT   YTTERBIUM

TRANSITION TEMPERATURES
BT1   TEMPERATURE
BT2   THERMODYNAMIC PROPERTIES
BT3   PHYSICAL PROPERTIES
BT4   PROPERTIES
NT1   BOILING POINT
NT1   DEW POINT
NT1   FREEZING POINT
NT1   MELTING POINT
RT   PHASE CHANGES

TRANSLATIONS
BT1   DOCUMENTS
RT   DATA COLLECTIONS
RT   INFORMATION HANDLING

TRANSMISSION
NT1   LIGHT TRANSMISSION
NT1   SOUND TRANSMISSION
RT   ABSORPTION (PHYSICS)
RT   ATTENUATION
RT   REFLECTION
RT   WAVE MOTION

TRANSMISSION (WATER WAVES)
USE   **WAVE PROPAGATION**

TRANSMISSION DISEASES
USE   **DISEASE TRANSMISSION**

TRANSMISSION LOSS
UF   absorption loss
UF   reflection loss
UF   refraction loss
UF   scattering loss
UF   sound transmission loss
RT   SOUND TRANSMISSION

TRANSMISSOMETERS
BT1   LIGHT MEASURING INSTRUMENTS
BT2   MEASURING DEVICES
RT   LIGHT ABSORPTION
RT   LIGHT SCATTERING
RT   PARTICLE CONCENTRATION
RT   TRANSPARENCY

TRANSMITTANCE
BT1   OPTICAL PROPERTIES
BT2   PHYSICAL PROPERTIES
BT3   PROPERTIES
NT1   BEAM TRANSMITTANCE
RT   ATTENUANCE
RT   LIGHT ATTENUATION
RT   LIGHT PENETRATION
RT   OPTICAL WATER TYPES
RT   TURBIDITY
RT   WATER TRANSPARENCY

TRANSPARENCY
BT1   OPTICAL PROPERTIES
BT2   PHYSICAL PROPERTIES
BT3   PROPERTIES
NT1   WATER TRANSPARENCY
RT   LIGHT ABSORPTION
RT   LIGHT REFRACTION
RT   LIGHT TRANSMISSION
RT   NEPHELOMETERS
RT   REFRACTION
RT   TRANSMISSOMETERS
RT   TURBIDITY

TRANSPARENCY (WATER)
USE   **WATER TRANSPARENCY**

TRANSPARENCY METERS
USE   **BEAM TRANSMITTANCE METERS**

TRANSPIRATION
SN   Added in 1980
RT   CARBON CYCLE
RT   CUTICLES
RT   DEHYDRATION
RT   EVAPORATION
RT   EVAPOTRANSPIRATION
RT   HYDROLOGIC CYCLE
RT   PHOTOSYNTHESIS
RT   RESPIRATION
RT   STOMATA
RT   WATER BALANCE
RT   WATER CONTENT

TRANSPLANTATION
SN   Artificial introduction of
        organisms into habitats where they
        do not occur naturally. Before 1982
        search STOCKING (ORGANISMS)
UF   transplantation techniques
RT   AQUACULTURE DEVELOPMENT
RT   ARTIFICIAL LAKES
RT   HERBIVOROUS FISH
RT   INTRODUCED SPECIES
RT   SEED (AQUACULTURE)
RT   SEEDING (AQUACULTURE)
RT   SPORT FISHING
RT   STOCKING (ORGANISMS)

TRANSPLANTATION TECHNIQUES
USE   **TRANSPLANTATION**

TRANSPLANTS
SN   The tissue or organ grafted or
        transplanted from one individual
        either to another part of the same
        individual or to a different one.
        Added in 1980
UF   biological transplantation
UF   grafts
RT   BODY ORGANS
RT   ORGAN REMOVAL
RT   TISSUES

TRANSPONDER ARRAYS
BT1   ACOUSTIC ARRAYS
BT2   ARRAYS
RT   ACOUSTIC EQUIPMENT
RT   TRANSPONDERS

TRANSPONDER NAVIGATION
USE   **ACOUSTIC NAVIGATION**

TRANSPONDERS
NT1   ACOUSTIC TRANSPONDERS
NT2   SONAR TRANSPONDERS
RT   ACOUSTIC ARRAYS
RT   ELECTRONIC EQUIPMENT
RT   TRANSPONDER ARRAYS

TRANSPORT
SN   Use of a more specific term is
        recommended
RT   EKMAN TRANSPORT
RT   HEAT TRANSPORT
RT   MASS TRANSPORT
RT   SEDIMENT TRANSPORT
RT   SVERDRUP TRANSPORT
RT   TRANSPORT PROCESSES
RT   TRANSPORTATION
RT   VOLUME TRANSPORT

TRANSPORT (VEHICULAR)
USE   **TRANSPORTATION**

TRANSPORT AGENTS
USE   **PERMEASES**

ASFIS Thesaurus

TRANSPORT PROCESSES
NT1	ADVECTION
NT2	CONVECTION
NT3	ATMOSPHERIC CONVECTION
NT3	CELLULAR CONVECTION
NT3	FORCED CONVECTION
NT3	MANTLE CONVECTION
NT3	OCEANIC CONVECTION
NT2	HORIZONTAL ADVECTION
NT2	SALT ADVECTION
NT2	VERTICAL ADVECTION
NT1	DIFFUSION
NT2	ATMOSPHERIC DIFFUSION
NT2	MOLECULAR DIFFUSION
NT3	DOUBLE DIFFUSION
NT2	THERMAL DIFFUSION
NT2	TURBULENT DIFFUSION
RT	SALT FINGERS
RT	TRANSPORT
RT	WATER MOTION

TRANSPORTATION
SN	Carriage of goods and passengers
UF	transport (vehicular)
NT1	AIR TRANSPORTATION
NT1	MARINE TRANSPORTATION
RT	AIRCRAFT
RT	BOATS
RT	BRIDGES
RT	SHIPS
RT	SURFACE CRAFT
RT	TRANSPORT
RT	TUNNELS
RT	UNDERWATER VEHICLES
RT	VEHICLES

TRANSURANIC ELEMENTS
BT1	METALS
RT	AMERICIUM
RT	BERKELIUM
RT	CALIFORNIUM
RT	CURIUM
RT	EINSTEINIUM
RT	FERMIUM
RT	LAWRENCIUM
RT	MENDELEVIUM
RT	NEPTUNIUM
RT	NOBELIUM
RT	PLUTONIUM

TRANSVERSE BARS
UF	finger bars
BT1	NEARSHORE BARS
BT2	BEACH FEATURES
RT	TRANSVERSE BED FORMS

TRANSVERSE BED FORMS
BT1	BED FORMS
BT2	SEDIMENTARY STRUCTURES
RT	ANTIDUNES
RT	CHANNEL FLOW
RT	GRAVEL WAVES
RT	RIPPLE MARKS
RT	SAND PATCHES
RT	SAND RIPPLES
RT	SAND WAVES
RT	TRANSVERSE BARS
RT	UNIDIRECTIONAL FLOW

TRANSVERSE MIXING
BT1	WATER MIXING
RT	ESTUARINE DYNAMICS

TRAP FISHING
UF	trapping
BT1	CATCHING METHODS
RT	BAIT
RT	BAIT FISH
RT	CRAB FISHERIES
RT	CRUSTACEAN FISHERIES

TRAP FISHING (cont'd)
RT	FISHING
RT	GASTROPOD FISHERIES
RT	LOBSTER FISHERIES
RT	TRAP NETS

TRAP NETS
UF	fish traps
UF	fyke nets
UF	pound nets
UF	traps
BT1	FISHING NETS
BT2	FISHING GEAR
RT	COASTAL FISHERIES
RT	INLAND FISHERIES
RT	LAGOON FISHERIES
RT	POTS
RT	TRAP FISHING

TRAPPED WAVES
UF	bottom trapped waves
UF	coastal trapped waves
BT1	WATER WAVES
NT1	EDGE WAVES
NT1	KELVIN WAVES
NT2	EQUATORIAL TRAPPED WAVES
NT1	SHELF WAVES
NT1	SURF BEATS
RT	WAVE TRAPPING

TRAPPING
USE	**TRAP FISHING**

TRAPS
USE	**TRAP NETS**

TRASH FISH
SN	Fish and other aquatic organisms without commercial value for human food market
UF	industrial fish
UF	rough fish
BT1	FISH
BT2	AQUATIC ANIMALS
RT	COMMERCIAL SPECIES
RT	FISH MEAL PROCESSING
RT	FISH OILS
RT	FISH WASTES

TRAVERSE TABLES
BT1	TABLES
BT2	DOCUMENTS
RT	NAVIGATIONAL TABLES

TRAWL NETS
UF	trawls
BT1	FISHING NETS
BT2	FISHING GEAR
NT1	BOTTOM TRAWLS
NT1	MIDWATER TRAWLS
RT	COASTAL FISHERIES
RT	DEMERSAL FISHERIES
RT	NET SOUNDERS
RT	OTTER BOARDS
RT	PELAGIC FISHERIES
RT	TRAWLERS
RT	TRAWLING

TRAWLERS
UF	beam trawlers
UF	otter trawlers
UF	pair trawlers
BT1	FISHING VESSELS
BT2	SURFACE CRAFT
BT3	VEHICLES
RT	DEMERSAL FISHERIES
RT	PELAGIC FISHERIES
RT	TRAWL NETS
RT	TRAWLING

TRAWLING
UF	pair trawling
BT1	CATCHING METHODS
NT1	BOTTOM TRAWLING
RT	BOTTOM TRAWLS
RT	FISHING
RT	FLATFISH FISHERIES
RT	GADOID FISHERIES
RT	NET FISHING
RT	NET SOUNDERS
RT	OTTER BOARDS
RT	SONAR
RT	TENSOMETERS
RT	TRAWL NETS
RT	TRAWLERS

TRAWLS
USE	**TRAWL NETS**

TRAY CULTURE
SN	Added in 1982
BT1	AQUACULTURE TECHNIQUES
RT	OYSTER CULTURE

TREATIES
USE	**INTERNATIONAL AGREEMENTS**

TREATMENT FOR DISEASES
USE	**THERAPY**

TRENCHES
USE	**TRENCHES (OCEANIC)**

TRENCHES (OCEANIC)
SN	Before 1982 search TRENCHES
UF	oceanic trenches
UF	submarine trenches
UF	trenches
BT1	SUBMARINE FEATURES
BT2	TOPOGRAPHIC FEATURES
RT	BENIOFF ZONE
RT	CONTINENTAL MARGINS
RT	CONVERGING PLATE BOUNDARIES
RT	DEEP-SEA FURROWS
RT	FOREARC BASINS
RT	HEAT FLOW
RT	ISLAND ARCS
RT	PLATE CONVERGENCE
RT	POTENTIAL TEMPERATURE
RT	RELIEF FORMS
RT	SUBDUCTION ZONES
RT	VALLEYS

TRENCHES (PIPELINES)
RT	OCEAN FLOOR
RT	PIPELINES
RT	SLOPE STABILITY
RT	SUBMARINE CABLES
RT	TRENCHING

TRENCHING
UF	ditching
UF	ploughing trenches
RT	BURYING
RT	DREDGING
RT	OCEAN FLOOR
RT	PIPELINE CONSTRUCTION
RT	PLOUGHS
RT	SOIL MECHANICS
RT	TRENCHES (PIPELINES)

TRIASSIC
SN	Before 1982 search TRIASSIC PERIOD
BT1	MESOZOIC
BT2	GEOLOGICAL TIME

TRIBUTARIES
BT1	RIVERS
BT2	INLAND WATERS
RT	DISTRIBUTARIES
RT	FLUVIAL MORPHOLOGY

TRICHLOROETHYLENE
BT1	CHLORINATED HYDROCARBONS
BT2	HALOGENATED HYDROCARBONS
BT3	HYDROCARBONS
BT4	ORGANIC COMPOUNDS

TRIPLE JUNCTIONS
RT	PLATE BOUNDARIES
RT	PLATES

TRITIUM
BT1	HYDROGEN ISOTOPES
BT2	ISOTOPES

TROLL-LINES
USE	**LINES**

TROLLERS
USE	**LINERS**

TROLLING
BT1	LINE FISHING
BT2	CATCHING METHODS
RT	LINERS
RT	LINES

TROPHIC LEVELS
RT	BIOLOGICAL PRODUCTION
RT	CARNIVORES
RT	ECOSYSTEMS
RT	ENERGY FLOW
RT	FEEDING BEHAVIOUR
RT	FOOD CHAINS
RT	HERBIVORES
RT	OMNIVORES
RT	TROPHODYNAMIC CYCLE

TROPHIC RELATIONSHIPS
SN	Added in 1980
RT	FOOD CHAINS
RT	FOOD WEBS
RT	INTERSPECIFIC RELATIONSHIPS
RT	INTRASPECIFIC RELATIONSHIPS
RT	TROPHIC STRUCTURE
RT	TROPHODYNAMIC CYCLE

TROPHIC STATUS
USE	**TROPHIC STRUCTURE**

TROPHIC STRUCTURE
SN	Added in 1980
UF	trophic status
UF	trophic zonality
RT	ECOSYSTEMS
RT	TROPHIC RELATIONSHIPS

TROPHIC ZONALITY
USE	**TROPHIC STRUCTURE**

TROPHODYNAMIC CYCLE
UF	food cycle
BT1	CYCLES
RT	BIOGENIC MATERIAL
RT	BIOLOGICAL PRODUCTION
RT	ENERGY FLOW
RT	FEEDING BEHAVIOUR
RT	FOOD WEBS
RT	HETEROTROPHIC ORGANISMS
RT	NUTRITIONAL REQUIREMENTS
RT	TROPHIC LEVELS
RT	TROPHIC RELATIONSHIPS

TROPICAL AQUACULTURE
USE	**WARM-WATER AQUACULTURE**

TROPICAL CLIMATE
USE	**TROPICAL ENVIRONMENT**

TROPICAL CLIMATOLOGY
USE	**TROPICAL METEOROLOGY**

TROPICAL CYCLONES
USE	**HURRICANES**

TROPICAL DEPRESSIONS
SN	Before 1982 search also TROPICAL CYCLONES
UF	cyclones (tropical)
UF	tropical storms
BT1	ATMOSPHERIC DEPRESSIONS
NT1	HURRICANES
RT	ATMOSPHERIC DISTURBANCES
RT	EASTERLY WAVES
RT	TROPICAL METEOROLOGY
RT	WEATHER FORECASTING

TROPICAL EASTERLIES
USE	**TRADE WINDS**

TROPICAL ENVIRONMENT
SN	For global treatment of regional aspects of tropical waters use WORLD TROPICAL REGIONS in Geographic Authority List
UF	tropical climate
BT1	ENVIRONMENTS
RT	ATOLLS
RT	DRY SEASON
RT	MONSOONS
RT	RAINY SEASON
RT	TROPICAL LAKES
RT	TROPICAL METEOROLOGY
RT	TROPICAL OCEANOGRAPHY

TROPICAL FISH
SN	Added in 1980
BT1	FISH
BT2	AQUATIC ANIMALS
RT	CORAL REEFS
RT	HERBIVOROUS FISH
RT	MARINE FISH
RT	ORNAMENTAL FISH

TROPICAL LAKES
BT1	LAKES
BT2	INLAND WATERS
RT	DRY SEASON
RT	RAINY SEASON
RT	TROPICAL ENVIRONMENT

TROPICAL METEOROLOGY
UF	tropical climatology
BT1	METEOROLOGY
RT	EASTERLY WAVES
RT	EQUATORIAL DYNAMICS
RT	EQUATORIAL TROUGH
RT	HURRICANES
RT	MONSOONS
RT	TRADE WINDS
RT	TROPICAL DEPRESSIONS
RT	TROPICAL ENVIRONMENT
RT	TROPICAL OCEANOGRAPHY

TROPICAL OCEANOGRAPHY
BT1	OCEANOGRAPHY
BT2	EARTH SCIENCES
RT	EQUATORIAL CIRCULATION
RT	EQUATORIAL DYNAMICS
RT	HURRICANE WAVES
RT	MONSOON REVERSAL
RT	MONSOONS
RT	TROPICAL ENVIRONMENT

TROPICAL OCEANOGRAPHY (cont'd)
RT	TROPICAL METEOROLOGY

TROPICAL STORMS
USE	**TROPICAL DEPRESSIONS**

TROPISM
NT1	CHEMOTROPISM
NT1	GEOTROPISM
NT1	PHOTOTROPISM
NT1	RHEOTROPISM
RT	BEHAVIOUR
RT	KINESIS
RT	ORIENTATION BEHAVIOUR
RT	STIMULI
RT	TAXIS

TROPOPAUSE
BT1	EARTH ATMOSPHERE
BT2	PLANETARY ATMOSPHERES
RT	STRATOSPHERE
RT	TROPOSPHERE

TROPOSPHERE
BT1	EARTH ATMOSPHERE
BT2	PLANETARY ATMOSPHERES
RT	AIR TEMPERATURE
RT	ATMOSPHERIC BOUNDARY LAYER
RT	ATMOSPHERIC FRONTS
RT	JET STREAM
RT	METEOROLOGICAL DATA
RT	STRATOSPHERE
RT	TROPOPAUSE
RT	WEATHER

TROUT FISHERIES
USE	**SALMON FISHERIES**

TSUNAMI GENERATION
BT1	WAVE GENERATION
RT	EARTHQUAKES
RT	LANDSLIDES
RT	TSUNAMIS

TSUNAMI PREDICTION
BT1	PREDICTION
RT	TSUNAMIS
RT	WARNING SERVICES

TSUNAMIS
UF	seismic sea waves
UF	tunamis
BT1	SURFACE WATER WAVES
BT2	WATER WAVES
RT	CATASTROPHIC WAVES
RT	DISASTERS
RT	EARTHQUAKES
RT	EDGE WAVES
RT	FLOODING
RT	FLOODS
RT	PREDICTION
RT	SEA LEVEL VARIATIONS
RT	SHALLOW-WATER WAVES
RT	SURFACE GRAVITY WAVES
RT	TIDAL WAVES
RT	TSUNAMI GENERATION
RT	TSUNAMI PREDICTION
RT	VOLCANIC ERUPTIONS
RT	WARNING SERVICES
RT	WAVE EFFECTS

TUBE DWELLERS
SN	Organisms living in a constructed tube. Added in 1980
UF	tube dwelling organisms
UF	tubiculous organisms
BT1	AQUATIC ORGANISMS
RT	BENTHOS

TUBE DWELLING ORGANISMS
USE   **TUBE DWELLERS**

TUBERCULOSIS
SN   Added in 1980
UF   mycobacterial infections
BT1   BACTERIAL DISEASES
BT2   INFECTIOUS DISEASES
BT3   DISEASES
RT   ANTIBIOTICS
RT   FISH DISEASES
RT   INFECTIOUS DISEASES

TUBICULOUS ORGANISMS
USE   **TUBE DWELLERS**

TUBING
SN   Use for tubular construction and
structural components
RT   CYLINDERS
RT   NODE CONSTRUCTION
RT   PIPES
RT   STEEL

TUGS
BT1   SHIPS
BT2   SURFACE CRAFT
BT3   VEHICLES
RT   SUPPORT SHIPS
RT   TOWING

TUMBLING DISEASE
USE   **WHIRLING DISEASE**

TUMORS
USE   **TUMOURS**

TUMOURS
UF   carcinoma
UF   hepatoma
UF   neoplasms
UF   sarcoma
UF   tumors
BT1   DISEASES
RT   CARCINOGENESIS
RT   CARCINOGENS
RT   FISH DISEASES
RT   GILL DISEASE
RT   MORTALITY
RT   THERAPY

TUNA AND TUNA-LIKE FISHERIES
USE   **TUNA FISHERIES**

TUNA FISHERIES
SN   Added in 1980
UF   albacore fisheries
UF   billfisheries
UF   bonito fisheries
UF   king mackerel fisheries
UF   skipjack tuna fisheries
UF   swordfish fisheries
UF   tuna and tuna-like fisheries
BT1   FINFISH FISHERIES
BT2   FISHERIES
RT   BAIT CULTURE
RT   BAIT FISHING
RT   LONGLINING
RT   MACKEREL FISHERIES
RT   MARINE FISHERIES
RT   MIGRATORY SPECIES
RT   PELAGIC FISHERIES
RT   POLE-LINE FISHING
RT   PURSE SEINING
RT   SPORT FISHING

TUNAMIS
USE   **TSUNAMIS**

TUNGSTEN
BT1   CHEMICAL ELEMENTS
RT   METALS
RT   TRACE ELEMENTS
RT   TRACE METALS
RT   TUNGSTEN COMPOUNDS
RT   TUNGSTEN ISOTOPES

TUNGSTEN COMPOUNDS
RT   CHEMICAL COMPOUNDS
RT   TUNGSTEN

TUNGSTEN ISOTOPES
BT1   ISOTOPES
RT   TUNGSTEN

TUNNELS
RT   BRIDGES
RT   STRAITS
RT   TRANSPORTATION

TURBIDIMETERS
UF   turbidity sensors
BT1   MEASURING DEVICES
RT   LIGHT MEASURING INSTRUMENTS
RT   OCEANOGRAPHIC EQUIPMENT
RT   TURBIDITY

TURBIDITES
BT1   CLASTICS
BT2   SEDIMENTS
RT   DEEP-SEA FANS
RT   SEDIMENTARY ROCKS
RT   TERRIGENOUS SEDIMENTS
RT   TURBIDITY CURRENTS

TURBIDITY
BT1   PHYSICAL PROPERTIES
BT2   PROPERTIES
RT   ABSORPTION SPECTRA
RT   AEROSOLS
RT   COLLOIDS
RT   DETRITUS
RT   HAZE
RT   LIGHT ABSORPTION
RT   LIGHT ATTENUATION
RT   LIGHT PENETRATION
RT   LIGHT SCATTERING
RT   NEPHELOID LAYER
RT   NEPHELOMETERS
RT   OPTICAL PROPERTIES
RT   PARTICLE CONCENTRATION
RT   PARTICLE DISTRIBUTION
RT   PARTICLE SIZE
RT   RIVER PLUMES
RT   SUSPENDED INORGANIC MATTER
RT   SUSPENDED ORGANIC MATTER
RT   SUSPENDED PARTICULATE MATTER
RT   TRANSMITTANCE
RT   TRANSPARENCY
RT   TURBIDIMETERS
RT   TURBIDITY CURRENTS
RT   TURBULENCE
RT   VISIBILITY UNDERWATER
RT   WATER COLOUR
RT   WATER PROPERTIES
RT   WATER TRANSPARENCY

TURBIDITY CURRENT STRUCTURES
BT1   SEDIMENTARY STRUCTURES
RT   FLOW STRUCTURES
RT   OLISTOLITHS
RT   OLISTOSTROMES
RT   TURBIDITY CURRENTS

TURBIDITY CURRENTS
UF   suspension currents
BT1   SEDIMENT GRAVITY FLOWS
BT2   SEDIMENT MOVEMENT
RT   ABYSSAL ZONE
RT   BOTTOM CURRENTS
RT   COHESIONLESS SEDIMENTS
RT   CONTINENTAL SLOPE
RT   DEEP-SEA FANS
RT   DENSITY FLOW
RT   EARTHQUAKES
RT   FANS
RT   NEPHELOID LAYER
RT   SEDIMENT TRANSPORT
RT   SUBMARINE CABLE BREAKS
RT   SUBMARINE CANYONS
RT   TURBIDITES
RT   TURBIDITY
RT   TURBIDITY CURRENT STRUCTURES

TURBIDITY SENSORS
USE   **TURBIDIMETERS**

TURBINES
BT1   MOTORS
RT   POWER PLANTS
RT   PROPULSION SYSTEMS

TURBULENCE
UF   isotropic turbulence
BT1   FLUID MOTION
NT1   ATMOSPHERIC TURBULENCE
NT2   CLEAR AIR TURBULENCE
NT2   GUSTS
NT1   OCEANIC TURBULENCE
RT   DIFFUSION
RT   EDDY CONDUCTIVITY
RT   EDDY DIFFUSIVITY
RT   EDDY VISCOSITY
RT   REYNOLDS STRESSES
RT   RHODAMINE B-DYE
RT   TURBIDITY
RT   TURBULENCE MEASUREMENT
RT   TURBULENT BOUNDARY LAYER
RT   TURBULENT DIFFUSION
RT   TURBULENT FLOW
RT   TURBULENT TRANSFER
RT   VORTICES
RT   VORTICITY
RT   WAKES
RT   WATER CIRCULATION
RT   WAVE DISSIPATION
RT   WAVE INTERACTIONS

TURBULENCE MEASUREMENT
BT1   FLOW MEASUREMENT
BT2   MEASUREMENT
RT   ANEMOMETERS
RT   ATMOSPHERIC TURBULENCE
RT   OCEANIC TURBULENCE
RT   TURBULENCE
RT   WIND MEASURING EQUIPMENT

TURBULENT BOUNDARY LAYER
BT1   BOUNDARY LAYERS
BT2   LAYERS
RT   LAMINAR BOUNDARY LAYER
RT   REYNOLDS STRESSES
RT   TURBULENCE
RT   TURBULENT FLOW

TURBULENT DIFFUSION
UF   eddy diffusion
BT1   DIFFUSION
BT2   TRANSPORT PROCESSES
RT   ATMOSPHERIC DIFFUSION
RT   ATMOSPHERIC TURBULENCE
RT   DYE DISPERSION
RT   EDDY CONDUCTION
RT   EDDY DIFFUSIVITY

TURBULENT DIFFUSION (cont'd)
RT   EDDY VISCOSITY
RT   MIXING PROCESSES
RT   OCEANIC TURBULENCE
RT   TURBULENCE

TURBULENT ENERGY
USE   **EDDY KINETIC ENERGY**

TURBULENT ENTRAINMENT
BT1   FLUID MOTION
RT   BUOYANT JETS
RT   MIXING PROCESSES
RT   PLUMES
RT   SALT-WEDGE ESTUARIES
RT   SEPARATION
RT   TURBULENT FLOW

TURBULENT EXCHANGE
USE   **EDDY FLUX**

TURBULENT FLOW
BT1   FLUID FLOW
BT2   FLUID MOTION
NT1   CAVITATION
RT   ATMOSPHERIC TURBULENCE
RT   CHANNEL FLOW
RT   EDDY VISCOSITY
RT   LAMINAR FLOW
RT   MULTIPHASE FLOW
RT   OCEANIC TURBULENCE
RT   REYNOLDS NUMBER
RT   REYNOLDS STRESSES
RT   TURBULENCE
RT   TURBULENT BOUNDARY LAYER
RT   TURBULENT ENTRAINMENT
RT   TURBULENT SHEAR FLOW

TURBULENT HEAT TRANSFER
USE   **EDDY CONDUCTION**

TURBULENT JETS
USE   **JETS**

TURBULENT SHEAR FLOW
BT1   SHEAR FLOW
BT2   FLUID FLOW
BT3   FLUID MOTION
RT   TURBULENT FLOW

TURBULENT SHEAR STRESSES
USE   **REYNOLDS STRESSES**

TURBULENT TRANSFER
RT   TURBULENCE

TURIONS
SN   Added in 1980
BT1   PLANT REPRODUCTIVE STRUCTURES
BT2   PLANT ORGANS
BT3   BODY ORGANS
RT   AQUATIC PLANTS

TURNOVER
USE   **OVERTURN**

TURTLE CULTURE
BT1   AQUACULTURE
RT   AQUATIC REPTILES
RT   CULTURES
RT   TURTLE FISHERIES

TURTLE FISHERIES
SN   Added in 1982
BT1   FISHERIES
RT   TURTLE CULTURE

TWINE
USE   **YARNS**

TWO PHASE FLOW
USE   **MULTIPHASE FLOW**

TYPE LOCALITIES
SN   Specific geographic area in which
       the type specimens were first
       collected. Added in 1980
RT   DISTRIBUTION RECORDS
RT   HOLOTYPES
RT   NEW TAXA

TYPE SPECIMENS
USE   **HOLOTYPES**

TYPHOONS
USE   **HURRICANES**

TYPOLOGY
SN   The study of types as of
       constitutional types. Added in 1980
RT   ECOTYPES
RT   EVOLUTION
RT   GENOTYPES
RT   HOLOTYPES
RT   PHENOTYPES
RT   TAXONOMY

TYROSINE
BT1   AMINO ACIDS
BT2   ORGANIC ACIDS
BT3   ORGANIC COMPOUNDS

UDN
USE   **ULCERATIVE DERMAL NECROSIS**

ULCER DISEASE
USE   **VIBRIOSIS**

ULCERATIVE DERMAL NECROSIS
SN   Added in 1982
UF   udn
BT1   FISH DISEASES
BT2   ANIMAL DISEASES
BT3   DISEASES
RT   NECROSES

ULTRAMAFIC ROCKS
BT1   IGNEOUS ROCKS
BT2   ROCKS
NT1   OPHIOLITES
NT1   PERIDOTITE

ULTRASONIC DEVICES
UF   ultrasonic equipment
RT   ULTRASONIC TRANSDUCERS
RT   ULTRASONICS

ULTRASONIC EQUIPMENT
USE   **ULTRASONIC DEVICES**

ULTRASONIC TESTING
USE   **NONDESTRUCTIVE TESTING**

ULTRASONIC TRACKING
USE   **TRACKING**

ULTRASONIC TRANSDUCERS
BT1   TRANSDUCERS
RT   ULTRASONIC DEVICES

ULTRASONICS
BT1   ACOUSTICS
BT2   PHYSICS
RT   ULTRASONIC DEVICES

ULTRASTRUCTURE
SN   Used only as a qualifier
UF   fine structure (biology)
UF   finestructure (biology)
RT   BIOTECHNOLOGY
RT   CELLS
RT   ELECTRON MICROSCOPY
RT   TISSUES

ULTRAVIOLET RADIATION
SN   Wavelength range between 0.02-0.4
       microns
BT1   ELECTROMAGNETIC RADIATION
BT2   RADIATIONS
RT   LIGHT
RT   OZONE
RT   SOLAR RADIATION
RT   STERILIZATION
RT   THERMAL RADIATION
RT   ULTRAVIOLET STERILIZATION

ULTRAVIOLET STERILIZATION
SN   The sterilization of water by
       passing it near sources of
       ultraviolet radiation. Added in 1980
BT1   STERILIZATION
RT   AQUACULTURE SYSTEMS
RT   LABORATORY CULTURE
RT   ULTRAVIOLET RADIATION

UMBILICALS
BT1   CABLES
RT   DIVING SUITS
RT   ELECTRIC CABLES
RT   LIFE SUPPORT SYSTEMS
RT   POWER CABLES
RT   TETHERED VEHICLES

UNCONTROLLED SPAWNING
USE   **WILD SPAWNING**

UNCONVENTIONAL RESOURCES
SN   Added in 1982
UF   nonconventional resources
BT1   NATURAL RESOURCES
BT2   RESOURCES
RT   EXPLORATORY FISHING
RT   FISHERY DEVELOPMENT
RT   FOOD RESOURCES
RT   LIVING RESOURCES
RT   POTENTIAL RESOURCES
RT   POTENTIAL YIELD

UNDER-ICE ENVIRONMENT
USE   **EPONTIC ENVIRONMENT**

UNDER-ICE ORGANISMS
USE   **EPONTIC ORGANISMS**

UNDER KEEL CLEARANCE
USE   **KEEL CLEARANCE**

UNDERCURRENTS
BT1   WATER CURRENTS
BT2   WATER MOTION
NT1   EQUATORIAL UNDERCURRENTS
NT1   WESTERN BOUNDARY UNDERCURRENTS
RT   COASTAL COUNTERCURRENTS
RT   OCEAN CURRENTS

UNDERDEVELOPED COUNTRIES
USE   **DEVELOPING COUNTRIES**

UNDERGROUND WATER
USE   **GROUND WATER**

ASFIS Thesaurus

UNDERKEEL CLEARANCE
USE **KEEL CLEARANCE**

UNDERSEA WARFARE
UF anti-submarine warfare
BT1 SECURITY
RT ACOUSTIC TRACKING SYSTEMS
RT MILITARY OCEANOGRAPHY
RT MILITARY OPERATIONS
RT RADIOACTIVE CONTAMINATION
RT SEABED CONVENTIONS
RT SONAR COUNTERMEASURES
RT SONAR DETECTION
RT SUBMARINES
RT UNDERWATER EXPLOSIONS

UNDERTOW
BT1 NEARSHORE CURRENTS
BT2 WATER CURRENTS
BT3 WATER MOTION
RT BREAKERS
RT RIP CURRENTS
RT SURF ZONE
RT WAVES ON BEACHES

UNDERUTILIZED SPECIES
SN Commercial species which are not
fully utilized. Added in 1982
BT1 COMMERCIAL SPECIES
BT2 SPECIES
BT3 TAXA
RT LIVING RESOURCES
RT PLANT UTILIZATION
RT SHARK UTILIZATION
RT UTILIZATION

UNDERWATER ACCESS
SN Pertains to underwater installations
BT1 ACCESS
RT UNDERWATER INSPECTION

UNDERWATER ACOUSTICS
USE **ACOUSTICS**

UNDERWATER AMBIENT NOISE
USE **AMBIENT NOISE**

UNDERWATER BIOTELEMETRY
USE **BIOTELEMETRY**

UNDERWATER CAMERAS
BT1 CAMERAS
BT2 PHOTOGRAPHIC EQUIPMENT
BT3 EQUIPMENT
RT LIGHT SOURCES
RT UNDERWATER EQUIPMENT
RT UNDERWATER PHOTOGRAPHY
RT UNDERWATER TELEVISION
RT VISIBILITY UNDERWATER

UNDERWATER CONNECTORS
USE **CONNECTORS**

UNDERWATER ENGINEERING
USE **OFFSHORE ENGINEERING**

UNDERWATER EQUIPMENT
BT1 EQUIPMENT
RT ARCHAEOLOGY
RT DIVING TOOLS
RT SONAR
RT UNDERWATER CAMERAS
RT UNDERWATER EXPLOITATION
RT UNDERWATER PHOTOGRAPHY
RT UNDERWATER TELEVISION
RT UNDERWATER VEHICLES
RT WORKING UNDERWATER

UNDERWATER EROSION
USE **BOTTOM EROSION**

UNDERWATER ESCARPMENTS
USE **SUBMARINE SCARPS**

UNDERWATER EXPLOITATION
BT1 EXPLOITATION
RT EXCLUSIVE ECONOMIC ZONE
RT MINERAL RESOURCES
RT OFFSHORE ENGINEERING
RT OIL SEEPAGES
RT OIL WELLS
RT PIPELINES
RT RESOURCE MANAGEMENT
RT SONAR
RT TECHNOLOGY
RT UNDERWATER EQUIPMENT

UNDERWATER EXPLORATION
BT1 EXPLORATION
RT ARCHAEOLOGY
RT BATHYSPHERES
RT CORING
RT DEEP-SEA DIVING
RT DIVING
RT DIVING SURVEYS
RT DRILLING
RT EXCLUSIVE RIGHTS
RT GEOGRAPHICAL EXPLORATION
RT GEOLOGICAL SURVEYS
RT MINERAL RESOURCES
RT OFFSHORE ENGINEERING
RT PHOTOGRAPHY
RT SEAFLOOR MAPPING
RT SURVEYING UNDERWATER
RT UNDERWATER PHOTOGRAPHY
RT UNDERWATER TELEVISION
RT UNDERWATER VEHICLES

UNDERWATER EXPLOSIONS
BT1 EXPLOSIONS
RT NUCLEAR EXPLOSIONS
RT RADIOACTIVE CONTAMINATION
RT UNDERSEA WARFARE

UNDERWATER HABITATS
SN Seabed chambers for human
occupation. Before 1982 search
ARTIFICIAL HABITATS
UF artificial habitats
UF chambers (one-atmosphere)
UF habitats (artificial)
UF human habitats
UF seabed habitats
BT1 UNDERWATER STRUCTURES
BT2 OFFSHORE STRUCTURES
BT3 HYDRAULIC STRUCTURES
RT ACCOMMODATION
RT AIR CONDITIONING
RT CAISSONS
RT DIVING BELLS
RT HABITAT
RT LIFE SUPPORT SYSTEMS
RT OCEAN FLOOR
RT WORK PLATFORMS
RT WORKING UNDERWATER

UNDERWATER ICE PROFILES
USE **ICE CANOPY**

UNDERWATER INSPECTION
BT1 INSPECTION
RT MAINTENANCE
RT UNDERWATER ACCESS

UNDERWATER LIGHT SOURCES
USE **LIGHT SOURCES**

UNDERWATER MEDICINE
UF diving medicine
BT1 MEDICINE
BT2 HEALTH AND SAFETY
RT BONE NECROSIS
RT DECOMPRESSION SICKNESS
RT DEEP-SEA DIVING
RT DISEASES
RT DIVING
RT DIVING PHYSIOLOGY
RT HYPERCAPNIA
RT HYPERTHERMIA
RT HYPOTHERMIA
RT HYPOXIA
RT LIFE SUPPORT SYSTEMS
RT MANNED VEHICLES
RT NITROGEN NARCOSIS
RT SUBMERSIBLES

UNDERWATER NAVIGATION
USE **NAVIGATION UNDERWATER**

UNDERWATER NOISE
BT1 NOISE (SOUND)
NT1 REVERBERATION
NT2 BOTTOM REVERBERATION
RT ACOUSTICS
RT AMBIENT NOISE

UNDERWATER OBJECT LOCATION
BT1 LOCATING
RT SALVAGING
RT SEARCH AND RESCUE
RT SONAR
RT WRECK LOCATION

UNDERWATER PHOTOGRAPHS
BT1 PHOTOGRAPHS
BT2 AUDIOVISUAL MATERIAL
BT3 DOCUMENTS
NT1 BOTTOM PHOTOGRAPHS
RT DIVING
RT UNDERWATER PHOTOGRAPHY

UNDERWATER PHOTOGRAPHY
BT1 PHOTOGRAPHY
BT2 IMAGERY
BT3 REMOTE SENSING
RT BOTTOM PHOTOGRAPHS
RT DIVING
RT LIGHT SOURCES
RT PHOTOGRAPHIC EQUIPMENT
RT SURVEYING UNDERWATER
RT UNDERWATER CAMERAS
RT UNDERWATER EQUIPMENT
RT UNDERWATER EXPLORATION
RT UNDERWATER PHOTOGRAPHS
RT VISIBILITY UNDERWATER
RT WORKING UNDERWATER

UNDERWATER PROPULSION
UF underwater propulsion systems
BT1 PROPULSION SYSTEMS
RT BATTERIES
RT DIESEL ENGINES
RT NUCLEAR PROPULSION
RT UNDERWATER VEHICLES

UNDERWATER PROPULSION SYSTEMS
USE **UNDERWATER PROPULSION**

UNDERWATER RESEARCH VESSELS
USE **UNDERWATER VEHICLES**

UNDERWATER SOUND TRANSMISSION
    USE   **SOUND WAVES**

UNDERWATER STRUCTURES
    SN   Work platforms and equipment
            located and fixed to seabed
    BT1   OFFSHORE STRUCTURES
    BT2   HYDRAULIC STRUCTURES
    NT1   PIPELINES
    NT2   FLOWLINES
    NT2   GATHERING LINES
    NT1   UNDERWATER HABITATS
    NT1   WELLHEADS
    RT   GUIDE LINES
    RT   OFFSHORE ENGINEERING
    RT   OIL TANKS
    RT   STRUCTURES
    RT   WORK PLATFORMS
    RT   WORKING UNDERWATER

UNDERWATER SURVEYING
    USE   **SURVEYING UNDERWATER**

UNDERWATER TELEVISION
    BT1   TELEVISION SYSTEMS
    BT2   COMMUNICATION SYSTEMS
    RT   DIVING
    RT   LIGHT SOURCES
    RT   UNDERWATER CAMERAS
    RT   UNDERWATER EQUIPMENT
    RT   UNDERWATER EXPLORATION
    RT   VIDEOTAPE RECORDINGS
    RT   VISIBILITY UNDERWATER

UNDERWATER TOOLS
    USE   **DIVING TOOLS**

UNDERWATER TOPOGRAPHY
    USE   **BOTTOM TOPOGRAPHY**

UNDERWATER TRACKING SYSTEMS
    USE   **ACOUSTIC TRACKING SYSTEMS**

UNDERWATER VEHICLES
    SN   Before 1982 search UNDERWATER
            RESEARCH VESSELS
    UF   underwater research vessels
    BT1   VEHICLES
    NT1   FREE-SWIMMING VEHICLES
    NT1   MANNED VEHICLES
    NT2   DIVING BELLS
    NT2   OBSERVATION CHAMBERS
    NT3   BATHYSPHERES
    NT2   SUBMARINES
    NT3   SUBMARINE TANKERS
    NT2   SUBMERSIBLES
    NT3   LOCKOUT SUBMERSIBLES
    NT3   WET SUBMERSIBLES
    NT1   SELF-PROPELLED VEHICLES
    NT1   TETHERED VEHICLES
    NT1   UNMANNED VEHICLES
    NT2   SEABED VEHICLES
    NT2   TETHERED FREE-SWIMMING VEHICLES
    NT2   TOWED VEHICLES
    NT3   GLORIA
    NT3   UNDULATORS
    NT2   UNTETHERED VEHICLES
    RT   BALLAST TANKS
    RT   DEPLOYMENT
    RT   DIVING PHYSIOLOGY
    RT   INSTRUMENT PLATFORMS
    RT   MANIPULATORS
    RT   MARINE TRANSPORTATION
    RT   MOTHER SHIPS
    RT   PROPULSION SYSTEMS
    RT   RECOVERY
    RT   SHIP MODELS
    RT   SHIP TECHNOLOGY
    RT   SHIPPING
    RT   TOWED BODIES

UNDERWATER VEHICLES (cont'd)
    RT   TOWED BODY DESIGN
    RT   TOWED SENSORS
    RT   TRANSPORTATION
    RT   UNDERWATER EQUIPMENT
    RT   UNDERWATER EXPLORATION
    RT   UNDERWATER PROPULSION
    RT   WORK PLATFORMS

UNDERWATER VIEWING
    USE   **VIEWING UNDERWATER**

UNDERWATER VISIBILITY
    USE   **VISIBILITY UNDERWATER**

UNDERWATER WELLHEADS
    USE   **WELLHEADS**

UNDERWATER WORK
    USE   **WORKING UNDERWATER**

UNDULATORS
    UF   batfish
    BT1   TOWED VEHICLES
    BT2   UNMANNED VEHICLES
    BT3   UNDERWATER VEHICLES
    BT4   VEHICLES
    RT   OCEANOGRAPHIC EQUIPMENT
    RT   TOWED SENSORS

UNIDIRECTIONAL FLOW
    BT1   FLUID MOTION
    RT   CHANNEL FLOW
    RT   OSCILLATORY FLOW
    RT   RESIDUAL FLOW
    RT   STREAM FLOW
    RT   TRANSVERSE BED FORMS

UNIT STOCKS
    SN   Self-sustaining genetic entities.
            Added in 1982
    BT1   STOCKS
    RT   POPULATION GENETICS
    RT   SUBPOPULATIONS

UNIVERSITIES
    USE   **EDUCATION ESTABLISHMENTS**

UNLOADING
    USE   **FISH HANDLING**

UNMANNED SUBMERSIBLES
    USE   **UNMANNED VEHICLES**

UNMANNED VEHICLES
    SN   Unmanned underwater vehicles
            capable of self-propulsion and
            manoeuvrability
    UF   remotely operated vehicles
    UF   rovs
    UF   submersibles (unmanned)
    UF   unmanned submersibles
    BT1   UNDERWATER VEHICLES
    BT2   VEHICLES
    NT1   SEABED VEHICLES
    NT1   TETHERED FREE-SWIMMING VEHICLES
    NT1   TOWED VEHICLES
    NT2   GLORIA
    NT2   UNDULATORS
    NT1   UNTETHERED VEHICLES
    RT   MANNED VEHICLES

UNSATURATED HYDROCARBONS
    BT1   HYDROCARBONS
    BT2   ORGANIC COMPOUNDS
    NT1   ALKENES
    NT2   ETHENE
    NT1   ALKYNES
    NT2   ETHYNE
    NT1   AROMATIC HYDROCARBONS

UNSATURATED HYDROCARBONS (cont'd)
    NT2   BENZENE
    NT2   NAPHTHALENE
    NT2   PCB
    NT2   XYLENE
    NT1   POLYUNSATURATED HYDROCARBONS
    NT2   SQUALENE
    NT2   TERPENES

UNSTEADY FLOW
    BT1   FLUID MOTION
    RT   BAROTROPIC INSTABILITY
    RT   LAMINAR FLOW
    RT   MULTIPHASE FLOW

UNSTEADY STATE
    RT   EQUILIBRIUM
    RT   INSTABILITY
    RT   STEADY STATE

UNTETHERED VEHICLES
    SN   Self-propelled, self-powered
            unmanned underwater vehicles
            controlled by acoustic command
    BT1   UNMANNED VEHICLES
    BT2   UNDERWATER VEHICLES
    BT3   VEHICLES
    RT   FREE-SWIMMING VEHICLES
    RT   REMOTE CONTROL
    RT   SELF-PROPELLED VEHICLES
    RT   WET SUBMERSIBLES

UPLIFT
    BT1   EPEIROGENY
    BT2   TECTONICS
    BT3   GEOLOGY
    BT4   EARTH SCIENCES
    RT   EMERGENT SHORELINES
    RT   PROGRADATION
    RT   RAISED BEACHES
    RT   REGRESSIONS
    RT   SUBSIDENCE

UPPER ATMOSPHERE
    BT1   EARTH ATMOSPHERE
    BT2   PLANETARY ATMOSPHERES
    NT1   IONOSPHERE

UPPER LAYERS (LAKES)
    USE   **EPILIMNION**

UPPER LAYERS (OCEAN)
    USE   **UPPER OCEAN**

UPPER MANTLE
    UF   outer mantle
    BT1   EARTH MANTLE
    BT2   EARTH STRUCTURE
    RT   ASTHENOSPHERE
    RT   LITHOSPHERE
    RT   LOWER MANTLE

UPPER OCEAN
    SN   The ocean above and including the
            permanent thermocline
    UF   upper layers (ocean)
    RT   OCEANIC BOUNDARY LAYER
    RT   OCEANS
    RT   PERMANENT THERMOCLINE
    RT   SURFACE LAYERS
    RT   SURFACE MIXED LAYER
    RT   SURFACE WATER MASSES

UPPER TERTIARY
    USE   **NEOGENE**

ASFIS Thesaurus

UPSTREAM MIGRATIONS
  USE   **ANADROMOUS MIGRATIONS**

UPWARD IRRADIANCE
  BT1   IRRADIANCE

UPWARD LONG WAVE RADIATION
  BT1   TERRESTRIAL RADIATION
  BT2   ELECTROMAGNETIC RADIATION
  BT3   RADIATIONS

UPWELLING
  BT1   VERTICAL WATER MOVEMENT
  BT2   WATER MOTION
  NT1   COASTAL UPWELLING
  NT1   EQUATORIAL UPWELLING
  RT   ARTIFICIAL UPWELLING
  RT   BIOLOGICAL PRODUCTION
  RT   CIRCULATION
  RT   COASTAL CURRENTS
  RT   DIVERGENCE
  RT   DIVERGENCE ZONES
  RT   DOWNWELLING
  RT   EKMAN PUMPING
  RT   EKMAN TRANSPORT
  RT   FERTILITY
  RT   FOG
  RT   LONGSHORE CURRENTS
  RT   MIXING PROCESSES
  RT   NEARSHORE CURRENTS
  RT   NUTRIENTS (MINERAL)
  RT   OCEANIC DIVERGENCES
  RT   VERTICAL ADVECTION
  RT   WATER MIXING
  RT   WIND-DRIVEN CURRENTS
  RT   WINDS

URANIUM
  BT1   CHEMICAL ELEMENTS
  RT   ACTINIDES
  RT   DISSOLVED CHEMICALS
  RT   RADIOACTIVITY
  RT   TRANSITION ELEMENTS
  RT   URANIUM COMPOUNDS
  RT   URANIUM ISOTOPES

URANIUM COMPOUNDS
  BT1   ACTINIDE COMPOUNDS
  RT   CHEMICAL COMPOUNDS
  RT   URANIUM

URANIUM-HELIUM DATING
  BT1   RADIOMETRIC DATING
  BT2   GEOCHRONOMETRY
  RT   HELIUM ISOTOPES
  RT   URANIUM ISOTOPES

URANIUM ISOTOPES
  BT1   ISOTOPES
  RT   URANIUM
  RT   URANIUM-HELIUM DATING
  RT   URANIUM-234/URANIUM-238 RATIO

URANIUM-234/URANIUM-238 RATIO
  RT   RADIOMETRIC DATING
  RT   URANIUM ISOTOPES

URBAN DEVELOPMENT
  USE   **URBANIZATION**

URBAN RUNOFF
  BT1   RUNOFF
  BT2   DRAINAGE WATER
  BT3   WATER

URBANIZATION
  UF   urban development
  RT   COASTAL ZONE MANAGEMENT
  RT   DRAINAGE WATER
  RT   POLLUTION

UREA
  BT1   ORGANIC COMPOUNDS
  RT   AMMONIA
  RT   CHEMICAL COMPOUNDS
  RT   FEED
  RT   FERTILIZERS
  RT   NITROGEN COMPOUNDS
  RT   URINE

URINARY SYSTEM
  SN   Added in 1980
  BT1   ANATOMICAL STRUCTURES
  RT   KIDNEYS
  RT   URINE

URINE
  BT1   EXCRETORY PRODUCTS
  RT   BODY FLUIDS
  RT   KIDNEYS
  RT   SEWAGE
  RT   UREA
  RT   URINARY SYSTEM
  RT   WATER BALANCE

USAGE
  USE   **UTILIZATION**

USE OF WATER
  USE   **WATER USE**

UTILIZATION
  SN   Used only as a qualifier. Added in
          1982
  UF   application
  UF   usage
  NT1   PLANT UTILIZATION
  NT1   SHARK UTILIZATION
  NT1   WASTE UTILIZATION
  NT1   WATER USE
  RT   MARKETING
  RT   PROCESSING FISHERY PRODUCTS
  RT   UNDERUTILIZED SPECIES

VACCINATION
  SN   Added in 1980
  BT1   IMMUNIZATION
  RT   DISEASE RESISTANCE
  RT   DISEASES
  RT   IMMUNITY
  RT   IMMUNOLOGY
  RT   IMMUNOPRECIPITATION
  RT   INFECTIOUS DISEASES
  RT   VACCINES

VACCINES
  SN   Added in 1980
  UF   bacterial vaccines
  UF   fungal vaccines
  UF   viral vaccines
  BT1   DRUGS
  NT1   BACTERINS
  RT   ANTIBODIES
  RT   ANTIGENS
  RT   IMMUNITY
  RT   IMMUNIZATION
  RT   IMMUNOLOGY
  RT   IMMUNOPRECIPITATION
  RT   TOXICOLOGY
  RT   VACCINATION

VALINE
  BT1   AMINO ACIDS
  BT2   ORGANIC ACIDS
  BT3   ORGANIC COMPOUNDS

VALLEYS
  BT1   LANDFORMS
  BT2   TOPOGRAPHIC FEATURES
  NT1   RIVER VALLEYS
  RT   CHANNELS
  RT   DEEP-SEA FURROWS
  RT   DROWNED VALLEYS
  RT   EROSION
  RT   FRACTURE ZONES
  RT   GEOMORPHOLOGY
  RT   GLACIERS
  RT   MEDIAN VALLEYS
  RT   RELIEF FORMS
  RT   RIFT VALLEYS
  RT   RIFT ZONES
  RT   RIVER BASINS
  RT   RIVERS
  RT   SUBMARINE CANYONS
  RT   SUBMARINE VALLEYS
  RT   TRENCHES (OCEANIC)
  RT   WATERSHEDS

VALLICULTURE
  SN   Lagoon culture where sluices open
          and close the mouth of the lagoon.
          Added in 1982
  BT1   AQUACULTURE SYSTEMS
  RT   BRACKISHWATER AQUACULTURE
  RT   COASTAL LAGOONS
  RT   CULTURES
  RT   EXTENSIVE CULTURE
  RT   LAGOONS
  RT   POND CULTURE

VANADIUM
  BT1   CHEMICAL ELEMENTS
  RT   FERROMANGANESE NODULES
  RT   METALS
  RT   TRACE ELEMENTS
  RT   TRACE METALS
  RT   TRANSITION ELEMENTS
  RT   VANADIUM COMPOUNDS
  RT   VANADIUM ISOTOPES

VANADIUM COMPOUNDS
  RT   CHEMICAL COMPOUNDS
  RT   VANADIUM

VANADIUM ISOTOPES
  BT1   ISOTOPES
  RT   VANADIUM

VANE DEVICES
  RT   GEOLOGICAL EQUIPMENT
  RT   GEOTECHNICAL DATA
  RT   MEASURING DEVICES
  RT   SHEAR STRENGTH
  RT   SOIL MECHANICS
  RT   VANE SHEAR TESTING

VANE SHEAR TESTING
  RT   COHESIVE SEDIMENTS
  RT   IN SITU MEASUREMENTS
  RT   SHEAR STRENGTH
  RT   VANE DEVICES

VANES
  UF   current meter vanes
  UF   wind vanes
  RT   DIRECTION INDICATORS

VAPORIZATION
  BT1   PHASE CHANGES
  NT1   EVAPORATION
  NT2   EVAPOTRANSPIRATION
  NT1   SUBLIMATION
  RT   CAVITATION
  RT   VAPORIZATION HEAT

VAPORIZATION HEAT
UF	latent heat of vaporization
BT1	ENTHALPY
BT2	THERMODYNAMIC PROPERTIES
BT3	PHYSICAL PROPERTIES
BT4	PROPERTIES
RT	CONDENSATION
RT	EVAPORATION
RT	VAPORIZATION

VAPOUR PRESSURE
UF	vapour tension
UF	water vapour pressure
BT1	PRESSURE
BT2	PHYSICAL PROPERTIES
BT3	PROPERTIES
NT1	SATURATION VAPOUR PRESSURE
RT	BOWEN RATIO
RT	COLLIGATIVE PROPERTIES
RT	CONDENSATION
RT	HUMIDITY
RT	MIXING RATIO
RT	RELATIVE HUMIDITY
RT	THERMODYNAMIC PROPERTIES
RT	WATER VAPOUR

VAPOUR TENSION
USE	**VAPOUR PRESSURE**

VARIABILITY
SN	Used only as a qualifier
BT1	TEMPORAL VARIATIONS
RT	EQUILIBRIUM
RT	NONLINEARITY
RT	WIND CONSTANCY

VARIANCE ANALYSIS
SN	Includes covariance. Used only as a qualifier
BT1	STATISTICAL ANALYSIS
BT2	MATHEMATICAL ANALYSIS
NT1	MULTIVARIATE ANALYSIS
RT	CORRELATION ANALYSIS
RT	NUMERICAL TAXONOMY
RT	REGRESSION ANALYSIS

VARIATIONS (MAGNETIC)
USE	**MAGNETIC VARIATIONS**

VARIATIONS (PHENOTYPIC)
USE	**PHENOTYPIC VARIATIONS**

VARIATIONS (SPACE)
USE	**SPATIAL VARIATIONS**

VARIATIONS (TIME)
USE	**TEMPORAL VARIATIONS**

VARVES
BT1	BEDDING STRUCTURES
BT2	SEDIMENTARY STRUCTURES
RT	GEOCHRONOMETRY
RT	GLACIAL DEPOSITS
RT	LAKE DEPOSITS
RT	TELECONNECTIONS

VASCULAR SYSTEM
USE	**CIRCULATORY SYSTEM**

VECTORS
NT1	BIOLOGICAL VECTORS
NT1	CURL (VECTORS)
NT2	WIND STRESS CURL
NT1	CURRENT VECTORS
RT	HODOGRAPHS
RT	VELOCITY
RT	WIND VECTORS

VEGETAL FOSSILS
UF	plant fossils
BT1	FOSSILS
NT1	FOSSIL DIATOMS
NT1	FOSSIL POLLEN
NT1	FOSSIL SPORES

VEGETATION CONTROL
USE	**PLANT CONTROL**

VEGETATION COVER
SN	Plants covering the surface of water bodies or littoral zone
RT	DUNE STABILIZATION
RT	FRESHWATER WEEDS
RT	HABITAT IMPROVEMENT (BIOLOGICAL)
RT	PLANT CONTROL

VEGETATIVE REPRODUCTION
BT1	REPRODUCTION
RT	ASEXUAL REPRODUCTION
RT	BUDDING
RT	PLANT REPRODUCTIVE STRUCTURES
RT	RHIZOMES

VEHICLES
SN	Use of a more specific term is recommended
NT1	AIRCRAFT
NT2	HELICOPTERS
NT1	BUOY SYSTEMS
NT1	DEFENCE CRAFT
NT1	INSTRUMENT PLATFORMS
NT2	STABILIZED PLATFORMS
NT3	TOWERS
NT2	WAVE FOLLOWERS
NT1	SATELLITES
NT2	COMMUNICATION SATELLITES
NT2	NAVIGATIONAL SATELLITES
NT2	SCIENTIFIC SATELLITES
NT1	SURFACE CRAFT
NT2	BARGES
NT3	CRANE BARGES
NT3	PIPELAYING BARGES
NT2	BOATS
NT2	CANOES
NT2	CATAMARANS
NT2	DREDGERS
NT2	DRILLING VESSELS
NT2	EMERGENCY VESSELS
NT2	FISHING VESSELS
NT3	CATCHERS
NT3	GILLNETTERS
NT3	LINERS
NT3	SEINERS
NT3	TRAWLERS
NT2	HOVERCRAFT
NT2	HYDROFOILS
NT2	ICE BREAKERS
NT2	INFLATABLE CRAFT
NT2	LIFEBOATS
NT2	MINING VESSELS
NT2	RESEARCH VESSELS
NT2	ROW BOATS
NT2	SHIPS
NT3	CABLE SHIPS
NT3	LIGHTERS
NT3	LIGHTSHIPS
NT3	MERCHANT SHIPS
NT4	BULK CARRIERS
NT4	CONTAINER SHIPS
NT4	PASSENGER SHIPS
NT4	SELECTED SHIPS
NT4	TANKER SHIPS
NT3	MOTOR BOATS
NT3	PROTECTION VESSELS
NT3	SAILING SHIPS
NT4	YACHTS
NT3	SUPPLY BOATS
NT3	SUPPORT SHIPS

VEHICLES (cont'd)
NT4	FACTORY SHIPS
NT4	MOTHER SHIPS
NT3	TUGS
NT3	WEATHER SHIPS
NT2	SURVEY VESSELS
NT1	UNDERWATER VEHICLES
NT2	FREE-SWIMMING VEHICLES
NT2	MANNED VEHICLES
NT3	DIVING BELLS
NT3	OBSERVATION CHAMBERS
NT4	BATHYSPHERES
NT3	SUBMARINES
NT4	SUBMARINE TANKERS
NT3	SUBMERSIBLES
NT4	LOCKOUT SUBMERSIBLES
NT4	WET SUBMERSIBLES
NT2	SELF-PROPELLED VEHICLES
NT2	TETHERED VEHICLES
NT2	UNMANNED VEHICLES
NT3	SEABED VEHICLES
NT3	TETHERED FREE-SWIMMING VEHICLES
NT3	TOWED VEHICLES
NT4	GLORIA
NT4	UNDULATORS
NT3	UNTETHERED VEHICLES
NT1	WORK PLATFORMS
NT2	DRILLING PLATFORMS
NT2	PRODUCTION PLATFORMS
RT	AMPHIBIOUS VEHICLES
RT	EVACUATION
RT	MANOEUVRABILITY
RT	PROPULSION SYSTEMS
RT	SHIPPING
RT	STEERING SYSTEMS
RT	TRANSPORTATION
RT	WAKES

VEINS
USE	**BLOOD VESSELS**

VELIGERS
SN	Added in 1980
BT1	MOLLUSCAN LARVAE
BT2	INVERTEBRATE LARVAE
BT3	LARVAE
BT4	DEVELOPMENTAL STAGES
RT	MEROPLANKTON
RT	METAMORPHOSIS

VELOCITY
UF	absolute velocity
UF	speed
NT1	CURRENT VELOCITY
NT2	STREAM FLOW RATE
NT1	GROUP VELOCITY
NT1	ORBITAL VELOCITY
NT1	PHASE VELOCITY
NT1	SEISMIC VELOCITIES
NT2	COMPRESSIONAL WAVE VELOCITIES
NT2	SHEAR WAVE VELOCITIES
NT1	SETTLING RATE
NT1	SHIP SPEED
NT1	SOUND VELOCITY
NT1	WAVE DRIFT VELOCITY
NT1	WAVE VELOCITY
NT1	WIND SPEED
RT	ACCELERATION
RT	KINEMATICS
RT	VECTORS
RT	VELOCITY PROFILES
RT	FIELDS

VELOCITY GRADIENTS
RT	CURRENT PROFILES
RT	CURRENT VELOCITY
RT	GRADIENTS
RT	VERTICAL SHEAR
RT	WIND PROFILES
RT	WIND SPEED

VELOCITY MEASUREMENT (WATER)
USE **CURRENT MEASUREMENT**

VELOCITY MICROSTRUCTURE
BT1 MICROSTRUCTURE
BT2 SPATIAL VARIATIONS
RT CURRENT VELOCITY

VELOCITY PROFILERS
UF profiling current meters
BT1 PROFILERS
RT CURRENT MEASURING EQUIPMENT
RT CURRENT PROFILES
RT CURRENT VELOCITY
RT CYCLESONDE
RT DROPSONDE
RT FREE-FALL PROFILERS
RT SHEAR PROBES

VELOCITY PROFILES
BT1 VERTICAL PROFILES
BT2 PROFILES
NT1 CURRENT PROFILES
NT1 WIND PROFILES
RT VELOCITY
RT VERTICAL SHEAR
RT VORTEX SHEDDING

VELOCITY SECTIONS
BT1 HYDROGRAPHIC SECTIONS
BT2 VERTICAL SECTIONS
BT3 MAP GRAPHICS
BT4 GRAPHICS
RT CURRENT PROFILES
RT CURRENT VELOCITY

VENOM APPARATUS
RT BIOLOGICAL POISONS
RT NOXIOUS ORGANISMS
RT POISONOUS FISH
RT SECRETORY ORGANS
RT STINGING ORGANS

VENOMS
USE **BIOLOGICAL POISONS**

VENTILATION
RT AIR CONDITIONING
RT LIFE SUPPORT SYSTEMS

VENTS (HYDROTHERMAL)
USE **HYDROTHERMAL SPRINGS**

VENULES
USE **BLOOD VESSELS**

VERMICULITE
BT1 CLAY MINERALS
BT2 SILICATE MINERALS
BT3 MINERALS

VERNACULAR NAMES
UF common names
UF local names
RT AQUATIC ANIMALS
RT AQUATIC MAMMALS
RT AQUATIC PLANTS
RT AQUATIC REPTILES
RT CHECK LISTS
RT COMMERCIAL SPECIES
RT FISH
RT FISHERY RESOURCES
RT FRESHWATER CRUSTACEANS
RT FRESHWATER MOLLUSCS
RT MARINE CRUSTACEANS
RT MARINE MOLLUSCS
RT MARINE ORGANISMS
RT TERMINOLOGY

VERTEBRAE
BT1 BONES
BT2 ENDOSKELETON
BT3 SKELETON
BT4 MUSCULOSKELETAL SYSTEM
RT SPINAL CORD
RT VERTEBRAE COUNTS

VERTEBRAE COUNTS
BT1 MERISTIC COUNTS
RT ENDOSKELETON
RT VERTEBRAE

VERTEBRATE ZOOLOGY
UF chordate zoology
BT1 ZOOLOGY
BT2 BIOLOGY
NT1 HERPETOLOGY
NT1 ICHTHYOLOGY
NT1 MAMMALOGY
NT2 CETOLOGY
NT1 ORNITHOLOGY
NT1 OSTEOLOGY
RT BEHAVIOUR
RT BIOGEOGRAPHY
RT TAXONOMY

VERTICAL ADVECTION
UF vertical transport
BT1 ADVECTION
BT2 TRANSPORT PROCESSES
RT UPWELLING
RT VERTICAL MOTION
RT VERTICAL WATER MOVEMENT
RT WATER COLUMN

VERTICAL COSINE RESPONSE
USE **COSINE RESPONSE**

VERTICAL DISTRIBUTION
SN Use for distribution of aquatic
organisms. Use VERTICAL PROFILES
for physical and chemical properties
UF bathymetric distribution
BT1 GEOGRAPHICAL DISTRIBUTION
BT2 DISTRIBUTION
RT BATHYMETRIC CHARTS
RT BIOLOGICAL RHYTHMS
RT DIURNAL VARIATIONS
RT ECOLOGICAL ZONATION
RT FINESTRUCTURE
RT OXYGEN PROFILES
RT OXYGEN SECTIONS
RT SALINITY SECTIONS
RT SEASONAL VARIATIONS
RT SPATIAL VARIATIONS
RT TEMPERATURE SECTIONS
RT THERMOCLINE
RT VERTICAL MIGRATIONS
RT VERTICAL PROFILES
RT VERTICAL SECTIONS

VERTICAL MIGRATIONS
BT1 MIGRATIONS
RT BIOLOGICAL RHYTHMS
RT DIURNAL VARIATIONS
RT ENVIRONMENTAL EFFECTS
RT LIGHT EFFECTS
RT NYCTIMERAL RHYTHMS
RT ORIENTATION
RT PHENOLOGY
RT PHOTOPERIODICITY
RT PHOTOTAXIS
RT PHOTOTROPISM
RT SOLAR ECLIPSE
RT VERTICAL DISTRIBUTION

VERTICAL MIXING
BT1 WATER MIXING
RT DOUBLE DIFFUSION
RT VERTICAL WATER MOVEMENT

VERTICAL MOTION
RT ATMOSPHERIC MOTION
RT FLUID MOTION
RT VERTICAL ADVECTION
RT VERTICAL WATER MOVEMENT

VERTICAL MOVEMENTS (GEOLOGY)
USE **EPEIROGENY**

VERTICAL PROFILES
SN Plots of physical
properties/parameters against
depth/height
BT1 PROFILES
NT1 DENSITY PROFILES
NT1 OXYGEN PROFILES
NT1 SALINITY PROFILES
NT1 STD PROFILES
NT1 TEMPERATURE PROFILES
NT1 VELOCITY PROFILES
NT2 CURRENT PROFILES
NT2 WIND PROFILES
RT CTD OBSERVATIONS
RT CTD PROFILERS
RT FINESTRUCTURE
RT GRADIENTS
RT HORIZONTAL PROFILES
RT HYDROGRAPHIC SECTIONS
RT PROFILERS
RT PROFILING
RT STD PROFILERS
RT T/S DIAGRAMS
RT VERTICAL DISTRIBUTION
RT VERTICAL SECTIONS
RT WATER COLUMN

VERTICAL PROFILING
RT PROFILING

VERTICAL SECTIONS
BT1 MAP GRAPHICS
BT2 GRAPHICS
BT3 AUDIOVISUAL MATERIAL
BT4 DOCUMENTS
NT1 GEOLOGICAL SECTIONS
NT1 HYDROGRAPHIC SECTIONS
NT2 BATHYMETRIC PROFILES
NT2 DENSITY SECTIONS
NT2 OXYGEN SECTIONS
NT2 SALINITY SECTIONS
NT2 TEMPERATURE SECTIONS
NT2 VELOCITY SECTIONS
RT ECHOSOUNDER PROFILES
RT SEISMIC PROFILES
RT VERTICAL DISTRIBUTION
RT VERTICAL PROFILES

VERTICAL SHEAR
BT1 SHEAR
RT EKMAN LAYERS
RT RELATIVE VORTICITY
RT RICHARDSON NUMBER
RT SHEAR FLOW
RT SHEAR PROBES
RT VELOCITY GRADIENTS
RT VELOCITY PROFILES
RT WIND SHEAR

VERTICAL STABILITY
UF static stability
BT1 STABILITY
RT BRUNT-VAISALA FREQUENCY
RT INSTABILITY
RT POTENTIAL DENSITY
RT POTENTIAL TEMPERATURE

VERTICAL STABILITY (cont'd)
RT   STATIC INSTABILITY
RT   TEMPERATURE INVERSIONS

VERTICAL STRUCTURE (WATER BODIES)
USE   **WATER COLUMN**

VERTICAL TECTONICS
BT1   TECTONICS
BT2   GEOLOGY
BT3   EARTH SCIENCES
RT   EPEIROGENY
RT   ISOSTASY

VERTICAL TRANSPORT
USE   **VERTICAL ADVECTION**

VERTICAL WATER MOVEMENT
SN   Use of a more specific term is
          recommended
BT1   WATER MOTION
NT1   CABBELING
NT1   CASCADING
NT1   DOWNWELLING
NT1   OVERTURN
NT1   UPWELLING
NT2   COASTAL UPWELLING
NT2   EQUATORIAL UPWELLING
RT   MERIDIONAL OCEANIC CIRCULATION
RT   VERTICAL ADVECTION
RT   VERTICAL MIXING
RT   VERTICAL MOTION

VESSEL SEIZURE
USE   **SURVEILLANCE AND ENFORCEMENT**

VESSELS
USE   **SURFACE CRAFT**

VIBRATION
UF   strumming
RT   DAMPING
RT   ELASTIC WAVES
RT   NOISE (SOUND)
RT   OSCILLATIONS
RT   RESONANCE
RT   RESONANT FREQUENCY

VIBRATORY CORERS
UF   vibro-corers
BT1   CORERS
BT2   SEDIMENT SAMPLERS
BT3   SAMPLERS

VIBRIO INFECTIONS
USE   **VIBRIOSIS**

VIBRIOSIS
SN   A fish disease caused by Vibno
          anguillarum. Added in 1980
UF   red pest
UF   spotted pest
UF   ulcer disease
UF   vibrio infections
BT1   BACTERIAL DISEASES
BT2   INFECTIOUS DISEASES
BT3   DISEASES
RT   FISH DISEASES

VIBRO-CORERS
USE   **VIBRATORY CORERS**

VIDEO NETWORKS
USE   **TELEVISION SYSTEMS**

VIDEO TAPES
USE   **VIDEOTAPE RECORDINGS**

VIDEOTAPE RECORDINGS
UF   video tapes
BT1   AUDIOVISUAL MATERIAL
BT2   DOCUMENTS
RT   FILMS
RT   MAGNETIC TAPE RECORDINGS
RT   MAGNETIC TAPES
RT   RECORDS
RT   UNDERWATER TELEVISION

VIEWING UNDERWATER
UF   underwater viewing
RT   VISIBILITY UNDERWATER

VIRAL DISEASES
BT1   INFECTIOUS DISEASES
BT2   DISEASES
RT   ANTIBIOTICS
RT   BIOLOGICAL CONTROL
RT   DRUGS
RT   FISH DISEASES
RT   IMMUNIZATION
RT   SEPTICAEMIA
RT   VIROLOGY
RT   VIRUSES

VIRAL HAEMORRHAGIC SEPTICAEMIA
USE   **SEPTICAEMIA**

VIRAL VACCINES
USE   **VACCINES**

VIROLOGISTS
BT1   MICROBIOLOGISTS
BT2   BIOLOGISTS
BT3   SCIENTIFIC PERSONNEL
BT4   PERSONNEL
RT   DIRECTORIES
RT   MICROBIOLOGY
RT   VIROLOGY

VIROLOGY
BT1   MICROBIOLOGY
BT2   BIOLOGY
RT   VIRAL DISEASES
RT   VIROLOGISTS
RT   VIRUSES

VIRUSES
SN   In ASFA-1, used as taxonomic
          descriptor; in ASFA-2, used as
          subject descriptor
BT1   MICROORGANISMS
RT   BACTERIOPHAGES
RT   BIOLOGICAL CONTROL
RT   MICROBIAL CONTAMINATION
RT   STERILIZATION
RT   VIRAL DISEASES
RT   VIROLOGY

VISCOSITY
BT1   MECHANICAL PROPERTIES
BT2   PHYSICAL PROPERTIES
BT3   PROPERTIES
NT1   DYNAMIC VISCOSITY
NT1   EDDY VISCOSITY
NT1   KINEMATIC VISCOSITY
NT1   MOLECULAR VISCOSITY
RT   BOTTOM STRESS
RT   CAPILLARITY
RT   RHEOLOGY
RT   STOKES LAW
RT   WATER PROPERTIES
RT   WAVE DISSIPATION

VISCOSITY COEFFICIENTS
BT1   EXCHANGE COEFFICIENTS
NT1   EDDY VISCOSITY COEFFICIENT
NT1   MOLECULAR VISCOSITY COEFFICIENTS
RT   EDDY VISCOSITY

VISIBILITY
NT1   VISIBILITY UNDERWATER
RT   ATMOSPHERIC OPTICAL PHENOMENA
RT   FOG
RT   HAZE
RT   OPTICS

VISIBILITY UNDERWATER
UF   underwater visibility
BT1   VISIBILITY
RT   DIVING
RT   EXTINCTION COEFFICIENT
RT   LIGHT SOURCES
RT   SECCHI DISCS
RT   TURBIDITY
RT   UNDERWATER CAMERAS
RT   UNDERWATER PHOTOGRAPHY
RT   UNDERWATER TELEVISION
RT   VIEWING UNDERWATER
RT   VISION
RT   WORKING UNDERWATER

VISIBLE AND NEAR-INFRARED IMAGERY
USE   **SATELLITE PHOTOGRAPHY**

VISIBLE RADIATION
USE   **LIGHT**

VISION
BT1   SENSE FUNCTIONS
RT   COLOUR
RT   EYES
RT   LIGHT STIMULI
RT   OPTICS
RT   PHOTORECEPTION
RT   PHOTORECEPTORS
RT   RETINAS
RT   VISIBILITY UNDERWATER
RT   VISUAL PIGMENTS
RT   VISUAL STIMULI

VISUAL AIDS
USE   **AUDIOVISUAL MATERIAL**

VISUAL INSPECTION
SN   Visual inspection for organoleptic
          quality of seafood. Added in 1980
BT1   INSPECTION
RT   QUALITY ASSURANCE
RT   QUALITY CONTROL

VISUAL PIGMENTS
SN   Added in 1980
UF   light sensitive pigments
UF   rhodopsin
BT1   PIGMENTS
BT2   GLYCOSIDES
BT3   CARBOHYDRATES
BT4   ORGANIC COMPOUNDS
RT   RETINAS
RT   VISION
RT   VISUAL STIMULI

VISUAL STIMULI
SN   Added in 1980
BT1   STIMULI
RT   DOMINANCE HIERARCHIES
RT   EYES
RT   RETINAS
RT   VISION
RT   VISUAL PIGMENTS

VITAMIN A
SN   Before 1982 search VITAMINS
UF   carotenes
BT1   VITAMINS
RT   DIETS
RT   FEED COMPOSITION
RT   FOOD ADDITIVES

VITAMIN A (cont'd)
RT	HUMAN FOOD
RT	NUTRITIONAL REQUIREMENTS
RT	VITAMIN DEFICIENCIES

VITAMIN B
SN	Before 1982 search VITAMINS
UF	biotin
UF	riboflavin
UF	thiamine
UF	vitamin b complex
BT1	VITAMINS
RT	DIETS
RT	FOOD ADDITIVES
RT	GROWTH REGULATORS
RT	HUMAN FOOD
RT	NUTRITIONAL REQUIREMENTS
RT	RIBOSE
RT	VITAMIN DEFICIENCIES

VITAMIN B COMPLEX
USE	**VITAMIN B**

VITAMIN C
SN	Before 1982 search VITAMINS
UF	ascorbic acid
BT1	VITAMINS
RT	DIETS
RT	FEED COMPOSITION
RT	FOOD ADDITIVES
RT	HUMAN FOOD
RT	NUTRITIONAL REQUIREMENTS
RT	VITAMIN DEFICIENCIES

VITAMIN D
SN	Before 1982 search VITAMINS
UF	calciferol
UF	cholocalciferol
BT1	VITAMINS
RT	CALCIFICATION
RT	DIETS
RT	FOOD ADDITIVES
RT	HUMAN FOOD
RT	NUTRITIONAL REQUIREMENTS
RT	STEROIDS
RT	VITAMIN DEFICIENCIES

VITAMIN DEFICIENCIES
UF	avitaminosis
UF	vitamin deficiency
BT1	DIETARY DEFICIENCIES
RT	DEFICIENCY DISEASES
RT	NUTRIENT DEFICIENCY
RT	NUTRITION DISORDERS
RT	NUTRITIONAL REQUIREMENTS
RT	NUTRITIVE VALUE
RT	VITAMIN A
RT	VITAMIN B
RT	VITAMIN C
RT	VITAMIN D
RT	VITAMIN E
RT	VITAMINS

VITAMIN DEFICIENCY
USE	**VITAMIN DEFICIENCIES**

VITAMIN E
SN	Before 1982 search VITAMINS
UF	fertility vitamin
UF	tocopherol
BT1	VITAMINS
RT	DIETS
RT	FOOD ADDITIVES
RT	GROWTH
RT	HUMAN FOOD
RT	NUTRITIONAL REQUIREMENTS
RT	STERILITY
RT	VITAMIN DEFICIENCIES

VITAMINS
NT1	VITAMIN A
NT1	VITAMIN B
NT1	VITAMIN C
NT1	VITAMIN D
NT1	VITAMIN E
RT	BIOCHEMISTRY
RT	COENZYMES
RT	CULTURE MEDIA
RT	DIETS
RT	DRUGS
RT	FATS
RT	FOOD ADDITIVES
RT	GROWTH REGULATORS
RT	HUMAN FOOD
RT	NUTRITIONAL REQUIREMENTS
RT	NUTRITIVE VALUE
RT	VITAMIN DEFICIENCIES

VITELLOGENESIS
SN	Yolk formation
RT	EGGS
RT	EMBRYOLOGY
RT	EMBRYONIC DEVELOPMENT
RT	MORPHOGENESIS
RT	OOGENESIS
RT	ORGANOGENESIS
RT	YOLK

VIVIPARITY
SN	Giving birth to living young which have already reached an advanced stage of development
UF	viviparous
RT	OVIPARITY
RT	SEXUAL REPRODUCTION

VIVIPAROUS
USE	**VIVIPARITY**

VOCAL BEHAVIOUR
USE	**VOCALIZATION BEHAVIOUR**

VOCAL CORDS
USE	**VOCAL ORGANS**

VOCAL ORGANS
SN	Added in 1980
UF	vocal cords
UF	vocal sacs
BT1	ANIMAL ORGANS
BT2	BODY ORGANS
RT	LARYNX
RT	SOUND PRODUCTION
RT	VOCALIZATION BEHAVIOUR

VOCAL SACS
USE	**VOCAL ORGANS**

VOCALIZATION BEHAVIOUR
UF	vocal behaviour
BT1	BEHAVIOUR
RT	ANIMAL COMMUNICATION
RT	AQUATIC MAMMALS
RT	AUDITORY ORGANS
RT	AUDITORY STIMULI
RT	BIOACOUSTICS
RT	CETOLOGY
RT	SOUND PRODUCTION
RT	VOCAL ORGANS

VOES
USE	**COASTAL INLETS**

VOID RATIO
RT	GEOTECHNICAL DATA
RT	PERMEABILITY
RT	POROSITY
RT	RATIOS
RT	SOIL MECHANICS

VOID RATIO (cont'd)
RT	VOIDS

VOIDS
RT	PERCOLATION
RT	PERMEABILITY
RT	POROSITY
RT	SOIL MECHANICS
RT	VOID RATIO

VOLATILE COMPOUNDS
SN	Added in 1982
RT	AMMONIA
RT	CHEMICAL COMPOUNDS
RT	FISH SPOILAGE
RT	SULPHUR COMPOUNDS

VOLATILE HYDROCARBONS
BT1	PETROLEUM HYDROCARBONS
BT2	HYDROCARBONS
BT3	ORGANIC COMPOUNDS

VOLCANIC ASH
UF	ash (volcanic)
UF	dust (volcanic)
UF	volcanic dust
BT1	VOLCANIC ROCKS
BT2	IGNEOUS ROCKS
BT3	ROCKS
RT	ASH LAYERS
RT	ASHES
RT	BENTONITE
RT	CLIMATIC CHANGES
RT	DISCOLOURED WATER
RT	DUST CLOUDS
RT	EOLIAN DEPOSITS
RT	EOLIAN DUST
RT	EOLIAN TRANSPORT
RT	TERRIGENOUS SEDIMENTS
RT	VOLCANIC ERUPTIONS

VOLCANIC BELTS
RT	VOLCANISM
RT	VOLCANOES

VOLCANIC BRECCIA
BT1	TEPHRA
BT2	VOLCANIC ROCKS
BT3	IGNEOUS ROCKS
BT4	ROCKS
RT	BRECCIA

VOLCANIC DUST
USE	**VOLCANIC ASH**

VOLCANIC ERUPTIONS
RT	DISASTERS
RT	DUST CLOUDS
RT	GEOLOGICAL HAZARDS
RT	SUBMARINE VOLCANOES
RT	TEPHRA
RT	TSUNAMIS
RT	VOLCANIC ASH
RT	VOLCANIC ISLANDS
RT	VOLCANOES

VOLCANIC GLASS
UF	basaltic glass
BT1	VOLCANIC ROCKS
BT2	IGNEOUS ROCKS
BT3	ROCKS
RT	DEVITRIFICATION
RT	GLASS
RT	IGNIMBRITES
RT	OBSIDIAN
RT	VOLCANOGENIC DEPOSITS

VOLCANIC ISLANDS
BT1	OCEANIC ISLANDS
BT2	ISLANDS
BT3	LANDFORMS
BT4	TOPOGRAPHIC FEATURES
RT	ALKALI BASALTS
RT	ISLAND ARCS
RT	SUBMARINE VOLCANOES
RT	VOLCANIC ERUPTIONS
RT	VOLCANISM
RT	VOLCANOES

VOLCANIC LAPILLI
BT1	TEPHRA
BT2	VOLCANIC ROCKS
BT3	IGNEOUS ROCKS
BT4	ROCKS

VOLCANIC ROCKS
UF	pyroclastics
BT1	IGNEOUS ROCKS
BT2	ROCKS
NT1	ANDESITE
NT1	BASALTS
NT2	ALKALI BASALTS
NT2	OCEANITE
NT2	THOLEIITE
NT2	THOLEIITIC BASALT
NT1	LAVA
NT2	PILLOW LAVA
NT1	PALAGONITE
NT1	PUMICE
NT1	RHYOLITES
NT1	TEPHRA
NT2	IGNIMBRITES
NT2	VOLCANIC BRECCIA
NT2	VOLCANIC LAPILLI
NT1	VOLCANIC ASH
NT1	VOLCANIC GLASS
RT	ALLOCHTHONOUS DEPOSITS
RT	VOLCANISM
RT	VOLCANOES
RT	VOLCANOGENIC DEPOSITS

VOLCANIC SEDIMENTS
USE	**VOLCANOGENIC DEPOSITS**

VOLCANICITY
USE	**VOLCANISM**

VOLCANISM
SN	Before 1982 search SUBMARINE VOLCANOES
UF	volcanicity
UF	vulcanism
RT	ACTIVE MARGINS
RT	HOT SPOTS
RT	ISLAND ARCS
RT	MAGMA
RT	OCEANIC ISLANDS
RT	PLATE BOUNDARIES
RT	VOLCANIC BELTS
RT	VOLCANIC ISLANDS
RT	VOLCANIC ROCKS
RT	VOLCANOES
RT	VOLCANOGENIC DEPOSITS

VOLCANOES
SN	Before 1982 search SUBMARINE VOLCANOES
NT1	SUBMARINE VOLCANOES
RT	LAVA FLOWS
RT	VOLCANIC BELTS
RT	VOLCANIC ERUPTIONS
RT	VOLCANIC ISLANDS
RT	VOLCANIC ROCKS
RT	VOLCANISM
RT	VOLCANOGENIC DEPOSITS

VOLCANOGENIC DEPOSITS
UF	volcanic sediments
BT1	SEDIMENTS
RT	TERRIGENOUS SEDIMENTS
RT	VOLCANIC GLASS
RT	VOLCANIC ROCKS
RT	VOLCANISM
RT	VOLCANOES

VOLTAMMETRY
RT	ELECTROANALYSIS
RT	ELECTROLYSIS
RT	POLAROGRAPHY

VOLUME
SN	Descriptor to be used only as a qualifier
UF	capacity (volume)
BT1	DIMENSIONS
NT1	ICE VOLUME
RT	LAKES
RT	RESERVOIRS (WATER)
RT	SIZE
RT	SPECIFIC VOLUME

VOLUME SCATTERING FUNCTION
BT1	OPTICAL PROPERTIES
BT2	PHYSICAL PROPERTIES
BT3	PROPERTIES
RT	IRRADIANCE
RT	LIGHT SCATTERING
RT	SCATTERANCE METERS

VOLUME TRANSPORT
UF	mass transport (water currents)
RT	CURRENT VELOCITY
RT	TRANSPORT
RT	WATER CURRENTS

VOLUMETRIC ANALYSIS
RT	ANALYSIS
RT	TITRATION

VORTEX SHEDDING
RT	CURRENT FORCES
RT	VELOCITY PROFILES

VORTICES
RT	CAVITATION
RT	CURRENT RINGS
RT	FLUID MOTION
RT	LANGMUIR CIRCULATION
RT	LEE EDDIES
RT	MIXING LENGTH
RT	ROTATING FLUIDS
RT	TORNADOES
RT	TURBULENCE
RT	VORTICITY
RT	WATERSPOUTS

VORTICITY
NT1	ABSOLUTE VORTICITY
NT1	ENSTROPHY
NT1	PLANETARY VORTICITY
NT1	POTENTIAL VORTICITY
NT1	RELATIVE VORTICITY
RT	ATMOSPHERIC MOTION
RT	BETA-PLANE
RT	CORIOLIS FORCE
RT	CURL (VECTORS)
RT	EARTH ROTATION
RT	HYDRODYNAMICS
RT	POTENTIAL FLOW
RT	ROTATION
RT	TURBULENCE
RT	VORTICES
RT	WATER MOTION

VULCANISM
USE	**VOLCANISM**

VULNERABILITY
BT1	BIOLOGICAL PROPERTIES
BT2	PROPERTIES
RT	CATCHABILITY
RT	FISHING GEAR
RT	FISHING MORTALITY
RT	RESOURCE AVAILABILITY

WAKES
RT	HYDRODYNAMICS
RT	SHIP MOTION
RT	SHIP SPEED
RT	SURFACE CRAFT
RT	TURBULENCE
RT	VEHICLES

WARM-BLOODED ANIMALS
USE	**HOMOIOTHERMY**

WARM FRONTS
USE	**ATMOSPHERIC FRONTS**

WARM-WATER AQUACULTURE
SN	Culture of warm-water organisms. Added in 1982
UF	tropical aquaculture
BT1	AQUACULTURE TECHNIQUES
RT	ORNAMENTAL FISH
RT	THERMAL AQUACULTURE

WARNING DEVICES
USE	**ALARM SYSTEMS**

WARNING SERVICES
BT1	INFORMATION CENTRES
BT2	ORGANIZATIONS
NT1	STORM TIDE WARNING SERVICES
RT	ALARM SYSTEMS
RT	DISASTERS
RT	EARTHQUAKE PREDICTION
RT	ENVIRONMENTAL MONITORING
RT	ICEBERG DETECTION
RT	POLLUTION MONITORING
RT	PREDICTION
RT	SAFETY DEVICES
RT	STORM SURGE PREDICTION
RT	TSUNAMI PREDICTION
RT	TSUNAMIS

WARNING SYSTEMS
RT	ALARM SYSTEMS
RT	SAFETY DEVICES

WARSHIPS
USE	**DEFENCE CRAFT**

WASTE DISPOSAL
UF	chemical waste disposal
UF	disposal (waste)
NT1	RADIOACTIVE WASTE DISPOSAL
NT1	SEWAGE DISPOSAL
RT	GAS FLARING
RT	INCINERATION
RT	OCEAN DUMPING
RT	RADIOACTIVE WASTES
RT	RIPARIAN RIGHTS
RT	SANITARY ENGINEERING
RT	SEWAGE PONDS
RT	WASTE DISPOSAL SITES
RT	WASTE TREATMENT
RT	WASTES
RT	WATER POLLUTION

ASFIS Thesaurus

WASTE DISPOSAL SITES
SN	Offshore sites selected for dumping of wastes
UF	dumping grounds
RT	ENVIRONMENTAL MONITORING
RT	OCEAN DUMPING
RT	RADIOACTIVE WASTE DISPOSAL
RT	SITE SELECTION
RT	SITE SURVEYS
RT	SPOIL
RT	WASTE DISPOSAL
RT	WASTES

WASTE HEAT
SN	Heated or thermal effluents produced by power plants
BT1	HEAT
BT2	ENERGY
RT	FOSSIL FUELED POWER PLANTS
RT	HEAT TRANSFER
RT	NUCLEAR POWER PLANTS
RT	POWER PLANTS
RT	THERMAL AQUACULTURE
RT	THERMAL POLLUTION
RT	WASTES

WASTE TREATMENT
NT1	SEWAGE TREATMENT
NT1	SLUDGE TREATMENT
NT1	WASTEWATER TREATMENT
RT	ANAEROBIC DIGESTION
RT	DECANTATION
RT	DECANTATION TANKS
RT	DOMESTIC WASTES
RT	ENVIRONMENT MANAGEMENT
RT	SANITARY ENGINEERING
RT	WASTE DISPOSAL
RT	WASTES
RT	WATER POLLUTION TREATMENT

WASTE UTILIZATION
SN	Added in 1982
UF	fish waste utilization
BT1	UTILIZATION
RT	FISH WASTES
RT	WASTES
RT	WASTEWATER AQUACULTURE

WASTE WATER
BT1	WATER
RT	AGRICULTURAL POLLUTION
RT	AGRICULTURAL RUNOFF
RT	AQUACULTURE EFFLUENTS
RT	AQUACULTURE REGULATIONS
RT	DRAINAGE WATER
RT	INDUSTRIAL WASTES
RT	IRRIGATION
RT	SANITARY ENGINEERING
RT	SEWAGE
RT	SEWAGE DISPOSAL
RT	STORMWATER RUNOFF
RT	WASTES
RT	WASTEWATER TREATMENT
RT	WATER ANALYSIS
RT	WATER POLLUTION
RT	WATER RECLAMATION

WASTES
UF	effluents
UF	refuses
NT1	AQUACULTURE EFFLUENTS
NT1	DOMESTIC WASTES
NT1	DREDGE SPOIL
NT1	FISH WASTES
NT1	INDUSTRIAL WASTES
NT1	MINE TAILINGS
NT1	OIL WASTES
NT1	ORGANIC WASTES
NT1	PULP WASTES
NT1	RADIOACTIVE WASTES

WASTES (cont'd)
NT1	SEWAGE
NT1	SLUDGE
RT	AIR POLLUTION
RT	BRACKISHWATER POLLUTION
RT	BYPRODUCTS
RT	FRESHWATER POLLUTION
RT	INFLUENTS
RT	MANURE
RT	MARINE POLLUTION
RT	OCEAN DUMPING
RT	POLLUTANTS
RT	POLLUTION
RT	PRODUCTS
RT	WASTE DISPOSAL
RT	WASTE DISPOSAL SITES
RT	WASTE HEAT
RT	WASTE TREATMENT
RT	WASTE UTILIZATION
RT	WASTE WATER
RT	WATER POLLUTION

WASTEWATER AQUACULTURE
SN	Use of sewage and residual water for aquaculture purposes. Added in 1980
BT1	AQUACULTURE TECHNIQUES
RT	AGROPISCICULTURE
RT	DOMESTIC WASTES
RT	EUTROPHICATION
RT	FISH CULTURE
RT	OPEN SYSTEMS
RT	SLUDGE
RT	SUSPENDED ORGANIC MATTER
RT	WASTE UTILIZATION
RT	WASTEWATER TREATMENT

WASTEWATER RECYCLING
USE	**WASTEWATER TREATMENT**

WASTEWATER TREATMENT
SN	Including recycling of waste waters
UF	wastewater recycling
BT1	WASTE TREATMENT
RT	AQUACULTURE EFFLUENTS
RT	BIODEGRADATION
RT	REVERSE OSMOSIS
RT	SANITARY ENGINEERING
RT	SEWAGE TREATMENT
RT	WASTE WATER
RT	WASTEWATER AQUACULTURE
RT	WATER TREATMENT

WATER
SN	Use of a more specific term is recommended; consult terms listed below. Added in 1982
NT1	BOTTOM WATER
NT1	BRACKISH WATER
NT1	COOLING WATER
NT1	DISCOLOURED WATER
NT1	DISTILLED WATER
NT1	DRAINAGE WATER
NT2	RUNOFF
NT3	AGRICULTURAL RUNOFF
NT3	STORMWATER RUNOFF
NT3	URBAN RUNOFF
NT1	FRESH WATER
NT1	GROUND WATER
NT1	HEAVY WATER
NT1	IRRIGATION WATER
NT1	JUVENILE WATER
NT1	MELT WATER
NT1	PORE WATER
NT1	RAIN
NT1	RIVER WATER
NT1	SALINE WATER
NT1	SEA WATER
NT2	ARTIFICIAL SEAWATER
NT2	DENSE WATER

WATER (cont'd)
NT2	FOSSIL SEA WATER
NT2	STANDARD SEA WATER
NT1	STAGNANT WATER
NT1	SURFACE WATER
NT1	WASTE WATER
RT	ADIABATIC TEMPERATURE GRADIENT
RT	AQUATIC ENVIRONMENT
RT	CHEMICAL PROPERTIES
RT	DEAD WATER
RT	FLUIDS
RT	HYDROGEN COMPOUNDS
RT	HYDROGRAPHY
RT	HYDROLOGIC CYCLE
RT	HYDROLOGY
RT	HYDROMETEORS
RT	HYDROSPHERE
RT	HYDROSTATIC PRESSURE
RT	ICE
RT	LIMNOLOGY
RT	OCEANOGRAPHY
RT	OIL-WATER INTERFACE
RT	RECREATIONAL WATERS
RT	SHALLOW WATER
RT	T/S DIAGRAMS
RT	WATER ANALYSIS
RT	WATER BALANCE
RT	WATER CIRCULATION
RT	WATER COLOUR
RT	WATER CONSERVATION
RT	WATER CONTENT
RT	WATER CURRENTS
RT	WATER DENSITY
RT	WATER DEPTH
RT	WATER FILTERS
RT	WATER FILTRATION
RT	WATER HARDNESS
RT	WATER LEVELS
RT	WATER MANAGEMENT
RT	WATER MASSES
RT	WATER MIXING
RT	WATER MOTION
RT	WATER POLICY
RT	WATER POLLUTION
RT	WATER PROPERTIES
RT	WATER QUALITY
RT	WATER RESOURCES
RT	WATER RIGHTS
RT	WATER RIPPLES
RT	WATER SAMPLING
RT	WATER SPRINGS
RT	WATER SUPPLY
RT	WATER TABLE
RT	WATER TEMPERATURE
RT	WATER TRANSPARENCY
RT	WATER TREATMENT
RT	WATER TYPES
RT	WATER USE
RT	WATER VAPOUR
RT	WATER WAVES

WATER-AIR EXCHANGES
USE	**AIR-WATER EXCHANGES**

WATER ANALYSIS
SN	Before 1982 search also WATER ANALYSIS (BIOLOGICAL), WATER ANALYSIS (CHEMICAL) and WATER ANALYSIS (PHYSICAL)
UF	water analysis (biological)
UF	water analysis (chemical)
UF	water analysis (physical)
NT1	SHIPBOARD ANALYSIS
RT	ANALYSIS
RT	ANALYTICAL TECHNIQUES
RT	AUTOMATED RECORDING
RT	CHEMICAL ANALYSIS
RT	CHEMICAL COMPOSITION
RT	CHEMICAL LIMNOLOGY
RT	CHEMICAL OCEANOGRAPHY

WATER ANALYSIS (cont'd)			**WATER BODIES** (cont'd)			**WATER COLOUR** (cont'd)	
RT	CHEMICAL OXYGEN DEMAND		RT	RESERVOIRS (WATER)		RT	COLORIMETRIC TECHNIQUES
RT	CHEMICAL PROPERTIES		RT	RIVERS		RT	DISCOLOURED WATER
RT	CHEMISTRY		RT	WATER BUDGET		RT	GELBSTOFF
RT	COMPOSITION		RT	WATER COLUMN		RT	LIGHT ABSORPTION
RT	DISSOLVED GASES					RT	MULTISPECTRAL SCANNERS
RT	FRESHWATER ECOLOGY		**WATER BOTTLES**			RT	SPECTRAL COMPOSITION
RT	HYDROCARBON ANALYSIS		USE	**WATER SAMPLERS**		RT	SUSPENDED INORGANIC MATTER
RT	INDICATOR SPECIES					RT	SUSPENDED ORGANIC MATTER
RT	LIMNOLOGY		**WATER BUDGET**			RT	SUSPENDED PARTICULATE MATTER
RT	MARINE ECOLOGY		RT	EUSTATIC CHANGES		RT	TURBIDITY
RT	MICROBIOLOGY		RT	EVAPORATION		RT	WATER
RT	MICROORGANISMS		RT	HEAT BUDGET		RT	WATER PROPERTIES
RT	NUTRIENTS (MINERAL)		RT	HYDROLOGIC CYCLE		RT	WATER TRANSPARENCY
RT	OCEANOGRAPHY		RT	HYDROLOGY			
RT	PHYSICAL LIMNOLOGY		RT	HYDROSPHERE		**WATER COLUMN**	
RT	PHYSICAL OCEANOGRAPHY		RT	ICE VOLUME		UF	vertical structure (water bodies)
RT	PHYSICAL PROPERTIES		RT	INFLOW		BT1	LAYERS
RT	POLLUTANT IDENTIFICATION		RT	INLAND WATERS		NT1	DEEP LAYER
RT	POLLUTION DETECTION		RT	OUTFLOW		NT1	MIXED LAYER
RT	SALINITY MEASUREMENT		RT	RIVER DISCHARGE		NT2	BOTTOM MIXED LAYER
RT	TRACE ELEMENTS		RT	RIVER OUTFLOW		NT2	SURFACE MIXED LAYER
RT	WASTE WATER		RT	SALT BUDGET		NT1	SURFACE LAYERS
RT	WATER		RT	WATER BODIES		NT2	NEAR-SURFACE LAYER
RT	WATER HARDNESS		RT	WATER EXCHANGE		NT2	SURFACE MICROLAYER
RT	WATER POLLUTION					RT	BENTHIC BOUNDARY LAYER
RT	WATER QUALITY		**WATER CHANNELS**			RT	BOTTOM MIXED LAYER
RT	WATER SAMPLING		USE	**CHANNELS**		RT	EPILIMNION
RT	WATER TEMPERATURE					RT	HEAT BUDGET
RT	WATER TREATMENT		**WATER CIRCULATING SYSTEMS**			RT	HYDROSPHERE
			USE	**RECIRCULATING SYSTEMS**		RT	HYPOLIMNION
WATER ANALYSIS (BIOLOGICAL)						RT	PARTICULATE FLUX
USE	**WATER ANALYSIS**		**WATER CIRCULATION**			RT	STRATIFICATION
			SN	Circulation in oceans and inland		RT	THERMOCLINE
WATER ANALYSIS (CHEMICAL)				water bodies. Use of a more		RT	VERTICAL ADVECTION
USE	**WATER ANALYSIS**			specific term is recommended		RT	VERTICAL PROFILES
			UF	circulation (water)		RT	WATER BODIES
WATER ANALYSIS (PHYSICAL)			BT1	WATER MOTION			
USE	**WATER ANALYSIS**		NT1	LAKE DYNAMICS		**WATER CONSERVATION**	
			NT1	OCEAN CIRCULATION		SN	Concerning only the different types
WATER AUTHORITIES			NT2	ABYSSAL CIRCULATION			of water resources
BT1	ORGANIZATIONS		NT2	EQUATORIAL CIRCULATION		BT1	CONSERVATION
RT	POLLUTION CONTROL		NT2	GYRES		RT	EVAPORATION REDUCTION
RT	WATER CONSERVATION		NT2	MERIDIONAL OCEANIC CIRCULATION		RT	MARINE PARKS
RT	WATER MANAGEMENT		NT2	OCEANIC EDDIES		RT	RIVER BASIN MANAGEMENT
RT	WATER RESOURCES		NT3	CURRENT RINGS		RT	WATER
			NT3	MESOSCALE EDDIES		RT	WATER AUTHORITIES
WATER BALANCE			NT2	THERMOHALINE CIRCULATION		RT	WATER MANAGEMENT
RT	EVAPOTRANSPIRATION		NT3	HALINE CIRCULATION		RT	WATER POLICY
RT	EXCRETION		NT1	SHELF DYNAMICS		RT	WATER POLLUTION
RT	EXCRETORY PRODUCTS		NT2	BAY DYNAMICS		RT	WATER QUALITY
RT	KIDNEYS		NT2	ESTUARINE DYNAMICS		RT	WATER RESOURCES
RT	METABOLISM		NT2	FJORD DYNAMICS		RT	WATER USE
RT	OSMOSIS		NT2	NEARSHORE DYNAMICS			
RT	TRANSPIRATION		NT2	SHELF EDGE DYNAMICS		**WATER CONTENT**	
RT	URINE		NT1	SURFACE CIRCULATION		UF	moisture content
RT	WATER		NT1	WIND-DRIVEN CIRCULATION		RT	BIOCHEMICAL COMPOSITION
			RT	AERATION		RT	DEHYDRATION
WATER BLOOMS			RT	CIRCULATION		RT	DEWATERING
USE	**ALGAL BLOOMS**		RT	CORIOLIS FORCE		RT	DRYING
			RT	DIFFUSION		RT	EVAPOTRANSPIRATION
WATER BODIES			RT	FLUID MOTION		RT	GEOTECHNICAL DATA
SN	Surface waters of the Earth. Use of		RT	GYRES		RT	GRAIN SIZE
	a narrower term is recommended		RT	HYDRODYNAMICS		RT	HUMIDITY
UF	surface water bodies		RT	HYDROGRAPHY		RT	HYGROMETRY
RT	BAYS		RT	HYDROLOGIC CYCLE		RT	PORE PRESSURE
RT	CHANNELS		RT	PHYSICAL LIMNOLOGY		RT	PORE WATER
RT	COASTAL INLETS		RT	PHYSICAL OCEANOGRAPHY		RT	PORE WATER SAMPLERS
RT	COASTAL WATERS		RT	THERMAL STRATIFICATION		RT	POROSITY
RT	ESTUARIES		RT	TURBULENCE		RT	SEDIMENT ANALYSIS
RT	FJORDS		RT	WATER		RT	SEDIMENT PROPERTIES
RT	HEAT CONTENT		RT	WATER CURRENTS		RT	TRANSPIRATION
RT	HYDROSPHERE		RT	WATER MASSES		RT	WATER
RT	INLAND SEAS		RT	WATER MIXING		RT	WET BULK DENSITY
RT	INLAND WATERS					RT	WET WEIGHT
RT	LAGOONS		**WATER COLOUR**				
RT	LAKES		BT1	COLOUR			
RT	MARGINAL SEAS		BT2	OPTICAL PROPERTIES			
RT	OCEANS		BT3	PHYSICAL PROPERTIES			
RT	RECREATIONAL WATERS		BT4	PROPERTIES			

WATER CURRENT DATA
USE   **CURRENT DATA**

WATER CURRENT DATA AND OBSERVATIONS
USE   **CURRENT OBSERVATIONS**

WATER CURRENTS
UF	water flow
BT1	WATER MOTION
NT1	BOTTOM CURRENTS
NT2	ABYSSAL CURRENTS
NT2	BENTHIC CURRENTS
NT1	BOUNDARY CURRENTS
NT2	EASTERN BOUNDARY CURRENTS
NT2	WESTERN BOUNDARY CURRENTS
NT1	COASTAL CURRENTS
NT1	COUNTERCURRENTS
NT2	COASTAL COUNTERCURRENTS
NT2	EQUATORIAL COUNTERCURRENTS
NT1	GRADIENT CURRENTS
NT1	INERTIAL CURRENTS
NT1	LAKE CURRENTS
NT1	NEARSHORE CURRENTS
NT2	LONGSHORE CURRENTS
NT2	RIP CURRENTS
NT2	UNDERTOW
NT1	OCEAN CURRENTS
NT1	SHELF CURRENTS
NT1	SLOPE CURRENTS
NT1	STREAM FLOW
NT1	SUBSURFACE CURRENTS
NT2	DEEP CURRENTS
NT1	SURFACE CURRENTS
NT2	CONTOUR CURRENTS
NT1	TIDAL CURRENTS
NT2	EBB CURRENTS
NT2	FLOOD CURRENTS
NT2	ROTARY CURRENTS
NT1	UNDERCURRENTS
NT2	EQUATORIAL UNDERCURRENTS
NT2	WESTERN BOUNDARY UNDERCURRENTS
NT1	WIND-DRIVEN CURRENTS
RT	BOTTOM TOPOGRAPHY EFFECTS
RT	CHANNELS
RT	CIRCULATION
RT	CURRENT CHARTS
RT	CURRENT DATA
RT	CURRENT DIRECTION
RT	CURRENT FORCES
RT	CURRENT MEANDERING
RT	CURRENT MEASUREMENT
RT	CURRENT MEASURING EQUIPMENT
RT	CURRENT METERS
RT	CURRENT POWER
RT	CURRENT PREDICTION
RT	CURRENT REVERSAL
RT	CURRENT ROSES
RT	CURRENT SCOURING
RT	CURRENT VECTORS
RT	DENSITY FLOW
RT	DYE DISPERSION
RT	ENERGY SPECTRA
RT	FLUID FLOW
RT	FLUID MOTION
RT	HEAT TRANSPORT
RT	HORIZONTAL MOTION
RT	OCEAN CIRCULATION
RT	PHYSICAL LIMNOLOGY
RT	PHYSICAL OCEANOGRAPHY
RT	RESIDUAL FLOW
RT	RHEOTAXIS
RT	RHEOTROPISM
RT	RHODAMINE B-DYE
RT	STREAMLINES
RT	VOLUME TRANSPORT
RT	WATER
RT	WATER CIRCULATION

WATER CYCLE
USE   **HYDROLOGIC CYCLE**

WATER DENSITY
UF	density (water)
BT1	DENSITY
BT2	PHYSICAL PROPERTIES
BT3	PROPERTIES
NT1	IN SITU DENSITY
NT1	POTENTIAL DENSITY
NT1	RELATIVE DENSITY
NT1	SIGMA-T
RT	BUOYANCY
RT	CABBELING
RT	CHLORINITY
RT	CHLOROSITY
RT	DENSITY CHARTS
RT	DENSITY FIELD
RT	DENSITY FRONTS
RT	DENSITY GRADIENTS
RT	DENSITY INTERFACES
RT	DENSITY MEASUREMENT
RT	DENSITY PROFILES
RT	DENSITY SECTIONS
RT	DENSITY STRATIFICATION
RT	FREEZING POINT
RT	HYDROSTATIC PRESSURE
RT	ISOPYCNIC SURFACES
RT	ISOPYCNICS
RT	KNUDSEN TABLES
RT	MONIN-OBUKHOV LENGTH
RT	PYCNOCLINE
RT	SALINITY
RT	SPECIFIC VOLUME
RT	SPECIFIC VOLUME ANOMALIES
RT	WATER
RT	WATER PROPERTIES

WATER DEPTH
UF	nautical bottom
BT1	DEPTH
BT2	DIMENSIONS
RT	AQUATIC ENVIRONMENT
RT	BATHYMETERS
RT	BATHYMETRIC CHARTS
RT	BATHYMETRIC DATA
RT	BATHYMETRIC PROFILES
RT	BATHYMETRIC SURVEYS
RT	BATHYMETRY
RT	BATHYTHERMOGRAPHIC DATA
RT	BATHYTHERMOGRAPHS
RT	BOTTOM TOPOGRAPHY
RT	DEEP CURRENTS
RT	DEEP WATER
RT	DEPTH RECORDERS
RT	HYDROGRAPHIC SURVEYING
RT	HYDROGRAPHIC SURVEYS
RT	ISOBATHS
RT	PARTICLE MOTION
RT	SATURATION DEPTH
RT	SHALLOW WATER
RT	SOUNDINGS
RT	WATER
RT	WATER WAVE PARAMETERS
RT	WAVE ATTENUATION
RT	WIND WAVE PARAMETERS

WATER DEPTH MEASUREMENT
USE   **BATHYMETRY**

WATER DESALTING
USE   **DESALINATION**

WATER EXCHANGE
SN	Net exchange of water between adjacent water bodies
RT	CONSERVATION OF SALT
RT	HEAT TRANSPORT
RT	INFLOW
RT	OUTFLOW

WATER EXCHANGE (cont'd)
RT	STRAITS
RT	WATER BUDGET

WATER FILTERS
BT1	FILTERS
RT	AQUARIOLOGY
RT	WATER
RT	WATER FILTRATION

WATER FILTRATION
SN	Removal of ions and organic matter from water
UF	filtration (water)
BT1	FILTRATION
RT	AERATION
RT	AQUACULTURE EQUIPMENT
RT	AQUARIA
RT	AQUARIOLOGY
RT	CENTRIFUGATION
RT	RECIRCULATING SYSTEMS
RT	SANITARY ENGINEERING
RT	SEWAGE TREATMENT
RT	SLUDGE TREATMENT
RT	WATER
RT	WATER FILTERS
RT	WATER PURIFICATION
RT	WATER QUALITY
RT	WATER TREATMENT

WATER FLOW
USE   **WATER CURRENTS**

WATER HARDNESS
UF	hardness (water)
BT1	PHYSICAL PROPERTIES
BT2	PROPERTIES
RT	ALKALINITY
RT	CALCIUM
RT	CALCIUM COMPOUNDS
RT	CARBONATES
RT	CHEMICAL PROPERTIES
RT	SOAPS
RT	WATER
RT	WATER ANALYSIS
RT	WATER PROPERTIES
RT	WATER QUALITY

WATER LEVEL MEASUREMENT
BT1	MEASUREMENT
NT1	SEA LEVEL MEASUREMENT
RT	WATER LEVELS
RT	WAVE MEASUREMENT

WATER LEVELS
SN	Use for lakes, rivers, reservoirs etc. For oceans use MEAN SEA LEVEL and STERIC SEA LEVEL. Before 1984 search also WATER LEVELS (LAKES)
UF	stages (water)
UF	water levels (lakes)
RT	AGROPISCICULTURE
RT	AQUACULTURE DEVELOPMENT
RT	DROUGHTS
RT	FLOODS
RT	LAKE DYNAMICS
RT	LAKES
RT	LEVELS
RT	MEAN SEA LEVEL
RT	RESERVOIRS (WATER)
RT	SEA LEVEL
RT	STERIC SEA LEVEL
RT	WATER
RT	WATER LEVEL MEASUREMENT
RT	WIND SETUP

WATER LEVELS (LAKES)
USE   **WATER LEVELS**

WATER MANAGEMENT ·
BT1   RESOURCE MANAGEMENT
BT2   MANAGEMENT
RT   FLOOD CONTROL
RT   IRRIGATION WATER
RT   POLLUTION CONTROL
RT   RIVER BASIN MANAGEMENT
RT   WATER
RT   WATER AUTHORITIES
RT   WATER CONSERVATION
RT   WATER·POLICY
RT   WATER RESOURCES
RT   WATER SUPPLY

WATER MASS INTRUSIONS
NT1   BOLUSES
RT   OUTFLOW WATERS
RT   WATER MASSES

WATER MASSES
NT1   DEEP-WATER MASSES
NT1   INTERMEDIATE WATER MASSES
NT1   OUTFLOW WATERS
NT1   SLOPE WATER
NT1   SUBSURFACE WATER
NT1   SURFACE WATER MASSES
NT1   WATER TYPES
NT2   OPTICAL WATER TYPES
RT   AGE OF SEAWATER
RT   CABBELING
RT   CARBON/NITROGEN RATIO
RT   CONSERVATIVE PROPERTIES
RT   CONVERGENCE ZONES
RT   CORE LAYER METHOD
RT   CORE LAYERS (WATER)
RT   DIVERGENCE ZONES
RT   ENVIRONMENTAL FACTORS
RT   FRONTOGENESIS
RT   HYDROGRAPHY
RT   IN SITU DENSITY
RT   INDICATOR SPECIES
RT   INDICATORS
RT   NON-CONSERVATIVE PROPERTIES
RT   OCEANIC CONVERGENCES
RT   OCEANOGRAPHY
RT   OPTICAL CLASSIFICATION
RT   PYCNOCLINE
RT   SALINITY
RT   SEA WATER
RT   T/S DIAGRAMS
RT   THERMOCLINE
RT   THERMOSTADS
RT   WATER
RT   WATER CIRCULATION
RT   WATER MASS INTRUSIONS
RT   WATER MIXING
RT   WATER PROPERTIES
RT   WATER TEMPERATURE

WATER MIXING
UF   mixing (water)
NT1   TIDAL MIXING
NT1   TRANS-ISOPYCNAL MIXING
NT1   TRANSVERSE MIXING
NT1   VERTICAL MIXING
RT   AERATION
RT   BUOYANT JETS
RT   CABBELING
RT   CIRCULATION
RT   CORE LAYER METHOD
RT   DESTRATIFICATION
RT   DIFFUSION
RT   DISPERSION
RT   DOWNWELLING
RT   ESTUARINE DYNAMICS
RT   MIXING PROCESSES
RT   OVERTURN

WATER MIXING (cont'd)
RT   PLUMES
RT   RIVER PLUMES
RT   THERMAL PLUMES
RT   UPWELLING
RT   WATER
RT   WATER CIRCULATION
RT   WATER MASSES
RT   WATER MOTION

WATER MOTION
SN   Motion in oceans and inland water
         bodies
UF   water movements
NT1   LEE EDDIES
NT1   MEANDERING
NT2   CURRENT MEANDERING
NT2   RIVER MEANDERS
NT1   VERTICAL WATER MOVEMENT
NT2   CABBELING
NT2   CASCADING
NT2   DOWNWELLING
NT2   OVERTURN
NT2   UPWELLING
NT3   COASTAL UPWELLING
NT3   EQUATORIAL UPWELLING
NT1   WATER CIRCULATION
NT2   LAKE DYNAMICS
NT2   OCEAN CIRCULATION
NT3   ABYSSAL CIRCULATION
NT3   EQUATORIAL CIRCULATION
NT3   GYRES
NT3   MERIDIONAL OCEANIC CIRCULATION
NT3   OCEANIC EDDIES
NT4   CURRENT RINGS
NT4   MESOSCALE EDDIES
NT3   THERMOHALINE CIRCULATION
NT4   HALINE CIRCULATION
NT2   SHELF DYNAMICS
NT3   BAY DYNAMICS
NT3   ESTUARINE DYNAMICS
NT3   FJORD DYNAMICS
NT3   NEARSHORE DYNAMICS
NT3   SHELF EDGE DYNAMICS
NT2   SURFACE CIRCULATION
NT2   WIND-DRIVEN CIRCULATION
NT1   WATER CURRENTS
NT2   BOTTOM CURRENTS
NT3   ABYSSAL CURRENTS
NT3   BENTHIC CURRENTS
NT2   BOUNDARY CURRENTS
NT3   EASTERN BOUNDARY CURRENTS
NT3   WESTERN BOUNDARY CURRENTS
NT2   COASTAL CURRENTS
NT2   COUNTERCURRENTS
NT3   COASTAL COUNTERCURRENTS
NT3   EQUATORIAL COUNTERCURRENTS
NT2   GRADIENT CURRENTS
NT2   INERTIAL CURRENTS
NT2   LAKE CURRENTS
NT2   NEARSHORE CURRENTS
NT3   LONGSHORE CURRENTS
NT3   RIP CURRENTS
NT3   UNDERTOW
NT2   OCEAN CURRENTS
NT2   SHELF CURRENTS
NT2   SLOPE CURRENTS
NT2   STREAM FLOW
NT2   SUBSURFACE CURRENTS
NT3   DEEP CURRENTS
NT2   SURFACE CURRENTS
NT3   CONTOUR CURRENTS
NT2   TIDAL CURRENTS
NT3   EBB CURRENTS
NT3   FLOOD CURRENTS
NT3   ROTARY CURRENTS
NT2   UNDERCURRENTS
NT3   EQUATORIAL UNDERCURRENTS
NT3   WESTERN BOUNDARY UNDERCURRENTS
NT2   WIND-DRIVEN CURRENTS

WATER MOTION (cont'd)
NT1   WATER WAVE MOTION
RT   FLUID DYNAMICS
RT   MOTION
RT   OCEANIC TURBULENCE
RT   PLANETARY WAVES
RT   TRANSPORT PROCESSES
RT   VORTICITY
RT   WATER
RT   WATER MIXING

WATER MOVEMENTS
USE   **WATER MOTION**

WATER-OIL INTERFACE
USE   **OIL-WATER INTERFACE**

WATER OIL SEPARATION
USE   **OIL WATER SEPARATION**

WATER POLICY
SN   Added in 1980
BT1   POLICIES
RT   FLOOD CONTROL
RT   GOVERNMENTS
RT   IRRIGATION
RT   IRRIGATION WATER
RT   NAVIGATION
RT   RECREATIONAL WATERS
RT   WATER
RT   WATER CONSERVATION
RT   WATER MANAGEMENT
RT   WATER QUALITY
RT   WATER RESOURCES
RT   WATER SUPPLY

WATER POLLUTION
UF   aquatic pollution
UF   pollution (water)
BT1   POLLUTION
NT1   BRACKISHWATER POLLUTION
NT1   FRESHWATER POLLUTION
NT1   GROUNDWATER POLLUTION
NT1   MARINE POLLUTION
RT   AIR POLLUTION
RT   AVOIDANCE REACTIONS
RT   CHEMICAL OXYGEN DEMAND
RT   CHEMICAL POLLUTION
RT   ENVIRONMENTAL LEGISLATION
RT   INDUSTRIAL WASTES
RT   OIL POLLUTION
RT   ORGANIC WASTES
RT   OUTFALLS
RT   POLLUTANTS
RT   POLLUTION CONTROL
RT   POLLUTION EFFECTS
RT   POLLUTION MAPS
RT   POLLUTION MONITORING
RT   RADIOACTIVE CONTAMINATION
RT   RECREATIONAL WATERS
RT   RIPARIAN RIGHTS
RT   SEWAGE DISPOSAL
RT   THERMAL POLLUTION
RT   WASTE DISPOSAL
RT   WASTE WATER
RT   WASTES
RT   WATER
RT   WATER ANALYSIS
RT   WATER CONSERVATION
RT   WATER POLLUTION TREATMENT
RT   WATER RESOURCES
RT   WATER USE

WATER POLLUTION CONTROL
USE   **POLLUTION CONTROL**

ASFIS Thesaurus

WATER POLLUTION EFFECTS		
USE	**POLLUTION EFFECTS**	
WATER POLLUTION TREATMENT		
BT1	WATER TREATMENT	
RT	ADSORPTION	
RT	AERATION	
RT	BIODEGRADATION	
RT	BRACKISHWATER POLLUTION	
RT	CHEMICAL DEGRADATION	
RT	COAGULATION	
RT	DECANTATION	
RT	DECANTATION TANKS	
RT	FRESHWATER POLLUTION	
RT	HARBOURS	
RT	HYGIENE	
RT	MARINE POLLUTION	
RT	OIL REMOVAL	
RT	POLLUTION CONTROL	
RT	POLLUTION MONITORING	
RT	PUBLIC HEALTH	
RT	SANITARY ENGINEERING	
RT	SELF PURIFICATION	
RT	WASTE TREATMENT	
RT	WATER POLLUTION	
RT	WATER PURIFICATION	
RT	WATER QUALITY CONTROL	
WATER PRESSURE		
USE	**HYDROSTATIC PRESSURE**	
WATER PROPERTIES		
SN	Use of a more specific term is recommended	
BT1	PROPERTIES	
RT	ACIDITY	
RT	ACOUSTIC DATA	
RT	ALKALINITY	
RT	AUTOMATED RECORDING	
RT	BRACKISH WATER	
RT	CHEMICAL OXYGEN DEMAND	
RT	CHEMICAL PROPERTIES	
RT	CHLORINITY	
RT	CHLOROSITY	
RT	COMPRESSIBILITY	
RT	DISSOLVED OXYGEN	
RT	DISSOLVED SALTS	
RT	ENVIRONMENTAL CHARTS	
RT	ENVIRONMENTAL FACTORS	
RT	EUTROPHICATION	
RT	EVAPORATION	
RT	FRESH WATER	
RT	INDICATORS	
RT	OCEANOGRAPHIC TABLES	
RT	ORGANOLEPTIC PROPERTIES	
RT	PH	
RT	PHYSICAL LIMNOLOGY	
RT	PHYSICAL OCEANOGRAPHY	
RT	PHYSICAL PROPERTIES	
RT	PHYSICOCHEMICAL PROPERTIES	
RT	REDOX POTENTIAL	
RT	RELATIVE DENSITY	
RT	SALINE WATER	
RT	SALINITY	
RT	STANDARD DEPTHS	
RT	SURFACE PROPERTIES	
RT	SURFACE TENSION	
RT	THERMAL CONDUCTIVITY	
RT	THERMAL DIFFUSIVITY	
RT	THERMAL EXPANSION	
RT	TRACE ELEMENTS	
RT	TURBIDITY	
RT	VISCOSITY	
RT	WATER	
RT	WATER COLOUR	
RT	WATER DENSITY	
RT	WATER HARDNESS	
RT	WATER MASSES	
RT	WATER QUALITY	
RT	WATER SAMPLERS	

WATER PROPERTIES (cont'd)		
RT	WATER STRUCTURE	
RT	WATER TEMPERATURE	
RT	WATER TRANSPARENCY	
WATER PUMPS		
SN	Added in 1982	
UF	pumps (water)	
BT1	PUMPS	
RT	AQUACULTURE EQUIPMENT	
RT	AQUARIA	
RT	AQUARIUM CULTURE	
RT	HARVESTING MACHINES	
RT	POND CULTURE	
RT	RECIRCULATING SYSTEMS	
RT	SALVAGE EQUIPMENT	
WATER PURIFICATION		
SN	Physical and chemical treatment for water purification	
UF	purification (water)	
BT1	WATER TREATMENT	
RT	AERATION	
RT	AQUACULTURE TECHNIQUES	
RT	CENTRIFUGATION	
RT	CHLORINATION	
RT	COAGULATION	
RT	DECHLORINATION	
RT	DESALINATION	
RT	DISINFECTANTS	
RT	DISINFECTION	
RT	ION EXCHANGE	
RT	OXYGENATION	
RT	PLANT UTILIZATION	
RT	POLLUTION CONTROL	
RT	PUBLIC HEALTH	
RT	SANITARY ENGINEERING	
RT	SELF PURIFICATION	
RT	SEPARATION	
RT	WATER FILTRATION	
RT	WATER POLLUTION TREATMENT	
RT	WATER QUALITY	
WATER QUALITY		
UF	water standards	
RT	AQUACULTURE EFFLUENTS	
RT	AQUACULTURE REGULATIONS	
RT	BATHING	
RT	BIOCHEMICAL OXYGEN DEMAND	
RT	CHEMICAL OXYGEN DEMAND	
RT	CHEMICAL PROPERTIES	
RT	DEOXYGENATION	
RT	EUTROPHICATION	
RT	HAZARD ASSESSMENT	
RT	HYGIENE	
RT	INDICATOR SPECIES	
RT	ODOUR	
RT	ORGANIC WASTES	
RT	ORGANOLEPTIC PROPERTIES	
RT	OXYGEN DEMAND	
RT	POLLUTION MAPS	
RT	POLLUTION MONITORING	
RT	RADIOACTIVITY	
RT	RECREATIONAL WATERS	
RT	SITE SELECTION	
RT	TASTE	
RT	WATER	
RT	WATER ANALYSIS	
RT	WATER CONSERVATION	
RT	WATER FILTRATION	
RT	WATER HARDNESS	
RT	WATER POLICY	
RT	WATER PROPERTIES	
RT	WATER PURIFICATION	
RT	WATER QUALITY CONTROL	
RT	WATER RESOURCES	
RT	WATER SAMPLERS	
RT	WATER SAMPLING	
RT	WATER SUPPLY	

WATER QUALITY CONTROL		
BT1	CONTROL	
RT	AERATION	
RT	POLLUTION CONTROL	
RT	QUALITY CONTROL	
RT	WATER POLLUTION TREATMENT	
RT	WATER QUALITY	
RT	WATER SAMPLING	
RT	WATER TREATMENT	
WATER RECLAMATION		
UF	reclamation (water)	
BT1	RECLAMATION	
RT	WASTE WATER	
RT	WATER RESOURCES	
WATER RESERVOIRS		
USE	**RESERVOIRS (WATER)**	
WATER RESOURCES		
SN	Mainly different types of water bodies or water sources of inland regions	
BT1	NATURAL RESOURCES	
BT2	RESOURCES	
RT	ATMOSPHERIC PRECIPITATIONS	
RT	DESALINATION	
RT	DROUGHTS	
RT	FRESHWATER LAKES	
RT	GLACIERS	
RT	GROUND WATER	
RT	HYDROELECTRIC POWER	
RT	HYDROLOGIC CYCLE	
RT	ICEBERGS	
RT	INLAND WATER ENVIRONMENT	
RT	LAGOONS	
RT	LAKES	
RT	PONDS	
RT	RECREATIONAL WATERS	
RT	RENEWABLE RESOURCES	
RT	RESERVOIRS (WATER)	
RT	RESOURCE CONSERVATION	
RT	RESOURCE DEVELOPMENT	
RT	RIVERS	
RT	SALT LAKES	
RT	SPRING STREAMS	
RT	WATER	
RT	WATER AUTHORITIES	
RT	WATER CONSERVATION	
RT	WATER MANAGEMENT	
RT	WATER POLICY	
RT	WATER POLLUTION	
RT	WATER QUALITY	
RT	WATER RECLAMATION	
RT	WATER USE	
WATER RIGHTS		
SN	Added in 1980	
BT1	RIGHTS	
NT1	RIPARIAN RIGHTS	
RT	AQUACULTURE	
RT	BOUNDARIES	
RT	EXCLUSIVE RIGHTS	
RT	IRRIGATION	
RT	IRRIGATION WATER	
RT	LAKE RECLAMATION	
RT	LEGISLATION	
RT	RANCHING	
RT	RENTAL	
RT	WATER	
RT	WATER SUPPLY	
RT	WATER USE	
RT	WATER USE REGULATIONS	
WATER RIPPLES		
UF	ripples (water)	
BT1	CAPILLARY WAVES	
BT2	SURFACE WATER WAVES	
BT3	WATER WAVES	
RT	WATER	

WATER RUNUP			**WATER SUPPLY** (cont'd)			**WATER TEMPERATURE** (cont'd)		
USE	**WAVE RUNUP**		RT	WATER		RT	THERMAL STRUCTURE
			RT	WATER MANAGEMENT		RT	THERMOCLINE
WATER SAMPLERS			RT	WATER POLICY		RT	THERMOMETERS
UF	water bottles		RT	WATER QUALITY		RT	THERMORECEPTORS
BT1	SAMPLERS		RT	WATER RIGHTS		RT	THERMOSTADS
NT1	KNUDSEN SAMPLERS		RT	WATER TREATMENT		RT	WATER
NT1	NANSEN BOTTLES		RT	WATER USE		RT	WATER ANALYSIS
NT1	NISKIN SAMPLERS					RT	WATER MASSES
RT	HYDROGRAPHIC WIRE		**WATER SURFACE SALINITY**			RT	WATER PROPERTIES
RT	LIMNOLOGICAL EQUIPMENT		USE	**SURFACE SALINITY**		RT	WATER TYPES
RT	MESSENGERS						
RT	OCEANOGRAPHIC EQUIPMENT		**WATER SURFACE SLOPE**			**WATER TRANSPARENCY**	
RT	PORE WATER SAMPLERS		USE	**SURFACE SLOPE**		UF	transparency (water)
RT	REVERSING THERMOMETERS					BT1	TRANSPARENCY
RT	WATER PROPERTIES		**WATER SURFACE TEMPERATURE**			BT2	OPTICAL PROPERTIES
RT	WATER QUALITY		USE	**SURFACE TEMPERATURE**		BT3	PHYSICAL PROPERTIES
RT	WATER SAMPLES					BT4	PROPERTIES
RT	WATER SAMPLING		**WATER SURFACE TOPOGRAPHY**			RT	BEAM TRANSMITTANCE METERS
			USE	**SURFACE TOPOGRAPHY**		RT	EXTINCTION COEFFICIENT
WATER SAMPLES						RT	LIGHT ABSORPTION
BT1	SAMPLES		**WATER TABLE**			RT	LIGHT ATTENUATION
RT	CHEMICAL ANALYSIS		RT	DRAINAGE WATER		RT	LIGHT PENETRATION
RT	SAMPLE STORAGE		RT	GROUND WATER		RT	LIGHT REFRACTION
RT	STORAGE CONDITIONS		RT	RIVER VALLEYS		RT	LIGHT SCATTERING
RT	STORAGE EFFECTS		RT	WATER		RT	NEPHELOMETERS
RT	WATER SAMPLERS		RT	WATERSHEDS		RT	TRANSMITTANCE
RT	WATER SAMPLING					RT	TURBIDITY
			WATER TANKS			RT	WATER
WATER SAMPLING			USE	**TANKS**		RT	WATER COLOUR
BT1	SAMPLING					RT	WATER PROPERTIES
RT	ENVIRONMENTAL SURVEYS		**WATER TEMPERATURE**				
RT	HELICOPTERS		BT1	TEMPERATURE		**WATER TREATMENT**	
RT	LIMNOLOGICAL DATA		BT2	THERMODYNAMIC PROPERTIES		NT1	DESALINATION
RT	LIMNOLOGICAL EQUIPMENT		BT3	PHYSICAL PROPERTIES		NT1	WATER POLLUTION TREATMENT
RT	LIMNOLOGY		BT4	PROPERTIES		NT1	WATER PURIFICATION
RT	OCEANOGRAPHIC DATA		NT1	BOTTOM TEMPERATURE		RT	AERATION
RT	OCEANOGRAPHIC EQUIPMENT		NT1	IN SITU TEMPERATURE		RT	AQUACULTURE EQUIPMENT
RT	OCEANOGRAPHIC SURVEYS		NT1	PALAEOTEMPERATURE		RT	BIOFILTERS
RT	OCEANOGRAPHY		NT1	SURFACE TEMPERATURE		RT	COAGULATION
RT	WATER		NT2	BUCKET TEMPERATURE		RT	DECANTATION
RT	WATER ANALYSIS		NT2	INTAKE TEMPERATURE		RT	DECHLORINATION
RT	WATER QUALITY		NT2	SURFACE RADIATION TEMPERATURE		RT	ION EXCHANGE
RT	WATER QUALITY CONTROL		RT	ABIOTIC FACTORS		RT	OIL WATER SEPARATION
RT	WATER SAMPLERS		RT	AIR TEMPERATURE		RT	OXYGENATION
RT	WATER SAMPLES		RT	AXBTs		RT	WASTEWATER TREATMENT
			RT	BATHYTHERMOGRAPHIC DATA		RT	WATER
WATER SEEPAGES			RT	BATHYTHERMOGRAPHS		RT	WATER ANALYSIS
USE	**SUBMARINE SPRINGS**		RT	CABBELING		RT	WATER FILTRATION
			RT	COLD SEASON		RT	WATER QUALITY CONTROL
WATER SPRINGS			RT	CTD PROFILERS		RT	WATER SUPPLY
SN	Use of a more specific term is		RT	DICOTHERMAL LAYER			
	recommended		RT	ELECTRICAL CONDUCTIVITY		**WATER TYPES**	
UF	freshwater springs		RT	ENVIRONMENTAL CHARTS		BT1	WATER MASSES
UF	springs (water)		RT	EVAPORATION		NT1	OPTICAL WATER TYPES
NT1	GEOTHERMAL SPRINGS		RT	GEOTHERMAL SPRINGS		RT	CORE LAYER METHOD
NT2	HYDROTHERMAL SPRINGS		RT	HEAT CONTENT		RT	CORE LAYERS (WATER)
NT1	HOT SPRINGS		RT	HYDROCLIMATE		RT	HYDROGRAPHY
NT1	SPRING STREAMS		RT	HYDROGRAPHY		RT	SALINITY
NT1	SUBMARINE SPRINGS		RT	IN SITU DENSITY		RT	SEA WATER
RT	FRESH WATER		RT	ISOTHERMS		RT	T/S DIAGRAMS
RT	GROUND WATER		RT	LIMNOLOGICAL DATA		RT	WATER
RT	INLAND WATER ENVIRONMENT		RT	OCEANOGRAPHIC DATA		RT	WATER TEMPERATURE
RT	LOTIC ENVIRONMENT		RT	PHYSICAL LIMNOLOGY			
RT	SEEPAGES		RT	PHYSICAL OCEANOGRAPHY		**WATER USE**	
RT	WATER		RT	POTENTIAL TEMPERATURE		SN	Added in 1980
			RT	REFRACTIVE INDEX		UF	use of water
WATER STANDARDS			RT	REVERSING THERMOMETERS		UF	water utilization
USE	**WATER QUALITY**		RT	SEDIMENT TEMPERATURE		BT1	UTILIZATION
			RT	STD PROFILERS		RT	AQUACULTURE
WATER STRUCTURE			RT	T/S DIAGRAMS		RT	FISHERIES
RT	WATER PROPERTIES		RT	TEMPERATURE CHARTS		RT	HYDROLOGY
			RT	TEMPERATURE DATA		RT	LAND USE
WATER SUPPLY			RT	TEMPERATURE EFFECTS		RT	POWER PLANTS
SN	Added in 1980		RT	TEMPERATURE GRADIENTS		RT	RECLAMATION
RT	ARTIFICIAL UPWELLING		RT	TEMPERATURE PROFILES		RT	RECREATIONAL WATERS
RT	DESALINATION PLANTS		RT	TEMPERATURE SECTIONS		RT	WATER
RT	NATURAL RESOURCES		RT	THERMAL MICROSTRUCTURE		RT	WATER CONSERVATION
RT	SANITARY ENGINEERING		RT	THERMAL POLLUTION		RT	WATER POLLUTION
RT	SURFACE WATER		RT	THERMAL STRATIFICATION		RT	WATER RESOURCES

WATER USE (cont'd)		
RT	WATER RIGHTS	
RT	WATER SUPPLY	
RT	WATER USE REGULATIONS	
WATER USE REGULATIONS		
SN	Policy and ownership of land and	
	inland waters	
BT1	LEGISLATION	
RT	LEGAL ASPECTS	
RT	WATER RIGHTS	
RT	WATER USE	
WATER UTILIZATION		
USE	**WATER USE**	
WATER VAPOUR		
BT1	GASES	
BT2	FLUIDS	
RT	CONDENSATION	
RT	DEW POINT	
RT	GREENHOUSE EFFECT	
RT	HUMIDITY	
RT	HYDROMETEORS	
RT	HYGROMETERS	
RT	HYGROMETRY	
RT	MIXING RATIO	
RT	MOISTURE TRANSFER	
RT	SATURATION VAPOUR PRESSURE	
RT	SOLAR RADIATION	
RT	SPECIFIC HUMIDITY	
RT	SUBLIMATION	
RT	VAPOUR PRESSURE	
RT	WATER	
WATER VAPOUR PRESSURE		
USE	**VAPOUR PRESSURE**	
WATER VAPOUR TRANSFER		
USE	**MOISTURE TRANSFER**	
WATER WAVE FORECASTING		
USE	**WAVE FORECASTING**	
WATER WAVE MOTION		
BT1	WATER MOTION	
RT	DYNAMICAL OCEANOGRAPHY	
RT	FLUID MOTION	
RT	WAVE DISSIPATION	
RT	WAVE DYNAMICS	
RT	WAVE GENERATION	
RT	WAVE INTERACTIONS	
RT	WAVE PROCESSES ON BEACHES	
RT	WAVE PROPAGATION	
RT	WAVE RUNUP	
WATER WAVE PARAMETERS		
RT	DURATION	
RT	FETCH	
RT	WATER DEPTH	
RT	WATER WAVES	
RT	WAVE PROPERTIES	
RT	WIND SPEED	
RT	WIND STRESS	
WATER WAVE PROPAGATION		
USE	**WAVE PROPAGATION**	
WATER WAVE STATISTICS		
USE	**WAVE STATISTICS**	
WATER WAVES		
UF	waves (water)	
NT1	DEEP-WATER WAVES	
NT1	GRAVITY WAVES	
NT1	INERTIAL WAVES	
NT1	INTERNAL WAVES	
NT2	INTERNAL TIDES	
NT2	LEE WAVES	
NT1	LINEAR WAVES	

WATER WAVES (cont'd)		
NT1	NONLINEAR WAVES	
NT2	FINITE AMPLITUDE WAVES	
NT2	STOKES WAVES	
NT1	OSCILLATORY WAVES	
NT2	PROGRESSIVE WAVES	
NT2	STANDING WAVES	
NT1	SHALLOW-WATER WAVES	
NT2	CNOIDAL WAVES	
NT2	SOLITARY WAVES	
NT2	TIDAL BORES	
NT1	SURFACE GRAVITY WAVES	
NT1	SURFACE WATER WAVES	
NT2	BREAKING WAVES	
NT3	BREAKERS	
NT3	SPILLING WAVES	
NT3	SURF	
NT3	WHITECAPS	
NT2	CAPILLARY WAVES	
NT3	WATER RIPPLES	
NT2	CONSTRUCTIVE WAVES	
NT2	LONG-CRESTED WAVES	
NT2	SEICHES	
NT3	HARBOUR OSCILLATIONS	
NT2	SHORT-CRESTED WAVES	
NT2	SIGNIFICANT WAVES	
NT2	STORM SURGES	
NT3	HURRICANE WAVES	
NT3	NEGATIVE STORM SURGES	
NT2	SWELL	
NT3	ROLLERS	
NT2	TIDAL WAVES	
NT2	TSUNAMIS	
NT2	WIND WAVES	
NT1	TOPOGRAPHIC WAVES	
NT1	TRAPPED WAVES	
NT2	EDGE WAVES	
NT2	KELVIN WAVES	
NT3	EQUATORIAL TRAPPED WAVES	
NT2	SHELF WAVES	
NT2	SURF BEATS	
RT	ENERGY SPECTRA	
RT	GROUP VELOCITY	
RT	ORBITAL VELOCITY	
RT	OVERTOPPING	
RT	OVERWASH	
RT	PARTICLE MOTION	
RT	PHASE VELOCITY	
RT	PHYSICAL LIMNOLOGY	
RT	PHYSICAL OCEANOGRAPHY	
RT	PLANETARY WAVES	
RT	WATER	
RT	WATER WAVE PARAMETERS	
RT	WAVE ATTENUATION	
RT	WAVE CRESTS	
RT	WAVE DIFFRACTION	
RT	WAVE DISPERSION	
RT	WAVE DISSIPATION	
RT	WAVE DRIFT VELOCITY	
RT	WAVE EFFECTS	
RT	WAVE GAUGES	
RT	WAVE GENERATION	
RT	WAVE GENERATORS	
RT	WAVE GROUPS	
RT	WAVE INTERACTIONS	
RT	WAVE PROPAGATION	
RT	WAVE PROPERTIES	
RT	WAVE RECORDERS	
RT	WAVE SLOPE	
RT	WAVE STATISTICS	
RT	WAVE TRAINS	
RT	WAVE TRAPPING	
RT	WAVE-WAVE INTERACTION	
WATER WAVES ACTION		
USE	**WAVE EFFECTS**	

WATER WEED UTILIZATION		
USE	**PLANT UTILIZATION**	
WATERSHED (DIVIDE)		
USE	**WATERSHEDS**	
WATERSHEDS		
UF	watershed (divide)	
RT	ATMOSPHERIC PRECIPITATIONS	
RT	CATCHMENT AREA	
RT	DRAINAGE WATER	
RT	FLOOD CONTROL	
RT	FLOOD FORECASTING	
RT	GROUND WATER	
RT	HYDROLOGY	
RT	LAKE BASINS	
RT	RIVER BASINS	
RT	RUNOFF	
RT	STREAM FLOW	
RT	VALLEYS	
RT	WATER TABLE	
WATERSPOUTS		
RT	ATMOSPHERIC MOTION	
RT	HURRICANES	
RT	TORNADOES	
RT	VORTICES	
WAVE ACTION		
UF	density (wave action)	
UF	wave action density	
BT1	WAVE EFFECTS	
RT	EXPOSED HABITATS	
RT	SHIP MOTION	
WAVE ACTION DENSITY		
USE	**WAVE ACTION**	
WAVE AGE		
BT1	AGE	
RT	RATIOS	
RT	WAVE FORECASTING	
RT	WAVE VELOCITY	
RT	WIND SPEED	
WAVE-AIR INTERACTION		
SN	Wave effects on air flow over water	
BT1	WAVE INTERACTIONS	
RT	AIR FLOW OVER WATER	
RT	ATMOSPHERIC BOUNDARY LAYER	
RT	MOMENTUM TRANSFER	
RT	WAVE EFFECTS	
RT	WIND PROFILES	
WAVE AMPLITUDE		
BT1	AMPLITUDE	
BT2	DIMENSIONS	
NT1	TIDAL AMPLITUDE	
RT	WAVE ATTENUATION	
RT	WAVE HEIGHT	
RT	WAVE PROPERTIES	
WAVE ANALYSIS		
NT1	TIDAL ANALYSIS	
RT	ANALYSIS	
RT	SURFACE WATER WAVES	
WAVE ATTENUATION		
SN	Use for natural decrease of	
	amplitude	
UF	attenuation (water waves)	
BT1	WAVE DISSIPATION	
BT2	ENERGY DISSIPATION	
BT3	ENERGY TRANSFER	
NT1	SOUND ATTENUATION	
RT	ATTENUATION	
RT	PARTICLE MOTION	
RT	WATER DEPTH	
RT	WATER WAVES	
RT	WAVE AMPLITUDE	

WAVE ATTENUATION (cont'd)
RT	WAVE DAMPING
RT	WAVE PROPAGATION
RT	WAVE SCATTERING

WAVE BREAKING
BT1	WAVE DISSIPATION
BT2	ENERGY DISSIPATION
BT3	ENERGY TRANSFER
NT1	WHITECAPPING
RT	BREAKING WAVES
RT	INTERNAL WAVE BREAKING
RT	TIDAL BORES
RT	WAVE CRESTS
RT	WAVE DYNAMICS
RT	WAVE PROCESSES ON BEACHES
RT	WAVES ON BEACHES

WAVE BUOYS
BT1	DATA BUOYS
BT2	BUOYS
RT	ACCELEROMETERS
RT	HEAVING
RT	WAVE DIRECTION SENSORS
RT	WAVE MEASURING EQUIPMENT
RT	WAVE POWER DEVICES

WAVE CELERITY
USE	WAVE VELOCITY

WAVE CLIMATE
RT	CLIMATE
RT	CLIMATOLOGICAL CHARTS
RT	DESIGN WAVE
RT	ENVIRONMENTAL CHARTS
RT	ENVIRONMENTAL CONDITIONS
RT	OCEANOGRAPHIC ATLASES
RT	SEA STATE
RT	WAVE FORCES
RT	WIND WAVES

WAVE CONTROL (WATER WAVES)
USE	WAVE DAMPING

WAVE CRESTS
RT	BREAKING WAVES
RT	LONG-CRESTED WAVES
RT	SHORT-CRESTED WAVES
RT	WATER WAVES
RT	WAVE BREAKING
RT	WAVE GEOMETRY
RT	WAVE SLOPE

WAVE-CURRENT INTERACTION
BT1	WAVE INTERACTIONS
RT	GIANT WAVES
RT	INTERACTIONS
RT	LONGSHORE CURRENTS
RT	MOMENTUM TRANSFER
RT	RIP CURRENTS

WAVE-CUT PLATFORMS
UF	beach platforms
UF	erosion platforms
UF	strandflats
BT1	BEACH FEATURES
RT	CLIFFS
RT	EROSION FEATURES
RT	EROSION SURFACES
RT	INTERTIDAL SEDIMENTATION
RT	STRANDLINES
RT	TERRACES
RT	WAVE SCOURING

WAVE DAMPING
SN	Induced reduction in water wave amplitude
UF	damping (water waves)
UF	wave control (water waves)
BT1	DAMPING

WAVE DAMPING (cont'd)
RT	BREAKWATERS
RT	SHIP MOTION
RT	SURFACE FILMS
RT	SURFACE WATER WAVES
RT	WAVE ATTENUATION
RT	WAVE DISSIPATION

WAVE DATA
SN	Data on water waves
UF	wave records
BT1	DATA
RT	OCEANOGRAPHIC DATA
RT	WAVE STATISTICS

WAVE DECAY
USE	WAVE DISSIPATION

WAVE DIFFRACTION
SN	Use only for water waves and specify type of wave
UF	diffraction (water waves)
BT1	DIFFRACTION
RT	WATER WAVES
RT	WAVE INTERACTIONS
RT	WAVE PROPAGATION

WAVE DIRECTION
BT1	DIRECTION
RT	DIRECTIONAL SPECTRA
RT	LONG-CRESTED WAVES
RT	SHORT-CRESTED WAVES
RT	WAVE DIRECTION SENSORS
RT	WAVE PROPERTIES

WAVE DIRECTION SENSORS
BT1	WAVE MEASURING EQUIPMENT
BT2	MEASURING DEVICES
RT	SENSORS
RT	WAVE BUOYS
RT	WAVE DIRECTION

WAVE DISPERSION
SN	Use only for water waves and specify type of wave
UF	dispersion (water waves)
BT1	DISPERSION
RT	ATTENUATION
RT	GROUP VELOCITY
RT	PHASE VELOCITY
RT	WATER WAVES
RT	WAVE GROUPS
RT	WAVE MOTION
RT	WAVE PROPAGATION
RT	WAVE TRAINS

WAVE DISSIPATION
SN	Use only for water waves and specify type of wave
UF	dissipation (water waves)
UF	wave decay
UF	wave energy dissipation (water waves)
BT1	ENERGY DISSIPATION
BT2	ENERGY TRANSFER
NT1	TIDAL DISSIPATION
NT1	WAVE ATTENUATION
NT2	SOUND ATTENUATION
NT1	WAVE BREAKING
NT2	WHITECAPPING
RT	BOTTOM FRICTION
RT	BREAKING WAVES
RT	MOLECULAR VISCOSITY
RT	OCEANIC TURBULENCE
RT	SURF ZONE
RT	TURBULENCE
RT	VISCOSITY
RT	WATER WAVE MOTION
RT	WATER WAVES
RT	WAVE DAMPING
RT	WAVE ENERGY

WAVE DISSIPATION (cont'd)
RT	WAVE SCATTERING
RT	WHITECAPPING

WAVE DRIFT VELOCITY
UF	mass transport velocity
UF	stokes drift
BT1	VELOCITY
RT	MASS TRANSPORT
RT	ORBITAL VELOCITY
RT	PARTICLE MOTION
RT	WATER WAVES
RT	WAVE DYNAMICS

WAVE DYNAMICS
NT1	TIDAL DYNAMICS
RT	BAY DYNAMICS
RT	WATER WAVE MOTION
RT	WAVE BREAKING
RT	WAVE DRIFT VELOCITY

WAVE EFFECTS
UF	water waves action
NT1	WAVE ACTION
RT	BACKWASH
RT	BEACH CUSPS
RT	BEACH EROSION
RT	BEACH MORPHOLOGY
RT	BEACH PROFILES
RT	BUOY MOTION
RT	CAPSIZING
RT	FLOODING
RT	REFLECTANCE
RT	SEDIMENT TRANSPORT
RT	SHIP LOSSES
RT	SHIP MOTION
RT	TSUNAMIS
RT	WATER WAVES
RT	WAVE ENERGY
RT	WAVE FORCES
RT	WAVE-AIR INTERACTION
RT	WAVES ON BEACHES

WAVE ENERGY
SN	Used for the natural energy bound up in the motion of water waves. For exploitation of that energy use WAVE POWER
BT1	ENERGY
NT1	TIDAL ENERGY
RT	ENERGY DISSIPATION
RT	ENERGY TRANSFER
RT	WAVE DISSIPATION
RT	WAVE EFFECTS
RT	WAVE POWER
RT	WAVE POWER DEVICES
RT	WAVE SPECTRA

WAVE ENERGY DISSIPATION (WATER WAVES)
USE	WAVE DISSIPATION

WAVE ENERGY SPECTRA
USE	WAVE SPECTRA

WAVE FETCH
USE	FETCH

WAVE FOLLOWERS
UF	sea surface followers
UF	surface followers
BT1	INSTRUMENT PLATFORMS
BT2	VEHICLES
RT	AIR-WATER EXCHANGES
RT	WAVE MEASURING EQUIPMENT
RT	WAVE TANKS

ASFIS Thesaurus

WAVE FORCES
UF	impact (waves)
UF	slamming
UF	wave load
UF	wave pressure
BT1	LOADS (FORCES)
BT2	FORCES (MECHANICS)
RT	DESIGN WAVE
RT	FLOW AROUND OBJECTS
RT	HYDRODYNAMICS
RT	MORISON'S EQUATION
RT	OFFSHORE STRUCTURES
RT	SHIP MOTION
RT	WAVE CLIMATE
RT	WAVE EFFECTS

WAVE FORECASTING
UF	water wave forecasting
UF	wave forecasts
BT1	WAVE PREDICTING
BT2	PREDICTION
RT	DESIGN WAVE
RT	MICROSEISMS
RT	SHIP ROUTEING
RT	SIGNIFICANT WAVE HEIGHT
RT	WAVE AGE
RT	WAVE HINDCASTING

WAVE FORECASTS
USE	**WAVE FORECASTING**

WAVE FORMATION (WATER WAVES)
USE	**WAVE GENERATION**

WAVE FREQUENCY
SN	Before 1982 search WAVE PERIOD
BT1	FREQUENCY
RT	WAVE PERIOD
RT	WAVE PROPERTIES
RT	WAVE SPECTRA

WAVE GAGES
USE	**WAVE GAUGES**

WAVE GAUGES
SN	Before 1986 search also WAVE METERS
UF	wave gages
UF	wave meters
BT1	WAVE MEASURING EQUIPMENT
BT2	MEASURING DEVICES
RT	CAPILLARY WAVES
RT	WATER WAVES
RT	WAVE RECORDERS

WAVE GENERATION
SN	Use only for water waves and specify type of wave generation (water waves)
UF	wave formation (water waves)
UF	wave growth (water waves)
NT1	INTERNAL WAVE GENERATION
NT1	STORM SURGE GENERATION
NT1	TSUNAMI GENERATION
NT1	WIND WAVE GENERATION
RT	CALVING
RT	ENERGY TRANSFER
RT	WATER WAVE MOTION
RT	WATER WAVES
RT	WAVE GENERATORS

WAVE GENERATORS
SN	Mechanical devices used to generate water waves in wave tanks
RT	LABORATORY EQUIPMENT
RT	WATER WAVES
RT	WAVE GENERATION
RT	WAVE TANKS

WAVE GEOMETRY
SN	Search also SURFACE GEOMETRY before 1982
UF	surface geometry (water waves)
UF	wave shape
UF	wave topography
RT	SURFACE PROPERTIES
RT	SURFACE WATER WAVES
RT	WAVE CRESTS
RT	WAVE HEIGHT
RT	WAVE SLOPE
RT	WAVE STATISTICS

WAVE GROUPS
RT	GROUP VELOCITY
RT	WATER WAVES
RT	WAVE DISPERSION
RT	WAVE STATISTICS
RT	WAVE TRAINS

WAVE GROWTH (WATER WAVES)
USE	**WAVE GENERATION**

WAVE HEIGHT
SN	Use for surface water waves except tides
NT1	SIGNIFICANT WAVE HEIGHT
RT	DESIGN WAVE
RT	EXTREME WAVES
RT	GIANT WAVES
RT	SIGNIFICANT WAVES
RT	WAVE AMPLITUDE
RT	WAVE GEOMETRY
RT	WAVE PROPERTIES
RT	WAVE STATISTICS

WAVE HINDCASTING
UF	hindcasting (waves)
BT1	WAVE PREDICTING
BT2	PREDICTION
RT	WAVE FORECASTING

WAVE-ICE INTERACTION
SN	Influence of floating ice on water wave propagation and vice versa
BT1	WAVE INTERACTIONS
RT	FLOATING ICE
RT	ICE-WATER INTERFACE
RT	INTERACTIONS

WAVE-INDUCED LOADING
BT1	LOADS (FORCES)
BT2	FORCES (MECHANICS)
RT	CYCLIC LOADING
RT	PORE PRESSURE
RT	WAVE-SEABED INTERACTION

WAVE INTERACTIONS
SN	Use only for water waves
NT1	NONLINEAR WAVE INTERACTIONS
NT1	RESONANT WAVE INTERACTION
NT1	WAVE-AIR INTERACTION
NT1	WAVE-CURRENT INTERACTION
NT1	WAVE-ICE INTERACTION
NT1	WAVE-SEABED INTERACTION
NT1	WAVE TRAPPING
NT1	WAVE-WAVE INTERACTION
NT2	SHORT WAVE-LONG WAVE INTERACTIONS
NT2	SURFACE WAVE-INTERNAL WAVE INTERACTIONS
NT2	TIDE-SURGE INTERACTION
NT1	WIND-WAVE INTERACTION
RT	AIR FLOW OVER WATER
RT	ATMOSPHERIC BOUNDARY LAYER
RT	ENERGY TRANSFER
RT	MOMENTUM TRANSFER
RT	SHEAR FLOW
RT	SURFACE LAYERS
RT	TURBULENCE
RT	WATER WAVE MOTION

WAVE INTERACTIONS (cont'd)
RT	WATER WAVES
RT	WAVE DIFFRACTION
RT	WAVE REFLECTION
RT	WAVE REFRACTION
RT	WAVES ON BEACHES

WAVE LOAD
USE	**WAVE FORCES**

WAVE MEASUREMENT
RT	GLITTER
RT	LASER ALTIMETRY
RT	MICROWAVE IMAGERY
RT	PHOTOGRAMMETRY
RT	RADAR ALTIMETRY
RT	RADAR IMAGERY
RT	SATELLITE ALTIMETRY
RT	STEREOPHOTOGRAPHY
RT	WATER LEVEL MEASUREMENT
RT	WAVE MEASURING EQUIPMENT

WAVE MEASURING EQUIPMENT
UF	wave staff sensors
UF	wave staffs
BT1	MEASURING DEVICES
NT1	WAVE DIRECTION SENSORS
NT1	WAVE GAUGES
RT	ECHOSOUNDERS
RT	OCEANOGRAPHIC EQUIPMENT
RT	PRESSURE SENSORS
RT	RADAR ALTIMETERS
RT	SURFACE WATER WAVES
RT	WAVE BUOYS
RT	WAVE FOLLOWERS
RT	WAVE MEASUREMENT
RT	WAVE MEASURING PLATFORMS
RT	WAVE RECORDERS
RT	WAVE SLOPE FOLLOWERS
RT	WAVE TANKS

WAVE MEASURING PLATFORMS
RT	RADAR ALTIMETRY
RT	WAVE MEASURING EQUIPMENT

WAVE METERS
USE	**WAVE GAUGES**

WAVE MOTION
SN	Use only for general works on wave phenomena
UF	wave theory
UF	waves
RT	ABSORPTION
RT	ABSORPTION (PHYSICS)
RT	ATTENUATION
RT	DIFFRACTION
RT	REFLECTION
RT	REFRACTION
RT	TRANSMISSION
RT	WAVE DISPERSION

WAVE NUMBER
RT	WAVE PROPERTIES
RT	WAVE SPECTRA
RT	WAVELENGTH

WAVE OVERTOPPING
USE	**OVERTOPPING**

WAVE PARTICLE MOTION
USE	**PARTICLE MOTION**

WAVE PARTICLE VELOCITY
USE	**ORBITAL VELOCITY**

WAVE PERIOD
RT	SIGNIFICANT WAVES
RT	SURGES
RT	WAVE FREQUENCY
RT	WAVE PROPERTIES
RT	WAVE STATISTICS

WAVE PHASE
RT	WAVE PROPERTIES

WAVE POWER
SN	Utilizing the energy of waves as a source of power
BT1	POWER FROM THE SEA
BT2	ENERGY RESOURCES
BT3	NATURAL RESOURCES
BT4	RESOURCES
RT	HYDROELECTRIC POWER
RT	TIDAL POWER
RT	WAVE ENERGY
RT	WAVE POWER DEVICES

WAVE POWER DEVICES
BT1	ELECTRIC POWER SOURCES
RT	HYDROELECTRIC POWER PLANTS
RT	WAVE BUOYS
RT	WAVE ENERGY
RT	WAVE POWER

WAVE POWER SPECTRA
USE	**WAVE SPECTRA**

WAVE PREDICTING
SN	Use only for prediction of wind waves
BT1	PREDICTION
NT1	WAVE FORECASTING
NT1	WAVE HINDCASTING
RT	SEA STATE
RT	WAVE PROPERTIES

WAVE PRESSURE
USE	**WAVE FORCES**

WAVE PROCESSES ON BEACHES
NT1	WAVE RUNUP
NT1	WAVE SETDOWN
NT1	WAVE SETUP
RT	BEACHES
RT	LONGSHORE CURRENTS
RT	ROCKY SHORES
RT	WATER WAVE MOTION
RT	WAVE BREAKING
RT	WAVES ON BEACHES

WAVE PROPAGATION
SN	Use only for water waves and specify type of wave
UF	propagation (water waves)
UF	transmission (water waves)
UF	water wave propagation
UF	wave transmission
NT1	TIDAL PROPAGATION
RT	WATER WAVE MOTION
RT	WATER WAVES
RT	WAVE ATTENUATION
RT	WAVE DIFFRACTION
RT	WAVE DISPERSION
RT	WAVE REFLECTION
RT	WAVE REFRACTION
RT	WAVE SCATTERING

WAVE PROPERTIES
RT	PHYSICAL PROPERTIES
RT	SEISMIC WAVES
RT	SOUND WAVES
RT	WATER WAVE PARAMETERS
RT	WATER WAVES
RT	WAVE AMPLITUDE
RT	WAVE DIRECTION
RT	WAVE FREQUENCY

WAVE PROPERTIES (cont'd)
RT	WAVE HEIGHT
RT	WAVE NUMBER
RT	WAVE PERIOD
RT	WAVE PHASE
RT	WAVE PREDICTING
RT	WAVE SLOPE
RT	WAVE SPECTRA
RT	WAVE STATISTICS
RT	WAVE STEEPNESS
RT	WAVE VELOCITY
RT	WAVELENGTH
RT	WIND WAVE PARAMETERS

WAVE RECORDERS
UF	capacitance wire wave recorders
UF	shipborne wave recorders
UF	surface wave recorders
BT1	RECORDING EQUIPMENT
BT2	EQUIPMENT
RT	ACCELEROMETERS
RT	WATER WAVES
RT	WAVE GAUGES
RT	WAVE MEASURING EQUIPMENT
RT	WIND WAVES

WAVE RECORDS
USE	**WAVE DATA**

WAVE REFLECTION
SN	Use only for water waves and specify type of wave
UF	reflection (water waves)
BT1	REFLECTION
RT	STANDING WAVES
RT	WAVE INTERACTIONS
RT	WAVE PROPAGATION

WAVE REFRACTION
SN	Before 1982 search also REFRACTION (WATER WAVES). Use only for water waves and specify type of wave
UF	refraction (water waves)
BT1	REFRACTION
RT	BEACH CUSPS
RT	BOTTOM TOPOGRAPHY EFFECTS
RT	SHALLOW WATER
RT	WAVE INTERACTIONS
RT	WAVE PROPAGATION
RT	WAVE REFRACTION DIAGRAMS
RT	WAVES ON BEACHES

WAVE REFRACTION DIAGRAMS
BT1	GRAPHS
BT2	GRAPHICS
BT3	AUDIOVISUAL MATERIAL
BT4	DOCUMENTS
RT	CAUSTICS
RT	ORTHOGONALS
RT	WAVE REFRACTION

WAVE RUNUP
SN	Before 1986 search also SWASH
UF	surges (beach)
UF	swash
UF	water runup
BT1	WAVE PROCESSES ON BEACHES
RT	BACKWASH
RT	BREAKWATERS
RT	SEA WALLS
RT	WATER WAVE MOTION
RT	WAVES ON BEACHES

WAVE SAND RIPPLES
USE	**SAND RIPPLES**

WAVE SCATTERING
SN	Use only for water waves
UF	scattering (water waves)
RT	WAVE ATTENUATION
RT	WAVE DISSIPATION
RT	WAVE PROPAGATION

WAVE SCOURING
SN	Before 1983 search CURRENT SCOURING
BT1	SCOURING
BT2	EROSION
RT	BED FORMS
RT	BOTTOM EROSION
RT	CURRENT SCOURING
RT	SHALLOW WATER
RT	SHALLOW WATER WAVES
RT	SURFACE WATER WAVES
RT	WAVE-CUT PLATFORMS

WAVE-SEABED INTERACTION
BT1	WAVE INTERACTIONS
RT	BED FORMS
RT	BENTHIC BOUNDARY LAYER
RT	BOTTOM PRESSURE
RT	CYCLIC LOADING
RT	INTERACTIONS
RT	SEDIMENT-WATER INTERFACE
RT	WAVE-INDUCED LOADING

WAVE SETDOWN
BT1	WAVE PROCESSES ON BEACHES
RT	SEA LEVEL
RT	SEA LEVEL VARIATIONS
RT	SURF BEATS
RT	WAVE SETUP
RT	WAVES ON BEACHES

WAVE SETUP
UF	setup (wave)
BT1	WAVE PROCESSES ON BEACHES
RT	BEACH CUSPS
RT	COAST DEFENCES
RT	LONGSHORE CURRENTS
RT	MASS TRANSPORT
RT	MOMENTUM TRANSFER
RT	SEA LEVEL
RT	SEA LEVEL VARIATIONS
RT	SURF BEATS
RT	WAVE SETDOWN
RT	WAVES ON BEACHES

WAVE SHAPE
USE	**WAVE GEOMETRY**

WAVE-SHORE INTERACTION
USE	**WAVES ON BEACHES**

WAVE SLOPE
RT	SAND WAVES
RT	SURFACE SLOPE
RT	WATER WAVES
RT	WAVE CRESTS
RT	WAVE GEOMETRY
RT	WAVE PROPERTIES
RT	WAVE SLOPE FOLLOWERS
RT	WAVE STEEPNESS

WAVE SLOPE FOLLOWERS
UF	slope followers
RT	WAVE MEASURING EQUIPMENT
RT	WAVE SLOPE

WAVE SPECTRA
UF	wave energy spectra
UF	wave power spectra
BT1	SPECTRA
RT	WAVE ENERGY
RT	WAVE FREQUENCY
RT	WAVE NUMBER
RT	WAVE PROPERTIES

WAVE SPECTRA (cont'd)
    RT   WAVE STATISTICS

WAVE STAFF SENSORS
    USE   **WAVE MEASURING EQUIPMENT**

WAVE STAFFS
    USE   **WAVE MEASURING EQUIPMENT**

WAVE STATISTICS
    UF   water wave statistics
    BT1   STATISTICS
    RT   DESIGN WAVE
    RT   WATER WAVES
    RT   WAVE DATA
    RT   WAVE GEOMETRY
    RT   WAVE GROUPS
    RT   WAVE HEIGHT
    RT   WAVE PERIOD
    RT   WAVE PROPERTIES
    RT   WAVE SPECTRA
    RT   WAVE VELOCITY

WAVE STEEPNESS
    RT   GRADIENTS
    RT   WAVE PROPERTIES
    RT   WAVE SLOPE

WAVE TANKS
    BT1   TANKS
    BT2   CONTAINERS
    RT   CALIBRATION
    RT   FLUMES
    RT   HYDRAULIC MODELS
    RT   LABORATORY EQUIPMENT
    RT   SCALE MODELS
    RT   TEST EQUIPMENT
    RT   TOWING TANKS
    RT   WAVE FOLLOWERS
    RT   WAVE GENERATORS
    RT   WAVE MEASURING EQUIPMENT

WAVE THEORY
    USE   **WAVE MOTION**

WAVE TOPOGRAPHY
    USE   **WAVE GEOMETRY**

WAVE TRAINS
    RT   BENJAMIN FEIR INSTABILITY
    RT   WATER WAVES
    RT   WAVE DISPERSION
    RT   WAVE GROUPS

WAVE TRANSMISSION
    USE   **WAVE PROPAGATION**

WAVE TRAPPING
    BT1   WAVE INTERACTIONS
    RT   TOPOGRAPHIC EFFECTS
    RT   TRAPPED WAVES
    RT   WATER WAVES

WAVE VELOCITY
    SN   Use only for water waves
    UF   wave celerity
    UF   wave velocity (water waves)
    BT1   VELOCITY
    RT   GROUP VELOCITY
    RT   ORBITAL VELOCITY
    RT   PHASE VELOCITY
    RT   SOUND WAVES
    RT   WAVE AGE
    RT   WAVE PROPERTIES
    RT   WAVE STATISTICS

WAVE VELOCITY (SEISMIC)
    USE   **SEISMIC VELOCITIES**

WAVE VELOCITY (SOUND)
    USE   **SOUND VELOCITY**

WAVE VELOCITY (WATER WAVES)
    USE   **WAVE VELOCITY**

WAVE-WAVE INTERACTION
    BT1   WAVE INTERACTIONS
    NT1   SHORT WAVE-LONG WAVE INTERACTIONS
    NT1   SURFACE WAVE-INTERNAL WAVE INTERACTIONS
    NT1   TIDE-SURGE INTERACTION
    RT   INTERACTIONS
    RT   RESONANT WAVE INTERACTION
    RT   WATER WAVES

WAVEFORM ANALYSIS
    RT   FOURIER ANALYSIS
    RT   HARMONIC ANALYSIS
    RT   SPECTRAL ANALYSIS

WAVELENGTH
    RT   WAVE NUMBER
    RT   WAVE PROPERTIES

WAVES
    USE   **WAVE MOTION**

WAVES (ACOUSTIC)
    USE   **SOUND WAVES**

WAVES (ELECTROMAGNETIC)
    USE   **ELECTROMAGNETIC RADIATION**

WAVES (PLANETARY)
    USE   **PLANETARY WAVES**

WAVES (SAND)
    USE   **SAND WAVES**

WAVES (SEISMIC)
    USE   **SEISMIC WAVES**

WAVES (SOUND)
    USE   **SOUND**

WAVES (WATER)
    USE   **WATER WAVES**

WAVES ON BEACHES
    UF   wave-shore interaction
    RT   BACKWASH
    RT   BREAKING WAVES
    RT   EDGE WAVES
    RT   NEARSHORE DYNAMICS
    RT   SHOALING
    RT   SHOALING WAVES
    RT   SURF
    RT   SURF ZONE
    RT   UNDERTOW
    RT   WAVE BREAKING
    RT   WAVE EFFECTS
    RT   WAVE INTERACTIONS
    RT   WAVE PROCESSES ON BEACHES
    RT   WAVE REFRACTION
    RT   WAVE RUNUP
    RT   WAVE SETDOWN
    RT   WAVE SETUP

WAX
    USE   **WAXES**

WAXES
    SN   Added in 1980
    UF   wax
    BT1   LIPIDS
    BT2   ORGANIC COMPOUNDS

WAXES (cont'd)
    RT   ANIMAL PRODUCTS
    RT   PETROLEUM

WEAR
    SN   As applied to materials
    RT   DETERIORATION
    RT   FRICTION
    RT   TOUGHNESS

WEATHER
    SN   State of the atmosphere at a given time as defined by the meteorological elements. Before 1982 search WEATHER CONDITIONS
    UF   atmospheric conditions
    UF   weather conditions
    BT1   CLIMATE
    NT1   STORMS
    RT   AIR TEMPERATURE
    RT   ANTICYCLONES
    RT   ATMOSPHERIC DEPRESSIONS
    RT   ATMOSPHERIC PRECIPITATIONS
    RT   ATMOSPHERIC PRESSURE
    RT   CLOUD COVER
    RT   CLOUDS
    RT   FOG
    RT   HUMIDITY
    RT   ICE CONDITIONS
    RT   ICING
    RT   LIGHTNING
    RT   METEOROLOGY
    RT   RAINFALL
    RT   SEA LEVEL PRESSURE
    RT   SEA STATE
    RT   TROPOSPHERE
    RT   WEATHER FORECASTING
    RT   WEATHER HAZARDS
    RT   WEATHER MAPS
    RT   WIND SPEED

WEATHER CONDITIONS
    USE   **WEATHER**

WEATHER FORECAST MAP
    USE   **WEATHER MAPS**

WEATHER FORECASTING
    UF   weather forecasts
    BT1   PREDICTION
    RT   ATMOSPHERIC FRONTS
    RT   ATMOSPHERIC PRESSURE
    RT   CLIMATE
    RT   CLIMATE PREDICTION
    RT   METEOROLOGY
    RT   SATELLITE SENSING
    RT   SHIP ROUTEING
    RT   STORMS
    RT   TROPICAL DEPRESSIONS
    RT   WEATHER
    RT   WEATHER MAPS
    RT   WEATHER SHIPS

WEATHER FORECASTS
    USE   **WEATHER FORECASTING**

WEATHER HAZARDS
    BT1   HAZARDS
    RT   DROUGHTS
    RT   FLOODS
    RT   HURRICANES
    RT   ICING
    RT   STORMS
    RT   WEATHER

WEATHER MAPS
    UF   weather forecast map
    BT1   METEOROLOGICAL CHARTS
    BT2   MAPS
    BT3   GRAPHICS

ASFIS Thesaurus

WEATHER MAPS (cont'd)
BT4	AUDIOVISUAL MATERIAL
RT	AIR TEMPERATURE
RT	FACSIMILE TRANSMISSION
RT	ISOBARS
RT	METEOROLOGICAL OBSERVATIONS
RT	WEATHER
RT	WEATHER FORECASTING
RT	WIND DIRECTION
RT	WIND SPEED

WEATHER ROUTEING
USE	**SHIP ROUTEING**

WEATHER SHIPS
UF	ocean weather ships
BT1	SHIPS
BT2	SURFACE CRAFT
BT3	VEHICLES
RT	DATA BUOYS
RT	INSTRUMENT PLATFORMS
RT	METEOROLOGICAL DATA
RT	METEOROLOGY
RT	OCEAN STATIONS
RT	OCEANOGRAPHIC DATA
RT	RESEARCH VESSELS
RT	WEATHER FORECASTING

WEATHERING
RT	ATMOSPHERIC PRECIPITATIONS
RT	CORROSION
RT	DEGRADATION
RT	DETRITUS
RT	ENVIRONMENTAL EFFECTS
RT	EROSION
RT	FATE
RT	GEOCHEMISTRY
RT	GEOMORPHOLOGY
RT	LEACHING
RT	SEDIMENT CHEMISTRY

WEED CUTTING
USE	**PLANT CONTROL**

WEEDS
NT1	FRESHWATER WEEDS
NT1	SEAWEEDS
RT	AQUATIC PLANTS
RT	PLANT CONTROL
RT	PLANT DISEASES
RT	PLANT PHYSIOLOGY
RT	PLANT POPULATIONS
RT	PLEUSTON
RT	SEA GRASS

WEEKLY
SN	Descriptor to be used only as a qualifier
BT1	PERIODICITY

WEGENER HYPOTHESIS
USE	**CONTINENTAL DRIFT**

WEIGHT
BT1	PHYSICAL PROPERTIES
BT2	PROPERTIES
NT1	DRY WEIGHT
NT1	MOLECULAR WEIGHT
NT1	WET WEIGHT
RT	DISPLACEMENT
RT	GRAVITY
RT	LENGTH-WEIGHT RELATIONSHIPS
RT	LOADS (FORCES)
RT	MASS
RT	PRESSURE
RT	SPECIFIC GRAVITY

WEIGHT-LENGTH RELATIONSHIPS
USE	**LENGTH-WEIGHT RELATIONSHIPS**

WEIRS
SN	Structures built across rivers or channels to raise the water level and divert it
BT1	BARRAGES
BT2	HYDRAULIC STRUCTURES
RT	CHANNELS
RT	DAMS
RT	FLOWMETERS
RT	HYDRAULIC ENGINEERING
RT	RIVER ENGINEERING
RT	RIVERS

WELDING
NT1	ELECTRIC ARC WELDING
NT1	EXPLOSIVE WELDING
NT1	WELDING UNDERWATER
RT	CUTTING
RT	HEAT AFFECTED ZONES
RT	LAMELLAR TEARING
RT	PIPELINE CONSTRUCTION

WELDING UNDERWATER
BT1	WELDING
RT	CUTTING UNDERWATER
RT	WORKING UNDERWATER

WELL COMPLETION
UF	completion (well)
UF	offshore completion
RT	DRILLING
RT	OIL WELLS

WELL LOGGING
BT1	LOGGING
RT	BOREHOLES

WELL WORKOVER OPERATIONS
UF	workovers
RT	OIL AND GAS PRODUCTION
RT	WORKOVER BARGES

WELLHEADS
UF	christmas trees
UF	underwater wellheads
BT1	UNDERWATER STRUCTURES
BT2	OFFSHORE STRUCTURES
BT3	HYDRAULIC STRUCTURES
RT	BLOWOUT PREVENTERS
RT	FLOWLINES
RT	MANIFOLDS
RT	OCEAN FLOOR
RT	SUBSEA PRODUCTION SYSTEMS
RT	TEMPLATES

WELLS (OIL AND GAS)
USE	**OIL WELLS**

WEST WIND DRIFT
RT	WESTERLIES

WESTERLIES
BT1	PLANETARY WINDS
BT2	WINDS
BT3	ATMOSPHERIC MOTION
NT1	EQUATORIAL WESTERLIES
RT	WEST WIND DRIFT

WESTERN BOUNDARY CURRENTS
BT1	BOUNDARY CURRENTS
BT2	WATER CURRENTS
BT3	WATER MOTION
RT	OCEAN CURRENTS
RT	WESTERN BOUNDARY UNDERCURRENTS
RT	WESTWARD INTENSIFICATION

WESTERN BOUNDARY UNDERCURRENTS
BT1	UNDERCURRENTS
BT2	WATER CURRENTS
BT3	WATER MOTION
RT	CONTOUR CURRENTS
RT	OCEAN CURRENTS
RT	WESTERN BOUNDARY CURRENTS

WESTWARD INTENSIFICATION
SN	Westward intensification of velocity of wind driven currents
RT	CURRENT VELOCITY
RT	PLANETARY VORTICITY
RT	WESTERN BOUNDARY CURRENTS

WET
SN	Used only as a qualifier
RT	DRY

WET BULK DENSITY
BT1	SEDIMENT DENSITY
BT2	DENSITY
BT3	PHYSICAL PROPERTIES
BT4	PROPERTIES
RT	GEOTECHNICAL DATA
RT	GRAIN SIZE
RT	POROSITY
RT	WATER CONTENT

WET SEASON
USE	**RAINY SEASON**

WET SUBMERSIBLES
BT1	SUBMERSIBLES
BT2	MANNED VEHICLES
BT3	UNDERWATER VEHICLES
BT4	VEHICLES
RT	UNTETHERED VEHICLES

WET WEIGHT
BT1	WEIGHT
BT2	PHYSICAL PROPERTIES
BT3	PROPERTIES
RT	DENSITY
RT	DRY WEIGHT
RT	SPECIFIC GRAVITY
RT	WATER CONTENT

WETLANDS
SN	Added in 1980
BT1	LANDFORMS
BT2	TOPOGRAPHIC FEATURES
NT1	MARSHES
NT2	SALT MARSHES
NT1	SWAMPS
NT2	MANGROVE SWAMPS
RT	AMPHIBIOUS VEHICLES
RT	AQUATIC ENVIRONMENT
RT	CHENIERS
RT	DELTAS
RT	FLOODING
RT	FRESH WATER
RT	LAND RECLAMATION
RT	STAGNANT WATER

WHALE STRANDING
USE	**STRANDING**

WHALEBONES
USE	**BALEENS**

WHALING
UF	whaling techniques
NT1	ARTISANAL WHALING
RT	ANIMAL OIL EXTRACTION
RT	AQUATIC MAMMALS
RT	BLUE WHALE UNIT
RT	CATCHERS
RT	CETOLOGISTS
RT	CETOLOGY

WHALING (cont'd)
RT   FACTORY SHIPS
RT   HUNTING
RT   MARINE MAMMALS
RT   QUOTA REGULATIONS
RT   WHALING REGULATIONS
RT   WHALING STATIONS
RT   WHALING STATISTICS
RT   WOUNDING
RT   WOUNDING GEAR

WHALING REGULATIONS
SN   Added in 1982
BT1   FISHERY REGULATIONS
BT2   LEGISLATION
RT   BLUE WHALE UNIT
RT   INTERNATIONAL AGREEMENTS
RT   WHALING

WHALING STATIONS
RT   CATCHERS
RT   WHALING

WHALING STATISTICS
SN   Catch tabulation of whales and allied species including derived industrial products
BT1   CATCH STATISTICS
BT2   FISHERY STATISTICS
RT   BLUE WHALE UNIT
RT   CATCHERS
RT   CETOLOGY
RT   WHALING
RT   WOUNDING

WHALING TECHNIQUES
USE   **WHALING**

WHELK FISHERIES
USE   **GASTROPOD FISHERIES**

WHIRLING DISEASE
SN   Added in 1980
UF   tumbling disease
BT1   FISH DISEASES
BT2   ANIMAL DISEASES
BT3   DISEASES
RT   FISH CULTURE
RT   FRESHWATER AQUACULTURE
RT   HUSBANDRY DISEASES
RT   PARASITIC DISEASES
RT   SWIM BLADDER

WHITE MUSCLES
USE   **MUSCLES**

WHITECAPPING
BT1   WAVE BREAKING
BT2   WAVE DISSIPATION
BT3   ENERGY DISSIPATION
BT4   ENERGY TRANSFER
RT   WAVE DISSIPATION
RT   WHITECAPS

WHITECAPS
BT1   BREAKING WAVES
BT2   SURFACE WATER WAVES
BT3   WATER WAVES
RT   FOAMS
RT   WHITECAPPING

WHITING FISHERIES
USE   **GADOID FISHERIES**

WIDTH
SN   Used only as a qualifier
UF   breadth
BT1   DIMENSIONS

WILD FISH STOCKS
USE   **STOCKS**

WILD SPAWNING
SN   Before 1982 search SPAWNING
UF   uncontrolled spawning
BT1   SPAWNING
RT   FISH CULTURE

WILDLIFE CONSERVATION
USE   **NATURE CONSERVATION**

WINCHES
BT1   LIFTING TACKLE
BT2   DECK EQUIPMENT
BT3   EQUIPMENT
RT   FISHING GEAR
RT   GEAR HANDLING
RT   HYDROGRAPHIC WIRE
RT   LIMNOLOGICAL EQUIPMENT
RT   OCEANOGRAPHIC EQUIPMENT
RT   ROPES
RT   TOWING
RT   WIRE ROPE

WIND
USE   **WINDS**

WIND ABRASION
RT   DUNES
RT   EOLIAN TRANSPORT
RT   SCOURING
RT   WINDS

WIND CONSTANCY
RT   VARIABILITY
RT   WIND POWER
RT   WIND SPEED

WIND DATA
BT1   METEOROLOGICAL DATA
BT2   DATA
RT   WIND DIRECTION
RT   WIND FIELDS
RT   WIND MEASUREMENT
RT   WIND SPEED
RT   WIND STRESS
RT   WINDS

WIND DIRECTION
BT1   DIRECTION
RT   ANEMOMETERS
RT   WEATHER MAPS
RT   WIND DATA
RT   WIND MEASUREMENT
RT   WIND ROSES
RT   WIND SPEED
RT   WIND VECTORS
RT   WINDROWS
RT   WINDS

WIND DRIFT (CURRENT)
USE   **WIND-DRIVEN CURRENTS**

WIND-DRIVEN CIRCULATION
BT1   WATER CIRCULATION
BT2   WATER MOTION
RT   OCEAN CIRCULATION
RT   SURFACE CIRCULATION
RT   SVERDRUP TRANSPORT
RT   THERMOHALINE CIRCULATION
RT   WIND-DRIVEN CURRENTS

WIND-DRIVEN CURRENTS
SN   Search also DRIFT CURRENTS
UF   barometric currents
UF   drift currents
UF   wind drift (current)
BT1   WATER CURRENTS
BT2   WATER MOTION

WIND-DRIVEN CURRENTS (cont'd)
RT   BIOLOGICAL DRIFT
RT   BOUNDARY CURRENTS
RT   COASTAL CURRENTS
RT   EKMAN SPIRAL
RT   LONGSHORE CURRENTS
RT   NEARSHORE CURRENTS
RT   OCEAN CURRENTS
RT   RIP CURRENTS
RT   SURFACE CURRENTS
RT   SURFACE EKMAN LAYER
RT   SVERDRUP TRANSPORT
RT   UPWELLING
RT   WIND WAVES
RT   WIND-DRIVEN CIRCULATION
RT   WINDS

WIND ENERGY
USE   **WIND POWER**

WIND EROSION
BT1   EROSION
RT   DUNES
RT   EROSION CONTROL
RT   SOIL CONSERVATION
RT   WINDS

WIND FIELDS
RT   WIND DATA
RT   WINDS

WIND FORCES
USE   **WIND PRESSURE**

WIND-GENERATED NOISE
USE   **SURFACE NOISE**

WIND GENERATED WAVES
USE   **WIND WAVES**

WIND LOADING
USE   **WIND PRESSURE**

WIND MEASUREMENT
BT1   FLOW MEASUREMENT
BT2   MEASUREMENT
RT   WIND DATA
RT   WIND DIRECTION
RT   WIND MEASURING EQUIPMENT
RT   WIND SPEED
RT   WINDS

WIND MEASURING EQUIPMENT
BT1   FLOW MEASURING EQUIPMENT
RT   ANEMOMETERS
RT   BALLOONS
RT   FLOWMETERS
RT   METEOROLOGICAL INSTRUMENTS
RT   RADIOSONDES
RT   TURBULENCE MEASUREMENT
RT   WIND MEASUREMENT
RT   WINDS

WIND POWER
UF   wind energy
BT1   ENERGY RESOURCES
BT2   NATURAL RESOURCES
BT3   RESOURCES
RT   POWER FROM THE SEA
RT   RENEWABLE RESOURCES
RT   WIND CONSTANCY
RT   WIND PRESSURE
RT   WIND SPEED
RT   WINDS

WIND PRESSURE
SN   The force exerted on a structure by wind. Before 1983 search also WIND FORCES
UF   wind forces

WIND PRESSURE (cont'd)
UF	wind loading
BT1	LOADS (FORCES)
BT2	FORCES (MECHANICS)
RT	OFFSHORE STRUCTURES
RT	WIND POWER
RT	WINDS

WIND PROFILES
UF	wind speed profiles
BT1	VELOCITY PROFILES
BT2	VERTICAL PROFILES
BT3	PROFILES
RT	ATMOSPHERIC BOUNDARY LAYER
RT	VELOCITY GRADIENTS
RT	WAVE-AIR INTERACTION
RT	WIND SHEAR
RT	WIND SPEED
RT	WINDS

WIND ROSES
BT1	MAP GRAPHICS
BT2	GRAPHICS
BT3	AUDIOVISUAL MATERIAL
BT4	DOCUMENTS
RT	CLIMATOLOGICAL CHARTS
RT	CURRENT ROSES
RT	WIND DIRECTION
RT	WIND SPEED
RT	WINDS

WIND SETUP
SN	Use for changes in still water level due to wind stress in enclosed bodies of water
UF	setup (wind)
UF	wind time
RT	LAKE DYNAMICS
RT	RESERVOIRS (WATER)
RT	STORM SURGES
RT	WATER LEVELS
RT	WIND STRESS

WIND SHEAR
BT1	SHEAR
RT	CURRENT SHEAR
RT	VERTICAL SHEAR
RT	WIND PROFILES
RT	WIND SPEED
RT	WIND VECTORS

WIND SPEED
UF	wind strength
UF	wind velocity
BT1	VELOCITY
RT	ANEMOMETERS
RT	BREEZES
RT	FLOWMETERS
RT	GALE FORCE WINDS
RT	GUSTS
RT	VELOCITY GRADIENTS
RT	WATER WAVE PARAMETERS
RT	WAVE AGE
RT	WEATHER
RT	WEATHER MAPS
RT	WIND CONSTANCY
RT	WIND DATA
RT	WIND DIRECTION
RT	WIND MEASUREMENT
RT	WIND POWER
RT	WIND PROFILES
RT	WIND ROSES
RT	WIND SHEAR
RT	WIND VECTORS
RT	WIND WAVE PARAMETERS
RT	WINDS

WIND SPEED PROFILES
USE	**WIND PROFILES**

WIND STRENGTH
USE	**WIND SPEED**

WIND STRESS
UF	surface stress
BT1	STRESS
BT2	FORCES (MECHANICS)
RT	ATMOSPHERIC BOUNDARY LAYER
RT	ATMOSPHERIC FORCING
RT	DRAG
RT	DRAG COEFFICIENT
RT	ICE DRIFT
RT	REYNOLDS STRESSES
RT	SHEAR STRESS
RT	SVERDRUP TRANSPORT
RT	WATER WAVE PARAMETERS
RT	WIND DATA
RT	WIND SETUP
RT	WIND STRESS CURL
RT	WIND WAVE GENERATION
RT	WIND WAVE PARAMETERS
RT	WIND-WAVE INTERACTION
RT	WINDS

WIND STRESS CURL
UF	curl of wind stress
BT1	CURL (VECTORS)
BT2	VECTORS
RT	WIND STRESS
RT	WIND VECTORS

WIND SYSTEMS
USE	**WINDS**

WIND TIME
USE	**WIND SETUP**

WIND TUNNELS
BT1	TANKS
BT2	CONTAINERS
RT	METEOROLOGICAL INSTRUMENTS
RT	TEST EQUIPMENT

WIND VANES
USE	**VANES**

WIND VECTORS
BT1	MAP GRAPHICS
BT2	GRAPHICS
BT3	AUDIOVISUAL MATERIAL
BT4	DOCUMENTS
RT	VECTORS
RT	WIND DIRECTION
RT	WIND SHEAR
RT	WIND SPEED
RT	WIND STRESS CURL
RT	WINDS

WIND VELOCITY
USE	**WIND SPEED**

WIND WAVE GENERATION
BT1	WAVE GENERATION
RT	AIR FLOW OVER WATER
RT	DRAG
RT	DRAG COEFFICIENT
RT	DURATION
RT	FETCH
RT	MOMENTUM TRANSFER
RT	SURFACE ROUGHNESS
RT	WIND STRESS
RT	WIND WAVES
RT	WIND-WAVE INTERACTION

WIND-WAVE INTERACTION
BT1	WAVE INTERACTIONS
RT	AIR FLOW OVER WATER
RT	WIND STRESS
RT	WIND WAVE GENERATION
RT	WIND WAVES

WIND WAVE PARAMETERS
RT	DURATION
RT	FETCH
RT	PARAMETERS
RT	WATER DEPTH
RT	WAVE PROPERTIES
RT	WIND SPEED
RT	WIND STRESS
RT	WIND WAVES

WIND WAVES
UF	wind generated waves
BT1	SURFACE WATER WAVES
BT2	WATER WAVES
RT	SURFACE GRAVITY WAVES
RT	SURGES
RT	SWELL
RT	WAVE CLIMATE
RT	WAVE RECORDERS
RT	WIND WAVE GENERATION
RT	WIND WAVE PARAMETERS
RT	WIND-DRIVEN CURRENTS
RT	WIND-WAVE INTERACTION

WINDROWS
BT1	SLICKS
RT	CELLULAR CONVECTION
RT	LANGMUIR CIRCULATION
RT	SURFACE FILMS
RT	SURFACE PROPERTIES
RT	WIND DIRECTION

WINDS
UF	wind
UF	wind systems
BT1	ATMOSPHERIC MOTION
NT1	GALE FORCE WINDS
NT1	GEOSTROPHIC WINDS
NT1	GRADIENT WINDS
NT1	LOCAL WINDS
NT2	BREEZES
NT3	LAND AND SEA BREEZES
NT3	LAND BREEZES
NT3	SEA BREEZES
NT2	MISTRAL
NT1	PLANETARY WINDS
NT2	MONSOONS
NT2	TRADE WINDS
NT3	EQUATORIAL EASTERLIES
NT2	WESTERLIES
NT3	EQUATORIAL WESTERLIES
RT	ANEMOMETERS
RT	ANTICYCLONES
RT	ATMOSPHERIC CIRCULATION
RT	ATMOSPHERIC PRESSURE
RT	ATMOSPHERIC TURBULENCE
RT	CLIMATE
RT	CLIMATOLOGY
RT	DURATION
RT	EOLIAN DUST
RT	EOLIAN PROCESSES
RT	EOLIAN TRANSPORT
RT	FETCH
RT	FLUID FLOW
RT	GUSTS
RT	HURRICANES
RT	LANGMUIR CIRCULATION
RT	METEOROLOGY
RT	SEA LEVEL PRESSURE
RT	STORMS
RT	TORNADOES
RT	UPWELLING
RT	WIND ABRASION

ASFIS Thesaurus

WINDS (cont'd)
RT	WIND DATA
RT	WIND DIRECTION
RT	WIND-DRIVEN CURRENTS
RT	WIND EROSION
RT	WIND FIELDS
RT	WIND MEASUREMENT
RT	WIND MEASURING EQUIPMENT
RT	WIND POWER
RT	WIND PRESSURE
RT	WIND PROFILES
RT	WIND ROSES
RT	WIND SPEED
RT	WIND STRESS
RT	WIND VECTORS

WINGS
SN	Before 1982 search LOCOMOTORY APPENDAGES
BT1	LOCOMOTORY APPENDAGES
BT2	ANIMAL APPENDAGES
RT	ANIMAL NAVIGATION
RT	AQUATIC BIRDS
RT	AQUATIC INSECTS

WINKLE FISHERIES
USE	**GASTROPOD FISHERIES**

WINKLER METHOD
BT1	ANALYTICAL TECHNIQUES
RT	DISSOLVED OXYGEN

WINNOWING
BT1	SEDIMENT SORTING
RT	PARTICLE SETTLING
RT	SEDIMENT TRANSPORT

WINTER
BT1	SEASONS
RT	OVERWINTERING TECHNIQUES
RT	WINTERKILL

WINTER EGGS
USE	**RESTING EGGS**

WINTERKILL
SN	The loss of animals in a lake, pond or other water body as a result of heavy ice cover or mid-winter anoxia affecting eutrophic lakes. Added in 1980
BT1	FISH KILL
RT	ANOXIC CONDITIONS
RT	ICE COVER
RT	LAKE ICE
RT	OVERWINTERING TECHNIQUES
RT	OXYGEN DEPLETION
RT	TEMPERATURE EFFECTS
RT	WINTER

WIRE ANGLE
RT	GRADIENTS
RT	HYDROGRAPHIC WIRE
RT	WIRE ANGLE INDICATORS

WIRE ANGLE INDICATORS
BT1	SLOPE INDICATORS
BT2	MEASURING DEVICES
RT	HYDROGRAPHIC WIRE
RT	WIRE ANGLE

WIRE ROPE
SN	Do not use for electric cables.
UF	steel wire
UF	wires
BT1	ROPES
NT1	HYDROGRAPHIC WIRE
RT	CABLE DYNAMICS
RT	CABLES

WIRE ROPE (cont'd)
RT	GUIDE LINES
RT	TENSOMETERS
RT	WINCHES

WIRES
USE	**WIRE ROPE**

WITHIN-YEAR VARIATIONS
USE	**SEASONAL VARIATIONS**

WOMEN
BT1	HUMAN RESOURCES
BT2	RESOURCES
RT	ARTISANAL FISHING
RT	FISHERMEN
RT	FISHERY DEVELOPMENT
RT	SOCIOLOGICAL ASPECTS

WOOD
BT1	MATERIALS

WORK BOATS
USE	**SUPPORT SHIPS**

WORK PLATFORMS
UF	platforms (work)
BT1	VEHICLES
NT1	DRILLING PLATFORMS
NT1	PRODUCTION PLATFORMS
RT	BARGES
RT	CABLE SHIPS
RT	DREDGERS
RT	DRILLING VESSELS
RT	FACTORY SHIPS
RT	FISHING VESSELS
RT	FIXED PLATFORMS
RT	OFFSHORE STRUCTURES
RT	SURFACE CRAFT
RT	UNDERWATER HABITATS
RT	UNDERWATER STRUCTURES
RT	UNDERWATER VEHICLES

WORKERS
USE	**PERSONNEL**

WORKING UNDERWATER
UF	divers work
UF	underwater work
RT	CAISSONS
RT	DIVING
RT	DIVING BELLS
RT	DIVING INDUSTRY
RT	DIVING PHYSIOLOGY
RT	DIVING SURVEYS
RT	DIVING TOOLS
RT	LIGHT SOURCES
RT	LOCATIONS (WORKING)
RT	SATURATION DIVING
RT	SURVEYING UNDERWATER
RT	UNDERWATER EQUIPMENT
RT	UNDERWATER HABITATS
RT	UNDERWATER PHOTOGRAPHY
RT	UNDERWATER STRUCTURES
RT	VISIBILITY UNDERWATER
RT	WELDING UNDERWATER

WORKOVER BARGES
BT1	MOBILE PLATFORMS
BT2	FLOATING STRUCTURES
BT3	OFFSHORE STRUCTURES
BT4	HYDRAULIC STRUCTURES
RT	BARGES
RT	WELL WORKOVER OPERATIONS

WORKOVERS
USE	**WELL WORKOVER OPERATIONS**

WORKSHOPS
USE	**CONFERENCES**

WORLD
SN	Use for worldwide studies, e.g. economics, commodity statistics. For world geographic descriptors, see World Entries Facet in Geographic Authority List
RT	ECONOMICS
RT	INDUSTRIAL PRODUCTS STATISTICS
RT	RESOURCES
RT	SOCIOLOGICAL ASPECTS
RT	TRADE

WORM CULTURE
SN	Added in 1982
BT1	AQUACULTURE
RT	ARTIFICIAL FEEDING
RT	BAIT
RT	FOOD ORGANISMS
RT	FROG CULTURE
RT	WORM FISHING

WORM FISHING
SN	Fishing with worms as bait. Added in 1980
BT1	CATCHING METHODS
RT	ANGLING
RT	BAIT FISHING
RT	FISHING
RT	WORM CULTURE

WOUNDING
BT1	CATCHING METHODS
RT	FISHING
RT	HUNTING
RT	WHALING
RT	WHALING STATISTICS
RT	WOUNDING GEAR

WOUNDING GEAR
UF	harpoons
UF	impaling gear
BT1	FISHING GEAR
RT	HUNTING
RT	PELAGIC FISHERIES
RT	SPEAR FISHING
RT	WHALING
RT	WOUNDING

WOUNDS
USE	**INJURIES**

WRECK LOCATION
BT1	DETECTION
RT	LOCATING
RT	SURVEYING UNDERWATER
RT	UNDERWATER OBJECT LOCATION
RT	WRECKS

WRECK MARKS
USE	**OBSTACLE MARKS**

WRECK RECOVERY
USE	**SALVAGING**

WRECKS
RT	FLOTSAM
RT	NAVIGATIONAL HAZARDS
RT	SALVAGING
RT	SHIP LOSSES
RT	SHIPPING
RT	WRECK LOCATION

X-RAY ANALYSIS
USE	**X-RAY SPECTROSCOPY**

X-RAY DIFFRACTION ANALYSIS
BT1	X-RAY SPECTROSCOPY
BT2	SPECTROSCOPIC TECHNIQUES
BT3	ANALYTICAL TECHNIQUES
RT	DIFFRACTION

X-RAY EMISSION ANALYSIS
BT1	X-RAY SPECTROSCOPY
BT2	SPECTROSCOPIC TECHNIQUES
BT3	ANALYTICAL TECHNIQUES

X-RAY FLUORESCENCE ANALYSIS
BT1	X-RAY SPECTROSCOPY
BT2	SPECTROSCOPIC TECHNIQUES
BT3	ANALYTICAL TECHNIQUES

X-RAY INSPECTION
SN	Added in 1980
BT1	INSPECTION
RT	QUALITY CONTROL
RT	X-RAY SPECTROSCOPY
RT	X-RAYS

X-RAY SPECTROSCOPY
SN	Before 1982 search also X-RAY ANALYSIS
UF	x-ray analysis
BT1	SPECTROSCOPIC TECHNIQUES
BT2	ANALYTICAL TECHNIQUES
NT1	X-RAY DIFFRACTION ANALYSIS
NT1	X-RAY EMISSION ANALYSIS
NT1	X-RAY FLUORESCENCE ANALYSIS
RT	ANALYSIS
RT	CHEMICAL ANALYSIS
RT	RADIOGRAPHY
RT	X-RAY INSPECTION
RT	X-RAYS

X-RAYS
BT1	ELECTROMAGNETIC RADIATION
BT2	RADIATIONS
RT	X-RAY INSPECTION
RT	X-RAY SPECTROSCOPY

XANTHOPHORES
USE	**CHROMATOPHORES**

XANTHOPHYLLS
BT1	PHOTOSYNTHETIC PIGMENTS
BT2	PIGMENTS
BT3	GLYCOSIDES
BT4	CARBOHYDRATES
RT	PHOTOSYNTHESIS

XBTs
UF	expendable bathythermographs
BT1	BATHYTHERMOGRAPHS
BT2	PROFILERS
RT	AXBTs
RT	THERMISTORS

XENON
BT1	CHEMICAL ELEMENTS
RT	RARE GASES
RT	XENON ISOTOPES

XENON ISOTOPES
BT1	ISOTOPES
RT	XENON

XYLENE
BT1	AROMATIC HYDROCARBONS
BT2	UNSATURATED HYDROCARBONS
BT3	HYDROCARBONS
BT4	ORGANIC COMPOUNDS

XYLOSE
BT1	MONOSACCHARIDES
BT2	SACCHARIDES
BT3	CARBOHYDRATES
BT4	ORGANIC COMPOUNDS
RT	ALDEHYDES

YACHT HARBOURS
USE	**MARINAS**

YACHTING
BT1	RECREATION
RT	SAILS
RT	YACHTS

YACHTS
BT1	SAILING SHIPS
BT2	SHIPS
BT3	SURFACE CRAFT
BT4	VEHICLES
RT	MARINAS
RT	RECREATION
RT	RECREATIONAL WATERS
RT	SAILS
RT	YACHTING

YARNS
UF	twine
BT1	GEAR MATERIALS
BT2	MATERIALS
RT	FISHING NETS
RT	LINES
RT	SYNTHETIC FIBRES

YAW
USE	**YAWING**

YAW RESPONSE
BT1	DYNAMIC RESPONSE
BT2	INSTRUMENT RESPONSES
RT	BUOY MOTION EFFECTS
RT	YAWING

YAWING
UF	yaw
BT1	SHIP MOTION
RT	BUOY MOTION
RT	BUOY MOTION EFFECTS
RT	DYNAMIC RESPONSE
RT	ROLLING
RT	YAW RESPONSE

YEAR TO YEAR VARIATIONS
USE	**ANNUAL VARIATIONS**

YEARBOOKS
USE	**DIRECTORIES**

YEARLY CHANGES
USE	**ANNUAL VARIATIONS**

YEASTS
BT1	MICROORGANISMS
RT	FERMENTATION
RT	SINGLE CELL PROTEINS

YELLOW SUBSTANCE
USE	**GELBSTOFF**

YELLOW TAIL FISHERIES
USE	**CARANGID FISHERIES**

YIELD
UF	yield tables
NT1	POTENTIAL YIELD
RT	BIOLOGICAL PRODUCTION
RT	BIOMASS
RT	FISHING MORTALITY
RT	OVERFISHING
RT	POPULATION NUMBER

YIELD (cont'd)
RT	RECRUITMENT
RT	STOCK ASSESSMENT
RT	YIELD PREDICTIONS

YIELD POINT
BT1	MECHANICAL PROPERTIES
BT2	PHYSICAL PROPERTIES
BT3	PROPERTIES
RT	COLLAPSE STRENGTH
RT	DEFORMATION
RT	STRENGTH

YIELD PREDICTIONS
BT1	PREDICTION
RT	YIELD

YIELD TABLES
USE	**YIELD**

YOLK
SN	Added in 1980
RT	CYTOPLASM
RT	EGGS
RT	FATS
RT	PROTEINS
RT	VITELLOGENESIS

YTTERBIUM
BT1	CHEMICAL ELEMENTS
RT	RARE EARTHS
RT	TRANSITION ELEMENTS
RT	YTTERBIUM COMPOUNDS
RT	YTTERBIUM ISOTOPES

YTTERBIUM COMPOUNDS
RT	CHEMICAL COMPOUNDS
RT	YTTERBIUM

YTTERBIUM ISOTOPES
BT1	ISOTOPES
RT	YTTERBIUM

YTTRIUM
BT1	CHEMICAL ELEMENTS
RT	ALKALINE EARTH METALS
RT	YTTRIUM COMPOUNDS
RT	YTTRIUM ISOTOPES

YTTRIUM COMPOUNDS
RT	CHEMICAL COMPOUNDS
RT	YTTRIUM

YTTRIUM ISOTOPES
BT1	ISOTOPES
RT	YTTRIUM

ZEOLITE FACIES
BT1	METAMORPHIC FACIES
BT2	FACIES
RT	ZEOLITES

ZEOLITES
BT1	SILICATE MINERALS
BT2	MINERALS
NT1	ANALCITE
NT1	CLINOPTILONITE
NT1	HEULANDITE
NT1	PHILLIPSITE
RT	METAMORPHIC ROCKS
RT	ZEOLITE FACIES

ZINC
BT1	CHEMICAL ELEMENTS
RT	FERROMANGANESE NODULES
RT	HEAVY METALS
RT	HOT BRINES
RT	METALLIFEROUS SEDIMENTS
RT	METALS
RT	TRACE ELEMENTS

ASFIS Thesaurus

ZINC (cont'd)
RT   ZINC COMPOUNDS
RT   ZINC ISOTOPES

ZINC COMPOUNDS
RT   CHEMICAL COMPOUNDS
RT   ZINC

ZINC ISOTOPES
BT1   ISOTOPES
RT   ZINC

ZIRCON
BT1   SILICATE MINERALS
BT2   MINERALS
RT   PLACERS
RT   ZIRCONIUM

ZIRCONIUM
BT1   CHEMICAL ELEMENTS
RT   FERROMANGANESE NODULES
RT   METALS
RT   TRACE METALS
RT   ZIRCON
RT   ZIRCONIUM COMPOUNDS
RT   ZIRCONIUM ISOTOPES

ZIRCONIUM COMPOUNDS
RT   CHEMICAL COMPOUNDS
RT   ZIRCONIUM

ZIRCONIUM ISOTOPES
BT1   ISOTOPES
RT   ZIRCONIUM

ZOEAE
SN   Added in 1980
BT1   CRUSTACEAN LARVAE
BT2   INVERTEBRATE LARVAE
BT3   LARVAE
BT4   DEVELOPMENTAL STAGES
RT   MARINE CRUSTACEANS

ZONAL DISTRIBUTION
SN   Distribution East-West between or
        along lines of latitude. Used only
        as a qualifier
BT1   GEOGRAPHICAL DISTRIBUTION
BT2   DISTRIBUTION
RT   HYDROGRAPHIC SECTIONS
RT   MERIDIONAL DISTRIBUTION

ZONAL WIND SYSTEMS
USE   **PLANETARY WINDS**

ZONATION (ECOLOGICAL)
USE   **ECOLOGICAL ZONATION**

ZOOBENTHOS
UF   benthic fauna
BT1   BENTHOS
BT2   AQUATIC COMMUNITIES
RT   AQUATIC ANIMALS
RT   BENTHOS COLLECTING DEVICES
RT   ECOLOGICAL ZONATION

ZOOGEOGRAPHY
USE   **BIOGEOGRAPHY**

ZOOLOGICAL DRAWINGS
USE   **ILLUSTRATIONS**

ZOOLOGISTS
SN   Added in 1980
BT1   BIOLOGISTS
BT2   SCIENTIFIC PERSONNEL
BT3   PERSONNEL
NT1   CARCINOLOGISTS
NT1   ENTOMOLOGISTS
NT1   ICHTHYOLOGISTS

ZOOLOGISTS (cont'd)
NT1   MALACOLOGISTS
NT1   MAMMALOGISTS
NT2   CETOLOGISTS
NT1   ORNITHOLOGISTS
RT   ANIMAL PHYSIOLOGISTS
RT   DIRECTORIES
RT   TAXONOMISTS
RT   ZOOLOGY

ZOOLOGY
BT1   BIOLOGY
NT1   CONCHOLOGY
NT1   INVERTEBRATE ZOOLOGY
NT2   CARCINOLOGY
NT2   ENTOMOLOGY
NT2   MALACOLOGY
NT1   VERTEBRATE ZOOLOGY
NT2   HERPETOLOGY
NT2   ICHTHYOLOGY
NT2   MAMMALOGY
NT3   CETOLOGY
NT2   ORNITHOLOGY
NT2   OSTEOLOGY
RT   ANIMAL PHYSIOLOGY
RT   ANIMAL POPULATIONS
RT   AQUATIC ANIMALS
RT   BEHAVIOUR
RT   BIOGEOGRAPHY
RT   ECOLOGY
RT   EMBRYOLOGY
RT   ICHTHYOLOGISTS
RT   INSTINCT
RT   PALAEONTOLOGY
RT   SPECIES
RT   TAXONOMY
RT   ZOOLOGISTS
RT   ZOOPLANKTON

ZOOPLANKTON
UF   animal plankton
UF   macroplankton
BT1   PLANKTON
BT2   AQUATIC COMMUNITIES
NT1   HOLOPLANKTON
NT1   ICHTHYOPLANKTON
NT1   MEROPLANKTON
NT1   SAPROPLANKTON
RT   AQUATIC ANIMALS
RT   FOOD ORGANISMS
RT   ICHTHYOPLANKTON SURVEYS
RT   NEKTON COLLECTING DEVICES
RT   PLANKTON COLLECTING DEVICES
RT   PLANKTONOLOGY
RT   SCATTERING LAYERS
RT   SECONDARY PRODUCTION
RT   ZOOLOGY
RT   ZOOPLANKTON CULTURE

ZOOPLANKTON CULTURE
BT1   AQUACULTURE
RT   ARTIFICIAL AERATION
RT   ARTIFICIAL FEEDING
RT   BRINE SHRIMP CULTURE
RT   CONTINUOUS CULTURE
RT   CONTROLLED CONDITIONS
RT   CULTURED ORGANISMS
RT   CULTURES
RT   LABORATORY CULTURE
RT   LARVAE
RT   LARVAL DEVELOPMENT
RT   REARING
RT   ZOOPLANKTON

ZOOSEMIOTICS
USE   **ANIMAL COMMUNICATION**

ZOOSPORES
USE   **SPORES**

ZOOXANTHELLAE
SN   Symbiotic unicellular yellow-green
        algae occuring in some
        radiolarians, flatworms and polyps
BT1   ALGAE
RT   SYMBIONTS

ZYGOTES
SN   Added in 1982
RT   REPRODUCTION
RT   SEXUAL CELLS

0 GROUP
USE   **AGE GROUPS**

APPENDICES

ASFIS Thesaurus

List of Descriptors Classified by Facet

ASFIS Thesaurus
List of Descriptors by Facet

Operations

ABSORPTION SPECTROSCOPY
ACCEPTANCE TESTS
ACOUSTIC EMISSION
ACOUSTIC HOLOGRAPHY
ACOUSTIC IMAGERY
ACOUSTIC NAVIGATION
ACOUSTIC TELEMETRY
ACOUSTIC TOMOGRAPHY
ACQUISITION
ACTIVATION ANALYSIS
AERATION
AERIAL PHOTOGRAPHY
AERIAL SURVEYS
AEROMAGNETIC SURVEYS
AGE DETERMINATION
AGRICULTURE
AGROPISCICULTURE
AIR CONDITIONING
AIR SAMPLING
AIR TRANSPORTATION
AIRBORNE SENSING
ALGAL CULTURE
ALPHA SPECTROSCOPY
ALTIMETRY
ANAESTHESIA
ANALYSIS
ANALYTICAL TECHNIQUES
ANCHORING
ANGLING
ANIMAL OIL EXTRACTION
APPROXIMATION
AQUACULTURE
AQUACULTURE ENTERPRISES
AQUACULTURE TECHNIQUES
AQUARIUM CULTURE
ARTIFICIAL AERATION
ARTIFICIAL FEEDING
ARTISANAL FISHING
ARTISANAL WHALING
ATTRACTING TECHNIQUES
AUTOCORRELATION
AUTOMATED CARTOGRAPHY
AUTOMATED RECORDING
AUTOMATION
AUTORADIOGRAPHY
BAIT CULTURE
BAIT FISHING
BASELINE STUDIES
BATCH CULTURE
BATCH PROCESSING
BATHING
BATHYMETRIC SURVEYS
BATHYMETRY
BERTHING
BIOAERATION
BIOASSAYS
BIOCHEMICAL ANALYSIS
BIOLOGICAL CONTROL
BIOLOGICAL SAMPLING
BIOLOGICAL SURVEYS
BIOTELEMETRY
BIOTESTING
BLASTING
BLOWOUT CONTROL
BOTTOM CULTURE
BOTTOM TRAWLING
BOUSSINESQ APPROXIMATION
BRACKISHWATER AQUACULTURE
BRINE SHRIMP CULTURE
BUBBLING
BURYING
CABLE LAYING
CAGE CULTURE
CALIBRATION

CALORIMETRY
CANNING
CANOE FISHERIES
CARANGID FISHERIES
CASTRATION
CATCHING METHODS
CATHODIC PROTECTION
CELESTIAL NAVIGATION
CELL CULTURE
CENSUS
CENTRIFUGATION
CEPHALOPOD FISHERIES
CERTIFICATION
CHEMICAL ANALYSIS
CHEMICAL CONTROL
CHEMICAL EXTRACTION
CHILLING STORAGE
CHLORINATION
CHROMATOGRAPHIC TECHNIQUES
CLAM CULTURE
CLAM FISHERIES
CLASSIFICATION
CLEANING
CLIMATE PREDICTION
CLOSURE APPROXIMATION
CLUPEOID FISHERIES
COASTAL FISHERIES
COATING PROCESSES
COLD BRANDING
COLD STORAGE
COLLISION AVOIDANCE
COLORIMETRIC TECHNIQUES
COMMERCIAL FISHING
COMMUNICATION
COMPARATIVE STUDIES
COMPUTATION
CONNECTING
CONSTRUCTION
CONTAINMENT
CONTINUOUS CULTURE
CONTROL
CONVOLUTION
CORAL FARMING
CORE ANALYSIS
CORE HANDLING
CORE LAYER METHOD
CORE RECOVERY
CORING
CORRELATION ANALYSIS
CORROSION CONTROL
COST ANALYSIS
CRAB CULTURE
CRAB FISHERIES
CRAYFISH CULTURE
CRITICAL PATH METHOD
CROSS CORRELATION·
CRUISES
CRUSTACEAN CULTURE
CRUSTACEAN FISHERIES
CULLING
CULTURES
CURING
CURRENT MEASUREMENT
CURRENT PREDICTION
CUTTING
CUTTING UNDERWATER
DAMPING
DATA ACQUISITION
DATA PROCESSING
DATA REDUCTION
DATA RETRIEVAL
DATA STORAGE
DATA TRANSMISSION
DE-ICING
DEAD RECKONING
DEBUBBLING
DECANTATION
DECHLORINATION
DECOMPRESSION

DECONVOLUTION
DEEP-SEA DIVING
DEEP-SEA DRILLING
DEEP-SEA FISHERIES
DEEP-SEA MINING
DEMERSAL FISHERIES
DENSITY MEASUREMENT
DEPLOYMENT
DEPTH CONTROL
DEPTH MEASUREMENT
DESALINATION
DESIGN
DETECTION
DETOXIFICATION
DEWATERING
DIRECTION FINDING
DISEASE CONTROL
DISEASE DETECTION
DISINFECTION
DIVING
DIVING INDUSTRY
DIVING SURVEYS
DOMESTICATION
DOPPLER NAVIGATION
DREDGING
DRESSING
DRILLING
DRYING
DUNE STABILIZATION
DYNAMIC ANALYSIS
DYNAMIC POSITIONING
EARTHQUAKE PREDICTION
ECHINODERM FISHERIES
ECHO RANGING
ECHO SURVEYS
ECHOSOUNDING
ECONOMIC ANALYSIS
ELECTRIC ARC WELDING
ELECTRIC FISHING
ELECTRICAL EXPLORATION
ELECTROANALYSIS
ELECTROMAGNETIC EXPLORATION
ELECTRON MICROSCOPY
ELECTROPHORESIS
EMISSION SPECTROSCOPY
ENVIRONMENTAL MONITORING
ENVIRONMENTAL SURVEYS
EROSION CONTROL
ESTUARINE FISHERIES
EULERIAN CURRENT MEASUREMENT
EVACUATION
EVALUATION
EVAPORATION REDUCTION
EXCAVATION UNDERWATER
EXPEDITIONS
EXPERIMENTAL CULTURE
EXPERIMENTAL FISHING
EXPERIMENTAL RESEARCH
EXPLORATION
EXPLORATORY FISHING
EXPLOSIVE FISHING
EXPLOSIVE WELDING
EXTENSIVE CULTURE
EYESTALK EXTIRPATION
FACSIMILE TRANSMISSION
FEASIBILITY STUDIES
FEE FISHING
FEED PREPARATION
FEEDING EXPERIMENTS
FILLETTING
FILTRATION
FIN RAY COUNTS
FINANCING
FINFISH FISHERIES
FINITE DIFFERENCE METHOD
FINITE ELEMENT METHOD
FIRE FIGHTING
FIRE PREVENTION
FISH CULTURE

ASFIS Thesaurus
List of Descriptors by Facet

FISH DETECTION	HAZARD ASSESSMENT	LOGGING
FISH HANDLING	HEADING	LONG-TERM PLANNING
FISH INSPECTION	HEATING	LONGLINING
FISH MEAL PROCESSING	HIGH SEAS FISHERIES	MACKEREL FISHERIES
FISH OIL EXTRACTION	HOLE RE-ENTRY	MAGNETIC EXPLORATION
FISH POISONING	HOLOGRAPHY	MAGNETOTELLURIC METHODS
FISH SIZING	HUNTING	MAINTENANCE
FISH STORAGE	HURRICANE TRACKING	MAPPING
FISH UTILIZATION	HYBRID CULTURE	MARINE AQUACULTURE
FISHERIES	HYDROCARBON ANALYSIS	MARINE FISHERIES
FISHERY INDUSTRY	HYDROGRAPHIC SURVEYING	MARINE TRANSPORTATION
FISHERY SURVEYS	HYDROGRAPHIC SURVEYS	MARKET RESEARCH
FISHING	HYGIENE	MARKETING
FISHING BY DIVING	HYPOPHYSECTOMY	MARKING
FISHING OPERATIONS	HYPSOMETRY	MASS CULTURE
FISHING WITHOUT GEAR	ICE BREAKING	MASS SPECTROSCOPY
FIXATION	ICE FISHING	MATERIALS TESTING
FLATFISH FISHERIES	ICE FORECASTING	MATHEMATICAL ANALYSIS
FLOOD CONTROL	ICE PREVENTION	MATHEMATICAL PROGRAMMING
FLOOD FORECASTING	ICE ROUTEING	MAXIMUM ENTROPY SPECTRAL ANALYSIS
FLOW MEASUREMENT	ICEBERG DETECTION	MEASUREMENT
FLUORESCENCE MICROSCOPY	ICHTHYOPLANKTON SURVEYS	MECHANIZATION
FLUORESCENCE SPECTROSCOPY	IDENTIFICATION	MERISTIC COUNTS
FOREIGN FISHING	IMAGE ENHANCEMENT	METHODOLOGY
FOREST INDUSTRY	IMAGE PROCESSING	MICROBIOLOGICAL ANALYSIS
FOULING CONTROL	IMAGERY	MICROBIOLOGICAL CULTURE
FOURIER ANALYSIS	IMAGING TECHNIQUES	MICROSCOPY
FOURIER TRANSFORMS	IMMUNIZATION	MICROWAVE IMAGERY
FREEZE-DRYING	IMMUNOPRECIPITATION	MILITARY OPERATIONS
FREEZING STORAGE	IN SITU MEASUREMENTS	MINERAL EXPLORATION
FREQUENCY ANALYSIS	INCINERATION	MINERAL INDUSTRY
FRESHWATER AQUACULTURE	INDUCED BREEDING	MINERAL PROCESSING
FROG CULTURE	INDUSTRIAL PRODUCTION	MINING
FUNCTIONAL ANALYSIS	INDUSTRIES	MODELLING
GADOID FISHERIES	INERTIAL GUIDANCE	MOHOLE PROJECT
GAME THEORY	INERTIAL NAVIGATION	MOLLUSC CULTURE
GAMMA SPECTROSCOPY	INFRARED IMAGERY	MOLLUSC FISHERIES
GAS CHROMATOGRAPHY	INFRARED SPECTROSCOPY	MONITORING
GAS FLARING	INLAND FISHERIES	MONOCULTURE
GAS OIL SEPARATION	INSPECTION	MONOSEX CULTURE
GAS PROCESSING	INSTALLATION	MOORING RECOVERY
GAS PRODUCTION	INSTRUMENT DEPTH MEASUREMENT	MULLET FISHERIES
GAS WATER SEPARATION	INTENSIVE CULTURE	MULTISHIP EXPEDITIONS
GASTROPOD FISHERIES	INTERCALIBRATION	MULTISPECIES FISHERIES
GEAR CONSTRUCTION	INTERCOMPARISON	MULTIVARIATE ANALYSIS
GEAR HANDLING	INTERFEROMETRY	MUSSEL CULTURE
GEOCHEMICAL SURVEYS	INTERMEDIATE FISHING	MUSSEL FISHERIES
GEOCHRONOMETRY	ION SELECTIVE ELECTRODE ANALYSIS	NAVIGATION
GEOGRAPHICAL EXPLORATION	IRRADIATION	NAVIGATION IN ICE
GEOLOGICAL CORRELATION	IRRIGATION	NAVIGATION UNDER ICE
GEOLOGICAL SURVEYS	ISENTROPIC ANALYSIS	NAVIGATION UNDERWATER
GEOPHYSICAL EXPLORATION	ISOTOPE DILUTION	NET FISHING
GEOPHYSICAL SURVEYS	ISOTOPE FRACTIONATION	NEUTRON ACTIVATION ANALYSIS
GEOSENSING	JIGGING	NODE CONSTRUCTION
GEOSTROPHIC METHOD	KRILL FISHERIES	NOISE REDUCTION
GEOTHERMAL EXPLORATION	LABORATORY CULTURE	NONDESTRUCTIVE TESTING
GEOTHERMAL MEASUREMENT	LAGOON FISHERIES	NUCLEAR MAGNETIC RESONANCE
GILLRAKER COUNTS	LAGRANGIAN CURRENT MEASUREMENT	NUMERICAL ANALYSIS
GRADING	LAKE FISHERIES	OCEAN DUMPING
GRAFTING	LAKE RECLAMATION	OCEANOGRAPHIC SURVEYS
GRANULOMETRY	LAND RECLAMATION	OFF-BOTTOM CULTURE
GRAPHIC METHODS	LAPLACE TRANSFORMATION	OFFSHORE DOCKING
GRAPHICAL ANALYSIS	LASER ALTIMETRY	OFFSHORE OPERATIONS
GRAPPLING	LASER BATHYMETRY	OIL AND GAS EXPLORATION
GRAVIMETRIC TECHNIQUES	LAUNCHING	OIL AND GAS INDUSTRY
GRAVITY EXPLORATION	LEAST SQUARES METHOD	OIL AND GAS PRODUCTION
GRAVITY SURVEYS	LEVELLING	OIL PRODUCTION
GROUTING	LICENSING	OIL RECOVERY
GUTTING	LIFTING	OIL REMOVAL
HABITAT IMPROVEMENT	LIGHT FISHING	OIL TREATING
HABITAT IMPROVEMENT (BIOLOGICAL)	LIGHT MEASUREMENT	OIL WATER SEPARATION
HABITAT IMPROVEMENT (CHEMICAL)	LIGHT MICROSCOPY	OPERATIONS RESEARCH
HABITAT IMPROVEMENT (FERTILIZATION)	LIMNOLOGICAL SURVEYS	OPTICAL CLASSIFICATION
HABITAT IMPROVEMENT (PHYSICAL)	LINE FISHING	ORGAN REMOVAL
HALOGENATION	LINEAR PROGRAMMING	OTOLITH READING
HANDLING	LIVE STORAGE	OVERWINTERING TECHNIQUES
HANDLINING	LOBSTER CULTURE	OXYGEN ISOTOPE DATING
HARMONIC ANALYSIS	LOBSTER FISHERIES	OYSTER CULTURE
HARVESTING	LOCATING	OYSTER FISHERIES

ASFIS Thesaurus
List of Descriptors by Facet

OZONATION
PACKING FISHERY PRODUCTS
PALAEO STUDIES
PARAMETERIZATION
PARASITE CONTROL
PATTERN RECOGNITION
PEARL CULTURE
PEARL FISHERIES
PELAGIC FISHERIES
PERCOID FISHERIES
PERFORMANCE ASSESSMENT
PERT
PERTURBATION METHOD
PEST CONTROL
PHOTOGRAPHY
PHOTOMETRY
PHYTOPLANKTON CULTURE
PIGGING
PILE DRIVING
PIPE LAYING
PIPELINE CONSTRUCTION
PIPELINE CROSSING
PIPELINE PROTECTION
PLACER MINING
PLANKTON SURVEYS
PLANT CONTROL
PLANT CULTURE
PLANT UTILIZATION
PLOTTING
POLAR EXPLORATION
POLAROGRAPHY
POLE-LINE FISHING
POLLUTANT IDENTIFICATION
POLLUTION CONTROL
POLLUTION DETECTION
POLLUTION MONITORING
POLLUTION SURVEYS
POLYCULTURE
POND CONSTRUCTION
POND CULTURE
POPULATION CONTROL
POSITION FIXING
POT FISHING
POTASSIUM-ARGON DATING
PRAWN CULTURE
PREDATOR CONTROL
PREDICTION
PRESERVATION (FISHERY PRODUCTS)
PRESSURE MEASUREMENT
PRICING
PROBABILITY THEORY
PROCEDURES
PROCESSING FISHERY PRODUCTS
PRODUCT DEVELOPMENT
PROFILING
PROPHYLAXIS
PUMP FISHING
PUMPING
PURCHASING
PURSE SEINING
QUALITY ASSURANCE
QUALITY CONTROL
RACEWAY CULTURE
RACIAL STUDIES
RADAR ALTIMETRY
RADAR IMAGERY
RADAR NAVIGATION
RADIO NAVIGATION
RADIO TELEMETRY
RADIOACTIVE LABELLING
RADIOACTIVE WASTE DISPOSAL
RADIOCARBON DATING
RADIOGRAPHY
RADIOMETRIC DATING
RAFT CULTURE
RANCHING
REARING
RECLAMATION
RECOVERY

RECREATION
REDFISH FISHERIES
REEF FISHERIES
REFRIGERATION
REGIONAL PLANNING
REGRESSION ANALYSIS
REMOTE CONTROL
REMOTE SENSING
REMOVAL
REPAIR
REPLACING
REPTILE CULTURE
RESEARCH
RESEARCH PROGRAMMES
RESEARCH PROPOSALS
RESERVOIR FISHERIES
RESOURCE EXPLORATION
RESOURCE SURVEYS
RESPONSE ANALYSIS
RICE FIELD AQUACULTURE
RIGHTING
RIVER FISHERIES
ROE FISHERIES
RUBIDIUM-STRONTIUM DATING
SALINITY MEASUREMENT
SALMON FISHERIES
SALVAGING
SAMPLE STORAGE
SAMPLING
SATELLITE ALTIMETRY
SATELLITE NAVIGATION
SATELLITE PHOTOGRAPHY
SATELLITE SENSING
SATURATION DIVING
SCALE READING
SCALLOP CULTURE
SCALLOP FISHERIES
SCOUR PROTECTION
SCUBA DIVING
SEA LEVEL MEASUREMENT
SEAFLOOR MAPPING
SEAFLOOR SAMPLING
SEARCH AND RESCUE
SEAWEED CULTURE
SEAWEED HARVESTING
SEAWEED PROCESSING
SEDIMENT ANALYSIS
SEDIMENT SAMPLING
SEED COLLECTION
SEED PRODUCTION
SEEDING (AQUACULTURE)
SEINING
SEISMIC DATA PROCESSING
SEISMIC EXPLORATION
SEISMIC REFLECTION PROFILING
SEISMIC REFRACTION PROFILING
SELECTIVE BREEDING
SELECTIVE FEEDING
SEPARATION
SEWAGE DISPOSAL
SEWAGE TREATMENT
SHARK FISHERIES
SHELLFISH CULTURE
SHELLFISH FISHERIES
SHIP DESIGN
SHIP HANDLING
SHIP ROUTEING
SHIPBOARD ANALYSIS
SHORAN
SHORT-TERM PLANNING
SHRIMP CULTURE
SHRIMP FISHERIES
SIGNAL PROCESSING
SILO CULTURE
SIMULATION
SITE SELECTION
SITE SURVEYS
SLUDGE TREATMENT
SMALL SCALE AQUACULTURE

SONAR COUNTERMEASURES
SONAR DETECTION
SONAR IMAGERY
SOUND MEASUREMENT
SOUNDINGS
SPEAR FISHING
SPECTRAL ANALYSIS
SPECTROCHEMICAL ANALYSIS
SPECTROSCOPIC TECHNIQUES
SPONGE CULTURE
SPONGE FISHERIES
SPORT FISHING
SQUAT LOBSTER FISHERIES
SQUID CULTURE
STABILIZING
STAINING
STANDARDIZATION
STATION KEEPING
STATISTICAL ANALYSIS
STATISTICAL SAMPLING
STEREOPHOTOGRAPHY
STERILIZATION
STOCK ASSESSMENT
STOCK IDENTIFICATION
STOCKING (ORGANISMS)
STORAGE
STORM SURGE PREDICTION
STRATIGRAPHIC CORRELATION
STRIPPING ANALYSIS
STRUCTURAL ANALYSIS
STUPEFYING METHODS
SUB-BOTTOM PROFILING
SURFING
SURVEYING
SURVEYING UNDERWATER
SURVEYS
SWAMP FISHERIES
SYSTEM ANALYSIS
TAGGING
TANK CLEANING
TANKER LOADING
TASTE TESTS
TECHNOLOGY TRANSFER
TELEMETRY
TEMPERATURE MEASUREMENT
TESTING
TESTS
THAWING
THERAPY
THERMAL AQUACULTURE
THORIUM-230/THORIUM-232 DATING
TIDAL ANALYSIS
TIDAL PREDICTION
TIME SERIES ANALYSIS
TISSUE CULTURE
TITRATION
TOPOGRAPHIC SURVEYING
TOWED BODY DESIGN
TOWING
TOXICITY TESTS
TRACER TECHNIQUES
TRACKING
TRAINING
TRANSPLANTATION
TRANSPORTATION
TRAP FISHING
TRAWLING
TRAY CULTURE
TRENCHING
TROLLING
TSUNAMI PREDICTION
TUNA FISHERIES
TURBULENCE MEASUREMENT
TURTLE CULTURE
TURTLE FISHERIES
ULTRAVIOLET STERILIZATION
UNDERWATER EXPLORATION
UNDERWATER INSPECTION
UNDERWATER OBJECT LOCATION

UNDERWATER PHOTOGRAPHY
URANIUM-HELIUM DATING
VACCINATION
VALLICULTURE
VANE SHEAR TESTING
VARIANCE ANALYSIS
VENTILATION
VERTEBRAE COUNTS
VERTICAL PROFILING
VIEWING UNDERWATER
VISUAL INSPECTION
VOLTAMMETRY
VOLUMETRIC ANALYSIS
WARM-WATER AQUACULTURE
WASTE DISPOSAL
WASTE TREATMENT
WASTEWATER TREATMENT
WATER ANALYSIS
WATER FILTRATION
WATER LEVEL MEASUREMENT
WATER POLLUTION TREATMENT
WATER PURIFICATION
WATER QUALITY CONTROL
WATER RECLAMATION
WATER SAMPLING
WATER TREATMENT
WAVE ANALYSIS
WAVE DAMPING
WAVE FORECASTING
WAVE HINDCASTING
WAVE MEASUREMENT
WAVE PREDICTING
WAVEFORM ANALYSIS
WEATHER FORECASTING
WELDING
WELDING UNDERWATER
WELL COMPLETION
WELL LOGGING
WELL WORKOVER OPERATIONS
WHALING
WIND MEASUREMENT
WINKLER METHOD
WORKING UNDERWATER
WORM CULTURE
WORM FISHING
WRECK LOCATION
X-RAY DIFFRACTION ANALYSIS
X-RAY EMISSION ANALYSIS
X-RAY FLUORESCENCE ANALYSIS
X-RAY INSPECTION
X-RAY SPECTROSCOPY
YACHTING
YIELD PREDICTIONS
ZOOPLANKTON CULTURE

ASFIS Thesaurus
List of Descriptors by Facet

Properties and Characteristics

ABSOLUTE AGE
ABSOLUTE HUMIDITY
ABSOLUTE VORTICITY
ABSORPTANCE
ABUNDANCE
ACCELERATION
ACCEPTABILITY
ACIDITY
ACOUSTIC IMPEDANCE
ACOUSTIC PROPERTIES
ADHESION
AGE
AGE AT RECRUITMENT
AGE COMPOSITION
AGE OF SEAWATER
AGE OF TIDE
AIR TEMPERATURE
ALBEDO
ALKALINITY
AMPLITUDE
ANELASTICITY
ANGULAR DISTRIBUTION
ANGULAR MOMENTUM
ANISOTROPY
ANNUAL
AREA
ASH CONTENT
ATMOSPHERIC PRESSURE
ATTENUANCE
AVAILABILITY
BAROCLINIC INSTABILITY
BAROTROPIC INSTABILITY
BEACH SLOPE
BEAM TRANSMITTANCE
BEARING CAPACITY
BED ROUGHNESS
BENJAMIN FEIR INSTABILITY
BIENNIAL
BIOCHEMICAL COMPOSITION
BIOLOGICAL AGE
BIOLOGICAL PROPERTIES
BIOMASS
BLOOD PRESSURE
BODY BURDEN
BODY CONDITIONS
BODY SHAPE
BODY SIZE
BODY TEMPERATURE
BODY WEIGHT
BOILING POINT
BOTTOM PRESSURE
BOTTOM TEMPERATURE
BOTTOM TOW
BRITTLENESS
BRUNT-VAISALA FREQUENCY
BUCKET TEMPERATURE
BUOYANCY
CALORIES
CAPACITANCE
CAPACITY
CATCH COMPOSITION
CATCHABILITY
CHEMICAL COMPOSITION
CHEMICAL PROPERTIES
CHLORINITY
CHLOROSITY
CLOUD HEIGHT
COLD RESISTANCE
COLLAPSE STRENGTH
COLLIGATIVE PROPERTIES
COLOUR
COMMERCIAL AVAILABILITY
COMMUNITY COMPOSITION
COMPOSITION

COMPRESSIBILITY
COMPRESSIONAL WAVE VELOCITIES
COMPRESSIVE STRENGTH
CONSERVATIVE PROPERTIES
CONTROL RESISTANCE
CORE ORIENTATION
CORIOLIS ACCELERATION
CRUSTAL STRUCTURE
CRUSTAL THICKNESS
CURL (VECTORS)
CURRENT DENSITY
CURRENT DIRECTION
CURRENT VELOCITY
DAILY
DEFORMATION
DENSITY
DEPTH
DEW POINT
DIGESTIBILITY
DIMENSIONS
DIRECTION
DISPLACEMENT
DISTANCE
DOUBLE DIFFUSIVE INSTABILITY
DOWNWARD IRRADIANCE
DRUG RESISTANCE
DRY
DRY WEIGHT
DURATION
DYNAMIC HEIGHT
DYNAMIC VISCOSITY
EARTH AGE
EARTH CURVATURE
ECOLOGICAL EFFICIENCY
ECOSYSTEM RESILIENCE
EDDY CONDUCTIVITY
EDDY DIFFUSIVITY
EDDY FLUX
EDDY VISCOSITY
EFFICIENCY
ELASTICITY
ELECTRIC IMPEDANCE
ELECTRIC POTENTIAL
ELECTRICAL CONDUCTIVITY
ELECTRICAL PROPERTIES
ELECTRICAL RESISTIVITY
ENSTROPHY
ENTHALPY
ENTROPY
ENVIRONMENTAL CONDITIONS
EQUILIBRIUM
EURYHALINITY
EURYTHERMY
EXCHANGE CAPACITY
EXPOSURE TOLERANCE
FECUNDITY
FEED COMPOSITION
FEED EFFICIENCY
FERTILITY
FETCH
FIELDS
FLEXIBILITY
FOOD AVAILABILITY
FOOD COMPOSITION
FREE ENERGY
FREEZING POINT
FREQUENCY
FUNCTIONAL MORPHOLOGY
FUSION HEAT
GAS SOLUBILITY
GEAR SELECTIVITY
GEOTHERMAL PROPERTIES
GRADIENTS
GRAIN ORIENTATION
GRAIN PACKING
GRAIN PROPERTIES
GRAIN SHAPE
GRAIN SIZE
HEAT CONTENT

HEIGHT
HETEROSIS
HIGH FREQUENCY
HIGH PRESSURE EFFECTS
HORIZONTAL
HOURLY
HUMIDITY
HYDROSTATIC PRESSURE
HYPERBARIC
ICE PROPERTIES
ICE THICKNESS
ICE VOLUME
IMMUNITY
IMPEDANCE
IN SITU DENSITY
IN SITU TEMPERATURE
INSTABILITY
INTAKE TEMPERATURE
IRRADIANCE
ISOSTATIC SEA LEVEL
ISOTROPY
KEEL CLEARANCE
KELVIN-HELMHOLTZ INSTABILITY
KINEMATIC EDDY VISCOSITY
KINEMATIC VISCOSITY
LENGTH
LIGHT INTENSITY
LONGEVITY
LOW FREQUENCY
LOW TEMPERATURE
MAGNETIC FIELD ELEMENTS
MAGNETIC INCLINATION
MAGNETIC INTENSITY
MAGNETIC PERMEABILITY
MAGNETIC PROPERTIES
MAGNETIC SUSCEPTIBILITY
MANOEUVRABILITY
MASS
MEAN SEA LEVEL
MECHANICAL PROPERTIES
MELTING POINT
MESH SELECTIVITY
MINERAL COMPOSITION
MIXED LAYER DEPTH
MIXING LENGTH
MODES
MOLECULAR STRUCTURE
MOLECULAR VISCOSITY
MOLECULAR WEIGHT
MOMENTUM
MOMENTUM TRANSFER
MONIN-OBUKHOV LENGTH
MONTHLY
MORPHOMETRY
NON-CONSERVATIVE PROPERTIES
NONLINEARITY
NUTRITIONAL REQUIREMENTS
NUTRITIVE VALUE
ODOUR
OIL IN WATER CONTENT
OPTICAL PROPERTIES
ORBITAL VELOCITY
ORGANOLEPTIC PROPERTIES
ORIENTATION
OSMOTIC PRESSURE
OXIC CONDITIONS
OXYGEN ISOTOPE RATIO
PALAEOSALINITY
PALAEOTEMPERATURE
PALAEOTOPOGRAPHY
PALATABILITY
PARTICLE CONCENTRATION
PARTICLE DISTRIBUTION
PARTICLE SIZE
PENETRATION DEPTH
PERIODICITY
PERMANENCE
PERMEABILITY
PERSISTENCE

ASFIS Thesaurus
List of Descriptors by Facet

PH
PHASE VELOCITY
PHYSICAL PROPERTIES
PHYSICOCHEMICAL PROPERTIES
PLANETARY VORTICITY
PLASTICITY
POLLUTION TOLERANCE
POPULATION CHARACTERISTICS
POPULATION DENSITY
POPULATION NUMBER
POPULATION STRUCTURE
PORE PRESSURE
POROSITY
POTENTIAL DENSITY
POTENTIAL ENERGY
POTENTIAL TEMPERATURE
POTENTIAL VORTICITY
PRESSURE
PRESSURE FIELD
PROPERTIES
QUALITY
RADIANCE
RADIATION BALANCE
REDOX POTENTIAL
REFLECTANCE
REFRACTIVE INDEX
RELATIVE DENSITY
RELATIVE HUMIDITY
RELATIVE VORTICITY
RELIABILITY
REMANENT MAGNETIZATION
RESOLUTION
RESONANT FREQUENCY
RESOURCE AVAILABILITY
ROCK DEFORMATION
ROUGHNESS
SALINITY
SALINITY MICROSTRUCTURE
SALINITY TOLERANCE
SATURATION DEPTH
SATURATION VAPOUR PRESSURE
SEA LEVEL
SEA LEVEL PRESSURE
SEA STATE
SEASONALITY
SECONDARY SEXUAL CHARACTERS
SEDIMENT COMPOSITION
SEDIMENT DENSITY
SEDIMENT MOVEMENT
SEDIMENT PROPERTIES
SEDIMENT STABILITY
SEDIMENT STRUCTURE
SEDIMENT TEMPERATURE
SEDIMENT TEXTURE
SEISMIC VELOCITIES
SETTLING RATE
SEX
SEX CHARACTERS
SEX RATIO
SEXUAL MATURITY
SHAPE
SHEAR STRENGTH
SHEAR WAVE VELOCITIES
SHIP PERFORMANCE
SHIP SPEED
SHIP STABILITY
SIGMA-T
SILL DEPTH
SIZE
SIZE DISTRIBUTION
SLOPE STABILITY
SOLUBILITY
SOUND INTENSITY
SOUND PRESSURE
SOUND VELOCITY
SPECIES DIVERSITY
SPECIFIC GRAVITY
SPECIFIC HEAT
SPECIFIC HUMIDITY

SPECIFIC VOLUME
SPECIFICITY
SPECTRAL COMPOSITION
STABILITY
STATIC INSTABILITY
STEADY STATE
STENOHALINITY
STENOTHERMY
STERIC SEA LEVEL
STERILITY
STOCKING DENSITY
STORAGE CONDITIONS
STORAGE LIFE
STRAIN
STREAM FLOW RATE
STRENGTH
SUBLIMATION HEAT
SURFACE POTENTIAL
SURFACE PROPERTIES
SURFACE RADIATION TEMPERATURE
SURFACE ROUGHNESS
SURFACE SALINITY
SURFACE SLOPE
SURFACE TEMPERATURE
TARGET STRENGTH
TASTE
TEMPERATURE
TEMPERATURE (AIR-SEA)
TEMPERATURE TOLERANCE
TENSILE STRENGTH
TEXTURE
THERMAL DIFFUSIVITY
THERMAL EXPANSION
THERMAL MICROSTRUCTURE
THERMODYNAMIC EQUILIBRIUM
THERMODYNAMIC PROPERTIES
THICKNESS
THIXOTROPY
TIDAL AMPLITUDE
TIDAL CONSTITUENTS
TIDAL RANGE
TIDAL RESONANCE
TIDE GENERATING POTENTIAL
TOLERANCE
TOLERANCES (DIMENSIONAL)
TOUGHNESS
TOXICITY
TOXICITY TOLERANCE
TRANSITION TEMPERATURES
TRANSMITTANCE
TRANSPARENCY
TROPHIC STRUCTURE
TURBIDITY
ULTRASTRUCTURE
UNSTEADY STATE
UPWARD IRRADIANCE
URANIUM-234/URANIUM-238 RATIO
VAPORIZATION HEAT
VAPOUR PRESSURE
VELOCITY
VELOCITY MICROSTRUCTURE
VERTICAL STABILITY
VISCOSITY
VISIBILITY
VISIBILITY UNDERWATER
VOLUME
VORTICITY
VULNERABILITY
WATER BUDGET
WATER COLOUR
WATER CONTENT
WATER DENSITY
WATER DEPTH
WATER HARDNESS
WATER LEVELS
WATER PROPERTIES
WATER QUALITY
WATER STRUCTURE
WATER TEMPERATURE

WATER TRANSPARENCY
WATER WAVE PARAMETERS
WAVE AGE
WAVE AMPLITUDE
WAVE CLIMATE
WAVE DIRECTION
WAVE DRIFT VELOCITY
WAVE FREQUENCY
WAVE GEOMETRY
WAVE HEIGHT
WAVE NUMBER
WAVE PERIOD
WAVE PHASE
WAVE PROPERTIES
WAVE SLOPE
WAVE STEEPNESS
WAVE VELOCITY
WAVELENGTH
WEEKLY
WEIGHT
WET
WET BULK DENSITY
WET WEIGHT
WIDTH
WIND DIRECTION
WIND FIELDS
WIND SPEED
WIND STRESS CURL
WIND WAVE PARAMETERS
WIRE ANGLE
YIELD POINT

ASFIS Thesaurus
List of Descriptors by Facet

Phenomena

ABLATION
ABNORMALITIES
ABSORPTION (PHYSICS)
ABYSSAL CIRCULATION
ABYSSAL CURRENTS
ACCIDENTS
ACCLIMATION
ACCLIMATIZATION
ACCRETION
ACCUMULATION
ACID RAIN
ACIDIFICATION
ACTIVITY PATTERNS
ADAPTATIONS
ADIABATIC LAPSE RATES
ADIABATIC PROCESSES
ADIABATIC TEMPERATURE GRADIENT
ADSORPTION
ADVECTION
AEROBIC RESPIRATION
AESTIVATION
AGEOSTROPHIC FLOW
AGGREGATION
AGGRESSIVE BEHAVIOUR
AGING
AGONISTIC BEHAVIOUR
AGRICULTURAL POLLUTION
AIR BUBBLES
AIR EXPOSURE
AIR FLOW OVER LAND
AIR FLOW OVER WATER
AIR POLLUTION
AIR-SEA COUPLING
AIR-SEA INTERACTION
AIR-WATER EXCHANGES
AIR-WATER TEMPERATURE DIFFERENCE
AIRGLOW
ALBINISM
ALGAL BLOOMS
ALGAL SETTLEMENTS
ALLERGIC REACTIONS
ALTERNATE REPRODUCTION
AMBIENT NOISE
AMINATION
ANABOLISM
ANADROMOUS MIGRATIONS
ANAEMIA
ANAEROBIC DIGESTION
ANAEROBIC RESPIRATION
ANAEROBIOSIS
ANDROGENESIS
ANIMAL COMMUNICATION
ANIMAL DISEASES
ANIMAL METABOLISM
ANIMAL NAVIGATION
ANIMAL NUTRITION
ANNUAL VARIATIONS
ANOMALIES
ANOXIA
ANOXIC CONDITIONS
ANTARCTIC CONVERGENCE
ANTARCTIC FRONT
ANTICYCLONES
ANTICYCLONIC MOTION
ARTIFICIAL UPWELLING
ASEXUAL REPRODUCTION
ASPHYXIA
ASTRONOMICAL TIDES
ATMOSPHERE EVOLUTION
ATMOSPHERIC CIRCULATION
ATMOSPHERIC CONVECTION
ATMOSPHERIC CONVERGENCES
ATMOSPHERIC DEPRESSIONS
ATMOSPHERIC DIFFUSION

ATMOSPHERIC DISTURBANCES
ATMOSPHERIC ELECTRICITY
ATMOSPHERIC FORCING
ATMOSPHERIC FRONTS
ATMOSPHERIC MOTION
ATMOSPHERIC OPTICAL PHENOMENA
ATMOSPHERIC PRECIPITATIONS
ATMOSPHERIC TIDES
ATMOSPHERIC TURBULENCE
ATTENUATION
AUDITION
AUDITORY STIMULI
AURORA
AUTHIGENESIS
AUTOLYSIS
AUTOTOMY
AUTOTROPHY
AVOIDANCE REACTIONS
BACKSCATTER
BACKWASH
BACTERIAL DISEASES
BAROCLINIC FIELD
BAROCLINIC MODE
BAROCLINIC MOTION
BAROMETRIC WAVES
BAROTROPIC FIELD
BAROTROPIC MODE
BAROTROPIC MOTION
BAROTROPIC TIDES
BASALT-SEAWATER INTERACTION
BAY DYNAMICS
BEACH ACCRETION
BEACH EROSION
BEACH NOURISHMENT
BEHAVIOUR
BEHAVIOURAL RESPONSES
BENTHIC CURRENTS
BENTHIC FRONTS
BETA SPIRALS
BILLOWS
BIOACCUMULATION
BIOCHEMICAL CYCLES
BIOCHEMICAL OXYGEN DEMAND
BIOCHEMICAL PHENOMENA
BIODEGRADATION
BIOELECTRICITY
BIOEROSION
BIOGENESIS
BIOGEOCHEMICAL CYCLE
BIOLOGICAL AGING
BIOLOGICAL ATTACHMENT
BIOLOGICAL CLOCKS
BIOLOGICAL DAMAGE
BIOLOGICAL DEVELOPMENT
BIOLOGICAL DRIFT
BIOLOGICAL FERTILIZATION
BIOLOGICAL NOISE
BIOLOGICAL PHENOMENA
BIOLOGICAL PRODUCTION
BIOLOGICAL RAFTING
BIOLOGICAL RESISTANCE
BIOLOGICAL RHYTHMS
BIOLOGICAL SETTLEMENT
BIOLOGICAL SPECIATION
BIOLOGICAL STRESS
BIOLUMINESCENCE
BIOPOLYMORPHISM
BIOSELECTION
BIOSYNTHESIS
BIOTIC BARRIERS
BIOTIC PRESSURE
BIOTURBATION
BIPOLAR DISTRIBUTION
BLOOD CIRCULATION
BLOWOUTS
BODY WAVES
BOIL DISEASE
BOLUSES
BONE NECROSIS

BOTTOM CURRENTS
BOTTOM EROSION
BOTTOM FRICTION
BOTTOM REVERBERATION
BOTTOM SCATTERING
BOTTOM STRESS
BOTTOM TOPOGRAPHY EFFECTS
BOTULISM
BOUGUER ANOMALIES
BOUNDARY CURRENTS
BRACKISHWATER POLLUTION
BREAKERS
BREAKING WAVES
BREEDING
BREEZES
BUBBLE BURSTING
BUBBLE DISEASE
BUBBLES
BUDDING
BUOY MOTION
BUOY MOTION EFFECTS
BUOYANCY FLUX
BUOYANT JETS
CABBELING
CALCIFICATION
CALCITE DISSOLUTION
CALCITIZATION
CALVING
CAMOUFLAGE
CANNIBALISM
CAPILLARITY
CAPILLARY WAVES
CAPSIZING
CARBON CYCLE
CARBON FIXATION
CARBOXYLATION
CARCINOGENESIS
CASCADING
CATABOLISM
CATADROMOUS MIGRATIONS
CATAGENESIS
CATASTROPHIC WAVES
CATENARY
CAVITATION
CELL DIFFERENTIATION
CELL DIVISION
CELL FUSION
CELLULAR CONVECTION
CEMENTATION
CENTRIFUGAL FORCE
CENTRIPETAL FORCE
CHANDLER WOBBLE
CHANNEL FLOW
CHEMICAL CYCLES
CHEMICAL DEGRADATION
CHEMICAL EQUILIBRIUM
CHEMICAL OXYGEN DEMAND
CHEMICAL PLUMES
CHEMICAL POLLUTION
CHEMICAL PRECIPITATION
CHEMICAL REACTIONS
CHEMICAL SPECIATION
CHEMICAL SPILLS
CHEMICAL STIMULI
CHEMILUMINESCENCE
CHEMORECEPTION
CHEMOSYNTHESIS
CHEMOTAXIS
CHEMOTROPISM
CHERTIFICATION
CHROMATIC ADAPTATIONS
CHROMATIC BEHAVIOUR
CIGUATERA
CIRCADIAN RHYTHMS
CIRCULATION
CLEANING BEHAVIOUR
CLEAR AIR TURBULENCE
CLIMATE
CLIMATIC CHANGES

ASFIS Thesaurus
List of Descriptors by Facet

CLOUD COVER
CLOUDS
CNOIDAL WAVES
COAGULATION
COAST EFFECT
COASTAL COUNTERCURRENTS
COASTAL CURRENTS
COASTAL EROSION
COASTAL JETS
COASTAL UPWELLING
COLLISIONS
COLONIZATION
COMMENSALISM
COMPACTION
COMPETITION
COMPETITIVE BEHAVIOUR
COMPRESSION
CONDENSATION
CONSERVATION OF ANGULAR MOMENTUM
CONSERVATION OF ENERGY
CONSERVATION OF HEAT
CONSERVATION OF MASS
CONSERVATION OF MOMENTUM
CONSERVATION OF SALT
CONSERVATION OF VORTICITY
CONSERVATION PRINCIPLES
CONSOLIDATION
CONSTRUCTIVE WAVES
CONTINENTAL DRIFT
CONTOUR CURRENTS
CONVECTION
CONVERGENCE
CONVERGENCE ZONES
COOLING
COPRECIPITATION
CORIOLIS FORCE
CORROSION
COSINE RESPONSE
COSMIC RADIATION
COUETTE FLOW
COUNTERCURRENTS
COURTSHIP
CRACK PROPAGATION
CRACKING (CORROSION)
CRACKS
CREEP
CRITICAL FLOW
CRUSTAL ACCRETION
CRUSTAL ADJUSTMENT
CRUSTAL SHORTENING
CULTURE EFFECTS
CURRENT FORCES
CURRENT MARKS
CURRENT MEANDERING
CURRENT REVERSAL
CURRENT RINGS
CURRENT SCOURING
CURRENT SHEAR
CYCLES
CYCLIC LOADING
CYCLOGENESIS
CYCLOMORPHOSIS
CYCLONES
CYCLONIC MOTION
DAMAGE
DEAD WATER
DEAMINATION
DEBRIS FLOW
DECALCIFICATION
DECARBOXYLATION
DECOMPRESSION SICKNESS
DEEP CURRENTS
DEEP WATER FORMATION
DEEP-WATER WAVES
DEFAECATION
DEFECTS
DEFENCE MECHANISMS
DEFICIENCY DISEASES
DEFLECTION

DEFLOCCULATION
DEGASSING
DEGENERATION
DEGLACIATION
DEGRADATION
DEHYDRATION
DELTAIC SEDIMENTATION
DEMINERALIZATION
DENITRIFICATION
DENSITY DEPENDENCE
DENSITY FIELD
DENSITY FLOW
DENSITY FRONTS
DENSITY STRATIFICATION
DENUDATION
DEOXYGENATION
DEPOLYMERIZATION
DESICCATION
DESORPTION
DESTRATIFICATION
DESTRUCTIVE WAVES
DETERIORATION
DEVITRIFICATION
DIAGENESIS
DIALYSIS
DIAPAUSE
DIAPIRISM
DIASTROPHISM
DIETARY DEFICIENCIES
DIFFERENTIAL DISTRIBUTION
DIFFRACTION
DIFFUSION
DIGESTION
DILUTION
DISASTERS
DISCOLOURATION
DISEASE RESISTANCE
DISEASE TRANSMISSION
DISEASES
DISPERSION
DISPLAY BEHAVIOUR
DISSOCIATION
DISSOLUTION
DISTILLATION
DISTRIBUTION
DIURNAL TIDES
DIURNAL VARIATIONS
DIVERGENCE
DIVING ACCIDENTS
DIVING HAZARDS
DOLOMITIZATION
DOMINANCE HIERARCHIES
DOPPLER EFFECT
DORMANCY
DOUBLE DIFFUSION
DOWNWARD LONG WAVE RADIATION
DOWNWELLING
DRAG
DRIFT
DROUGHT RESISTANCE
DROUGHTS
DROWNING
DUST CLOUDS
DYE DISPERSION
DYNAMIC HEIGHT ANOMALY
DYNAMIC LOADS
DYNAMIC RESPONSE
EARTH ROTATION
EARTH TIDES
EARTH TILT
EARTHQUAKE LOADING
EARTHQUAKES
EASTERLY WAVES
EASTERN BOUNDARY CURRENTS
EBB CURRENTS
ECHOES
ECHOLOCATION
ECOLOGICAL BALANCE
ECOLOGICAL CRISIS

ECOLOGICAL DISTRIBUTION
ECOLOGICAL SUCCESSION
ECOSYSTEM DISTURBANCE
ECTOPARASITISM
EDDY CONDUCTION
EDDY KINETIC ENERGY
EDGE WAVES
EKMAN PUMPING
EKMAN SPIRAL
EKMAN TRANSPORT
EL NINO PHENOMENA
ELASTIC WAVES
ELECTRIC CHARGE
ELECTRIC CURRENTS
ELECTRIC FIELDS
ELECTRIC STIMULI
ELECTRICITY
ELECTRODIALYSIS
ELECTROLYSIS
ELECTROMAGNETIC RADIATION
ELECTROMAGNETISM
ELECTRONIC NOISE
EMBRITTLEMENT
EMBRYONIC DEVELOPMENT
EMERGENCE
EMERGENCIES
EMISSIVITY
ENCYSTMENT
ENDEMISM
ENDOPARASITISM
ENERGY
ENERGY BALANCE
ENERGY BUDGET
ENERGY DISSIPATION
ENERGY FLOW
ENERGY TRANSFER
ENTRAINMENT
ENVIRONMENTAL DISEASES
ENVIRONMENTAL EFFECTS
ENVIRONMENTAL IMPACT
ENZYMATIC ACTIVITY
ENZYMOLYSIS
EOLIAN PROCESSES
EOLIAN TRANSPORT
EPEIROGENY
EPIBIOSIS
EPIDEMICS
EQUATORIAL CIRCULATION
EQUATORIAL COUNTERCURRENTS
EQUATORIAL DYNAMICS
EQUATORIAL EASTERLIES
EQUATORIAL TRAPPED WAVES
EQUATORIAL TROUGH
EQUATORIAL UNDERCURRENTS
EQUATORIAL UPWELLING
EQUATORIAL WAVES
EQUATORIAL WESTERLIES
EQUILIBRIUM TIDES
EROSION
ERYTHROPOIESIS
ESCAPEMENT
ESTUARINE CHEMISTRY
ESTUARINE DYNAMICS
ESTUARINE FRONT
ESTUARINE SEDIMENTATION
ESTUARINE TIDES
EUSTATIC CHANGES
EUTROPHICATION
EVAPORATION
EVAPOTRANSPIRATION
EVOLUTION
EXCRETION
EXOPHTHALMIA
EXPLORATORY BEHAVIOUR
EXPLOSIONS
EXTRATERRESTRIAL RADIATION
EXTREME WAVES
FAILURES
FATIGUE (MATERIALS)

ASFIS Thesaurus
List of Descriptors by Facet

FEEDING	GEOTHERMAL ENERGY	HYDROSTATIC BEHAVIOUR
FEEDING BEHAVIOUR	GEOTHERMAL GRADIENT	HYDROTHERMAL ACTIVITY
FEEDING MIGRATIONS	GEOTROPISM	HYDROTHERMAL ALTERATION
FERMENTATION	GERMINATION	HYDROTHERMAL FLOW
FINESTRUCTURE	GIANT WAVES	HYPERCAPNIA
FINITE AMPLITUDE WAVES	GILL DISEASE	HYPERTHERMIA
FIRE	GLACIAL EROSION	HYPERTROPHY
FIRE HAZARDS	GLACIAL SEDIMENTATION	HYPOTHERMIA
FISH DISEASES	GLACIAL TRANSPORT	HYPOXIA
FISH KILL	GLACIATION	ICE ACCRETION
FISH SPOILAGE	GLITTER	ICE BREAKUP
FISHING MORTALITY	GRADIENT CURRENTS	ICE CONDITIONS
FJORD DYNAMICS	GRADIENT WINDS	ICE COVER
FLIGHT BEHAVIOUR	GRAIN FLOW	ICE DRIFT
FLOATING	GRAVEL WAVES	ICE FORMATION
FLOCCULATION	GRAVITATION	ICE FRONTS
FLOOD CURRENTS	GRAVITY	ICE JAMS
FLOODING	GRAVITY ANOMALIES	ICE LOADS
FLOODS	GRAVITY EFFECTS	ICE MELTING
FLOTATION	GRAVITY FIELD	ICE PRESSURE
FLOW AROUND OBJECTS	GRAVITY WAVES	ICE RAFTING
FLOW OVER SURFACES	GRAZING	ICEBERG SCOURING
FLOW STRUCTURES	GREENFLASH	ICING
FLUID FLOW	GREENHOUSE EFFECT	IMMERSION EFFECTS
FLUID MOTION	GROUND MOTION	IMMIGRATIONS
FLUIDIZATION	GROUNDINGS	IMPINGEMENT
FLUIDIZED SEDIMENT FLOW	GROUNDWATER POLLUTION	IMPLOSIONS
FLUORESCENCE	GROUP EFFECTS	IMPRESSED CURRENTS
FLUSHING	GROUP VELOCITY	IMPRINTING
FLUTE CASTS	GROWTH	INBREEDING
FLUVIAL SEDIMENTATION	GUSTS	INCUBATION
FLUVIAL TRANSPORT	GYRES	INERTIA
FLYING	HABITAT SELECTION	INERTIAL CURRENTS
FOG	HAEMATOLOGICAL DISEASES	INERTIAL OSCILLATIONS
FOOD ABSORPTION	HAEMOPOIESIS	INERTIAL WAVES
FOOD CHAINS	HAEMORRHAGE	INFECTIOUS DISEASES
FOOD CONSUMPTION	HALINE CIRCULATION	INFESTATION
FOOD CONVERSION	HALMYROLYSIS	INFLOW
FOOD POISONING	HARBOUR OSCILLATIONS	INFRARED RADIATION
FOOD PREFERENCES	HATCHING	INGESTION
FOOD WEBS	HAZARDS	INJURIES
FORCED CONVECTION	HAZE	INSOLATION
FORCED OSCILLATIONS	HEAT	INSONIFICATION
FORCES	HEAT BALANCE	INSTINCT
FORCES (MECHANICS)	HEAT BUDGET	INSTRUMENT RESPONSES
FORM DRAG	HEAT CONDUCTION	INTERFACE PHENOMENA
FORWARD SCATTERING	HEAT EXCHANGE	INTERFACIAL WAVES
FOULING	HEAT FLOW	INTERNAL TIDES
FRACTURES	HEAT SINKS	INTERNAL WAVE BREAKING
FREAK WAVES	HEAT STORAGE	INTERNAL WAVE EFFECTS
FREE AIR ANOMALIES	HEAT TRANSFER	INTERNAL WAVE GENERATION
FREEZING	HEAT TRANSPORT	INTERNAL WAVES
FRESHWATER POLLUTION	HEAVE RESONANCE	INTERSPECIFIC RELATIONSHIPS
FRICTION	HEAVE RESPONSE	INTERTIDAL SEDIMENTATION
FRONTAL FEATURES	HEAVING	INTERTROPICAL CONVERGENCE ZONE
FRONTOGENESIS	HERMAPHRODITISM	INTRASPECIFIC RELATIONSHIPS
FRONTS	HETEROTROPHY	INVERSIONS
FUNGAL DISEASES	HIBERNATION	ION ACCUMULATION
GALE FORCE WINDS	HIGH PRESSURE RIDGES	ION ASSOCIATION
GAMETOGENESIS	HIGH PRESSURE SYSTEMS	ION EXCHANGE
GAMMA RADIATION	HIGH WATER	ION TRANSPORT
GAS EXCHANGE	HIGHEST ASTRONOMICAL TIDES	IONIZING RADIATION
GAS SEEPAGES	HOMING BEHAVIOUR	ISENTROPIC PROCESSES
GAS TURBATION	HOMOIOTHERMY	ISOLATING MECHANISMS
GENETIC ABNORMALITIES	HORIZONTAL ADVECTION	ISOMERIZATION
GENETIC DRIFT	HORIZONTAL DISTRIBUTION	ISOSTASY
GENETIC ISOLATION	HORIZONTAL MOTION	ISOTHERMAL PROCESSES
GEOCHEMICAL CYCLE	HOST PREFERENCES	JET STREAM
GEOGRAPHICAL DISTRIBUTION	HUMAN DISEASES	JETS
GEOGRAPHICAL ISOLATION	HURRICANE WAVES	KELVIN WAVES
GEOID ANOMALIES	HURRICANES	KINESIS
GEOLOGICAL DISTRIBUTION	HUSBANDRY DISEASES	KINETIC ENERGY
GEOLOGICAL HAZARDS	HYBRIDIZATION	KURTOSIS
GEOMAGNETIC FIELD	HYDRATION	LACTATION
GEOSTROPHIC EQUILIBRIUM	HYDRAULIC JUMP	LACUSTRINE SEDIMENTATION
GEOSTROPHIC FLOW	HYDROCLIMATE	LAGOONAL SEDIMENTATION
GEOSTROPHIC TRANSPORT	HYDROLOGIC CYCLE	LAKE CURRENTS
GEOSTROPHIC WINDS	HYDROLYSIS	LAKE DYNAMICS
GEOSTROPHY	HYDROMETEORS	LAMELLAR TEARING

ASFIS Thesaurus
List of Descriptors by Facet

LAMINAR FLOW
LAMPREY ATTACHMENT
LAND AND SEA BREEZES
LAND BREEZES
LANDSLIDES
LANGMUIR CIRCULATION
LARVAL DEVELOPMENT
LARVAL SETTLEMENT
LATENT HEAT TRANSFER
LAVA FLOWS
LEACHING
LEAKS
LEARNING BEHAVIOUR
LEE EDDIES
LEE WAVES
LESIONS
LIFE CYCLE
LIFE HISTORY
LIGHT
LIGHT ABSORPTION
LIGHT ATTENUATION
LIGHT DIFFRACTION
LIGHT DISPERSION
LIGHT EFFECTS
LIGHT FIELDS
LIGHT PENETRATION
LIGHT PROPAGATION
LIGHT REFLECTION
LIGHT REFRACTION
LIGHT SCATTERING
LIGHT STIMULI
LIGHT TRANSMISSION
LIGHTNING
LINEAR WAVES
LIQUEFACTION
LIQUEFIED SEDIMENT FLOW
LITHIFICATION
LITHOGENESIS
LOADS (FORCES)
LOCAL MOVEMENTS
LOCAL WINDS
LOCOMOTION
LONG-CRESTED WAVES
LONG-PERIOD TIDES
LONG-TERM CHANGES
LONGITUDINAL DISPERSION
LONGSHORE CURRENTS
LONGSHORE SEDIMENT TRANSPORT
LOVE WAVES
LOW PRESSURE SYSTEMS
LOW PRESSURE TROUGHS
LOW TIDE
LOWEST ASTRONOMICAL TIDES
LUMINESCENCE
LUNAR DIURNAL TIDES
LUNAR SEMIDIURNAL TIDES
LUNAR TIDES
MAGNETIC ANOMALIES
MAGNETIC FIELDS
MAGNETIC REVERSALS
MAGNETIC VARIATIONS
MAGNETISM
MALARIA
MAN-INDUCED EFFECTS
MANTLE CONVECTION
MANTLE PLUMES
MARINE POLLUTION
MASS EXTINCTIONS
MASS GRAVITY TRANSPORT (SEDIMENTS)
MASS MOVEMENT
MASS TRANSFER
MASS TRANSPORT
MEANDERING
MECHANICAL STIMULI
MEIOSIS
MELTING
MERIDIONAL ATMOSPHERIC CIRCULATION
MERIDIONAL DISTRIBUTION
MERIDIONAL OCEANIC CIRCULATION

MEROMIXIS
MESOSCALE EDDIES
MESOSCALE FEATURES
METABOLIC DISORDERS
METABOLISM
METAL FATIGUE
METALLOGENESIS
METAMORPHISM
METAMORPHOSIS
METASOMATISM
METEOROLOGICAL TIDES
METHANOGENESIS
MICROBIAL CONTAMINATION
MICROEARTHQUAKES
MICROSEISMS
MICROSTRUCTURE
MICROWAVES
MIGRATIONS
MIMICRY
MINERALIZATION
MIRAGES
MISTRAL
MITOSIS
MIXING PROCESSES
MOISTURE TRANSFER
MOLECULAR DIFFUSION
MONSOON REVERSAL
MONSOONS
MONTHLY DISTRIBUTION
MOON PHASES
MOORING MOTION EFFECTS
MORPHOGENESIS
MORTALITY
MOTION
MOTION EFFECTS
MOULTING
MULTIPHASE FLOW
MUTATIONS
NARCOSIS
NATURAL MORTALITY
NATURAL SELECTION
NAVIGATIONAL HAZARDS
NEAP TIDES
NEARSHORE CURRENTS
NEARSHORE DYNAMICS
NEARSHORE SEDIMENTATION
NECROSES
NEGATIVE STORM SURGES
NEOTENY
NESTING
NEUROSECRETION
NEW RECORDS
NITROGEN CYCLE
NITROGEN FIXATION
NITROGEN NARCOSIS
NODAL TIDES
NOISE (SOUND)
NONLINEAR WAVE INTERACTIONS
NONLINEAR WAVES
NORTH ATLANTIC POLAR FRONT
NUCLEAR ENERGY
NUCLEAR EXPLOSIONS
NUCLEAR RADIATIONS
NUTRIENT CYCLES
NUTRIENT DEFICIENCY
NUTRITION
NUTRITION DISORDERS
NUTRITIONAL TYPES
NYCTIMERAL RHYTHMS
OBDUCTION
OBSTACLE MARKS
OCEAN CIRCULATION
OCEAN CURRENTS
OCEAN LOADING
OCEAN TIDES
OCEANIC CONVECTION
OCEANIC CONVERGENCES
OCEANIC DIVERGENCES
OCEANIC EDDIES

OCEANIC FRONTS
OCEANIC RESPONSE
OCEANIC TURBULENCE
OCEANIZATION
OCEANODROMOUS MIGRATIONS
OIL POLLUTION
OIL SEEPAGES
OIL SPILLS
OLFACTION
OOGENESIS
ORGANOGENESIS
ORIENTATION BEHAVIOUR
OROGENY
ORTHOTIDES
OSCILLATIONS
OSCILLATORY FLOW
OSCILLATORY WAVES
OSMOREGULATION
OSMOSIS
OSMOTIC ADAPTATIONS
OUTFLOW
OVERCROWDING
OVERFLOW
OVERTOPPING
OVERTURN
OVERWASH
OVERWINTERING
OVIPARITY
OVOVIVIPARITY
OVULATION
OXIDATION
OXYGEN CONSUMPTION
OXYGEN DEMAND
OXYGEN DEPLETION
OXYGENATION
P-WAVES
PALAEOCLIMATE
PALAEOCURRENTS
PALAEOMAGNETISM
PARASITE ATTACHMENT
PARASITE RESISTANCE
PARASITIC CASTRATION
PARASITIC DISEASES
PARASITISM
PARENTAL BEHAVIOUR
PARTHENOGENESIS
PARTICLE MOTION
PARTICLE SCATTERING
PARTICLE SETTLING
PARTICULATE FLUX
PARTURITION
PECKING ORDER
PEDUNCLE DISEASE
PELAGIC SEDIMENTATION
PERCOLATION
PERIODIC VARIATIONS
PERTURBATIONS
PETROGENESIS
PH EFFECTS
PHAGOCYTOSIS
PHASE CHANGES
PHENOTYPIC VARIATIONS
PHOSPHATIZATION
PHOSPHORESCENCE
PHOSPHORUS CYCLE
PHOTOCHEMICAL REACTIONS
PHOTOLYSIS
PHOTOPERIODICITY
PHOTOPERIODS
PHOTORECEPTION
PHOTOSYNTHESIS
PHOTOTAXIS
PHOTOTROPISM
PIPE BUCKLING
PITCH RESONANCE
PITCH RESPONSE
PITCHING
PLANETARY WAVES
PLANETARY WINDS

ASFIS Thesaurus
List of Descriptors by Facet

PLANT DISEASES
PLANT METABOLISM
PLANT NUTRITION
PLASTIC FLOW
PLATE CONVERGENCE
PLATE DIVERGENCE
PLATE MOTION
PLOUGHMARKS
PLUMBLINE DEFLECTION
PLUMES
POCK MARKS
POIKILOTHERMY
POLAR AIR MASSES
POLAR CONVERGENCES
POLAR FRONTS
POLAR WANDERING
POLARIZATION
POLE TIDES
POLLINATION
POLLUTANT PERSISTENCE
POLLUTION
POLLUTION DISPERSION
POLLUTION EFFECTS
POLYMERIZATION
POLYSPERMY
POPULATION FUNCTIONS
POTADROMOUS MIGRATIONS
POTENTIAL FLOW
POWER CONSUMPTION
PREDATION
PREGNANCY
PRESSURE EFFECTS
PRESSURE GRADIENTS
PREY SELECTION
PRIMARY PRODUCTION
PROGRADATION
PROGRESSIVE WAVES
PROTANDRY
PROTECTIVE BEHAVIOUR
PROTEIN DEFICIENCY
PROTEIN DENATURATION
PROTEIN SYNTHESIS
PROTOZOAN DISEASES
PROVENANCE
PYROLYSIS
QUANTITATIVE DISTRIBUTION
QUARTER DIURNAL TIDES
QUASI-GEOSTROPHIC MOTION
RADAR CLUTTER
RADIATION HAZARDS
RADIATION LEAKS
RADIATIONAL TIDES
RADIATIONS
RADIATIVE TRANSFER
RADIO WAVES
RADIOACTIVE CONTAMINATION
RADIOACTIVITY
RAFTING
RAINFALL
RANDOM PROCESSES
RAY PATHS
RAYLEIGH WAVES
RECRUITMENT
RED TIDES
REDMOUTH DISEASE
REDOX REACTIONS
REDUCTION
REEF FORMATION
REFLECTED GLOBAL RADIATION
REFLECTION
REFRACTION
REGENERATION
REGIONAL VARIATIONS
REGRESSIONS
RENEWAL
REPRODUCTION
REPRODUCTIVE BEHAVIOUR
REPRODUCTIVE CYCLE
RESIDUAL FLOW

RESISTANCE MECHANISMS
RESONANCE
RESONANT WAVE INTERACTION
RESPIRATION
RESUSPENSION
RETROGRADATION
REVERBERATION
REVERSE OSMOSIS
REYNOLDS STRESSES
RHEOTAXIS
RHEOTROPISM
RIFTING
RIP CURRENTS
RIVER DISCHARGE
RIVER MEANDERS
RIVER OUTFLOW
RIVER PLUMES
ROCK MECHANICS
ROLL RESONANCE
ROLL RESPONSE
ROLLERS
ROLLING
ROSSBY PARAMETER
ROTARY CURRENTS
ROTATING FLUIDS
ROTATION
S-WAVES
SALINE INTRUSION
SALINITY EFFECTS
SALINITY GRADIENTS
SALINITY STRATIFICATION
SALT ADVECTION
SALT BUDGET
SALT FINGERS
SALT FLUX
SALT WEDGES
SALTATION
SAMPLE CONTAMINATION
SATURATION
SCALING
SCHOOLING BEHAVIOUR
SCOURING
SEA BREEZES
SEA LEVEL CHANGES
SEA LEVEL VARIATIONS
SEA SICKNESS
SEAFLOOR SPREADING
SEAQUAKES
SEASONAL DISTRIBUTION
SEASONAL VARIATIONS
SEAWATER EVOLUTION
SECONDARY PRODUCTION
SECRETION
SEDIMENT DISTRIBUTION
SEDIMENT DYNAMICS
SEDIMENT GRAVITY FLOWS
SEDIMENT MIXING
SEDIMENT NOISE
SEDIMENT POLLUTION
SEDIMENT SORTING
SEDIMENT TRANSPORT
SEDIMENT-WATER EXCHANGES
SEDIMENTATION
SEEPAGES
SEICHES
SEISMIC ACTIVITY
SEISMIC ATTENUATION
SEISMIC DIFFRACTION
SEISMIC PROPAGATION
SEISMIC REFLECTION
SEISMIC REFRACTION
SEISMIC SCATTERING
SEISMIC WAVES
SELF FERTILIZATION
SELF PURIFICATION
SEMIDIURNAL TIDES
SENSE FUNCTIONS
SENSIBLE HEAT
SENSIBLE HEAT TRANSFER

SEPARATION PROCESSES
SEPTICAEMIA
SERPENTINITIZATION
SETTLEMENT (STRUCTURAL)
SETTLING BEHAVIOUR
SEX DETERMINATION
SEX REVERSAL
SEXUAL BEHAVIOUR
SEXUAL DIMORPHISM
SEXUAL ISOLATION
SEXUAL REPRODUCTION
SEXUAL SELECTION
SHALLOW-WATER TIDES
SHALLOW-WATER WAVES
SHARK ATTACKS
SHEAR
SHEAR FLOW
SHEAR STRESS
SHELF CURRENTS
SHELF DYNAMICS
SHELF EDGE DYNAMICS
SHELF EDGE FRONTS
SHELF FRONTS
SHELF SEDIMENTATION
SHELF WAVES
SHIP DRIFT
SHIP LOSSES
SHIP MOTION
SHIPPING NOISE
SHOALING
SHOALING WAVES
SHORT-CRESTED WAVES
SHORT-TERM CHANGES
SHORT WAVE-LONG WAVE INTERACTIONS
SIGNIFICANT WAVE HEIGHT
SIGNIFICANT WAVES
SILICIFICATION
SILICON CYCLE
SILTING
SINKING
SLIDES
SLOPE CURRENTS
SLOPE PROCESSES
SLUMPING
SNOW
SOCIAL BEHAVIOUR
SOFAR CHANNEL
SOIL EROSION
SOLAR ACTIVITY
SOLAR DIURNAL TIDES
SOLAR ECLIPSE
SOLAR RADIATION
SOLAR SEMIDIURNAL TIDES
SOLAR-TERRESTRIAL ACTIVITY
SOLAR TIDES
SOLE MARKS
SOLIDIFICATION
SOLITARY WAVES
SOLITONS
SOLVATION
SOLVENT EXTRACTION
SORPTION
SOUND
SOUND ABSORPTION
SOUND ATTENUATION
SOUND CHANNELS
SOUND DIFFRACTION
SOUND DISPERSION
SOUND GENERATION
SOUND PRODUCTION
SOUND PROPAGATION
SOUND REFLECTION
SOUND REFRACTION
SOUND SCATTERING
SOUND SOURCES
SOUND TRANSMISSION
SOUND WAVES
SOUTHERN OSCILLATION
SPALLING

ASFIS Thesaurus
List of Descriptors by Facet

SPATIAL VARIATIONS
SPAWNING
SPAWNING MIGRATIONS
SPECIES EXTINCTION
SPECIFIC VOLUME ANOMALIES
SPEECH DISTORTION
SPERMATOGENESIS
SPILLING WAVES
SPINDOWN
SPINUP
SPOROGENESIS
SPRAY
SPRING TIDES
STANDING WAVES
STARVATION
STIMULI
STOKES WAVES
STONELEY WAVES
STORAGE EFFECTS
STORM SURGE GENERATION
STORM SURGES
STORMS
STRANDING
STRATIFICATION
STRATIFIED FLOW
STRATIFIED SHEAR FLOW
STREAM FLOW
STRESS
STRESS CORROSION
STRESS-STRAIN RELATIONS
SUBDUCTION
SUBLETHAL EFFECTS
SUBLIMATION
SUBMARINE CABLE BREAKS
SUBMERGENCE
SUBSIDENCE
SUBSTRATE PREFERENCES
SUBSURFACE CURRENTS
SUBTROPICAL CONVERGENCES
SULPHATE REDUCTION
SUNBURN
SUPERSATURATION
SURF
SURF BEATS
SURFACE ACTIVITY
SURFACE CIRCULATION
SURFACE CLUTTER
SURFACE CURRENTS
SURFACE GRAVITY WAVES
SURFACE NOISE
SURFACE SEISMIC WAVES
SURFACE TENSION
SURFACE WATER WAVES
SURFACE WAVE-INTERNAL WAVE INTERACTIONS
SURGE RESPONSE
SURGES
SURGING
SURVIVAL
SUSPENSION
SVERDRUP TRANSPORT
SWAYING
SWELL
SWIMMING
SYMBIOSIS
SYMPTOMS
SYNERGISM
TACTILE FUNCTIONS
TACTILE STIMULI
TAGGING MORTALITY
TASTE FUNCTIONS
TAXIS
TELECONNECTIONS
TELLURIC CURRENTS
TEMPERATURE ANOMALIES
TEMPERATURE DIFFERENCES
TEMPERATURE EFFECTS
TEMPERATURE GRADIENTS
TEMPERATURE INVERSIONS
TEMPERATURE PREFERENCES

TEMPORAL DISTRIBUTION
TEMPORAL VARIATIONS
TENSION
TERRESTRIAL RADIATION
TERRITORIALITY
THERMAL CONDUCTIVITY
THERMAL DECOMPOSITION
THERMAL DIFFUSION
THERMAL DOMES
THERMAL FRONTS
THERMAL PLUMES
THERMAL POLLUTION
THERMAL RADIATION
THERMAL STIMULI
THERMAL STRATIFICATION
THERMAL STRUCTURE
THERMOCLINE DECAY
THERMODYNAMIC ACTIVITY
THERMOHALINE CIRCULATION
THERMOREGULATION
THERMOSTADS
THERMOSTERIC ANOMALIES
THUNDERSTORMS
TIDAL BORES
TIDAL CURRENTS
TIDAL CYCLES
TIDAL DISSIPATION
TIDAL DYNAMICS
TIDAL EFFECTS
TIDAL ENERGY
TIDAL FRICTION
TIDAL MIXING
TIDAL MOTION
TIDAL OSCILLATIONS
TIDAL PERTURBATION
TIDAL PROPAGATION
TIDAL WAVES
TIDE-SURGE INTERACTION
TIDES
TOPOGRAPHIC EFFECTS
TOPOGRAPHIC WAVES
TORNADOES
TORQUE
TOTAL MORTALITY
TRACTION
TRADE WIND INVERSION
TRADE WINDS
TRANS-ISOPYCNAL MIXING
TRANSGRESSIONS
TRANSMISSION
TRANSMISSION LOSS
TRANSPIRATION
TRANSPORT PROCESSES
TRANSVERSE MIXING
TRAPPED WAVES
TROPHIC RELATIONSHIPS
TROPHODYNAMIC CYCLE
TROPICAL DEPRESSIONS
TROPISM
TSUNAMI GENERATION
TSUNAMIS
TUBERCULOSIS
TUMOURS
TURBIDITY CURRENTS
TURBULENCE
TURBULENT DIFFUSION
TURBULENT ENTRAINMENT
TURBULENT FLOW
TURBULENT SHEAR FLOW
TURBULENT TRANSFER
ULCERATIVE DERMAL NECROSIS
ULTRAVIOLET RADIATION
UNDERCURRENTS
UNDERTOW
UNDERWATER EXPLOSIONS
UNDERWATER NOISE
UNIDIRECTIONAL FLOW
UNSTEADY FLOW
UPLIFT

UPWARD LONG WAVE RADIATION
UPWELLING
VAPORIZATION
VARIABILITY
VEGETATIVE REPRODUCTION
VELOCITY GRADIENTS
VERTICAL ADVECTION
VERTICAL DISTRIBUTION
VERTICAL MIGRATIONS
VERTICAL MIXING
VERTICAL MOTION
VERTICAL SHEAR
VERTICAL TECTONICS
VERTICAL WATER MOVEMENT
VIBRATION
VIBRIOSIS
VIRAL DISEASES
VISION
VISUAL STIMULI
VITAMIN DEFICIENCIES
VITELLOGENESIS
VIVIPARITY
VOCALIZATION BEHAVIOUR
VOIDS
VOLCANIC ERUPTIONS
VOLCANISM
VOLUME TRANSPORT
VORTEX SHEDDING
VORTICES
WAKES
WASTE HEAT
WATER BALANCE
WATER CIRCULATION
WATER CURRENTS
WATER EXCHANGE
WATER MASS INTRUSIONS
WATER MIXING
WATER MOTION
WATER POLLUTION
WATER RIPPLES
WATER WAVE MOTION
WATER WAVES
WATERSPOUTS
WAVE ACTION
WAVE-AIR INTERACTION
WAVE ATTENUATION
WAVE BREAKING
WAVE CRESTS
WAVE-CURRENT INTERACTION
WAVE DIFFRACTION
WAVE DISPERSION
WAVE DISSIPATION
WAVE DYNAMICS
WAVE EFFECTS
WAVE ENERGY
WAVE FORCES
WAVE GENERATION
WAVE GROUPS
WAVE-ICE INTERACTION
WAVE-INDUCED LOADING
WAVE INTERACTIONS
WAVE MOTION
WAVE PROCESSES ON BEACHES
WAVE PROPAGATION
WAVE REFLECTION
WAVE REFRACTION
WAVE RUNUP
WAVE SCATTERING
WAVE SCOURING
WAVE-SEABED INTERACTION
WAVE SETDOWN
WAVE SETUP
WAVE TRAINS
WAVE TRAPPING
WAVE-WAVE INTERACTION
WAVES ON BEACHES
WEAR
WEATHER
WEATHER HAZARDS

ASFIS Thesaurus
List of Descriptors by Facet

WEATHERING
WEST WIND DRIFT
WESTERLIES
WESTERN BOUNDARY CURRENTS
WESTERN BOUNDARY UNDERCURRENTS
WESTWARD INTENSIFICATION
WHIRLING DISEASE
WHITECAPPING
WHITECAPS
WILD SPAWNING
WIND ABRASION
WIND CONSTANCY
WIND-DRIVEN CIRCULATION
WIND-DRIVEN CURRENTS
WIND EROSION
WIND PRESSURE
WIND SETUP
WIND SHEAR
WIND STRESS
WIND WAVE GENERATION
WIND-WAVE INTERACTION
WIND WAVES
WINDS
WINNOWING
WINTERKILL
WOUNDING
X-RAYS
YAW RESPONSE
YAWING
ZONAL DISTRIBUTION

ASFIS Thesaurus
List of Descriptors by Facet

Materials

ACANSTEROL
ACETATE
ACETONE
ACRYLIC ACID
ACRYLICS
ACTIN
ACTINIDE COMPOUNDS
ACTINIDES
ACTINIUM
ACTINIUM COMPOUNDS
ACTINIUM ISOTOPES
ACYCLIC HYDROCARBONS
ADDITIVES
ADHESIVES
ADP
AEROSOLS
AGAR
AGAROSE
AGENTS
AGGREGATES
AGRICULTURAL RUNOFF
AIR
ALANINE
ALARM SUBSTANCES
ALBUMINS
ALCOHOLS
ALDEHYDES
ALDRIN
ALGICIDES
ALGINATES
ALGINIC ACID
ALICYCLIC HYDROCARBONS
ALKALI BASALTS
ALKALI METAL COMPOUNDS
ALKALI METALS
ALKALINE EARTH METAL COMPOUNDS
ALKALINE EARTH METALS
ALKALOIDS
ALKENES
ALKYNES
ALLOCHTHONOUS DEPOSITS
ALLOYS
ALLUVIAL DEPOSITS
ALUMINIUM
ALUMINIUM COMPOUNDS
ALUMINIUM ISOTOPES
AMBERGRIS
AMERICIUM
AMERICIUM COMPOUNDS
AMERICIUM ISOTOPES
AMINES
AMINO ACIDS
AMMONIA
AMMONIUM CHLORIDE
AMMONIUM COMPOUNDS
AMP
AMPHIBOLES
AMPHIBOLITES
ANAESTHETICS
ANALCITE
ANATASE
ANDALUSITE
ANDESITE
ANHYDRITE
ANIMAL PRODUCTS
ANIONS
ANISOTROPIC ROCKS
ANORTHITE
ANORTHOCLASE
ANORTHOSITE
ANOXIC SEDIMENTS
ANTIBIOTICS
ANTICOAGULANTS
ANTIFOULING SUBSTANCES

ANTIFREEZES
ANTIGENS
ANTIHELMINTHIC AGENTS
ANTIMONY
ANTIMONY COMPOUNDS
ANTIMONY ISOTOPES
ANTIOXIDANTS
ANTIPARASITIC AGENTS
ANTIPROTOZOAL AGENTS
APATITE
AQUACULTURE EFFLUENTS
AQUACULTURE PRODUCTS
AQUATIC DRUGS
ARABINOSE
ARACHIDONIC ACID
ARAGONITE
ARENACEOUS DEPOSITS
ARENITES
ARGILLACEOUS DEPOSITS
ARGININE
ARGON
ARGON ISOTOPES
AROMATIC HYDROCARBONS
AROMATICS
ARSENATES
ARSENIC
ARSENIC COMPOUNDS
ARSENIC ISOTOPES
ARTIFICIAL SEAWATER
ARTIFICIAL SEAWEED
ARTIFICIAL SUBSTRATA
ASBESTOS
ASH LAYERS
ASHES
ASPARTIC ACID
ASPHALT
ASTATINE
ASTATINE COMPOUNDS
ASTATINE ISOTOPES
ATMOSPHERIC GASES
ATMOSPHERIC PARTICULATES
ATP
AUGITE
AUTHIGENIC MINERALS
AUTOCHTHONOUS DEPOSITS
AUXINS
AZINES
BACTERINS
BACTERIOCIDES
BALANCED DIETS
BALANCED RATIONS
BARITE
BARIUM
BARIUM COMPOUNDS
BARIUM ISOTOPES
BASALTS
BASIC DIETS
BATHOLITHS
BAUXITE
BEACHROCK
BED LOAD
BENTONITE
BENZENE
BERKELIUM
BERKELIUM COMPOUNDS
BERKELIUM ISOTOPES
BERYLLIUM
BERYLLIUM COMPOUNDS
BERYLLIUM ISOTOPES
BICARBONATES
BILE
BIOCALCARENITE
BIODEGRADABLE SUBSTANCES
BIOGENIC MATERIAL
BIOLOGICAL POISONS
BIOLOGICAL POLLUTANTS
BIOTITE
BIRNESSITE
BISMUTH

BISMUTH COMPOUNDS
BISMUTH ISOTOPES
BITUMENS
BOEHMITE
BORATE MINERALS
BORAX
BORIC ACID
BORON
BORON COMPOUNDS
BORON ISOTOPES
BOTTOM WATER
BOULDER CLAY
BOULDERS
BRACKISH WATER
BREATHING MIXTURES
BRECCIA
BRINES
BROMIC ACID
BROMIDES
BROMINATED HYDROCARBONS
BROMINE
BROMINE COMPOUNDS
BROMINE ISOTOPES
BRUCITE
BUFFERS
BUOYANCY MATERIALS
BURROWS
BUTANE
BYPRODUCTS
CADMIUM
CADMIUM COMPOUNDS
CADMIUM ISOTOPES
CAESIUM
CAESIUM COMPOUNDS
CAESIUM ISOTOPES
CAESIUM 137
CALCARENITE
CALCAREOUS OOZE
CALCITE
CALCIUM
CALCIUM CARBONATES
CALCIUM COMPOUNDS
CALCIUM ISOTOPES
CALCIUM PHOSPHATES
CALCIUM SULPHATES
CALCRETE
CALIFORNIUM
CALIFORNIUM COMPOUNDS
CALIFORNIUM ISOTOPES
CANNED PRODUCTS
CAP ROCKS
CARBOHYDRATES
CARBON
CARBON COMPOUNDS
CARBON DIOXIDE
CARBON ISOTOPES
CARBON MONOXIDE
CARBON SULPHIDES
CARBON 13
CARBON 14
CARBONATE MINERALS
CARBONATE ROCKS
CARBONATE SEDIMENTS
CARBONATES
CARBONIC ACID
CARBONIC ANHYDRASE
CARBOXYLIC ACID SALTS
CARCINOGENS
CARNALLITE
CAROTENOIDS
CARRAGEENINS
CASSITERITE
CATALYSTS
CATIONS
CAVIAR
CELESTITE
CELLULOSE
CERAMICS
CERIUM

ASFIS Thesaurus
List of Descriptors by Facet

CERIUM COMPOUNDS
CERIUM ISOTOPES
CHALK
CHELATES
CHEMICAL COMPOUNDS
CHEMICAL ELEMENTS
CHEMICAL POLLUTANTS
CHEMICAL SEDIMENTS
CHERTS
CHILLED PRODUCTS
CHITIN
CHITOSAN
CHLORIC ACID
CHLORIDES
CHLORINATED HYDROCARBONS
CHLORINE
CHLORINE COMPOUNDS
CHLORINE ISOTOPES
CHLORITE
CHLOROFORM
CHLOROPHYLLS
CHOLESTEROL
CHOLINE
CHOLINESTERASE INHIBITORS
CHROMATIC PIGMENTS
CHROMITE
CHROMIUM
CHROMIUM COMPOUNDS
CHROMIUM ISOTOPES
CIGUATOXIN
CITRATES
CLASTICS
CLAY MINERALS
CLAYS
CLINOPTILONITE
COAGULANTS
COAL
COATING MATERIALS
COBALT
COBALT COMPOUNDS
COBALT ISOTOPES
COBBLESTONE
COENZYMES
COHESIONLESS SEDIMENTS
COHESIVE SEDIMENTS
COLLOIDAL CLAY
COLLOIDS
COMPLEX LIPIDS
COMPOSITE MATERIALS
COMPRESSED GAS
CONCRETE
CONCRETIONS
CONGLOMERATES
CONSTRUCTION MATERIALS
CONTOURITES
COOLING WATER
COPPER
COPPER COMPOUNDS
COPPER ISOTOPES
CORAL
CORES
COSMIC DUST
COSMIC SPHERULES
CRISTOBALITE
CRUDE OIL
CULTCH
CULTURE MEDIA
CURED PRODUCTS
CURIUM
CURIUM COMPOUNDS
CURIUM ISOTOPES
CYANIDES
CYSTEINE
CYSTINE
CYTOCHROMES
DDE
DDT
DEHYDROGENASES
DELTAIC DEPOSITS

DENSE WATER
DERIVED LIPIDS
DETERGENTS
DETRITAL DEPOSITS
DETRITUS
DEUTERIUM
DEUTERIUM COMPOUNDS
DIAMONDS
DIAPIRS
DIATOM OOZE
DIATOMITES
DIELDRIN
DIETS
DISCOLOURED WATER
DISINFECTANTS
DISPERSANTS
DISSOLVED CHEMICALS
DISSOLVED GASES
DISSOLVED INORGANIC MATTER
DISSOLVED ORGANIC CARBON
DISSOLVED ORGANIC MATTER
DISSOLVED ORGANIC NITROGEN
DISSOLVED ORGANIC PHOSPHORUS
DISSOLVED OXYGEN
DISSOLVED SALTS
DISTILLED WATER
DNA
DODECANE
DOLOMITE
DOLOSTONE
DOMESTIC WASTES
DRAINAGE WATER
DREDGE SPOIL
DREDGED SAMPLES
DRIED PRODUCTS
DRILLING FLUIDS
DROPLETS
DRUGS
DUST
DYES
DYSPROSIUM
DYSPROSIUM COMPOUNDS
DYSPROSIUM ISOTOPES
ECDYSONS
ECTOCRINES
EINSTEINIUM
EINSTEINIUM COMPOUNDS
EINSTEINIUM ISOTOPES
ELECTRICAL INSULATION
ELECTROLYTES
EMULSIONS
ENDOTOXINS
ENZYME INHIBITORS
ENZYMES
EOLIAN DEPOSITS
EOLIAN DUST
EPOXY RESINS
EPSOMITE
ERBIUM
ERBIUM COMPOUNDS
ERBIUM ISOTOPES
ESTERS
ETHANE
ETHENE
ETHYNE
EUROPIUM
EUROPIUM ISOTOPES
EVAPORITES
EXCRETORY PRODUCTS
EXTRATERRESTRIAL MATERIAL
FAECAL PELLETS
FALLOUT
FAST ICE
FATS
FATTY ACIDS
FEED
FELDSPARS
FERMENTED PRODUCTS
FERMIUM

FERMIUM COMPOUNDS
FERMIUM ISOTOPES
FERROMANGANESE NODULES
FERROMANGANESE OXIDES
FERROUS ALLOYS
FERRUGINOUS DEPOSITS
FERTILIZERS
FISH FILLETS
FISH FLOUR
FISH GLUE
FISH MEAL
FISH OILS
FISH REPELLENTS
FISH SILAGE
FISH WASTES
FISHERY PRODUCTS
FISSION PRODUCTS
FIXATIVES
FLINT
FLOATING ICE
FLOTSAM
FLUID MUD
FLUIDS
FLUORIDES
FLUORINATED HYDROCARBONS
FLUORINE
FLUORINE COMPOUNDS
FLUORINE ISOTOPES
FLUORITE
FLUVIAL DEPOSITS
FLY ASH
FLYSCH
FOAMS
FOOD
FOOD ADDITIVES
FORAMINIFERAL OOZE
FOSSIL FUELS
FOSSIL SEA WATER
FRANCIUM
FRANCIUM COMPOUNDS
FRANCIUM ISOTOPES
FRANCOLITE
FREEZE-DRIED PRODUCTS
FREONS
FRESH WATER
FRESHWATER ICE
FROZEN PRODUCTS
FUCOSE
FUCOSTEROL
FUELS
FULLERS EARTH
FULVIC ACIDS
FUMARIC ACID
FUNGICIDES
GABBROS
GADOLINIUM
GADOLINIUM COMPOUNDS
GADOLINIUM ISOTOPES
GALLIUM
GALLIUM COMPOUNDS
GALLIUM ISOTOPES
GARNET
GAS CONDENSATES
GAS HYDRATES
GASES
GEAR MATERIALS
GELBSTOFF
GELS
GEOLOGICAL SAMPLES
GERMANIUM
GERMANIUM COMPOUNDS
GERMANIUM ISOTOPES
GIBBSITE
GLACIAL DEPOSITS
GLACIAL ERRATICS
GLACIERS
GLASS
GLASS-REINFORCED PLASTICS
GLAUCONITE

ASFIS Thesaurus
List of Descriptors by Facet

GLOBIGERINA OOZE
GLOBULINS
GLUCOSAMINE
GLUCOSE
GLUTAMIC ACID
GLYCEROL
GLYCINE
GLYCOGEN
GLYCOLIC ACID
GLYCOPROTEINS
GLYCOSIDES
GOETHITE
GOLD
GOLD COMPOUNDS
GOLD ISOTOPES
GRANITE
GRAPHITE
GRAVEL
GRAYWACKE
GREENSCHISTS
GREIGITE
GROUND WATER
GROWTH REGULATORS
GUANO
GYPSUM
HAEMATITE
HAEMOCYANINS
HAFNIUM
HAFNIUM COMPOUNDS
HAFNIUM ISOTOPES
HAIL
HALIDE MINERALS
HALIDES
HALITE
HALOGEN COMPOUNDS
HALOGENATED HYDROCARBONS
HALOGENS
HAZARDOUS MATERIALS
HEAVY METALS
HEAVY MINERALS
HEAVY WATER
HELIUM
HELIUM ISOTOPES
HEPARIN
HERBICIDES
HEULANDITE
HEXOSAMINES
HISTAMINES
HISTONES
HOLMIUM
HOLMIUM COMPOUNDS
HOLMIUM ISOTOPES
HORMONES
HORNBLENDE
HOT BRINES
HUMAN FOOD
HUMIC ACIDS
HUMUS
HYDRATES
HYDROBIOTITE
HYDROCARBONS
HYDROGEN
HYDROGEN COMPOUNDS
HYDROGEN IONS
HYDROGEN ISOTOPES
HYDROGEN SULPHIDE
HYDROLASES
HYDROMAGNESITE
HYDROTHERMAL DEPOSITS
HYDROTHERMAL SOLUTIONS
HYDROXIDES
HYDROXYLAMINES
ICE
ICE KEELS
ICE NUCLEI
ICEBERGS
ICHTHYOCIDES
IGNEOUS DIKES
IGNEOUS INTRUSIONS

IGNEOUS ROCKS
IGNIMBRITES
ILLITE
ILLUSTRATIONS
ILMENITE
INDIUM
INDIUM COMPOUNDS
INDIUM ISOTOPES
INDUSTRIAL PRODUCTS
INDUSTRIAL WASTES
INHIBITORS
INORGANIC ACIDS
INORGANIC COMPOUNDS
INORGANIC MATTER
INSECTICIDES
INSULATING MATERIALS
INSULIN
IODATES
IODIDES
IODINATED HYDROCARBONS
IODINE
IODINE COMPOUNDS
IODINE ISOTOPES
IODOMETHANE
ION PAIRS
IONIUM
IONS
IRIDIUM
IRIDIUM COMPOUNDS
IRIDIUM ISOTOPES
IRON
IRON COMPOUNDS
IRON ISOTOPES
IRON OXIDES
IRON PHOSPHATES
IRON SILICATES
IRON SULPHIDES
IRONSTONE
IRRIGATION WATER
ISOENZYMES
ISOMERASES
ISOTOPES
ISOTROPIC MATERIALS
JAROSITE
JASPILITE
KAINITE
KANSITE
KAOLIN
KAOLINITE
KEROGEN
KETONES
KIMBERLITES
KRILL PRODUCTS
KRYPTON
KRYPTON ISOTOPES
KYANITE
LAKE DEPOSITS
LAKE ICE
LAND ICE
LANTHANIUM
LANTHANIUM COMPOUNDS
LANTHANIUM ISOTOPES
LAVA
LAWRENCIUM
LAWRENCIUM COMPOUNDS
LAWRENCIUM ISOTOPES
LEAD
LEAD COMPOUNDS
LEAD ISOTOPES
LEAD 210
LEADS
LEUCINE
LIGANDS
LIGASES
LIMESTONE
LIMONITE
LIPIDS
LIPOPROTEINS
LIQUEFIED NATURAL GAS

LIQUEFIED PETROLEUM GAS
LIQUIDS
LITHIUM
LITHIUM COMPOUNDS
LITHIUM ISOTOPES
LITHOFACIES
LITTORAL DEPOSITS
LIVESTOCK FOOD
LUBRICANTS
LUCIFERIN
LUTETIUM
LUTETIUM COMPOUNDS
LUTETIUM ISOTOPES
LUTITES
LYASES
LYSINE
MAFIC MAGMA
MAGHEMITE
MAGMA
MAGNESITE
MAGNESIUM
MAGNESIUM COMPOUNDS
MAGNESIUM FLUORIDES
MAGNESIUM ISOTOPES
MAGNESIUM PHOSPHATES
MAGNESIUM SILICATES
MAGNESIUM SULPHATES
MAGNETITE
MAJOR CONSTITUENTS
MANGANESE
MANGANESE COMPOUNDS
MANGANESE DEPOSITS
MANGANESE DIOXIDE
MANGANESE ISOTOPES
MANGANESE MINERALS
MANGANESE OXIDES
MANGANITE
MANNOSE
MANURE
MARCASITE
MARL
MARLSTONE
MATERIALS
MELANGES
MELT WATER
MEMBRANES
MENDELEVIUM
MENDELEVIUM COMPOUNDS
MENDELEVIUM ISOTOPES
MERCURY
MERCURY COMPOUNDS
MERCURY ISOTOPES
METABOLITES
METAL IONS
METALLIFEROUS SEDIMENTS
METALS
METAMORPHIC ROCKS
METHANE
METHIONINE
METHYL MERCURY
MICAS
MILK
MINCED PRODUCTS
MINE TAILINGS
MINERAL ASSEMBLAGES
MINERAL DEPOSITS
MINERAL SAMPLES
MINERALS
MIXED GAS
MOISTURE
MOLECULES
MOLLUSCICIDES
MOLYBDENUM
MOLYBDENUM COMPOUNDS
MOLYBDENUM ISOTOPES
MONAZITE
MONOMOLECULAR FILMS
MONOSACCHARIDES
MONTMORILLONITE

ASFIS Thesaurus
List of Descriptors by Facet

MORAINES
MUCINS
MUCOPOLYSACCHARIDES
MUCUS
MUD
MUDSTONE
MUSCOVITE
MUTAGENS
MYOGLOBINS
MYOSIN
NANNOFOSSIL OOZE
NAPHTHALENE
NAPPES
NARCOTICS
NATURAL GAS
NEODYMIUM
NEODYMIUM COMPOUNDS
NEODYMIUM ISOTOPES
NEON
NEON ISOTOPES
NEPTUNIUM
NEPTUNIUM COMPOUNDS
NEPTUNIUM ISOTOPES
NESTS
NETTING MATERIALS
NEUROTOXINS
NEUROTRANSMITTERS
NEW PRODUCTS
NICKEL
NICKEL COMPOUNDS
NICKEL ISOTOPES
NICOTINIC ACID
NIOBIUM
NIOBIUM COMPOUNDS
NIOBIUM ISOTOPES
NITRATES
NITRIC ACIDS
NITRIFICATION
NITRITES
NITROGEN
NITROGEN COMPOUNDS
NITROGEN ISOTOPES
NITROSAMINES
NITROUS OXIDE
NOBELIUM
NOBELIUM COMPOUNDS
NOBELIUM ISOTOPES
NODULES
NON-NEWTONIAN FLUIDS
NONFERROUS ALLOYS
NONTRONITE
NUCLEIC ACIDS
NUCLEOTIDES
NUTRIENTS (MINERAL)
OBSIDIAN
OCEANITE
OIL
OIL AND GAS
OIL SANDS
OIL SHALE
OIL SLICKS
OIL WASTES
OLEIC ACID
OLISTOLITHS
OLISTOSTROMES
OLIVINE
OOIDS
OOLITES
OOZES
OPAL
OPHIOLITES
ORES
ORGANIC ACIDS
ORGANIC CARBON
ORGANIC COMPOUNDS
ORGANIC CONSTITUENTS
ORGANIC MATTER
ORGANIC NITROGEN
ORGANIC PHOSPHORUS

ORGANIC SEDIMENTS
ORGANIC WASTES
ORGANOMETALLIC COMPLEXES
ORGANOMETALLIC COMPOUNDS
ORNITHINE
ORTHOCLASE
ORTHOPHOSPHATE
OSMIUM
OSMIUM COMPOUNDS
OSMIUM ISOTOPES
OXIC SEDIMENTS
OXIDE MINERALS
OXIDES
OXIDOREDUCTASES
OXYGEN
OXYGEN COMPOUNDS
OXYGEN ISOTOPES
OXYGEN MAXIMUM LAYER
OXYGEN MINIMUM LAYER
OZONE
PACK ICE
PACKING MATERIALS
PAINTS
PALAGONITE
PALLADIUM
PALLADIUM COMPOUNDS
PALLADIUM ISOTOPES
PALYGORSKITE
PARTICULATE ORGANIC CARBON
PARTICULATE ORGANIC MATTER
PARTICULATE ORGANIC NITROGEN
PARTICULATE ORGANIC PHOSPHORUS
PARTICULATES
PCB
PEARLS
PEAT
PEBBLES
PELAGIC CLAY
PELAGIC SEDIMENTS
PELLET FEEDS
PEPTIDES
PEPTONES
PERIDOTITE
PERMAFROST
PERMEASES
PESTICIDES
PETROLEUM
PETROLEUM HYDROCARBONS
PETROLEUM RESIDUES
PHENOLS
PHENYLALANINE
PHEROMONES
PHILLIPSITE
PHOSPHATE DEPOSITS
PHOSPHATE MINERALS
PHOSPHATE ROCKS
PHOSPHATES
PHOSPHORIC ACID
PHOSPHORITE
PHOSPHORITE NODULES
PHOSPHORUS
PHOSPHORUS COMPOUNDS
PHOSPHORUS ISOTOPES
PHOTOSYNTHETIC PIGMENTS
PHTHALATE ESTERS
PHYTOHORMONES
PIGMENTS
PILLOW LAVA
PLACERS
PLAGIOCLASE
PLASTIC COATINGS
PLASTIC DEBRIS
PLASTICS
PLATINUM
PLATINUM COMPOUNDS
PLATINUM ISOTOPES
PLUTONIUM
PLUTONIUM COMPOUNDS
PLUTONIUM ISOTOPES

PLUTONS
POLLUTANTS
POLLUTION INDICATORS
POLONIUM
POLONIUM COMPOUNDS
POLONIUM ISOTOPES
POLYHALITE
POLYMERS
POLYNYAS
POLYPEPTIDES
POLYSACCHARIDES
POLYUNSATURATED FATTY ACIDS
POLYUNSATURATED HYDROCARBONS
PORCELLANITE
PORE WATER
PORPHYRINS
POTASH DEPOSITS
POTASSIUM
POTASSIUM COMPOUNDS
POTASSIUM ISOTOPES
POWDERED PRODUCTS
PRASEODYMIUM
PRASEODYMIUM COMPOUNDS
PRASEODYMIUM ISOTOPES
PRESERVATIVES
PRESTRESSED CONCRETE
PRIMERS
PROCESSED FISHERY PRODUCTS
PRODUCTS
PROLINE
PROMETHIUM
PROMETHIUM COMPOUNDS
PROMETHIUM ISOTOPES
PROPANE
PROTACTINIUM
PROTACTINIUM COMPOUNDS
PROTACTINIUM ISOTOPES
PROTEINS
PTEROPOD OOZE
PULP WASTES
PUMICE
PURINES
PYRIDINES
PYRIMIDINES
PYRITE
PYROLUSITE
PYROPHYLLITE
PYROXENES
PYRRHOTITE
PYRROLIDINE
QUARTZ
QUARTZITE
QUICKSANDS
QUINOLINES
RADIOACTIVE AEROSOLS
RADIOACTIVE MATERIALS
RADIOACTIVE POLLUTANTS
RADIOACTIVE TRACERS
RADIOACTIVE WASTES
RADIOISOTOPES
RADIOLARIAN OOZE
RADIOLARITE
RADIUM
RADIUM COMPOUNDS
RADIUM ISOTOPES
RADON
RADON ISOTOPES
RAIN
RARE EARTHS
RARE GASES
RARE RESOURCES
RAW MATERIALS
REINFORCED CONCRETE
RELICT SEDIMENTS
REPELLENTS
RESUSPENDED SEDIMENTS
RHENIUM
RHENIUM COMPOUNDS
RHENIUM ISOTOPES

ASFIS Thesaurus
List of Descriptors by Facet

RHODAMINE B-DYE
RHODIUM
RHODIUM COMPOUNDS
RHODIUM ISOTOPES
RHYOLITES
RIBOSE
RIVER WATER
RNA
ROCKS
ROTENONE
RUBBER
RUBIDIUM
RUBIDIUM COMPOUNDS
RUBIDIUM ISOTOPES
RUDITES
RUNOFF
RUTHENIUM
RUTHENIUM COMPOUNDS
RUTHENIUM ISOTOPES
RUTILE
SACCHARIDES
SALINE WATER
SALT DEPOSITS
SALT NUCLEI
SALT PARTICLES
SALTS
SAMARIUM
SAMARIUM COMPOUNDS
SAMARIUM ISOTOPES
SAMPLES
SAND
SANDSTONE
SAPONINS
SAPONITE
SAPROPELITE
SAPROPELS
SATURATED HYDROCARBONS
SCANDIUM
SCANDIUM COMPOUNDS
SCANDIUM ISOTOPES
SCHISTS
SEA ICE
SEA WATER
SEABED DEPOSITS
SEAFOOD
SEAWEED PRODUCTS
SECRETORY PRODUCTS
SEDIMENT LOAD
SEDIMENT SAMPLES
SEDIMENTARY ROCKS
SEDIMENTS
SELENIUM
SELENIUM COMPOUNDS
SELENIUM ISOTOPES
SEPIOLITE
SERINE
SERPENTINITE
SEWAGE
SEX HORMONES
SHALE
SHALLOW WATER
SHINGLE
SIDERITE
SILICA
SILICATE MINERALS
SILICATES
SILICEOUS OOZE
SILICEOUS ROCKS
SILICEOUS SEDIMENTS
SILICIC ACID
SILICON
SILICON COMPOUNDS
SILICON ISOTOPES
SILLS
SILT
SILTSTONE
SILVER
SILVER COMPOUNDS
SILVER ISOTOPES

SITOSTEROLS
SLATES
SLICKS
SLOPE WATER
SLUDGE
SLURRIES
SMECTITE
SMOKE
SOAPS
SODIUM
SODIUM CHLORIDE
SODIUM COMPOUNDS
SODIUM ISOTOPES
SOILS
SOLID IMPURITIES
SOLUTES
SOLUTIONS
SOLVENTS
SPOIL
SQUALENE
STAGNANT WATER
STAINLESS STEEL
STANDARD SEA WATER
STARCH
STEEL
STEROIDS
STEROLS
STICKWATER
STOMACH CONTENT
STORMWATER RUNOFF
STRONTIUM
STRONTIUM COMPOUNDS
STRONTIUM ISOTOPES
SUBMARINE CEMENTS
SUBSURFACE DEPOSITS
SULPHATE MINERALS
SULPHATES
SULPHIDE DEPOSITS
SULPHIDE MINERALS
SULPHIDES
SULPHITES
SULPHONATES
SULPHUR
SULPHUR COMPOUNDS
SULPHUR DIOXIDE
SULPHUR ISOTOPES
SULPHUR OXIDES
SULPHURIC ACID
SURFACE FILMS
SURFACTANTS
SUSPENDED INORGANIC MATTER
SUSPENDED LOAD
SUSPENDED ORGANIC MATTER
SUSPENDED PARTICULATE MATTER
SYNTHETIC FIBRES
TABULAR BERGS
TANTALUM
TANTALUM COMPOUNDS
TANTALUM ISOTOPES
TAR
TAR BALLS
TECHNETIUM
TECHNETIUM COMPOUNDS
TECHNETIUM ISOTOPES
TELLURIUM
TELLURIUM COMPOUNDS
TELLURIUM ISOTOPES
TEPHRA
TERATOGENS
TERBIUM
TERBIUM COMPOUNDS
TERBIUM ISOTOPES
TERPENES
TERRIGENOUS SEDIMENTS
TETRODOTOXIN
THALLIUM
THALLIUM COMPOUNDS
THALLIUM ISOTOPES
THOLEIITE

THOLEIITIC BASALT
THORIUM
THORIUM COMPOUNDS
THORIUM ISOTOPES
THREONINE
THULIUM
THULIUM COMPOUNDS
THULIUM ISOTOPES
TIDAL DEPOSITS
TIN
TIN COMPOUNDS
TIN ISOTOPES
TITANITE
TITANIUM
TITANIUM COMPOUNDS
TITANIUM ISOTOPES
TODOROKITE
TOTAL ORGANIC CARBON
TOURMALINE
TOWED BODIES
TOXICANTS
TRACE ELEMENTS
TRACE METALS
TRACERS
TRANSFERASES
TRANSITION ELEMENT COMPOUNDS
TRANSITION ELEMENTS
TRANSURANIC ELEMENTS
TRICHLOROETHYLENE
TRITIUM
TUNGSTEN
TUNGSTEN COMPOUNDS
TUNGSTEN ISOTOPES
TURBIDITES
TYROSINE
ULTRAMAFIC ROCKS
UNSATURATED HYDROCARBONS
URANIUM
URANIUM COMPOUNDS
URANIUM ISOTOPES
URBAN RUNOFF
UREA
URINE
VACCINES
VALINE
VANADIUM
VANADIUM COMPOUNDS
VANADIUM ISOTOPES
VERMICULITE
VITAMIN A
VITAMIN B
VITAMIN C
VITAMIN D
VITAMIN E
VITAMINS
VOLATILE COMPOUNDS
VOLATILE HYDROCARBONS
VOLCANIC ASH
VOLCANIC BRECCIA
VOLCANIC GLASS
VOLCANIC LAPILLI
VOLCANIC ROCKS
VOLCANOGENIC DEPOSITS
WASTE WATER
WASTES
WASTEWATER AQUACULTURE
WATER
WATER SAMPLES
WATER VAPOUR
WAXES
WINDROWS
WOOD
XANTHOPHYLLS
XENON
XENON ISOTOPES
XYLENE
XYLOSE
YTTERBIUM
YTTERBIUM COMPOUNDS

ASFIS Thesaurus
List of Descriptors by Facet

YTTERBIUM ISOTOPES
YTTRIUM
YTTRIUM COMPOUNDS
YTTRIUM ISOTOPES
ZEOLITES
ZINC
ZINC COMPOUNDS
ZINC ISOTOPES
ZIRCON
ZIRCONIUM
ZIRCONIUM COMPOUNDS
ZIRCONIUM ISOTOPES

ASFIS Thesaurus
List of Descriptors by Facet

Intellectual Tools

ABSORPTION SPECTRA
ABSTRACTS
ACCOMMODATION
ACCURACY
ACOUSTIC DATA
ACOUSTIC IMAGES
ACOUSTIC MODELS
ACRONYMS
AERIAL PHOTOGRAPHS
ALGORITHMS
ALMANACS
AMPHIDROMIC SYSTEMS
ANALOG MODELS
ANALOG RECORDS
ANALOGS
ANALYTICAL ERRORS
ANNUAL REPORTS
AQUACULTURE STATISTICS
ARCHIVES
ARTIFICIAL INTELLIGENCE
ATLASES
AUDIO RECORDINGS
AUDIOVISUAL MATERIAL
BATHYMETRIC CHARTS
BATHYMETRIC DATA
BATHYMETRIC PROFILES
BATHYTHERMOGRAMS
BATHYTHERMOGRAPHIC DATA
BEACH PROFILES
BEAUFORT SCALE
BENCH MARKS
BIBLIOGRAPHIC INFORMATION
BIBLIOGRAPHIES
BIOGRAPHIES
BIOLOGICAL CHARTS
BIOLOGICAL COLLECTIONS
BIOLOGICAL DATA
BLOOD GROUPS
BOOK CATALOGUES
BOTTOM PHOTOGRAPHS
BOUGUER GRAVITY CHARTS
BOUNDARY VALUE PROBLEMS
BROCHURES
CATALOGUES
CATCH STATISTICS
CATCH/EFFORT
CAUSTICS
CHART CATALOGUES
CHART DATUM
CHECK LISTS
CLASSIFICATION SYSTEMS
CLASSIFIED DOCUMENTS
CLIMATIC DATA
CLIMATOLOGICAL CHARTS
CODEX STANDARDS
COLLECTED PAPERS
COLLECTIONS
COMPUTER PROGRAMS
CONDITION FACTOR
CONSERVATION EQUATIONS
CONTOURS
CONTROL CHARTS
CONVERSION TABLES
COORDINATE SYSTEMS
CORANGE CHARTS
CORRECTIONS
COTIDAL CHARTS
COTIDAL LINES
CRUISE REPORTS
CTD OBSERVATIONS
CURRENT CHARTS
CURRENT DATA
CURRENT ELLIPSES
CURRENT METER DATA

CURRENT OBSERVATIONS
CURRENT PROFILES
CURRENT ROSES
CURRENT SPECTRA
CURRENT VECTORS
DATA
DATA COLLECTIONS
DATA REPORTS
DECOMPRESSION TABLES
DENSITY CHARTS
DENSITY GRADIENTS
DENSITY PROFILES
DENSITY SECTIONS
DESIGN WAVE
DIFFERENTIAL EQUATIONS
DIGITAL RECORDS
DIRECTIONAL SPECTRA
DIRECTORIES
DISTRIBUTION RECORDS
DOCUMENTS
ECHOSOUNDER PROFILES
ECONOMIC MODELS
EIGENFUNCTIONS
ENCYCLOPAEDIAS
ENERGY SPECTRA
ENGINEERING DRAWINGS
ENVIRONMENTAL CHARTS
EQUATION OF CONTINUITY
EQUATIONS
EQUATIONS OF MOTION
EQUATIONS OF STATE
ERRORS
EXPEDITION REPORTS
EXPERIMENTAL DATA
FESTSCHRIFTEN
FILMS
FILMSTRIPS
FISH CATCH STATISTICS
FISH CONVERSION FACTORS
FISHERMEN STATISTICS
FISHERY CHARTS
FISHERY DATA
FISHERY STATISTICS
FISHING EFFORT
FISHING POWER
FISHING TIME
FISHING VESSELS STATISTICS
FORMULAE
FREE AIR GRAVITY CHARTS
FREQUENCY SPECTRA
GAUSSIAN DISTRIBUTION
GAZETEERS
GEODETIC COORDINATES
GEOGRAPHICAL COORDINATES
GEOGRAPHICAL REFERENCE SYSTEMS
GEOLOGICAL COLLECTIONS
GEOLOGICAL DATA
GEOLOGICAL MAPS
GEOLOGICAL SECTIONS
GEOPHYSICAL DATA
GEOTECHNICAL DATA
GEOTHERMAL DATA
GLOSSARIES
GRAPHICS
GRAPHS
GRAVITY CHARTS
GRAVITY CORRECTIONS
GRAVITY DATA
GROWTH CURVES
HODOGRAPHS
HORIZONTAL PROFILES
HUNTING STATISTICS
HYDRODYNAMIC EQUATIONS
HYDROGRAPHIC CHARTS
HYDROGRAPHIC DATA
HYDROGRAPHIC SECTIONS
HYDROSTATIC EQUATION
HYPSOMETRIC CURVES
ICE CHARTS

ICE OBSERVATIONS
IDENTIFICATION KEYS
INDUSTRIAL PRODUCTS STATISTICS
INSTRUMENT HANDBOOKS
INTEGRAL EQUATIONS
INVENTORIES
ISOBARS
ISOBATHS
ISOCHRONES
ISOHALINES
ISOHYETS
ISOMAGNETIC LINES
ISOPACH MAPS
ISOPACHS
ISOPLETHS
ISOPYCNICS
ISOSTERES
ISOTHERMS
KALMAN FILTERS
KNUDSEN TABLES
KORTWEG DEVRIES EQUATION
LANDING STATISTICS
LAPLACE EQUATION
LATITUDE
LATTICE CHARTS
LECTURES
LENGTH-WEIGHT RELATIONSHIPS
LIMNOLOGICAL DATA
LITERATURE REVIEWS
LOGBOOKS
LONG-TERM RECORDS
LONGITUDE
MAGNETIC ANOMALY CHARTS
MAGNETIC CHARTS
MAGNETIC DATA
MAGNETIC TAPE RECORDINGS
MAGNETIC TAPES
MANUALS
MAP GRAPHICS
MAP PROJECTIONS
MAPS
MARSDEN SQUARES
MATHEMATICAL MODELS
METEOROLOGICAL CHARTS
METEOROLOGICAL DATA
METEOROLOGICAL OBSERVATIONS
METEOROLOGICAL TABLES
MICROFORMS
MINERAL COLLECTIONS
MODELS
MORISON'S EQUATION
MUSEUM COLLECTIONS
NAUTICAL ALMANACS
NAVIER-STOKES EQUATIONS
NAVIGATIONAL CHARTS
NAVIGATIONAL TABLES
NONLINEAR EQUATIONS
OCEANOGRAPHIC ATLASES
OCEANOGRAPHIC DATA
OCEANOGRAPHIC TABLES
ORTHOGONALS
OXYGEN PROFILES
OXYGEN SECTIONS
PARAMETERS
PATENTS
PERSONAL BIBLIOGRAPHIES
PHOTOGRAPHS
PILOT CHARTS
PLANKTON EQUIVALENTS
POISSON'S EQUATION
POLLUTION DATA
POLLUTION MAPS
POPULATION FACTORS
PRACTICAL SALINITY SCALE
PROFILES
PROGRAMMES
PROGRESS REPORTS
RECORDS
REPORT LITERATURE

ASFIS Thesaurus
List of Descriptors by Facet

RICHTER SCALE
SAILING DIRECTIONS
SALINITY CHARTS
SALINITY DATA
SALINITY PROFILES
SALINITY SCALES
SALINITY SECTIONS
SALINITY TABLES
SATELLITE MOSAICS
SCATTER DIAGRAMS
SEA STATE SCALES
SEAWEED STATISTICS
SEDIMENT COLLECTIONS
SEISMIC DATA
SEISMIC PROFILES
SEISMIC REFLECTION PROFILES
SEISMIC REFRACTION PROFILES
SEISMOGRAMS
SHELLFISH CATCH STATISTICS
SHORT-TERM RECORDS
SIGNAL-TO-NOISE RATIO
SKEWNESS
SOUND SPECTRA
SPECIFICATIONS
SPECTRA
SPLINES
SPORT FISHING STATISTICS
STANDARD DEPTHS
STANDARD SIGNALS
STANDARDS
STATION LISTS
STATISTICAL MODELS
STATISTICAL TABLES
STD OBSERVATIONS
STD PROFILES
STOCHASTIC PROCESSES
STOKES LAW
STREAM FUNCTIONS
STREAMLINES
SWATHS
SYNONYMY
SYNOPSIS
TABLES
TEMPERATURE CHARTS
TEMPERATURE DATA
TEMPERATURE PROFILES
TEMPERATURE SECTIONS
THALWEG
THESAURUS
TIDAL CHARTS
TIDAL CURVES
TIDAL EQUATIONS
TIDAL MODELS
TIDAL RECORDS
TIDE TABLES
TIME SERIES
TOPOGRAPHIC MAPS
TRACK CHARTS
TRAINING AIDS
TRANSLATIONS
TRAVERSE TABLES
T/S DIAGRAMS
UNDERWATER PHOTOGRAPHS
VELOCITY PROFILES
VELOCITY SECTIONS
VERNACULAR NAMES
VERTICAL PROFILES
VERTICAL SECTIONS
VIDEOTAPE RECORDINGS
VOID RATIO
WAVE DATA
WAVE REFRACTION DIAGRAMS
WAVE SPECTRA
WAVE STATISTICS
WEATHER MAPS
WHALING STATISTICS
WIND DATA
WIND PROFILES
WIND ROSES

WIND VECTORS

ASFIS Thesaurus
List of Descriptors by Facet

Equipment and Structures

ACCELEROMETERS
ACOUSTIC ARRAYS
ACOUSTIC BEACONS
ACOUSTIC COMMAND SYSTEMS
ACOUSTIC CURRENT METERS
ACOUSTIC EQUIPMENT
ACOUSTIC INSULATION
ACOUSTIC PINGERS
ACOUSTIC TRACKING SYSTEMS
ACOUSTIC TRANSDUCERS
ACOUSTIC TRANSPONDERS
ACTINOMETERS
ACTIVE SONAR
AIR GUNS
AIRBORNE EQUIPMENT
AIRCRAFT
AIRPORTS
ALARM SYSTEMS
ALTIMETERS
AMPHIBIOUS VEHICLES
ANCHORS
ANEMOMETERS
ANODES
AQUACULTURE EQUIPMENT
AQUACULTURE FACILITIES
AQUACULTURE SYSTEMS
AQUARIA
ARRAYS
ARTICULATED COLUMNS
ARTIFICIAL HARBOURS
ARTIFICIAL ISLANDS
ARTIFICIAL REEFS
AUTOMATED FISHING PLATFORMS
AUTOPILOTS
AXBTS
BACTERIA COLLECTING DEVICES
BACTERIAL COUNTERS
BAIT
BALLAST
BALLAST TANKS
BALLOONS
BARGES
BAROMETERS
BARRAGES
BARRIERS
BATHYMETERS
BATHYSPHERES
BATHYTHERMOGRAPHS
BATTERIES
BEACH SEINES
BEAM TRANSMITTANCE METERS
BENTHOS COLLECTING DEVICES
BIOFILTERS
BLOWOUT PREVENTERS
BOAT SEINES
BOATS
BOOMERS
BOREHOLES
BOTTOM TRAWLS
BREAKWATERS
BREATHING APPARATUS
BREEDING PONDS
BRIDGES
BUBBLE BARRIERS
BULK CARRIERS
BUOY HULLS
BUOY MOORING SYSTEMS
BUOY SYSTEMS
BUOYANCY FLOATS
BUOYS
CABLE DEPRESSORS
CABLE SHIPS
CABLES
CAGES

CAISSONS
CALCULATORS
CAMERAS
CANOES
CAST NETS
CATAMARANS
CATCHERS
CATHODES
CELL COUNTERS
CENTRIFUGES
CHAIN
CHRONOMETERS
COAST DEFENCES
COASTAL STRUCTURES
COAXIAL CABLES
COLLECTING DEVICES
COMMUNICATION SATELLITES
COMMUNICATION SYSTEMS
COMPASSES
COMPONENTS
COMPRESSORS
COMPUTERS
CONCRETE STRUCTURES
CONDUCTIVITY SENSORS
CONNECTORS
CONTAINER SHIPS
CONTAINERS
COOLING SYSTEMS
CORERS
COSINE COLLECTORS
COUNTERS
COUPLED BODIES
CRANE BARGES
CRANES
CTD PROFILERS
CULTURE TANKS
CURRENT MEASURING EQUIPMENT
CURRENT METER ARRAYS
CURRENT METER MOORINGS
CURRENT METERS
CURRENT SENSORS
CYCLESONDE
CYLINDERS
CYLINDRICAL STRUCTURES
DAMS
DATA BUOYS
DATA CONVERTERS
DATA LOGGERS
DAVITS
DECANTATION TANKS
DECCA
DECK COMPRESSION CHAMBERS
DECK EQUIPMENT
DECKS
DECOMPRESSION CHAMBERS
DEEP-SEA TIDE GAUGES
DEEP-WATER TERMINALS
DEFENCE CRAFT
DEICING EQUIPMENT
DENSITOMETERS
DENSITY MEASURING EQUIPMENT
DEPRESSORS
DEPTH RECORDERS
DESALINATION PLANTS
DETECTORS
DETONATORS
DIESEL ENGINES
DIRECTION INDICATORS
DISCUS-SHAPED BUOYS
DISTRESS SIGNALS
DIVING BELLS
DIVING EQUIPMENT
DIVING SUITS
DIVING TOOLS
DOPPLER SONAR
DREDGERS
DREDGES
DREDGES (GEOLOGY)
DRIFT BOTTLES

DRIFT CARDS
DRIFTERS
DRIFTING DATA BUOYS
DRIFTING STATIONS
DRILL PIPE
DRILL STRING
DRILLING EQUIPMENT
DRILLING PLATFORMS
DRILLING RIGS
DRILLING VESSELS
DRILLS
DROGUES
DROPSONDE
ECHO INTEGRATORS
ECHOSOUNDERS
EGG COUNTERS
ELECTRIC CABLES
ELECTRIC FENCES
ELECTRIC GENERATORS
ELECTRIC POWER SOURCES
ELECTRICAL EQUIPMENT
ELECTRIFIED GEAR
ELECTROACOUSTIC DEVICES
ELECTRODES
ELECTRONIC EQUIPMENT
EMERGENCY VESSELS
ENCLOSURES
ENTANGLING NETS
EQUIPMENT
EVAPORATION TANKS
EXPLODING WIRE
EXPLOSIVES
FACTORY SHIPS
FAIRINGS
FEEDING EQUIPMENT
FENDERS
FERRY TERMINALS
FIBRE GLASS
FIBRE ROPE (NATURAL)
FIBRE ROPE (SYNTHETIC)
FILTERS
FIRE EXTINGUISHERS
FISH COUNTERS
FISH PUMPS
FISHERY INDUSTRY EQUIPMENT
FISHERY INDUSTRY PLANTS
FISHING BARRIERS
FISHING BUOYS
FISHING GEAR
FISHING HARBOURS
FISHING NETS
FISHING VESSELS
FISHWAYS
FIXED PLATFORMS
FLOATING BARRIERS
FLOATING CAGES
FLOATING HOSES
FLOATING STRUCTURES
FLOW MEASURING EQUIPMENT
FLOWLINES
FLOWMETERS
FLUMES
FLUORIMETERS
FOSSIL FUELED POWER PLANTS
FOUNDATIONS
FREE-FALL CORERS
FREE-FALL INSTRUMENTS
FREE-FALL PROFILERS
FREE-SWIMMING VEHICLES
GAS EXPLODERS
GAS TERMINALS
GATHERING LINES
GAUGES
GEIGER COUNTERS
GEK
GEOLOGICAL EQUIPMENT
GEOPHYSICAL EQUIPMENT
GEOTHERMAL EQUIPMENT
GILLNETS

ASFIS Thesaurus
List of Descriptors by Facet

GILLNETTERS
GLORIA
GRABS
GRAPPLING GEAR
GRAVITY CORERS
GRAVITY METERS
GRAVITY PLATFORMS
GROYNES
GUIDE LINES
GUIDING DEVICES
GUYED TOWERS
GYROCOMPASSES
GYROSCOPES
HARBOUR MODELS
HARVESTING MACHINES
HATCHERIES
HEAT EXCHANGERS
HEAT PROBES
HEAVE COMPENSATORS
HELICOPTERS
HELIDECKS
HOOKS
HOSES
HOVERCRAFT
HULLS
HYDRAULIC MODELS
HYDRAULIC STRUCTURES
HYDRAULIC SYSTEMS
HYDROELECTRIC POWER PLANTS
HYDROFOILS
HYDROGRAPHIC WIRE
HYDROMETERS
HYDROPHONES
HYGROMETERS
ICE BARRIERS
ICE BREAKERS
ICE RAFTS
IMPELLERS
INCLINOMETERS
INFLATABLE CRAFT
INFRARED DETECTORS
INSTRUMENT PLATFORMS
INSTRUMENTS
IRRADIANCE METERS
JACKUP PLATFORMS
JELLY BOTTLES
JOINTS
KNUDSEN SAMPLERS
LABORATORY EQUIPMENT
LAMPARA NETS
LARGE SPAR BUOYS
LASER ALTIMETERS
LASER BATHYMETERS
LASERS
LEGS (STRUCTURAL)
LIDAR
LIFE JACKETS
LIFE SAVING EQUIPMENT
LIFE SUPPORT SYSTEMS
LIFEBOATS
LIFT-NETS
LIFTING TACKLE
LIGHT MEASURING INSTRUMENTS
LIGHT SOURCES
LIGHTERS
LIGHTHOUSES
LIGHTING SYSTEMS
LIGHTSHIPS
LIMNOLOGICAL EQUIPMENT
LINERS
LINES
LOADING BUOYS
LOCKOUT SUBMERSIBLES
LORAN
MACHINERY
MAGNETOMETERS
MAGNETS
MANIFOLDS
MANIPULATORS

MANNED VEHICLES
MANOMETERS
MARINAS
MARKER BUOYS
MASTS
MEASURING DEVICES
MERCHANT SHIPS
MESH GAUGES
MESSENGERS
METEOROLOGICAL INSTRUMENTS
MICROMETER CALIPERS
MICROPHONES
MICROPROCESSORS
MICROSCOPES
MICROWAVE RADAR
MICROWAVE RADIOMETERS
MIDWATER TRAWLS
MINING EQUIPMENT
MINING VESSELS
MOBILE PLATFORMS
MODULES
MONITORING SYSTEMS
MOORING BUOYS
MOORING LINES
MOORING SYSTEMS
MOTHER SHIPS
MOTOR BOATS
MOTORS
MULTIBEAM SONAR
MULTISPECTRAL SCANNERS
NANSEN BOTTLES
NAVIGATION SYSTEMS
NAVIGATIONAL AIDS
NAVIGATIONAL BUOYS
NAVIGATIONAL SATELLITES
NEKTON COLLECTING DEVICES
NEPHELOMETERS
NET SOUNDERS
NETS
NISKIN SAMPLERS
NUCLEAR POWER PLANTS
NUCLEAR PROPULSION
OBSERVATION CHAMBERS
OCEAN BOTTOM SEISMOMETERS
OCEANOGRAPHIC EQUIPMENT
OFFSHORE EQUIPMENT
OFFSHORE STRUCTURES
OFFSHORE TERMINALS
OIL REFINERIES
OIL TANKS
OIL WELLS
OMEGA
ONE-ATMOSPHERE SYSTEMS
OPEN SYSTEMS
OPTICAL FILTERS
OPTICAL INSTRUMENTS
OTEC PLANTS
OTTER BOARDS
OUTFALLS
PARTICLE COUNTERS
PASSENGER SHIPS
PASSIVE SONAR
PENETROMETERS
PERFORATED STRUCTURES
PH SENSORS
PHOTOGRAPHIC EQUIPMENT
PHOTOMETERS
PIERS
PIEZOELECTRIC TRANSDUCERS
PILED PLATFORMS
PILES
PINGERS
PIPE STRINGERS
PIPELAYING BARGES
PIPELINE PIGS
PIPELINES
PIPES
PISTON CORERS
PLANKTON COLLECTING DEVICES

PLOUGHS
PONTOONS
PORE WATER SAMPLERS
PORT INSTALLATIONS
POSITIONING SYSTEMS
POTS
POWER CABLES
POWER PLANTS
PRESSURE GAUGES
PRESSURE SENSORS
PRESSURE VESSELS
PROCESS PLANTS
PRODUCTION PLATFORMS
PROFILERS
PROPELLERS
PROPULSION SYSTEMS
PROTECTION VESSELS
PROTECTIVE CLOTHING
PROTOTYPES
PSYCHROMETERS
PUMP STATIONS
PUMPS
PURSE SEINES
PYRANOMETERS
PYRGEOMETERS
PYRHELIOMETERS
QUANTA METERS
QUARTZ CLOCKS
QUARTZ PRESSURE SENSORS
QUARTZ TEMPERATURE SENSORS
RADAR
RADAR ALTIMETERS
RADIANCE METERS
RADIO
RADIO AIDS
RADIO BUOYS
RADIOMETERS
RADIOSONDES
RAIN GAUGES
RECIRCULATING SYSTEMS
RECORDING EQUIPMENT
REFRIGERATORS
RELEASE MECHANISMS
REMOTE SENSING EQUIPMENT
RESEARCH VESSELS
RESISTIVITY PROBES
RESPIROMETERS
REVERSING THERMOMETERS
RIGGING
RIPRAP
RISER CABLES
RISER PIPES
ROBOTS
ROPES
ROW BOATS
RUBBLEMOUND BREAKWATERS
SACRIFICIAL ANODES
SAFETY DEVICES
SAILING SHIPS
SAILS
SALINITY MEASURING EQUIPMENT
SALINOMETERS
SALVAGE EQUIPMENT
SAMPLERS
SAND STRUCTURES
SATELLITE COMMUNICATION
SATELLITES
SCALE MODELS
SCATTERANCE METERS
SCATTEROMETERS
SCIENTIFIC SATELLITES
SCREENS
SEA WALLS
SEABED DRIFTERS
SEABED VEHICLES
SEALS (STOPPERS)
SECCHI DISCS
SEDIMENT SAMPLERS
SEDIMENT TRAPS

ASFIS Thesaurus
List of Descriptors by Facet

SEINE NETS
SEINERS
SEISMIC ARRAYS
SEISMIC ENERGY SOURCES
SEISMIC EQUIPMENT
SEISMOMETERS
SELECTED SHIPS
SELF-PROPELLED VEHICLES
SEMISUBMERSIBLE PLATFORMS
SENSORS
SEWAGE PONDS
SHAPED CHARGES
SHEAR PROBES
SHELTERS
SHIP HULLS
SHIP MODELS
SHIP MOORING SYSTEMS
SHIPBOARD EQUIPMENT
SHIPS
SIDE SCAN SONAR
SILT METERS
SIMULATORS
SINGLE POINT MOORINGS
SLIDES (PHOTOGRAPHIC)
SLOPE INDICATORS
SODAR
SOFAR
SOFAR FLOATS
SOLAR CELLS
SONAR
SONAR ARRAYS
SONAR RECEIVERS
SONAR TARGETS
SONAR TRANSDUCERS
SONAR TRANSPONDERS
SONIC TAGS
SONOBUOYS
SONOGRAPHS
SOUND GENERATORS
SOUND RECORDERS
SOUNDING LINES
SPAR BUOYS
SPARKERS
SPECTROPHOTOMETERS
SPEEDOMETERS
SPHERES
STABILIZED PLATFORMS
STABILIZERS
STD PROFILERS
STEEL STRUCTURES
STEERING SYSTEMS
STORAGE TANKS
STORM SURGE BARRIERS
STRAIN GAUGES
STRAIN SEISMOMETERS
STRATIGRAPHIC TRAPS
STREAMERS
STRUCTURES
SUBMARINE CABLES
SUBMARINE TANKERS
SUBMARINES
SUBMERGED CAGES
SUBMERSIBLE PLATFORMS
SUBMERSIBLES
SUBSEA PRODUCTION SYSTEMS
SUBSURFACE DRIFTERS
SUPPLY BOATS
SUPPORT SHIPS
SUPPRESSORS
SURFACE CRAFT
SURFACE DRIFTERS
SURROUNDING NETS
SURVEY VESSELS
SURVEYING EQUIPMENT
SWALLOW FLOATS
SYNTHETIC APERTURE RADAR
TAGS
TANKER SHIPS
TANKER TERMINALS

TANKS
TELEPHONE SYSTEMS
TELEVISION SYSTEMS
TELEX
TELLUROMETERS
TEMPLATES
TENSION LEG PLATFORMS
TENSOMETERS
TEST EQUIPMENT
TETHERED FREE-SWIMMING VEHICLES
TETHERED VEHICLES
THERMAL INSULATION
THERMISTOR CHAINS
THERMISTORS
THERMOCOUPLE ARRAYS
THERMOCOUPLES
THERMOMETERS
THRUSTERS
TIDAL BARRAGES
TIDAL POWER PLANTS
TIDE GAUGES
TILTMETERS
TOWED SENSORS
TOWED VEHICLES
TOWERS
TOWING LINES
TOWING TANKS
TRANSDUCER ARRAYS
TRANSDUCERS
TRANSFER CHAMBERS
TRANSMISSOMETERS
TRANSPONDER ARRAYS
TRANSPONDERS
TRAP NETS
TRAWL NETS
TRAWLERS
TUBING
TUGS
TUNNELS
TURBIDIMETERS
TURBINES
ULTRASONIC DEVICES
ULTRASONIC TRANSDUCERS
UMBILICALS
UNDERWATER CAMERAS
UNDERWATER EQUIPMENT
UNDERWATER HABITATS
UNDERWATER PROPULSION
UNDERWATER STRUCTURES
UNDERWATER TELEVISION
UNDERWATER VEHICLES
UNDULATORS
UNMANNED VEHICLES
UNTETHERED VEHICLES
VANE DEVICES
VANES
VEHICLES
VELOCITY PROFILERS
VIBRATORY CORERS
WARNING SYSTEMS
WATER FILTERS
WATER PUMPS
WATER SAMPLERS
WAVE BUOYS
WAVE DIRECTION SENSORS
WAVE FOLLOWERS
WAVE GAUGES
WAVE GENERATORS
WAVE MEASURING EQUIPMENT
WAVE MEASURING PLATFORMS
WAVE POWER DEVICES
WAVE RECORDERS
WAVE SLOPE FOLLOWERS
WAVE TANKS
WEATHER SHIPS
WEIRS
WELLHEADS
WET SUBMERSIBLES
WHALING STATIONS

WINCHES
WIND MEASURING EQUIPMENT
WIND TUNNELS
WIRE ANGLE INDICATORS
WIRE ROPE
WORK PLATFORMS
WORKOVER BARGES
WOUNDING GEAR
WRECKS
XBTS
YACHTS
YARNS

ASFIS Thesaurus
List of Descriptors by Facet

Sciences and Technology

ACOUSTICS
AERODYNAMICS
AETIOLOGY
ALGOLOGY
ANATOMY
ANIMAL MORPHOLOGY
ANIMAL PHYSIOLOGY
AQUACULTURE ECONOMICS
AQUARIOLOGY
AQUATIC SCIENCES
ARCHAEOLOGY
ASTRONOMY
ATMOSPHERIC CHEMISTRY
ATMOSPHERIC PHYSICS
ATMOSPHERIC SCIENCES
AUTECOLOGY
AVIAN PHYSIOLOGY
BACTERIOLOGY
BEACH MORPHOLOGY
BIOACOUSTICS
BIOCHEMISTRY
BIOCLIMATOLOGY
BIOENERGETICS
BIOGENY
BIOGEOCHEMISTRY
BIOGEOGRAPHY
BIOLOGY
BIOMETRICS
BIOPHYSICS
BIOSTRATIGRAPHY
BIOTECHNOLOGY
BOTANY
BRACKISHWATER ECOLOGY
BRIGHT SPOT TECHNOLOGY
CABLE DYNAMICS
CARCINOLOGY
CARTOGRAPHY
CELL MORPHOLOGY
CETOLOGY
CHEMICAL ENGINEERING
CHEMICAL KINETICS
CHEMICAL LIMNOLOGY
CHEMICAL OCEANOGRAPHY
CHEMISTRY
CHEMOTAXONOMY
CHRONOSTRATIGRAPHY
CIVIL ENGINEERING
CLIMATOLOGY
CLOUD PHYSICS
COASTAL ENGINEERING
COASTAL GEODESY
COASTAL MORPHOLOGY
COASTAL OCEANOGRAPHY
CONCHOLOGY
CRYOBIOLOGY
CYTOCHEMISTRY
CYTOLOGY
DIVING PHYSIOLOGY
DOCUMENTATION
DYNAMICAL OCEANOGRAPHY
DYNAMICS
EARTH SCIENCES
ECOLOGY
ECONOMETRICS
ECONOMICS
ECOPHYSIOLOGY
ELECTRICAL ENGINEERING
ELECTROCHEMISTRY
ELECTROPHYSIOLOGY
EMBRYOLOGY
ENDOCRINOLOGY
ENGINEERING
ENTOMOLOGY
EPIDEMIOLOGY

ETHOLOGY
FIBRE OPTICS
FISH PHYSIOLOGY
FISHERY BIOLOGY
FISHERY ECONOMICS
FISHERY ENGINEERING
FISHERY LIMNOLOGY
FISHERY OCEANOGRAPHY
FISHERY SCIENCES
FISHERY TECHNOLOGY
FISHING TECHNOLOGY
FLUID DYNAMICS
FLUID MECHANICS
FLUVIAL MORPHOLOGY
FOOD TECHNOLOGY
FRESHWATER ECOLOGY
FRESHWATER SCIENCES
GEAR RESEARCH
GENECOLOGY
GENETICS
GEOCHEMISTRY
GEODESY
GEOGRAPHY
GEOLOGY
GEOMAGNETISM
GEOMORPHOLOGY
GEOPHYSICS
GEOTECHNOLOGY
GLACIAL GEOLOGY
GRAVIMETRY
HAEMATOLOGY
HERPETOLOGY
HISTOCHEMISTRY
HISTOLOGY
HISTOPATHOLOGY
HUMAN PHYSIOLOGY
HYDRAULIC ENGINEERING
HYDRAULICS
HYDROBIOLOGY
HYDRODYNAMICS
HYDROGRAPHY
HYDROLOGY
HYDROSTATICS
HYGROMETRY
ICHTHYOLOGY
IMMUNOLOGY
INFORMATION HANDLING
INFORMATION RETRIEVAL
INVERTEBRATE ZOOLOGY
KARYOLOGY
KINEMATICS
KINETICS
LAKE MORPHOLOGY
LIMNOLOGY
LITHOLOGY
MAGNETOSTRATIGRAPHY
MALACOLOGY
MAMMALIAN PHYSIOLOGY
MAMMALOGY
MARINE ECOLOGY
MARINE GEODESY
MARINE GEOLOGY
MARINE SCIENCES
MARINE TECHNOLOGY
MATERIALS TECHNOLOGY
MATHEMATICS
MECHANICS
MEDICINE
METALLURGY
METEOROLOGY
MICROBIOLOGY
MICROPALAEONTOLOGY
MICROPHOTOGRAPHY
MILITARY OCEANOGRAPHY
MINERALOGY
MYCOLOGY
NEUROPHYSIOLOGY
NUCLEAR PHYSICS
NUMERICAL TAXONOMY

OCEANOGRAPHY
OFFSHORE ENGINEERING
ONTOGENY
OPTICS
ORGANISM MORPHOLOGY
ORNITHOLOGY
OSTEOLOGY
OXYGEN ISOTOPE STRATIGRAPHY
PALAEOCEANOGRAPHY
PALAEOCLIMATOLOGY
PALAEOECOLOGY
PALAEOLIMNOLOGY
PALAEONTOLOGY
PALYNOLOGY
PARASITOLOGY
PATHOLOGY
PETROLEUM ENGINEERING
PETROLEUM GEOLOGY
PETROLOGY
PHARMACOLOGY
PHENOTYPES
PHOTOCHEMISTRY
PHOTOGRAMMETRY
PHYLOGENETICS
PHYLOGENY
PHYSICAL LIMNOLOGY
PHYSICAL OCEANOGRAPHY
PHYSICS
PHYSIOLOGY
PHYTOSOCIOLOGY
PLANKTONOLOGY
PLANT MORPHOLOGY
PLANT PHYSIOLOGY
PLATE TECTONICS
POLAR METEOROLOGY
POLAR OCEANOGRAPHY
POPULATION DYNAMICS
POPULATION GENETICS
RADIO OCEANOGRAPHY
RADIOCHEMISTRY
RADIOECOLOGY
RADIONUCLIDE KINETICS
RHEOLOGY
RIVER ENGINEERING
SANITARY ENGINEERING
SEDIMENT CHEMISTRY
SEDIMENTOLOGY
SEISMIC STRATIGRAPHY
SEISMOLOGY
SEROLOGICAL STUDIES
SEROLOGICAL TAXONOMY
SHELF GEOLOGY
SHIP TECHNOLOGY
SOIL MECHANICS
SPELAEOLOGY
STATISTICS
STRATIGRAPHY
STRUCTURAL DYNAMICS
STRUCTURAL ENGINEERING
STRUCTURAL GEOLOGY
SURFACE CHEMISTRY
SYNECOLOGY
TAXONOMY
TECHNOLOGY
TECTONICS
TECTONOPHYSICS
TERATOLOGY
THERMODYNAMICS
TOXICOLOGY
TROPICAL METEOROLOGY
TROPICAL OCEANOGRAPHY
TYPOLOGY
ULTRASONICS
UNDERWATER MEDICINE
VERTEBRATE ZOOLOGY
VIROLOGY
ZOOLOGY

ASFIS Thesaurus
List of Descriptors by Facet

Organisms

ABDOMEN
ADRENAL GLANDS
ADULTS
AEROBIC BACTERIA
AGE GROUPS
AGGLUTININS
AIR-BREATHING FISH
ALGAE
ALIMENTARY ORGANS
ALLOPATRIC POPULATIONS
AMOEBOCYTES
AMPHIBIOTIC SPECIES
AMPHIHALINE SPECIES
ANADROMOUS SPECIES
ANAEROBIC BACTERIA
ANATOMICAL STRUCTURES
ANIMAL APPENDAGES
ANIMAL FOSSILS
ANIMAL ORGANS
ANIMAL POPULATIONS
ANIMAL REPRODUCTIVE ORGANS
ANTENNAE
ANTIBODIES
AQUATIC ANIMALS
AQUATIC BIRDS
AQUATIC COMMUNITIES
AQUATIC INSECTS
AQUATIC MAMMALS
AQUATIC ORGANISMS
AQUATIC PLANTS
AQUATIC REPTILES
ASSOCIATED SPECIES
ATTACHMENT ORGANS
AUDITORY ORGANS
AUTONOMIC NERVOUS SYSTEM
BACTERIA
BACTERIOPHAGES
BAIT FISH
BALANCE ORGANS
BALEENS
BARBELS
BENTHOS
BIOCOENOSIS
BIOLOGICAL MEMBRANES
BIOLOGICAL VECTORS
BIOTA
BIRD EGGS
BLADDERS
BLOOD
BLOOD CELLS
BLOOD VESSELS
BODY CAVITIES
BODY FLUIDS
BODY ORGANS
BODY REGIONS
BODY WALLS
BONES
BONY FINS
BORING ORGANISMS
BRACKISHWATER FISH
BRACKISHWATER MOLLUSCS
BRAIN
BRINE SHRIMP EGGS
BROOD STOCKS
BUDS
BURROWING ORGANISMS
BYSSUS
CARAPACE
CARCASSES
CARNIVORES
CARTILAGE
CATADROMOUS SPECIES
CAVERNICOLOUS SPECIES
CELL CONSTITUENTS

CELL INCLUSIONS
CELL MEMBRANES
CELL ORGANELLES
CELL WALLS
CELLS
CENTRAL NERVOUS SYSTEM
CEPHALOTHORAX
CHEMORECEPTORS
CHLOROPLASTS
CHROMATOPHORES
CHROMOSOMES
CILIA
CIRCULATORY SYSTEM
CLIMAX COMMUNITY
CLONES
CLUTCH
COARSE FISH
COCCOLITHS
COELOM
COELOMIC FLUIDS
COLONIES
COMMENSALS
COMMERCIAL SPECIES
COMPETITORS
COMPOUND EYES
CONIDIA
CONNECTIVE TISSUES
COSMOPOLITE SPECIES
CRUSTACEAN LARVAE
CRYOPLANKTON
CULTURED ORGANISMS
CUTICLES
CYSTS
CYTOPLASM
DANGEROUS ORGANISMS
DECOMPOSERS
DETRITUS FEEDERS
DEVELOPMENTAL STAGES
DIATOMS
DIGESTIVE GLANDS
DIGESTIVE SYSTEM
DIGESTIVE TRACT
DOMESTIC SPECIES
DOMINANT SPECIES
ECOLOGICAL AGGREGATIONS
ECOLOGICAL ASSOCIATIONS
ECOPHENE
ECOTYPES
ECTOPARASITES
EGGS
ELECTRIC ORGANS
EMBRYOS
ENDEMIC SPECIES
ENDOCRINE GLANDS
ENDOPARASITES
ENDOSKELETON
EPIBIONTS
EPIPHYTES
EPIPSAMMON
EPITHELIA
EPIZOITES
EPONTIC ORGANISMS
ERYTHROCYTES
ESTUARINE ORGANISMS
EXCRETORY ORGANS
EXOCRINE GLANDS
EXOSKELETON
EYES
EYESTALKS
FEATHERS
FEMALES
FILTER FEEDERS
FINGERLINGS
FINS
FISH
FISH EGGS
FISH LARVAE
FLAGELLA

FOETUS
FOOD FISH
FOOD ORGANISMS
FORAGE FISH
FORAMINIFERA
FOSSIL ASSEMBLAGES
FOSSIL DIATOMS
FOSSIL FORAMINIFERA
FOSSIL POLLEN
FOSSIL PTEROPODS
FOSSIL RADIOLARIA
FOSSIL SPORES
FOSSILS
FOULING ORGANISMS
FRESHWATER CRUSTACEANS
FRESHWATER FISH
FRESHWATER MOLLUSCS
FRESHWATER ORGANISMS
FRESHWATER WEEDS
FRY
FUNGI
GALL BLADDER
GAME FISH
GANGLIA
GEMMULES
GENES
GENOMES
GENOTYPES
GILLS
GLANDS
GOLGI APPARATUS
GUANO BIRDS
HAEMOGLOBINS
HAEMOLYMPH
HEAD
HEART
HEPATOPANCREAS
HERBIVORES
HERBIVOROUS FISH
HETEROTROPHIC ORGANISMS
HOLDFASTS
HOLOPLANKTON
HOLOTYPES
HOSTS
HYBRIDS
HYPOTHALAMUS
ICHTHYOPLANKTON
INDICATOR SPECIES
INSECT EGGS
INSECT LARVAE
INSTARS
INTEGUMENTARY SYSTEM
INTESTINES
INTRODUCED SPECIES
INVERTEBRATE LARVAE
JUVENILES
KARYOTYPES
KELPS
KELT
KIDNEYS
LACCOLITHS
LARVAE
LARYNX
LATERAL LINE
LEAVES
LEUKOCYTES
LIVER
LIVING FOSSILS
LOCOMOTORY APPENDAGES
LOPHOPHORES
LUMINOUS ORGANISMS
LUNGS
LYMPH
LYMPHATIC SYSTEM
LYMPHOCYTES
MACROPHAGES
MALES
MANTLE
MANTLE CAVITY

ASFIS Thesaurus
List of Descriptors by Facet

MARINE BIRDS
MARINE CRUSTACEANS
MARINE FISH
MARINE INVERTEBRATES
MARINE MAMMALS
MARINE MOLLUSCS
MARINE ORGANISMS
MASTICATORY STOMACH
MECHANORECEPTORS
MEGALOPS
MEIOBENTHOS
MEROPLANKTON
MICROORGANISMS
MIGRATORY SPECIES
MOLLUSCAN LARVAE
MOUTH PARTS
MUSCLES
MUSCULOSKELETAL SYSTEM
NANNOPLANKTON
NATURAL POPULATIONS
NAUPLII
NEKTON
NERVES
NERVOUS SYSTEM
NERVOUS TISSUES
NEURONS
NEUROSECRETORY SYSTEM
NEUSTON
NEW CLASSES
NEW FAMILIES
NEW GENERA
NEW ORDERS
NEW SPECIES
NEW TAXA
NEW VARIETIES
NOXIOUS ORGANISMS
NUCLEI
NYMPHS
OLFACTORY ORGANS
OMNIVORES
ORGANISM AGGREGATIONS
ORNAMENTAL FISH
OTOLITHS
OVARIES
PANCREAS
PARASITES
PATHOGENIC BACTERIA
PATHOGENS
PEARL OYSTERS
PERIPHERAL NERVOUS SYSTEM
PERIPHYTON
PHENOLOGY
PHOTOPHORES
PHOTORECEPTORS
PHYLLOSOMAE
PHYTOBENTHOS
PHYTOPLANKTON
PINEAL ORGAN
PITUITARY GLAND
PLACENTA
PLANKTON
PLANKTON FEEDERS
PLANT ORGANS
PLANT POPULATIONS
PLANT REPRODUCTIVE STRUCTURES
PLEUSTON
POISONOUS FISH
POISONOUS ORGANISMS
POLLEN
POLYPLOIDS
POLYPS
PREDATORS
PROTISTS
PSAMMON
PUPAE
PUPS
PYLORIC CAECA
RADULAE
RARE SPECIES

RECEPTORS
REEF FISH
RELICT SPECIES
RESPIRATORY ORGANS
RESPIRATORY PIGMENTS
RESPIRATORY SYSTEM
RESTING EGGS
RESTING SPORES
RESTING STAGES
RETINAS
RHIZOMES
RIBOSOMES
ROES
ROOTS
SAPROBIONTS
SAPROPHYTES
SAPROPLANKTON
SAPROZOITES
SCALES
SCAVENGERS
SEA GRASS
SEAWEEDS
SECRETORY ORGANS
SEDENTARY SPECIES
SEED (AQUACULTURE)
SEMEN
SENSE ORGANS
SENSE TENTACLES
SERUM
SESSILE SPECIES
SESTON
SEXUAL CELLS
SHELLFISH
SHELLS
SIBLING SPECIES
SINGLE CELL PROTEINS
SKELETON
SKIN
SKULL
SMOLTS
SPAT
SPAWNING POPULATIONS
SPECIES
SPERM
SPERMATOPHORES
SPINAL CORD
SPLEEN
SPONGES
SPORANGIA
SPORES
STATOCYSTS
STEMS
STINGING ORGANS
STOCKS
STOMACH
STOMATA
SUBPOPULATIONS
SWIM BLADDER
SYMBIONTS
SYMPATRIC POPULATIONS
SYNAPSES
TACTILE ORGANS
TARGET CELLS
TASTE ORGANS
TAXA
TEETH
TELSON
TENTACLES
TEST ORGANISMS
TESTES
THALLUS
THERMORECEPTORS
THORAX
THYMUS
THYROID
TISSUES
TRACHEA
TRANSPLANTS
TRASH FISH

TROPICAL FISH
TUBE DWELLERS
TURIONS
UNDERUTILIZED SPECIES
UNIT STOCKS
URINARY SYSTEM
VEGETAL FOSSILS
VEGETATION COVER
VELIGERS
VENOM APPARATUS
VERTEBRAE
VIRUSES
VISUAL PIGMENTS
VOCAL ORGANS
WEEDS
WINGS
YEASTS
YOLK
ZOEAE
ZOOBENTHOS
ZOOPLANKTON
ZOOXANTHELLAE
ZYGOTES

ASFIS Thesaurus
List of Descriptors by Facet

Earth, Space and Time Concepts

ABYSSAL HILLS
ABYSSAL PLAINS
ABYSSAL ZONE
ABYSSOBENTHIC ZONE
ABYSSOPELAGIC ZONE
ACTIVE MARGINS
AIR-ICE INTERFACE
AIR MASSES
AIR-WATER INTERFACE
ALGAL MATS
ALLUVIAL FANS
ALLUVIAL TERRACES
AMPHIBOLITE FACIES
ANCHORAGES
ANOXIC BASINS
ANTARCTIC ZONE
ANTICLINES
ANTICLINORIA
ANTIDUNES
APHOTIC ZONE
AQUATIC ENVIRONMENT
ARCHIPELAGIC APRONS
ARCHIPELAGOES
ARCTIC ZONE
ARID ENVIRONMENTS
ARTIFICIAL LAKES
ARTIFICIAL SPAWNING GROUNDS
ASEISMIC RIDGES
ASEISMIC ZONES
ASTHENOSPHERE
ATMOSPHERIC BOUNDARY LAYER
ATOLL LAGOONS
ATOLLS
AUTUMN
AZIMUTH
BACKSHORE
BACKWATERS
BANKS (TOPOGRAPHY)
BARRIER BEACHES
BARRIER ISLANDS
BARRIER REEFS
BARRIER SPITS
BASEMENT ROCK
BASINS
BATHYAL-BENTHIC ZONE
BATHYAL ZONE
BATHYPELAGIC ZONE
BAYS
BEACH CUSPS
BEACH FEATURES
BEACH RIDGES
BEACHES
BED FORMS
BEDDING STRUCTURES
BENIOFF ZONE
BENTHIC BOUNDARY LAYER
BENTHIC ENVIRONMENT
BERMS
BETA-PLANE
BIOFACIES
BIOGENIC DEPOSITS
BIOGENIC SEDIMENTARY STRUCTURES
BIOHERMS
BIOLOGICAL HALF LIFE
BIOTOPES
BOTTOM EKMAN LAYER
BOTTOM MIXED LAYER
BOTTOM TOPOGRAPHY
BOTTOMSET BEDS
BOUDINAGE
BOUNDARIES
BOUNDARY LAYERS
BRACKISHWATER ENVIRONMENT
BREAK-POINT BARS

BREEDING SEASONS
BREEDING SITES
CAMBRIAN
CANALS
CARBONATE COMPENSATION DEPTH
CARBONIFEROUS
CATCHMENT AREA
CAVES
CAYS
CENOZOIC
CHANNELS
CHENIER PLAINS
CHENIERS
CLIFFS
CLIMATIC ZONES
CLINES
COASTAL BOUNDARY LAYER
COASTAL INLETS
COASTAL LAGOONS
COASTAL LANDFORMS
COASTAL WATERS
COASTAL ZONE
COASTS
COMPENSATION DEPTH
CONTINENTAL BORDERLAND
CONTINENTAL CRUST
CONTINENTAL MARGINS
CONTINENTAL RIDGES
CONTINENTAL RISE
CONTINENTAL SHELVES
CONTINENTAL SLOPE
CONTINENTS
CONVERGING PLATE BOUNDARIES
COOLING PONDS
CORAL REEFS
CORANGE LINES
CORE LAYERS (WATER)
CRATONS
CRETACEOUS
CRUISE STATIONS
CRYOSPHERE
CUSPATE FORELANDS
DATUM LEVELS
DAYTIME
DEEP LAYER
DEEP-SEA CHANNELS
DEEP-SEA FANS
DEEP-SEA FURROWS
DEEP WATER
DEEP-WATER MASSES
DELTAIC FEATURES
DELTAS
DENSITY INTERFACES
DEPOSITION FEATURES
DESERTS
DEVONIAN
DICOTHERMAL LAYER
DISCONTINUITY LAYERS
DISPHOTIC ZONE
DISTRIBUTARIES
DIURNAL THERMOCLINE
DIVERGENCE ZONES
DIVERGING PLATE BOUNDARIES
DOMES
DROWNED VALLEYS
DRY SEASON
DUNES
DYNAMIC TOPOGRAPHY
DYSTROPHIC LAKES
EARTH
EARTH ATMOSPHERE
EARTH CORE
EARTH CRUST
EARTH HISTORY
EARTH MANTLE
EARTH ORBIT
EARTH STRUCTURE
ECOCLINES
ECOLOGICAL ZONATION

ECOSYSTEMS
EKMAN LAYERS
EMBANKMENTS
EMERGENT SHORELINES
ENVIRONMENTS
EOCENE
EPICENTRES
EPILIMNION
EPIPELAGIC ZONE
EPONTIC ENVIRONMENT
EQUATOR
EROSION FEATURES
EROSION SURFACES
ESCARPMENTS
ESKERS
ESTUARIES
EULITTORAL ZONE
EUPHOTIC ZONE
EUTROPHIC LAKES
EUTROPHIC WATERS
EXPOSED HABITATS
FACIES
FANS
FAULT SCARPS
FAULT ZONES
FAULTS
FAUNAL PROVINCES
FISH PONDS
FISHING GROUNDS
FIXED STATIONS
FJORDS
FLAW LEADS
FLOOD PLAINS
FLUSHING TIME
FLUVIAL FEATURES
FOLDS
FOREARC BASINS
FORESET BEDS
FORESHORE
FOSSILIZED TRACKS
FRACTURE ZONES
FRESHWATER LAKES
FRINGING REEFS
GAS CONDENSATE FIELDS
GAS FIELDS
GEOCLINES
GEOID
GEOLOGICAL HISTORY
GEOLOGICAL STRUCTURES
GEOLOGICAL TIME
GEOSYNCLINES
GEOTHERMAL SPRINGS
GLACIAL FEATURES
GLACIAL LAKES
GRABEN
GREENSCHIST FACIES
GROWING PONDS
GUYOTS
HABITAT
HALOCLINE
HARBOURS
HEADLANDS
HEAT AFFECTED ZONES
HIATUSES
HIGH SEAS
HOLOCENE
HOME RANGE
HORIZON
HOT SPOTS
HOT SPRINGS
HYDROSPHERE
HYDROTHERMAL FIELDS
HYDROTHERMAL SPRINGS
HYPOLIMNION
ICE AGES
ICE CANOPY
ICE CAPS
ICE EDGE
ICE FIELDS

ASFIS Thesaurus
List of Descriptors by Facet

ICE FOOT
ICE-FREE PERIODS
ICE ISLANDS
ICE-OIL INTERFACE
ICE RIDGES
ICE SHELVES
ICE-WATER INTERFACE
IMPOUNDMENTS
INFLUENTS
INLAND LAGOONS
INLAND SEAS
INLAND WATER ENVIRONMENT
INLAND WATERS
INLETS (WATERWAYS)
INSHORE STATIONS
INTERFACES
INTERGLACIAL PERIODS
INTERMEDIATE WATER MASSES
INTERNATIONAL BOUNDARIES
INTEROCEAN CANALS
INTERSTITIAL ENVIRONMENT
INTERTIDAL ENVIRONMENT
IONOSPHERE
ISENTROPIC SURFACES
ISLAND ARCS
ISLAND SLOPE
ISLANDS
ISOBARIC SURFACES
ISOPYCNIC SURFACES
ISOSTERIC SURFACES
JURASSIC
JUVENILE WATER
LAGOONS
LAKE BASINS
LAKE SHORES
LAKES
LAMINAR BOUNDARY LAYER
LAND BRIDGES
LANDFORMS
LAYERS
LENITIC ENVIRONMENT
LEVEES
LEVEL OF NO MOTION
LEVELS
LITHOSPHERE
LITTORAL ZONE
LOCATIONS (WORKING)
LONGSHORE BARS
LOTIC ENVIRONMENT
LOW-VELOCITY LAYER
LOWER MANTLE
LYSOCLINE
MAGMA CHAMBERS
MANGROVE SWAMPS
MARGINAL BASINS
MARGINAL FIELDS
MARGINAL SEAS
MARINE ENVIRONMENT
MARINE PARKS
MARSHES
MEDIAN LINES
MEDIAN VALLEYS
MEROMICTIC LAKES
MESOPELAGIC ZONE
MESOSPHERE (EARTH)
MESOZOIC
MESSINIAN
METALIMNION
METAMORPHIC FACIES
MICROCONTINENTS
MICROHABITATS
MICROTOPOGRAPHY
MID-OCEAN RIDGES
MILITARY PORTS
MIOCENE
MIXED LAYER
MOHO
MOON
MOUNTAINS

MUD BANKS
MUD FLATS
NAVIGATIONAL CHANNELS
NEAR-SURFACE LAYER
NEARSHORE BARS
NEOGENE
NEPHELOID LAYER
NERITIC PROVINCE
NICHES
NIGHTTIME
NURSERY GROUNDS
NURSERY PONDS
OCEAN-ATMOSPHERE SYSTEM
OCEAN BASINS
OCEAN FLOOR
OCEAN-ICE-ATMOSPHERE SYSTEM
OCEAN STATIONS
OCEANIC BOUNDARY LAYER
OCEANIC CRUST
OCEANIC DESERTS
OCEANIC ISLANDS
OCEANIC PROVINCE
OCEANOGRAPHIC STATIONS
OCEANS
OFFSHORE
OIL AND GAS FIELDS
OIL FIELDS
OIL-GAS INTERFACE
OIL RESERVOIRS
OIL-WATER INTERFACE
OLIGOCENE
OLIGOTROPHIC LAKES
OPTICAL WATER TYPES
ORDOVICIAN
OUTCROPS
OUTER CONTINENTAL SHELF
OUTFLOW WATERS
OXBOW LAKES
OYSTER REEFS
PALAEOCENE
PALAEOENVIRONMENTS
PALAEOGENE
PALAEOLATITUDE
PALAEOSHORELINES
PALAEOZOIC
PARTIALLY-MIXED ESTUARIES
PASSIVE MARGINS
PELAGIC ENVIRONMENT
PERMANENT THERMOCLINE
PERMIAN
PHANEROZOIC
PHYSIOGRAPHIC PROVINCES
PILLOW STRUCTURES
PITS
PLAINS
PLANETARY ATMOSPHERES
PLATE BOUNDARIES
PLATE MARGINS
PLATEAUX
PLATES
PLATFORMS (GEOLOGY)
PLAYAS
PLEISTOCENE
PLIO-PLEISTOCENE BOUNDARY
PLIOCENE
POLAR WATERS
POLAR ZONES
POLDERS
POLE POSITIONS
PONDS
PRECAMBRIAN
PYCNOCLINE
QUATERNARY
RAINY SEASON
RAISED BEACHES
RECREATIONAL WATERS
REDDS
REEFS
REFERENCE LEVELS

REFUGES
REGIONS
RELICT LAKES
RELICT SHORELINES
RELIEF FORMS
RESERVOIRS (WATER)
RESIDENCE TIME
RESPONSE TIME
RIA COASTS
RICE FIELDS
RIDGES
RIFT VALLEYS
RIFT ZONES
RIP CHANNELS
RIPPLE MARKS
RIVER BANKS
RIVER BASINS
RIVER BEDS
RIVER VALLEYS
RIVERS
ROCKY SHORES
RUNNELS
SABKHAS
SALINITY MAXIMUM LAYER
SALINITY MINIMUM LAYER
SALT DOMES
SALT LAKES
SALT MARSHES
SALT-WEDGE ESTUARIES
SANCTUARIES
SAND BANKS
SAND BARS
SAND PATCHES
SAND RIBBONS
SAND RIPPLES
SAND WAVES
SCATTERING LAYERS
SCOUR AND FILL
SCOUR HOLLOWS
SCOUR MARKS
SEA SURFACE
SEABIGHTS
SEACHANNELS
SEAKNOLLS
SEAMOATS
SEAMOUNT CHAINS
SEAMOUNTS
SEASONAL THERMOCLINE
SEASONS
SEDIMENT DRIFTS
SEDIMENT-WATER INTERFACE
SEDIMENTARY BASINS
SEDIMENTARY ENVIRONMENTS
SEDIMENTARY STRUCTURES
SEISMIC DISCONTINUITIES
SEISMIC LAYERS
SEISMIC RIDGES
SEISMIC ZONES
SEMI-ENCLOSED SEAS
SHEAR ZONE
SHELF EDGE
SHELF FACIES
SHELF SEAS
SHELTERED HABITATS
SHIP CANALS
SHIPPING LANES
SHOALS
SIAL
SILURIAN
SIMA
SLOPE ENVIRONMENT
SLOPES (TOPOGRAPHY)
SLUMP STRUCTURES
SPAWNING GROUNDS
SPAWNING SEASONS
SPITS
SPLASH ZONE
SPREADING CENTRES
SPRING

ASFIS Thesaurus
List of Descriptors by Facet

SPRING STREAMS
STACKS
STANDARD OCEAN SECTIONS
STOCKING PONDS
STRAITS
STRANDLINES
STRATOSPHERE
STRIP MINE LAKES
STROMATOLITES
STRUCTURAL BASINS
STRUCTURAL DOMES
SUBAEREAL TOPOGRAPHY
SUBDUCTION ZONES
SUBLITTORAL ZONE
SUBMARINE BANKS
SUBMARINE CANYONS
SUBMARINE FEATURES
SUBMARINE PLATEAUX
SUBMARINE RIDGES
SUBMARINE SCARPS
SUBMARINE SPRINGS
SUBMARINE TROUGHS
SUBMARINE VALLEYS
SUBMARINE VOLCANOES
SUBMERGED SHORELINES
SUBSTRATA
SUBSURFACE WATER
SUBTROPICAL ZONES
SUMMER
SUN
SUPRALITTORAL ZONE
SURF ZONE
SURFACE EKMAN LAYER
SURFACE LAYERS
SURFACE MICROLAYER
SURFACE MIXED LAYER
SURFACE TOPOGRAPHY
SURFACE WATER
SURFACE WATER MASSES
SURFACES
SWAMPS
SYNCLINES
SYNCLINORIA
TEMPERATE ZONES
TEMPERATURE MAXIMUM LAYER
TEMPERATURE MINIMUM LAYER
TEMPORARY PONDS
TERRACES
TERTIARY
THERMOCLINE
TIDAL DATUM
TIDAL FLATS
TIDAL INLETS
TOMBOLOS
TOPOGRAPHIC FEATURES
TOPOGRAPHY
TOPOGRAPHY (GEOLOGY)
TOPSET BEDS
TRACE FOSSILS
TRANSFORM FAULTS
TRANSFORM PLATE BOUNDARIES
TRANSVERSE BARS
TRANSVERSE BED FORMS
TRENCHES (OCEANIC)
TRENCHES (PIPELINES)
TRIASSIC
TRIBUTARIES
TRIPLE JUNCTIONS
TROPICAL ENVIRONMENT
TROPICAL LAKES
TROPOPAUSE
TROPOSPHERE
TURBIDITY CURRENT STRUCTURES
TURBULENT BOUNDARY LAYER
TYPE LOCALITIES
UPPER ATMOSPHERE
UPPER MANTLE
UPPER OCEAN
VALLEYS

VARVES
VOLCANIC BELTS
VOLCANIC ISLANDS
VOLCANOES
WASTE DISPOSAL SITES
WATER BODIES
WATER COLUMN
WATER MASSES
WATER SPRINGS
WATER TABLE
WATER TYPES
WATERSHEDS
WAVE-CUT PLATFORMS
WETLANDS
WINTER
WORLD
ZEOLITE FACIES

ASFIS Thesaurus
List of Descriptors by Facet

Organizational, Socioeconomic, Legal and Personnel Aspects

ACCESS
ACCIDENT PREVENTION
ALGOLOGISTS
ALLOCATION SYSTEMS
ANIMAL PHYSIOLOGISTS
AQUACULTURE DEVELOPMENT
AQUACULTURE REGULATIONS
AQUACULTURISTS
BACTERIOLOGISTS
BILATERAL AGREEMENTS
BIOLOGICAL INSTITUTIONS
BIOLOGISTS
BLUE WHALE UNIT
BOATING
BOTANICAL RESOURCES
BOTANISTS
BY CATCH
CAPTURE FISHERY ECONOMICS
CARCINOLOGISTS
CAREERS
CARGOES
CETOLOGISTS
COASTAL STATES
COASTAL ZONE MANAGEMENT
COASTGUARDS
COLD SEASON
COMMERCE
COMMERCIAL LEGISLATION
COMMON PROPERTY RESOURCES
COMPANIES
CONCESSIONS
CONFERENCES
CONSERVATION
CONSULTANTS
CONSUMERS
CONTIGUOUS ZONES
CONTRACTORS
CONTRACTS
COOPERATIVES
COSTS
COUNTRIES
CREW
CURRENT POWER
CURRICULA
DATA CENTRES
DEPLETION
DEVELOPED COUNTRIES
DEVELOPING COUNTRIES
DEVELOPMENT POTENTIAL
DEVELOPMENT PROJECTS
DISPUTES
DIVERS
DIVING REGULATIONS
ECOLOGISTS
ECONOMIC FEASIBILITY
ECONOMISTS
ECOSYSTEM MANAGEMENT
EDUCATION
EDUCATION ESTABLISHMENTS
ELECTROMAGNETIC POWER
ENERGY RESOURCES
ENGINEERS
ENTOMOLOGISTS
ENVIRONMENT MANAGEMENT
ENVIRONMENTAL LEGISLATION
ENVIRONMENTAL PROTECTION
EXCLUSIVE ECONOMIC ZONE
EXCLUSIVE RIGHTS
EXHIBITIONS
EXPERTS
EXPLOITATION
EXPLORATION RIGHTS

EXTENDED JURISDICTION
FEASIBILITY
FELLOWSHIPS
FINANCIAL INSTITUTIONS
FINANCIAL MANAGEMENT
FINANCIAL RESOURCES
FISH CONSUMPTION
FISH INSPECTION REGULATIONS
FISHERMEN
FISHERY BIOLOGISTS
FISHERY BOUNDARIES
FISHERY DEVELOPMENT
FISHERY DISPUTES
FISHERY INDUSTRY LEGISLATION
FISHERY INSTITUTIONS
FISHERY MANAGEMENT
FISHERY ORGANIZATIONS
FISHERY POLICY
FISHERY PROTECTION
FISHERY REGULATIONS
FISHERY RESOURCES
FISHING RIGHTS
FOOD RESOURCES
FRESHWATER ECOLOGISTS
FRESHWATER SCIENTISTS
FUEL ECONOMY
GENETICISTS
GEOLOGICAL INSTITUTIONS
GEOLOGISTS
GEOTHERMAL POWER
GOVERNMENT POLICY
GOVERNMENTS
GRANTS
HARBOUR REGULATIONS
HEALTH AND SAFETY
HISTORICAL ACCOUNT
HUMAN RESOURCES
HYDROELECTRIC POWER
ICHTHYOLOGISTS
ILLEGAL FISHING
INFORMATION CENTRES
INFORMATION SCIENTISTS
INFORMATION SERVICES
INSTITUTIONAL RESOURCES
INSURANCE
INTERNATIONAL AGREEMENTS
INTERNATIONAL COOPERATION
INTERNATIONAL LAW
INTERNATIONAL ORGANIZATIONS
INTERNATIONAL POLICY
INTERNATIONAL WATERS
INVESTMENTS
JOINT VENTURES
JURISDICTION
LABORATORIES
LABOUR
LABOUR COSTS
LABOUR LEGISLATION
LAND USE
LANDLOCKED STATES
LAW OF THE SEA
LEASES
LEGAL ASPECTS
LEGISLATION
LIABILITY
LIBRARIANS
LIBRARIES
LICENCES
LIMNOLOGICAL INSTITUTIONS
LIVING RESOURCES
MALACOLOGISTS
MAMMALOGISTS
MANAGEMENT
MARINE ECOLOGISTS
MARINE RESOURCES
MARINE SCIENTISTS
MARITIME LEGISLATION
MESH REGULATIONS
METEOROLOGISTS

MICROBIOLOGISTS
MINERAL RESOURCES
MINING LEGISLATION
MORATORIA
MULTIPLE USE OF RESOURCES
MUSEUMS
MYCOLOGISTS
NATIONAL PLANNING
NATURAL RESOURCES
NATURE CONSERVATION
NAVAL BASES
NAVIGATION POLICY
NAVIGATION REGULATIONS
NONRENEWABLE RESOURCES
OBITUARIES
OCEAN POLICY
OCEAN SPACE
OCEANOGRAPHIC INSTITUTIONS
OIL AND GAS LEGISLATION
OIL RESERVES
OPERATIONAL COSTS
ORGANIZATIONS
ORNITHOLOGISTS
OTEC
OVEREXPLOITATION
OVERFISHING
PERMITS
PERSONNEL
PHYSIOLOGISTS
PLANNING
PLANT PHYSIOLOGISTS
POLICIES
POLITICAL ASPECTS
POLLUTION CONVENTION
POLLUTION LEGISLATION
POTENTIAL RESOURCES
POTENTIAL YIELD
POWER FROM THE SEA
PRODUCTION COST
PRODUCTION MANAGEMENT
PROPERTY RIGHTS
PROTECTED RESOURCES
PROTECTION
PUBLIC ACCESS
PUBLIC HEALTH
PUBLICITY MATERIAL
QUARANTINE REGULATIONS
QUOTA REGULATIONS
RADIATION PROTECTION
RENEWABLE RESOURCES
RENTAL
RESEARCH INSTITUTIONS
RESOURCE CONSERVATION
RESOURCE DEPLETION
RESOURCE DEVELOPMENT
RESOURCE MANAGEMENT
RESOURCES
RIGHTS
RIPARIAN RIGHTS
RISKS
RIVER BASIN MANAGEMENT
SAFETY REGULATIONS
SALINITY POWER
SCIENTIFIC PERSONNEL
SEABED CONVENTIONS
SEABED PROTECTION
SEAMANSHIP
SEASON REGULATIONS
SECURITY
SHARED STOCKS
SHARK UTILIZATION
SHIPPING
SHORE PROTECTION
SIZE-LIMIT REGULATIONS
SOCIOLOGICAL ASPECTS
SOIL CONSERVATION
SOLAR POWER
SORTING CENTRES
STATISTICIANS

ASFIS Thesaurus
List of Descriptors by Facet

STORM TIDE WARNING SERVICES
SURVEILLANCE AND ENFORCEMENT
SURVIVAL AT SEA
TAXES
TAXONOMISTS
TECHNICAL FEASIBILITY
TECHNICIANS
TERRITORIAL WATERS
THERMAL POWER
TIDAL POWER
TRADE
TRADE ORGANIZATIONS
TRAFFIC MANAGEMENT
TRAINING CENTRES
UNCONVENTIONAL RESOURCES
UNDERSEA WARFARE
UNDERWATER ACCESS
UNDERWATER EXPLOITATION
URBANIZATION
UTILIZATION
VIROLOGISTS
WARNING SERVICES
WASTE UTILIZATION
WATER AUTHORITIES
WATER CONSERVATION
WATER MANAGEMENT
WATER POLICY
WATER RESOURCES
WATER RIGHTS
WATER SUPPLY
WATER USE
WATER USE REGULATIONS
WAVE POWER
WHALING REGULATIONS
WIND POWER
WOMEN
YIELD
ZOOLOGISTS

Constants

ABSORPTION COEFFICIENT
ASSOCIATION CONSTANTS
BOWEN RATIO
BULK MODULUS
CARBON ISOTOPE RATIO
CARBON/NITROGEN RATIO
CARBON/PHOSPHORUS RATIO
COEFFICIENTS
CONDUCTIVITY RATIO
CONSTANTS
DIELECTRIC CONSTANT
DIFFUSION COEFFICIENTS
DIMENSIONLESS NUMBERS
DRAG COEFFICIENT
EDDY VISCOSITY COEFFICIENT
ELASTIC CONSTANTS
EXCHANGE COEFFICIENTS
EXTINCTION COEFFICIENT
FROUDE NUMBER
GREEN'S FUNCTION
HARMONIC FUNCTIONS
MIXING RATIO
MOLECULAR VISCOSITY COEFFICIENTS
POISSON'S RATIO
PRANDTL NUMBER
RATIOS
REYNOLDS NUMBER
RICHARDSON NUMBER
ROSSBY NUMBER
SCATTERING COEFFICIENT
SHEAR MODULUS
SOLAR CONSTANT
STABILITY CONSTANTS
TIDAL CONSTANTS
VISCOSITY COEFFICIENTS
VOLUME SCATTERING FUNCTION

ASFIS Thesaurus
List of Descriptors by Facet

Residual Concepts

ABIOTIC FACTORS
ANNUAL RANGE
ANTHROPOGENIC FACTORS
BIOTIC FACTORS
BOUNDARY CONDITIONS
CAPTIVITY
CONTROLLED CONDITIONS
CONVERSION FACTORS
CORIOLIS PARAMETERS
CORRELATION
CRUISE PROGRAMMES
ENVIRONMENTAL FACTORS
EXTREME VALUES
FATE
INDICATORS
INTERACTIONS
LATITUDINAL VARIATIONS
LETHAL EFFECTS
LETHAL LIMITS
LIMITING FACTORS
MORTALITY CAUSES
TERMINOLOGY
TRANSPORT
TROPHIC LEVELS
VECTORS

Alphabetic List of Terms

ASFIS Thesaurus
Alphabetical List of Terms

A

ABDOMEN
ABIOTIC FACTORS
ABLATION
ABNORMALITIES
ABSOLUTE AGE
ABSOLUTE HUMIDITY
ABSOLUTE VORTICITY
ABSORPTANCE
ABSORPTION (PHYSICS)
ABSORPTION COEFFICIENT
ABSORPTION SPECTRA
ABSORPTION SPECTROSCOPY
ABSTRACTS
ABUNDANCE
ABYSSAL CIRCULATION
ABYSSAL CURRENTS
ABYSSAL HILLS
ABYSSAL PLAINS
ABYSSAL ZONE
ABYSSOBENTHIC ZONE
ABYSSOPELAGIC ZONE
ACANSTEROL
ACCELERATION
ACCELEROMETERS
ACCEPTABILITY
ACCEPTANCE TESTS
ACCESS
ACCIDENT PREVENTION
ACCIDENTS
ACCLIMATION
ACCLIMATIZATION
ACCOMMODATION
ACCRETION
ACCUMULATION
ACCURACY
ACETATE
ACETONE
ACID RAIN
ACIDIFICATION
ACIDITY
ACOUSTIC ARRAYS
ACOUSTIC BEACONS
ACOUSTIC COMMAND SYSTEMS
ACOUSTIC CURRENT METERS
ACOUSTIC DATA
ACOUSTIC EMISSION
ACOUSTIC EQUIPMENT
ACOUSTIC HOLOGRAPHY
ACOUSTIC IMAGERY
ACOUSTIC IMAGES
ACOUSTIC IMPEDANCE
ACOUSTIC INSULATION
ACOUSTIC MODELS
ACOUSTIC NAVIGATION
ACOUSTIC PINGERS
ACOUSTIC PROPERTIES
ACOUSTIC TELEMETRY
ACOUSTIC TOMOGRAPHY
ACOUSTIC TRACKING SYSTEMS
ACOUSTIC TRANSDUCERS
ACOUSTIC TRANSPONDERS
ACOUSTICS
ACQUISITION
ACRONYMS
ACRYLIC ACID
ACRYLICS
ACTIN
ACTINIDE COMPOUNDS
ACTINIDES
ACTINIUM
ACTINIUM COMPOUNDS
ACTINIUM ISOTOPES
ACTINOMETERS
ACTIVATION ANALYSIS
ACTIVE MARGINS

ACTIVE SONAR
ACTIVITY PATTERNS
ACYCLIC HYDROCARBONS
ADAPTATIONS
ADDITIVES
ADHESION
ADHESIVES
ADIABATIC LAPSE RATES
ADIABATIC PROCESSES
ADIABATIC TEMPERATURE GRADIENT
ADP
ADRENAL GLANDS
ADSORPTION
ADULTS
ADVECTION
AERATION
AERIAL PHOTOGRAPHS
AERIAL PHOTOGRAPHY
AERIAL SURVEYS
AEROBIC BACTERIA
AEROBIC RESPIRATION
AERODYNAMICS
AEROMAGNETIC SURVEYS
AEROSOLS
AESTIVATION
AETIOLOGY
AGAR
AGAROSE
AGE
AGE AT RECRUITMENT
AGE COMPOSITION
AGE DETERMINATION
AGE GROUPS
AGE OF SEAWATER
AGE OF TIDE
AGENTS
AGEOSTROPHIC FLOW
AGGLUTININS
AGGREGATES
AGGREGATION
AGGRESSIVE BEHAVIOUR
AGING
AGONISTIC BEHAVIOUR
AGRICULTURAL POLLUTION
AGRICULTURAL RUNOFF
AGRICULTURE
AGROPISCICULTURE
AIR
AIR BUBBLES
AIR CONDITIONING
AIR EXPOSURE
AIR FLOW OVER LAND
AIR FLOW OVER WATER
AIR GUNS
AIR MASSES
AIR POLLUTION
AIR SAMPLING
AIR TEMPERATURE
AIR TRANSPORTATION
AIR-BREATHING FISH
AIR-ICE INTERFACE
AIR-SEA COUPLING
AIR-SEA INTERACTION
AIR-WATER EXCHANGES
AIR-WATER INTERFACE
AIR-WATER TEMPERATURE DIFFERENCE
AIRBORNE EQUIPMENT
AIRBORNE SENSING
AIRCRAFT
AIRGLOW
AIRPORTS
ALANINE
ALARM SUBSTANCES
ALARM SYSTEMS
ALBEDO
ALBINISM
ALBUMINS

ALCOHOLS
ALDEHYDES
ALDRIN
ALGAE
ALGAL BLOOMS
ALGAL CULTURE
ALGAL MATS
ALGAL SETTLEMENTS
ALGICIDES
ALGINATES
ALGINIC ACID
ALGOLOGISTS
ALGOLOGY
ALGORITHMS
ALICYCLIC HYDROCARBONS
ALIMENTARY ORGANS
ALKALI BASALTS
ALKALI METAL COMPOUNDS
ALKALI METALS
ALKALINE EARTH METAL COMPOUNDS
ALKALINE EARTH METALS
ALKALINITY
ALKALOIDS
ALKENES
ALKYNES
ALLERGIC REACTIONS
ALLOCATION SYSTEMS
ALLOCHTHONOUS DEPOSITS
ALLOPATRIC POPULATIONS
ALLOYS
ALLUVIAL DEPOSITS
ALLUVIAL FANS
ALLUVIAL TERRACES
ALMANACS
ALPHA SPECTROSCOPY
ALTERNATE REPRODUCTION
ALTIMETERS
ALTIMETRY
ALUMINIUM
ALUMINIUM COMPOUNDS
ALUMINIUM ISOTOPES
AMBERGRIS
AMBIENT NOISE
AMERICIUM
AMERICIUM COMPOUNDS
AMERICIUM ISOTOPES
AMINATION
AMINES
AMINO ACIDS
AMMONIA
AMMONIUM CHLORIDE
AMMONIUM COMPOUNDS
AMOEBOCYTES
AMP
AMPHIBIOTIC SPECIES
AMPHIBIOUS VEHICLES
AMPHIBOLES
AMPHIBOLITE FACIES
AMPHIBOLITES
AMPHIDROMIC SYSTEMS
AMPHIHALINE SPECIES
AMPLITUDE
ANABOLISM
ANADROMOUS MIGRATIONS
ANADROMOUS SPECIES
ANAEMIA
ANAEROBIC BACTERIA
ANAEROBIC DIGESTION
ANAEROBIC RESPIRATION
ANAEROBIOSIS
ANAESTHESIA
ANAESTHETICS
ANALCITE
ANALOG MODELS
ANALOG RECORDS
ANALOGS
ANALYSIS
ANALYTICAL ERRORS

ASFIS Thesaurus
Alphabetical List of Terms

ANALYTICAL TECHNIQUES
ANATASE
ANATOMICAL STRUCTURES
ANATOMY
ANCHORAGES
ANCHORING
ANCHORS
ANDALUSITE
ANDESITE
ANDROGENESIS
ANELASTICITY
ANEMOMETERS
ANGLING
ANGULAR DISTRIBUTION
ANGULAR MOMENTUM
ANHYDRITE
ANIMAL APPENDAGES
ANIMAL COMMUNICATION
ANIMAL DISEASES
ANIMAL FOSSILS
ANIMAL METABOLISM
ANIMAL MORPHOLOGY
ANIMAL NAVIGATION
ANIMAL NUTRITION
ANIMAL OIL EXTRACTION
ANIMAL ORGANS
ANIMAL PHYSIOLOGISTS
ANIMAL PHYSIOLOGY
ANIMAL POPULATIONS
ANIMAL PRODUCTS
ANIMAL REPRODUCTIVE ORGANS
ANIONS
ANISOTROPIC ROCKS
ANISOTROPY
ANNUAL
ANNUAL RANGE
ANNUAL REPORTS
ANNUAL VARIATIONS
ANODES
ANOMALIES
ANORTHITE
ANORTHOCLASE
ANORTHOSITE
ANOXIA
ANOXIC BASINS
ANOXIC CONDITIONS
ANOXIC SEDIMENTS
ANTARCTIC CONVERGENCE
ANTARCTIC FRONT
ANTARCTIC ZONE
ANTENNAE
ANTHROPOGENIC FACTORS
ANTIBIOTICS
ANTIBODIES
ANTICLINES
ANTICLINORIA
ANTICOAGULANTS
ANTICYCLONES
ANTICYCLONIC MOTION
ANTIDUNES
ANTIFOULING SUBSTANCES
ANTIFREEZES
ANTIGENS
ANTIHELMINTHIC AGENTS
ANTIMONY
ANTIMONY COMPOUNDS
ANTIMONY ISOTOPES
ANTIOXIDANTS
ANTIPARASITIC AGENTS
ANTIPROTOZOAL AGENTS
APATITE
APHOTIC ZONE
APPROXIMATION
AQUACULTURE
AQUACULTURE DEVELOPMENT
AQUACULTURE ECONOMICS
AQUACULTURE EFFLUENTS

AQUACULTURE ENTERPRISES
AQUACULTURE EQUIPMENT
AQUACULTURE FACILITIES
AQUACULTURE PRODUCTS
AQUACULTURE REGULATIONS
AQUACULTURE STATISTICS
AQUACULTURE SYSTEMS
AQUACULTURE TECHNIQUES
AQUACULTURISTS
AQUARIA
AQUARIOLOGY
AQUARIUM CULTURE
AQUATIC ANIMALS
AQUATIC BIRDS
AQUATIC COMMUNITIES
AQUATIC DRUGS
AQUATIC ENVIRONMENT
AQUATIC INSECTS
AQUATIC MAMMALS
AQUATIC ORGANISMS
AQUATIC PLANTS
AQUATIC REPTILES
AQUATIC SCIENCES
ARABINOSE
ARACHIDONIC ACID
ARAGONITE
ARCHAEOLOGY
ARCHIPELAGIC APRONS
ARCHIPELAGOES
ARCHIVES
ARCTIC ZONE
AREA
ARENACEOUS DEPOSITS
ARENITES
ARGILLACEOUS DEPOSITS
ARGININE
ARGON
ARGON ISOTOPES
ARID ENVIRONMENTS
AROMATIC HYDROCARBONS
AROMATICS
ARRAYS
ARSENATES
ARSENIC
ARSENIC COMPOUNDS
ARSENIC ISOTOPES
ARTICULATED COLUMNS
ARTIFICIAL AERATION
ARTIFICIAL FEEDING
ARTIFICIAL HARBOURS
ARTIFICIAL INTELLIGENCE
ARTIFICIAL ISLANDS
ARTIFICIAL LAKES
ARTIFICIAL REEFS
ARTIFICIAL SEAWATER
ARTIFICIAL SEAWEED
ARTIFICIAL SPAWNING GROUNDS
ARTIFICIAL SUBSTRATA
ARTIFICIAL UPWELLING
ARTISANAL FISHING
ARTISANAL WHALING
ASBESTOS
ASEISMIC RIDGES
ASEISMIC ZONES
ASEXUAL REPRODUCTION
ASH CONTENT
ASH LAYERS
ASHES
ASPARTIC ACID
ASPHALT
ASPHYXIA
ASSOCIATED SPECIES
ASSOCIATION CONSTANTS
ASTATINE
ASTATINE COMPOUNDS
ASTATINE ISOTOPES
ASTHENOSPHERE

ASTRONOMICAL TIDES
ASTRONOMY
ATLASES
ATMOSPHERE EVOLUTION
ATMOSPHERIC BOUNDARY LAYER
ATMOSPHERIC CHEMISTRY
ATMOSPHERIC CIRCULATION
ATMOSPHERIC CONVECTION
ATMOSPHERIC CONVERGENCES
ATMOSPHERIC DEPRESSIONS
ATMOSPHERIC DIFFUSION
ATMOSPHERIC DISTURBANCES
ATMOSPHERIC ELECTRICITY
ATMOSPHERIC FORCING
ATMOSPHERIC FRONTS
ATMOSPHERIC GASES
ATMOSPHERIC MOTION
ATMOSPHERIC OPTICAL PHENOMENA
ATMOSPHERIC PARTICULATES
ATMOSPHERIC PHYSICS
ATMOSPHERIC PRECIPITATIONS
ATMOSPHERIC PRESSURE
ATMOSPHERIC SCIENCES
ATMOSPHERIC TIDES
ATMOSPHERIC TURBULENCE
ATOLL LAGOONS
ATOLLS
ATP
ATTACHMENT ORGANS
ATTENUANCE
ATTENUATION
ATTRACTING TECHNIQUES
AUDIO RECORDINGS
AUDIOVISUAL MATERIAL
AUDITION
AUDITORY ORGANS
AUDITORY STIMULI
AUGITE
AURORA
AUTECOLOGY
AUTHIGENESIS
AUTHIGENIC MINERALS
AUTOCHTHONOUS DEPOSITS
AUTOCORRELATION
AUTOLYSIS
AUTOMATED CARTOGRAPHY
AUTOMATED FISHING PLATFORMS
AUTOMATED RECORDING
AUTOMATION
AUTONOMIC NERVOUS SYSTEM
AUTOPILOTS
AUTORADIOGRAPHY
AUTOTOMY
AUTOTROPHY
AUTUMN
AUXINS
AVAILABILITY
AVIAN PHYSIOLOGY
AVOIDANCE REACTIONS
AXBTs
AZIMUTH
AZINES

B

BACKSCATTER
BACKSHORE
BACKWASH
BACKWATERS
BACTERIA
BACTERIA COLLECTING DEVICES
BACTERIAL COUNTERS
BACTERIAL DISEASES
BACTERINS
BACTERIOCIDES
BACTERIOLOGISTS
BACTERIOLOGY
BACTERIOPHAGES

ASFIS Thesaurus
Alphabetical List of Terms

BAIT
BAIT CULTURE
BAIT FISH
BAIT FISHING
BALANCE ORGANS
BALANCED DIETS
BALANCED RATIONS
BALEENS
BALLAST
BALLAST TANKS
BALLOONS
BANKS (TOPOGRAPHY)
BARBELS
BARGES
BARITE
BARIUM
BARIUM COMPOUNDS
BARIUM ISOTOPES
BAROCLINIC FIELD
BAROCLINIC INSTABILITY
BAROCLINIC MODE
BAROCLINIC MOTION
BAROMETERS
BAROMETRIC WAVES
BAROTROPIC FIELD
BAROTROPIC INSTABILITY
BAROTROPIC MODE
BAROTROPIC MOTION
BAROTROPIC TIDES
BARRAGES
BARRIER BEACHES
BARRIER ISLANDS
BARRIER REEFS
BARRIER SPITS
BARRIERS
BASALT-SEAWATER INTERACTION
BASALTS
BASELINE STUDIES
BASEMENT ROCK
BASIC DIETS
BASINS
BATCH CULTURE
BATCH PROCESSING
BATHING
BATHOLITHS
BATHYAL ZONE
BATHYAL-BENTHIC ZONE
BATHYMETERS
BATHYMETRIC CHARTS
BATHYMETRIC DATA
BATHYMETRIC PROFILES
BATHYMETRIC SURVEYS
BATHYMETRY
BATHYPELAGIC ZONE
BATHYSPHERES
BATHYTHERMOGRAMS
BATHYTHERMOGRAPHIC DATA
BATHYTHERMOGRAPHS
BATTERIES
BAUXITE
BAY DYNAMICS
BAYS
BEACH ACCRETION
BEACH CUSPS
BEACH EROSION
BEACH FEATURES
BEACH MORPHOLOGY
BEACH NOURISHMENT
BEACH PROFILES
BEACH RIDGES
BEACH SEINES
BEACH SLOPE
BEACHES
BEACHROCK
BEAM TRANSMITTANCE
BEAM TRANSMITTANCE METERS
BEARING CAPACITY

BEAUFORT SCALE
BED FORMS
BED LOAD
BED ROUGHNESS
BEDDING STRUCTURES
BEHAVIOUR
BEHAVIOURAL RESPONSES
BENCH MARKS
BENIOFF ZONE
BENJAMIN FEIR INSTABILITY
BENTHIC BOUNDARY LAYER
BENTHIC CURRENTS
BENTHIC ENVIRONMENT
BENTHIC FRONTS
BENTHOS
BENTHOS COLLECTING DEVICES
BENTONITE
BENZENE
BERKELIUM
BERKELIUM COMPOUNDS
BERKELIUM ISOTOPES
BERMS
BERTHING
BERYLLIUM
BERYLLIUM COMPOUNDS
BERYLLIUM ISOTOPES
BETA SPIRALS
BETA-PLANE
BIBLIOGRAPHIC INFORMATION
BIBLIOGRAPHIES
BICARBONATES
BIENNIAL
BILATERAL AGREEMENTS
BILE
BILLOWS
BIOACCUMULATION
BIOACOUSTICS
BIOAERATION
BIOASSAYS
BIOCALCARENITE
BIOCHEMICAL ANALYSIS
BIOCHEMICAL COMPOSITION
BIOCHEMICAL CYCLES
BIOCHEMICAL OXYGEN DEMAND
BIOCHEMICAL PHENOMENA
BIOCHEMISTRY
BIOCLIMATOLOGY
BIOCOENOSIS
BIODEGRADABLE SUBSTANCES
BIODEGRADATION
BIOELECTRICITY
BIOENERGETICS
BIOEROSION
BIOFACIES
BIOFILTERS
BIOGENESIS
BIOGENIC DEPOSITS
BIOGENIC MATERIAL
BIOGENIC SEDIMENTARY STRUCTURES
BIOGENY
BIOGEOCHEMICAL CYCLE
BIOGEOCHEMISTRY
BIOGEOGRAPHY
BIOGRAPHIES
BIOHERMS
BIOLOGICAL AGE
BIOLOGICAL AGING
BIOLOGICAL ATTACHMENT
BIOLOGICAL CHARTS
BIOLOGICAL CLOCKS
BIOLOGICAL COLLECTIONS
BIOLOGICAL CONTROL
BIOLOGICAL DAMAGE
BIOLOGICAL DATA
BIOLOGICAL DEVELOPMENT
BIOLOGICAL DRIFT
BIOLOGICAL FERTILIZATION

BIOLOGICAL HALF LIFE
BIOLOGICAL INSTITUTIONS
BIOLOGICAL MEMBRANES
BIOLOGICAL NOISE
BIOLOGICAL PHENOMENA
BIOLOGICAL POISONS
BIOLOGICAL POLLUTANTS
BIOLOGICAL PRODUCTION
BIOLOGICAL PROPERTIES
BIOLOGICAL RAFTING
BIOLOGICAL RESISTANCE
BIOLOGICAL RHYTHMS
BIOLOGICAL SAMPLING
BIOLOGICAL SETTLEMENT
BIOLOGICAL SPECIATION
BIOLOGICAL STRESS
BIOLOGICAL SURVEYS
BIOLOGICAL VECTORS
BIOLOGISTS
BIOLOGY
BIOLUMINESCENCE
BIOMASS
BIOMETRICS
BIOPHYSICS
BIOPOLYMORPHISM
BIOSELECTION
BIOSTRATIGRAPHY
BIOSYNTHESIS
BIOTA
BIOTECHNOLOGY
BIOTELEMETRY
BIOTESTING
BIOTIC BARRIERS
BIOTIC FACTORS
BIOTIC PRESSURE
BIOTITE
BIOTOPES
BIOTURBATION
BIPOLAR DISTRIBUTION
BIRD EGGS
BIRNESSITE
BISMUTH
BISMUTH COMPOUNDS
BISMUTH ISOTOPES
BITUMENS
BLADDERS
BLASTING
BLOOD
BLOOD CELLS
BLOOD CIRCULATION
BLOOD GROUPS
BLOOD PRESSURE
BLOOD VESSELS
BLOWOUT CONTROL
BLOWOUT PREVENTERS
BLOWOUTS
BLUE WHALE UNIT
BOAT SEINES
BOATING
BOATS
BODY BURDEN
BODY CAVITIES
BODY CONDITIONS
BODY FLUIDS
BODY ORGANS
BODY REGIONS
BODY SHAPE
BODY SIZE
BODY TEMPERATURE
BODY WALLS
BODY WAVES
BODY WEIGHT
BOEHMITE
BOIL DISEASE
BOILING POINT
BOLUSES
BONE NECROSIS
BONES

ASFIS Thesaurus
Alphabetical List of Terms

BONY FINS
BOOK CATALOGUES
BOOMERS
BORATE MINERALS
BORAX
BOREHOLES
BORIC ACID
BORING ORGANISMS
BORON
BORON COMPOUNDS
BORON ISOTOPES
BOTANICAL RESOURCES
BOTANISTS
BOTANY
BOTTOM CULTURE
BOTTOM CURRENTS
BOTTOM EKMAN LAYER
BOTTOM EROSION
BOTTOM FRICTION
BOTTOM MIXED LAYER
BOTTOM PHOTOGRAPHS
BOTTOM PRESSURE
BOTTOM REVERBERATION
BOTTOM SCATTERING
BOTTOM STRESS
BOTTOM TEMPERATURE
BOTTOM TOPOGRAPHY
BOTTOM TOPOGRAPHY EFFECTS
BOTTOM TOW
BOTTOM TRAWLING
BOTTOM TRAWLS
BOTTOM WATER
BOTTOMSET BEDS
BOTULISM
BOUDINAGE
BOUGUER ANOMALIES
BOUGUER GRAVITY CHARTS
BOULDER CLAY
BOULDERS
BOUNDARIES
BOUNDARY CONDITIONS
BOUNDARY CURRENTS
BOUNDARY LAYERS
BOUNDARY VALUE PROBLEMS
BOUSSINESQ APPROXIMATION
BOWEN RATIO
BRACKISH WATER
BRACKISHWATER AQUACULTURE
BRACKISHWATER ECOLOGY
BRACKISHWATER ENVIRONMENT
BRACKISHWATER FISH
BRACKISHWATER MOLLUSCS
BRACKISHWATER POLLUTION
BRAIN
BREAK-POINT BARS
BREAKERS
BREAKING WAVES
BREAKWATERS
BREATHING APPARATUS
BREATHING MIXTURES
BRECCIA
BREEDING
BREEDING PONDS
BREEDING SEASONS
BREEDING SITES
BREEZES
BRIDGES
BRIGHT SPOT TECHNOLOGY
BRINE SHRIMP CULTURE
BRINE SHRIMP EGGS
BRINES
BRITTLENESS
BROCHURES
BROMIC ACID
BROMIDES
BROMINATED HYDROCARBONS
BROMINE

BROMINE COMPOUNDS
BROMINE ISOTOPES
BROOD STOCKS
BRUCITE
BRUNT-VAISALA FREQUENCY
BUBBLE BARRIERS
BUBBLE BURSTING
BUBBLE DISEASE
BUBBLES
BUBBLING
BUCKET TEMPERATURE
BUDDING
BUDS
BUFFERS
BULK CARRIERS
BULK MODULUS
BUOY HULLS
BUOY MOORING SYSTEMS
BUOY MOTION
BUOY MOTION EFFECTS
BUOY SYSTEMS
BUOYANCY
BUOYANCY FLOATS
BUOYANCY FLUX
BUOYANCY MATERIALS
BUOYANT JETS
BUOYS
BURROWING ORGANISMS
BURROWS
BURYING
BUTANE
BY CATCH
BYPRODUCTS
BYSSUS

C

CABBELING
CABLE DEPRESSORS
CABLE DYNAMICS
CABLE LAYING
CABLE SHIPS
CABLES
CADMIUM
CADMIUM COMPOUNDS
CADMIUM ISOTOPES
CAESIUM
CAESIUM COMPOUNDS
CAESIUM ISOTOPES
CAESIUM 137
CAGE CULTURE
CAGES
CAISSONS
CALCARENITE
CALCAREOUS OOZE
CALCIFICATION
CALCITE
CALCITE DISSOLUTION
CALCITIZATION
CALCIUM
CALCIUM CARBONATES
CALCIUM COMPOUNDS
CALCIUM ISOTOPES
CALCIUM PHOSPHATES
CALCIUM SULPHATES
CALCRETE
CALCULATORS
CALIBRATION
CALIFORNIUM
CALIFORNIUM COMPOUNDS
CALIFORNIUM ISOTOPES
CALORIES
CALORIMETRY
CALVING
CAMBRIAN
CAMERAS
CAMOUFLAGE

CANALS
CANNED PRODUCTS
CANNIBALISM
CANNING
CANOE FISHERIES
CANOES
CAP ROCKS
CAPACITANCE
CAPACITY
CAPILLARITY
CAPILLARY WAVES
CAPSIZING
CAPTIVITY
CAPTURE FISHERY ECONOMICS
CARANGID FISHERIES
CARAPACE
CARBOHYDRATES
CARBON
CARBON COMPOUNDS
CARBON CYCLE
CARBON DIOXIDE
CARBON FIXATION
CARBON ISOTOPE RATIO
CARBON ISOTOPES
CARBON MONOXIDE
CARBON SULPHIDES
CARBON 13
CARBON 14
CARBON/NITROGEN RATIO
CARBON/PHOSPHORUS RATIO
CARBONATE COMPENSATION DEPTH
CARBONATE MINERALS
CARBONATE ROCKS
CARBONATE SEDIMENTS
CARBONATES
CARBONIC ACID
CARBONIC ANHYDRASE
CARBONIFEROUS
CARBOXYLATION
CARBOXYLIC ACID SALTS
CARCASSES
CARCINOGENESIS
CARCINOGENS
CARCINOLOGISTS
CARCINOLOGY
CAREERS
CARGOES
CARNALLITE
CARNIVORES
CAROTENOIDS
CARRAGEENINS
CARTILAGE
CARTOGRAPHY
CASCADING
CASSITERITE
CAST NETS
CASTRATION
CATABOLISM
CATADROMOUS MIGRATIONS
CATADROMOUS SPECIES
CATAGENESIS
CATALOGUES
CATALYSTS
CATAMARANS
CATASTROPHIC WAVES
CATCH COMPOSITION
CATCH STATISTICS
CATCH/EFFORT
CATCHABILITY
CATCHERS
CATCHING METHODS
CATCHMENT AREA
CATENARY
CATHODES
CATHODIC PROTECTION
CATIONS
CAUSTICS
CAVERNICOLOUS SPECIES

ASFIS Thesaurus
Alphabetical List of Terms

CAVES
CAVIAR
CAVITATION
CAYS
CELESTIAL NAVIGATION
CELESTITE
CELL CONSTITUENTS
CELL COUNTERS
CELL CULTURE
CELL DIFFERENTIATION
CELL DIVISION
CELL FUSION
CELL INCLUSIONS
CELL MEMBRANES
CELL MORPHOLOGY
CELL ORGANELLES
CELL WALLS
CELLS
CELLULAR CONVECTION
CELLULOSE
CEMENTATION
CENOZOIC
CENSUS
CENTRAL NERVOUS SYSTEM
CENTRIFUGAL FORCE
CENTRIFUGATION
CENTRIFUGES
CENTRIPETAL FORCE
CEPHALOPOD FISHERIES
CEPHALOTHORAX
CERAMICS
CERIUM
CERIUM COMPOUNDS
CERIUM ISOTOPES
CERTIFICATION
CETOLOGISTS
CETOLOGY
CHAIN
CHALK
CHANDLER WOBBLE
CHANNEL FLOW
CHANNELS
CHART CATALOGUES
CHART DATUM
CHECK LISTS
CHELATES
CHEMICAL ANALYSIS
CHEMICAL COMPOSITION
CHEMICAL COMPOUNDS
CHEMICAL CONTROL
CHEMICAL CYCLES
CHEMICAL DEGRADATION
CHEMICAL ELEMENTS
CHEMICAL ENGINEERING
CHEMICAL EQUILIBRIUM
CHEMICAL EXTRACTION
CHEMICAL KINETICS
CHEMICAL LIMNOLOGY
CHEMICAL OCEANOGRAPHY
CHEMICAL OXYGEN DEMAND
CHEMICAL PLUMES
CHEMICAL POLLUTANTS
CHEMICAL POLLUTION
CHEMICAL PRECIPITATION
CHEMICAL PROPERTIES
CHEMICAL REACTIONS
CHEMICAL SEDIMENTS
CHEMICAL SPECIATION
CHEMICAL SPILLS
CHEMICAL STIMULI
CHEMILUMINESCENCE
CHEMISTRY
CHEMORECEPTION
CHEMORECEPTORS
CHEMOSYNTHESIS
CHEMOTAXIS
CHEMOTAXONOMY

CHEMOTROPISM
CHENIER PLAINS
CHENIERS
CHERTIFICATION
CHERTS
CHILLED PRODUCTS
CHILLING STORAGE
CHITIN
CHITOSAN
CHLORIC ACID
CHLORIDES
CHLORINATED HYDROCARBONS
CHLORINATION
CHLORINE
CHLORINE COMPOUNDS
CHLORINE ISOTOPES
CHLORINITY
CHLORITE
CHLOROFORM
CHLOROPHYLLS
CHLOROPLASTS
CHLOROSITY
CHOLESTEROL
CHOLINE
CHOLINESTERASE INHIBITORS
CHROMATIC ADAPTATIONS
CHROMATIC BEHAVIOUR
CHROMATIC PIGMENTS
CHROMATOGRAPHIC TECHNIQUES
CHROMATOPHORES
CHROMITE
CHROMIUM
CHROMIUM COMPOUNDS
CHROMIUM ISOTOPES
CHROMOSOMES
CHRONOMETERS
CHRONOSTRATIGRAPHY
CIGUATERA
CIGUATOXIN
CILIA
CIRCADIAN RHYTHMS
CIRCULATION
CIRCULATORY SYSTEM
CITRATES
CIVIL ENGINEERING
CLAM CULTURE
CLAM FISHERIES
CLASSIFICATION
CLASSIFICATION SYSTEMS
CLASSIFIED DOCUMENTS
CLASTICS
CLAY MINERALS
CLAYS
CLEANING
CLEANING BEHAVIOUR
CLEAR AIR TURBULENCE
CLIFFS
CLIMATE
CLIMATE PREDICTION
CLIMATIC CHANGES
CLIMATIC DATA
CLIMATIC ZONES
CLIMATOLOGICAL CHARTS
CLIMATOLOGY
CLIMAX COMMUNITY
CLINES
CLINOPTILONITE
CLONES
CLOSURE APPROXIMATION
CLOUD COVER
CLOUD HEIGHT
CLOUD PHYSICS
CLOUDS
CLUPEOID FISHERIES
CLUTCH
CNOIDAL WAVES
COAGULANTS

COAGULATION
COAL
COARSE FISH
COAST DEFENCES
COAST EFFECT
COASTAL BOUNDARY LAYER
COASTAL COUNTERCURRENTS
COASTAL CURRENTS
COASTAL ENGINEERING
COASTAL EROSION
COASTAL FISHERIES
COASTAL GEODESY
COASTAL INLETS
COASTAL JETS
COASTAL LAGOONS
COASTAL LANDFORMS
COASTAL MORPHOLOGY
COASTAL OCEANOGRAPHY
COASTAL STATES
COASTAL STRUCTURES
COASTAL UPWELLING
COASTAL WATERS
COASTAL ZONE
COASTAL ZONE MANAGEMENT
COASTGUARDS
COASTS
COATING MATERIALS
COATING PROCESSES
COAXIAL CABLES
COBALT
COBALT COMPOUNDS
COBALT ISOTOPES
COBBLESTONE
COCCOLITHS
CODEX STANDARDS
COEFFICIENTS
COELOM
COELOMIC FLUIDS
COENZYMES
COHESIONLESS SEDIMENTS
COHESIVE SEDIMENTS
COLD BRANDING
COLD RESISTANCE
COLD SEASON
COLD STORAGE
COLLAPSE STRENGTH
COLLECTED PAPERS
COLLECTING DEVICES
COLLECTIONS
COLLIGATIVE PROPERTIES
COLLISION AVOIDANCE
COLLISIONS
COLLOIDAL CLAY
COLLOIDS
COLONIES
COLONIZATION
COLORIMETRIC TECHNIQUES
COLOUR
COMMENSALISM
COMMENSALS
COMMERCE
COMMERCIAL AVAILABILITY
COMMERCIAL FISHING
COMMERCIAL LEGISLATION
COMMERCIAL SPECIES
COMMON PROPERTY RESOURCES
COMMUNICATION
COMMUNICATION SATELLITES
COMMUNICATION SYSTEMS
COMMUNITY COMPOSITION
COMPACTION
COMPANIES
COMPARATIVE STUDIES
COMPASSES
COMPENSATION DEPTH
COMPETITION
COMPETITIVE BEHAVIOUR
COMPETITORS

COMPLEX LIPIDS
COMPONENTS
COMPOSITE MATERIALS
COMPOSITION
COMPOUND EYES
COMPRESSED GAS
COMPRESSIBILITY
COMPRESSION
COMPRESSIONAL WAVE VELOCITIES
COMPRESSIVE STRENGTH
COMPRESSORS
COMPUTATION
COMPUTER PROGRAMS
COMPUTERS
CONCESSIONS
CONCHOLOGY
CONCRETE
CONCRETE STRUCTURES
CONCRETIONS
CONDENSATION
CONDITION FACTOR
CONDUCTIVITY RATIO
CONDUCTIVITY SENSORS
CONFERENCES
CONGLOMERATES
CONIDIA
CONNECTING
CONNECTIVE TISSUES
CONNECTORS
CONSERVATION
CONSERVATION EQUATIONS
CONSERVATION OF ANGULAR MOMENTUM
CONSERVATION OF ENERGY
CONSERVATION OF HEAT
CONSERVATION OF MASS
CONSERVATION OF MOMENTUM
CONSERVATION OF SALT
CONSERVATION OF VORTICITY
CONSERVATION PRINCIPLES
CONSERVATIVE PROPERTIES
CONSOLIDATION
CONSTANTS
CONSTRUCTION
CONSTRUCTION MATERIALS
CONSTRUCTIVE WAVES
CONSULTANTS
CONSUMERS
CONTAINER SHIPS
CONTAINERS
CONTAINMENT
CONTIGUOUS ZONES
CONTINENTAL BORDERLAND
CONTINENTAL CRUST
CONTINENTAL DRIFT
CONTINENTAL MARGINS
CONTINENTAL RIDGES
CONTINENTAL RISE
CONTINENTAL SHELVES
CONTINENTAL SLOPE
CONTINENTS
CONTINUOUS CULTURE
CONTOUR CURRENTS
CONTOURITES
CONTOURS
CONTRACTORS
CONTRACTS
CONTROL
CONTROL CHARTS
CONTROL RESISTANCE
CONTROLLED CONDITIONS
CONVECTION
CONVERGENCE
CONVERGENCE ZONES
CONVERGING PLATE BOUNDARIES
CONVERSION FACTORS
CONVERSION TABLES
CONVOLUTION

COOLING
COOLING PONDS
COOLING SYSTEMS
COOLING WATER
COOPERATIVES
COORDINATE SYSTEMS
COPPER
COPPER COMPOUNDS
COPPER ISOTOPES
COPRECIPITATION
CORAL
CORAL FARMING
CORAL REEFS
CORANGE CHARTS
CORANGE LINES
CORE ANALYSIS
CORE HANDLING
CORE LAYER METHOD
CORE LAYERS (WATER)
CORE ORIENTATION
CORE RECOVERY
CORERS
CORES
CORING
CORIOLIS ACCELERATION
CORIOLIS FORCE
CORIOLIS PARAMETERS
CORRECTIONS
CORRELATION
CORRELATION ANALYSIS
CORROSION
CORROSION CONTROL
COSINE COLLECTORS
COSINE RESPONSE
COSMIC DUST
COSMIC RADIATION
COSMIC SPHERULES
COSMOPOLITE SPECIES
COST ANALYSIS
COSTS
COTIDAL CHARTS
COTIDAL LINES
COUETTE FLOW
COUNTERCURRENTS
COUNTERS
COUNTRIES
COUPLED BODIES
COURTSHIP
CRAB CULTURE
CRAB FISHERIES
CRACK PROPAGATION
CRACKING (CORROSION)
CRACKS
CRANE BARGES
CRANES
CRATONS
CRAYFISH CULTURE
CREEP
CRETACEOUS
CREW
CRISTOBALITE
CRITICAL FLOW
CRITICAL PATH METHOD
CROSS CORRELATION
CRUDE OIL
CRUISE PROGRAMMES
CRUISE REPORTS
CRUISE STATIONS
CRUISES
CRUSTACEAN CULTURE
CRUSTACEAN FISHERIES
CRUSTACEAN LARVAE
CRUSTAL ACCRETION
CRUSTAL ADJUSTMENT
CRUSTAL SHORTENING
CRUSTAL STRUCTURE
CRUSTAL THICKNESS

CRYOBIOLOGY
CRYOPLANKTON
CRYOSPHERE
CTD OBSERVATIONS
CTD PROFILERS
CULLING
CULTCH
CULTURE EFFECTS
CULTURE MEDIA
CULTURE TANKS
CULTURED ORGANISMS
CULTURES
CURED PRODUCTS
CURING
CURIUM
CURIUM COMPOUNDS
CURIUM ISOTOPES
CURL (VECTORS)
CURRENT CHARTS
CURRENT DATA
CURRENT DENSITY
CURRENT DIRECTION
CURRENT ELLIPSES
CURRENT FORCES
CURRENT MARKS
CURRENT MEANDERING
CURRENT MEASUREMENT
CURRENT MEASURING EQUIPMENT
CURRENT METER ARRAYS
CURRENT METER DATA
CURRENT METER MOORINGS
CURRENT METERS
CURRENT OBSERVATIONS
CURRENT POWER
CURRENT PREDICTION
CURRENT PROFILES
CURRENT REVERSAL
CURRENT RINGS
CURRENT ROSES
CURRENT SCOURING
CURRENT SENSORS
CURRENT SHEAR
CURRENT SPECTRA
CURRENT VECTORS
CURRENT VELOCITY
CURRICULA
CUSPATE FORELANDS
CUTICLES
CUTTING
CUTTING UNDERWATER
CYANIDES
CYCLES
CYCLESONDE
CYCLIC LOADING
CYCLOGENESIS
CYCLOMORPHOSIS
CYCLONES
CYCLONIC MOTION
CYLINDERS
CYLINDRICAL STRUCTURES
CYSTEINE
CYSTINE
CYSTS
CYTOCHEMISTRY
CYTOCHROMES
CYTOLOGY
CYTOPLASM

D

DAILY
DAMAGE
DAMPING
DAMS
DANGEROUS ORGANISMS
DATA
DATA ACQUISITION
DATA BUOYS

ASFIS Thesaurus
Alphabetical List of Terms

DATA CENTRES
DATA COLLECTIONS
DATA CONVERTERS
DATA LOGGERS
DATA PROCESSING
DATA REDUCTION
DATA REPORTS
DATA RETRIEVAL
DATA STORAGE
DATA TRANSMISSION
DATUM LEVELS
DAVITS
DAYTIME
DDE
DDT
DE-ICING
DEAD RECKONING
DEAD WATER
DEAMINATION
DEBRIS FLOW
DEBUBBLING
DECALCIFICATION
DECANTATION
DECANTATION TANKS
DECARBOXYLATION
DECCA
DECHLORINATION
DECK COMPRESSION CHAMBERS
DECK EQUIPMENT
DECKS
DECOMPOSERS
DECOMPRESSION
DECOMPRESSION CHAMBERS
DECOMPRESSION SICKNESS
DECOMPRESSION TABLES
DECONVOLUTION
DEEP CURRENTS
DEEP LAYER
DEEP WATER
DEEP WATER FORMATION
DEEP-SEA CHANNELS
DEEP-SEA DIVING
DEEP-SEA DRILLING
DEEP-SEA FANS
DEEP-SEA FISHERIES
DEEP-SEA FURROWS
DEEP-SEA MINING
DEEP-SEA TIDE GAUGES
DEEP-WATER MASSES
DEEP-WATER TERMINALS
DEEP-WATER WAVES
DEFAECATION
DEFECTS
DEFENCE CRAFT
DEFENCE MECHANISMS
DEFICIENCY DISEASES
DEFLECTION
DEFLOCCULATION
DEFORMATION
DEGASSING
DEGENERATION
DEGLACIATION
DEGRADATION
DEHYDRATION
DEHYDROGENASES
DEICING EQUIPMENT
DELTAIC DEPOSITS
DELTAIC FEATURES
DELTAIC SEDIMENTATION
DELTAS
DEMERSAL FISHERIES
DEMINERALIZATION
DENITRIFICATION
DENSE WATER
DENSITOMETERS
DENSITY
DENSITY CHARTS

DENSITY DEPENDENCE
DENSITY FIELD
DENSITY FLOW
DENSITY FRONTS
DENSITY GRADIENTS
DENSITY INTERFACES
DENSITY MEASUREMENT
DENSITY MEASURING EQUIPMENT
DENSITY PROFILES
DENSITY SECTIONS
DENSITY STRATIFICATION
DENUDATION
DEOXYGENATION
DEPLETED STOCKS
DEPLETION
DEPLOYMENT
DEPOLYMERIZATION
DEPOSITION FEATURES
DEPRESSORS
DEPTH
DEPTH CONTROL
DEPTH MEASUREMENT
DEPTH RECORDERS
DERIVED LIPIDS
DESALINATION
DESALINATION PLANTS
DESERTS
DESICCATION
DESIGN
DESIGN WAVE
DESORPTION
DESTRATIFICATION
DESTRUCTIVE WAVES
DETECTION
DETECTORS
DETERGENTS
DETERIORATION
DETONATORS
DETOXIFICATION
DETRITAL DEPOSITS
DETRITUS
DETRITUS FEEDERS
DEUTERIUM
DEUTERIUM COMPOUNDS
DEVELOPED COUNTRIES
DEVELOPING COUNTRIES
DEVELOPMENT POTENTIAL
DEVELOPMENT PROJECTS
DEVELOPMENTAL STAGES
DEVITRIFICATION
DEVONIAN
DEW POINT
DEWATERING
DIAGENESIS
DIALYSIS
DIAMONDS
DIAPAUSE
DIAPIRISM
DIAPIRS
DIASTROPHISM
DIATOM OOZE
DIATOMITES
DIATOMS
DICOTHERMAL LAYER
DIELDRIN
DIELECTRIC CONSTANT
DIESEL ENGINES
DIETARY DEFICIENCIES
DIETS
DIFFERENTIAL DISTRIBUTION
DIFFERENTIAL EQUATIONS
DIFFRACTION
DIFFUSION
DIFFUSION COEFFICIENTS
DIGESTIBILITY
DIGESTION
DIGESTIVE GLANDS

DIGESTIVE SYSTEM
DIGESTIVE TRACT
DIGITAL RECORDS
DILUTION
DIMENSIONLESS NUMBERS
DIMENSIONS
DIRECTION
DIRECTION FINDING
DIRECTION INDICATORS
DIRECTIONAL SPECTRA
DIRECTORIES
DISASTERS
DISCOLOURATION
DISCOLOURED WATER
DISCONTINUITY LAYERS
DISCUS-SHAPED BUOYS
DISEASE CONTROL
DISEASE DETECTION
DISEASE RESISTANCE
DISEASE TRANSMISSION
DISEASES
DISINFECTANTS
DISINFECTION
DISPERSANTS
DISPERSION
DISPHOTIC ZONE
DISPLACEMENT
DISPLAY BEHAVIOUR
DISPUTES
DISSOCIATION
DISSOLUTION
DISSOLVED CHEMICALS
DISSOLVED GASES
DISSOLVED INORGANIC MATTER
DISSOLVED ORGANIC CARBON
DISSOLVED ORGANIC MATTER
DISSOLVED ORGANIC NITROGEN
DISSOLVED ORGANIC PHOSPHORUS
DISSOLVED OXYGEN
DISSOLVED SALTS
DISTANCE
DISTILLATION
DISTILLED WATER
DISTRESS SIGNALS
DISTRIBUTARIES
DISTRIBUTION
DISTRIBUTION RECORDS
DIURNAL THERMOCLINE
DIURNAL TIDES
DIURNAL VARIATIONS
DIVERGENCE
DIVERGENCE ZONES
DIVERGING PLATE BOUNDARIES
DIVERS
DIVING
DIVING ACCIDENTS
DIVING BELLS
DIVING EQUIPMENT
DIVING HAZARDS
DIVING INDUSTRY
DIVING PHYSIOLOGY
DIVING REGULATIONS
DIVING SUITS
DIVING SURVEYS
DIVING TOOLS
DNA
DOCUMENTATION
DOCUMENTS
DODECANE
DOLOMITE
DOLOMITIZATION
DOLOSTONE
DOMES
DOMESTIC SPECIES
DOMESTIC WASTES
DOMESTICATION
DOMINANCE HIERARCHIES
DOMINANT SPECIES

DOPPLER EFFECT
DOPPLER NAVIGATION
DOPPLER SONAR
DORMANCY
DOUBLE DIFFUSION
DOUBLE DIFFUSIVE INSTABILITY
DOWNWARD IRRADIANCE
DOWNWARD LONG WAVE RADIATION
DOWNWELLING
DRAG
DRAG COEFFICIENT
DRAINAGE WATER
DREDGE SPOIL
DREDGED SAMPLES
DREDGERS
DREDGES
DREDGES (GEOLOGY)
DREDGING
DRESSING
DRIED PRODUCTS
DRIFT
DRIFT BOTTLES
DRIFT CARDS
DRIFTERS
DRIFTING DATA BUOYS
DRIFTING STATIONS
DRILL PIPE
DRILL STRING
DRILLING
DRILLING EQUIPMENT
DRILLING FLUIDS
DRILLING PLATFORMS
DRILLING RIGS
DRILLING VESSELS
DRILLS
DROGUES
DROPLETS
DROPSONDE
DROUGHT RESISTANCE
DROUGHTS
DROWNED VALLEYS
DROWNING
DRUG RESISTANCE
DRUGS
DRY
DRY SEASON
DRY WEIGHT
DRYING
DUNE STABILIZATION
DUNES
DURATION
DUST
DUST CLOUDS
DYE DISPERSION
DYES
DYNAMIC ANALYSIS
DYNAMIC HEIGHT
DYNAMIC HEIGHT ANOMALY
DYNAMIC LOADS
DYNAMIC POSITIONING
DYNAMIC RESPONSE
DYNAMIC TOPOGRAPHY
DYNAMIC VISCOSITY
DYNAMICAL OCEANOGRAPHY
DYNAMICS
DYSPROSIUM
DYSPROSIUM COMPOUNDS
DYSPROSIUM ISOTOPES
DYSTROPHIC LAKES

E

EARTH
EARTH AGE
EARTH ATMOSPHERE
EARTH CORE
EARTH CRUST

EARTH CURVATURE
EARTH HISTORY
EARTH MANTLE
EARTH ORBIT
EARTH ROTATION
EARTH SCIENCES
EARTH STRUCTURE
EARTH TIDES
EARTH TILT
EARTHQUAKE LOADING
EARTHQUAKE PREDICTION
EARTHQUAKES
EASTERLY WAVES
EASTERN BOUNDARY CURRENTS
EBB CURRENTS
ECDYSONS
ECHINODERM FISHERIES
ECHO INTEGRATORS
ECHO RANGING
ECHO SURVEYS
ECHOES
ECHOLOCATION
ECHOSOUNDER PROFILES
ECHOSOUNDERS
ECHOSOUNDING
ECOCLINES
ECOLOGICAL AGGREGATIONS
ECOLOGICAL ASSOCIATIONS
ECOLOGICAL BALANCE
ECOLOGICAL CRISIS
ECOLOGICAL DISTRIBUTION
ECOLOGICAL EFFICIENCY
ECOLOGICAL SUCCESSION
ECOLOGICAL ZONATION
ECOLOGISTS
ECOLOGY
ECONOMETRICS
ECONOMIC ANALYSIS
ECONOMIC FEASIBILITY
ECONOMIC MODELS
ECONOMICS
ECONOMISTS
ECOPHENE
ECOPHYSIOLOGY
ECOSYSTEM DISTURBANCE
ECOSYSTEM MANAGEMENT
ECOSYSTEM RESILIENCE
ECOSYSTEMS
ECOTYPES
ECTOCRINES
ECTOPARASITES
ECTOPARASITISM
EDDY CONDUCTION
EDDY CONDUCTIVITY
EDDY DIFFUSIVITY
EDDY FLUX
EDDY KINETIC ENERGY
EDDY VISCOSITY
EDDY VISCOSITY COEFFICIENT
EDGE WAVES
EDUCATION
EDUCATION ESTABLISHMENTS
EFFICIENCY
EGG COUNTERS
EGGS
EIGENFUNCTIONS
EINSTEINIUM
EINSTEINIUM COMPOUNDS
EINSTEINIUM ISOTOPES
EKMAN LAYERS
EKMAN PUMPING
EKMAN SPIRAL
EKMAN TRANSPORT
EL NINO PHENOMENA
ELASTIC CONSTANTS
ELASTIC WAVES
ELASTICITY

ELECTRIC ARC WELDING
ELECTRIC CABLES
ELECTRIC CHARGE
ELECTRIC CURRENTS
ELECTRIC FENCES
ELECTRIC FIELDS
ELECTRIC FISHING
ELECTRIC GENERATORS
ELECTRIC IMPEDANCE
ELECTRIC ORGANS
ELECTRIC POTENTIAL
ELECTRIC POWER SOURCES
ELECTRIC STIMULI
ELECTRICAL CONDUCTIVITY
ELECTRICAL ENGINEERING
ELECTRICAL EQUIPMENT
ELECTRICAL EXPLORATION
ELECTRICAL INSULATION
ELECTRICAL PROPERTIES
ELECTRICAL RESISTIVITY
ELECTRICITY
ELECTRIFIED GEAR
ELECTROACOUSTIC DEVICES
ELECTROANALYSIS
ELECTROCHEMISTRY
ELECTRODES
ELECTRODIALYSIS
ELECTROLYSIS
ELECTROLYTES
ELECTROMAGNETIC EXPLORATION
ELECTROMAGNETIC POWER
ELECTROMAGNETIC RADIATION
ELECTROMAGNETISM
ELECTRON MICROSCOPY
ELECTRONIC EQUIPMENT
ELECTRONIC NOISE
ELECTROPHORESIS
ELECTROPHYSIOLOGY
EMBANKMENTS
EMBRITTLEMENT
EMBRYOLOGY
EMBRYONIC DEVELOPMENT
EMBRYOS
EMERGENCE
EMERGENCIES
EMERGENCY VESSELS
EMERGENT SHORELINES
EMISSION SPECTROSCOPY
EMISSIVITY
EMULSIONS
ENCLOSURES
ENCYCLOPAEDIAS
ENCYSTMENT
ENDEMIC SPECIES
ENDEMISM
ENDOCRINE GLANDS
ENDOCRINOLOGY
ENDOPARASITES
ENDOPARASITISM
ENDOSKELETON
ENDOTOXINS
ENERGY
ENERGY BALANCE
ENERGY BUDGET
ENERGY DISSIPATION
ENERGY FLOW
ENERGY RESOURCES
ENERGY SPECTRA
ENERGY TRANSFER
ENGINEERING
ENGINEERING DRAWINGS
ENGINEERS
ENSTROPHY
ENTANGLING NETS
ENTHALPY
ENTOMOLOGISTS
ENTOMOLOGY
ENTRAINMENT

ASFIS Thesaurus
Alphabetical List of Terms

ENTROPY
ENVIRONMENT MANAGEMENT
ENVIRONMENTAL CHARTS
ENVIRONMENTAL CONDITIONS
ENVIRONMENTAL DISEASES
ENVIRONMENTAL EFFECTS
ENVIRONMENTAL FACTORS
ENVIRONMENTAL IMPACT
ENVIRONMENTAL LEGISLATION
ENVIRONMENTAL MONITORING
ENVIRONMENTAL PROTECTION
ENVIRONMENTAL SURVEYS
ENVIRONMENTS
ENZYMATIC ACTIVITY
ENZYME INHIBITORS
ENZYMES
ENZYMOLYSIS
EOCENE
EOLIAN DEPOSITS
EOLIAN DUST
EOLIAN PROCESSES
EOLIAN TRANSPORT
EPEIROGENY
EPIBIONTS
EPIBIOSIS
EPICENTRES
EPIDEMICS
EPIDEMIOLOGY
EPILIMNION
EPIPELAGIC ZONE
EPIPHYTES
EPIPSAMMON
EPITHELIA
EPIZOITES
EPONTIC ENVIRONMENT
EPONTIC ORGANISMS
EPOXY RESINS
EPSOMITE
EQUATION OF CONTINUITY
EQUATIONS
EQUATIONS OF MOTION
EQUATIONS OF STATE
EQUATOR
EQUATORIAL CIRCULATION
EQUATORIAL COUNTERCURRENTS
EQUATORIAL DYNAMICS
EQUATORIAL EASTERLIES
EQUATORIAL TRAPPED WAVES
EQUATORIAL TROUGH
EQUATORIAL UNDERCURRENTS
EQUATORIAL UPWELLING
EQUATORIAL WAVES
EQUATORIAL WESTERLIES
EQUILIBRIUM
EQUILIBRIUM TIDES
EQUIPMENT
ERBIUM
ERBIUM COMPOUNDS
ERBIUM ISOTOPES
EROSION
EROSION CONTROL
EROSION FEATURES
EROSION SURFACES
ERRORS
ERYTHROCYTES
ERYTHROPOIESIS
ESCAPEMENT
ESCARPMENTS
ESKERS
ESTERS
ESTUARIES
ESTUARINE CHEMISTRY
ESTUARINE DYNAMICS
ESTUARINE FISHERIES
ESTUARINE FRONT
ESTUARINE ORGANISMS
ESTUARINE SEDIMENTATION

ESTUARINE TIDES
ETHANE
ETHENE
ETHOLOGY
ETHYNE
EULERIAN CURRENT MEASUREMENT
EULITTORAL ZONE
EUPHOTIC ZONE
EUROPIUM
EUROPIUM COMPOUNDS
EUROPIUM ISOTOPES
EURYHALINITY
EURYTHERMY
EUSTATIC CHANGES
EUTROPHIC LAKES
EUTROPHIC WATERS
EUTROPHICATION
EVACUATION
EVALUATION
EVAPORATION
EVAPORATION REDUCTION
EVAPORATION TANKS
EVAPORITES
EVAPOTRANSPIRATION
EVOLUTION
EXCAVATION UNDERWATER
EXCHANGE CAPACITY
EXCHANGE COEFFICIENTS
EXCLUSIVE ECONOMIC ZONE
EXCLUSIVE RIGHTS
EXCRETION
EXCRETORY ORGANS
EXCRETORY PRODUCTS
EXHIBITIONS
EXOCRINE GLANDS
EXOPHTHALMIA
EXOSKELETON
EXPEDITION REPORTS
EXPEDITIONS
EXPERIMENTAL CULTURE
EXPERIMENTAL DATA
EXPERIMENTAL FISHING
EXPERIMENTAL RESEARCH
EXPERTS
EXPLODING WIRE
EXPLOITATION
EXPLORATION
EXPLORATION RIGHTS
EXPLORATORY BEHAVIOUR
EXPLORATORY FISHING
EXPLOSIONS
EXPLOSIVE FISHING
EXPLOSIVE WELDING
EXPLOSIVES
EXPOSED HABITATS
EXPOSURE TOLERANCE
EXTENDED JURISDICTION
EXTENSIVE CULTURE
EXTINCTION COEFFICIENT
EXTRATERRESTRIAL MATERIAL
EXTRATERRESTRIAL RADIATION
EXTREME VALUES
EXTREME WAVES
EYES
EYESTALK EXTIRPATION
EYESTALKS

F

FACIES
FACSIMILE TRANSMISSION
FACTORY SHIPS
FAECAL PELLETS
FAILURES
FAIRINGS
FALLOUT
FANS

FAST ICE
FATE
FATIGUE (MATERIALS)
FATS
FATTY ACIDS
FAULT SCARPS
FAULT ZONES
FAULTS
FAUNAL PROVINCES
FEASIBILITY
FEASIBILITY STUDIES
FEATHERS
FECUNDITY
FEE FISHING
FEED
FEED COMPOSITION
FEED EFFICIENCY
FEED PREPARATION
FEEDING
FEEDING BEHAVIOUR
FEEDING EQUIPMENT
FEEDING EXPERIMENTS
FEEDING MIGRATIONS
FELDSPARS
FELLOWSHIPS
FEMALES
FENDERS
FERMENTATION
FERMENTED PRODUCTS
FERMIUM
FERMIUM COMPOUNDS
FERMIUM ISOTOPES
FERROMANGANESE NODULES
FERROMANGANESE OXIDES
FERROUS ALLOYS
FERRUGINOUS DEPOSITS
FERRY TERMINALS
FERTILITY
FERTILIZERS
FESTSCHRIFTEN
FETCH
FIBRE GLASS
FIBRE OPTICS
FIBRE ROPE (NATURAL)
FIBRE ROPE (SYNTHETIC)
FIELDS
FILLETTING
FILMS
FILMSTRIPS
FILTER FEEDERS
FILTERS
FILTRATION
FIN RAY COUNTS
FINANCIAL INSTITUTIONS
FINANCIAL MANAGEMENT
FINANCIAL RESOURCES
FINANCING
FINESTRUCTURE
FINFISH FISHERIES
FINGERLINGS
FINITE AMPLITUDE WAVES
FINITE DIFFERENCE METHOD
FINITE ELEMENT METHOD
FINS
FIRE
FIRE EXTINGUISHERS
FIRE FIGHTING
FIRE HAZARDS
FIRE PREVENTION
FISH
FISH CATCH STATISTICS
FISH CONSUMPTION
FISH CONVERSION FACTORS
FISH COUNTERS
FISH CULTURE
FISH DETECTION
FISH DISEASES
FISH EGGS

ASFIS Thesaurus
Alphabetical List of Terms

FISH FILLETS
FISH FLOUR
FISH GLUE
FISH HANDLING
FISH INSPECTION
FISH INSPECTION REGULATIONS
FISH KILL
FISH LARVAE
FISH MEAL
FISH MEAL PROCESSING
FISH OIL EXTRACTION
FISH OILS
FISH PHYSIOLOGY
FISH POISONING
FISH PONDS
FISH PUMPS
FISH REPELLENTS
FISH SILAGE
FISH SIZING
FISH SPOILAGE
FISH STORAGE
FISH UTILIZATION
FISH WASTES
FISHERIES
FISHERMEN
FISHERMEN STATISTICS
FISHERY BIOLOGISTS
FISHERY BIOLOGY
FISHERY BOUNDARIES
FISHERY CHARTS
FISHERY DATA
FISHERY DEVELOPMENT
FISHERY DISPUTES
FISHERY ECONOMICS
FISHERY ENGINEERING
FISHERY INDUSTRY
FISHERY INDUSTRY EQUIPMENT
FISHERY INDUSTRY LEGISLATION
FISHERY INDUSTRY PLANTS
FISHERY INSTITUTIONS
FISHERY LIMNOLOGY
FISHERY MANAGEMENT
FISHERY OCEANOGRAPHY
FISHERY ORGANIZATIONS
FISHERY POLICY
FISHERY PRODUCTS
FISHERY PROTECTION
FISHERY REGULATIONS
FISHERY RESOURCES
FISHERY SCIENCES
FISHERY STATISTICS
FISHERY SURVEYS
FISHERY TECHNOLOGY
FISHING
FISHING BARRIERS
FISHING BUOYS
FISHING BY DIVING
FISHING EFFORT
FISHING GEAR
FISHING GROUNDS
FISHING HARBOURS
FISHING MORTALITY
FISHING NETS
FISHING OPERATIONS
FISHING POWER
FISHING RIGHTS
FISHING TECHNOLOGY
FISHING TIME
FISHING VESSELS
FISHING VESSELS STATISTICS
FISHING WITHOUT GEAR
FISHWAYS
FISSION PRODUCTS
FIXATION
FIXATIVES
FIXED PLATFORMS
FIXED STATIONS

FJORD DYNAMICS
FJORDS
FLAGELLA
FLATFISH FISHERIES
FLAW LEADS
FLEXIBILITY
FLIGHT BEHAVIOUR
FLINT
FLOATING
FLOATING BARRIERS
FLOATING CAGES
FLOATING HOSES
FLOATING ICE
FLOATING STRUCTURES
FLOCCULATION
FLOOD CONTROL
FLOOD CURRENTS
FLOOD FORECASTING
FLOOD PLAINS
FLOODING
FLOODS
FLOTATION
FLOTSAM
FLOW AROUND OBJECTS
FLOW MEASUREMENT
FLOW MEASURING EQUIPMENT
FLOW OVER SURFACES
FLOW STRUCTURES
FLOWLINES
FLOWMETERS
FLUID DYNAMICS
FLUID FLOW
FLUID MECHANICS
FLUID MOTION
FLUID MUD
FLUIDIZATION
FLUIDIZED SEDIMENT FLOW
FLUIDS
FLUMES
FLUORESCENCE
FLUORESCENCE MICROSCOPY
FLUORESCENCE SPECTROSCOPY
FLUORIDES
FLUORIMETERS
FLUORINATED HYDROCARBONS
FLUORINE
FLUORINE COMPOUNDS
FLUORINE ISOTOPES
FLUORITE
FLUSHING
FLUSHING TIME
FLUTE CASTS
FLUVIAL DEPOSITS
FLUVIAL FEATURES
FLUVIAL MORPHOLOGY
FLUVIAL SEDIMENTATION
FLUVIAL TRANSPORT
FLY ASH
FLYING
FLYSCH
FOAMS
FOETUS
FOG
FOLDS
FOOD
FOOD ABSORPTION
FOOD ADDITIVES
FOOD AVAILABILITY
FOOD CHAINS
FOOD COMPOSITION
FOOD CONSUMPTION
FOOD CONVERSION
FOOD FISH
FOOD ORGANISMS
FOOD POISONING
FOOD PREFERENCES
FOOD RESOURCES

FOOD TECHNOLOGY
FOOD WEBS
FORAGE FISH
FORAMINIFERA
FORAMINIFERAL OOZE
FORCED CONVECTION
FORCED OSCILLATIONS
FORCES
FORCES (MECHANICS)
FOREARC BASINS
FOREIGN FISHING
FORESET BEDS
FORESHORE
FOREST INDUSTRY
FORM DRAG
FORMULAE
FORWARD SCATTERING
FOSSIL ASSEMBLAGES
FOSSIL DIATOMS
FOSSIL FORAMINIFERA
FOSSIL FUELED POWER PLANTS
FOSSIL FUELS
FOSSIL POLLEN
FOSSIL PTEROPODS
FOSSIL RADIOLARIA
FOSSIL SEA WATER
FOSSIL SPORES
FOSSILIZED TRACKS
FOSSILS
FOULING
FOULING CONTROL
FOULING ORGANISMS
FOUNDATIONS
FOURIER ANALYSIS
FOURIER TRANSFORMS
FRACTURE ZONES
FRACTURES
FRANCIUM
FRANCIUM COMPOUNDS
FRANCIUM ISOTOPES
FRANCOLITE
FREAK WAVES
FREE AIR ANOMALIES
FREE AIR GRAVITY CHARTS
FREE ENERGY
FREE-FALL CORERS
FREE-FALL INSTRUMENTS
FREE-FALL PROFILERS
FREE-SWIMMING VEHICLES
FREEZE-DRIED PRODUCTS
FREEZE-DRYING
FREEZING
FREEZING POINT
FREEZING STORAGE
FREONS
FREQUENCY
FREQUENCY ANALYSIS
FREQUENCY SPECTRA
FRESH WATER
FRESHWATER AQUACULTURE
FRESHWATER CRUSTACEANS
FRESHWATER ECOLOGISTS
FRESHWATER ECOLOGY
FRESHWATER FISH
FRESHWATER ICE
FRESHWATER LAKES
FRESHWATER MOLLUSCS
FRESHWATER ORGANISMS
FRESHWATER POLLUTION
FRESHWATER SCIENCES
FRESHWATER SCIENTISTS
FRESHWATER WEEDS
FRICTION
FRINGING REEFS
FROG CULTURE
FRONTAL FEATURES
FRONTOGENESIS
FRONTS

ASFIS Thesaurus
Alphabetical List of Terms

FROUDE NUMBER
FROZEN PRODUCTS
FRY
FUCOSE
FUCOSTEROL
FUEL ECONOMY
FUELS
FULLERS EARTH
FULVIC ACIDS
FUMARIC ACID
FUNCTIONAL ANALYSIS
FUNCTIONAL MORPHOLOGY
FUNGAL DISEASES
FUNGI
FUNGICIDES
FUSION HEAT

G

GABBROS
GADOID FISHERIES
GADOLINIUM
GADOLINIUM COMPOUNDS
GADOLINIUM ISOTOPES
GALE FORCE WINDS
GALL BLADDER
GALLIUM
GALLIUM COMPOUNDS
GALLIUM ISOTOPES
GAME FISH
GAME THEORY
GAMETOGENESIS
GAMMA RADIATION
GAMMA SPECTROSCOPY
GANGLIA
GARNET
GAS CHROMATOGRAPHY
GAS CONDENSATE FIELDS
GAS CONDENSATES
GAS EXCHANGE
GAS EXPLODERS
GAS FIELDS
GAS FLARING
GAS HYDRATES
GAS OIL SEPARATION
GAS PROCESSING
GAS PRODUCTION
GAS SEEPAGES
GAS SOLUBILITY
GAS TERMINALS
GAS TURBATION
GAS WATER SEPARATION
GASES
GASTROPOD FISHERIES
GATHERING LINES
GAUGES
GAUSSIAN DISTRIBUTION
GAZETEERS
GEAR CONSTRUCTION
GEAR HANDLING
GEAR MATERIALS
GEAR RESEARCH
GEAR SELECTIVITY
GEIGER COUNTERS
GEK
GELBSTOFF
GELS
GEMMULES
GENECOLOGY
GENES
GENETIC ABNORMALITIES
GENETIC DRIFT
GENETIC ISOLATION
GENETICISTS
GENETICS
GENOMES
GENOTYPES

GEOCHEMICAL CYCLE
GEOCHEMICAL SURVEYS
GEOCHEMISTRY
GEOCHRONOMETRY
GEOCLINES
GEODESY
GEODETIC COORDINATES
GEOGRAPHICAL COORDINATES
GEOGRAPHICAL DISTRIBUTION
GEOGRAPHICAL EXPLORATION
GEOGRAPHICAL ISOLATION
GEOGRAPHICAL REFERENCE SYSTEMS
GEOGRAPHY
GEOID
GEOID ANOMALIES
GEOLOGICAL COLLECTIONS
GEOLOGICAL CORRELATION
GEOLOGICAL DATA
GEOLOGICAL DISTRIBUTION
GEOLOGICAL EQUIPMENT
GEOLOGICAL HAZARDS
GEOLOGICAL HISTORY
GEOLOGICAL INSTITUTIONS
GEOLOGICAL MAPS
GEOLOGICAL SAMPLES
GEOLOGICAL SECTIONS
GEOLOGICAL STRUCTURES
GEOLOGICAL SURVEYS
GEOLOGICAL TIME
GEOLOGISTS
GEOLOGY
GEOMAGNETIC FIELD
GEOMAGNETISM
GEOMORPHOLOGY
GEOPHYSICAL DATA
GEOPHYSICAL EQUIPMENT
GEOPHYSICAL EXPLORATION
GEOPHYSICAL SURVEYS
GEOPHYSICS
GEOSENSING
GEOSTROPHIC EQUILIBRIUM
GEOSTROPHIC FLOW
GEOSTROPHIC METHOD
GEOSTROPHIC TRANSPORT
GEOSTROPHIC WINDS
GEOSTROPHY
GEOSYNCLINES
GEOTECHNICAL DATA
GEOTECHNOLOGY
GEOTHERMAL DATA
GEOTHERMAL ENERGY
GEOTHERMAL EQUIPMENT
GEOTHERMAL EXPLORATION
GEOTHERMAL GRADIENT
GEOTHERMAL MEASUREMENT
GEOTHERMAL POWER
GEOTHERMAL PROPERTIES
GEOTHERMAL SPRINGS
GEOTROPISM
GERMANIUM
GERMANIUM COMPOUNDS
GERMANIUM ISOTOPES
GERMINATION
GIANT WAVES
GIBBSITE
GILL DISEASE
GILLNETS
GILLNETTERS
GILLRAKER COUNTS
GILLS
GLACIAL DEPOSITS
GLACIAL EROSION
GLACIAL ERRATICS
GLACIAL FEATURES
GLACIAL GEOLOGY
GLACIAL LAKES
GLACIAL SEDIMENTATION

GLACIAL TRANSPORT
GLACIATION
GLACIERS
GLANDS
GLASS
GLASS-REINFORCED PLASTICS
GLAUCONITE
GLITTER
GLOBIGERINA OOZE
GLOBULINS
GLORIA
GLOSSARIES
GLUCOSAMINE
GLUCOSE
GLUTAMIC ACID
GLYCEROL
GLYCINE
GLYCOGEN
GLYCOLIC ACID
GLYCOPROTEINS
GLYCOSIDES
GOETHITE
GOLD
GOLD COMPOUNDS
GOLD ISOTOPES
GOLGI APPARATUS
GOVERNMENT POLICY
GOVERNMENTS
GRABEN
GRABS
GRADIENT CURRENTS
GRADIENT WINDS
GRADIENTS
GRADING
GRAFTING
GRAIN FLOW
GRAIN ORIENTATION
GRAIN PACKING
GRAIN PROPERTIES
GRAIN SHAPE
GRAIN SIZE
GRANITE
GRANTS
GRANULOMETRY
GRAPHIC METHODS
GRAPHICAL ANALYSIS
GRAPHICS
GRAPHITE
GRAPHS
GRAPPLING
GRAPPLING GEAR
GRAVEL
GRAVEL WAVES
GRAVIMETRIC TECHNIQUES
GRAVIMETRY
GRAVITATION
GRAVITY
GRAVITY ANOMALIES
GRAVITY CHARTS
GRAVITY CORERS
GRAVITY CORRECTIONS
GRAVITY DATA
GRAVITY EFFECTS
GRAVITY EXPLORATION
GRAVITY FIELD
GRAVITY METERS
GRAVITY PLATFORMS
GRAVITY SURVEYS
GRAVITY WAVES
GRAYWACKE
GRAZING
GREEN'S FUNCTION
GREENFLASH
GREENHOUSE EFFECT
GREENSCHIST FACIES
GREENSCHISTS
GREIGITE
GROUND MOTION

ASFIS Thesaurus
Alphabetical List of Terms

GROUND WATER
GROUNDINGS
GROUNDWATER POLLUTION
GROUP EFFECTS
GROUP VELOCITY
GROUTING
GROWING PONDS
GROWTH
GROWTH CURVES
GROWTH REGULATORS
GROYNES
GUANO
GUANO BIRDS
GUIDE LINES
GUIDING DEVICES
GUSTS
GUTTING
GUYED TOWERS
GUYOTS
GYPSUM
GYRES
GYROCOMPASSES
GYROSCOPES

H

HABITAT
HABITAT IMPROVEMENT
HABITAT IMPROVEMENT (BIOLOGICAL)
HABITAT IMPROVEMENT (CHEMICAL)
HABITAT IMPROVEMENT (FERTILIZATION)
HABITAT IMPROVEMENT (PHYSICAL)
HABITAT SELECTION
HAEMATITE
HAEMATOLOGICAL DISEASES
HAEMATOLOGY
HAEMOCYANINS
HAEMOGLOBINS
HAEMOLYMPH
HAEMOPOIESIS
HAEMORRHAGE
HAFNIUM
HAFNIUM COMPOUNDS
HAFNIUM ISOTOPES
HAIL
HALIDE MINERALS
HALIDES
HALINE CIRCULATION
HALITE
HALMYROLYSIS
HALOCLINE
HALOGEN COMPOUNDS
HALOGENATED HYDROCARBONS
HALOGENATION
HALOGENS
HANDLING
HANDLINING
HARBOUR MODELS
HARBOUR OSCILLATIONS
HARBOUR REGULATIONS
HARBOURS
HARMONIC ANALYSIS
HARMONIC FUNCTIONS
HARVESTING
HARVESTING MACHINES
HATCHERIES
HATCHING
HAZARD ASSESSMENT
HAZARDOUS MATERIALS
HAZARDS
HAZE
HEAD
HEADING
HEADLANDS
HEALTH AND SAFETY
HEART
HEAT

HEAT AFFECTED ZONES
HEAT BALANCE
HEAT BUDGET
HEAT CONDUCTION
HEAT CONTENT
HEAT EXCHANGE
HEAT EXCHANGERS
HEAT FLOW
HEAT PROBES
HEAT SINKS
HEAT STORAGE
HEAT TRANSFER
HEAT TRANSPORT
HEATING
HEAVE COMPENSATORS
HEAVE RESONANCE
HEAVE RESPONSE
HEAVING
HEAVY METALS
HEAVY MINERALS
HEAVY WATER
HEIGHT
HELICOPTERS
HELIDECKS
HELIUM
HELIUM ISOTOPES
HEPARIN
HEPATOPANCREAS
HERBICIDES
HERBIVORES
HERBIVOROUS FISH
HERMAPHRODITISM
HERPETOLOGY
HETEROSIS
HETEROTROPHIC ORGANISMS
HETEROTROPHY
HEULANDITE
HEXOSAMINES
HIATUSES
HIBERNATION
HIGH FREQUENCY
HIGH PRESSURE EFFECTS
HIGH PRESSURE RIDGES
HIGH PRESSURE SYSTEMS
HIGH SEAS
HIGH SEAS FISHERIES
HIGH WATER
HIGHEST ASTRONOMICAL TIDES
HISTAMINES
HISTOCHEMISTRY
HISTOLOGY
HISTONES
HISTOPATHOLOGY
HISTORICAL ACCOUNT
HODOGRAPHS
HOLDFASTS
HOLE RE-ENTRY
HOLMIUM
HOLMIUM COMPOUNDS
HOLMIUM ISOTOPES
HOLOCENE
HOLOGRAPHY
HOLOPLANKTON
HOLOTYPES
HOME RANGE
HOMING BEHAVIOUR
HOMOIOTHERMY
HOOKS
HORIZON
HORIZONTAL
HORIZONTAL ADVECTION
HORIZONTAL DISTRIBUTION
HORIZONTAL MOTION
HORIZONTAL PROFILES
HORMONES
HORNBLENDE
HOSES

HOST PREFERENCES
HOSTS
HOT BRINES
HOT SPOTS
HOT SPRINGS
HOURLY
HOVERCRAFT
HULLS
HUMAN DISEASES
HUMAN FOOD
HUMAN PHYSIOLOGY
HUMAN RESOURCES
HUMIC ACIDS
HUMIDITY
HUMUS
HUNTING
HUNTING STATISTICS
HURRICANE TRACKING
HURRICANE WAVES
HURRICANES
HUSBANDRY DISEASES
HYBRID CULTURE
HYBRIDIZATION
HYBRIDS
HYDRATES
HYDRATION
HYDRAULIC ENGINEERING
HYDRAULIC JUMP
HYDRAULIC MODELS
HYDRAULIC STRUCTURES
HYDRAULIC SYSTEMS
HYDRAULICS
HYDROBIOLOGY
HYDROBIOTITE
HYDROCARBON ANALYSIS
HYDROCARBONS
HYDROCLIMATE
HYDRODYNAMIC EQUATIONS
HYDRODYNAMICS
HYDROELECTRIC POWER
HYDROELECTRIC POWER PLANTS
HYDROFOILS
HYDROGEN
HYDROGEN COMPOUNDS
HYDROGEN IONS
HYDROGEN ISOTOPES
HYDROGEN SULPHIDE
HYDROGRAPHIC CHARTS
HYDROGRAPHIC DATA
HYDROGRAPHIC SECTIONS
HYDROGRAPHIC SURVEYING
HYDROGRAPHIC SURVEYS
HYDROGRAPHIC WIRE
HYDROGRAPHY
HYDROLASES
HYDROLOGIC CYCLE
HYDROLOGY
HYDROLYSIS
HYDROMAGNESITE
HYDROMETEORS
HYDROMETERS
HYDROPHONES
HYDROSPHERE
HYDROSTATIC BEHAVIOUR
HYDROSTATIC EQUATION
HYDROSTATIC PRESSURE
HYDROSTATICS
HYDROTHERMAL ACTIVITY
HYDROTHERMAL ALTERATION
HYDROTHERMAL DEPOSITS
HYDROTHERMAL FIELDS
HYDROTHERMAL FLOW
HYDROTHERMAL SOLUTIONS
HYDROTHERMAL SPRINGS
HYDROXIDES
HYDROXYLAMINES
HYGIENE
HYGROMETERS

ASFIS Thesaurus
Alphabetical List of Terms

HYGROMETRY
HYPERBARIC
HYPERCAPNIA
HYPERTHERMIA
HYPERTROPHY
HYPOLIMNION
HYPOPHYSECTOMY
HYPOTHALAMUS
HYPOTHERMIA
HYPOXIA
HYPSOMETRIC CURVES
HYPSOMETRY

I

ICE
ICE ACCRETION
ICE AGES
ICE BARRIERS
ICE BREAKERS
ICE BREAKING
ICE BREAKUP
ICE CANOPY
ICE CAPS
ICE CHARTS
ICE CONDITIONS
ICE COVER
ICE DRIFT
ICE EDGE
ICE FIELDS
ICE FISHING
ICE FOOT
ICE FORECASTING
ICE FORMATION
ICE FRONTS
ICE ISLANDS
ICE JAMS
ICE KEELS
ICE LOADS
ICE MELTING
ICE NUCLEI
ICE OBSERVATIONS
ICE PRESSURE
ICE PREVENTION
ICE PROPERTIES
ICE RAFTING
ICE RAFTS
ICE RIDGES
ICE ROUTEING
ICE SHELVES
ICE THICKNESS
ICE VOLUME
ICE-FREE PERIODS
ICE-OIL INTERFACE
ICE-WATER INTERFACE
ICEBERG DETECTION
ICEBERG SCOURING
ICEBERGS
ICHTHYOCIDES
ICHTHYOLOGISTS
ICHTHYOLOGY
ICHTHYOPLANKTON
ICHTHYOPLANKTON SURVEYS
ICING
IDENTIFICATION
IDENTIFICATION KEYS
IGNEOUS DIKES
IGNEOUS INTRUSIONS
IGNEOUS ROCKS
IGNIMBRITES
ILLEGAL FISHING
ILLITE
ILLUSTRATIONS
ILMENITE
IMAGE ENHANCEMENT
IMAGE PROCESSING
IMAGERY

IMAGING TECHNIQUES
IMMERSION EFFECTS
IMMIGRATIONS
IMMUNITY
IMMUNIZATION
IMMUNOLOGY
IMMUNOPRECIPITATION
IMPEDANCE
IMPELLERS
IMPINGEMENT
IMPLOSIONS
IMPOUNDMENTS
IMPRESSED CURRENTS
IMPRINTING
IN SITU DENSITY
IN SITU MEASUREMENTS
IN SITU TEMPERATURE
INBREEDING
INCINERATION
INCLINOMETERS
INCUBATION
INDICATOR SPECIES
INDICATORS
INDIUM
INDIUM COMPOUNDS
INDIUM ISOTOPES
INDUCED BREEDING
INDUSTRIAL PRODUCTION
INDUSTRIAL PRODUCTS
INDUSTRIAL PRODUCTS STATISTICS
INDUSTRIAL WASTES
INDUSTRIES
INERTIA
INERTIAL CURRENTS
INERTIAL GUIDANCE
INERTIAL NAVIGATION
INERTIAL OSCILLATIONS
INERTIAL WAVES
INFECTIOUS DISEASES
INFESTATION
INFLATABLE CRAFT
INFLOW
INFLUENTS
INFORMATION CENTRES
INFORMATION HANDLING
INFORMATION RETRIEVAL
INFORMATION SCIENTISTS
INFORMATION SERVICES
INFRARED DETECTORS
INFRARED IMAGERY
INFRARED RADIATION
INFRARED SPECTROSCOPY
INGESTION
INHIBITORS
INJURIES
INLAND FISHERIES
INLAND LAGOONS
INLAND SEAS
INLAND WATER ENVIRONMENT
INLAND WATERS
INLETS (WATERWAYS)
INORGANIC ACIDS
INORGANIC COMPOUNDS
INORGANIC MATTER
INSECT EGGS
INSECT LARVAE
INSECTICIDES
INSHORE STATIONS
INSOLATION
INSONIFICATION
INSPECTION
INSTABILITY
INSTALLATION
INSTARS
INSTINCT
INSTITUTIONAL RESOURCES
INSTRUMENT DEPTH MEASUREMENT

INSTRUMENT HANDBOOKS
INSTRUMENT PLATFORMS
INSTRUMENT RESPONSES
INSTRUMENTS
INSULATING MATERIALS
INSULIN
INSURANCE
INTAKE TEMPERATURE
INTEGRAL EQUATIONS
INTEGUMENTARY SYSTEM
INTENSIVE CULTURE
INTERACTIONS
INTERCALIBRATION
INTERCOMPARISON
INTERFACE PHENOMENA
INTERFACES
INTERFACIAL WAVES
INTERFEROMETRY
INTERGLACIAL PERIODS
INTERMEDIATE FISHING
INTERMEDIATE WATER MASSES
INTERNAL TIDES
INTERNAL WAVE BREAKING
INTERNAL WAVE EFFECTS
INTERNAL WAVE GENERATION
INTERNAL WAVES
INTERNATIONAL AGREEMENTS
INTERNATIONAL BOUNDARIES
INTERNATIONAL COOPERATION
INTERNATIONAL LAW
INTERNATIONAL ORGANIZATIONS
INTERNATIONAL POLICY
INTERNATIONAL WATERS
INTEROCEAN CANALS
INTERSPECIFIC RELATIONSHIPS
INTERSTITIAL ENVIRONMENT
INTERTIDAL ENVIRONMENT
INTERTIDAL SEDIMENTATION
INTERTROPICAL CONVERGENCE ZONE
INTESTINES
INTRASPECIFIC RELATIONSHIPS
INTRODUCED SPECIES
INVENTORIES
INVERSIONS
INVERTEBRATE LARVAE
INVERTEBRATE ZOOLOGY
INVESTMENTS
IODATES
IODIDES
IODINATED HYDROCARBONS
IODINE
IODINE COMPOUNDS
IODINE ISOTOPES
IODOMETHANE
ION ACCUMULATION
ION ASSOCIATION
ION EXCHANGE
ION PAIRS
ION SELECTIVE ELECTRODE ANALYSIS
ION TRANSPORT
IONIUM
IONIZING RADIATION
IONOSPHERE
IONS
IRIDIUM
IRIDIUM COMPOUNDS
IRIDIUM ISOTOPES
IRON
IRON COMPOUNDS
IRON ISOTOPES
IRON OXIDES
IRON PHOSPHATES
IRON SILICATES
IRON SULPHIDES
IRONSTONE
IRRADIANCE
IRRADIANCE METERS
IRRADIATION

ASFIS Thesaurus
Alphabetical List of Terms

IRRIGATION
IRRIGATION WATER
ISENTROPIC ANALYSIS
ISENTROPIC PROCESSES
ISENTROPIC SURFACES
ISLAND ARCS
ISLAND SLOPE
ISLANDS
ISOBARIC SURFACES
ISOBARS
ISOBATHS
ISOCHRONES
ISOENZYMES
ISOHALINES
ISOHYETS
ISOLATING MECHANISMS
ISOMAGNETIC LINES
ISOMERASES
ISOMERIZATION
ISOPACH MAPS
ISOPACHS
ISOPLETHS
ISOPYCNIC SURFACES
ISOPYCNICS
ISOSTASY
ISOSTATIC SEA LEVEL
ISOSTERES
ISOSTERIC SURFACES
ISOTHERMAL PROCESSES
ISOTHERMS
ISOTOPE DILUTION
ISOTOPE FRACTIONATION
ISOTOPES
ISOTROPIC MATERIALS
ISOTROPY

J

JACKUP PLATFORMS
JAROSITE
JASPILITE
JELLY BOTTLES
JET STREAM
JETS
JIGGING
JOINT VENTURES
JOINTS
JURASSIC
JURISDICTION
JUVENILE WATER
JUVENILES

K

KAINITE
KALMAN FILTERS
KANSITE
KAOLIN
KAOLINITE
KARYOLOGY
KARYOTYPES
KEEL CLEARANCE
KELPS
KELT
KELVIN WAVES
KELVIN-HELMHOLTZ INSTABILITY
KEROGEN
KETONES
KIDNEYS
KIMBERLITES
KINEMATIC EDDY VISCOSITY
KINEMATIC VISCOSITY
KINEMATICS
KINESIS
KINETIC ENERGY
KINETICS
KNUDSEN SAMPLERS

KNUDSEN TABLES
KORTWEG DEVRIES EQUATION
KRILL FISHERIES
KRILL PRODUCTS
KRYPTON
KRYPTON ISOTOPES
KURTOSIS
KYANITE

L

LABORATORIES
LABORATORY CULTURE
LABORATORY EQUIPMENT
LABOUR
LABOUR COSTS
LABOUR LEGISLATION
LACCOLITHS
LACTATION
LACUSTRINE SEDIMENTATION
LAGOON FISHERIES
LAGOONAL SEDIMENTATION
LAGOONS
LAGRANGIAN CURRENT MEASUREMENT
LAKE BASINS
LAKE CURRENTS
LAKE DEPOSITS
LAKE DYNAMICS
LAKE FISHERIES
LAKE ICE
LAKE MORPHOLOGY
LAKE RECLAMATION
LAKE SHORES
LAKES
LAMELLAR TEARING
LAMINAR BOUNDARY LAYER
LAMINAR FLOW
LAMPARA NETS
LAMPREY ATTACHMENT
LAND AND SEA BREEZES
LAND BREEZES
LAND BRIDGES
LAND ICE
LAND RECLAMATION
LAND USE
LANDFORMS
LANDING STATISTICS
LANDLOCKED STATES
LANDSLIDES
LANGMUIR CIRCULATION
LANTHANIUM
LANTHANIUM COMPOUNDS
LANTHANIUM ISOTOPES
LAPLACE EQUATION
LAPLACE TRANSFORMATION
LARGE SPAR BUOYS
LARVAE
LARVAL DEVELOPMENT
LARVAL SETTLEMENT
LARYNX
LASER ALTIMETERS
LASER ALTIMETRY
LASER BATHYMETERS
LASER BATHYMETRY
LASERS
LATENT HEAT TRANSFER
LATERAL LINE
LATITUDE
LATITUDINAL VARIATIONS
LATTICE CHARTS
LAUNCHING
LAVA
LAVA FLOWS
LAW OF THE SEA
LAWRENCIUM
LAWRENCIUM COMPOUNDS
LAWRENCIUM ISOTOPES

LAYERS
LEACHING
LEAD
LEAD COMPOUNDS
LEAD ISOTOPES
LEAD 210
LEADS
LEAKS
LEARNING BEHAVIOUR
LEASES
LEAST SQUARES METHOD
LEAVES
LECTURES
LEE EDDIES
LEE WAVES
LEGAL ASPECTS
LEGISLATION
LEGS (STRUCTURAL)
LENGTH
LENGTH-WEIGHT RELATIONSHIPS
LENITIC ENVIRONMENT
LESIONS
LETHAL EFFECTS
LETHAL LIMITS
LEUCINE
LEUKOCYTES
LEVEES
LEVEL OF NO MOTION
LEVELLING
LEVELS
LIABILITY
LIBRARIANS
LIBRARIES
LICENCES
LICENSING
LIDAR
LIFE CYCLE
LIFE HISTORY
LIFE JACKETS
LIFE SAVING EQUIPMENT
LIFE SUPPORT SYSTEMS
LIFEBOATS
LIFT-NETS
LIFTING
LIFTING TACKLE
LIGANDS
LIGASES
LIGHT
LIGHT ABSORPTION
LIGHT ATTENUATION
LIGHT DIFFRACTION
LIGHT DISPERSION
LIGHT EFFECTS
LIGHT FIELDS
LIGHT FISHING
LIGHT INTENSITY
LIGHT MEASUREMENT
LIGHT MEASURING INSTRUMENTS
LIGHT MICROSCOPY
LIGHT PENETRATION
LIGHT PROPAGATION
LIGHT REFLECTION
LIGHT REFRACTION
LIGHT SCATTERING
LIGHT SOURCES
LIGHT STIMULI
LIGHT TRANSMISSION
LIGHTERS
LIGHTHOUSES
LIGHTING SYSTEMS
LIGHTNING
LIGHTSHIPS
LIMESTONE
LIMITING FACTORS
LIMNOLOGICAL DATA
LIMNOLOGICAL EQUIPMENT
LIMNOLOGICAL INSTITUTIONS
LIMNOLOGICAL SURVEYS

ASFIS Thesaurus
Alphabetical List of Terms

LIMNOLOGY
LIMONITE
LINE FISHING
LINEAR PROGRAMMING
LINEAR WAVES
LINERS
LINES
LIPIDS
LIPOPROTEINS
LIQUEFACTION .
LIQUEFIED NATURAL GAS
LIQUEFIED PETROLEUM GAS
LIQUEFIED SEDIMENT FLOW
LIQUIDS
LITERATURE REVIEWS
LITHIFICATION
LITHIUM
LITHIUM COMPOUNDS
LITHIUM ISOTOPES
LITHOFACIES
LITHOGENESIS
LITHOLOGY
LITHOSPHERE
LITTORAL DEPOSITS
LITTORAL ZONE
LIVE STORAGE
LIVER
LIVESTOCK FOOD
LIVING FOSSILS
LIVING RESOURCES
LOADING BUOYS
LOADS (FORCES)
LOBSTER CULTURE
LOBSTER FISHERIES
LOCAL MOVEMENTS
LOCAL WINDS
LOCATING
LOCATIONS (WORKING)
LOCKOUT SUBMERSIBLES
LOCOMOTION
LOCOMOTORY APPENDAGES
LOGBOOKS
LOGGING
LONG-CRESTED WAVES
LONG-PERIOD TIDES
LONG-TERM CHANGES
LONG-TERM PLANNING
LONG-TERM RECORDS
LONGEVITY
LONGITUDE
LONGITUDINAL DISPERSION
LONGLINING
LONGSHORE BARS
LONGSHORE CURRENTS
LONGSHORE SEDIMENT TRANSPORT
LOPHOPHORES
LORAN
LOTIC ENVIRONMENT
LOVE WAVES
LOW FREQUENCY
LOW PRESSURE SYSTEMS
LOW PRESSURE TROUGHS
LOW TEMPERATURE
LOW TIDE
LOW-VELOCITY LAYER
LOWER MANTLE
LOWEST ASTRONOMICAL TIDES
LUBRICANTS
LUCIFERIN
LUMINESCENCE
LUMINOUS ORGANISMS
LUNAR DIURNAL TIDES
LUNAR SEMIDIURNAL TIDES
LUNAR TIDES
LUNGS
LUTETIUM
LUTETIUM COMPOUNDS

LUTETIUM ISOTOPES
LUTITES
LYASES
LYMPH
LYMPHATIC SYSTEM
LYMPHOCYTES
LYSINE
LYSOCLINE

M

MACHINERY
MACKEREL FISHERIES
MACROPHAGES
MAFIC MAGMA
MAGHEMITE
MAGMA
MAGMA CHAMBERS
MAGNESITE
MAGNESIUM
MAGNESIUM COMPOUNDS
MAGNESIUM FLUORIDES
MAGNESIUM ISOTOPES
MAGNESIUM PHOSPHATES
MAGNESIUM SILICATES
MAGNESIUM SULPHATES
MAGNETIC ANOMALIES
MAGNETIC ANOMALY CHARTS
MAGNETIC CHARTS
MAGNETIC DATA
MAGNETIC EXPLORATION
MAGNETIC FIELD ELEMENTS
MAGNETIC FIELDS
MAGNETIC INCLINATION
MAGNETIC INTENSITY
MAGNETIC PERMEABILITY
MAGNETIC PROPERTIES
MAGNETIC REVERSALS
MAGNETIC SUSCEPTIBILITY
MAGNETIC TAPE RECORDINGS
MAGNETIC TAPES
MAGNETIC VARIATIONS
MAGNETISM
MAGNETITE
MAGNETOMETERS
MAGNETOSTRATIGRAPHY
MAGNETOTELLURIC METHODS
MAGNETS
MAINTENANCE
MAJOR CONSTITUENTS
MALACOLOGISTS
MALACOLOGY
MALARIA
MALES
MAMMALIAN PHYSIOLOGY
MAMMALOGISTS
MAMMALOGY
MAN-INDUCED EFFECTS
MANAGEMENT
MANGANESE
MANGANESE COMPOUNDS
MANGANESE DEPOSITS
MANGANESE DIOXIDE
MANGANESE ISOTOPES
MANGANESE MINERALS
MANGANESE OXIDES
MANGANITE
MANGROVE SWAMPS
MANIFOLDS
MANIPULATORS
MANNED VEHICLES
MANNOSE
MANOEUVRABILITY
MANOMETERS
MANTLE
MANTLE CAVITY
MANTLE CONVECTION

MANTLE PLUMES
MANUALS
MANURE
MAP GRAPHICS
MAP PROJECTIONS
MAPPING
MAPS
MARCASITE
MARGINAL BASINS
MARGINAL FIELDS
MARGINAL SEAS
MARINAS
MARINE AQUACULTURE
MARINE BIRDS
MARINE CRUSTACEANS
MARINE ECOLOGISTS
MARINE ECOLOGY
MARINE ENVIRONMENT
MARINE FISH
MARINE FISHERIES
MARINE GEODESY
MARINE GEOLOGY
MARINE INVERTEBRATES
MARINE MAMMALS
MARINE MOLLUSCS
MARINE ORGANISMS
MARINE PARKS
MARINE POLLUTION
MARINE RESOURCES
MARINE SCIENCES
MARINE SCIENTISTS
MARINE TECHNOLOGY
MARINE TRANSPORTATION
MARITIME LEGISLATION
MARKER BUOYS
MARKET RESEARCH
MARKETING
MARKING
MARL
MARLSTONE
MARSDEN SQUARES
MARSHES
MASS
MASS CULTURE
MASS EXTINCTIONS
MASS GRAVITY TRANSPORT (SEDIMENTS)
MASS MOVEMENT
MASS SPECTROSCOPY
MASS TRANSFER
MASS TRANSPORT
MASTICATORY STOMACH
MASTS
MATERIALS
MATERIALS TECHNOLOGY
MATERIALS TESTING
MATHEMATICAL ANALYSIS
MATHEMATICAL MODELS
MATHEMATICAL PROGRAMMING
MATHEMATICS
MAXIMUM ENTROPY SPECTRAL ANALYSIS
MEAN SEA LEVEL
MEANDERING
MEASUREMENT
MEASURING DEVICES
MECHANICAL PROPERTIES
MECHANICAL STIMULI
MECHANICS
MECHANIZATION
MECHANORECEPTORS
MEDIAN LINES
MEDIAN VALLEYS
MEDICINE
MEGALOPS
MEIOBENTHOS
MEIOSIS
MELANGES
MELT WATER
MELTING

ASFIS Thesaurus
Alphabetical List of Terms

MELTING POINT
MEMBRANES
MENDELEVIUM
MENDELEVIUM COMPOUNDS
MENDELEVIUM ISOTOPES
MERCHANT SHIPS
MERCURY
MERCURY COMPOUNDS
MERCURY ISOTOPES
MERIDIONAL ATMOSPHERIC CIRCULATION
MERIDIONAL DISTRIBUTION
MERIDIONAL OCEANIC CIRCULATION
MERISTIC COUNTS
MEROMICTIC LAKES
MEROMIXIS
MEROPLANKTON
MESH GAUGES
MESH REGULATIONS
MESH SELECTIVITY
MESOPELAGIC ZONE
MESOSCALE EDDIES
MESOSCALE FEATURES
MESOSPHERE (EARTH)
MESOZOIC
MESSENGERS
MESSINIAN
METABOLIC DISORDERS
METABOLISM
METABOLITES
METAL FATIGUE
METAL IONS
METALIMNION
METALLIFEROUS SEDIMENTS
METALLOGENESIS
METALLURGY
METALS
METAMORPHIC FACIES
METAMORPHIC ROCKS
METAMORPHISM
METAMORPHOSIS
METASOMATISM
METEOROLOGICAL CHARTS
METEOROLOGICAL DATA
METEOROLOGICAL INSTRUMENTS
METEOROLOGICAL OBSERVATIONS
METEOROLOGICAL TABLES
METEOROLOGICAL TIDES
METEOROLOGISTS
METEOROLOGY
METHANE
METHANOGENESIS
METHIONINE
METHODOLOGY
METHYL MERCURY
MICAS
MICROBIAL CONTAMINATION
MICROBIOLOGICAL ANALYSIS
MICROBIOLOGICAL CULTURE
MICROBIOLOGISTS
MICROBIOLOGY
MICROCONTINENTS
MICROEARTHQUAKES
MICROFORMS
MICROHABITATS
MICROMETER CALIPERS
MICROORGANISMS
MICROPALAEONTOLOGY
MICROPHONES
MICROPHOTOGRAPHY
MICROPROCESSORS
MICROSCOPES
MICROSCOPY
MICROSEISMS
MICROSTRUCTURE
MICROTOPOGRAPHY
MICROWAVE IMAGERY
MICROWAVE RADAR

MICROWAVE RADIOMETERS
MICROWAVES
MID-OCEAN RIDGES
MIDWATER TRAWLS
MIGRATIONS
MIGRATORY SPECIES
MILITARY OCEANOGRAPHY
MILITARY OPERATIONS
MILITARY PORTS
MILK
MIMICRY
MINCED PRODUCTS
MINE TAILINGS
MINERAL ASSEMBLAGES
MINERAL COLLECTIONS
MINERAL COMPOSITION
MINERAL DEPOSITS
MINERAL EXPLORATION
MINERAL INDUSTRY
MINERAL PROCESSING
MINERAL RESOURCES
MINERAL SAMPLES
MINERALIZATION
MINERALOGY
MINERALS
MINING
MINING EQUIPMENT
MINING LEGISLATION
MINING VESSELS
MIOCENE
MIRAGES
MISTRAL
MITOSIS
MIXED GAS
MIXED LAYER
MIXED LAYER DEPTH
MIXING LENGTH
MIXING PROCESSES
MIXING RATIO
MOBILE PLATFORMS
MODELLING
MODELS
MODES
MODULES
MOHO
MOHOLE PROJECT
MOISTURE
MOISTURE TRANSFER
MOLECULAR DIFFUSION
MOLECULAR STRUCTURE
MOLECULAR VISCOSITY
MOLECULAR VISCOSITY COEFFICIENTS
MOLECULAR WEIGHT
MOLECULES
MOLLUSC CULTURE
MOLLUSC FISHERIES
MOLLUSCAN LARVAE
MOLLUSCICIDES
MOLYBDENUM
MOLYBDENUM COMPOUNDS
MOLYBDENUM ISOTOPES
MOMENTUM
MOMENTUM TRANSFER
MONAZITE
MONIN-OBUKHOV LENGTH
MONITORING
MONITORING SYSTEMS
MONOCULTURE
MONOMOLECULAR FILMS
MONOSACCHARIDES
MONOSEX CULTURE
MONSOON REVERSAL
MONSOONS
MONTHLY
MONTHLY DISTRIBUTION
MONTMORILLONITE
MOON

MOON PHASES
MOORING BUOYS
MOORING LINES
MOORING MOTION EFFECTS
MOORING RECOVERY
MOORING SYSTEMS
MORAINES
MORATORIA
MORISON'S EQUATION
MORPHOGENESIS
MORPHOMETRY
MORTALITY
MORTALITY CAUSES
MOTHER SHIPS
MOTION
MOTION EFFECTS
MOTOR BOATS
MOTORS
MOULTING
MOUNTAINS
MOUTH PARTS
MUCINS
MUCOPOLYSACCHARIDES
MUCUS
MUD
MUD BANKS
MUD FLATS
MUDSTONE
MULLET FISHERIES
MULTIBEAM SONAR
MULTIPHASE FLOW
MULTIPLE USE OF RESOURCES
MULTISHIP EXPEDITIONS
MULTISPECIES FISHERIES
MULTISPECTRAL SCANNERS
MULTIVARIATE ANALYSIS
MUSCLES
MUSCOVITE
MUSCULOSKELETAL SYSTEM
MUSEUM COLLECTIONS
MUSEUMS
MUSSEL CULTURE
MUSSEL FISHERIES
MUTAGENS
MUTATIONS
MYCOLOGISTS
MYCOLOGY
MYOGLOBINS
MYOSIN

N

NANNOFOSSIL OOZE
NANNOPLANKTON
NANSEN BOTTLES
NAPHTHALENE
NAPPES
NARCOSIS
NARCOTICS
NATIONAL PLANNING
NATURAL GAS
NATURAL MORTALITY
NATURAL POPULATIONS
NATURAL RESOURCES
NATURAL SELECTION
NATURE CONSERVATION
NAUPLII
NAUTICAL ALMANACS
NAVAL BASES
NAVIER-STOKES EQUATIONS
NAVIGATION
NAVIGATION IN ICE
NAVIGATION POLICY
NAVIGATION REGULATIONS
NAVIGATION SYSTEMS
NAVIGATION UNDER ICE
NAVIGATION UNDERWATER
NAVIGATIONAL AIDS

ASFIS Thesaurus
Alphabetical List of Terms

NAVIGATIONAL BUOYS
NAVIGATIONAL CHANNELS
NAVIGATIONAL CHARTS
NAVIGATIONAL HAZARDS
NAVIGATIONAL SATELLITES
NAVIGATIONAL TABLES
NEAP TIDES
NEAR-SURFACE LAYER
NEARSHORE BARS
NEARSHORE CURRENTS
NEARSHORE DYNAMICS
NEARSHORE SEDIMENTATION
NECROSES
NEGATIVE STORM SURGES
NEKTON
NEKTON COLLECTING DEVICES
NEODYMIUM
NEODYMIUM COMPOUNDS
NEODYMIUM ISOTOPES
NEOGENE
NEON
NEON ISOTOPES
NEOTENY
NEPHELOID LAYER
NEPHELOMETERS
NEPTUNIUM
NEPTUNIUM COMPOUNDS
NEPTUNIUM ISOTOPES
NERITIC PROVINCE
NERVES
NERVOUS SYSTEM
NERVOUS TISSUES
NESTING
NESTS
NET FISHING
NET SOUNDERS
NETS
NETTING MATERIALS
NEURONES
NEUROPHYSIOLOGY
NEUROSECRETION
NEUROSECRETORY SYSTEM
NEUROTOXINS
NEUROTRANSMITTERS
NEUSTON
NEUTRON ACTIVATION ANALYSIS
NEW CLASSES
NEW FAMILIES
NEW GENERA
NEW ORDERS
NEW PRODUCTS
NEW RECORDS
NEW SPECIES
NEW TAXA
NEW VARIETIES
NICHES
NICKEL
NICKEL COMPOUNDS
NICKEL ISOTOPES
NICOTINIC ACID
NIGHTTIME
NIOBIUM
NIOBIUM COMPOUNDS
NIOBIUM ISOTOPES
NISKIN SAMPLERS
NITRATES
NITRIC ACIDS
NITRIFICATION
NITRITES
NITROGEN
NITROGEN COMPOUNDS
NITROGEN CYCLE
NITROGEN FIXATION
NITROGEN ISOTOPES
NITROGEN NARCOSIS
NITROSAMINES
NITROUS OXIDE

NOBELIUM
NOBELIUM COMPOUNDS
NOBELIUM ISOTOPES
NODAL TIDES
NODE CONSTRUCTION
NODULES
NOISE (SOUND)
NOISE REDUCTION
NON-CONSERVATIVE PROPERTIES
NON-NEWTONIAN FLUIDS
NONDESTRUCTIVE TESTING
NONFERROUS ALLOYS
NONLINEAR EQUATIONS
NONLINEAR WAVE INTERACTIONS
NONLINEAR WAVES
NONLINEARITY
NONRENEWABLE RESOURCES
NONTRONITE
NORTH ATLANTIC POLAR FRONT
NOXIOUS ORGANISMS
NUCLEAR ENERGY
NUCLEAR EXPLOSIONS
NUCLEAR MAGNETIC RESONANCE
NUCLEAR PHYSICS
NUCLEAR POWER PLANTS
NUCLEAR PROPULSION
NUCLEAR RADIATIONS
NUCLEI
NUCLEIC ACIDS
NUCLEOTIDES
NUMERICAL ANALYSIS
NUMERICAL TAXONOMY
NURSERY GROUNDS
NURSERY PONDS
NUTRIENT CYCLES
NUTRIENT DEFICIENCY
NUTRIENTS (MINERAL)
NUTRITION
NUTRITION DISORDERS
NUTRITIONAL REQUIREMENTS
NUTRITIONAL TYPES
NUTRITIVE VALUE
NYCTIMERAL RHYTHMS
NYMPHS

O

OBDUCTION
OBITUARIES
OBSERVATION CHAMBERS
OBSIDIAN
OBSTACLE MARKS
OCEAN BASINS
OCEAN BOTTOM SEISMOMETERS
OCEAN CIRCULATION
OCEAN CURRENTS
OCEAN DUMPING
OCEAN FLOOR
OCEAN LOADING
OCEAN POLICY
OCEAN SPACE
OCEAN STATIONS
OCEAN TIDES
OCEAN-ATMOSPHERE SYSTEM
OCEAN-ICE-ATMOSPHERE SYSTEM
OCEANIC BOUNDARY LAYER
OCEANIC CONVECTION
OCEANIC CONVERGENCES
OCEANIC CRUST
OCEANIC DESERTS
OCEANIC DIVERGENCES
OCEANIC EDDIES
OCEANIC FRONTS
OCEANIC ISLANDS
OCEANIC PROVINCE
OCEANIC RESPONSE
OCEANIC TURBULENCE

OCEANITE
OCEANIZATION
OCEANODROMOUS MIGRATIONS
OCEANOGRAPHIC ATLASES
OCEANOGRAPHIC DATA
OCEANOGRAPHIC EQUIPMENT
OCEANOGRAPHIC INSTITUTIONS
OCEANOGRAPHIC STATIONS
OCEANOGRAPHIC SURVEYS
OCEANOGRAPHIC TABLES
OCEANOGRAPHY
OCEANS
ODOUR
OFF-BOTTOM CULTURE
OFFSHORE
OFFSHORE DOCKING
OFFSHORE ENGINEERING
OFFSHORE EQUIPMENT
OFFSHORE OPERATIONS
OFFSHORE STRUCTURES
OFFSHORE TERMINALS
OIL
OIL AND GAS
OIL AND GAS EXPLORATION
OIL AND GAS FIELDS
OIL AND GAS INDUSTRY
OIL AND GAS LEGISLATION
OIL AND GAS PRODUCTION
OIL FIELDS
OIL IN WATER CONTENT
OIL POLLUTION
OIL PRODUCTION
OIL RECOVERY
OIL REFINERIES
OIL REMOVAL
OIL RESERVES
OIL RESERVOIRS
OIL SANDS
OIL SEEPAGES
OIL SHALE
OIL SLICKS
OIL SPILLS
OIL TANKS
OIL TREATING
OIL WASTES
OIL WATER SEPARATION
OIL WELLS
OIL-GAS INTERFACE
OIL-WATER INTERFACE
OLEIC ACID
OLFACTION
OLFACTORY ORGANS
OLIGOCENE
OLIGOTROPHIC LAKES
OLISTOLITHS
OLISTOSTROMES
OLIVINE
OMEGA
OMNIVORES
ONE-ATMOSPHERE SYSTEMS
ONTOGENY
OOGENESIS
OOIDS
OOLITES
OOZES
OPAL
OPEN SYSTEMS
OPERATIONAL COSTS
OPERATIONS RESEARCH
OPHIOLITES
OPTICAL CLASSIFICATION
OPTICAL FILTERS
OPTICAL INSTRUMENTS
OPTICAL PROPERTIES
OPTICAL WATER TYPES
OPTICS
ORBITAL VELOCITY
ORDOVICIAN

ASFIS Thesaurus
Alphabetical List of Terms

ORES
ORGAN REMOVAL
ORGANIC ACIDS
ORGANIC CARBON
ORGANIC COMPOUNDS
ORGANIC CONSTITUENTS
ORGANIC MATTER
ORGANIC NITROGEN
ORGANIC PHOSPHORUS
ORGANIC SEDIMENTS
ORGANIC WASTES
ORGANISM AGGREGATIONS
ORGANISM MORPHOLOGY
ORGANIZATIONS
ORGANOGENESIS
ORGANOLEPTIC PROPERTIES
ORGANOMETALLIC COMPLEXES
ORGANOMETALLIC COMPOUNDS
ORIENTATION
ORIENTATION BEHAVIOUR
ORNAMENTAL FISH
ORNITHINE
ORNITHOLOGISTS
ORNITHOLOGY
OROGENY
ORTHOCLASE
ORTHOGONALS
ORTHOPHOSPHATE
ORTHOTIDES
OSCILLATIONS
OSCILLATORY FLOW
OSCILLATORY WAVES
OSMIUM
OSMIUM COMPOUNDS
OSMIUM ISOTOPES
OSMOREGULATION
OSMOSIS
OSMOTIC ADAPTATIONS
OSMOTIC PRESSURE
OSTEOLOGY
OTEC
OTEC PLANTS
OTOLITH READING
OTOLITHS
OTTER BOARDS
OUTCROPS
OUTER CONTINENTAL SHELF
OUTFALLS
OUTFLOW
OUTFLOW WATERS
OVARIES
OVERCROWDING
OVEREXPLOITATION
OVERFISHING
OVERFLOW
OVERTOPPING
OVERTURN
OVERWASH
OVERWINTERING
OVERWINTERING TECHNIQUES
OVIPARITY
OVOVIVIPARITY
OVULATION
OXBOW LAKES
OXIC CONDITIONS
OXIC SEDIMENTS
OXIDATION
OXIDE MINERALS
OXIDES
OXIDOREDUCTASES
OXYGEN
OXYGEN COMPOUNDS
OXYGEN CONSUMPTION
OXYGEN DEMAND
OXYGEN DEPLETION
OXYGEN ISOTOPE DATING
OXYGEN ISOTOPE RATIO

OXYGEN ISOTOPE STRATIGRAPHY
OXYGEN ISOTOPES
OXYGEN MAXIMUM LAYER
OXYGEN MINIMUM LAYER
OXYGEN PROFILES
OXYGEN SECTIONS
OXYGENATION
OYSTER CULTURE
OYSTER FISHERIES
OYSTER REEFS
OZONATION
OZONE

P

P-WAVES
PACK ICE
PACKING FISHERY PRODUCTS
PACKING MATERIALS
PAINTS
PALAEO STUDIES
PALAEOCEANOGRAPHY
PALAEOCENE
PALAEOCLIMATE
PALAEOCLIMATOLOGY
PALAEOCURRENTS
PALAEOECOLOGY
PALAEOENVIRONMENTS
PALAEOGENE
PALAEOLATITUDE
PALAEOLIMNOLOGY
PALAEOMAGNETISM
PALAEONTOLOGY
PALAEOSALINITY
PALAEOSHORELINES
PALAEOTEMPERATURE
PALAEOTOPOGRAPHY
PALAEOZOIC
PALAGONITE
PALATABILITY
PALLADIUM
PALLADIUM COMPOUNDS
PALLADIUM ISOTOPES
PALYGORSKITE
PALYNOLOGY
PANCREAS
PARAMETERIZATION
PARAMETERS
PARASITE ATTACHMENT
PARASITE CONTROL
PARASITE RESISTANCE
PARASITES
PARASITIC CASTRATION
PARASITIC DISEASES
PARASITISM
PARASITOLOGY
PARENTAL BEHAVIOUR
PARTHENOGENESIS
PARTIALLY-MIXED ESTUARIES
PARTICLE CONCENTRATION
PARTICLE COUNTERS
PARTICLE DISTRIBUTION
PARTICLE MOTION
PARTICLE SCATTERING
PARTICLE SETTLING
PARTICLE SIZE
PARTICULATE FLUX
PARTICULATE ORGANIC CARBON
PARTICULATE ORGANIC MATTER
PARTICULATE ORGANIC NITROGEN
PARTICULATE ORGANIC PHOSPHORUS
PARTICULATES
PARTURITION
PASSENGER SHIPS
PASSIVE MARGINS
PASSIVE SONAR
PATENTS

PATHOGENIC BACTERIA
PATHOGENS
PATHOLOGY
PATTERN RECOGNITION
PCB
PEARL CULTURE
PEARL FISHERIES
PEARL OYSTERS
PEARLS
PEAT
PEBBLES
PECKING ORDER
PEDUNCLE DISEASE
PELAGIC CLAY
PELAGIC ENVIRONMENT
PELAGIC FISHERIES
PELAGIC SEDIMENTATION
PELAGIC SEDIMENTS
PELLET FEEDS
PENETRATION DEPTH
PENETROMETERS
PEPTIDES
PEPTONES
PERCOID FISHERIES
PERCOLATION
PERFORATED STRUCTURES
PERFORMANCE ASSESSMENT
PERIDOTITE
PERIODIC VARIATIONS
PERIODICITY
PERIPHERAL NERVOUS SYSTEM
PERIPHYTON
PERMAFROST
PERMANENCE
PERMANENT THERMOCLINE
PERMEABILITY
PERMEASES
PERMIAN
PERMITS
PERSISTENCE
PERSONAL BIBLIOGRAPHIES
PERSONNEL
PERT
PERTURBATION METHOD
PERTURBATIONS
PEST CONTROL
PESTICIDES
PETROGENESIS
PETROLEUM
PETROLEUM ENGINEERING
PETROLEUM GEOLOGY
PETROLEUM HYDROCARBONS
PETROLEUM RESIDUES
PETROLOGY
PH
PH EFFECTS
PH SENSORS
PHAGOCYTOSIS
PHANEROZOIC
PHARMACOLOGY
PHASE CHANGES
PHASE VELOCITY
PHENOLOGY
PHENOLS
PHENOTYPES
PHENOTYPIC VARIATIONS
PHENYLALANINE
PHEROMONES
PHILLIPSITE
PHOSPHATE DEPOSITS
PHOSPHATE MINERALS
PHOSPHATE ROCKS
PHOSPHATES
PHOSPHATIZATION
PHOSPHORESCENCE
PHOSPHORIC ACID
PHOSPHORITE
PHOSPHORITE NODULES

ASFIS Thesaurus
Alphabetical List of Terms

PHOSPHORUS
PHOSPHORUS COMPOUNDS
PHOSPHORUS CYCLE
PHOSPHORUS ISOTOPES
PHOTOCHEMICAL REACTIONS
PHOTOCHEMISTRY
PHOTOGRAMMETRY
PHOTOGRAPHIC EQUIPMENT
PHOTOGRAPHS
PHOTOGRAPHY
PHOTOLYSIS
PHOTOMETERS
PHOTOMETRY
PHOTOPERIODICITY
PHOTOPERIODS
PHOTOPHORES
PHOTORECEPTION
PHOTORECEPTORS
PHOTOSYNTHESIS
PHOTOSYNTHETIC PIGMENTS
PHOTOTAXIS
PHOTOTROPISM
PHTHALATE ESTERS
PHYLLOSOMAE
PHYLOGENETICS
PHYLOGENY
PHYSICAL LIMNOLOGY
PHYSICAL OCEANOGRAPHY
PHYSICAL PROPERTIES
PHYSICOCHEMICAL PROPERTIES
PHYSICS
PHYSIOGRAPHIC PROVINCES
PHYSIOLOGISTS
PHYSIOLOGY
PHYTOBENTHOS
PHYTOHORMONES
PHYTOPLANKTON
PHYTOPLANKTON CULTURE
PHYTOSOCIOLOGY
PIERS
PIEZOELECTRIC TRANSDUCERS
PIGGING
PIGMENTS
PILE DRIVING
PILED PLATFORMS
PILES
PILLOW LAVA
PILLOW STRUCTURES
PILOT CHARTS
PINEAL ORGAN
PINGERS
PIPE BUCKLING
PIPE LAYING
PIPE STRINGERS
PIPELAYING BARGES
PIPELINE CONSTRUCTION
PIPELINE CROSSING
PIPELINE PIGS
PIPELINE PROTECTION
PIPELINES
PIPES
PISTON CORERS
PITCH RESONANCE
PITCH RESPONSE
PITCHING
PITS
PITUITARY GLAND
PLACENTA
PLACER MINING
PLACERS
PLAGIOCLASE
PLAINS
PLANETARY ATMOSPHERES
PLANETARY VORTICITY
PLANETARY WAVES
PLANETARY WINDS
PLANKTON

PLANKTON COLLECTING DEVICES
PLANKTON EQUIVALENTS
PLANKTON FEEDERS
PLANKTON SURVEYS
PLANKTONOLOGY
PLANNING
PLANT CONTROL
PLANT CULTURE
PLANT DISEASES
PLANT METABOLISM
PLANT MORPHOLOGY
PLANT NUTRITION
PLANT ORGANS
PLANT PHYSIOLOGISTS
PLANT PHYSIOLOGY
PLANT POPULATIONS
PLANT REPRODUCTIVE STRUCTURES
PLANT UTILIZATION
PLASTIC COATINGS
PLASTIC DEBRIS
PLASTIC FLOW
PLASTICITY
PLASTICS
PLATE BOUNDARIES
PLATE CONVERGENCE
PLATE DIVERGENCE
PLATE MARGINS
PLATE MOTION
PLATE TECTONICS
PLATEAUX
PLATES
PLATFORMS (GEOLOGY)
PLATINUM
PLATINUM COMPOUNDS
PLATINUM ISOTOPES
PLAYAS
PLEISTOCENE
PLEUSTON
PLIO-PLEISTOCENE BOUNDARY
PLIOCENE
PLOTTING
PLOUGHMARKS
PLOUGHS
PLUMBLINE DEFLECTION
PLUMES
PLUTONIUM
PLUTONIUM COMPOUNDS
PLUTONIUM ISOTOPES
PLUTONS
POCK MARKS
POIKILOTHERMY
POISONOUS FISH
POISONOUS ORGANISMS
POISSON'S EQUATION
POISSON'S RATIO
POLAR AIR MASSES
POLAR CONVERGENCES
POLAR EXPLORATION
POLAR FRONTS
POLAR METEOROLOGY
POLAR OCEANOGRAPHY
POLAR WANDERING
POLAR WATERS
POLAR ZONES
POLARIZATION
POLAROGRAPHY
POLDERS
POLE POSITIONS
POLE TIDES
POLE-LINE FISHING
POLICIES
POLITICAL ASPECTS
POLLEN
POLLINATION
POLLUTANT IDENTIFICATION
POLLUTANT PERSISTENCE
POLLUTANTS

POLLUTION
POLLUTION CONTROL
POLLUTION CONVENTION
POLLUTION DATA
POLLUTION DETECTION
POLLUTION DISPERSION
POLLUTION EFFECTS
POLLUTION INDICATORS
POLLUTION LEGISLATION
POLLUTION MAPS
POLLUTION MONITORING
POLLUTION SURVEYS
POLLUTION TOLERANCE
POLONIUM
POLONIUM COMPOUNDS
POLONIUM ISOTOPES
POLYCULTURE
POLYHALITE
POLYMERIZATION
POLYMERS
POLYNYAS
POLYPEPTIDES
POLYPLOIDS
POLYPS
POLYSACCHARIDES
POLYSPERMY
POLYUNSATURATED FATTY ACIDS
POLYUNSATURATED HYDROCARBONS
POND CONSTRUCTION
POND CULTURE
PONDS
PONTOONS
POPULATION CHARACTERISTICS
POPULATION CONTROL
POPULATION DENSITY
POPULATION DYNAMICS
POPULATION FACTORS
POPULATION FUNCTIONS
POPULATION GENETICS
POPULATION NUMBER
POPULATION STRUCTURE
PORCELLANITE
PORE PRESSURE
PORE WATER
PORE WATER SAMPLERS
POROSITY
PORPHYRINS
PORT INSTALLATIONS
POSITION FIXING
POSITIONING SYSTEMS
POT FISHING
POTADROMOUS MIGRATIONS
POTASH DEPOSITS
POTASSIUM
POTASSIUM COMPOUNDS
POTASSIUM ISOTOPES
POTASSIUM-ARGON DATING
POTENTIAL DENSITY
POTENTIAL ENERGY
POTENTIAL FLOW
POTENTIAL RESOURCES
POTENTIAL TEMPERATURE
POTENTIAL VORTICITY
POTENTIAL YIELD
POTS
POWDERED PRODUCTS
POWER CABLES
POWER CONSUMPTION
POWER FROM THE SEA
POWER PLANTS
PRACTICAL SALINITY SCALE
PRANDTL NUMBER
PRASEODYMIUM
PRASEODYMIUM COMPOUNDS
PRASEODYMIUM ISOTOPES
PRAWN CULTURE
PRECAMBRIAN
PREDATION

PREDATOR CONTROL
PREDATORS
PREDICTION
PREGNANCY
PRESERVATION (FISHERY PRODUCTS)
PRESERVATIVES
PRESSURE
PRESSURE EFFECTS
PRESSURE FIELD
PRESSURE GAUGES
PRESSURE GRADIENTS
PRESSURE MEASUREMENT
PRESSURE SENSORS
PRESSURE VESSELS
PRESTRESSED CONCRETE
PREY SELECTION
PRICING
PRIMARY PRODUCTION
PRIMERS
PROBABILITY THEORY
PROCEDURES
PROCESS PLANTS
PROCESSED FISHERY PRODUCTS
PROCESSING FISHERY PRODUCTS
PRODUCT DEVELOPMENT
PRODUCTION COST
PRODUCTION MANAGEMENT
PRODUCTION PLATFORMS
PRODUCTS
PROFILERS
PROFILES
PROFILING
PROGRADATION
PROGRAMMES
PROGRESS REPORTS
PROGRESSIVE WAVES
PROLINE
PROMETHIUM
PROMETHIUM COMPOUNDS
PROMETHIUM ISOTOPES
PROPANE
PROPELLERS
PROPERTIES
PROPERTY RIGHTS
PROPHYLAXIS
PROPULSION SYSTEMS
PROTACTINIUM
PROTACTINIUM COMPOUNDS
PROTACTINIUM ISOTOPES
PROTANDRY
PROTECTED RESOURCES
PROTECTION
PROTECTION VESSELS
PROTECTIVE BEHAVIOUR
PROTECTIVE CLOTHING
PROTEIN DEFICIENCY
PROTEIN DENATURATION
PROTEIN SYNTHESIS
PROTEINS
PROTISTS
PROTOTYPES
PROTOZOAN DISEASES
PROVENANCE
PSAMMON
PSYCHROMETERS
PTEROPOD OOZE
PUBLIC ACCESS
PUBLIC HEALTH
PUBLICITY MATERIAL
PULP WASTES
PUMICE
PUMP FISHING
PUMP STATIONS
PUMPING
PUMPS
PUPAE
PUPS

PURCHASING
PURINES
PURSE SEINES
PURSE SEINING
PYCNOCLINE
PYLORIC CAECA
PYRANOMETERS
PYRGEOMETERS
PYRHELIOMETERS
PYRIDINES
PYRIMIDINES
PYRITE
PYROLUSITE
PYROLYSIS
PYROPHYLLITE
PYROXENES
PYRRHOTITE
PYRROLIDINE

Q

QUALITY
QUALITY ASSURANCE
QUALITY CONTROL
QUANTA METERS
QUANTITATIVE DISTRIBUTION
QUARANTINE REGULATIONS
QUARTER DIURNAL TIDES
QUARTZ
QUARTZ CLOCKS
QUARTZ PRESSURE SENSORS
QUARTZ TEMPERATURE SENSORS
QUARTZITE
QUASI-GEOSTROPHIC MOTION
QUATERNARY
QUICKSANDS
QUINOLINES
QUOTA REGULATIONS

R

RACEWAY CULTURE
RACIAL STUDIES
RADAR
RADAR ALTIMETERS
RADAR ALTIMETRY
RADAR CLUTTER
RADAR IMAGERY
RADAR NAVIGATION
RADIANCE
RADIANCE METERS
RADIATION BALANCE
RADIATION HAZARDS
RADIATION LEAKS
RADIATION PROTECTION
RADIATIONAL TIDES
RADIATIONS
RADIATIVE TRANSFER
RADIO
RADIO AIDS
RADIO BUOYS
RADIO NAVIGATION
RADIO OCEANOGRAPHY
RADIO TELEMETRY
RADIO WAVES
RADIOACTIVE AEROSOLS
RADIOACTIVE CONTAMINATION
RADIOACTIVE LABELLING
RADIOACTIVE MATERIALS
RADIOACTIVE POLLUTANTS
RADIOACTIVE TRACERS
RADIOACTIVE WASTE DISPOSAL
RADIOACTIVE WASTES
RADIOACTIVITY
RADIOCARBON DATING
RADIOCHEMISTRY
RADIOECOLOGY

RADIOGRAPHY
RADIOISOTOPES
RADIOLARIAN OOZE
RADIOLARITE
RADIOMETERS
RADIOMETRIC DATING
RADIONUCLIDE KINETICS
RADIOSONDES
RADIUM
RADIUM COMPOUNDS
RADIUM ISOTOPES
RADON
RADON ISOTOPES
RADULAE
RAFT CULTURE
RAFTING
RAIN
RAIN GAUGES
RAINFALL
RAINY SEASON
RAISED BEACHES
RANCHING
RANDOM PROCESSES
RARE EARTHS
RARE GASES
RARE RESOURCES
RARE SPECIES
RATIOS
RAW MATERIALS
RAY PATHS
RAYLEIGH WAVES
REARING
RECEPTORS
RECIRCULATING SYSTEMS
RECLAMATION
RECORDING EQUIPMENT
RECORDS
RECOVERY
RECREATION
RECREATIONAL WATERS
RECRUITMENT
RED TIDES
REDDS
REDFISH FISHERIES
REDMOUTH DISEASE
REDOX POTENTIAL
REDOX REACTIONS
REDUCTION
REEF FISH
REEF FISHERIES
REEF FORMATION
REEFS
REFERENCE LEVELS
REFLECTANCE
REFLECTED GLOBAL RADIATION
REFLECTION
REFRACTION
REFRACTIVE INDEX
REFRIGERATION
REFRIGERATORS
REFUGES
REGENERATION
REGIONAL PLANNING
REGIONAL VARIATIONS
REGIONS
REGRESSION ANALYSIS
REGRESSIONS
REINFORCED CONCRETE
RELATIVE DENSITY
RELATIVE HUMIDITY
RELATIVE VORTICITY
RELEASE MECHANISMS
RELIABILITY
RELICT LAKES
RELICT SEDIMENTS
RELICT SHORELINES
RELICT SPECIES
RELIEF FORMS

ASFIS Thesaurus
Alphabetical List of Terms

REMANENT MAGNETIZATION
REMOTE CONTROL
REMOTE SENSING
REMOTE SENSING EQUIPMENT
REMOVAL
RENEWABLE RESOURCES
RENEWAL
RENTAL
REPAIR
REPELLENTS
REPLACING
REPORT LITERATURE
REPRODUCTION
REPRODUCTIVE BEHAVIOUR
REPRODUCTIVE CYCLE
REPTILE CULTURE
RESEARCH
RESEARCH INSTITUTIONS
RESEARCH PROGRAMMES
RESEARCH PROPOSALS
RESEARCH VESSELS
RESERVOIR FISHERIES
RESERVOIRS (WATER)
RESIDENCE TIME
RESIDUAL FLOW
RESISTANCE MECHANISMS
RESISTIVITY PROBES
RESOLUTION
RESONANCE
RESONANT FREQUENCY
RESONANT WAVE INTERACTION
RESOURCE AVAILABILITY
RESOURCE CONSERVATION
RESOURCE DEPLETION
RESOURCE DEVELOPMENT
RESOURCE EXPLORATION
RESOURCE MANAGEMENT
RESOURCE SURVEYS
RESOURCES
RESPIRATION
RESPIRATORY ORGANS
RESPIRATORY PIGMENTS
RESPIRATORY SYSTEM
RESPIROMETERS
RESPONSE ANALYSIS
RESPONSE TIME
RESTING EGGS
RESTING SPORES
RESTING STAGES
RESUSPENDED SEDIMENTS
RESUSPENSION
RETINAS
RETROGRADATION
REVERBERATION
REVERSE OSMOSIS
REVERSING THERMOMETERS
REYNOLDS NUMBER
REYNOLDS STRESSES
RHENIUM
RHENIUM COMPOUNDS
RHENIUM ISOTOPES
RHEOLOGY
RHEOTAXIS
RHEOTROPISM
RHIZOMES
RHODAMINE B-DYE
RHODIUM
RHODIUM COMPOUNDS
RHODIUM ISOTOPES
RHYOLITES
RIA COASTS
RIBOSE
RIBOSOMES
RICE FIELD AQUACULTURE
RICE FIELDS
RICHARDSON NUMBER
RICHTER SCALE

RIDGES
RIFT VALLEYS
RIFT ZONES
RIFTING
RIGGING
RIGHTING
RIGHTS
RIP CHANNELS
RIP CURRENTS
RIPARIAN RIGHTS
RIPPLE MARKS
RIPRAP
RISER CABLES
RISER PIPES
RISKS
RIVER BANKS
RIVER BASIN MANAGEMENT
RIVER BASINS
RIVER BEDS
RIVER DISCHARGE
RIVER ENGINEERING
RIVER FISHERIES
RIVER MEANDERS
RIVER OUTFLOW
RIVER PLUMES
RIVER VALLEYS
RIVER WATER
RIVERS
RNA
ROBOTS
ROCK DEFORMATION
ROCK MECHANICS
ROCKS
ROCKY SHORES
ROE FISHERIES
ROES
ROLL RESONANCE
ROLL RESPONSE
ROLLERS
ROLLING
ROOTS
ROPES
ROSSBY NUMBER
ROSSBY PARAMETER
ROTARY CURRENTS
ROTATING FLUIDS
ROTATION
ROTENONE
ROUGHNESS
ROW BOATS
RUBBER
RUBBLEMOUND BREAKWATERS
RUBIDIUM
RUBIDIUM COMPOUNDS
RUBIDIUM ISOTOPES
RUBIDIUM-STRONTIUM DATING
RUDITES
RUNNELS
RUNOFF
RUTHENIUM
RUTHENIUM COMPOUNDS
RUTHENIUM ISOTOPES
RUTILE

S

S-WAVES
SABKHAS
SACCHARIDES
SACRIFICIAL ANODES
SAFETY DEVICES
SAFETY REGULATIONS
SAILING DIRECTIONS
SAILING SHIPS
SAILS
SALINE INTRUSION
SALINE WATER

SALINITY
SALINITY CHARTS
SALINITY DATA
SALINITY EFFECTS
SALINITY GRADIENTS
SALINITY MAXIMUM LAYER
SALINITY MEASUREMENT
SALINITY MEASURING EQUIPMENT
SALINITY MICROSTRUCTURE
SALINITY MINIMUM LAYER
SALINITY POWER
SALINITY PROFILES
SALINITY SCALES
SALINITY SECTIONS
SALINITY STRATIFICATION
SALINITY TABLES
SALINITY TOLERANCE
SALINOMETERS
SALMON FISHERIES
SALT ADVECTION
SALT BUDGET
SALT DEPOSITS
SALT DOMES
SALT FINGERS
SALT FLUX
SALT LAKES
SALT MARSHES
SALT NUCLEI
SALT PARTICLES
SALT WEDGES
SALT-WEDGE ESTUARIES
SALTATION
SALTS
SALVAGE EQUIPMENT
SALVAGING
SAMARIUM
SAMARIUM COMPOUNDS
SAMARIUM ISOTOPES
SAMPLE CONTAMINATION
SAMPLE STORAGE
SAMPLERS
SAMPLES
SAMPLING
SANCTUARIES
SAND
SAND BANKS
SAND BARS
SAND PATCHES
SAND RIBBONS
SAND RIPPLES
SAND STRUCTURES
SAND WAVES
SANDSTONE
SANITARY ENGINEERING
SAPONINS
SAPONITE
SAPROBIONTS
SAPROPELITE
SAPROPELS
SAPROPHYTES
SAPROPLANKTON
SAPROZOITES
SATELLITE ALTIMETRY
SATELLITE COMMUNICATION
SATELLITE MOSAICS
SATELLITE NAVIGATION
SATELLITE PHOTOGRAPHY
SATELLITE SENSING
SATELLITES
SATURATED HYDROCARBONS
SATURATION
SATURATION DEPTH
SATURATION DIVING
SATURATION VAPOUR PRESSURE
SCALE MODELS
SCALE READING
SCALES
SCALING

SCALLOP CULTURE
SCALLOP FISHERIES
SCANDIUM
SCANDIUM COMPOUNDS
SCANDIUM ISOTOPES
SCATTER DIAGRAMS
SCATTERANCE METERS
SCATTERING COEFFICIENT
SCATTERING LAYERS
SCATTEROMETERS
SCAVENGERS
SCHISTS
SCHOOLING BEHAVIOUR
SCIENTIFIC PERSONNEL
SCIENTIFIC SATELLITES
SCOUR AND FILL
SCOUR HOLLOWS
SCOUR MARKS
SCOUR PROTECTION
SCOURING
SCREENS
SCUBA DIVING
SEA BREEZES
SEA GRASS
SEA ICE
SEA LEVEL
SEA LEVEL CHANGES
SEA LEVEL MEASUREMENT
SEA LEVEL PRESSURE
SEA LEVEL VARIATIONS
SEA SICKNESS
SEA STATE
SEA STATE SCALES
SEA SURFACE
SEA WALLS
SEA WATER
SEABED CONVENTIONS
SEABED DEPOSITS
SEABED DRIFTERS
SEABED PROTECTION
SEABED VEHICLES
SEABIGHTS
SEACHANNELS
SEAFLOOR MAPPING
SEAFLOOR SAMPLING
SEAFLOOR SPREADING
SEAFOOD
SEAKNOLLS
SEALS (STOPPERS)
SEAMANSHIP
SEAMOATS
SEAMOUNT CHAINS
SEAMOUNTS
SEAQUAKES
SEARCH AND RESCUE
SEASON REGULATIONS
SEASONAL DISTRIBUTION
SEASONAL THERMOCLINE
SEASONAL VARIATIONS
SEASONALITY
SEASONS
SEAWATER EVOLUTION
SEAWEED CULTURE
SEAWEED HARVESTING
SEAWEED PROCESSING
SEAWEED PRODUCTS
SEAWEED STATISTICS
SEAWEEDS
SECCHI DISCS
SECONDARY PRODUCTION
SECONDARY SEXUAL CHARACTERS
SECRETION
SECRETORY ORGANS
SECRETORY PRODUCTS
SECURITY
SEDENTARY SPECIES
SEDIMENT ANALYSIS

SEDIMENT CHEMISTRY
SEDIMENT COLLECTIONS
SEDIMENT COMPOSITION
SEDIMENT DENSITY
SEDIMENT DISTRIBUTION
SEDIMENT DRIFTS
SEDIMENT DYNAMICS
SEDIMENT GRAVITY FLOWS
SEDIMENT LOAD
SEDIMENT MIXING
SEDIMENT MOVEMENT
SEDIMENT NOISE
SEDIMENT POLLUTION
SEDIMENT PROPERTIES
SEDIMENT SAMPLERS
SEDIMENT SAMPLES
SEDIMENT SAMPLING
SEDIMENT SORTING
SEDIMENT STABILITY
SEDIMENT STRUCTURE
SEDIMENT TEMPERATURE
SEDIMENT TEXTURE
SEDIMENT TRANSPORT
SEDIMENT TRAPS
SEDIMENT-WATER EXCHANGES
SEDIMENT-WATER INTERFACE
SEDIMENTARY BASINS
SEDIMENTARY ENVIRONMENTS
SEDIMENTARY ROCKS
SEDIMENTARY STRUCTURES
SEDIMENTATION
SEDIMENTOLOGY
SEDIMENTS
SEED (AQUACULTURE)
SEED COLLECTION
SEED PRODUCTION
SEEDING (AQUACULTURE)
SEEPAGES
SEICHES
SEINE NETS
SEINERS
SEINING
SEISMIC ACTIVITY
SEISMIC ARRAYS
SEISMIC ATTENUATION
SEISMIC DATA
SEISMIC DATA PROCESSING
SEISMIC DIFFRACTION
SEISMIC DISCONTINUITIES
SEISMIC ENERGY SOURCES
SEISMIC EQUIPMENT
SEISMIC EXPLORATION
SEISMIC LAYERS
SEISMIC PROFILES
SEISMIC PROPAGATION
SEISMIC REFLECTION
SEISMIC REFLECTION PROFILES
SEISMIC REFLECTION PROFILING
SEISMIC REFRACTION
SEISMIC REFRACTION PROFILES
SEISMIC REFRACTION PROFILING
SEISMIC RIDGES
SEISMIC SCATTERING
SEISMIC STRATIGRAPHY
SEISMIC VELOCITIES
SEISMIC WAVES
SEISMIC ZONES
SEISMOGRAMS
SEISMOLOGY
SEISMOMETERS
SELECTED SHIPS
SELECTIVE BREEDING
SELECTIVE FEEDING
SELENIUM
SELENIUM COMPOUNDS
SELENIUM ISOTOPES
SELF FERTILIZATION

SELF PURIFICATION
SELF-PROPELLED VEHICLES
SEMEN
SEMI-ENCLOSED SEAS
SEMIDIURNAL TIDES
SEMISUBMERSIBLE PLATFORMS
SENSE FUNCTIONS
SENSE ORGANS
SENSE TENTACLES
SENSIBLE HEAT
SENSIBLE HEAT TRANSFER
SENSORS
SEPARATION
SEPARATION PROCESSES
SEPIOLITE
SEPTICAEMIA
SERINE
SEROLOGICAL STUDIES
SEROLOGICAL TAXONOMY
SERPENTINITE
SERPENTINITIZATION
SERUM
SESSILE SPECIES
SESTON
SETTLEMENT (STRUCTURAL)
SETTLING BEHAVIOUR
SETTLING RATE
SEWAGE
SEWAGE DISPOSAL
SEWAGE PONDS
SEWAGE TREATMENT
SEX
SEX CHARACTERS
SEX DETERMINATION
SEX HORMONES
SEX RATIO
SEX REVERSAL
SEXUAL BEHAVIOUR
SEXUAL CELLS
SEXUAL DIMORPHISM
SEXUAL ISOLATION
SEXUAL MATURITY
SEXUAL REPRODUCTION
SEXUAL SELECTION
SHALE
SHALLOW WATER
SHALLOW-WATER TIDES
SHALLOW-WATER WAVES
SHAPE
SHAPED CHARGES
SHARED STOCKS
SHARK ATTACKS
SHARK FISHERIES
SHARK UTILIZATION
SHEAR
SHEAR FLOW
SHEAR MODULUS
SHEAR PROBES
SHEAR STRENGTH
SHEAR STRESS
SHEAR WAVE VELOCITIES
SHEAR ZONE
SHELF CURRENTS
SHELF DYNAMICS
SHELF EDGE
SHELF EDGE DYNAMICS
SHELF EDGE FRONTS
SHELF FACIES
SHELF FRONTS
SHELF GEOLOGY
SHELF SEAS
SHELF SEDIMENTATION
SHELF WAVES
SHELLFISH
SHELLFISH CATCH STATISTICS
SHELLFISH CULTURE
SHELLFISH FISHERIES
SHELLS

ASFIS Thesaurus
Alphabetical List of Terms

SHELTERED HABITATS
SHELTERS
SHINGLE
SHIP CANALS
SHIP DESIGN
SHIP DRIFT
SHIP HANDLING
SHIP HULLS
SHIP LOSSES
SHIP MODELS
SHIP MOORING SYSTEMS
SHIP MOTION
SHIP PERFORMANCE
SHIP ROUTEING
SHIP SPEED
SHIP STABILITY
SHIP TECHNOLOGY
SHIPBOARD ANALYSIS
SHIPBOARD EQUIPMENT
SHIPPING
SHIPPING LANES
SHIPPING NOISE
SHIPS
SHOALING
SHOALING WAVES
SHOALS
SHORAN
SHORE PROTECTION
SHORT WAVE-LONG WAVE INTERACTIONS
SHORT-CRESTED WAVES
SHORT-TERM CHANGES
SHORT-TERM PLANNING
SHORT-TERM RECORDS
SHRIMP CULTURE
SHRIMP FISHERIES
SIAL
SIBLING SPECIES
SIDE SCAN SONAR
SIDERITE
SIGMA-T
SIGNAL PROCESSING
SIGNAL-TO-NOISE RATIO
SIGNIFICANT WAVE HEIGHT
SIGNIFICANT WAVES
SILICA
SILICATE MINERALS
SILICATES
SILICEOUS OOZE
SILICEOUS ROCKS
SILICEOUS SEDIMENTS
SILICIC ACID
SILICIFICATION
SILICON
SILICON COMPOUNDS
SILICON CYCLE
SILICON ISOTOPES
SILL DEPTH
SILLS
SILO CULTURE
SILT
SILT METERS
SILTING
SILTSTONE
SILURIAN
SILVER
SILVER COMPOUNDS
SILVER ISOTOPES
SIMA
SIMULATION
SIMULATORS
SINGLE CELL PROTEINS
SINGLE POINT MOORINGS
SINKING
SITE SELECTION
SITE SURVEYS
SITOSTEROLS
SIZE

SIZE DISTRIBUTION
SIZE-LIMIT REGULATIONS
SKELETON
SKEWNESS
SKIN
SKULL
SLATES
SLICKS
SLIDES
SLIDES (PHOTOGRAPHIC)
SLOPE CURRENTS
SLOPE ENVIRONMENT
SLOPE INDICATORS
SLOPE PROCESSES
SLOPE STABILITY
SLOPE WATER
SLOPES (TOPOGRAPHY)
SLUDGE
SLUDGE TREATMENT
SLUMP STRUCTURES
SLUMPING
SLURRIES
SMALL SCALE AQUACULTURE
SMECTITE
SMOKE
SMOLTS
SNOW
SOAPS
SOCIAL BEHAVIOUR
SOCIOLOGICAL ASPECTS
SODAR
SODIUM
SODIUM CHLORIDE
SODIUM COMPOUNDS
SODIUM ISOTOPES
SOFAR
SOFAR CHANNEL
SOFAR FLOATS
SOIL CONSERVATION
SOIL EROSION
SOIL MECHANICS
SOILS
SOLAR ACTIVITY
SOLAR CELLS
SOLAR CONSTANT
SOLAR DIURNAL TIDES
SOLAR ECLIPSE
SOLAR POWER
SOLAR RADIATION
SOLAR SEMIDIURNAL TIDES
SOLAR TIDES
SOLAR-TERRESTRIAL ACTIVITY
SOLE MARKS
SOLID IMPURITIES
SOLIDIFICATION
SOLITARY WAVES
SOLITONS
SOLUBILITY
SOLUTES
SOLUTIONS
SOLVATION
SOLVENT EXTRACTION
SOLVENTS
SONAR
SONAR ARRAYS
SONAR COUNTERMEASURES
SONAR DETECTION
SONAR IMAGERY
SONAR RECEIVERS
SONAR TARGETS
SONAR TRANSDUCERS
SONAR TRANSPONDERS
SONIC TAGS
SONOBUOYS
SONOGRAPHS
SORPTION
SORTING CENTRES

SOUND
SOUND ABSORPTION
SOUND ATTENUATION
SOUND CHANNELS
SOUND DIFFRACTION
SOUND DISPERSION
SOUND GENERATION
SOUND GENERATORS
SOUND INTENSITY
SOUND MEASUREMENT
SOUND PRESSURE
SOUND PRODUCTION
SOUND PROPAGATION
SOUND RECORDERS
SOUND REFLECTION
SOUND REFRACTION
SOUND SCATTERING
SOUND SOURCES
SOUND SPECTRA
SOUND TRANSMISSION
SOUND VELOCITY
SOUND WAVES
SOUNDING LINES
SOUNDINGS
SOUTHERN OSCILLATION
SPALLING
SPAR BUOYS
SPARKERS
SPAT
SPATIAL VARIATIONS
SPAWNING
SPAWNING GROUNDS
SPAWNING MIGRATIONS
SPAWNING POPULATIONS
SPAWNING SEASONS
SPEAR FISHING
SPECIES
SPECIES DIVERSITY
SPECIES EXTINCTION
SPECIFIC GRAVITY
SPECIFIC HEAT
SPECIFIC HUMIDITY
SPECIFIC VOLUME
SPECIFIC VOLUME ANOMALIES
SPECIFICATIONS
SPECIFICITY
SPECTRA
SPECTRAL ANALYSIS
SPECTRAL COMPOSITION
SPECTROCHEMICAL ANALYSIS
SPECTROPHOTOMETERS
SPECTROSCOPIC TECHNIQUES
SPEECH DISTORTION
SPEEDOMETERS
SPELAEOLOGY
SPERM
SPERMATOGENESIS
SPERMATOPHORES
SPHERES
SPILLING WAVES
SPINAL CORD
SPINDOWN
SPINUP
SPITS
SPLASH ZONE
SPLEEN
SPLINES
SPOIL
SPONGE CULTURE
SPONGE FISHERIES
SPONGES
SPORANGIA
SPORES
SPOROGENESIS
SPORT FISHING
SPORT FISHING STATISTICS
SPRAY
SPREADING CENTRES

ASFIS Thesaurus
Alphabetical List of Terms

SPRING
SPRING STREAMS
SPRING TIDES
SQUALENE
SQUAT LOBSTER FISHERIES
SQUID CULTURE
STABILITY
STABILITY CONSTANTS
STABILIZED PLATFORMS
STABILIZERS
STABILIZING
STACKS
STAGNANT WATER
STAINING
STAINLESS STEEL
STANDARD DEPTHS
STANDARD OCEAN SECTIONS
STANDARD SEA WATER
STANDARD SIGNALS
STANDARDIZATION
STANDARDS
STANDING WAVES
STARCH
STARVATION
STATIC INSTABILITY
STATION KEEPING
STATION LISTS
STATISTICAL ANALYSIS
STATISTICAL MODELS
STATISTICAL SAMPLING
STATISTICAL TABLES
STATISTICIANS
STATISTICS
STATOCYSTS
STD OBSERVATIONS
STD PROFILERS
STD PROFILES
STEADY STATE
STEEL
STEEL STRUCTURES
STEERING SYSTEMS
STEMS
STENOHALINITY
STENOTHERMY
STEREOPHOTOGRAPHY
STERIC SEA LEVEL
STERILITY
STERILIZATION
STEROIDS
STEROLS
STICKWATER
STIMULI
STINGING ORGANS
STOCHASTIC PROCESSES
STOCK ASSESSMENT
STOCK IDENTIFICATION
STOCKING (ORGANISMS)
STOCKING DENSITY
STOCKING PONDS
STOCKS
STOKES LAW
STOKES WAVES
STOMACH
STOMACH CONTENT
STOMATA
STONELEY WAVES
STORAGE
STORAGE CONDITIONS
STORAGE EFFECTS
STORAGE LIFE
STORAGE TANKS
STORM SURGE BARRIERS
STORM SURGE GENERATION
STORM SURGE PREDICTION
STORM SURGES
STORM TIDE WARNING SERVICES
STORMS

STORMWATER RUNOFF
STRAIN
STRAIN GAUGES
STRAIN SEISMOMETERS
STRAITS
STRANDING
STRANDLINES
STRATIFICATION
STRATIFIED FLOW
STRATIFIED SHEAR FLOW
STRATIGRAPHIC CORRELATION
STRATIGRAPHIC TRAPS
STRATIGRAPHY
STRATOSPHERE
STREAM FLOW
STREAM FLOW RATE
STREAM FUNCTIONS
STREAMERS
STREAMLINES
STRENGTH
STRESS
STRESS CORROSION
STRESS-STRAIN RELATIONS
STRIP MINE LAKES
STRIPPING ANALYSIS
STROMATOLITES
STRONTIUM
STRONTIUM COMPOUNDS
STRONTIUM ISOTOPES
STRUCTURAL ANALYSIS
STRUCTURAL BASINS
STRUCTURAL DOMES
STRUCTURAL DYNAMICS
STRUCTURAL ENGINEERING
STRUCTURAL GEOLOGY
STRUCTURES
STUPEFYING METHODS
SUB-BOTTOM PROFILING
SUBAEREAL TOPOGRAPHY
SUBDUCTION
SUBDUCTION ZONES
SUBLETHAL EFFECTS
SUBLIMATION
SUBLIMATION HEAT
SUBLITTORAL ZONE
SUBMARINE BANKS
SUBMARINE CABLE BREAKS
SUBMARINE CABLES
SUBMARINE CANYONS
SUBMARINE CEMENTS
SUBMARINE FEATURES
SUBMARINE PLATEAUX
SUBMARINE RIDGES
SUBMARINE SCARPS
SUBMARINE SPRINGS
SUBMARINE TANKERS
SUBMARINE TROUGHS
SUBMARINE VALLEYS
SUBMARINE VOLCANOES
SUBMARINES
SUBMERGED CAGES
SUBMERGED SHORELINES
SUBMERGENCE
SUBMERSIBLE PLATFORMS
SUBMERSIBLES
SUBPOPULATIONS
SUBSEA PRODUCTION SYSTEMS
SUBSIDENCE
SUBSTRATA
SUBSTRATE PREFERENCES
SUBSURFACE CURRENTS
SUBSURFACE DEPOSITS
SUBSURFACE DRIFTERS
SUBSURFACE WATER
SUBTROPICAL CONVERGENCES
SUBTROPICAL ZONES
SULPHATE MINERALS

SULPHATE REDUCTION
SULPHATES
SULPHIDE DEPOSITS
SULPHIDE MINERALS
SULPHIDES
SULPHITES
SULPHONATES
SULPHUR
SULPHUR COMPOUNDS
SULPHUR DIOXIDE
SULPHUR ISOTOPES
SULPHUR OXIDES
SULPHURIC ACID
SUMMER
SUN
SUNBURN
SUPERSATURATION
SUPPLY BOATS
SUPPORT SHIPS
SUPPRESSORS
SUPRALITTORAL ZONE
SURF
SURF BEATS
SURF ZONE
SURFACE ACTIVITY
SURFACE CHEMISTRY
SURFACE CIRCULATION
SURFACE CLUTTER
SURFACE CRAFT
SURFACE CURRENTS
SURFACE DRIFTERS
SURFACE EKMAN LAYER
SURFACE FILMS
SURFACE GRAVITY WAVES
SURFACE LAYERS
SURFACE MICROLAYER
SURFACE MIXED LAYER
SURFACE NOISE
SURFACE POTENTIAL
SURFACE PROPERTIES
SURFACE RADIATION TEMPERATURE
SURFACE ROUGHNESS
SURFACE SALINITY
SURFACE SEISMIC WAVES
SURFACE SLOPE
SURFACE TEMPERATURE
SURFACE TENSION
SURFACE TOPOGRAPHY
SURFACE WATER
SURFACE WATER MASSES
SURFACE WATER WAVES
SURFACE WAVE-INTERNAL WAVE INTERACTIONS
SURFACES
SURFACTANTS
SURFING
SURGE RESPONSE
SURGES
SURGING
SURROUNDING NETS
SURVEILLANCE AND ENFORCEMENT
SURVEY VESSELS
SURVEYING
SURVEYING EQUIPMENT
SURVEYING UNDERWATER
SURVEYS
SURVIVAL
SURVIVAL AT SEA
SUSPENDED INORGANIC MATTER
SUSPENDED LOAD
SUSPENDED ORGANIC MATTER
SUSPENDED PARTICULATE MATTER
SUSPENSION
SVERDRUP TRANSPORT
SWALLOW FLOATS
SWAMP FISHERIES
SWAMPS
SWATHS
SWAYING

ASFIS Thesaurus
Alphabetical List of Terms

SWELL
SWIM BLADDER
SWIMMING
SYMBIONTS
SYMBIOSIS
SYMPATRIC POPULATIONS
SYMPTOMS
SYNAPSES
SYNCLINES
SYNCLINORIA
SYNECOLOGY
SYNERGISM
SYNONYMY
SYNOPSIS
SYNTHETIC APERTURE RADAR
SYNTHETIC FIBRES
SYSTEM ANALYSIS

T

T/S DIAGRAMS
TABLES
TABULAR BERGS
TACTILE FUNCTIONS
TACTILE ORGANS
TACTILE STIMULI
TAGGING
TAGGING MORTALITY
TAGS
TANK CLEANING
TANKER LOADING
TANKER SHIPS
TANKER TERMINALS
TANKS
TANTALUM
TANTALUM COMPOUNDS
TANTALUM ISOTOPES
TAR
TAR BALLS
TARGET CELLS
TARGET STRENGTH
TASTE
TASTE FUNCTIONS
TASTE ORGANS
TASTE TESTS
TAXA
TAXES
TAXIS
TAXONOMISTS
TAXONOMY
TECHNETIUM
TECHNETIUM COMPOUNDS
TECHNETIUM ISOTOPES
TECHNICAL FEASIBILITY
TECHNICIANS
TECHNOLOGY
TECHNOLOGY TRANSFER
TECTONICS
TECTONOPHYSICS
TEETH
TELECONNECTIONS
TELEMETRY
TELEPHONE SYSTEMS
TELEVISION SYSTEMS
TELEX
TELLURIC CURRENTS
TELLURIUM
TELLURIUM COMPOUNDS
TELLURIUM ISOTOPES
TELLUROMETERS
TELSON
TEMPERATE ZONES
TEMPERATURE
TEMPERATURE (AIR-SEA)
TEMPERATURE ANOMALIES
TEMPERATURE CHARTS
TEMPERATURE DATA

TEMPERATURE DIFFERENCES
TEMPERATURE EFFECTS
TEMPERATURE GRADIENTS
TEMPERATURE INVERSIONS
TEMPERATURE MAXIMUM LAYER
TEMPERATURE MEASUREMENT
TEMPERATURE MINIMUM LAYER
TEMPERATURE PREFERENCES
TEMPERATURE PROFILES
TEMPERATURE SECTIONS
TEMPERATURE TOLERANCE
TEMPLATES
TEMPORAL DISTRIBUTION
TEMPORAL VARIATIONS
TEMPORARY PONDS
TENSILE STRENGTH
TENSION
TENSION LEG PLATFORMS
TENSOMETERS
TENTACLES
TEPHRA
TERATOGENS
TERATOLOGY
TERBIUM
TERBIUM COMPOUNDS
TERBIUM ISOTOPES
TERMINOLOGY
TERPENES
TERRACES
TERRESTRIAL RADIATION
TERRIGENOUS SEDIMENTS
TERRITORIAL WATERS
TERRITORIALITY
TERTIARY
TEST EQUIPMENT
TEST ORGANISMS
TESTES
TESTING
TESTS
TETHERED FREE-SWIMMING VEHICLES
TETHERED VEHICLES
TETRODOTOXIN
TEXTURE
THALLIUM
THALLIUM COMPOUNDS
THALLIUM ISOTOPES
THALLUS
THALWEG
THAWING
THERAPY
THERMAL AQUACULTURE
THERMAL CONDUCTIVITY
THERMAL DECOMPOSITION
THERMAL DIFFUSION
THERMAL DIFFUSIVITY
THERMAL DOMES
THERMAL EXPANSION
THERMAL FRONTS
THERMAL INSULATION
THERMAL MICROSTRUCTURE
THERMAL PLUMES
THERMAL POLLUTION
THERMAL POWER
THERMAL RADIATION
THERMAL STIMULI
THERMAL STRATIFICATION
THERMAL STRUCTURE
THERMISTOR CHAINS
THERMISTORS
THERMOCLINE
THERMOCLINE DECAY
THERMOCOUPLE ARRAYS
THERMOCOUPLES
THERMODYNAMIC ACTIVITY
THERMODYNAMIC EQUILIBRIUM
THERMODYNAMIC PROPERTIES
THERMODYNAMICS

THERMOHALINE CIRCULATION
THERMOMETERS
THERMORECEPTORS
THERMOREGULATION
THERMOSTADS
THERMOSTERIC ANOMALIES
THESAURUS
THICKNESS
THIXOTROPY
THOLEIITE
THOLEIITIC BASALT
THORAX
THORIUM
THORIUM COMPOUNDS
THORIUM ISOTOPES
THORIUM-230/THORIUM-232 DATING
THREONINE
THRUSTERS
THULIUM
THULIUM COMPOUNDS
THULIUM ISOTOPES
THUNDERSTORMS
THYMUS
THYROID
TIDAL AMPLITUDE
TIDAL ANALYSIS
TIDAL BARRAGES
TIDAL BORES
TIDAL CHARTS
TIDAL CONSTANTS
TIDAL CONSTITUENTS
TIDAL CURRENTS
TIDAL CURVES
TIDAL CYCLES
TIDAL DATUM
TIDAL DEPOSITS
TIDAL DISSIPATION
TIDAL DYNAMICS
TIDAL EFFECTS
TIDAL ENERGY
TIDAL EQUATIONS
TIDAL FLATS
TIDAL FRICTION
TIDAL INLETS
TIDAL MIXING
TIDAL MODELS
TIDAL MOTION
TIDAL OSCILLATIONS
TIDAL PERTURBATION
TIDAL POWER
TIDAL POWER PLANTS
TIDAL PREDICTION
TIDAL PROPAGATION
TIDAL RANGE
TIDAL RECORDS
TIDAL RESONANCE
TIDAL WAVES
TIDE GAUGES
TIDE GENERATING POTENTIAL
TIDE TABLES
TIDE-SURGE INTERACTION
TIDES
TILTMETERS
TIME SERIES
TIME SERIES ANALYSIS
TIN
TIN COMPOUNDS
TIN ISOTOPES
TISSUE CULTURE
TISSUES
TITANITE
TITANIUM
TITANIUM COMPOUNDS
TITANIUM ISOTOPES
TITRATION
TODOROKITE
TOLERANCE
TOLERANCES (DIMENSIONAL)

ASFIS Thesaurus
Alphabetical List of Terms

TOMBOLOS
TOPOGRAPHIC EFFECTS
TOPOGRAPHIC FEATURES
TOPOGRAPHIC MAPS
TOPOGRAPHIC SURVEYING
TOPOGRAPHIC WAVES
TOPOGRAPHY
TOPOGRAPHY (GEOLOGY)
TOPSET BEDS
TORNADOES
TORQUE
TOTAL MORTALITY
TOTAL ORGANIC CARBON
TOUGHNESS
TOURMALINE
TOWED BODIES
TOWED BODY DESIGN
TOWED SENSORS
TOWED VEHICLES
TOWERS
TOWING
TOWING LINES
TOWING TANKS
TOXICANTS
TOXICITY
TOXICITY TESTS
TOXICITY TOLERANCE
TOXICOLOGY
TRACE ELEMENTS
TRACE FOSSILS
TRACE METALS
TRACER TECHNIQUES
TRACERS
TRACHEA
TRACK CHARTS
TRACKING
TRACTION
TRADE
TRADE ORGANIZATIONS
TRADE WIND INVERSION
TRADE WINDS
TRAFFIC MANAGEMENT
TRAINING
TRAINING AIDS
TRAINING CENTRES
TRANS-ISOPYCNAL MIXING
TRANSDUCER ARRAYS
TRANSDUCERS
TRANSFER CHAMBERS
TRANSFERASES
TRANSFORM FAULTS
TRANSFORM PLATE BOUNDARIES
TRANSGRESSIONS
TRANSITION ELEMENT COMPOUNDS
TRANSITION ELEMENTS
TRANSITION TEMPERATURES
TRANSLATIONS
TRANSMISSION
TRANSMISSION LOSS
TRANSMISSOMETERS
TRANSMITTANCE
TRANSPARENCY
TRANSPIRATION
TRANSPLANTATION
TRANSPLANTS
TRANSPONDER ARRAYS
TRANSPONDERS
TRANSPORT
TRANSPORT PROCESSES
TRANSPORTATION
TRANSURANIC ELEMENTS
TRANSVERSE BARS
TRANSVERSE BED FORMS
TRANSVERSE MIXING
TRAP FISHING
TRAP NETS
TRAPPED WAVES

TRASH FISH
TRAVERSE TABLES
TRAWL NETS
TRAWLERS
TRAWLING
TRAY CULTURE
TRENCHES (OCEANIC)
TRENCHES (PIPELINES)
TRENCHING
TRIASSIC
TRIBUTARIES
TRICHLOROETHYLENE
TRIPLE JUNCTIONS
TRITIUM
TROLLING
TROPHIC LEVELS
TROPHIC RELATIONSHIPS
TROPHIC STRUCTURE
TROPHODYNAMIC CYCLE
TROPICAL DEPRESSIONS
TROPICAL ENVIRONMENT
TROPICAL FISH
TROPICAL LAKES
TROPICAL METEOROLOGY
TROPICAL OCEANOGRAPHY
TROPISM
TROPOPAUSE
TROPOSPHERE
TSUNAMI GENERATION
TSUNAMI PREDICTION
TSUNAMIS
TUBE DWELLERS
TUBERCULOSIS
TUBING
TUGS
TUMOURS
TUNA FISHERIES
TUNGSTEN
TUNGSTEN COMPOUNDS
TUNGSTEN ISOTOPES
TUNNELS
TURBIDIMETERS
TURBIDITES
TURBIDITY
TURBIDITY CURRENT STRUCTURES
TURBIDITY CURRENTS
TURBINES
TURBULENCE
TURBULENCE MEASUREMENT
TURBULENT BOUNDARY LAYER
TURBULENT DIFFUSION
TURBULENT ENTRAINMENT
TURBULENT FLOW
TURBULENT SHEAR FLOW
TURBULENT TRANSFER
TURIONS
TURTLE CULTURE
TURTLE FISHERIES
TYPE LOCALITIES
TYPOLOGY
TYROSINE

U

ULCERATIVE DERMAL NECROSIS
ULTRAMAFIC ROCKS
ULTRASONIC DEVICES
ULTRASONIC TRANSDUCERS
ULTRASONICS
ULTRASTRUCTURE
ULTRAVIOLET RADIATION
ULTRAVIOLET STERILIZATION
UMBILICALS
UNCONVENTIONAL RESOURCES
UNDERCURRENTS
UNDERSEA WARFARE
UNDERTOW

UNDERUTILIZED SPECIES
UNDERWATER ACCESS
UNDERWATER CAMERAS
UNDERWATER EQUIPMENT
UNDERWATER EXPLOITATION
UNDERWATER EXPLORATION
UNDERWATER EXPLOSIONS
UNDERWATER HABITATS
UNDERWATER INSPECTION
UNDERWATER MEDICINE
UNDERWATER NOISE
UNDERWATER OBJECT LOCATION
UNDERWATER PHOTOGRAPHS
UNDERWATER PHOTOGRAPHY
UNDERWATER PROPULSION
UNDERWATER STRUCTURES
UNDERWATER TELEVISION
UNDERWATER VEHICLES
UNDULATORS
UNIDIRECTIONAL FLOW
UNIT STOCKS
UNMANNED VEHICLES
UNSATURATED HYDROCARBONS
UNSTEADY FLOW
UNSTEADY STATE
UNTETHERED VEHICLES
UPLIFT
UPPER ATMOSPHERE
UPPER MANTLE
UPPER OCEAN
UPWARD IRRADIANCE
UPWARD LONG WAVE RADIATION
UPWELLING
URANIUM
URANIUM COMPOUNDS
URANIUM ISOTOPES
URANIUM-HELIUM DATING
URANIUM-234/URANIUM-238 RATIO
URBAN RUNOFF
URBANIZATION
UREA
URINARY SYSTEM
URINE
UTILIZATION

V

VACCINATION
VACCINES
VALINE
VALLEYS
VALLICULTURE
VANADIUM
VANADIUM COMPOUNDS
VANADIUM ISOTOPES
VANE DEVICES
VANE SHEAR TESTING
VANES
VAPORIZATION
VAPORIZATION HEAT
VAPOUR PRESSURE
VARIABILITY
VARIANCE ANALYSIS
VARVES
VECTORS
VEGETAL FOSSILS
VEGETATION COVER
VEGETATIVE REPRODUCTION
VEHICLES
VELIGERS
VELOCITY
VELOCITY GRADIENTS
VELOCITY MICROSTRUCTURE
VELOCITY PROFILERS
VELOCITY PROFILES
VELOCITY SECTIONS
VENOM APPARATUS
VENTILATION

ASFIS Thesaurus
Alphabetical List of Terms

VERMICULITE
VERNACULAR NAMES
VERTEBRAE
VERTEBRAE COUNTS
VERTEBRATE ZOOLOGY
VERTICAL ADVECTION
VERTICAL DISTRIBUTION
VERTICAL MIGRATIONS
VERTICAL MIXING
VERTICAL MOTION
VERTICAL PROFILES
VERTICAL PROFILING
VERTICAL SECTIONS
VERTICAL SHEAR
VERTICAL STABILITY
VERTICAL TECTONICS
VERTICAL WATER MOVEMENT
VIBRATION
VIBRATORY CORERS
VIBRIOSIS
VIDEOTAPE RECORDINGS
VIEWING UNDERWATER
VIRAL DISEASES
VIROLOGISTS
VIROLOGY
VIRUSES
VISCOSITY
VISCOSITY COEFFICIENTS
VISIBILITY
VISIBILITY UNDERWATER
VISION
VISUAL INSPECTION
VISUAL PIGMENTS
VISUAL STIMULI
VITAMIN A
VITAMIN B
VITAMIN C
VITAMIN D
VITAMIN DEFICIENCIES
VITAMIN E
VITAMINS
VITELLOGENESIS
VIVIPARITY
VOCAL ORGANS
VOCALIZATION BEHAVIOUR
VOID RATIO
VOIDS
VOLATILE COMPOUNDS
VOLATILE HYDROCARBONS
VOLCANIC ASH
VOLCANIC BELTS
VOLCANIC BRECCIA
VOLCANIC ERUPTIONS
VOLCANIC GLASS
VOLCANIC ISLANDS
VOLCANIC LAPILLI
VOLCANIC ROCKS
VOLCANISM
VOLCANOES
VOLCANOGENIC DEPOSITS
VOLTAMMETRY
VOLUME
VOLUME SCATTERING FUNCTION
VOLUME TRANSPORT
VOLUMETRIC ANALYSIS
VORTEX SHEDDING
VORTICES
VORTICITY
VULNERABILITY

W

WAKES
WARM-WATER AQUACULTURE
WARNING SERVICES
WARNING SYSTEMS
WASTE DISPOSAL

WASTE DISPOSAL SITES
WASTE HEAT
WASTE TREATMENT
WASTE UTILIZATION
WASTE WATER
WASTES
WASTEWATER AQUACULTURE
WASTEWATER TREATMENT
WATER
WATER ANALYSIS
WATER AUTHORITIES
WATER BALANCE
WATER BODIES
WATER BUDGET
WATER CIRCULATION
WATER COLOUR
WATER COLUMN
WATER CONSERVATION
WATER CONTENT
WATER CURRENTS
WATER DENSITY
WATER DEPTH
WATER EXCHANGE
WATER FILTERS
WATER FILTRATION
WATER HARDNESS
WATER LEVEL MEASUREMENT
WATER LEVELS
WATER MANAGEMENT
WATER MASS INTRUSIONS
WATER MASSES
WATER MIXING
WATER MOTION
WATER POLICY
WATER POLLUTION
WATER POLLUTION TREATMENT
WATER PROPERTIES
WATER PUMPS
WATER PURIFICATION
WATER QUALITY
WATER QUALITY CONTROL
WATER RECLAMATION
WATER RESOURCES
WATER RIGHTS
WATER RIPPLES
WATER SAMPLERS
WATER SAMPLES
WATER SAMPLING
WATER SPRINGS
WATER STRUCTURE
WATER SUPPLY
WATER TABLE
WATER TEMPERATURE
WATER TRANSPARENCY
WATER TREATMENT
WATER TYPES
WATER USE
WATER USE REGULATIONS
WATER VAPOUR
WATER WAVE MOTION
WATER WAVE PARAMETERS
WATER WAVES
WATERSHEDS
WATERSPOUTS
WAVE ACTION
WAVE AGE
WAVE AMPLITUDE
WAVE ANALYSIS
WAVE ATTENUATION
WAVE BREAKING
WAVE BUOYS
WAVE CLIMATE
WAVE CRESTS
WAVE DAMPING
WAVE DATA
WAVE DIFFRACTION
WAVE DIRECTION

WAVE DIRECTION SENSORS
WAVE DISPERSION
WAVE DISSIPATION
WAVE DRIFT VELOCITY
WAVE DYNAMICS
WAVE EFFECTS
WAVE ENERGY
WAVE FOLLOWERS
WAVE FORCES
WAVE FORECASTING
WAVE FREQUENCY
WAVE GAUGES
WAVE GENERATION
WAVE GENERATORS
WAVE GEOMETRY
WAVE GROUPS
WAVE HEIGHT
WAVE HINDCASTING
WAVE INTERACTIONS
WAVE MEASUREMENT
WAVE MEASURING EQUIPMENT
WAVE MEASURING PLATFORMS
WAVE MOTION
WAVE NUMBER
WAVE PERIOD
WAVE PHASE
WAVE POWER
WAVE POWER DEVICES
WAVE PREDICTING
WAVE PROCESSES ON BEACHES
WAVE PROPAGATION
WAVE PROPERTIES
WAVE RECORDERS
WAVE REFLECTION
WAVE REFRACTION
WAVE REFRACTION DIAGRAMS
WAVE RUNUP
WAVE SCATTERING
WAVE SCOURING
WAVE SETDOWN
WAVE SETUP
WAVE SLOPE
WAVE SLOPE FOLLOWERS
WAVE SPECTRA
WAVE STATISTICS
WAVE STEEPNESS
WAVE TANKS
WAVE TRAINS
WAVE TRAPPING
WAVE VELOCITY
WAVE-AIR INTERACTION
WAVE-CURRENT INTERACTION
WAVE-CUT PLATFORMS
WAVE-ICE INTERACTION
WAVE-INDUCED LOADING
WAVE-SEABED INTERACTION
WAVE-WAVE INTERACTION
WAVEFORM ANALYSIS
WAVELENGTH
WAVES ON BEACHES
WAXES
WEAR
WEATHER
WEATHER FORECASTING
WEATHER HAZARDS
WEATHER MAPS
WEATHER SHIPS
WEATHERING
WEEDS
WEEKLY
WEIGHT
WEIRS
WELDING
WELDING UNDERWATER
WELL COMPLETION
WELL LOGGING
WELL WORKOVER OPERATIONS
WELLHEADS

ASFIS Thesaurus
Alphabetical List of Terms

WEST WIND DRIFT
WESTERLIES
WESTERN BOUNDARY CURRENTS
WESTERN BOUNDARY UNDERCURRENTS
WESTWARD INTENSIFICATION
WET
WET BULK DENSITY
WET SUBMERSIBLES
WET WEIGHT
WETLANDS
WHALING
WHALING REGULATIONS
WHALING STATIONS
WHALING STATISTICS
WHIRLING DISEASE
WHITECAPPING
WHITECAPS
WIDTH
WILD SPAWNING
WINCHES
WIND ABRASION
WIND CONSTANCY
WIND DATA
WIND DIRECTION
WIND EROSION
WIND FIELDS
WIND MEASUREMENT
WIND MEASURING EQUIPMENT
WIND POWER
WIND PRESSURE
WIND PROFILES
WIND ROSES
WIND SETUP
WIND SHEAR
WIND SPEED
WIND STRESS
WIND STRESS CURL
WIND TUNNELS
WIND VECTORS
WIND WAVE GENERATION
WIND WAVE PARAMETERS
WIND WAVES
WIND-DRIVEN CIRCULATION
WIND-DRIVEN CURRENTS
WIND-WAVE INTERACTION
WINDROWS
WINDS
WINGS
WINKLER METHOD
WINNOWING
WINTER
WINTERKILL
WIRE ANGLE
WIRE ANGLE INDICATORS
WIRE ROPE
WOMEN
WOOD
WORK PLATFORMS
WORKING UNDERWATER
WORKOVER BARGES
WORLD
WORM CULTURE
WORM FISHING
WOUNDING
WOUNDING GEAR
WRECK LOCATION
WRECKS

X

X-RAY DIFFRACTION ANALYSIS
X-RAY EMISSION ANALYSIS
X-RAY FLUORESCENCE ANALYSIS
X-RAY INSPECTION
X-RAY SPECTROSCOPY
X-RAYS
XANTHOPHYLLS

XBTs
XENON
XENON ISOTOPES
XYLENE
XYLOSE

Y

YACHTING
YACHTS
YARNS
YAW RESPONSE
YAWING
YEASTS
YIELD
YIELD POINT
YIELD PREDICTIONS
YOLK
YTTERBIUM
YTTERBIUM COMPOUNDS
YTTERBIUM ISOTOPES
YTTRIUM
YTTRIUM COMPOUNDS
YTTRIUM ISOTOPES

Z

ZEOLITE FACIES
ZEOLITES
ZINC
ZINC COMPOUNDS
ZINC ISOTOPES
ZIRCON
ZIRCONIUM
ZIRCONIUM COMPOUNDS
ZIRCONIUM ISOTOPES
ZOEAE
ZONAL DISTRIBUTION
ZOOBENTHOS
ZOOLOGISTS
ZOOLOGY
ZOOPLANKTON
ZOOPLANKTON CULTURE
ZOOXANTHELLAE
ZYGOTES

ASFIS Thesaurus Terminology Control Form

TERM

The above term should be:
- ☐ ADDED
- ☐ DELETED
- ☐ CHANGED

Because:

1) It does not appear in the thesaurus .... ☐
2) It is synonymous to another thesaurus term .... ☐
   a) The synonymous term is _____
3) It appears in the thesaurus with an incorrect relationship .... ☐
4) It appears in the thesaurus with an incorrect scope note .... ☐
5) It is spelled incorrectly .... ☐

Other reasons and/or comments:

SUGGESTED ENTRY

TERM

SCOPE NOTE

USE

USED FOR

BROADER TERM(S)

NARROWER TERM(S)

RELATED TERM(S)

From: **Date:** _____

Organization:

Address:

ASFIS Thesaurus Committee Comments

☐ Accepted   Reasons: **Date:** _____
☐ Changed
☐ Rejected

Effective for
year _____

Mail to: Fishery Information, Data and Statistics Service
          Fisheries Department
          FAO, Via delle Terme di Caracalla
          00100 Rome, Italy

ASFIS Thesaurus Terminology Control Form

TERM

The above term should be: ☐ ADDED
                                     ☐ DELETED
                                     ☐ CHANGED

Because:

1) It does not appear in the thesaurus .... ☐
2) It is synonymous to another thesaurus term .... ☐
    a) The synonymous term is _____
3) It appears in the thesaurus with an incorrect relationship .... ☐
4) It appears in the thesaurus with an incorrect scope note .... ☐
5) It is spelled incorrectly .... ☐

Other reasons and/or comments:

SUGGESTED ENTRY

TERM

SCOPE NOTE

USE

USED FOR

BROADER TERM(S)

NARROWER TERM(S)

RELATED TERM(S)

From: **Date:** _____

Organization:

Address:

ASFIS Thesaurus Committee Comments

☐ Accepted   Reasons: **Date:** _____
☐ Changed
☐ Rejected

Effective for
year _____

Mail to: Fishery Information, Data and Statistics Service
            Fisheries Department
            FAO, Via delle Terme di Caracalla
            00100 Rome, Italy

ASFIS Thesaurus Terminology Control Form

TERM

The above term should be: ☐ ADDED
                                     ☐ DELETED
                                     ☐ CHANGED

Because:

   1) It does not appear in the thesaurus .... ☐
   2) It is synonymous to another thesaurus term .... ☐
      a) The synonymcus term is _____ _____
   3) It appears in the thesaurus with an incorrect relationship .... ☐
   4) It appears in the thesaurus with an incorrect scope note .... ☐
   5) It is spelled incorrectly .... ☐

   Other reasons and/or comments:

SUGGESTED ENTRY

     TERM

     SCOPE NOTE

     USE

     USED FOR

     BROADER TERM(S)

     NARROWER TERM(S)

     RELATED TERM(S)

From: **Date:** _____

Organization:

Address:

ASFIS Thesaurus Committee Comments

☐ Accepted   Reasons: **Date:** _____
☐ Changed
☐ Rejected

Effective for
year _____

         Mail to: Fishery Information, Data and Statistics Service
                   Fisheries Department
                   FAO, Via delle Terme di Caracalla
                   00100 Rome, Italy